Everyday Mathematics®

The University of Chicago School Mathematics Project

Teacher's Lesson Guide

Volume 1

Grade 6

Wright Group

The McGraw·Hill Companies

Everyday Mathematics

The University of Chicago School Mathematics Project (UCSMP)
Max Bell, Director, UCSMP Elementary Materials Component; Director, *Everyday Mathematics* First Edition
James McBride, Director, *Everyday Mathematics* Second Edition
Andy Isaacs, Director, *Everyday Mathematics* Third Edition
Amy Dillard, Associate Director, *Everyday Mathematics* Third Edition

Authors
Max Bell, John Bretzlauf, Amy Dillard, Robert Hartfield, Andy Isaacs, James McBride, Ann McCarty*, Kathleen Pitvorec, Peter Saecker, Robert Balfanz†, William Carroll†
**Third Edition only* †*First Edition only*

Technical Art
Diana Barrie

Teacher in Residence
Denise Porter

Mathematics and Technology Advisor
James Flanders

ELL Consultant
Kathryn B. Chval

Contributors
Serena Hohmann, Barbara J.Kitz, Moira S. Rodgers, Linda Werner; Ann Brown, Sarah Busse, Terry DeJong, Craig Dezell, John Dini, James Flanders, Donna Goffron, Steve Heckley, Karen Hedberg, Deborah Arron Leslie, Sharon McHugh, Janet M. Meyers, Donna Owen, William D. Pattison, Marilyn Pavlak, Jane Picken, Kelly Porto, John Sabol, Rose Ann Simpson, Debbi Suhajda, Laura Sunseri, Andrea Tyrance, Kim Van Haitsma, Mary Wilson, Nancy Wilson, Jackie Winston, Carl Zmola, Theresa Zmola

Photo Credits
©Age Fotostock, p. 167; ©Martin Barraud/Getty Images, p. xxi *bottom;* ©Burke/Triolo Productions/Getty Images, p. 2 *left;* ©Corbis, pp. xxv, xxx *bottom,* 97, 240 *flags of Thailand, Colombia,* and *Libya,* 322; ©Sean Ellis/Getty Images, p. 166 *left;* ©Randy Faris/Corbis, p. 3; ©Getty Images, pp. cover *center,* xix *top,* 2 *bottom,* 17, 79, 87, 179, 240, 241, 253 *bottom,* 334 *bottom,* 335; ©iStock International Inc., pp. 166 *right,* 322 *right,* 323, 334 *top;* ©Kelly Kalhoefer/Getty Images, cover *top right;* ©Marka/Age Fotostock, p. 177; Courtesy of Mettler Toledo, p. 86 *bottom;* ©Jean Miele/Corbis, p. 101; ©Zoran Milich/Masterfile, p. 240 *top;* Courtesy of NorthernTool.com, p. 98; ©PhotoSpin, p. 86 *top;* ©Jeff Titcomb/Getty Images, p. xx *bottom;* ©Toysmith, p. xxii *top;* ©Jim Wark/Getty Images, p. 16; ©Stuart Westmoreland/Corbis, cover *bottom left;* ©John Wilkes/Getty Images, p. xxii *bottom;* ©M. Winkel/A.B./Zefa/Corbis, p. 322 *left.*

This material is based upon work supported by the National Science Foundation under Grant No. ESI-9252984. Any opinions, findings, conclusions, or recommendations expressed in the material are those of the authors and do not necessarily reflect the views of the National Science Foundation.

---

www.WrightGroup.com

Wright Group

Printed in the United States of America.

Send all inquiries to:
Wright Group/McGraw-Hill
P.O. Box 812960
Chicago, IL 60681

ISBN 0-07-603609-X

2 3 4 5 6 7 8 9 BAN 12 11 10 09 08 07 06

The University of Chicago School Mathematics Project (UCSMP)

Acknowledgements

The first edition of *Everyday Mathematics* was made possible by sustained support over several years from the GTE Corporation and the National Science Foundation; additional help came from the Amoco Foundation through its support of the University of Chicago School Mathematics Project (UCSMP). Earlier projects supported by the National Science Foundation, the National Institute of Education, and the Benton Foundation provided us with insights into the surprising capabilities of young children.

Development of the second edition of *Everyday Mathematics* was funded by the Everyday Learning Corporation and the authors; development of this third edition was supported by Wright Group/McGraw-Hill, the University of Chicago, and the authors.

For all three editions, many University of Chicago and UCSMP colleagues have been helpful. For this third edition, Deborah Arron Leslie, David W. Beer, Rachel Malpass McCall, Cheryl G. Moran, Mary Ellen Dairyko, Amy Dillard, Noreen Winningham, and Ann McCarty formed a committee that provided invaluable guidance on many key issues. We also acknowledge dedicated and resourceful assistance on production and technical tasks by many people at the University of Chicago and at Wright Group/McGraw-Hill.

Over the years that UCSMP has been working in schools, feedback and advice from teachers willing to take risks in trying development versions of our materials have been essential and enormously helpful. There are too many such teachers to list, but their contributions are gratefully acknowledged.

Andy Isaacs
Director, Third Edition

James McBride
Director, Second Edition

Max Bell
Director, First Edition

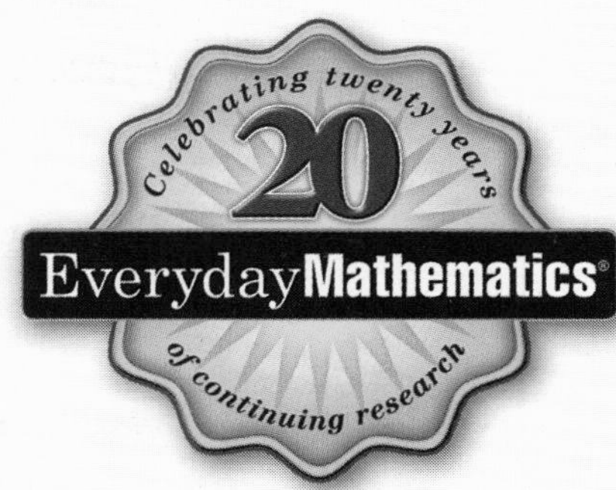

Contents

A Mission to Improve Mathematics

The University of Chicago School Mathematics Project

> "We, our funders, and our users believe strongly that even the best curricula of decades ago are not adequate for today's youth."
>
> University of Chicago School Mathematics Project

Everyday Mathematics was developed by the University of Chicago School Mathematics Project (UCSMP) in order to enable children in elementary grades to learn more mathematical content and become life-long mathematical thinkers.

- The National Science Foundation and Amoco, GTE, and other leading corporations supported the project through substantial, long-term funding.
- A strong partnership was developed among researchers, mathematics educators, classroom teachers, students, and administrators.
- A consistent, core author team at the University of Chicago School Mathematics Project collaborated on all grade levels to provide a cohesive and well-articulated Pre-K through Grade 6 curriculum.

Research Foundation

Everyday Mathematics began with the premise that students can, and must, learn more mathematics than has been expected from them in the past. This premise is based on research the UCSMP author team undertook prior to writing the curriculum. Following are some major findings of this research:

- The typical U.S. mathematics curriculum is arithmetic-driven, slow-paced with isolated instruction, and broad, without depth of content.
- International studies show that U.S. students learn much less mathematics than students in other countries.
- Children are capable of learning more mathematics in a richer curriculum.
- All children can be successful mathematical thinkers.
- Mathematics is meaningful to children when it is varied, rich, and rooted in real-world problems and applications.

Instructional Design

The *Everyday Mathematics* instructional design was carefully crafted to capitalize on student interest and maximize student learning.

- High expectations for all students
- Concepts and skills developed over time and in a wide variety of contexts
- Balance among mathematical strands
- Dynamic applications
- Multiple methods and strategies for problem solving
- Concrete modeling as a pathway to abstract understanding
- Collaborative learning in partner and small-group activities
- Cross-curricular applications and connections
- Built-in professional development for teachers

"Our teachers in Grades 6-8 tell me that students using the *Everyday Mathematics* program in earlier grades are arriving in their classrooms with a deeper understanding of mathematical concepts and are ready to start the year at a much higher level."

Principal Ken Tucker,
Florence Sawyer School Pre-K to 8

Meeting Standards, Achieving Results

The *Everyday Mathematics* program is celebrating 20 years of research and development. The program offers schools results unmatched by any other elementary mathematics program.

Research, Validation, Results

As part of the research for *Everyday Mathematics,* the authors at the University of Chicago School Mathematics Project examined successful curricula from around the world, researched how children learn mathematics, and studied the actual use of mathematics by people in their everyday lives. The results of this research was used to establish the mathematical content scope and sequence for the *Everyday Mathematics* program.

Field Testing

The program was written and field tested one grade-level at a time, beginning with kindergarten. Field tests gathered information from classroom teachers and students in three main areas: teacher preparation of materials, student response to materials, and student achievement. Based on teacher and student feedback, the authors revised the curriculum before *Everyday Mathematics* was published.

Learner Verification

The best way to show effectiveness of a program is to study it over time. Several independent research studies have been conducted which provide evidence for the effectiveness of *Everyday Mathematics*. For example, *Everyday Mathematics* was the focus of a five-year longitudinal study conducted by researchers at Northwestern University. Reports from this study and others are available through the University of Chicago School Mathematics Project or Wright Group/ McGraw-Hill.

***Everyday Mathematics* Timeline of Research and Development**

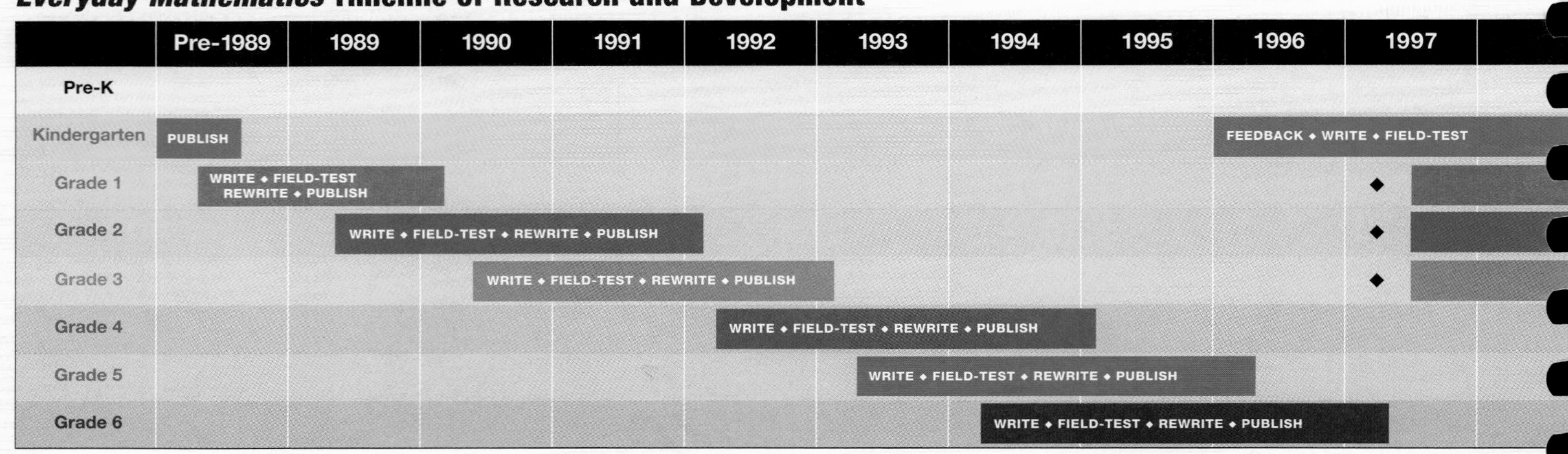

Tristate Student Achievement Study

The ARC Center, a National Science Foundation (NSF) funded project, located at the Consortium for Mathematics and its Applications (COMAP), completed a study on the effects of standards-based mathematics programs of student performance on state-mandated standardized tests in Massachusetts, Illinois, and Washington.

The findings in this report are based on the records of over 78,000 students: 39,701 who had used the *Everyday Mathematics* curriculum for at least two years, and 38,481 students from comparison schools. The students were carefully matched by reading level, socioeconomic status, and other variables.

Results showed that the average scores of students in the *Everyday Mathematics* schools were consistently higher than the average scores of students in the comparison schools. The results hold across different state-mandated tests and across topics ranging from computation, measurement, and geometry to algebra, problem-solving, and making connections. (A complete report is available from COMAP or Wright Group/Mcgraw Hill.)

A report based on 78,000 students showed that average standardized test scores were significantly higher for students in *Everyday Mathematics* schools than for students in comparison schools.

Closing the Gap

Many districts using the *Everyday Mathematics* program have helped minority students close any previously experienced achievement gap, while maintaining achievement growth in all other student categories. This helps schools and districts meet adequate yearly progress set forth by No Child Left Behind legislation. District information is available by contacting Wright Group/McGraw-Hill.

1998	1999	2000	2001	2002	2003	2004	2005	2006	2007	2008
			FEEDBACK ◆ WRITE ◆ FIELD-TEST ◆ PUBLISH					FEEDBACK ◆ WRITE FIELD-TEST ◆ PUBLISH		
PUBLISH — 2ND EDITION					▲	FEEDBACK ◆ WRITE ◆ FIELD-TEST ◆ PUBLISH — 3RD EDITION				
FEEDBACK ◆ WRITE ◆ FIELD-TEST ◆ PUBLISH — 2ND EDITION					▲	FEEDBACK ◆ WRITE ◆ FIELD-TEST ◆ PUBLISH — 3RD EDITION				
FEEDBACK ◆ WRITE ◆ FIELD-TEST ◆ PUBLISH — 2ND EDITION					▲	FEEDBACK ◆ WRITE ◆ FIELD-TEST ◆ PUBLISH — 3RD EDITION				
FEEDBACK ◆ WRITE ◆ FIELD-TEST ◆ PUBLISH — 2ND EDITION					▲	FEEDBACK ◆ WRITE ◆ FIELD-TEST ◆ PUBLISH — 3RD EDITION				
◆	FEEDBACK ◆ WRITE ◆ FIELD-TEST ◆ PUBLISH — 2ND EDITION				▲	FEEDBACK ◆ WRITE ◆ FIELD-TEST ◆ PUBLISH — 3RD EDITION				
◆	FEEDBACK ◆ WRITE ◆ FIELD-TEST ◆ PUBLISH — 2ND EDITION				▲	FEEDBACK ◆ WRITE ◆ FIELD-TEST ◆ PUBLISH — 3RD EDITION				
◆	FEEDBACK ◆ WRITE ◆ FIELD-TEST ◆ PUBLISH — 2ND EDITION				▲	FEEDBACK ◆ WRITE ◆ FIELD-TEST ◆ PUBLISH — 3RD EDITION				

◆ = 1st edition update ▲ = 2nd edition update — electronic components added

Rigorous Mathematics

Program Goals and Grade-Level Goals

Everyday Mathematics structures content into Grade-Level Goals and Program Goals. Program Goals are then organized by content strand and are carefully articulated across the grades. The content in each grade provides all students with a balanced mathematics curriculum that is rich in real-world problem-solving opportunities. The success of this approach to teaching mathematics is evident in students' improved scores on standardized tests.

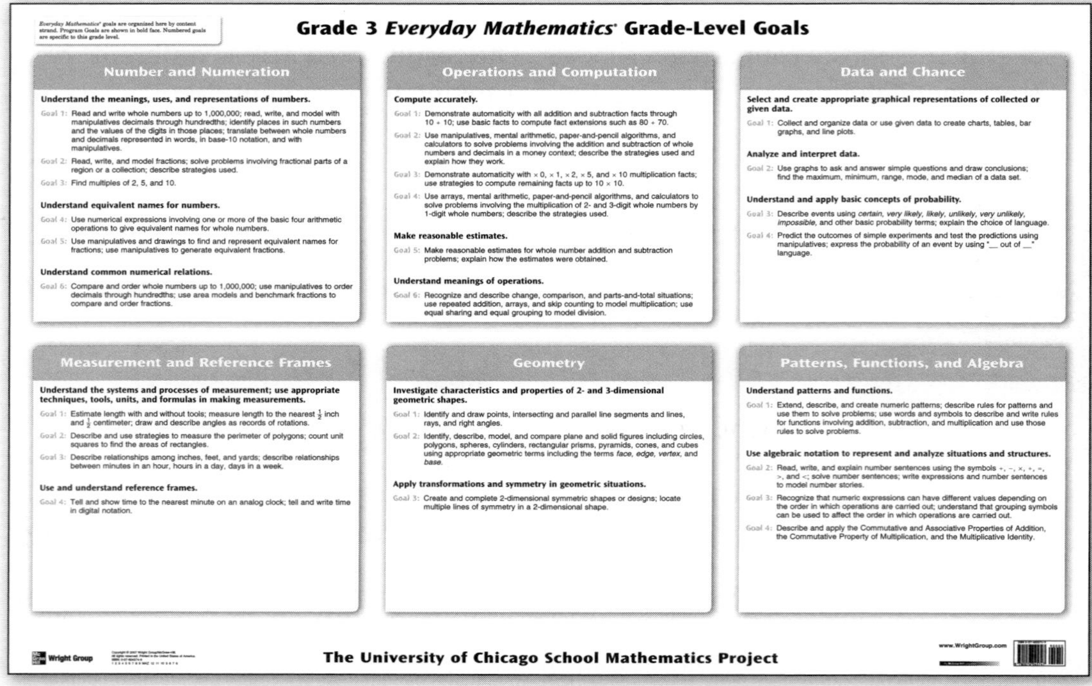

Everyday Mathematics® goals are organized here by content strand. Program Goals are shown in bold face. Numbered goals are specific to this grade level.

Grade 3 *Everyday Mathematics®* Grade-Level Goals

Number and Numeration

Understand the meanings, uses, and representations of numbers.

Goal 1: Read and write whole numbers up to 1,000,000; read, write, and model with manipulatives decimals through hundredths; identify places in such numbers and the values of the digits in those places; translate between whole numbers and decimals represented in words, in base-10 notation, and with manipulatives.

Goal 2: Read, write, and model fractions; solve problems involving fractional parts of a region or a collection; describe strategies used.

Goal 3: Find multiples of 2, 5, and 10.

Understand equivalent names for numbers.

Goal 4: Use numerical expressions involving one or more of the basic four arithmetic operations to give equivalent names for whole numbers.

Goal 5: Use manipulatives and drawings to find and represent equivalent names for fractions; use manipulatives to generate equivalent fractions.

Understand common numerical relations.

Goal 6: Compare and order whole numbers up to 1,000,000; use manipulatives to order decimals through hundredths; use area models and benchmark fractions to compare and order fractions.

Operations and Computation

Compute accurately.

Goal 1: Demonstrate automaticity with all addition and subtraction facts through 10 + 10; use basic facts to compute fact extensions such as 80 + 70.

Goal 2: Use manipulatives, mental arithmetic, paper-and-pencil algorithms, and calculators to solve problems involving the addition and subtraction of whole numbers and decimals in a money context; describe the strategies used and explain how they work.

Goal 3: Demonstrate automaticity with × 0, × 1, × 2, × 5, and × 10 multiplication facts; use strategies to compute remaining facts up to 10 × 10.

Goal 4: Use arrays, mental arithmetic, paper-and-pencil algorithms, and calculators to solve problems involving the multiplication of 2- and 3-digit whole numbers by 1-digit whole numbers; describe the strategies used.

Make reasonable estimates.

Goal 5: Make reasonable estimates for whole number addition and subtraction problems; explain how the estimates were obtained.

Understand meanings of operations.

Goal 6: Recognize and describe change, comparison, and parts-and-total situations; use repeated addition, arrays, and skip counting to model multiplication; use equal sharing and equal grouping to model division.

Data and Chance

Select and create appropriate graphical representations of collected or given data.

Goal 1: Collect and organize data or use given data to create charts, tables, bar graphs, and line plots.

Analyze and interpret data.

Goal 2: Use graphs to ask and answer simple questions and draw conclusions; find the maximum, minimum, range, mode, and median of a data set.

Understand and apply basic concepts of probability.

Goal 3: Describe events using *certain, very likely, likely, unlikely, very unlikely, impossible,* and other basic probability terms; explain the choice of language.

Goal 4: Predict the outcomes of simple experiments and test the predictions using manipulatives; express the probability of an event by using "__ out of __" language.

Measurement and Reference Frames

Understand the systems and processes of measurement; use appropriate techniques, tools, units, and formulas in making measurements.

Goal 1: Estimate length with and without tools; measure length to the nearest $\frac{1}{2}$ inch and $\frac{1}{2}$ centimeter; draw and describe angles as records of rotations.

Goal 2: Describe and use strategies to measure the perimeter of polygons; count unit squares to find the areas of rectangles.

Goal 3: Describe relationships among inches, feet, and yards; describe relationships between minutes in an hour, hours in a day, days in a week.

Use and understand reference frames.

Goal 4: Tell and show time to the nearest minute on an analog clock; tell and write time in digital notation.

Geometry

Investigate characteristics and properties of 2- and 3-dimensional geometric shapes.

Goal 1: Identify and draw points, intersecting and parallel line segments and lines, rays, and right angles.

Goal 2: Identify, describe, model, and compare plane and solid figures including circles, polygons, spheres, cylinders, rectangular prisms, pyramids, cones, and cubes using appropriate geometric terms including the terms *face, edge, vertex,* and *base.*

Apply transformations and symmetry in geometric situations.

Goal 3: Create and complete 2-dimensional symmetric shapes or designs; locate multiple lines of symmetry in a 2-dimensional shape.

Patterns, Functions, and Algebra

Understand patterns and functions.

Goal 1: Extend, describe, and create numeric patterns; describe rules for patterns and use them to solve problems; use words and symbols to describe and write rules for functions involving addition, subtraction, and multiplication and use those rules to solve problems.

Use algebraic notation to represent and analyze situations and structures.

Goal 2: Read, write, and explain number sentences using the symbols +, −, ×, ÷, =, >, and <; solve number sentences; write expressions and number sentences to model number stories.

Goal 3: Recognize that numeric expressions can have different values depending on the order in which operations are carried out; understand that grouping symbols can be used to affect the order in which operations are carried out.

Goal 4: Describe and apply the Commutative and Associative Properties of Addition, the Commutative Property of Multiplication, and the Multiplicative Identity.

Wright Group

The University of Chicago School Mathematics Project

www.WrightGroup.com

Grade 3 Grade-Level Goals Poster

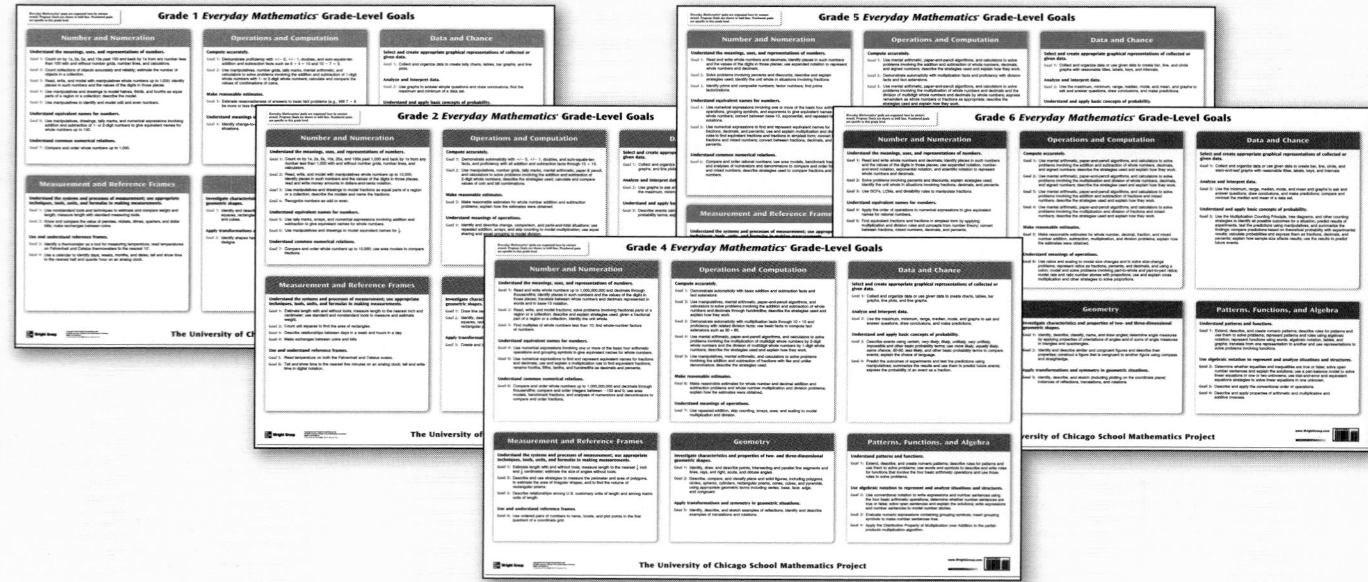

The *Everyday Mathematics* Program Goals are listed below. *Everyday Mathematics* Program Goals are organized by strand and extend across all grade levels.

Number and Numeration Strand

- Understand the meanings, uses, and representations of numbers
- Understand equivalent names for numbers
- Understand common numerical relations

Operations and Computation Strand

- Compute accurately
- Make reasonable estimates
- Understand meanings of operations

Data and Chance Strand

- Select and create appropriate graphical representations of collected or given data
- Analyze and interpret data
- Understand and apply basic concepts of probability

Measurement and Reference Frames Strand

- Understand the systems and processes of measurement; use appropriate techniques, tools, units, and formulas in making measurements
- Use and understand reference frames

Geometry Strand

- Investigate characteristics and properties of two- and three-dimensional geometric shapes
- Apply transformations and symmetry in geometric situations

Patterns, Functions, and Algebra Strand

- Understand patterns and functions
- Use algebraic notation to represent and analyze situations and structures

Everyday Mathematics®

Components at a Glance

The table below shows core materials that are used on a regular basis throughout *Everyday Mathematics*.

STUDENT MATERIALS

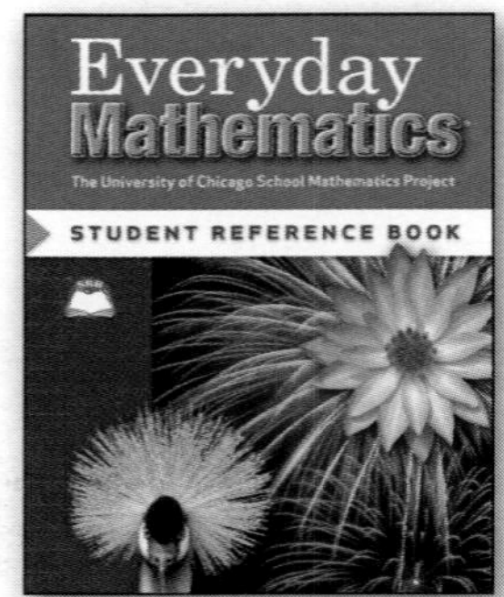

Student Reference Book (Grades 3-6) Contains explanations of key mathematical content, along with directions for the *Everyday Mathematics* games. This hardbound book supports student learning in the classroom and at home.

My Reference Book (Grades 1 and 2) This hardcover book is a child's first mathematical reference book. *My Reference Book* contains explanations of key concepts as well as directions for games.

Student Math Journal, Volumes 1 & 2 (Grades 1-6) These consumable books provide daily support for classroom instruction. They provide a long-term record of each student's mathematical development.

TEACHER MATERIALS

Teacher's Lesson Guide, Volumes 1 & 2 (Grades 1-6) The core of the *Everyday Mathematics* program, the *Teacher's Lesson Guide* provides teachers with easy-to-follow lessons organized by instructional unit, as well as built-in mathematical content support. Lessons include planning and assessment tips and multi-level differentiation strategies to support all learners.

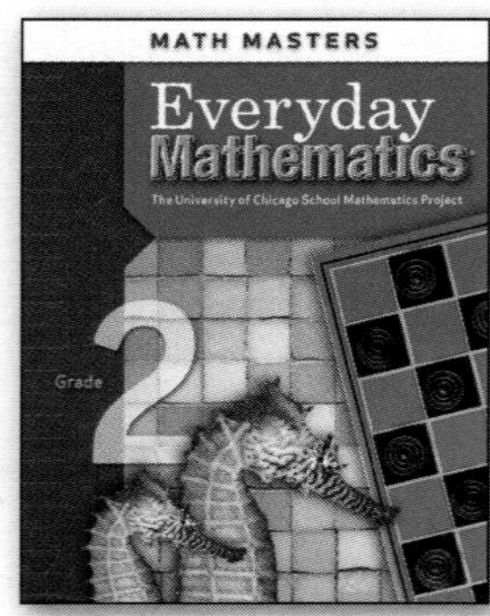

Math Masters (Grades 1-6) Blackline masters that support daily lesson activities. Includes Home/Study Links, lesson-specific masters, game masters, and project masters.

Minute Math®+ (Grades 1-3)
5-Minute Math (Grades 4-6)
Brief activities for transition time and for spare moments throughout the day.

TEACHER RESOURCES

Teacher's Reference Manual Contains comprehensive background information about mathematical content and program management for grades Early Childhood, 1-3, and 4-6.

Home Connection Handbook Enhances home-school communication for teachers and administrators. Includes masters for easy planning for grades Early Childhood, 1-3, and 4-6.

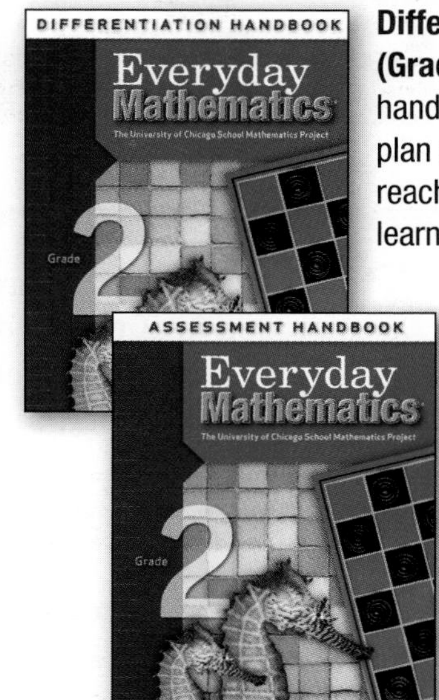

Differentiation Handbook (Grades 1-6) Grade-specific handbooks that help teachers plan strategically in order to reach the needs of diverse learners.

Assessment Handbook (Grades 1-6) Grade-specific handbooks provide explanations of key features of assessment in the *Everyday Mathematics* program. Includes all assessment masters.

TECHNOLOGY COMPONENTS

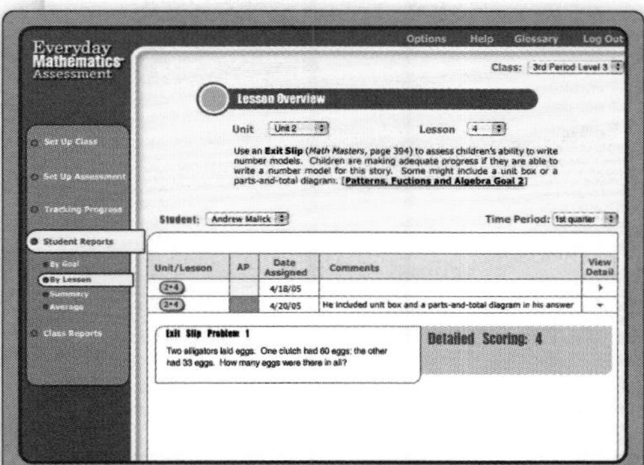

◀ **Assessment Management System (Grades K-6)** Web-based software that provides teachers with the opportunity to track student progress toward Grade-Level Goals.

Interactive Teacher's Lesson Guide (Grades K-6) Grade-level specific CD-ROM provides access to student and teacher materials. Content is searchable. ▶

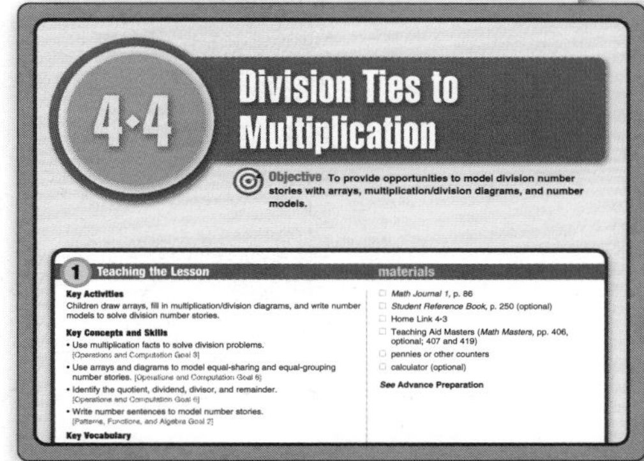

KINDERGARTEN MATERIALS

Kindergarten Teacher's Guide to Activities

Assessment Handbook

Math Masters

My First Math Book

Minute Math®

Resources for the Kindergarten Classroom

Everyday **Mathematics**

Planning and Instructional Support

Each unit organizer provides an overview of the content for the unit. Also included is support for ongoing learning and practice, problem solving, and differentiated instruction. Detailed content support relating to the unit instruction is provided in Mathematical Background.

Overview

Describes concepts and ideas that are the focus of the unit.

Contents

Includes the objective for every lesson.

Unit 4 Organizer

Multiplication and Division

Overview

Unit 4 focuses on the most common uses of multiplication and division—those involving multiples of equal groups, equal sharing, and equal grouping. In second grade, children worked with multiplication and division number stories and were introduced to the basic multiplication and division facts. This work is continued in third grade with the expectation that children will use arrays, mental arithmetic, paper-and-pencil algorithms, and calculators to solve problems involving the multiplication of 2-and 3-digit whole numbers by 1-digit whole numbers and describe the strategies used by the end of the school year. They are also expected to demonstrate automaticity with x0, x1, x2, x5, and x10 multiplication facts and use strategies to compute remaining facts up to 10x10.Unit 4 has three main areas of focus:

- To model and solve multiplication number stories and practice multiplication facts,
- To model and solve division number stories and practice division facts, and
- To explore the links between multiplication and division.

228 Unit 4 Multiplication and Division

Contents

Key Concepts and Skills

Lists the Key Concepts and Skills, the important mathematical ideas that are covered in each lesson.

Unit 4 Organizer

Learning In Perspective

Key Concepts and Skills

230 Unit 4 Multiplication and Division

Unit Organizer 231

Learning in Perspective

Identifies connections to prior and future content both within and across grade levels.

Ongoing Learning and Practice

Highlights essential activities which provide review and practice for maintaining skills. These activities include Math Boxes, Home/Study Links, games, and Extra Practice.

Ongoing Assessment

Includes the assessment opportunities in each lesson to assess progress toward Grade-Level Goals.

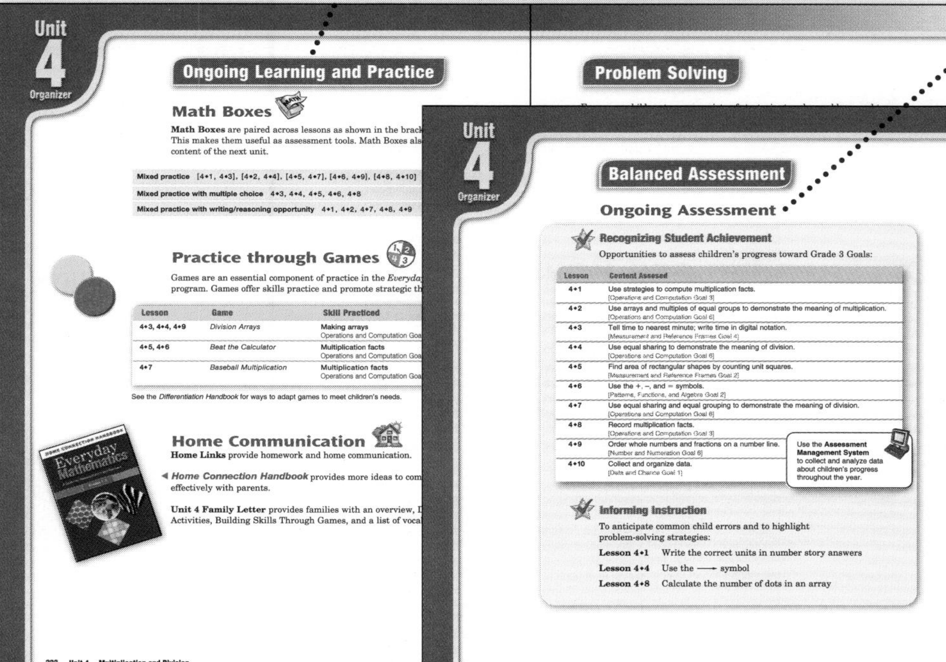

Assessment Support

Identifies useful pages in the *Assessment Handbook* for each unit.

Mathematical Background

Provides content support for important mathematical ideas in the unit.

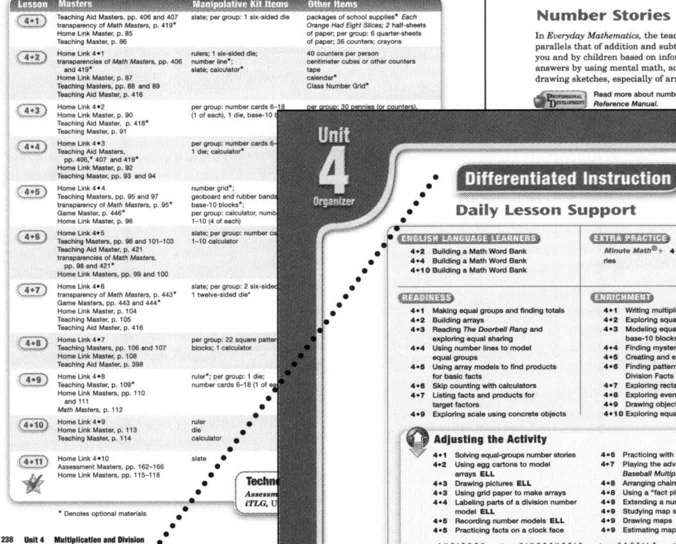

Differentiated Instruction

Highlights the many facets of differentiated instruction in each unit. Includes English Language Learner support, Enrichment, Readiness, Extra Practice, and Using the Projects.

Everyday Mathematics®

Instructional Plan

3-Part Lessons

1 Teaching the Lesson Provides main instructional activities for the lesson.

2 Ongoing Learning and Practice Supports previously introduced concepts and skills; essential for maintaining skills.

3 Differentiation Options Includes options for supporting the needs of all students; usually an extension of Part 1, Teaching the Lesson.

Getting Started

Contains quick mental math activities, Math Message (an independent warm-up), and follow-up suggestions for Home/Study Links.

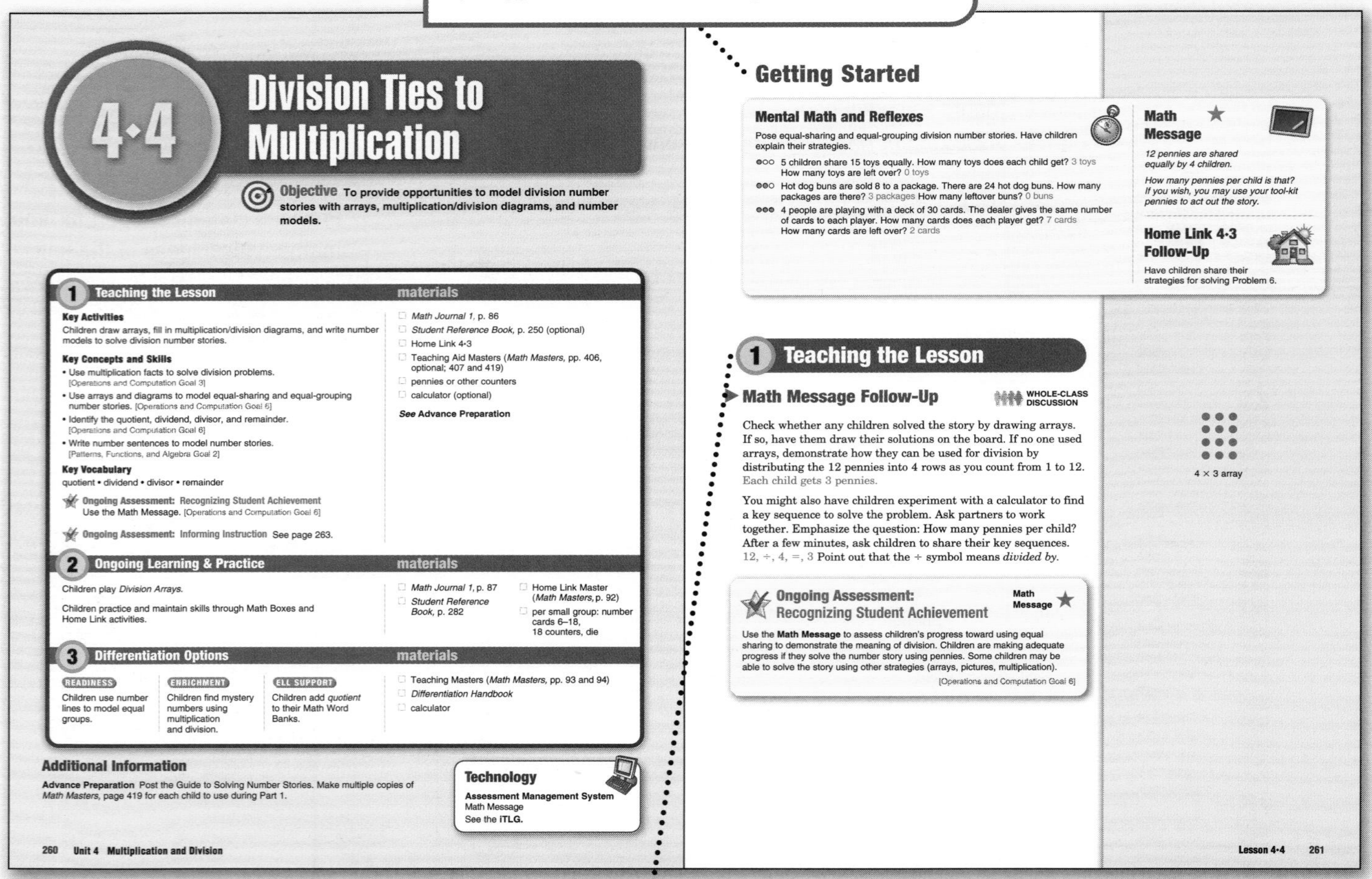

4•4 Division Ties to Multiplication

Objective To provide opportunities to model division number stories with arrays, multiplication/division diagrams, and number models.

1 Teaching the Lesson

Key Activities
Children draw arrays, fill in multiplication/division diagrams, and write number models to solve division number stories.

Key Concepts and Skills
- Use multiplication facts to solve division problems. [Operations and Computation Goal 3]
- Use arrays and diagrams to model equal-sharing and equal-grouping number stories. [Operations and Computation Goal 6]
- Identify the quotient, dividend, divisor, and remainder. [Operations and Computation Goal 6]
- Write number sentences to model number stories. [Patterns, Functions, and Algebra Goal 2]

Key Vocabulary
quotient • dividend • divisor • remainder

Ongoing Assessment: Recognizing Student Achievement Use the Math Message. [Operations and Computation Goal 6]

Ongoing Assessment: Informing Instruction See page 263.

materials
- ☐ *Math Journal 1*, p. 86
- ☐ *Student Reference Book*, p. 250 (optional)
- ☐ Home Link 4•3
- ☐ Teaching Aid Masters (*Math Masters*, pp. 406, optional; 407 and 419)
- ☐ pennies or other counters
- ☐ calculator (optional)

***See* Advance Preparation**

2 Ongoing Learning & Practice

Children play *Division Arrays*.

Children practice and maintain skills through Math Boxes and Home Link activities.

materials
- ☐ *Math Journal 1*, p. 87
- ☐ *Student Reference Book*, p. 282
- ☐ Home Link Master (*Math Masters*, p. 92)
- ☐ per small group: number cards 6–18, 18 counters, die

3 Differentiation Options

READINESS	ENRICHMENT	ELL SUPPORT
Children use number lines to model equal groups.	Children find mystery numbers using multiplication and division.	Children add *quotient* to their Math Word Banks.

materials
- ☐ Teaching Masters (*Math Masters*, pp. 93 and 94)
- ☐ *Differentiation Handbook*
- ☐ calculator

Additional Information

Advance Preparation Post the Guide to Solving Number Stories. Make multiple copies of *Math Masters*, page 419 for each child to use during Part 1.

Technology
Assessment Management System
Math Message
See the **iTLG.**

260 Unit 4 Multiplication and Division

Getting Started

Mental Math and Reflexes

Pose equal-sharing and equal-grouping division number stories. Have children explain their strategies.

●○○ 5 children share 15 toys equally. How many toys does each child get? 3 toys How many toys are left over? 0 toys

●●○ Hot dog buns are sold 8 to a package. There are 24 hot dog buns. How many packages are there? 3 packages How many leftover buns? 0 buns

●●● 4 people are playing with a deck of 30 cards. The dealer gives the same number of cards to each player. How many cards does each player get? 7 cards How many cards are left over? 2 cards

Math Message ★

12 pennies are shared equally by 4 children.

How many pennies per child is that? If you wish, you may use your tool-kit pennies to act out the story.

Home Link 4•3 Follow-Up

Have children share their strategies for solving Problem 6.

1 Teaching the Lesson

Math Message Follow-Up WHOLE-CLASS DISCUSSION

Check whether any children solved the story by drawing arrays. If so, have them draw their solutions on the board. If no one used arrays, demonstrate how they can be used for division by distributing the 12 pennies into 4 rows as you count from 1 to 12. Each child gets 3 pennies.

You might also have children experiment with a calculator to find a key sequence to solve the problem. Ask partners to work together. Emphasize the question: How many pennies per child? After a few minutes, ask children to share their key sequences. 12, ÷, 4, =, 3 Point out that the ÷ symbol means *divided by.*

4 × 3 array

Ongoing Assessment: Recognizing Student Achievement Math Message ★

Use the **Math Message** to assess children's progress toward using equal sharing to demonstrate the meaning of division. Children are making adequate progress if they solve the number story using pennies. Some children may be able to solve the story using other strategies (arrays, pictures, multiplication).

[Operations and Computation Goal 6]

Lesson 4•4 261

1 Teaching the Lesson

Main instructional activities for the lesson which introduce new content.

2 Ongoing Learning & Practice

Activities provide essential review and practice for maintaining skills. Includes *Everyday Mathematics* games appropriate for revisiting mathematics skills, as well as Math Boxes and Home/Study Links.

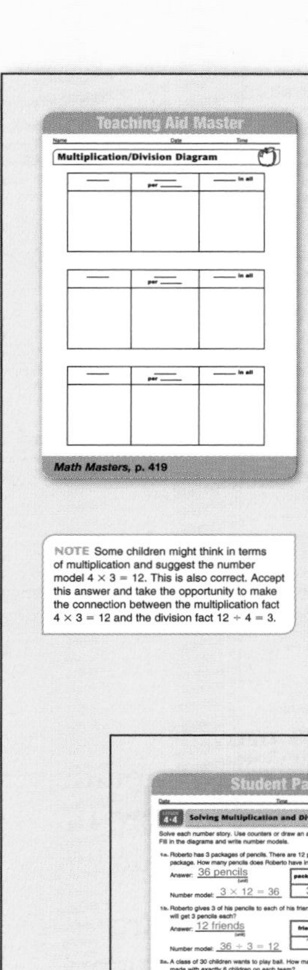

NOTE Some children might think in terms of multiplication and suggest the number model 4 × 3 = 12. This is also correct. Accept this answer and take the opportunity to make the connection between the multiplication fact 4 × 3 = 12 and the division fact 12 ÷ 4 = 3.

▶ **Using Number Models and Diagrams for Division Stories**

WHOLE-CLASS ACTIVITY

(*Math Masters,* p. 419)

With the 4-by-3 array from the Math Message left on the board, display a multiplication/division diagram (see below). Ask children to fill in the known numbers and identify the missing numbers in a diagram on *Math Masters,* page 419. The diagram is the same for division and multiplication—the diagram reinforces the inverse relationship between the two operations.

children	pennies per child	pennies in all
4	?	12

- Ask: *How many pennies per child?* 3 pennies
- Ask whether a volunteer can write a number model to match the story. 12 ÷ 4 = 3, $\frac{12}{4}$ = 3, or $4\overline{)12}$ with 3 above

Any of these notations can be read or thought of in a variety of ways: What is 12 divided by 4? How many 4s in 12? 4 goes into 12 how many times?

▷ The answer in each of the division number models, or the result of the division, is called the **quotient.**

▷ The **dividend** is the total before sharing.

▷ The **divisor** is the number of equal parts or the number in each equal part.

Adjusting the Activity ELL

Pose the following problem: *There are 15 pennies. Each child receives 4 pennies. How many children are there?*

Display or draw a multiplication/division diagram on the board. Ask children to fill in the known numbers and identify the missing number.

children	pennies per child	pennies in all
?	4	15

- Ask: *How many children are there?* 3 children
- Ask a volunteer to write a number model to match the story. 15 ÷ 4 → 3 R3, $\frac{15}{4}$ → 3 R3, $4\overline{)15}$ with 3R3 above
- For problems with remainders, use the same notations, but replace the = sign with an arrow. This arrow is read as *leads to, gives, results in,* or a similar expression.
- The **remainder** is the quantity left over when a set of objects is shared equally or separated into equal groups. You can expect children to use the word *remainder* when describing the result of a division problem.

Ongoing Assessment: Informing Instruction

Watch for children who are confused by the → symbol. Have them use the = symbol in their work. Continue to model problems using the → symbol so that children will become accustomed to the notation.

Pose additional problems as necessary. For each problem, fill in a multiplication/division diagram and write a number model.

- 23 candles are arranged with 3 in each row. How many rows are there? 7 rows; 23 ÷ 3 → 7 R2

NOTE Some children may think in terms of multiplication and suggest more than one number model to solve the problem. They might first use 3 × 4 = 12 and 4 × 4 = 16. Then 12 + 3 = 15 (or 15 − 12 = 3).

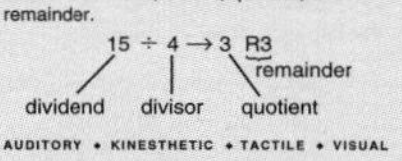

Adjusting the Activity ELL

Write the number model on the board and label the dividend, divisor, quotient, and remainder.

15 ÷ 4 → 3 R3 (dividend, divisor, quotient, remainder)

AUDITORY • KINESTHETIC • TACTILE • VISUAL

NOTE Explain that there are several symbols for division. The symbol ÷ is used for division in most textbooks and on calculators. The fraction notation symbol / is commonly used on computer keyboards, in newspapers, and in most other non-textbook situations. The symbol $\overline{)\ }$ is used mostly in textbooks when teaching the traditional long-division algorithm.

262 Unit 4

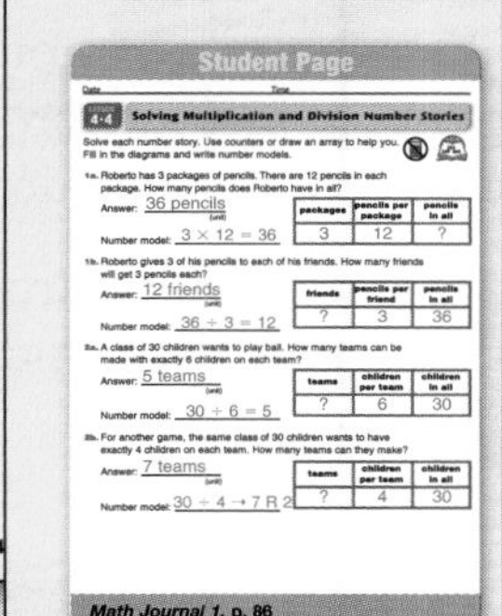

2 Ongoing Learning & Practice

▶ **Playing *Division Arrays***

SMALL-GROUP ACTIVITY

(*Student Reference Book,* p. 282)

Children practice modeling equal sharing by making arrays in *Division Arrays.* For detailed instructions, see Lesson 4-3 or page 282 in the *Student Reference Book.*

▶ **Math Boxes 4·4**

INDEPENDENT ACTIVITY

(*Math Journal 1,* p. 87)

Mixed Practice Math Boxes in this lesson are paired with Math Boxes in Lesson 4-2. The skill in Problem 6 previews Unit 5 content.

▶ **Home Link 4·4**

INDEPENDENT ACTIVITY

(*Math Masters,* p. 92)

Home Connection Children use division to solve number stories.

Student Page — Math Boxes — *Math Journal 1,* p. 87

Home Link Master — Division Number Stories — *Math Masters,* p. 92

3 Differentiation Options

READINESS

▶ **Making Equal Groups on a Number Line**

INDEPENDENT ACTIVITY 5–15 Min

(*Math Masters,* p. 93)

To provide experience with equal-grouping situations using a number-line model, have children solve equal-grouping problems by marking and counting hops on a number line.

ENRICHMENT

▶ **Finding the Mystery Number**

INDEPENDENT ACTIVITY 15–30 Min

(*Math Masters,* p. 94)

To apply children's understanding of the relationship between multiplication and division, have them find mystery numbers and identify patterns on *Math Masters,* page 94. When children have finished the page, have them share their ideas on why the Mystery Number is the same as the first number. Sample answer: First you multiply a number, then you subtract that number one time and divide by one less than you multiplied by.

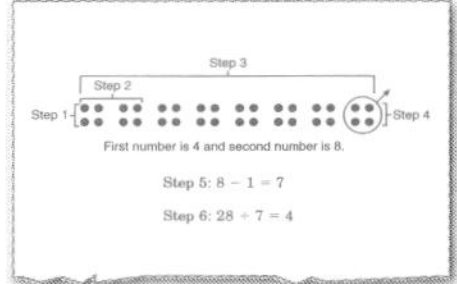

Sample answer for Start Number 4 and 2nd number 8

ELL SUPPORT

▶ **Building a Math Word Bank**

SMALL-GROUP ACTIVITY 5–15 Min

(*Differentiation Handbook*)

To provide language support for division, have children use the Word Bank template found in the *Differentiation Handbook.* Ask children to write *quotient* and *remainder,* draw a picture representing each word, and write other related words. See the *Differentiation Handbook* for more information.

Teaching Master — 4·4 Equal Groups — *Math Masters,* p. 93

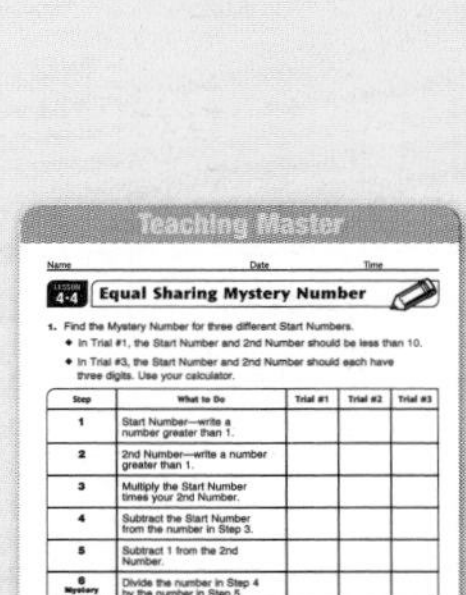

264 Unit 4 Multiplication and Division

Lesson 4·4 265

3 Differentiation Options

Includes Readiness activities which cover mathematical content necessary for student success in the lesson. English Language Learner support, Enrichment, and Extra Practice are also key features of the Differentiation Options.

Assessment

In *Everyday Mathematics,* assessment is like a motion picture revealing the development of each student's mathematical understanding over time, while giving the teacher useful feedback about the instructional needs of both individual students and the class as a whole.

Types of Assessment

Ongoing Assessment Lessons feature Ongoing Assessment: Recognizing Student Achievement and Ongoing Assessment: Informing Instruction.

Periodic Assessment Formal assessments, such as the Progress Check, are built into the *Everyday Mathematics* curriculum.

Purposes of Assessment

Formative Assessment Formative assessments provide information about students' current knowledge and abilities and are used for effectively planning future instruction. In *Everyday Mathematics,* this is called Informing Instruction.

Summative Assessment Summative assessments measure student growth and achievement. Summative assessments are included in each lesson as Recognizing Student Achievement.

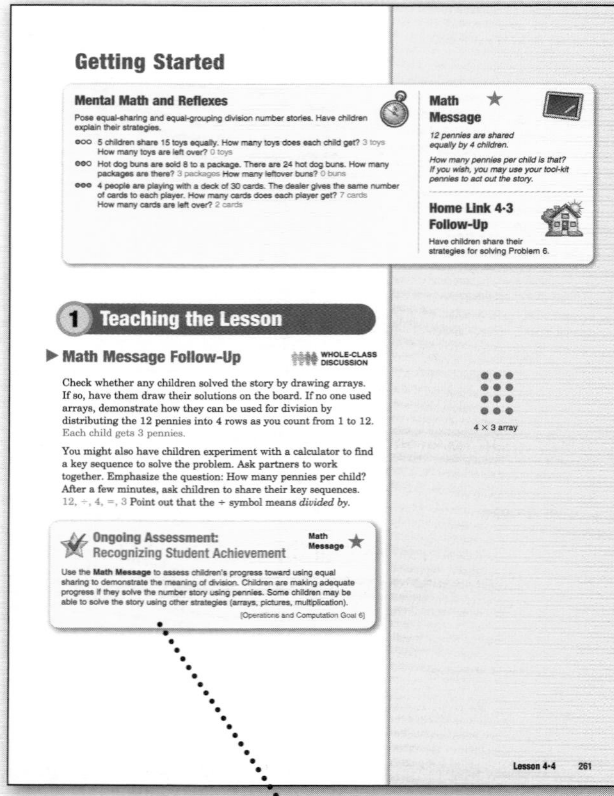

Getting Started

Mental Math and Reflexes

Pose equal-sharing and equal-grouping division number stories. Have children explain their strategies.

- 5 children share 15 toys equally. How many toys does each child get? 3 toys How many toys are left over? 0 toys
- Hot dog buns are sold 8 to a package. There are 24 hot dog buns. How many packages are there? 3 packages How many leftover buns? 0 buns
- 4 people are playing with a deck of 30 cards. The dealer gives the same number of cards to each player. How many cards does each player get? 7 cards How many cards are left over? 2 cards

Math Message

12 pennies are shared equally by 4 children.

How many pennies per child is that? If you wish, you may use your tool-kit pennies to act out the story.

Home Link 4·3 Follow-Up

Have children share their strategies for solving Problem 6.

1 Teaching the Lesson

▶ Math Message Follow-Up WHOLE-CLASS DISCUSSION

Check whether any children solved the story by drawing arrays. If so, have them draw their solutions on the board. If no one used arrays, demonstrate how they can be used for division by distributing the 12 pennies into 4 rows as you count from 1 to 12. Each child gets 3 pennies.

You might also have children experiment with a calculator to find a key sequence to solve the problem. Ask partners to work together. Emphasize the question: How many pennies per child? After a few minutes, ask children to share their key sequences. 12, ÷, 4, =, 3 Point out that the ÷ symbol means *divided by.*

4 × 3 array

Ongoing Assessment: Recognizing Student Achievement Math Message

Use the **Math Message** to assess children's progress toward using equal sharing to demonstrate the meaning of division. Children are making adequate progress if they solve the number story using pennies. Some children may be able to solve the story using other strategies (arrays, pictures, multiplication).

[Operations and Computation Goal 6]

Lesson 4·4 261

Recognizing Student Achievement

Each lesson contains a Recognizing Student Achievement note. The notes highlight tasks that can be used to monitor students' progress.

Informing Instruction

Suggests how to use observation of students' work to effectively adapt instruction.

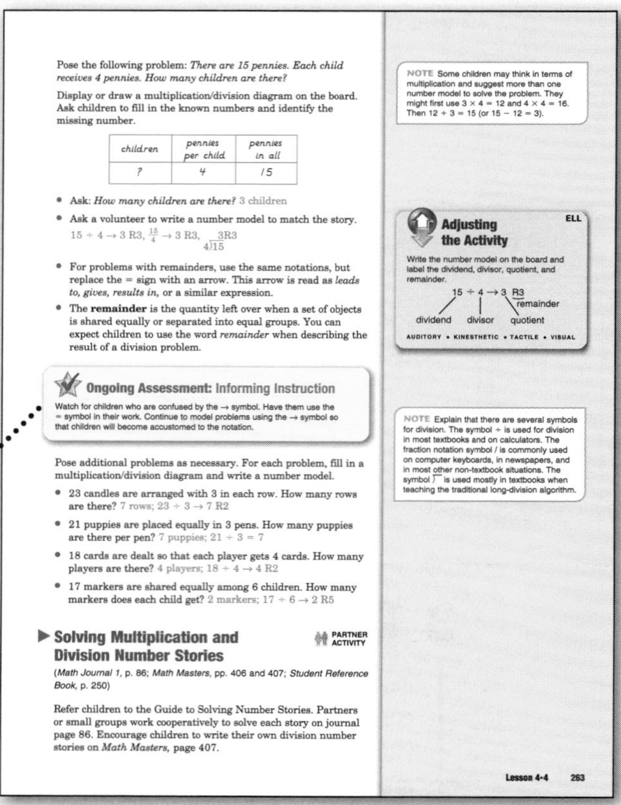

Pose the following problem: *There are 15 pennies. Each child receives 4 pennies. How many children are there?*

Display or draw a multiplication/division diagram on the board. Ask children to fill in the known numbers and identify the missing number.

children	pennies per child	pennies in all
?	4	15

- Ask: *How many children are there?* 3 children
- Ask a volunteer to write a number model to match the story. $15 \div 4 \rightarrow 3\ R3$, $\frac{15}{4} \rightarrow 3\ R3$, $4\overline{)15}$ 3R3
- For problems with remainders, use the same notations, but replace the = sign with an arrow. This arrow is read as *leads to, gives, results in,* or a similar expression.
- The **remainder** is the quantity left over when a set of objects is shared equally or separated into equal groups. You can expect children to use the word *remainder* when describing the result of a division problem.

Ongoing Assessment: Informing Instruction

Watch for children who are confused by the → symbol. Have them use the = symbol in their work. Continue to model problems using the → symbol so that children will become accustomed to the notation.

Pose additional problems as necessary. For each problem, fill in a multiplication/division diagram and write a number model.

- 23 candles are arranged with 3 in each row. How many rows are there? 7 rows; 23 ÷ 3 → 7 R2
- 21 puppies are placed equally in 3 pens. How many puppies are there per pen? 7 puppies; 21 ÷ 3 = 7
- 18 cards are dealt so that each player gets 4 cards. How many players are there? 4 players; 18 ÷ 4 → 4 R2
- 17 markers are shared equally among 6 children. How many markers does each child get? 2 markers; 17 ÷ 6 → 2 R5

▶ Solving Multiplication and Division Number Stories PARTNER ACTIVITY

(*Math Journal 1*, p. 86; *Math Masters*, pp. 406 and 407; *Student Reference Book*, p. 250)

Refer children to the Guide to Solving Number Stories. Partners or small groups work cooperatively to solve each story on journal page 86. Encourage children to write their own division number stories on *Math Masters,* page 407.

NOTE Some children may think in terms of multiplication and suggest more than one number model to solve the problem. They might first use 3 × 4 = 12 and 4 × 4 = 16. Then 12 + 3 = 15 (or 15 − 12 = 3).

Adjusting the Activity ELL

Write the number model on the board and label the dividend, divisor, quotient, and remainder.

15 ÷ 4 → 3 R3 (dividend, divisor, quotient, remainder)

AUDITORY • KINESTHETIC • TACTILE • VISUAL

NOTE Explain that there are several symbols for division. The symbol ÷ is used for division in most textbooks and on calculators. The fraction notation symbol / is commonly used on computer keyboards, in newspapers, and in most other non-textbook situations. The symbol $\overline{)\ }$ is used mostly in textbooks when teaching the traditional long-division algorithm.

Lesson 4·4 263

Progress Checks

Provides multiple assessment options. Includes Oral and Slate Assessments, Written Assessment, Open Response, and Self-Assessment.

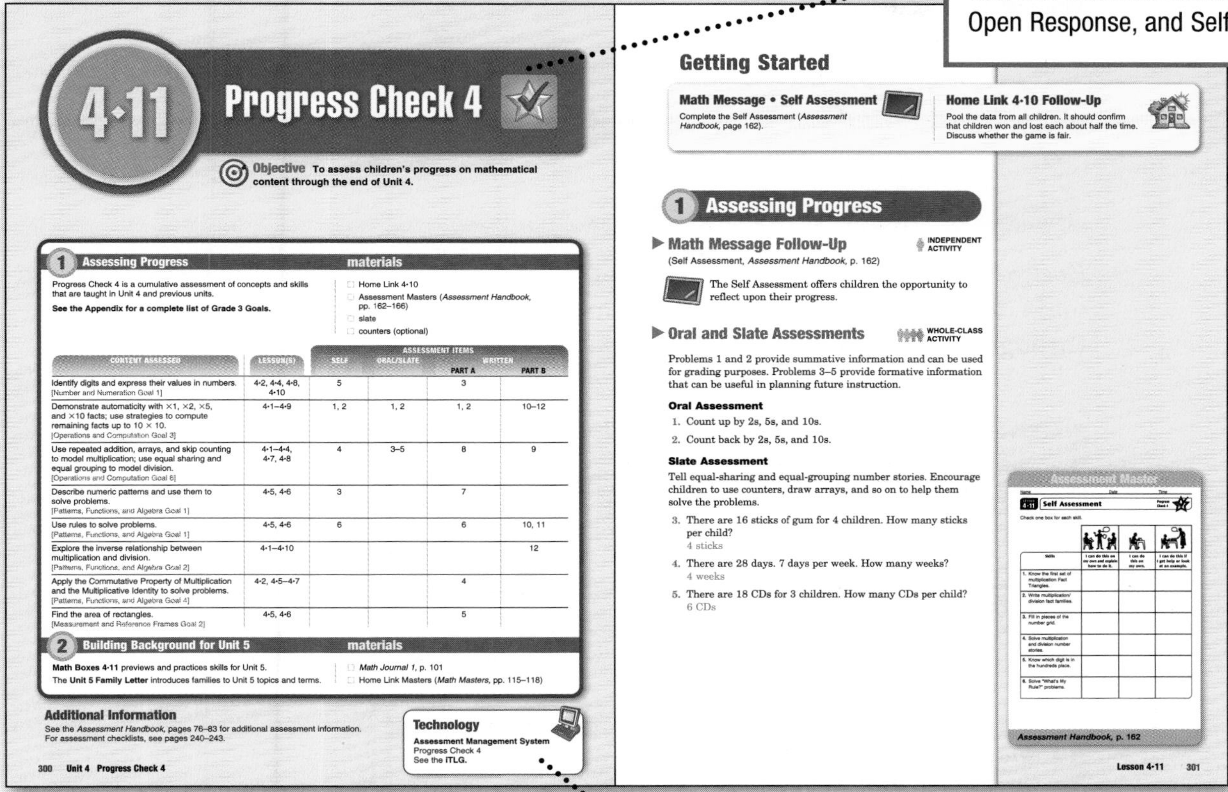

4·11 Progress Check 4

Objective To assess children's progress on mathematical content through the end of Unit 4.

1 Assessing Progress

Progress Check 4 is a cumulative assessment of concepts and skills that are taught in Unit 4 and previous units.

See the Appendix for a complete list of Grade 3 Goals.

materials

- Home Link 4-10
- Assessment Masters (*Assessment Handbook*, pp. 162–166)
- slate
- counters (optional)

Content Assessed	Lesson(s)	Self	Oral/Slate	Written Part A	Written Part B
Identify digits and express their values in numbers. [Number and Numeration Goal 1]	4-2, 4-4, 4-8, 4-10	5		3	
Demonstrate automaticity with ×1, ×2, ×5, and ×10 facts; use strategies to compute remaining facts up to 10 × 10. [Operations and Computation Goal 3]	4-1–4-9	1, 2	1, 2	1, 2	10–12
Use repeated addition, arrays, and skip counting to model multiplication; use equal sharing and equal grouping to model division. [Operations and Computation Goal 6]	4-1–4-4, 4-7, 4-8	4	3–5	8	9
Describe numeric patterns and use them to solve problems. [Patterns, Functions, and Algebra Goal 1]	4-5, 4-6	3		7	
Use rules to solve problems. [Patterns, Functions, and Algebra Goal 1]	4-5, 4-6	6		6	10, 11
Explore the inverse relationship between multiplication and division. [Patterns, Functions, and Algebra Goal 2]	4-1–4-10				12
Apply the Commutative Property of Multiplication and the Multiplicative Identity to solve problems. [Patterns, Functions, and Algebra Goal 4]	4-2, 4-5–4-7			4	
Find the area of rectangles. [Measurement and Reference Frames Goal 2]	4-5, 4-6			5	

2 Building Background for Unit 5

Math Boxes 4·11 previews and practices skills for Unit 5.

The **Unit 5 Family Letter** introduces families to Unit 5 topics and terms.

materials

- *Math Journal 1*, p. 101
- Home Link Masters (*Math Masters*, pp. 115–118)

Additional Information

See the *Assessment Handbook*, pages 76–83 for additional assessment information. For assessment checklists, see pages 240–243.

Technology

Assessment Management System Progress Check 4 See the **iTLG.**

300 Unit 4 Progress Check 4

Getting Started

Math Message • Self Assessment

Complete the Self Assessment (*Assessment Handbook*, page 162).

Home Link 4·10 Follow-Up

Pool the data from all children. It should confirm that children won and lost each about half the time. Discuss whether the game is fair.

1 Assessing Progress

▶ **Math Message Follow-Up** INDEPENDENT ACTIVITY

(Self Assessment, *Assessment Handbook*, p. 162)

The Self Assessment offers children the opportunity to reflect upon their progress.

▶ **Oral and Slate Assessments** WHOLE-CLASS ACTIVITY

Problems 1 and 2 provide summative information and can be used for grading purposes. Problems 3–5 provide formative information that can be useful in planning future instruction.

Oral Assessment

1. Count up by 2s, 5s, and 10s.
2. Count back by 2s, 5s, and 10s.

Slate Assessment

Tell equal-sharing and equal-grouping number stories. Encourage children to use counters, draw arrays, and so on to help them solve the problems.

3. There are 16 sticks of gum for 4 children. How many sticks per child? 4 sticks
4. There are 28 days. 7 days per week. How many weeks? 4 weeks
5. There are 18 CDs for 3 children. How many CDs per child? 6 CDs

Assessment Master — Self Assessment — *Assessment Handbook*, p. 162

Lesson 4·11 301

Written Assessment

Each Written Assessment has two parts: Part A Recognizing Student Achievement (summative assessment), and Part B Informing Instruction (formative assessment).

Assessment Management System

Web-based software provides teachers with the opportunity to monitor and document progress toward Grade-Level Goals.

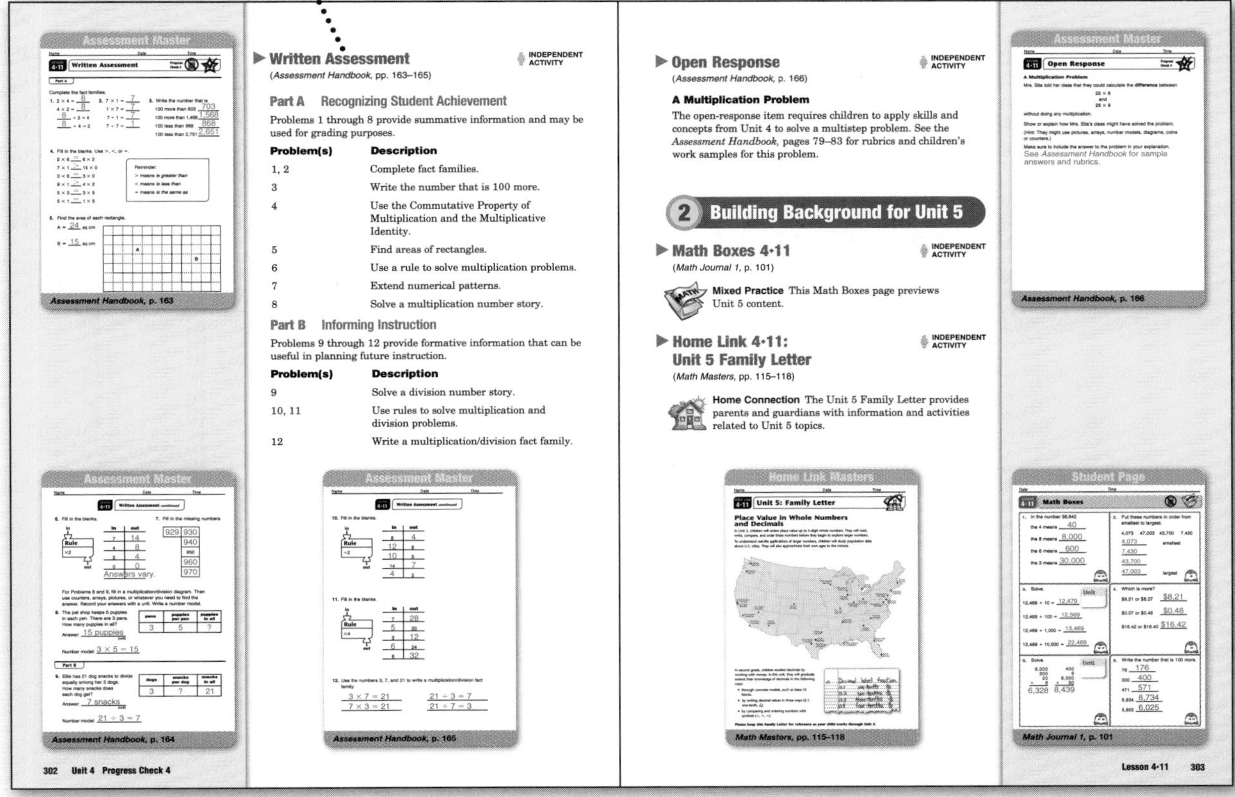

Assessment Master — Written Assessment — *Assessment Handbook*, p. 163

▶ **Written Assessment** INDEPENDENT ACTIVITY

(*Assessment Handbook*, pp. 163–165)

Part A Recognizing Student Achievement

Problems 1 through 8 provide summative information and may be used for grading purposes.

Problem(s)	Description
1, 2	Complete fact families.
3	Write the number that is 100 more.
4	Use the Commutative Property of Multiplication and the Multiplicative Identity.
5	Find areas of rectangles.
6	Use a rule to solve multiplication problems.
7	Extend numerical patterns.
8	Solve a multiplication number story.

Part B Informing Instruction

Problems 9 through 12 provide formative information that can be useful in planning future instruction.

Problem(s)	Description
9	Solve a division number story.
10, 11	Use rules to solve multiplication and division problems.
12	Write a multiplication/division fact family.

▶ **Open Response** INDEPENDENT ACTIVITY

(*Assessment Handbook*, p. 166)

A Multiplication Problem

The open-response item requires children to apply skills and concepts from Unit 4 to solve a multistep problem. See the *Assessment Handbook*, pages 79–83 for rubrics and children's work samples for this problem.

2 Building Background for Unit 5

▶ **Math Boxes 4·11** INDEPENDENT ACTIVITY

(*Math Journal 1*, p. 101)

Mixed Practice This Math Boxes page previews Unit 5 content.

▶ **Home Link 4·11: Unit 5 Family Letter** INDEPENDENT ACTIVITY

(*Math Masters*, pp. 115–118)

Home Connection The Unit 5 Family Letter provides parents and guardians with information and activities related to Unit 5 topics.

Assessment Master — Open Response — *Assessment Handbook*, p. 166

Assessment Master — *Assessment Handbook*, p. 164

Assessment Master — *Assessment Handbook*, p. 165

Home Link Masters — Unit 5: Family Letter — *Math Masters*, pp. 115–118

Student Page — Math Boxes — *Math Journal 1*, p. 101

302 Unit 4 Progress Check 4 | Lesson 4·11 303

Technology Support

Technology Options

Everyday Mathematics offers teachers and students many technology options to make teaching easier and learning more fun! These options are available through the internet or on CD-ROM.

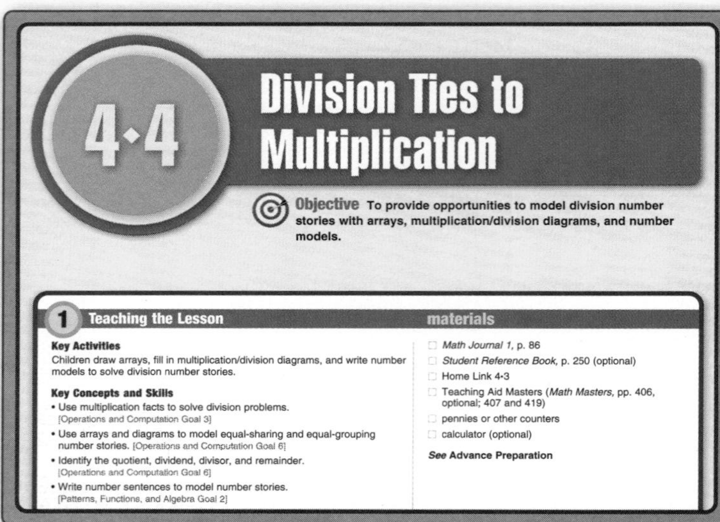

Interactive Teacher's Lesson Guide This grade-level specific software provides access to student and teacher materials. Content is searchable.

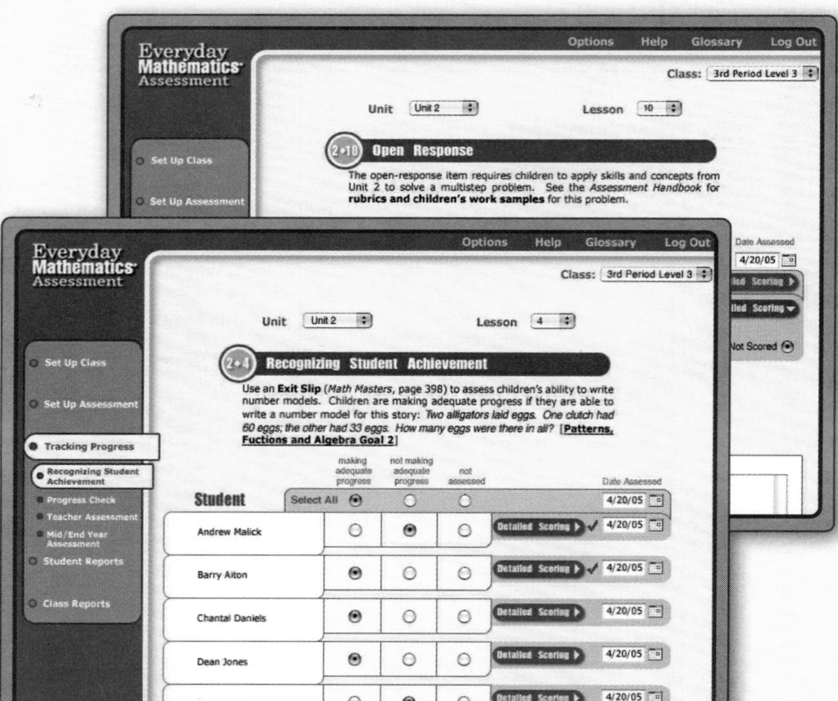

Assessment Management System Web-based software that provides teachers with the opportunity to track progress toward Grade-Level Goals.

Supporting Students and Home

Family Involvement

Within *Everyday Mathematics* there are several opportunities for supporting the home-school connection.

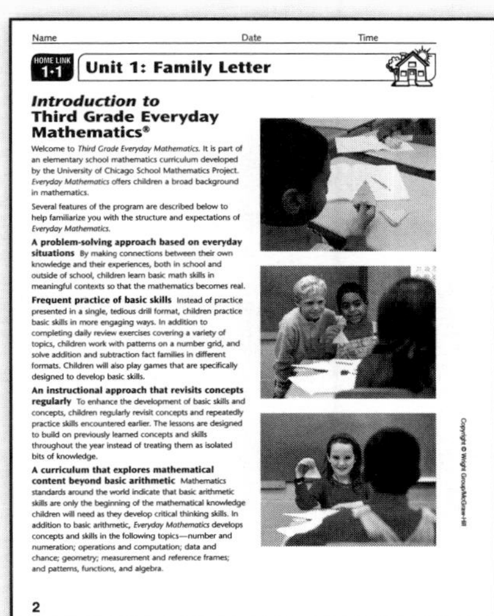

Name Date Time

HOME LINK 1•1 **Unit 1: Family Letter**

***Introduction to* Third Grade Everyday Mathematics®**

Welcome to *Third Grade Everyday Mathematics*. It is part of an elementary school mathematics curriculum developed by the University of Chicago School Mathematics Project. *Everyday Mathematics* offers children a broad background in mathematics.

Several features of the program are described below to help familiarize you with the structure and expectations of *Everyday Mathematics*.

A problem-solving approach based on everyday situations By making connections between their own knowledge and their experiences, both in school and outside of school, children learn basic math skills in meaningful contexts so that the mathematics becomes real.

Frequent practice of basic skills Instead of practice presented in a single, tedious drill format, children practice basic skills in more engaging ways. In addition to completing daily review exercises covering a variety of topics, children work with patterns on a number grid, and solve addition and subtraction fact families in different formats. Children will also play games that are specifically designed to develop basic skills.

An instructional approach that revisits concepts regularly To enhance the development of basic skills and concepts, children regularly revisit concepts and repeatedly practice skills encountered earlier. The lessons are designed to build on previously learned concepts and skills throughout the year instead of treating them as isolated bits of knowledge.

A curriculum that explores mathematical content beyond basic arithmetic Mathematics standards around the world indicate that basic arithmetic skills are only the beginning of the mathematical knowledge children will need as they develop critical thinking skills. In addition to basic arithmetic, *Everyday Mathematics* develops concepts and skills in the following topics—number and numeration; operations and computation; data and chance; geometry; measurement and reference frames; and patterns, functions, and algebra.

Copyright © Wright Group/McGraw-Hill

2

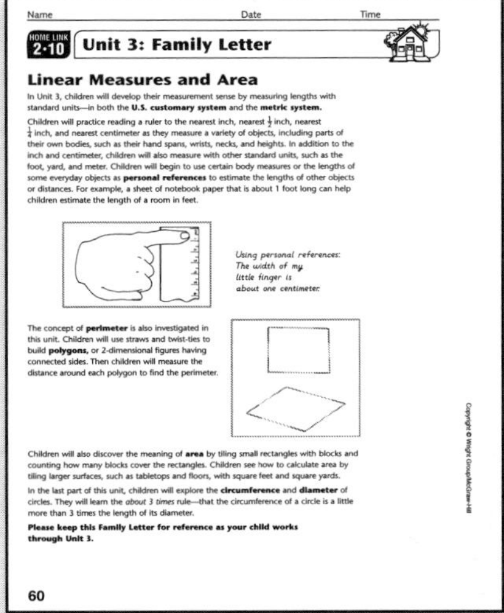

Name Date Time

HOME LINK 2•10 **Unit 3: Family Letter**

Linear Measures and Area

In Unit 3, children will develop their measurement sense by measuring lengths with standard units—in both the **U.S. customary system** and the **metric system.**

Children will practice reading a ruler to the nearest inch, nearest $\frac{1}{2}$ inch, nearest $\frac{1}{4}$ inch, and nearest centimeter as they measure a variety of objects, including parts of their own bodies, such as their hand spans, wrists, necks, and heights. In addition to the inch and centimeter, children will also measure with other standard units, such as the foot, yard, and meter. Children will begin to use certain body measures or the lengths of some everyday objects as **personal references** to estimate the lengths of other objects or distances. For example, a sheet of notebook paper that is about 1 foot long can help children estimate the length of a room in feet.

Using personal references: The width of my little finger is about one centimeter.

The concept of **perimeter** is also investigated in this unit. Children will use straws and twist-ties to build **polygons,** or 2-dimensional figures having connected sides. Then children will measure the distance around each polygon to find the perimeter.

Children will also discover the meaning of **area** by tiling small rectangles with blocks and counting how many blocks cover the rectangles. Children see how to calculate area by tiling larger surfaces, such as tabletops and floors, with square feet and square yards.

In the last part of this unit, children will explore the **circumference** and **diameter** of circles. They will learn the *about 3 times* rule—that the circumference of a circle is a little more than 3 times the length of its diameter.

Please keep this Family Letter for reference as your child works through Unit 3.

Copyright © Wright Group/McGraw-Hill

60

Family Letters Provide families with information on the *Everyday Mathematics* structure and curriculum. Each unit's Family Letter explains key content and vocabulary for the unit, directions for appropriate games, Do-Anytime Activities, and answers to most Home/Study Links for the unit.

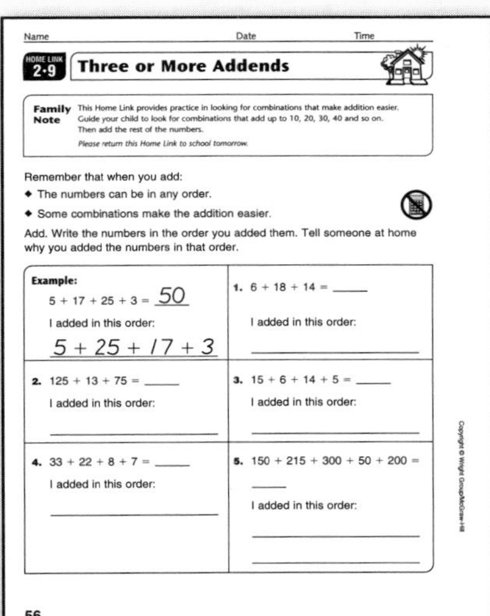

Name Date Time

HOME LINK 2•9 **Three or More Addends**

Family Note This Home Link provides practice in looking for combinations that make addition easier. Guide your child to look for combinations that add up to 10, 20, 30, 40 and so on. Then add the rest of the numbers.

Please return this Home Link to school tomorrow.

Remember that when you add:

- The numbers can be in any order.
- Some combinations make the addition easier.

Add. Write the numbers in the order you added them. Tell someone at home why you added the numbers in that order.

Example: 5 + 17 + 25 + 3 = 50 I added in this order: 5 + 25 + 17 + 3	**1.** 6 + 18 + 14 = ____ I added in this order: ____
2. 125 + 13 + 75 = ____ I added in this order: ____	**3.** 15 + 6 + 14 + 5 = ____ I added in this order: ____
4. 33 + 22 + 8 + 7 = ____ I added in this order: ____	**5.** 150 + 215 + 300 + 50 + 200 = ____ I added in this order: ____

Copyright © Wright Group/McGraw-Hill

56

Home Links/Study Links Each lesson has a Home/Study Link. Home/Study Links include extensions of lessons and ongoing review problems. They show families what students are doing in mathematics.

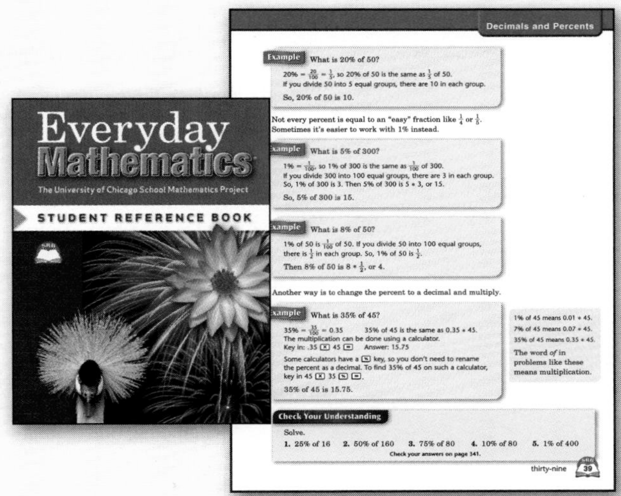

Decimals and Percents

Example What is 20% of 50?

20% = $\frac{20}{100}$ = $\frac{1}{5}$, so 20% of 50 is the same as $\frac{1}{5}$ of 50.
If you divide 50 into 5 equal groups, there are 10 in each group.

So, 20% of 50 is 10.

Not every percent is equal to an "easy" fraction like $\frac{1}{4}$ or $\frac{1}{5}$. Sometimes it's easier to work with 1% instead.

Example What is 5% of 300?

1% = $\frac{1}{100}$, so 1% of 300 is the same as $\frac{1}{100}$ of 300.
If you divide 300 into 100 equal groups, there are 3 in each group.
So, 1% of 300 is 3. Then 5% of 300 is 5 ∗ 3, or 15.

So, 5% of 300 is 15.

Example What is 8% of 50?

1% of 50 is $\frac{1}{100}$ of 50. If you divide 50 into 100 equal groups, there is $\frac{1}{2}$ in each group. So, 1% of 50 is $\frac{1}{2}$.

Then 8% of 50 is 8 ∗ $\frac{1}{2}$, or 4.

Another way is to change the percent to a decimal and multiply.

Example What is 35% of 45?

35% = $\frac{35}{100}$ = 0.35 35% of 45 is the same as 0.35 ∗ 45.
The multiplication can be done using a calculator.
Key in: .35 [×] 45 [=] Answer: 15.75

Some calculators have a [%] key, so you don't need to rename the percent as a decimal. To find 35% of 45 on such a calculator, key in 45 [×] 35 [%] [=].

35% of 45 is 15.75.

1% of 45 means 0.01 ∗ 45.
7% of 45 means 0.07 ∗ 45.
35% of 45 means 0.35 ∗ 45.
The word *of* in problems like these means multiplication.

Check Your Understanding

Solve.

1. 25% of 16 **2.** 50% of 160 **3.** 75% of 80 **4.** 10% of 80 **5.** 1% of 400

Check your answers on page 341.

thirty-nine 39

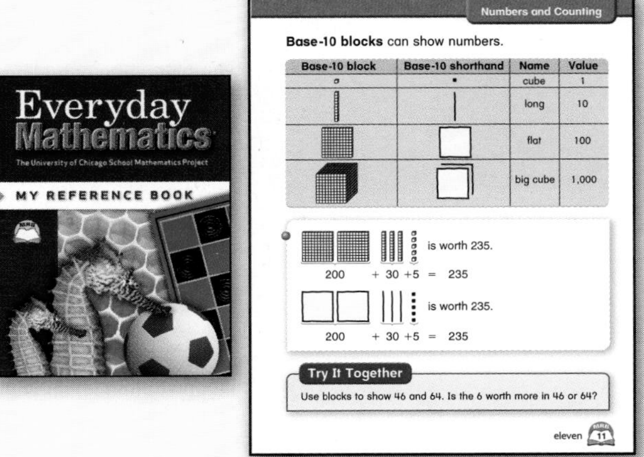

Numbers and Counting

Base-10 blocks can show numbers.

Base-10 block	Base-10 shorthand	Name	Value
		cube	1
		long	10
		flat	100
		big cube	1,000

is worth 235.

200 + 30 + 5 = 235

is worth 235.

200 + 30 + 5 = 235

Try It Together

Use blocks to show 46 and 64. Is the 6 worth more in 46 or 64?

eleven 11

Home Connection Handbook This teacher- and administrator-focused handbook provides support for communicating with families. Includes blackline masters for easier communication.

Student Reference Book and My Reference Book These books are resources that can be sent home to provide parents with support on lesson content. The reference books include explanations and examples of mathematical topics, as well as directions for *Everyday Mathematics* games.

Contents

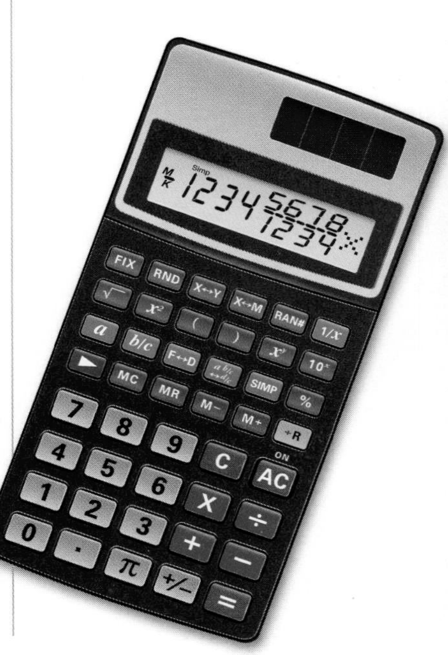

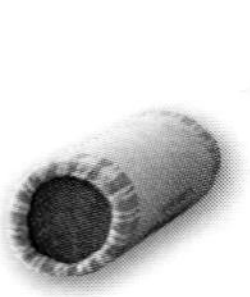

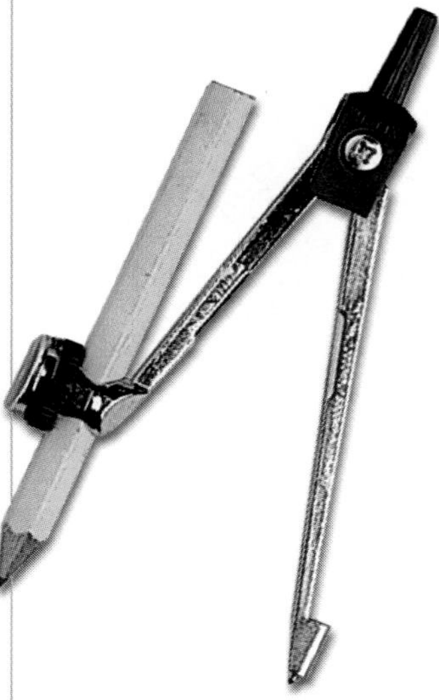

Volume 2

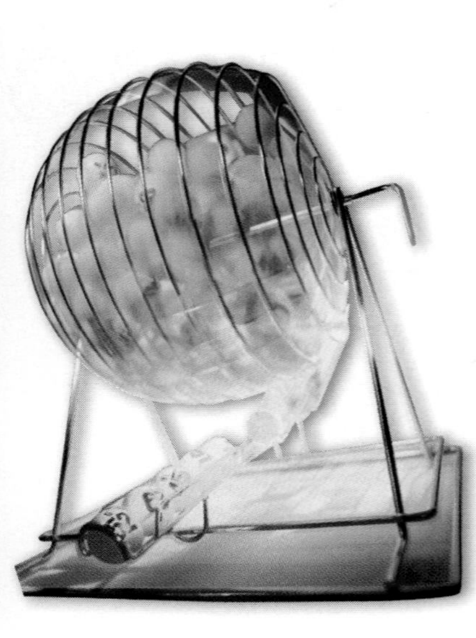

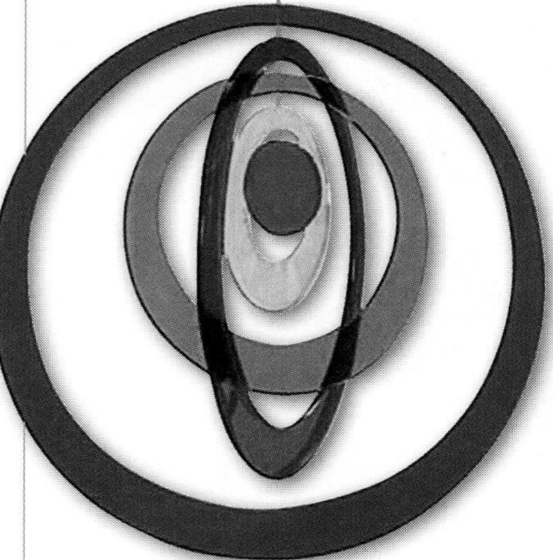

Welcome to *Everyday Mathematics*, the elementary school mathematics curriculum developed by the University of Chicago School Mathematics Project (UCSMP). *Everyday Mathematics* offers you and your students a broad, rich, and balanced experience in mathematics.

Sixth Grade Everyday Mathematics emphasizes the following content strands, skills, and concepts:

- **Number and Numeration** Reading, writing, and comparing whole numbers, signed numbers, fractions, decimals, and percents; reading, writing, and interpreting integer powers of 10; converting among standard, number-and-word, scientific, and expanded notations and among fractions, decimals, percents, and mixed numbers; renaming fractions and mixed numbers in simplest form.
- **Operations and Computation** Using paper-and-pencil algorithms for basic operations with whole numbers, fractions, and decimals; using mental arithmetic to compute exact answers and to estimate; performing operations with signed numbers and with numbers in scientific notation; solving problems using unit rates and ratios; solving proportions; using ratios in scale drawings and size-change factors in similar figures; rounding to any specified place; adding and subtracting fractions and mixed numbers with unlike denominators; multiplying and dividing fractions; applying divisibility rules to find least common multiples and greatest common factors.
- **Data and Chance** Expressing probabilities as fractions, decimals, and percents; using tree diagrams to analyze simple probabilistic situations; understanding that the sum of the probabilities for all possible outcomes of an experiment is 1; making predictions based on theoretical probabilities and understanding why actual outcomes may differ from predicted outcomes; constructing and interpreting line plots, stem-and-leaf plots, step graphs, circle graphs, bar graphs, and line graphs; understanding how changing the scale on the axes affects a graph; using and comparing measures of central tendency (mean, median, mode) to characterize and interpret data sets; understanding how changes in a data set may affect the mean, median, and mode; formulating a question, carrying out a survey or an experiment, recording data, and communicating results.
- **Measurement and Reference Frames** Measuring and estimating length to $\frac{1}{16}$ inch and 1 mm; estimating, measuring, and drawing angles; converting within and between customary and metric units of measure; using formulas to calculate areas, perimeters, circumferences, and volumes; naming, locating, and plotting points in all four quadrants of a coordinate grid.
- **Geometry** Comparing and contrasting properties of 2-dimensional and 3-dimensional figures; understanding congruence and similarity; visualizing, describing, and sketching translations, reflections, rotations, and size-change transformations; classifying angles; identifying angle relationships in triangles and quadrilaterals, in parallel lines cut by a transversal, and in intersecting and perpendicular lines—with and without tools; understanding and applying basic concepts in topology; classifying tessellations.

- **Patterns, Functions, and Algebra** Recognizing, describing, and extending complex patterns; finding the *n*th term in a sequence; using variables and open number sentences to represent problem situations; writing equations to fit given tables of numbers and line graphs; evaluating algebraic expressions; solving linear equations with one and two unknowns by performing the same operation(s) to both sides of the equation; representing linear functions as equations, in tables and graphs, and verbally as rules; translating from one such representation to another; understanding and applying the order of operations and the distributive property.

Throughout *Everyday Mathematics,* emphasis is placed on:

- A realistic approach to problem solving in everyday situations, applications, and purely mathematical contexts.
- Frequent and distributed practice of basic skills through ongoing program routines and mathematical games.
- An instructional approach that revisits topics regularly to ensure full concept development and long-term retention of learning.
- Activities that explore a wide variety of mathematical content and offer opportunities for students to apply their skills and understandings to geometry, measurement, and algebra.

Everyday Mathematics is a comprehensive program for students and teachers. During your first year teaching the program, you will become increasingly comfortable with the content, components, and strategies of *Sixth Grade Everyday Mathematics.* You and your students will experience mathematical processes as a part of everyday work and play. These processes will gradually shape students' ways of thinking about mathematics and will foster the development of their mathematical intuitions and understandings. By the end of the year, we think you will agree that the rewards are worth the effort.

Have an exciting year!

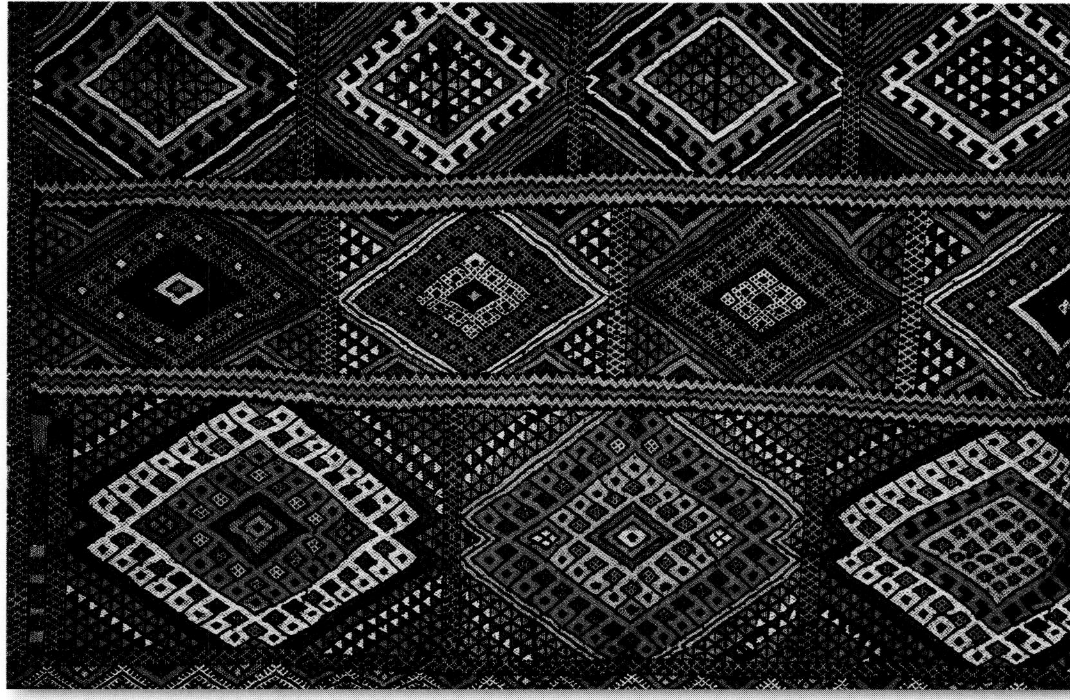

Professional Preparation

Components for *Sixth Grade* Everyday Mathematics

Go to...	When you need...	
Teacher's Lesson Guide	• daily lessons • daily assessment suggestions • readiness, enrichment, extra practice, and ELL suggestions	• unit support information • key vocabulary • Grade-Level Goals
Teacher's Reference Manual	• background on mathematical content • ideas for curriculum and classroom management	• a comprehensive glossary
Assessment Handbook	• suggestions for ongoing and periodic assessment • Program Goals and Grade-Level Goals for all grades	• Assessment Masters • sample rubrics for open-response items
Differentiation Handbook	• suggestions for meeting diverse needs	• unit-specific ideas
5-Minute Math	• brief activities for transition time and extra practice	
Content-by-Strand Poster	• key concepts and skills organized by content strand and paced by month	• Program Goals and Grade-Level Goals
Home Connection Handbook	• suggestions for home-school communication	
Student Reference Book	• concise explanations of mathematical concepts • worked examples	• game directions • a reference for students to read with teachers and/or parents and others
Math Masters	• blackline masters for lessons, Study Links, projects, teaching aids, and games	
Student Math Journal	• lesson support material for students to analyze and complete • activity sheets	• paired Math Boxes for mixed practice • a year-long record of each student's mathematical development

Suggested Reading & Lesson Preparation

In order to prepare for effective classroom and curriculum management, we suggest the following before you teach *Everyday Mathematics* for the first time.

- ☐ Review each component in your Teacher's Resource Package (TRP). Locate information and materials so you can find them throughout the school year. See the chart on p. xxvi.
- ☐ Browse through the *Teacher's Reference Manual,* the *Assessment Handbook,* the *Differentiation Handbook,* the *Home Connection Handbook,* and the *Student Reference Book.*
- ☐ Read the Management Guide in the *Teacher's Reference Manual,* which has many useful tips and explanations.
- ☐ Before you teach each unit, including Unit 1, read the Unit Organizer in the *Teacher's Lesson Guide* and refer to the Advance Preparation section in each lesson. Also read the relevant sections of the *Teacher's Reference Manual,* the *Assessment Handbook,* and the *Differentiation Handbook.*
- ☐ Prepare a daily math schedule. *Everyday Mathematics* lessons have several parts, which can be done at different times throughout the day. Your schedule should include time for Getting Started activities (Math Message, Mental Math and Reflexes, and Study Link Follow-Up); Teaching the Lesson; Ongoing Learning & Practice activities, including Math Boxes and games; and possibly Differentiation Options.
- ☐ Prepare materials that will be used throughout the year. Special items for consideration include:
    - For the Mental Math and Reflexes routine, gather slates and chalk (or dry erase boards and markers) and old socks for erasers.
    - Prepare a lost-and-found box for misplaced items.
    - Assign an ID number to each student to simplify matching students and manipulatives.
- ☐ Prepare a supply of paper:
  Blank $8\frac{1}{2}$ in. by 11 in. (full, half, and quarter-size sheets)
  Graph paper (1 centimeter; see *Math Masters,* page 408)
- ☐ Obtain the optional books listed in the literature links section of the Unit Organizer for upcoming units.

Organizing Your Classroom

Items for Display

Before the school year begins, we suggest that you gather the following items for classroom display. By taking time to prepare these items your first year, and laminating them if possible, you will be able to reuse them year after year. See the Management Guide of your *Teacher's Reference Manual* for more information and suggestions.

- ☐ Number Line (–35 to 180)
- ☐ Poster 1: Probability Meter (English/Spanish)
- ☐ Poster 2: The Real Number Line (English/Spanish)
- ☐ Poster 3: ∗, / Facts Table (English/Spanish)
- ☐ A Class Data Pad (for example, chart paper on an easel)

Classroom Setup

The following items should be considered as you set up your classroom for *Everyday Mathematics.* Try several arrangements until you find one that is comfortable and effective for you and your students. Visit other classrooms in your building to observe and discuss what works for your colleagues.

- ☐ Prepare and label a location in the classroom where students can deposit their written work such as Math Messages, Study Links, Exit Slips, and so on.
- ☐ Arrange the classroom to allow for easy access to manipulatives and to facilitate efficient transitions for individual, partner, and small-group activities.
- ☐ Organize class and individual manipulatives for easy access and efficient use of storage space.
- ☐ Allow space for math center(s). Selected games and activities can then be left in this space for ongoing practice or free exploration.
- ☐ Identify a place where the daily Math Message will be posted. See the *Teacher's Reference Manual* for information about the Math Message.
- ☐ One or more computers with Internet access can let students use software and Web sites that are recommended in *Sixth Grade Everyday Mathematics.*

Manipulatives

The table below lists the materials that are used on a regular basis throughout *Sixth Grade Everyday Mathematics*. Some lessons call for a few additional materials, which you or your students can bring in at the appropriate time.

Quantity	Item
1 per student	Calculator (Texas Instruments TI-15 or Casio fx-55 recommended)*
1 per student	Compass, Helix
1 pkg (2,000)	Connectors
1 set of 4 cups	Cup Set, Standard
1 per student	Dice, Dot
15 decks	Everything Math Deck
1 per student	Geometry Template (in student materials set)
1	Liter Pitcher
1	Liter Volume Cube
10	Metersticks, Dual Scale
1	Number Line, –35 to 180
1 set (250)	Pattern Blocks
1	Rocker Balance
1 per student	Slate or Marker Board
1 pkg (500)	Straws
15	Tape Measure, Retractable
1	Tape Measure, 30 m/100'
1 per student	Tool-kit Bags*
15	Transparent Mirrors

All of the items above are available from Wright Group/McGraw-Hill. They may be purchased either as a comprehensive classroom manipulatives kit or as individual components. The manipulatives kit provides appropriate quantities for a class of 25 and comes packaged in durable plastic tubs with labels.

* *Calculators and tool-kit bags are available from Wright Group/McGraw-Hill for individual purchase only.*

Additional Valuable Classroom Resources

- Base-10 Blocks (Thousands Block, Hundreds Flats, Tens Rods, Unit Cubes)
- Chalkboard Compass
- Geoboards, Two Sided (7" × 7")
- Overhead Projector Materials
- Overhead Calculator
- Rubber Bands

Instruction

The following sections introduce instructional procedures and suggestions for implementing *Everyday Mathematics.* We encourage you to read these pages and refer to them throughout the school year.

Program Routines

Everyday Mathematics uses a number of program routines that are incorporated throughout all grade levels. These routines provide a consistent and familiar format for ongoing practice and applications. Below is a list of the program routines you will encounter in *Sixth Grade Everyday Mathematics.* The lesson in which each routine is first used has been noted. Refer to the Management Guide in the *Teacher's Reference Manual* for more information.

Mental Math and Reflexes (Lesson 1-1)
Math Message (Lesson 1-1)
Games (Lesson 1-2)
Math Boxes (Lesson 1-1)
Study Links (Lesson 1-1)
"What's My Rule?" (Lesson 2-4)
Museums (Lesson 1-1)

Students who have used *Fifth Grade Everyday Mathematics* will be familiar with the above routines, so most can be reintroduced with a minimum of explanation.

Suggestions for building games into your instructional program:

- Include games as part of your daily morning routine.
- Devote the first or last 10 minutes of each math class to playing games from the current unit.
- Designate one math class per week as Games Day. Set up stations that feature the unit games. Ask parent volunteers to assist in the rotation of students through these stations.
- Set up a Games Corner that features some of the students' favorite games. Encourage students to visit this corner during free time. Change the games frequently to maintain student interest.

Games

A significant amount of practice in *Everyday Mathematics* is formatted as games, which are accordingly integral to the program and must not be omitted. Establish a games routine during the first unit and maintain it throughout the year. Once established, the routine will become self-sustaining, as much by the students' enthusiasm as by your effort. Make sure that all students are afforded time to play the games, especially those students who require the most practice.

Museums

Everyday Mathematics encourages the development of classroom museums, using a bulletin board or table where related items can be collected, categorized, and labeled. *Sixth Grade Everyday Mathematics* includes the following museums:

- Graphs Museum (Unit 1)
- Fractions, Decimals, and Percents Museum (Unit 4)
- Rates and Ratios Museum (Unit 8)
- Tessellations Museum (Unit 10)

Projects

Sixth Grade Everyday Mathematics provides eight optional projects, each of which includes an array of mathematics activities that focus on a theme of interest to students. The Unit Organizers in the *Teacher's Lesson Guide* include reminders about these projects at appropriate times throughout the year. Projects typically take one or two days to complete, depending upon how many of the suggested activities you incorporate. Projects involve a range of concepts and skills; integrate mathematics with science, social studies, history, and art; and allow you to assess students' abilities to apply the mathematics they have learned in cross-curricular contexts. Projects are also often memorable for students.

Refer to the Management Guide in the *Teacher's Reference Manual* and the Unit Organizers in the *Teacher's Lesson Guide* for more information. Detailed explanations for the projects are found at the back of the *Teacher's Lesson Guide*.

The *Sixth Grade Everyday Mathematics Student Reference Book* also includes a special set of Art and Design projects. Unlike the regular projects, which are intended for the entire class, the Art and Design projects are intended for individual students or small groups. You may find the Art and Design projects useful in adjusting the program to accommodate individual needs.

Assessment

Everyday Mathematics supports a balanced approach to assessment that provides information for guiding instruction and for evaluating student performance. Assessment takes place on an ongoing basis as students complete their everyday work and in special periodic assessments, such as the Progress Check lesson at the end of each unit. Information for assessment is gathered through teacher observations while students are working, and through students' written products.

Refer to the *Assessment Handbook* and the Unit Organizers in the *Teacher's Lesson Guide* for detailed information regarding student assessment.

Differentiation

Everyday Mathematics has been designed to accommodate a wide range of student backgrounds and abilities, including English language learners. The program also includes many tools and suggestions to help teachers differentiate instruction to meet students' diverse needs, including Readiness, Enrichment, Extra Practice and ELL Support activities in Part 3 of the lessons and Adjusting the Activity suggestions in Parts 1 and 2. Differentiated instruction gives students multiple options for taking in information, making sense of ideas, building skills, and communicating what they have learned.

Refer to the *Differentiation Handbook* and the Unit Organizers in the *Teacher's Lesson Guide* for detailed information about differentiation in *Everyday Mathematics.*

Providing for Home-School Connections

Comprehensive and consistent home-school communication is essential for successful implementation of *Everyday Mathematics*. The *Home Connection Handbook* has many suggestions and tools that can help you introduce parents and primary caregivers to the *Everyday Mathematics* curriculum. Grade-specific Family Letters and Study Links in the *Math Masters* book facilitate ongoing communication and engage parents as partners in the learning process. Individual assessment checklists in the *Assessment Handbook* are a valuable communication tool during parent conferences.

Refer to the *Home Connection Handbook* for more information.

4–6 Games Correlation Chart

Game	Grade 4 Lesson	Grade 5 Lesson	Grade 6 Lesson	Basic Facts	Operations	Calculator	Numeration	Geometry	Data	Algebra	Ref. Frames	Mental Math	Strategy
				Skill and Concept Areas									
Addition Top-It	1◆2	2◆2		●	●		●					●	
Algebra Election		4◆7	6◆11		●	●			●	●	●		●
Angle Tangle	6◆6	3◆6	5◆1		●			●			●		
Base-10 Exchange	4◆2						●						
Baseball Multiplication	3◆3	*		●	●							●	
Beat the Calculator	3◆5			●	●	●						●	
Build-It		8◆1	4◆2				●						●
Buzz and Bizz Buzz	3◆2				●		●						
Calculator 10,000	*				●	●							
Chances Are	7◆11								●				
Coin Top-It	4◆3				●		●					●	
Coordinate Search		12◆8									●		●
Credits/Debits Game	10◆6	7◆8	3◆7		●					●		●	
Credits/Debits Game (Advanced Version)	11◆6		6◆3		●					●		●	
Divisibility Dash		4◆4	2◆6	●	●		●					●	●
Division Arrays	3◆5			●	●							●	
Division Dash	6◆3	4◆2			●	●						●	
Division Top-It	*	4◆5	2◆7	●	●		●					●	
Doggone Decimal			2◆4		●	●	●					●	●
Estimation Squeeze		5◆5				●	●					●	
Exponent Ball		7◆1	2◆10		●	●	●					●	
Factor Bingo		1◆7		●	●		●					●	
Factor Captor		1◆4	3◆2	●	●		●					●	●
First to 100		4◆7	8◆12	●	●					●		●	
Fishing for Digits	2◆4				●	●	●						●
500		7◆8			●								
Frac-Tac-Toe		5◆7	4◆8		●		●					●	●
Fraction Action, Fraction Friction		8◆4	4◆4		●		●					●	
Fraction Capture		6◆9	4◆1		●								●
Fraction Match	7◆6						●					●	●
Fraction Of	7◆2	5◆11			●		●					●	●
Fraction/Percent Concentration	9◆3	5◆8			●		●					●	
Fraction Spin		8◆5			●		●						●
Fraction Top-It	7◆9	5◆1					●						
Fraction/Whole Number Top-It			6◆1		●		●						

Number indicates first exposure at grade level. *Available in the Games section of the *Student Reference Book.*

Games Correlation Chart *continued*

Game	Grade 4 Lesson	Grade 5 Lesson	Grade 6 Lesson	Basic Facts	Operations	Calculator	Numeration	Geometry	Data	Algebra	Ref. Frames	Mental Math	Strategy
				Skill and Concept Areas									
Getting to One	7•10		3•10			●	●			●			●
Grab Bag	7•3		7•1		●				●			●	●
Greedy			7•7						●			●	●
Grid Search	6•8										●		●
Hidden Treasure		9•1									●		●
High-Number Toss	2•7	2•10	1•2				●						●
High-Number Toss (Decimal Version)		2•5	1•11		●		●						●
Landmark Shark			1•5						●			●	●
Mixed Number Spin		8•3	4•7		●		●						●
Multiplication Bulls-Eye		2•7	2•5		●	●	●					●	
Multiplication Top-It	3•3	1•3	2•5	●	●		●					●	
Multiplication Wrestling	5•2		9•1	●	●		●			●		●	●
Name That Number	2•2	1•9	1•8	●	●		●			●		●	●
Number Top-It (7 digit numbers)	5•11	2•10	2•1				●						●
Number Top-It (decimals)	4•4	5•6					●						●
Over and Up Squares	6•9		1•6								●		●
Percent/Sector Match-Up			1•9				●						●
Polygon Capture		3•7	5•8					●					
Polygon Pair-Up	1•6							●					
Product Pile-Up	4•3			●			●					●	●
Rugs and Fences	9•2	11•4									●	●	●
Scientific Notation Toss		7•3	2•9				●						●
Sides and Angles: Triangles		3•6						●			●		
Solution Search			6•12		●					●			●
Spoon Scramble		12•6	5•4				●					●	
Spreadsheet Scramble			3•7		●					●		●	●
Subtraction Target Practice	2•9	2•3		●	●								
Subtraction Top-It	1•4			●	●		●					●	
3-D Shape Sort		11•2	5•10					●					
Top-It Games with Positive and Negative Numbers		7•10	6•4	●	●		●			●		●	
Venn Diagram Challenge			7•6					●	●				●
What's My Attribute Rule?		3•7						●		●			●
Where Do I Fit In?		3•6						●					
X and O—Tic Tac Toe			5•4								●		●

Number indicates first exposure at grade level. *Available in the Games section of the *Student Reference Book.*

Unit

1

Organizer

Collection, Display, and Interpretation of Data

Overview

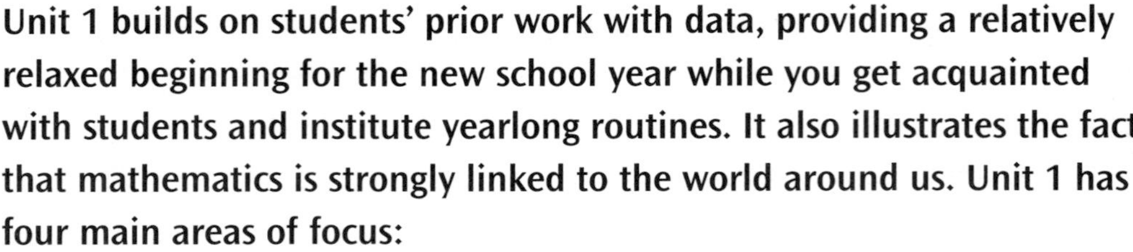

Unit 1 builds on students' prior work with data, providing a relatively relaxed beginning for the new school year while you get acquainted with students and institute yearlong routines. It also illustrates the fact that mathematics is strongly linked to the world around us. Unit 1 has four main areas of focus:

- To use the *Student Reference Book* to find information and solve problems,
- To find data landmarks, and to compare the median and mean for sets of data,
- To create, read, and interpret line plots, stem-and-leaf plots, broken-line graphs, bar graphs, step graphs, and circle graphs, and
- To analyze data displays and explain ways in which data can be presented to misrepresent or mislead.

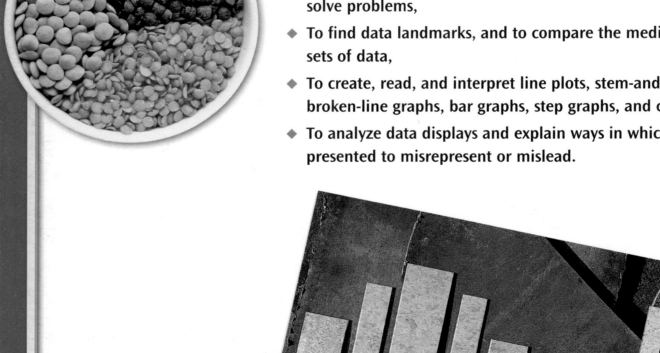

Contents

Unit 1 Organizer

Learning In Perspective

	Lesson Objectives	Links to the Past	Links to the Future
1•1	To use the *Student Reference Book* to find information and solve problems.	In Grade 5, students investigate the content and organization of the *Student Reference Book* by using it to solve problems and find information.	In Grade 6, students use the *Student Reference Book* as a resource for information on mathematical topics and terms, calculator functions, and *EM* game rules
1•2	To create and describe line plots; and to use data landmarks.	In Grade 5, students match descriptions of collected data with the line plots that represent them.	In Unit 3, students create, interpret, and write stories for mystery graphs.
1•3	To use stem-and-leaf plots for organizing and analyzing data.	In Grade 5, students use stem-and-leaf plots to organize data about hand and finger measures.	Grade 6 and after: Applications and maintenance.
1•4	To calculate and compare the median and mean of a data set.	In Grade 5, students describe prominent features of a data set and make distinctions between median and mean.	Grade 6 and after: Applications and maintenance.
1•5	To find the range, median, mode, and mean for sets of numbers.	In Grade 5, students identify landmarks in a given set or display.	Grade 6 and after: Applications and maintenance.
1•6	To create, read, and interpret broken-line graphs.	In Grade 5, students read and interpret line graphs of American Tour data. They use line graphs to represent rates.	Grade 6 and after: Students use line graphs to represent and interpret rates of change, make predicions, and draw conclusions.
1•7	To create, read, and interpret bar graphs.	In Grade 4, students use side-by-side bar graphs. In Grade 5, students create and interpret bar graphs.	Grade 6 and after: Application and maintenance.
1•8	To create, read, and interpret step graphs.	In Grade 5, students read and interpret graphs in which the horizontal axis represents time or distance.	After Grade 6, students continue to identify trends in data and find functions that model the data.
1•9	To review the Percent Circle; and to interpret circle graphs.	In Grade 5, students use a Percent Circle to draw and interpret circle graphs.	In Units 4, 5, and 8, students represent data with circle graphs. They calculate the degree measure of sectors and use protractors to draw circle graphs.
1•10	To find the perimeter and area of a rectangle; and to describe relationships between perimeter and area.	In Grade 5, students find the areas and perimeters of rectangles.	In Unit 8, students compare the perimeters and areas of similar polygons. In Unit 9, students use and apply the formulas for perimeter and area.
1•11	To analyze data displays and explain ways in which data can be presented to misrepresent or mislead.	In Grade 5, students analyze data displays and draw conclusions about the data represented.	After Grade 6, students examine the design of studies, the appropriateness of data analysis, and the validity of conclusions.
1•12	To determine whether a sample is random or biased; and to compare and analyze recall surveys.	In Grade 5, students conduct surveys and investigate the relationship between sample size and reliability of predictions.	After Grade 6, students examine the role of randomization in surveys and experiments.

	Key Concepts and Skills	Grade 6 Goals*
1•1	Express the place value of a digit in a decimal number.	Number and Numeration Goal 1
	Use algorithms to multiply multidigit whole numbers.	Operations and Computation Goal 2
	Estimate metric equivalents for customary linear measurements.	Measurement and Reference Frames Goal 1
	Name angles using three letters.	Geometry Goal 1
	Identify relation symbols.	Patterns, Functions, and Algebra Goal 2
1•2	Construct a line plot from collected data.	Data and Chance Goal 1
	Use the spread and shape of a line plot to draw conclusions about the data it represents.	Data and Chance Goal 2
	Identify landmarks of data sets.	Data and Chance Goal 2
1•3	Construct a stem-and-leaf plot from unsorted data.	Data and Chance Goal 1
	Compare different graphical representations of the same data.	Data and Chance Goal 2
	Identify landmarks of data (maximum, minimum, range, median, mode) displayed in stem-and-leaf plots.	Data and Chance Goal 2
1•4	Calculate and compare the median and mean of a data set.	Data and Chance Goal 2
	Examine how the median and the mean change as data change.	Data and Chance Goal 2
	Find the mode of a data set.	Data and Chance Goal 2
	Determine which landmark best represents a set of data—mean, median, or mode.	Data and Chance Goal 2
1•5	Mentally add, subtract, multiply, and divide whole numbers.	Operations and Computation Goals 1 and 2
	Calculate landmarks (range, median, mean, mode) of a data set.	Data and Chance Goal 2
	Predict how the landmarks of a data set change as the values of the data set change.	Data and Chance Goal 2
1•6	Construct broken-line graphs.	Data and Chance Goal 1
	Read and interpret broken-line and double broken-line graphs.	Data and Chance Goal 1
	Describe and predict patterns and trends represented by broken-line graphs.	Data and Chance Goal 2
1•7	Subtract multidigit whole numbers to find data ranges.	Operations and Computation Goal 1
	Construct a bar graph to represent a description of data.	Data and Chance Goal 1
	Read and interpret side-by-side and stacked bar graphs.	Data and Chance Goal 1
	Use a graph key to distinguish represented data.	Data and Chance Goal 1
	Use data ranges to read and interpret a stacked bar graph.	Data and Chance Goal 2
1•8	Read and interpret a data table and a step graph.	Data and Chance Goal 1
	Construct a step graph to represent data from a table.	Data and Chance Goal 1
	Compare the usefulness of various data representations.	Data and Chance Goal 2
1•9	Read and interpret circle graphs that have been constructed from survey data.	Data and Chance Goal 1
	Estimate percents on circle graphs.	Data and Chance Goal 1
	Use the Percent Circle to measure sectors to within ±2%.	Measurement and Reference Frames Goal 1
	Review the meaning of *radius*.	Measurement and Reference Frames Goal 2
1•10	Convert between fractions and decimals.	Number and Numeration Goal 5
	Multiply decimal numbers.	Operations and Computation Goal 2
	Calculate the areas of rectangles.	Measurement and Reference Frames Goal 2
	Use a graph to investigate the relationship between the perimeter and area of a rectangle.	Patterns, Functions, and Algebra Goal 1
1•11	Apply place-value concepts to read and round large numbers.	Number and Numeration Goal 1
	Use a calculator to compute products and quotients of whole numbers.	Operations and Computation Goal 2
	Interpret a pictograph and broken-line graph.	Data and Chance Goal 1
	Analyze examples of inaccurate or misleading displays of data.	Data and Chance Goal 2
1•12	Analyze, compare, and interpret side-by-side bar graphs.	Data and Chance Goal 1
	Extract numerical data from text.	Data and Chance Goal 2
	Examine the relationship between a sample and the population it represents.	Data and Chance Goal 3

* See the Appendix for a complete list of Grade 6 Goals.

Ongoing Learning and Practice

Math Boxes

Math Boxes are paired across lessons as shown in the brackets below. This makes them useful as assessment tools. Math Boxes also preview content of the next unit.

Mixed practice	[1•1, 1•3], [1•2, 1•4], [1•5, 1•7], [1•6, 1•8], [1•9, 1•11], [1•10, 1•12]
Mixed practice with multiple choice	1•2, 1•3, 1•5, 1•7, 1•8, 1•11, 1•12, 1•13
Mixed practice with writing/reasoning opportunity	1•1, 1•2, 1•6, 1•9

Practice through Games

Games are an essential component of practice in the *Everyday Mathematics* program. Games offer skills practice and promote strategic thinking.

Lesson	Game	Skill Practiced
1•2, 1•11	*High-Number Toss* (Whole Number Version)	**Reading, writing, and comparing whole numbers** Number and Numeration Goal 1
1•5, 1•6, 1•10	*Landmark Shark*	**Calculate landmarks (range, median, mean, mode) of data sets** Data and Chance Goal 2
1•6	*Over and Up Squares*	**Naming and plotting points in the first quadrant of a coordinate grid** Measurement and Reference Frames Goal 3
1•8	*Name That Number*	**Writing number sentences using order of operations** Patterns, Functions, and Algebra Goal 3
1•9	*Percent-Sector Match-Up*	**Estimating percents on circle graphs** Data and Chance Goal 1

See the *Differentiation Handbook* for ways to adapt games to meet students' needs.

Home Communication

Study Links provide homework and home communication.

◀ ***Home Connection Handbook*** provides more ideas to communicate effectively with parents.

Unit 1 Family Letter provides families with an overview, Do-Anytime Activities, Building Skills Through Games, and a list of vocabulary.

Problem Solving

Encourage students to use a variety of strategies to solve problems and to explain those strategies. Strategies that students might use in this unit:

- Using a reference book
- Using a diagram (line plot)
- Using logical reasoning
- Using computation
- Drawing and interpreting graphs
- Using estimation

Lessons that teach *through* problem solving, not just *about* problem solving

Lesson	Activity
1•1	Look for information in a reference book to solve problems.
1•2	Match line plots with statements describing data.
1•3	Compare different graphical representations of the same data set.
1•5	Predict how the landmarks of a data set change as values of the data set change.
1•6	Draw and interpret broken-line graphs about the climate in Omaha, Nebraska.
1•8	Solve postal rate, taxicab rate, and plumber's rate problems by using step graphs.
1•9	Draw conclusions about survey results that are presented in circle graphs.
1•10	Use a graph to find the largest area for a given perimeter.
1•11	Analyze data displays and present them to misrepresent or mislead.

See Chapter 18 in the *Teacher's Reference Manual* for more information about problem solving.

Planning Tips

Pacing

Pacing depends on a number of factors, such as students' individual needs and how long your school has been using *Everyday Mathematics.* At the beginning of Unit 1, review your *Content by Strand* Poster to help you set a monthly pace.

← MOST CLASSROOMS →

AUGUST	SEPTEMBER	OCTOBER

NCTM Standards

Unit 1 Lessons	1•1	1•2	1•3	1•4	1•5	1•6	1•7	1•8	1•9	1•10	1•11	1•12
NCTM Standards	1–10	5–10	5–10	1, 5–10	5–10	5–10	5–10	5–10	5–10	3–4, 6–10	5–10	1, 5–10

Content Standards: 1 Number and Operations, **2** Algebra, **3** Geometry, **4** Measurement, **5** Data Analysis and Probability
Process Standards: 6 Problem Solving, **7** Reasoning and Proof, **8** Communication, **9** Connections, **10** Representation

Balanced Assessment

Ongoing Assessment

Recognizing Student Achievement

Opportunities to assess students' progress toward Grade 6 Goals:

Lesson	Content Assessed
1•1	Multiply 2-digit whole numbers. [Operations and Computation Goal 2]
1•2	Demonstrate knowledge of landmark terms. [Data and Chance Goal 2]
1•3	Find the minimum, maximum, range, and mode of data displayed in a stem-and-leaf plot. [Data and Chance Goal 2]
1•4	Acknowledge the difference between median and mean. [Data and Chance Goal 2]
1•5	Construct a line plot and calculate the mean of a data set. [Data and Chance Goals 1 and 2]
1•6	Read data values from a broken-line graph. [Data and Chance Goal 1]
1•7	Construct a bar graph from a description of data. [Data and Chance Goal 1]
1•8	Draw a broken-line graph from a table of data values. [Data and Chance Goal 1]
1•9	Estimate and measure sector sizes using the Percent Circle. [Measurement and Reference Frames Goal 1]
1•10	Calculate data landmarks. Explain how data landmarks change as data values change. [Data and Chance Goal 2]
1•11	Read and interpret a broken-line graph. [Data and Chance Goal 2]
1•12	Read and interpret a side-by-side bar graph. [Data and Chance Goal 1]

Use the **Assessment Management System** to collect and analyze data about students' progress throughout the year.

Informing Instruction

To anticipate common student errors and to highlight problem-solving strategies:

Lesson 1•3 Keep track of recorded data values

Lesson 1•6 Recognize the subtle difference between data in a table and data in a graph

Lesson 1•7 Understand horizontal bar graphs

Lesson 1•8 Use solid and open dots to indicate inclusion of data values

Lesson 1•10 Understand that either side of a rectangle can be its length

Lesson 1•11 Recognize discrepancies between the size of figures in a pictograph and the numbers these figures are intended to represent

Periodic Assessment

1◆13 Progress Check 1

CONTENT ASSESSED	Self	Oral/Slate	Written	Open Response
	ASSESSMENT ITEMS			
Read, write, and represent whole and decimal numbers. [Number and Numeration Goal 1]		✔		
Create and use numerical expressions involving all four operations, parentheses, and order of operations to represent equivalent names for whole numbers. [Number and Numeration Goal 4]			✔	
Solve number stories involving addition and subtraction of whole numbers. [Operations and Computation Goal 1]			✔	
Know multiplication and division facts. [Operations and Computation Goal 2]			✔	
Solve problems involving multiplication and division of whole and decimal numbers. [Operations and Computation Goal 2]		✔	✔	
Create and interpret bar, line, and stem-and-leaf graphs for a set of data. [Data and Chance Goal 1]	✔		✔	
Find, compare, and use data landmarks to answer questions, draw conclusions, and make predictions. [Data and Chance Goal 2]	✔	✔	✔	✔
Estimate and measure circle graph sectors using the Percent Circle. [Measurement and Reference Frames Goal 1]	✔		✔	
Use formulas to calculate perimeter and area. [Measurement and Reference Frames Goal 2]		✔	✔	

Portfolio Opportunities

Opportunities to gather samples of students' mathematical writings, drawings, and creations to add balance to the assessment process:

- Constructing a back-to-back stem-and-leaf plot, **Lesson 1◆3**
- Explaining a strategy used to convert between centimeters and meters, **Lesson 1◆5**
- Completing a table; constructing and interpreting a step graph, **Lesson 1◆8**
- Using computer software to create a circle graph, **Lesson 1◆9**
- Drawing rectangles with given perimeters and finding a systematic way to determine perimeters, **Lesson 1◆10**
- Calculating the areas of rectangular regions and finding the sums and differences of these areas, **Lesson 1◆10**

Assessment Handbook

Unit 1 Assessment Support

- Grade 6 Goals, pp. 37–50
- Unit 1 Assessment Overview, pp. 52–59
- Unit 1 Open Response
  - Detailed rubric, p. 56
  - Sample student responses, pp. 57–59

Unit 1 Assessment Masters

- Unit 1 Self Assessment, p. 138
- Unit 1 Written Assessment, pp. 139–142
- Unit 1 Open Response, p. 143
- Unit 1 Class Checklist, pp. 228, 229, and 275
- Unit 1 Individual Profile of Progress, p. 226, 227, and 274
- Exit Slip, p. 283
- Math Logs, pp. 278–280
- Other Student Assessment Forms, pp. 276, 277, and 281

Differentiated Instruction

Daily Lesson Support

ENGLISH LANGUAGE LEARNERS

- **1•2** Building a Math Word Bank
- **1•6** Using the Graphs Museum to identify a type of graph
- **1•9** Building a Math Word Bank
- **1•10** Building a Math Word Bank

EXTRA PRACTICE

- **1•4** Solving custom-made Math Boxes
- **1•8** Constructing and analyzing a step graph
- **1•8** Solving custom-made Math Boxes

5-Minute Math **1•3** Finding range and mean of data set
- **1•5** Calculating landmarks for sets of numbers
- **1•7** Finding the landmarks for a data set containing negative numbers
- **1•11** Rounding numbers and estimating products
- **1•12** Estimating and calculating capacity equivalents

READINESS

- **1•1** Tabbing the *Student Reference Book*
- **1•2** Reading and constructing line plots
- **1•3** Constructing stem-and-leaf plots
- **1•4** Defining the mean of a data set
- **1•5** Analyzing landmarks of a data set
- **1•6** Playing *Over and Up Squares*
- **1•7** Interpreting simple bar graphs
- **1•8** Identifying jumps and intervals in a data set
- **1•9** Matching percents with the shaded regions that represent them
- **1•10** Determining dimensions of rectangles

ENRICHMENT

- **1•1** Reading *G is for Googol*
- **1•2** Examining the effects of outliers
- **1•3** Constructing stem-and-leaf plots
- **1•4** Using technology to find data landmarks
- **1•5** Calculating the mean of a data set
- **1•6** Generating a broken-line graph
- **1•7** Creating and analyzing a bar graph
- **1•9** Generating a circle graph
- **1•10** Solving a multistep area problem
- **1•11** Creating persuasive graphs
- **1•12** Collecting and analyzing survey data
- **1•12** Reading about a historical opinion poll

Adjusting the Activity

- **1•1** Highlighting unfamiliar math terms **ELL**
- **1•2** Discussing meanings of *landmark* **ELL**
- **1•3** Connecting setm-and-leaf plot and parts of plants **ELL**
- **1•4** Explaining how to use mean of a data set to find a sum of the data values
- **1•5** Playing *Landmark Shark* in teams
- **1•7** Drawing comparison diagrams
- **1•9** Checking work by adding percents **ELL**
- **1•10** Sketching rectangles **ELL**

AUDITORY • KINESTHETIC • TACTILE • VISUAL

Cross-Curricular Links

Science
Lesson 1•6 Students draw and interpret a broken-line graph showing climate data.
Lesson 1•7 Students read bar graphs showing weather conditions.

Health
Lesson 1•11 Students analyze a pictograph showing the leading causes of death.

History
Lesson 1•12 Students research a famous U.S. election.

Literature
Lesson 1•1 Students read *G is for Googol.*

Language Support

Everyday Mathematics provides lesson-specific suggestions to help all students, including non-native English speakers, to acquire, process, and express mathematical ideas.

Unit 1 Vocabulary

arc
area
bar graph
biased sample
broken-line graph
circle
circle graph
double-stem plot
graph key
interior of a circle
landmark
leaf
line graph
line plot
maximum
median
minimum
mode
mystery plot
Percent Circle
perimeter
precipitation
radius
random sample
range
recall survey
sample
sector
side-by-side bar graph
stacked bar graph
stem
stem-and-leaf plot
step graph

Connecting Math and Literacy

G Is for Googol: A Math Alphabet Book, by David M. Schwartz, Tricycle Press, 1998

Tiger Math, by Ann Whitehead Nagda, Henry Holt and Company, 2000

How to Lie with Statistics, by Darrell Huff, W. W. Norton, reissued 1993

Student Reference Book

pp. viii, 134, 136, 137, 140, 145, 212, 215, 323–326, and 329

Multiage Classroom ◆ Companion Lessons

Companion Lessons from Grade 5 can help you meet instructional needs of a multiage classroom. The full Scope and Sequence can be found in the Appendix.

Grade 5	1◆1	6◆4		10◆4, 10◆7		10◆4, 10◆6, 10◆7	10◆4, 10◆6, 10◆7	10◆4, 10◆6, 10◆7	5◆10, 5◆11	9◆7		
Grade 6	**1◆1**	**1◆2**	**1◆3**	**1◆4**	**1◆5**	**1◆6**	**1◆7**	**1◆8**	**1◆9**	**1◆10**	**1◆11**	**1◆12**

Professional Development

Teacher's Reference Manual Links

Lesson	Topic	Section
1◆1	Program Routines	1.2
	Reading Strategies	1.4.1
	Cooperative Groupings	4.1
1◆2, 1◆7	Line Plots and Bar Graphs	12.2.3
1◆3	Stem-and-Leaf Plots	12.2.3
1◆4, 1◆5	Data Landmarks Median and Mean	12.2.4
1◆6	Broken-Line Graphs	12.2.3

Lesson	Topic	Section
1◆8	Step Graphs	12.2.3
1◆9	Percent Circle	3.2.4
	Circle Graphs	12.2.3
1◆10	Area and Perimeter	14.3.1
	Relationships	14.4.2
1◆11	Persuasive Data and Graphs	12.2.4
1◆12	Samples and Surveys	12.2.2

Materials

Lesson	Masters	Manipulative Kit Items	Other Items
1•1	Study Link Masters, pp. 2–5 Teaching Master, p. 6	Geometry Template calculator	inch ruler; stick-on notes (5 per student)
1•2	Study Link 1•1 Teaching Aid Master, p. 404 Teaching Masters, pp. 7 and 9 Study Link Master, p. 8 Game Master, p. 454	per group: 1 six-sided die	scissors; 5 envelopes; 10 stick-on notes; per group: marker; large sheet of paper; metric ruler
1•3	Study Link 1•2 Study Link Master, p. 10 Teaching Masters, pp. 11 and 12		measuring tape
1•4	Study Link 1•3 Teaching Aid Masters, pp. 404 and 405 Study Link Master, p. 13 Teaching Master, p. 14	calculator	metric ruler; per student: 25 unit cubes; computer; spreadsheet/graphing software
1•5	Study Link 1•4 Game Masters, pp. 456 and 457 Study Link Master, p. 15 Teaching Masters, pp. 16 and 17	per group: 1 complete deck of number cards	index cards (10 per student); markers
1•6	Study Link 1•5 transparency of *Math Masters,* p. 18* Study Link Master, p. 19 Game Masters, pp. 456, 457, 465, and 466	per group: 1 complete deck of number cards 2 six-sided dice	straightedge; per group: 2 different-colored pencils; computer; spreadsheet/graphingsoftware
1•7	Study Link 1•6 transparency of *Math Masters,* p. 19* Study Link Master, p. 20 Teaching Master, p. 21		straightedge; computer; spreadsheet/graphing software
1•8	Study Link 1•7 Study Link Masters, pp. 22 and 23 Game Master, p. 462 Teaching Masters, pp. 24 and 25 Teaching Aid Master, p. 405	per group: 1 complete deck of number cards	straightedge; jumbo paper clips ($1\frac{13}{16}$" by $\frac{3}{8}$")
1•9	Study Link 1•8 Teaching Master, p. 26 transparencies of *Math Masters,* pp. 27* and 406* Study Link Masters, pp. 28 and 29 Game Masters, pp. 467–469	Geometry Template	straightedge; scissors; computer; spreadsheet/graphing software
1•10	Study Link 1•9 Teaching Aid Masters, pp. 404, 407, and 408 transparencies of *Math Masters,* pp. 30* and 407* Study Link Master, p. 31 Game Masters, pp. 456 and 457 Teaching Masters, pp. 32 and 33	per group: 1 complete deck of number cards calculator	
1•11	Study Link 1•10 Study Link Master, p. 34 Game Master, p. 455 Teaching Master, p. 35	calculator per group: 4 each of the number cards 0–9	
1•12	Study Link 1•11 Study Link Master, p. 36		computer; graphing software
1•13	Study Link 1•12 Assessment Masters, pp. 138–143 Study Link Masters, pp. 37–40		

* Denotes optional materials

Technology
Assessment Management System, Unit 1
iTLG, Unit 1

Mathematical Background

The discussion below highlights the major content ideas presented in Unit 1 and helps establish instructional priorities.

The *Student Reference Book* (Lesson 1◆1)

The *Student Reference Book* (*SRB*) provides a review of several mathematical topics and calculator usage, and also contains directions for various mathematical games, data tables, and a glossary of mathematical terms. Well organized and concise, the *SRB* allows students to easily reference necessary information on their own, thereby encouraging them to take responsibility for their own learning. This book also serves as a resource for parents helping their students at home and students who missed schoolwork during a period of absence.

From time to time, the SRB icon appears on journal pages, game masters, and Study Links to indicate pages in the *Student Reference Book* that contain relevant information about the topic at hand.

Read more about the *Student Reference Book* in Section 1.2.9, of the *Teacher's Reference Manual.*

Line Plots (Lesson 1◆2)

In Lesson 1-2, students read, analyze, and graph data using line plots. The "mystery-plot" approach in this lesson helps students match graphical representations with given situations. This approach can be used with data and graphs found in newspapers and other sources as well.

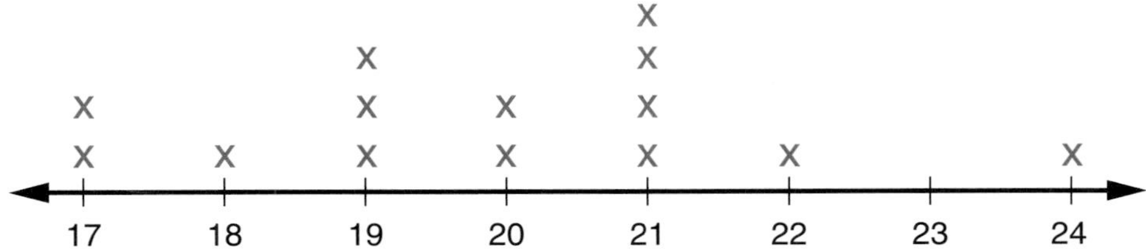

Students learn to discuss key characteristics of data after collecting and organizing it, especially landmarks such as *maximum, minimum, median, mode,* and *range.* They can use these landmarks as reference points when they analyze and interpret data, just as cartographers use landmarks when discussing map facts.

The data landmarks reviewed in this lesson have been the focus of informal data analysis since *Kindergarten Everyday Mathematics.* These simple methods of analyzing data can prove useful to five-year-olds as well as adults. The data sets and representations may become larger, more complex, and more difficult to collect, and the analysis may require more advanced procedures and statistical tools, but the basic ideas of data analysis will remain the same.

Read more about line plots in Section 12.2.3 of the *Teacher's Reference Manual.*

Stem-and-Leaf Plots

(Lesson 1◆3)

Girls' Heights (cm)

Stems (10s)	Leaves (1s)
13	8
14	3 5 6 8 9 9
15	0 6
16	0 4 7

Students also learn to use stem-and-leaf plots to analyze data in Lesson 1-3. They use this data representation to find landmarks such as *maximum, minimum, median, mode,* and *range.* Once students learn to read a stem-and-leaf plot, they construct several on their own. To construct a stem-and-leaf plot, a student begins by separating the digits of each number in the data set with a vertical line. The digits to the left of the line form the stems and the digits to the right form the leaves. A constructed stem-and-leaf plot for a sample of heights is shown at the left.

Read more about stem-and-leaf plots in Section 12.2.3 of the *Teacher's Reference Manual.*

Median and Mean

(Lessons 1◆4 and 1◆5)

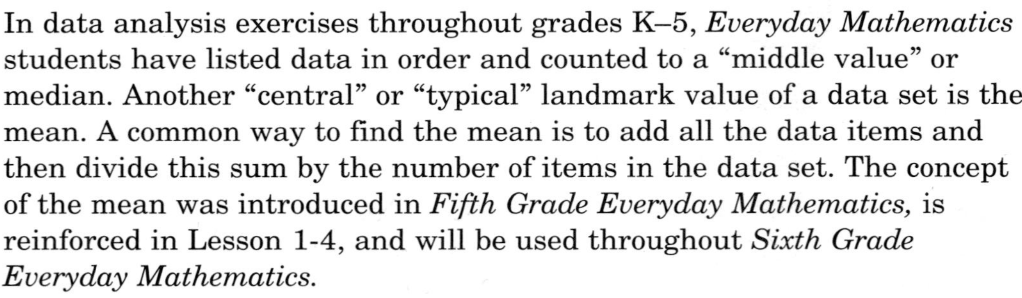

In data analysis exercises throughout grades K–5, *Everyday Mathematics* students have listed data in order and counted to a "middle value" or median. Another "central" or "typical" landmark value of a data set is the mean. A common way to find the mean is to add all the data items and then divide this sum by the number of items in the data set. The concept of the mean was introduced in *Fifth Grade Everyday Mathematics,* is reinforced in Lesson 1-4, and will be used throughout *Sixth Grade Everyday Mathematics.*

The median and the mean are often about the same for a set of data. Either the mean or the median works well in representing fairly uniform data; however, if a few data are poles apart from the rest, mean and median can be very different. In this case, one might be preferred as more "typical." See the following example.

Name	Michael	Juan	Kiriko	Jaime	Jonathan	Carmen	Chitra	Lee	Sofia
Yearly Income	$15,000	$17,500	$17,500	$20,000	$25,000	$30,000	$33,000	$40,000	$250,000

Median: $25,000 **Mean: $49,778**

In this example, Sofia's unusually high income "skews" the mean. The median is a more typical value for the data set.

Lesson 1-5 provides students with more experience finding landmarks of data sets by playing the *Landmark Shark* game.

See Section 12.2.4 of the *Teacher's Reference Manual* for more information about median and mean.

Note: Consider setting up a Graphs Museum in your classroom. Ask students to look in magazines and newspapers for examples of ways in which the graphs described in this unit are used to represent real-world data.

Broken-Line Graphs

(Lesson 1◆6)

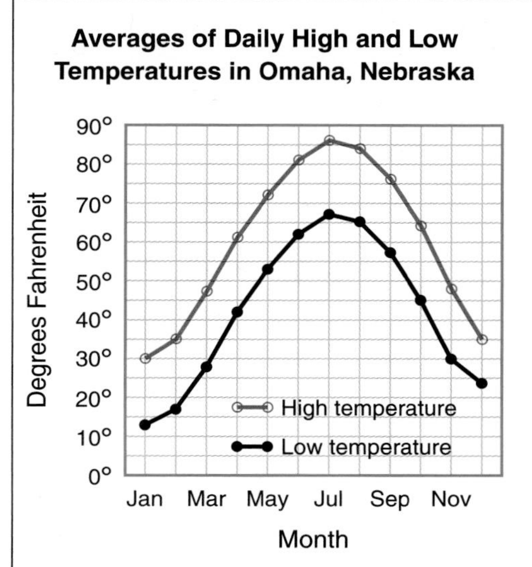

Lesson 1-6 provides students with methods to read, interpret, and construct broken-line graphs. Unlike other data sets, data for broken-line graphs consist of a few representative values from a large number of possible values, such as average monthly temperatures rather than average daily or hourly temperatures. Students construct these graphs by plotting discrete points or values. They then connect the plotted points to provide a picture of the overall change in data. This method of data representation works well for showing trends and the big picture. According to the graph, the average high temperature in Omaha in the month of May is about 70°F. However, the actual temperature on any given day in Omaha during May might be higher or lower than this average.

See Section 12.2.3 of the *Teacher's Reference Manual* for more information about broken-line graphs.

Bar Graphs

(Lesson 1◆7)

Students learn that the display of numerical information using a bar graph is useful when comparing data. A side-by-side bar graph allows them to make two kinds of comparisons at the same time. They develop the skills to construct and interpret various types of bar graphs, including the side-by-side and stacked bar graph, throughout this lesson.

To learn more about bar graphs, see Section 12.2.3 of the *Teacher's Reference Manual.*

Step Graphs

(Lesson 1◆8)

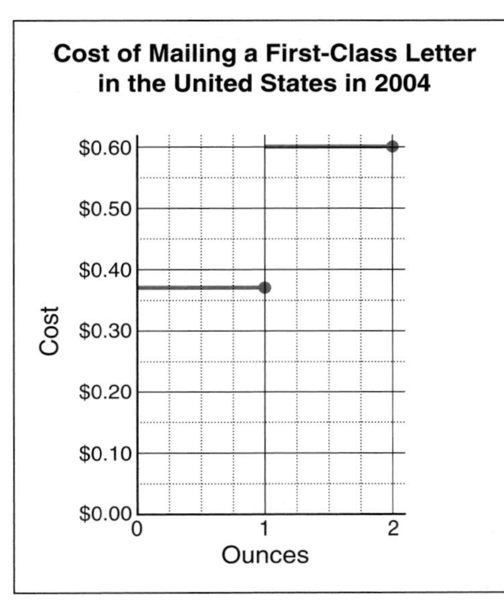

In this lesson, students encounter step graphs for the first time in the *Everyday Mathematics* curriculum. Step graphs depict situations in which data input and output remain constant for a certain period of time but show a sudden jump at the end of this time period. For example, in 2004, the cost of sending a first-class letter (as shown at the right), was 37 cents for any weight up to 1 ounce. This cost jumped to 60 cents when the weight was just over 1 ounce and remained constant up to 2 ounces. Identification and interpretation of such jumps might prove challenging for students at times. The dot at the right end of the first segment in the graph indicates that postage is still 37 cents at 1 ounce but increases to 60 cents for anything more than 1 ounce.

See Section 12.2.3 of the *Teacher's Reference Manual* for more information about step graphs.

The Percent Circle and Circle Graphs

(Lesson 1•9)

Circle graphs are effective visual displays for certain kinds of information and are among the most common statistical displays in newspapers and magazines. Often called "pie graphs," they show how the whole "pie" is divided into sectors.

In this lesson, students use the Percent Circle on the Geometry Template to read and draw circle graphs. The Percent Circle is like a full-circle protractor, except that the circumference is marked with percents instead of degrees. If the Percent Circle is being used for the first time, it might be helpful to practice using it prior to teaching students to work with this tool.

To learn more about the Percent Circle and circle graphs, see Section 14.11.2 of the *Teacher's Reference Manual.*

Using a Graph to Investigate Perimeter and Area (Lesson 1•10)

Students use graphs in this lesson to investigate the relationship between the perimeter and area of rectangles. The graphing activity in this lesson illustrates several key mathematical concepts:

- The essential difference between perimeter as the sum of the lengths and area as the product of lengths is highlighted. This seems to be confusing for many students (and adults), and it is crucial that they develop a good understanding of these concepts.
- Students are introduced to real world applications such as enclosing the largest possible area with a fixed amount of fence and the complementary problem of minimizing cost for a desired outcome. (Calculus courses in higher education use "derivates" to find such "maximums" and "minimums," but simple graphing works just as well.)

- The final graph of different areas for a given or fixed perimeter is a smooth curve called a "parabola" and is different from the other kinds of graphs encountered in this unit. This type of graph also begins the study of graphs of "quadratic functions" that students will encounter more in algebra, geometry, and calculus courses to come.

See Sections 14.3 and 14.4 of the *Teacher's Reference Manual* for more information about perimeter and area.

Persuasive Data and Graphs

(Lesson 1◆11)

Graphs often provide excellent pictorial representations that make reading and interpreting large data sets easy. Some graphs are simple and straightforward while others need to be read carefully to understand the messages conveyed. For example, if most of the data in a given situation are between \$10,000 and \$12,000, it makes sense to start the graphing scale at just under \$10,000 instead of at \$0. But students should be informed that choosing to use this scale might give the impression that small differences may be more significant than they really are.

Graphs can also be used to present information in a misleading manner. Pictographs with lavish graphics are often rigged to give particular impressions. The most flagrant deceptions use scale and areas of figures. Of course, such deception may not always be created on purpose, but it is deception, nonetheless.

For additional information about persuasive data and graphs, see Section 12.2.4 of the *Teacher's Reference Manual.*

Samples and Surveys

(Lesson 1◆12)

Most decisions made by businesses are based on surveys. Manufacturers survey consumers to help make changes to their products or create new products. Television stations survey viewers to learn about popular programs. Politicians, newspapers, and magazines survey people to obtain opinions on campaign issues and candidates. In this lesson, students analyze survey results with a critical eye to help make appropriate inferences. They also learn the difference between random and biased samples and the effect that using these samples can have on survey results.

See Section 12.2.2 of the *Teacher's Reference Manual* to learn more about samples and surveys.

Introduction to the *Student Reference Book*

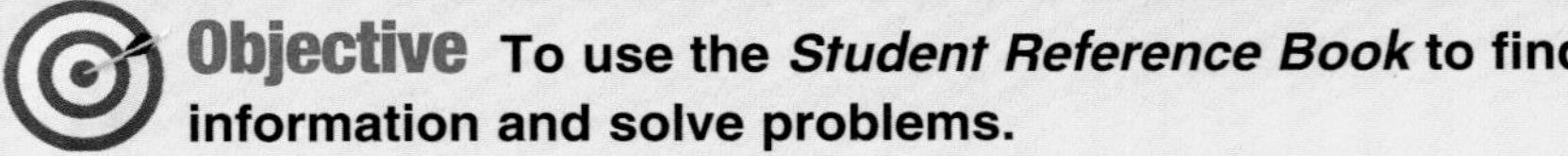

Objective To use the *Student Reference Book* to find information and solve problems.

1 Teaching the Lesson

Key Activities
Students examine the content and organization of the *Student Math Journal* and *Student Reference Book.*

Key Concepts and Skills
- Express the place value of a digit in a decimal number. [Number and Numeration Goal 1]
- Use algorithms to multiply multidigit whole numbers. [Operations and Computation Goal 2]
- Estimate metric equivalents for customary linear measurements. [Measurement and Reference Frames Goal 1]
- Name angles using three letters. [Geometry Goal 1]
- Identify relation symbols. [Patterns, Functions, and Algebra Goal 2]

Ongoing Assessment: Recognizing Student Achievement Use journal page 3. [Operations and Computation Goal 2]

materials
- ☐ *Math Journal 1,* pp. 1–4
- ☐ *Student Reference Book,* p. viii
- ☐ calculator

2 Ongoing Learning & Practice

Students practice and maintain skills by completing Math Boxes.

Students take home a Family Letter introducing *Everyday Mathematics* and Unit 1.

materials
- ☐ *Math Journal 1,* p. 5
- ☐ Study Link Masters (*Math Masters,* pp. 2–5)
- ☐ Geometry Template
- ☐ inch ruler

3 Differentiation Options

READINESS
Students become familiar with the *Student Reference Book* by using stick-on notes to tab sections.

ENRICHMENT
Students read *G Is for Googol: A Math Alphabet Book* by David M. Schwartz.

materials
- ☐ Teaching Master (*Math Masters,* p. 6)
- ☐ stick-on notes (5 per student)

***See* Advance Preparation**

Additional Information

Advance Preparation Obtain a copy of *G Is for Googol: A Math Alphabet Book* by David M. Schwartz (Tricycle Press, 1998).

Technology

Assessment Management System
Journal page 3, Problem 7
See the **iTLG**.

Getting Started

Mental Math and Reflexes

●○○ 3 * 9 27
30 * 9 270
30 * 900 27,000

●●○ 7 * 8 56
7 * 80 560
7 * 800 5,600

●●● 6 * 5 30
60 * 50 3,000
600 * 500 300,000

Math Message

Study your assigned topic on journal page 1 with your group. Find examples of this topic in Math Boxes and on journal pages. Record these page numbers.

NOTE Some students may benefit from doing the Readiness activity before beginning Part 1 of the lesson. See Part 3 for details.

1 Teaching the Lesson

▶ Math Message Follow-Up

WHOLE-CLASS ACTIVITY

(*Math Journal 1,* p. 1)

Divide students into groups. Assign each group one of the bulleted topics on journal page 1. Ask groups to share their examples. As a class, generate a list of concepts that students recognize from Grade 5. Discuss the advantages of working with familiar concepts and skills. Brainstorm ways in which these concepts and skills will be taken to the next level this year.

▶ Examining the *Student Reference Book*

WHOLE-CLASS DISCUSSION

(*Student Reference Book,* p. viii)

Have students read *Student Reference Book* page viii, "About the *Student Reference Book*." Point out the icon used in the journal to indicate *Student Reference Book* pages that relate to the current topic.

Choose a page in the *Student Reference Book,* preferably one with a topic familiar to students, such as "Extended Multiplication Facts" on page 18. Work through the page to model how students should use it. Have them try the Check Your Understanding problems and check their answers using the Answer Key.

▶ Using the *Student Reference Book*

PARTNER ACTIVITY

(*Math Journal 1,* pp. 2–4; *Student Reference Book*)

Students solve problems on various topics covered in *Everyday Mathematics*. At this point, focus students' attention on finding helpful pages in the *Student Reference Book* rather than on obtaining correct answers. The scoring—3 points for correct answers and 5 points for citing an appropriate page—emphasizes skill in locating pages.

Student Page

Date Time

LESSON 1·1 **Sixth Grade Everyday Mathematics**

Much of what you learned in the first years of *Everyday Mathematics* served as basic training in mathematics and its uses. In fourth and fifth grades, you built on this training and studied more sophisticated mathematics. This year, you will study new ideas—some of which your parents and older siblings may not have learned until high school. The authors, along with many other people, believe that sixth graders today can learn and do more mathematics than was thought possible 10 or 20 years ago.

Here are a few topics that you will discuss in *Sixth Grade Everyday Mathematics:*

- Practice and improve your number sense, measure sense, and estimation skills.
- Review and extend your arithmetic, calculator, and thinking skills by working with fractions, decimals, percents, large and small numbers, and negative numbers.
- Continue your study of variables, expressions, equations, and other topics in algebra.
- Expand your understanding of geometry, with a focus on compass-and-straightedge constructions, transformations of figures, and volumes of 3-dimensional figures.
- Explore probability and statistics.
- Carry out projects that investigate the uses of mathematics outside the classroom.

A *Student Reference Book* is included in the *Sixth Grade Everyday Mathematics* program. This resource book allows you to look up and review information on topics covered in mathematics both this year and in years past. The *Student Reference Book* also includes the rules of popular mathematical games; a glossary of mathematical terms; and reference information, such as tables of measures, fraction-decimal-percent conversion tables, and place-value charts. (Some of this information also appears at the back of your journal.)

This year's activities will help you appreciate the beauty and usefulness of mathematics. The authors hope you will enjoy *Sixth Grade Everyday Mathematics.* Most importantly, we want you to become more skilled at using mathematics so that you may better understand the world in which you live.

Math Journal 1, p. 1

Student Page

Date Time

LESSON 1·1 ***Student Reference Book* Scavenger Hunt**

Solve the problems on this page and on the next two pages. Use your *Student Reference Book* to help you.

Write the page number on which you found information in the *Student Reference Book* for each problem. You may not need to look for help in the *Student Reference Book*, but you will earn additional points for showing where you would look if you needed to.

Keep score as follows:

- 3 points for each correct answer
- 5 points for each correct page number of the *Student Reference Book*

Sample *SRB* page numbers given.

Problem Points | Page Points

1. Draw a diameter of the circle below.

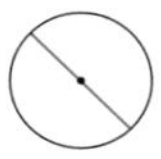

Student Reference Book, page 176

2. Write the formula for finding the area of a circle.
Formula: $A = \pi * r^2$
Student Reference Book, page 218

3. Find the equivalents for the measurements below.
1 mi = 1,760 yd
1 ft² = 144 in.²
1 in. = 2.54 cm
1 mi ≈ 1.6 km
Student Reference Book, page 371

***Math Journal 1*, p. 2**

NOTE If a "no calculator" icon appears next to a set of problems, students should not use their calculators.

Student Page

Date Time

LESSON 1·1 ***Student Reference Book* Scavenger Hunt** *cont.*

Problem Points | Page Points

4.

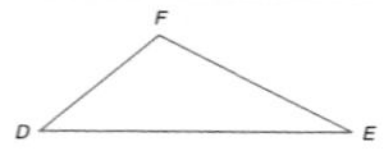

Name the angles for triangle *DEF*.
∠*FDE*, ∠*DEF*, ∠*EFD*
Student Reference Book, page 166

5. Write the symbol for *perpendicular*. ⊥
Student Reference Book, page 161

6. Find the mean for the data set: 24, 26, 21, 18, 26.
mean 23
Student Reference Book, page 137

★ 7. 46 ∗ 53 = 2,438
Student Reference Book, page 19 and 20

8. 3,380 = 438 + 2,942
Student Reference Book, page 13 and 14

9. Is 54,132 divisible by 6? yes
How can you tell without actually dividing?
It is divisible by both 2 and 3.
Student Reference Book, page 11

10. Explain why the number sentence $x + 5 < 8$ is an inequality.
It contains one of the symbols ≠, <, >, ≤, ≥.
Student Reference Book, page 241

***Math Journal 1*, p. 3**

Circulate and assist. Review the answers and the pages in the *Student Reference Book* where students found the information. Encourage students to cite multiple sources.

Ask students to calculate two scores—one for their total correct answers and one for their total correct page numbers.

Adjusting the Activity

ELL

Have students highlight unfamiliar math terms in each question and then locate these terms in the glossary of the *Student Reference Book*.

AUDITORY ◆ KINESTHETIC ◆ TACTILE ◆ VISUAL

Ongoing Assessment: Recognizing Student Achievement

Journal Page 3 Problem 7 ★

Use **journal page 3, Problem 7** to assess students' ability to multiply 2-digit whole numbers. Students are making adequate progress if they choose a reliable algorithm and are able to correctly calculate the product. Many students may be able to solve this problem without referring to the *Student Reference Book.*

[Operations and Computation Goal 2]

2 Ongoing Learning & Practice

▶ Math Boxes 1·1

INDEPENDENT ACTIVITY

(*Math Journal 1,* p. 5)

Mixed Practice The Math Boxes in this lesson are paired with Math Boxes in Lesson 1-3. The skill in Problem 4 previews Unit 2 content.

Writing/Reasoning Have students write their responses to the following: *Explain how you checked your answer to Problem 4a.* Sample answer: I added my answer to $2.96 to see if I got $4.83.

▶ Study Link: Unit 1 Family Letter

INDEPENDENT ACTIVITY

(*Math Masters,* pp. 2–5)

Home Connection The Study Link for Lesson 1-1 is a Family Letter. This Family Letter introduces *Everyday Mathematics* and describes Unit 1. It encourages parents and guardians to support their children by looking for examples of graphs and tables in newspapers and magazines. Consider setting aside a bulletin board or other display area for a Graphs Museum.

3 Differentiation Options

READINESS

PARTNER ACTIVITY

15–30 Min

▶ Tabbing Sections of the *Student Reference Book*

(*Math Masters,* p. 6)

Students follow the instructions for using stick-on notes to tab sections of the *Student Reference Book.* They discuss the ways that each tabbed section may be used throughout the year.

ENRICHMENT

PARTNER ACTIVITY

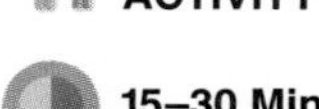

15–30 Min

▶ Reading about Mathematical Concepts and Terms

Literature Link The book *G Is for Googol* features mathematical concepts and terms from "A is for Abacus" to "Z is for Zillion." One question students often ask is raised under *W*—"When are we ever gonna use this stuff anyway?" Suggest that students use library or Internet sources to explore jobs that require knowledge of mathematics.

Planning Ahead

You can use computer software to quickly generate and analyze many of the graphs in this unit. Familiarize yourself with the graphing software you plan to use.

Teaching Master

Name ______ Date ______ Time ______

LESSON 1•1 **Tabbing the *Student Reference Book***

Some sections of the *Student Reference Book* appear in the table below.

1. Follow Steps 1–4. Then complete the table.

Step 1 Count out one stick-on note for each of the 5 section titles.

Step 2 Record a different section title on each stick-on note.

Step 3 Find the first page of each section. Make a tab for that section by attaching the appropriate stick-on note to the side of that first page.

Step 4 Record the page on which you placed each stick-on note.

Section Title	Page Number
Answer Key	412
Contents (Table of Contents)	iii
Games	301
Glossary	380
Index	422

Use your tabs and the table above to complete Problems 2–6.

2. Find and read the definition for **bar graph.**
3. Using your Index tab, find the page number(s) on which bar graphs are presented. Record the page number(s). pp. 138 and 139
4. Turn to the page(s) you recorded in Problem 3. What mathematical topic appears in the color strip at the top of the page? Data and Probability
5. Study the Check Your Understanding problem at the bottom of the page. On what page can you find the answer to the problem? p. 419

   To which tabbed section does this page belong? Answer Key
6. Using your Contents tab, find the mathematical topic under which *bar graphs* is listed. (It should be the same as the one you recorded in Problem 4.)

   What is the last page of this topic? p. 156

Math Masters, p. 6

Student Page

Date ______ Time ______

LESSON 1•1 ***Student Reference Book* Scavenger Hunt** *cont.*

	Problem Points	Page Points

11. In the decimal number 603,125.748
    a. what is the value of the 8? thousandths
    b. what digit is in the tenths place? 7

    Student Reference Book, page 28
12. Rename each fraction as a decimal.

    $\frac{1}{10}$ = 0.1 $\frac{1}{8}$ = 0.125

    Student Reference Book, page 372
13. What materials do you need to play *Landmark Shark?* Number cards, *Landmark Shark* cards, score sheet

    Student Reference Book, page 325
14. What is the height of a geometric solid, such as a prism? The shortest distance between its bases

    Student Reference Book, page 215
15. In Ms. McCarty's class, 9 out of 20 students are boys. Express the ratio of boys to the total number of students,
    a. using a fraction. $\frac{9}{20}$
    b. using a colon. 9:20

    Student Reference Book, page 117 and 118

Total Problem Points ______ Total Page Points ______

Total Points ______

Math Journal 1, p. 4

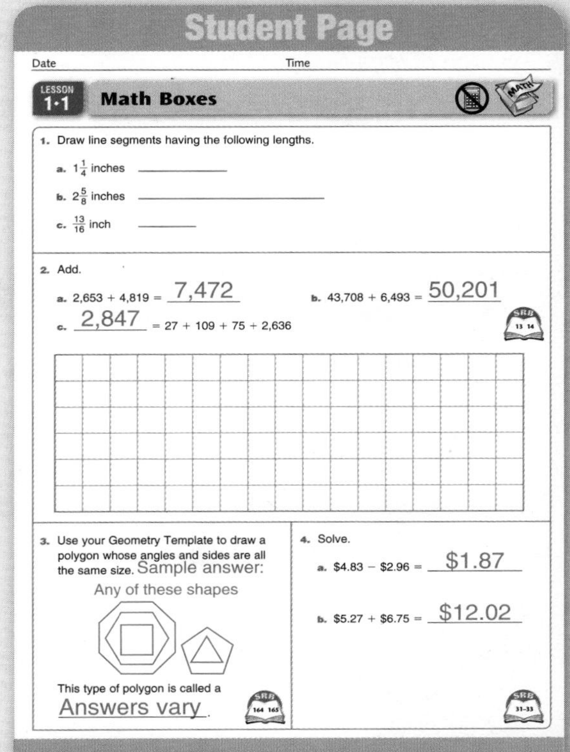

Student Page

Date ______ Time ______

LESSON 1•1 **Math Boxes**

1. Draw line segments having the following lengths.
   a. $1\frac{1}{4}$ inches
   b. $2\frac{5}{8}$ inches
   c. $\frac{13}{16}$ inch
2. Add.
   a. 2,653 + 4,819 = 7,472
   b. 43,708 + 6,493 = 50,201
   c. 2,847 = 27 + 109 + 75 + 2,636
3. Use your Geometry Template to draw a polygon whose angles and sides are all the same size. Sample answer: Any of these shapes

   This type of polygon is called a Answers vary.
4. Solve.
   a. \$4.83 − \$2.96 = \$1.87
   b. \$5.27 + \$6.75 = \$12.02

Math Journal 1, p. 5

1•2 Line Plots

Objectives To create and describe line plots; and to use data landmarks.

1 Teaching the Lesson

Key Activities

Students construct line plots from data they have collected about themselves. Then students match "mystery" line plots to each category of collected data. They also identify landmarks for each set of data.

Key Concepts and Skills

- Construct a line plot from collected data. [Data and Chance Goal 1]
- Use the spread and shape of a line plot to draw conclusions about the data it represents. [Data and Chance Goal 2]
- Identify landmarks of data sets. [Data and Chance Goal 2]

Key Vocabulary

line plot • mystery plot • landmark • minimum • maximum • median • mode • range

Ongoing Assessment: Recognizing Student Achievement Use an Exit Slip. [Data and Chance Goal 2]

materials

- ☐ *Student Reference Book,* p. 134
- ☐ *Math Journal 1,* pp. 6 and 7
- ☐ Study Link 1•1
- ☐ Teaching Aid Master (*Math Masters,* p. 404)
- ☐ Teaching Master (*Math Masters,* p. 7)
- ☐ scissors; 5 envelopes; 10 stick-on notes
- ☐ Per group: marker; large sheet of paper

See **Advance Preparation**

2 Ongoing Learning & Practice

Students practice reading, writing, and comparing numbers by playing the whole-number version of *High-Number Toss.*

Students practice and maintain skills through Math Boxes and Study Link activities.

materials

- ☐ *Math Journal 1,* p. 8
- ☐ *Student Reference Book,* p. 323
- ☐ Study Link Master (*Math Masters,* p. 8)
- ☐ Game Master (*Math Masters,* p. 454)
- ☐ 1 six-sided die per partnership
- ☐ metric ruler

3 Differentiation Options

READINESS

Students review how to read and construct a line plot.

ENRICHMENT

Students examine how an outlier affects the mean of a data set.

ELL SUPPORT

Students add landmark terms to their Math Word Banks.

materials

- ☐ *Student Reference Book,* p. 134
- ☐ Teaching Master (*Math Masters,* p. 9)
- ☐ *Differentiation Handbook*

Additional Information

Advance Preparation Assemble five envelopes for the mystery plot activity in Part 1. Use stick-on notes to prepare number-letter labels 1–5 and A–E. Affix one label to each envelope. Prepare a correspondence between letters and numbers for your reference only (A↔2, B↔4, and so on). Supply groups with one large sheet of paper and copies of *Math Masters,* page 7.

Technology

Assessment Management System
Exit Slip
See the **iTLG**.

Getting Started

Mental Math and Reflexes

Students solve multiplication problems. *Suggestions:*

●○○ How many 7s in 56? 8
How many 700s in 5,600? 8

●●○ How many 9s in 540? 60
How many 18s in 540? 30

●●● How many 5s in 600? 120
How many 50s in 6,000? 120

Draw attention to problems in which the dividend and divisor are multiplied by the same number and the quotient remains unchanged.

Math Message

Cut 1 copy of Math Masters, *page 7, into 5 pieces. Complete the statements at the top of journal page 6. Do not share your answers.*

Study Link 1·1 Follow-Up

Remind students to look in newspapers and magazines for graphs they can add to the classroom Graphs Museum.

NOTE Some students may benefit from doing the Readiness activity before beginning Part 1 of the lesson. See Part 3 for details.

▶ Math Message Follow-Up

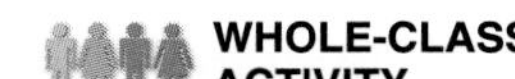
WHOLE-CLASS ACTIVITY

(*Math Masters,* p. 7; *Math Journal 1,* p. 6)

Have students copy their answers from the Math Message onto the five pieces from *Math Masters,* page 7 as follows:

1. On one of the five pieces, each student circles his or her answer to Statement A. (A blank has been provided for students to write in responses greater than 40.)
2. Students give the completed pieces to you.
3. Place the responses in the envelope labeled A. Discard any responses that have extra marks or labels.

Repeat this procedure for Statements B–E. Out of students' sight, replace the letter-labels with the corresponding number-labels.

▶ Making and Discussing Line Plots of the Data

SMALL-GROUP ACTIVITY

(*Student Reference Book,* p. 134)

Give each group a numbered envelope and a large sheet of paper. To support English language learners, review the meaning of *plot* in the context of this activity.

NOTE Some students may go to great lengths to try to identify their own responses while deciding which statement goes with which data set. You might consider switching envelopes with another class.

Teaching Master

Name ______ Date ______ Time ______

LESSON 1·2 **Survey Data**

Math Message

0
1 2 3 4 5 6 7 8 9 10
11 12 13 14 15 16 17 18 19 20
21 22 23 24 25 26 27 28 29 30
31 32 33 34 35 36 37 38 39 40
____

0
1 2 3 4 5 6 7 8 9 10
11 12 13 14 15 16 17 18 19 20
21 22 23 24 25 26 27 28 29 30
31 32 33 34 35 36 37 38 39 40
____

0
1 2 3 4 5 6 7 8 9 10
11 12 13 14 15 16 17 18 19 20
21 22 23 24 25 26 27 28 29 30
31 32 33 34 35 36 37 38 39 40
____

0
1 2 3 4 5 6 7 8 9 10
11 12 13 14 15 16 17 18 19 20
21 22 23 24 25 26 27 28 29 30
31 32 33 34 35 36 37 38 39 40
____

0
1 2 3 4 5 6 7 8 9 10
11 12 13 14 15 16 17 18 19 20
21 22 23 24 25 26 27 28 29 30
31 32 33 34 35 36 37 38 39 40
____

Math Masters, **p. 7**

Student Page

Date ______ Time ______

LESSON 1·2 **Mystery Plots and Landmarks**

Math Message

Complete the following statements. *Do not share your answers.* Estimate if you do not know the exact number. Answers vary.

A. I usually spend about ______ minutes taking a shower or a bath.

B. There is a total of ______ letters in my first, middle, and last names.

C. There are ______ people living in my home.

D. My shoe is about ______ centimeters long (to the nearest centimeter).

E. I watch about ______ hours of television per week.

Mystery Plots

You and your classmates will make **line plots** of the data from the Math Message above. You will then try to figure out which line plot, or **mystery plot**, goes with which statement in the Math Message.

Landmarks

After the class has agreed on the subject of each line plot, mark the number lines for each statement on the next page to show the following data **landmarks** for each statement set: **minimum, maximum, median,** and **mode.** Also record the **range.**

Example:

range 30 min

Math Journal 1, p. 6

Links to the Future

The activities in this lesson provide students with a foundation for this year's experiences using graphs to represent and communicate data. Analyzing and interpreting data is an *Everyday Mathematics* program goal.

Student Page

Date ______ Time ______

LESSON 1·2 **Mystery Plots and Landmarks** *continued*

Answers vary.

A. Shower/Bath Time (in minutes) range ______

B. Number of Letters in First, Middle, and Last Names range ______

C. Number of People Living in Home range ______

D. Length of Shoe (to nearest cm) range ______

E. Hours of Television Viewed per Week range ______

Math Journal 1, p. 7

Groups proceed as follows:

1. List the data in order from least to greatest.
2. Using markers and the large sheet of paper, draw a **line plot** of the data.
3. Write the envelope number on the line plot.
4. Post the line plots around the classroom.
5. Decide which line plot goes with which statement (A–E) in the Math Message. Groups should be ready to defend their answers.

Matching Line Plots with Statements and Landmarks

WHOLE-CLASS DISCUSSION

(*Math Journal 1*, pp. 6 and 7)

Pose questions such as the following:

- Which **mystery plot** matches each statement? Why?
- Is there a statement that definitely does not go with a certain line plot? Why?
- Which statement was easiest to identify by line plot? Which was most difficult? Why?

Students may offer reasoning similar to the following: "Minutes of shower/bath and hours of watching television could easily have the same range. However, shower/bath minutes will probably be below 15, while television hours will probably have values above 20."

Encourage students to consider the spreads and shapes of their line plots. After some discussion, reveal the correct statement for each line plot.

Ask students to identify the following **landmarks** for each set of data: **minimum, maximum, median, mode,** and **range.** Have them turn to journal page 7 and record these landmarks.

Adjusting the Activity

ELL

Landmarks are notable features of a locale in the same way that they are notable features of a data set. To support English language learners, discuss the similarities between the everyday and mathematical meanings of *landmark*. Label the landmarks on the group charts as shown in the example on journal page 6.

AUDITORY ◆ KINESTHETIC ◆ TACTILE ◆ VISUAL

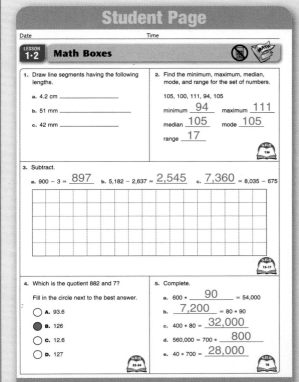

Ongoing Assessment: Recognizing Student Achievement

Exit Slip

Use an **Exit Slip** (*Math Masters,* p. 404) to assess students' understanding of landmark terms. (See next paragraph.) Students are making adequate progress if their methods and meanings demonstrate knowledge of an accurate definition.

Pose the following informal assessment item to students: Suppose a friend has trouble remembering the definitions for *minimum, maximum, median, mode,* and *range.* Describe a way to remember the meaning of each landmark term.

[Data and Chance Goal 2]

2 Ongoing Learning & Practice

▶ Playing *High-Number Toss* (Whole-Number Version)

PARTNER ACTIVITY

(*Student Reference Book,* p. 323; *Math Masters,* p. 454)

This is the whole-number version of the game introduced in *Fourth Grade Everyday Mathematics.* Have students read the game directions on page 323 in the *Student Reference Book.* Play a round against the class before having students play on their own. Provide each pair with a 6-sided die and record sheet (*Math Masters,* p. 454). Circulate and observe to get a sense of students' ability to read, write, and compare whole numbers to hundred-millions.

NOTE Games are integral to the *Everyday Mathematics* program. They provide an effective and interactive way to reinforce skills in Grade 6 Goals. Establish a games routine during Unit 1 and maintain it throughout the year. Make sure all students are given time to play the games, especially those who find traditional drill and practice tedious.

▶ Math Boxes 1•2

INDEPENDENT ACTIVITY

(*Math Journal 1,* p. 8)

Mixed Practice Math Boxes in this lesson are paired with Math Boxes in Lesson 1-4. The skills in Problems 4 and 5 preview Unit 2 content.

Writing/Reasoning Have students write their responses to the following: *Explain how you can check your answer to Problem 4 without using a calculator.* Sample answer: I multiplied my answer choice by 7 to see if I would get 882.

Game Master

Name ______ Date ______ Time ______

High-Number Toss Record Sheet (SRB 323)

Hundred-Millions	Ten-Millions	Millions	,	Hundred-Thousands	Ten-Thousands	Thousands	,	Hundreds	Tens	Ones

Player 1 ______ (Name) Player 2 ______ (Name)

Round	Player 1	>, <, =	Player 2
Sample	1 3 2 ∣ 6 132,000,000	>	3 5 6 ∣ 4 3,560,000
1	___ ___ ___ ∣ ___ ______		___ ___ ___ ∣ ___ ______
2	___ ___ ___ ∣ ___ ______		___ ___ ___ ∣ ___ ______
3	___ ___ ___ ∣ ___ ______		___ ___ ___ ∣ ___ ______
4	___ ___ ___ ∣ ___ ______		___ ___ ___ ∣ ___ ______
5	___ ___ ___ ∣ ___ ______		___ ___ ___ ∣ ___ ______

Math Masters, p. 454

Student Page

Date ______ Time ______

LESSON 1•2 **Math Boxes**

1. Draw line segments having the following lengths.
   a. 4.2 cm ______
   b. 51 mm ______
   c. 42 mm ______

2. Find the minimum, maximum, median, mode, and range for the set of numbers.
   105, 100, 111, 94, 105
   minimum 94 maximum 111
   median 105 mode 105
   range 17
   (SRB 136)

3. Subtract.
   a. 900 − 3 = 897 b. 5,182 − 2,637 = 2,545 c. 7,360 = 8,035 − 675
   (SRB 15-17)

4. Which is the quotient 882 and 7?
   Fill in the circle next to the best answer.
   ○ A. 93.6
   ● B. 126
   ○ C. 12.6
   ○ D. 127
   (SRB 22-24)

5. Complete.
   a. 600 ∗ 90 = 54,000
   b. 7,200 = 80 ∗ 90
   c. 400 ∗ 80 = 32,000
   d. 560,000 = 700 ∗ 800
   e. 40 ∗ 700 = 28,000
   (SRB 18)

Math Journal 1, p. 8

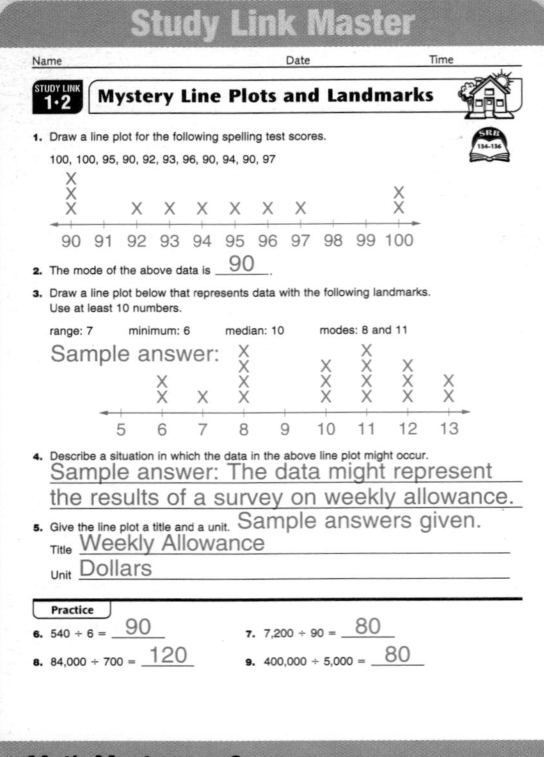

Study Link Master

Name Date Time

STUDY LINK 1·2 **Mystery Line Plots and Landmarks**

SRB 134-136

1. Draw a line plot for the following spelling test scores.

100, 100, 95, 90, 92, 93, 96, 90, 94, 90, 97

90 91 92 93 94 95 96 97 98 99 100

2. The mode of the above data is 90.

3. Draw a line plot below that represents data with the following landmarks. Use at least 10 numbers.

range: 7 minimum: 6 median: 10 modes: 8 and 11

Sample answer:

5 6 7 8 9 10 11 12 13

4. Describe a situation in which the data in the above line plot might occur.

Sample answer: The data might represent the results of a survey on weekly allowance.

5. Give the line plot a title and a unit. Sample answers given.

Title Weekly Allowance

Unit Dollars

Practice

6. 540 ÷ 6 = 90
7. 7,200 ÷ 90 = 80
8. 84,000 ÷ 700 = 120
9. 400,000 ÷ 5,000 = 80

Math Masters, p. 8

▶ Study Link 1·2

INDEPENDENT ACTIVITY

(*Math Masters*, p. 8)

Home Connection Students use a line plot to identify landmarks and draw a line plot to represent a given set of data. You may want to send the *Student Reference Book* home with students.

Consider assigning the Practice problems that appear at the bottom of most Study Links. Because these problems provide fact and computation practice, students should not use calculators to solve them. They may work the problems on the back of the page.

3 Differentiation Options

READINESS

SMALL-GROUP ACTIVITY

▶ Reviewing Line Plots

5–15 Min

(*Student Reference Book*, p. 134)

To provide experience with line plots, have students read page 134 of the *Student Reference Book* and complete Problem 2 of Check Your Understanding. Review answers.

ENRICHMENT

INDEPENDENT ACTIVITY

▶ Examining the Effects of Outliers

5–15 Min

(*Math Masters*, p. 9)

To extend students' knowledge of mean and median, have them find the mean and median of a data set with and without the outlier. Students compare the results and draw conclusions about the effect of an outlier on the mean and median of a data set.

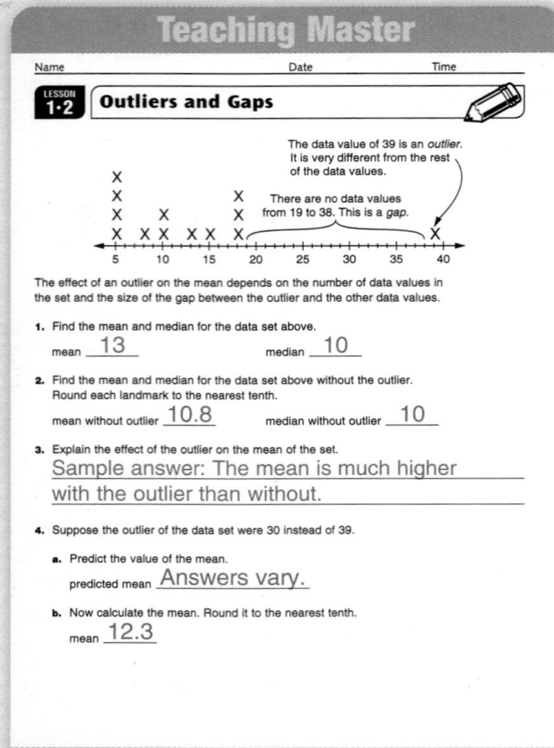

Teaching Master

Name Date Time

LESSON 1·2 **Outliers and Gaps**

The data value of 39 is an *outlier*. It is very different from the rest of the data values.

There are no data values from 19 to 38. This is a *gap*.

5 10 15 20 25 30 35 40

The effect of an outlier on the mean depends on the number of data values in the set and the size of the gap between the outlier and the other data values.

1. Find the mean and median for the data set above.

mean 13 median 10

2. Find the mean and median for the data set above without the outlier. Round each landmark to the nearest tenth.

mean without outlier 10.8 median without outlier 10

3. Explain the effect of the outlier on the mean of the set.

Sample answer: The mean is much higher with the outlier than without.

4. Suppose the outlier of the data set were 30 instead of 39.

a. Predict the value of the mean.

predicted mean Answers vary.

b. Now calculate the mean. Round it to the nearest tenth.

mean 12.3

Math Masters, p. 9

ELL SUPPORT

INDEPENDENT ACTIVITY

▶ Building a Math Word Bank

5–15 Min

(*Differentiation Handbook*)

To provide language support for data landmarks, have students use the Word Bank template found in the *Differentiation Handbook*. Ask students to write the terms *minimum, maximum, median,* and *mode* and then represent the terms with pictures and other words that describe them. See the *Differentiation Handbook* for more information.

Stem-and-Leaf Plots

Objective To use stem-and-leaf plots for organizing and analyzing data.

1 Teaching the Lesson

Key Activities

Students review the basics for stem-and-leaf plots. They utilize double stems to organize and display larger sets of data. Students determine the median, mode, and range from constructed stem-and-leaf plots.

Key Concepts and Skills

- Construct a stem-and-leaf plot from unsorted data. [Data and Chance Goal 1]
- Compare different graphical representations of the same data. [Data and Chance Goal 2]
- Identify landmarks of data (maximum, minimum, range, median, mode) displayed in stem-and-leaf plots. [Data and Chance Goal 2]

Key Vocabulary

minimum • maximum • range • mode • median • stem-and-leaf plot • stem • leaf • double-stem plot

Ongoing Assessment: Informing Instruction See page 30.

Ongoing Assessment: Recognizing Student Achievement Use journal page 11. [Data and Chance Goal 2]

materials

- ☐ *Math Journal 1,* pp. 9–11
- ☐ Study Link 1•2

2 Ongoing Learning & Practice

Students practice rounding numbers and estimating products.

Students practice and maintain skills through Math Boxes and Study Link activities.

materials

- ☐ *Math Journal 1,* pp. 12 and 13
- ☐ Study Link Master (*Math Masters,* p. 10)

3 Differentiation Options

READINESS

Students review how to read and construct a stem-and-leaf plot.

ENRICHMENT

Students use a back-to-back stem-and-leaf plot to display and compare two sets of data.

EXTRA PRACTICE

Students find the range and mean of data sets.

materials

- ☐ Teaching Masters (*Math Masters,* pp. 11 and 12)
- ☐ measuring tape
- ☐ *5-Minute Math,* pp. 116 and 198

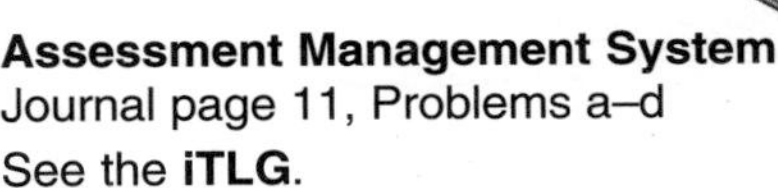

Technology

Assessment Management System
Journal page 11, Problems a–d
See the **iTLG**.

Getting Started

Mental Math and Reflexes

Students record dictated numbers on their slates or dry-erase boards and then round them to a specified place.

●○○ Round to the nearest hundred.
936; 575; 5,231; 67,351
900; 600; 5,200; 67,400

●●○ Round to the nearest thousand.
19,067; 33,733; 483,755; 96,502
19,000; 34,000; 484,000; 97,000

Math Message

Complete Problems 1–3 on journal page 9. Be prepared to discuss your answers.

Study Link 1·2 Follow-Up

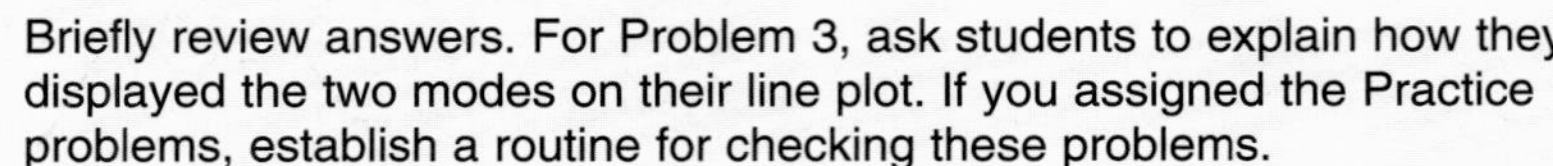

Briefly review answers. For Problem 3, ask students to explain how they displayed the two modes on their line plot. If you assigned the Practice problems, establish a routine for checking these problems.

Math Test Scores

Stems (100s and 10s)	Leaves (1s)
5	5 6 6 6
6	1 3 3 4 8
7	1 5
8	1 4 ④ 4 4 7 7 8 8
9	1 5 8 9 9
10	0 0

Cross out one data value from each end of the plot until only one (or two) remains.

Student Page

Date Time

LESSON 1·3 **Comparing Graphical Representations**

Math Message

a. Math Test Scores

Stems (100s and 10s)	Leaves (1s)
5	5 6 6 6
6	1 3 3 4 8
7	1 5
8	1 4 4 4 4 7 7 8 8
9	1 5 8 9 9
10	0 0

b. Math Test Scores

Number of Students; Scores: 50–59, 60–69, 70–79, 80–89, 90–99, 100–109

c. Math Test Scores

Scores	Number of Students
50–59	////
60–69	~~////~~
70–79	//
80–89	~~////~~ ////
90–99	~~////~~
100	//

d. Math Test Scores

50 55 60 65 70 75 80 85 90 95 100

1. Use pages 134, 135, and 138 of the *Student Reference Book* to identify each of the data representations (a–d) above.
   a. Stem-and-leaf plot b. Bar graph
   c. Tally chart (of grouped data) d. Line plot
2. Explain how these data representations are alike and how they are different.
   Each graph displays the same set of data. Only the stem-and-leaf plot and line plot show individual values. The stem-and-leaf plot shows the individual values more clearly.
3. Which graphical representation helps you identify the range, median, and mode most easily? Explain your choice. Sample answer:
   The stem-and-leaf plot displays individual values so it is easy to determine data landmarks.

Math Journal 1, p. 9

NOTE Some students may benefit from doing the Readiness activity before beginning Part 1 of the lesson. See Part 3 for details.

1 Teaching the Lesson

▶ Math Message Follow-Up

WHOLE-CLASS DISCUSSION

(*Math Journal 1,* p. 9)

Consider having students discuss their answers to Problem 2 of the Math Message in small groups. Then bring the class together to share the similarities and differences among Graphs a–d. Expect statements such as the following:

▷ The range of the numbers on each graph is the same.

▷ Each graph has the same title.

▷ The stem-and-leaf plot clearly displays individual data values. The other graphs are not as specific; they show general trends.

Ask students to read the leaves along one of the stems. Sample answer: 61, 63, 63, 64, 68 Ask: *How many test scores are greater than 95?* 5 *How many scores are less than 75?* 10

Expect that most students will be able to identify the **minimum** 55, **maximum** 100, **range** 45, and **mode** 84. Students will see that the procedure for finding a **median** is the same for stem-and-leaf plots as it is for line plots. In each case, students count from the smallest data value up to the middle one (or two) or from the largest value down to the middle one (or two). There are 27 numbers in the data set, so the middle value lies about halfway, near the 13th and 14th data values (27 ÷ 2).

NOTE Most students understand that the mode of a data set is the value that appears most often. However, students may not realize that a mode does not always exist or that a mode does not have to be unique.

▶ Constructing Double-Stem Plots

WHOLE-CLASS ACTIVITY

(*Math Journal 1,* pp. 10 and 11)

A **stem-and-leaf plot** is a useful way to organize data that are in a random order. Decide what unit to use for the stems and what unit to use for the leaves. The Old Faithful eruption data on journal page 10 involve a number of whole minutes and tenths of a minute. A duration of 4.9 minutes is split as 4 | 9 in the stem-and-leaf plot. The digits to the left of the vertical line form the **stem.** The digits to the right of the vertical line form the **leaf.** In the case of 4 | 9, the stem is 4 minutes and the leaf is 0.9 minute. The stem is written only once, but the leaves are listed every time they appear. In this way, individual data values are displayed. This individual display is an advantage of using a stem-and-leaf plot.

Adjusting the Activity

ELL

To support English language learners, make a connection between a stem-and-leaf plot and the similarly named parts of a plant or tree.

AUDITORY ◆ KINESTHETIC ◆ TACTILE ◆ VISUAL

Ask students to use the stem-and-leaf plot on journal page 10 to find the maximum, minimum, and range. After students have recorded these landmarks on the journal page, draw attention to the many leaves in the plot, particularly for stems 3 and 4. Long rows of leaves make it cumbersome to find the median. In cases like the eruption-duration data, in which many leaves fall on a few stems, students can split the stems to make a **double-stem plot.** In a double-stem plot, each stem having leaves that span from 0 to 9 is listed twice. Leaves 0 to 4 go on the upper stem, and leaves 5 to 9 go on the lower stem.

Duration of Old Faithful Eruptions
(Number of Observations: 48)

Stems (ones)	**Leaves** (tenths)
1	7 7 7 8 8 8 9 9 9
2	0 0 0 3 3 3
2	5 9 9
3	1 2 3 4 4
3	5 5 5 7 7 9 9 9
4	0 0 1 1 1 2 3 3
4	5 5 6 6 6 7 7 8 9

Notice that because the values of leaves for the first stem begin with 7, the first stem has not been split. The rows of leaves are shorter, so it is easier to find the median.

Student Page

Date Time

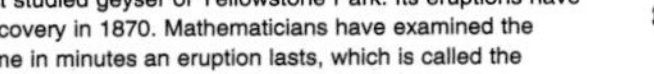

LESSON 1·3 **Old Faithful Erupts**

SRB 135 136

A geyser is a natural fountain of water and steam that erupts from the ground. Old Faithful is perhaps the most studied geyser of Yellowstone Park. Its eruptions have been recorded since its discovery in 1870. Mathematicians have examined the relationship between the time in minutes an eruption lasts, which is called the duration, and the time to the next eruption, which is called the interval.

Duration data appear in the table below.

Duration of Old Faithful Eruptions (in min)
(Number of Observations: 48)

4.9	1.7	2.3	3.5	2.3	3.9	4.3	2.5	3.4	4.8	4.1	1.9
4.6	4.1	2.9	3.7	3.4	1.7	1.7	3.3	4.0	4.6	3.1	2.9
4.1	4.6	2.0	3.5	4.2	4.7	1.8	4.0	1.8	1.9	2.3	2.0
4.5	3.7	3.9	3.9	1.9	4.3	3.2	4.7	3.5	2.0	1.8	4.5

A stem-and-leaf plot is a useful way to find landmarks when there are many data values in random order. The stem-and-leaf plot of the eruption data appears below.

Duration of Old Faithful Eruptions
(Number of Observations: 48)

Stems (ones)	**Leaves** (tenths)
1	7 7 7 8 8 8 9 9 9
2	0 0 0 3 3 3 5 9 9
3	1 2 3 4 4 5 5 5 7 7 9 9 9
4	0 0 1 1 1 2 3 3 5 5 6 6 6 7 7 8 9

The data in the plot are ordered, making it easier to determine data landmarks. Using the stem-and-leaf plot above, find the minimum, maximum, and range of the duration data.

a. minimum 1.7 b. maximum 4.9 c. range 3.2

Math Journal 1, p. 10

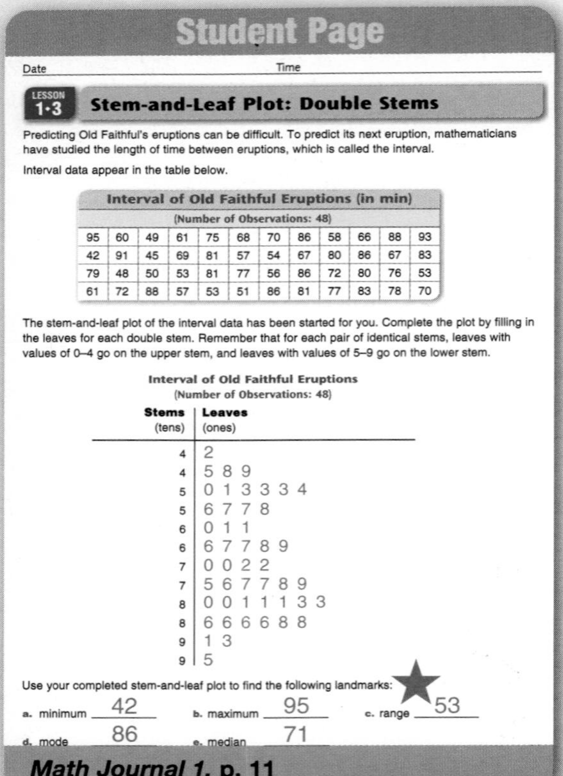

Student Page

Date Time

LESSON 1·3 **Stem-and-Leaf Plot: Double Stems**

Predicting Old Faithful's eruptions can be difficult. To predict its next eruption, mathematicians have studied the length of time between eruptions, which is called the interval.

Interval data appear in the table below.

Interval of Old Faithful Eruptions (in min)
(Number of Observations: 48)

95	60	49	61	75	68	70	86	58	66	88	93
42	91	45	69	81	57	54	67	80	86	67	83
79	48	50	53	81	77	56	86	72	80	76	53
61	72	88	57	53	51	86	81	77	83	78	70

The stem-and-leaf plot of the interval data has been started for you. Complete the plot by filling in the leaves for each double stem. Remember that for each pair of identical stems, leaves with values of 0–4 go on the upper stem, and leaves with values of 5–9 go on the lower stem.

Interval of Old Faithful Eruptions
(Number of Observations: 48)

Stems (tens)	Leaves (ones)
4	2
4	5 8 9
5	0 1 3 3 3 4
5	6 7 7 8
6	0 1 1
6	6 7 7 8 9
7	0 0 2 2
7	5 6 7 7 8 9
8	0 0 1 1 1 3 3
8	6 6 6 6 8 8
9	1 3
9	5

Use your completed stem-and-leaf plot to find the following landmarks:

a. minimum 42 b. maximum 95 c. range 53

d. mode 86 e. median 71

***Math Journal 1*, p. 11**

Circulate and assist as students work on journal page 11. The table on the page shows the time between eruptions in minutes. Have students complete the double-stem plot and find the maximum, minimum, range, median, and mode of the data set.

Ongoing Assessment: Informing Instruction

Watch for students who are having difficulty keeping track of data values that they have recorded in the plot and values that they still need to record. Encourage students to develop a system of crossing out values in the table once they've been recorded in the plot. Remind students to check that the number of leaves in their plot is the same as the number of values in the table.

Ongoing Assessment: Recognizing Student Achievement

Journal Page 11 Problems a–d

Use **journal page 11, Problems a–d** to assess students' ability to find the minimum, maximum, range, and mode of data displayed in a stem-and-leaf plot. Students are making adequate progress if they accurately calculate these landmarks from their constructed plots. Some students may be able to navigate the double stems to find the median (near the 24th and 25th values).

[Data and Chance Goal 2]

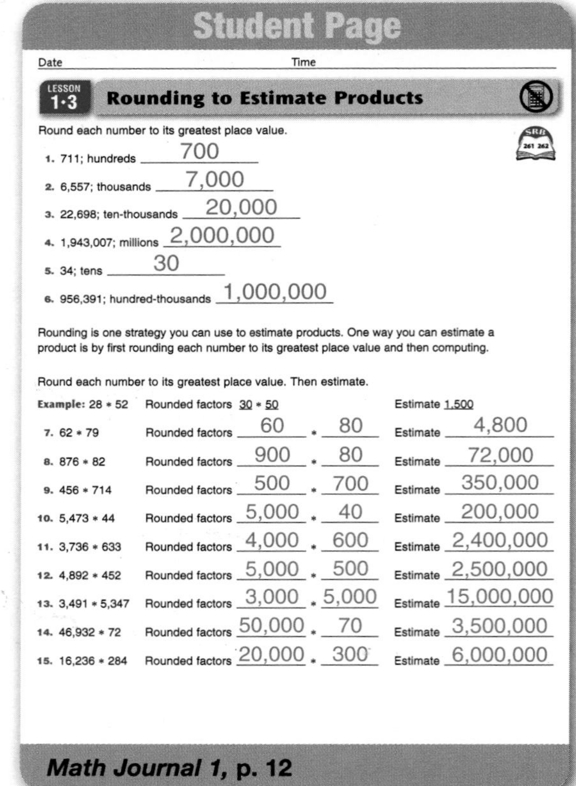

Student Page

Date Time

LESSON 1·3 **Rounding to Estimate Products**

SRB 241 242

Round each number to its greatest place value.

1. 711; hundreds 700
2. 6,557; thousands 7,000
3. 22,698; ten-thousands 20,000
4. 1,943,007; millions 2,000,000
5. 34; tens 30
6. 956,391; hundred-thousands 1,000,000

Rounding is one strategy you can use to estimate products. One way you can estimate a product is by first rounding each number to its greatest place value and then computing.

Round each number to its greatest place value. Then estimate.

Example: 28 ∗ 52	Rounded factors	30 ∗ 50	Estimate 1,500
7. 62 ∗ 79	Rounded factors	60 ∗ 80	Estimate 4,800
8. 876 ∗ 82	Rounded factors	900 ∗ 80	Estimate 72,000
9. 456 ∗ 714	Rounded factors	500 ∗ 700	Estimate 350,000
10. 5,473 ∗ 44	Rounded factors	5,000 ∗ 40	Estimate 200,000
11. 3,736 ∗ 633	Rounded factors	4,000 ∗ 600	Estimate 2,400,000
12. 4,892 ∗ 452	Rounded factors	5,000 ∗ 500	Estimate 2,500,000
13. 3,491 ∗ 5,347	Rounded factors	3,000 ∗ 5,000	Estimate 15,000,000
14. 46,932 ∗ 72	Rounded factors	50,000 ∗ 70	Estimate 3,500,000
15. 16,236 ∗ 284	Rounded factors	20,000 ∗ 300	Estimate 6,000,000

***Math Journal 1*, p. 12**

2 Ongoing Learning & Practice

▶ Rounding to Estimate Products

INDEPENDENT ACTIVITY

(*Math Journal 1,* p. 12)

The problems on journal page 12 provide practice rounding numbers and estimating products.

▶ Math Boxes 1·3

INDEPENDENT ACTIVITY

(*Math Journal 1,* p. 13)

Mixed Practice Math Boxes in this lesson are paired with Math Boxes in Lesson 1-1. The skill in Problem 4 previews Unit 2 content.

▶ Study Link 1·3

INDEPENDENT ACTIVITY

(*Math Masters,* p. 10)

Home Connection Students construct a stem-and-leaf plot for decimal number values.

Student Page

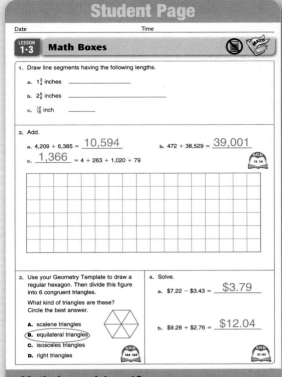

Date Time

LESSON 1·3 **Math Boxes**

1. Draw line segments having the following lengths.

a. $1\frac{3}{4}$ inches ______

b. $2\frac{6}{8}$ inches ______

c. $\frac{12}{16}$ inch ______

2. Add.

a. 4,209 + 6,385 = 10,594

b. 472 + 38,529 = 39,001

c. 1,366 = 4 + 263 + 1,020 + 79

SRB 13 14

3. Use your Geometry Template to draw a regular hexagon. Then divide this figure into 6 congruent triangles.

What kind of triangles are these? Circle the best answer.

A. scalene triangles

B. equilateral triangles (circled)

C. isosceles triangles

D. right triangles

SRB 164 165

4. Solve.

a. \$7.22 − \$3.43 = \$3.79

b. \$9.28 + \$2.76 = \$12.04

SRB 31-33

Math Journal 1, p. 13

Study Link Master

Name Date Time

STUDY LINK 1·3 **Stem-and-Leaf Plots**

SRB 133 134

Every day, there are many earthquakes worldwide. Most are too small for people to notice. Scientists refer to the size of an earthquake as its magnitude. Earthquakes are classified in categories from minor to great, depending on magnitude.

Class	Magnitude
Great	8.0 or more
Major	7–7.9
Strong	6–6.9
Moderate	5–5.9
Light	4–4.9
Minor	3–3.9

The table below shows the magnitude of 21 earthquakes that occurred on June 28, 2004.

Magnitude of Earthquakes Occurring June 28, 2004										
4.2	5.2	2.8	4.8	3.9	2.0	3.3	4.8	4.5	3.5	2.2
2.6	3.4	6.8	3.0	4.7	2.8	4.2	4.1	5.4	5.1	

1. Construct a stem-and-leaf plot of the earthquake magnitude data.

2. Use your stem-and-leaf plot to find the following landmarks.

a. range 4.8

b. mode(s) 2.8, 4.2, 4.8

c. median 4.1

Magnitude of Earthquakes Occurring on June 28, 2004

Stems (ones)	Leaves (tenths)
2	0 2 6 8 8
3	0 3 4 5 9
4	1 2 2 5 7 8 8
5	1 2 4
6	8

Practice

3. 6,400 ÷ 80 = 80

4. 121,000 ÷ 1,100 = 110

5. 3,000,000 ÷ 6,000 = 500

6. 600,000 ÷ 12,000 = 50

Math Masters, p. 10

3 Differentiation Options

READINESS

PARTNER ACTIVITY

▶ Reviewing Stem-and-Leaf Plots

15–30 Min

(*Math Masters,* p. 11)

To provide experience with stem-and-leaf plots, have students work in pairs to complete *Math Masters,* page 11 and then compare their answers. Have students describe the stem-and-leaf plot when sharing their results.

ENRICHMENT

INDEPENDENT ACTIVITY

▶ Reading and Constructing Back-to-Back Stem-and-Leaf Plots

15–30 Min

(*Math Masters,* p. 12)

To extend their knowledge of stem-and-leaf plots, have students study an example of a back-to-back stem-and-leaf plot. They then construct a back-to-back stem-and-leaf plot that has 2-digit stems.

EXTRA PRACTICE

SMALL-GROUP ACTIVITY

▶ *5-Minute Math*

5–15 Min

To offer more practice finding the range and mean of data sets, see *5-Minute Math,* pages 116 and 198.

Teaching Master

Name Date Time

LESSON 1·3 **Reviewing Stem-and-Leaf Plots**

Students in Mr. Conley's sixth-grade class measured how far they could reach and jump. Each student stood with legs together, feet flat on the floor, and one arm stretched up as high as possible. **Arm reach** was then measured from top fingertip to floor.

arm reach

1. Using a tape measure, measure your arm reach in inches. Record this measurement.

_____ in. Answers vary.

In the **standing jump,** each student stood with knees bent and then jumped forward as far as possible. The distance was measured from the starting line to the point closest to where the student's heels came down.

jump distance

Students displayed their results using two different stem-and-leaf plots.

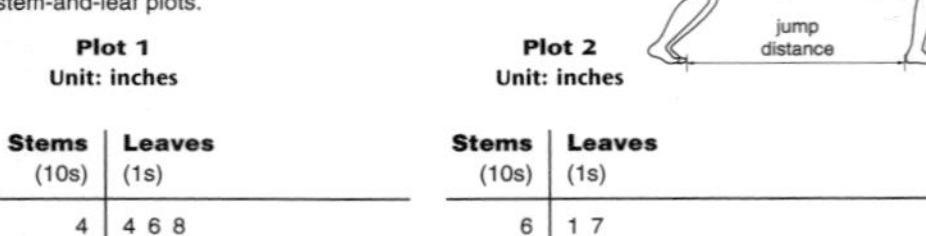

Plot 1
Unit: inches

Stems (10s)	Leaves (1s)
4	4 6 8
5	0 0 3 3 4 5 6 7 7 8 8 9
6	0 0 1 3 8 9

Plot 2
Unit: inches

Stems (10s)	Leaves (1s)
6	1 7
7	0 1 2 2 2 3 3 4 5 6 6 6 6 8 9 9
8	3 4 7

2. Use what you know about your arm reach to figure out which stem-and-leaf plot represents the class data for the standing jump.
   a. Which plot do you think it is? Plot 1
   b. Explain why you think so. Sample answer: The smallest number in Plot 2 is 61, which is more than 5 feet. Most sixth-grade students cannot jump that far.

Math Masters, p. 11

Teaching Master

Name Date Time

LESSON 1·3 **Back-to-Back Stem-and-Leaf Plots**

You can compare two related sets of data in a **back-to-back stem-and-leaf plot.** In this type of plot, the stem is written in the center, with one set of leaves to the right and another set of leaves to the left.

The ages of Wimbledon tennis champions in the women's and men's singles from 1993–2003 are shown in the back-to-back stem-and-leaf plot below.

Ages of Wimbledon Tennis Champions 1993–2003

Women Leaves (1s)	Stems (10s)	Men Leaves (1s)
7	1	
4 3 2 2 1 1 0	2	1 2 2 3 4
7 6	2	5 6 7 8 9
	3	0

1. How many women champions were in their twenties? 9
2. What is the mode age for women? 21, 22 For men? 22
3. What is the median age for women? 22 For men? 25

Students' Heights (in centimeters)	
Girls' Heights	**Boys' Heights**
162, 126, 134, 145, 127, 134, 143, 159, 147, 169, 164, 171, 163, 171, 154, 157	154, 137, 162, 147, 145, 174, 132, 151, 170, 161, 166, 136, 168, 155, 153, 143

4. The data table above shows students' heights in centimeters. Make a back-to-back stem-and-leaf plot to display the data. Use the 2-digit stems provided.

Students' Heights

Girls Leaves (1s)	Stems (10s)	Boys Leaves (1s)
7 6	12	
4 4	13	2 6 7
7 5 3	14	3 5 7
9 7 4	15	1 3 4 5
9 4 3 2	16	1 2 6 8
1 1	17	0 4

Math Masters, p. 12

Median and Mean

Objective To calculate and compare the median and mean of a data set.

1 Teaching the Lesson

Key Activities
Students find and compare the median and the mean of various data sets.

Key Concepts and Skills
- Calculate and compare the median and mean of a data set.
  [Data and Chance Goal 2]
- Examine how the median and the mean change as data change.
  [Data and Chance Goal 2]
- Find the mode of a data set.
  [Data and Chance Goal 2]
- Determine which landmark best represents a set of data—mean, median, or mode.
  [Data and Chance Goal 2]

Ongoing Assessment: Recognizing Student Achievement Use an Exit Slip.
[Data and Chance Goal 2]

materials
- ☐ *Math Journal 1,* pp. 14 and 15
- ☐ Study Link 1•3
- ☐ Teaching Aid Master (*Math Masters,* p. 404)
- ☐ calculator

2 Ongoing Learning & Practice

Students practice and maintain skills through Math Boxes and Study Link activities.

materials
- ☐ *Math Journal 1,* p. 16
- ☐ Study Link Master (*Math Masters,* p. 13)
- ☐ metric ruler

3 Differentiation Options

READINESS
Students use manipulatives to represent the mean and write number sentences that model how to find the mean.

ENRICHMENT
Students use computer software to find the median and mean of a data set.

EXTRA PRACTICE
Students complete teacher-generated Math Boxes.

materials
- ☐ Teaching Master (*Math Masters,* p. 14)
- ☐ Teaching Aid Master (*Math Masters,* p. 405)
- ☐ 25 unit cubes per student
- ☐ computer
- ☐ spreadsheet/graphing software

See **Advance Preparation**

Additional Information

Advance Preparation Consider having students use computer software for the optional Enrichment activity in Part 3.

Technology

Assessment Management System
Exit Slip
See the **iTLG**.

Getting Started

Mental Math and Reflexes

Students solve mental math problems such as the following:

●○○ Add 25 and 70. Take away 15. Triple the result. 240

●●○ Add 250 and 750. Divide by 10. Subtract 50. 50

●●● Add 35 and 65. Multiply by 5. Double the result. 1,000

Math Message

Complete Problem 1 on journal page 14.

Study Link 1·3 Follow-Up

Briefly review answers.

NOTE Some students may benefit from doing the Readiness activity before beginning Part 1 of the lesson. See Part 3 for details.

1 Teaching the Lesson

▶ Math Message Follow-Up

WHOLE-CLASS DISCUSSION

(*Math Journal 1,* p. 14)

Review the salary data in the table. Ask students to explain how the mean salary was calculated. Sample answer: Find the sum of the salaries and divide the sum by the number of employees.

Ask students to share their thoughts about which landmark (mean, median, or mode) best represents a typical annual salary at the company. Sample answer: Both the mean and mode are greater than $90,000. Because 9 of the 12 employees earn less than $90,000, the mean and mode do not seem to be good representations of the salaries. Since 7 of the 12 salaries are between $40,000 and $63,000, the median salary of $54,000 best represents the typical annual salary. To support English language learners, discuss the meaning of *typical* as well as *annual salary.*

Discuss how the mean and the median change as data change. Pose the following situation: *Suppose the salary of the company president increased to $350,000. How would this affect the mean salary?* The mean salary would increase. *How would the increase affect the median salary?* The median salary would remain the same. It is less affected by the maximum and minimum salaries than the mean salary is. Explore other situations that would affect the mean and median salaries.

Circulate and assist as students complete journal page 14. Bring the class together to share answers.

Student Page

Date ______ Time ______

LESSON 1·4 **Comparing the Median and Mean**

Math Message

A small office supply company has 12 employees. Their yearly salaries appear in the table, as well as the mean, median, and mode salaries.

1. Does the mean, the median, or the mode best represent the typical salary at the company? Explain.

   Sample answer: The mean and mode salaries are greater than $90,000. Because 9 of the 12 salaries are less than $65,000, the median salary seems the best representation of a typical salary at Fancy Font.

Salaries at Fancy Font Office Supplies

Job	Annual Salary
President	$275,000
Vice-President: Marketing	$185,000
Vice-President: Sales	$185,000
Marketing Manager	$62,500
Product Manager	$59,000
Sales Manager	$55,500
Promotions Manager	$52,500
Salesperson 1	$45,000
Salesperson 2	$43,500
Salesperson 3	$43,000
Administrative Assistant 1	$39,500
Administrative Assistant 2	$36,000
Mean salary	**$90,125**
Median salary	**$54,000**
Mode salary	**$185,000**

Median and Mean

Find the median and mean for each of the following sets of numbers.

2. 6, 9, 10, 15 — a. median 9.5 — b. mean 10
3. 0.50, 0.75, 1, 1.25, 0.80 — a. median 0.80 — b. mean 0.86
4. 123, 56, 92, 90, 88 — a. median 90 — b. mean 89.8

Math Journal 1, p. 14

Adjusting the Activity

Ask students to explain how they could use the mean salary to find the sum of the salaries.

AUDITORY ◆ KINESTHETIC ◆ TACTILE ◆ VISUAL

Comparing the Median and Mean of a Data Set

Relate the following situation to students.

Imagine that it is the end of the grading period. You have received the following test scores: 90, 88, 100, and 82. You have one more test to take before the end of the grading period.

Pose the following questions:

- **If your teacher bases your grade on the median of your test scores, will you be motivated to study for the last test?** Sample answer: No. There would not be much incentive to study. No matter how low my last test score is, my median score will not be lower than 88.
- **If your teacher bases your grade on the mean score, will you be motivated to study for the last test?** Sample answer: Yes. I will be motivated to study. The better test score I make, the higher my final grade will be.
- **Suppose you score 20 out of 100 on your final test. Will the median or the mean give a better picture of your overall performance?** Sample answer: The median (88) seems to give a better overall picture. The mean will be 76, which is 6 points lower than the lowest of my other test scores.
- **Suppose you score 95 out of 100 on your final test. Will the median or the mean give a better picture of your overall performance?** Sample answer: Both will be about 90.
- **Most teachers determine final grades by calculating the mean of the scores for each student. Why do you suppose they use the mean?** Sample answer: One or more low scores can significantly lower the mean of the scores. Using the mean gives students incentive to get high scores on all tests.
- **Can you think of a situation outside of school in which the mode of the data would be most useful?** Sample answers: A small grocery store that can stock only one brand of peanut butter would want to stock only the most requested brand. A political candidate often wants to know the most popular public opinion concerning an issue.

Student Page

Date ____________ Time ____________

LESSON 1·4 Data Landmarks

The 10 most successful coaches in the history of the National Football League (NFL) are listed in the table at the right, along with the number of games won through the end of the 2002 season.

Most Successful NFL Coaches

Coach	Games Won
Don Shula	347
George Halas	324
Tom Landry	270
Curly Lambeau	229
Chuck Noll	209
Dan Reeves	198
Chuck Knox	193
Paul Brown	170
Bud Grant	168
Steve Owen	155

Find the following landmarks for the data set displayed in the table.

1. median 203.5
2. maximum 347
3. minimum 155
4. mean 226.3
5. mode none
6. range 192

Try This

7. Denzel's first three test scores in math were 90, 100, and 90.
   a. What must Denzel score on his fourth test to keep his *mean* score at 90 or higher? 80 or higher
   b. What must Denzel score on his fourth test to keep his *median* test score at 90 or higher? Any score, even 0, will keep the median at 90 or higher.

***Math Journal 1,* p. 15**

▶ Finding Landmarks

PARTNER ACTIVITY

(*Math Journal 1,* p. 15)

Ask students to find the median of the following data sets:

10, 14, 12, 11, 12 12

10, 14, 12, 11, 12, 11 11.5

Draw their attention to the number of values in the second data set. Because the number of values is even, the median is the number halfway between the two middle values, or the mean of the two middle values.

Circulate and assist as students complete the journal page.

Ongoing Assessment: Recognizing Student Achievement

Exit Slip 

Use an **Exit Slip** (*Math Masters,* p. 404) to assess students' understanding of median and mean. Students are making adequate progress if they can acknowledge that the median is less affected by outliers than the mean is.

Pose the following informal assessment item to students: In 2004, baseball player Derek Jeter earned about $25 million in salary, bonuses, and endorsements. If you were to report the typical annual earnings for baseball players, would it be more accurate to report the mean or median earnings? Why?

[Data and Chance Goal 2]

2 Ongoing Learning & Practice

▶ Math Boxes 1·4

INDEPENDENT ACTIVITY

(*Math Journal 1,* p. 16)

Mixed Practice Math Boxes in this lesson are paired with Math Boxes in Lesson 1-2. The skills in Problems 4 and 5 are prerequisites for Unit 2.

▶ Study Link 1·4

INDEPENDENT ACTIVITY

(*Math Masters,* p. 13)

Home Connection Students construct stem-and-leaf plots and practice finding the mean and median of data sets.

Student Page

Date ____________ Time ____________

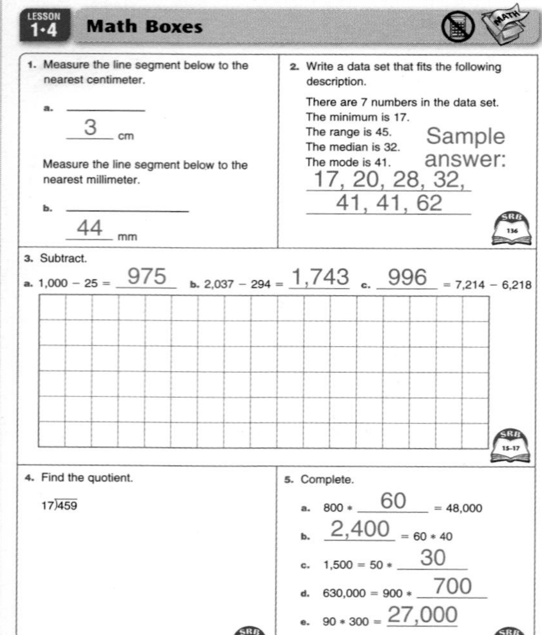

LESSON 1·4 Math Boxes

1. Measure the line segment below to the nearest centimeter.
   a. 3 cm
   Measure the line segment below to the nearest millimeter.
   b. 44 mm
2. Write a data set that fits the following description.
   There are 7 numbers in the data set.
   The minimum is 17.
   The range is 45.
   The median is 32.
   The mode is 41.
   Sample answer: 17, 20, 28, 32, 41, 41, 62
3. Subtract.
   a. 1,000 − 25 = 975 b. 2,037 − 294 = 1,743 c. 996 = 7,214 − 6,218
4. Find the quotient.
   17)459
   459 ÷ 17 = 27
5. Complete.
   a. 800 ∗ 60 = 48,000
   b. 2,400 = 60 ∗ 40
   c. 1,500 = 50 ∗ 30
   d. 630,000 = 900 ∗ 700
   e. 90 ∗ 300 = 27,000

***Math Journal 1,* p. 16**

3 Differentiation Options

READINESS

PARTNER ACTIVITY

▶ Defining the Mean

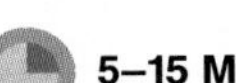
5–15 Min

(*Math Masters,* p. 14)

To provide experience with modeling and finding the mean, have students use unit cubes to represent data values. They redistribute, or even out, the unit cubes to find the mean value. Students then write a number sentence to model how they redistributed the unit cubes to help determine the mean of the data set.

ENRICHMENT

SMALL-GROUP ACTIVITY

▶ Using Technology to Find the Median and Mean

15–30 Min

Assign each group one of the data sets provided in the Data and Probability section of the *Student Reference Book.* Students use computer software to sort the values of a data set from least to greatest to calculate the median of the data set. They use a formula to calculate the mean of the same data set.

EXTRA PRACTICE

INDEPENDENT ACTIVITY

▶ Writing Custom-Made Math Boxes

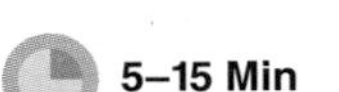
5–15 Min

(*Math Masters,* p. 405)

To provide extra practice, use *Math Masters,* page 405 to generate Math Box questions that focus on a particular concept or skill for which students need extra practice.

Study Link Master

Name Date Time

STUDY LINK 1•4 **Median and Mean**

Mia's quiz scores are 75, 70, 75, 85, 75, 85, 80, 95, and 80.

Nico's quiz scores are 55, 85, 95, 100, 75, 75, 65, 95, and 75.

1. Find each student's mean score. Mia 80 Nico 80

2. Make a stem-and-leaf plot for each student's scores.

a. **Mia's Quiz Scores**

Stems (100s and 10s)	Leaves (1s)
7	0 5 5 5
8	0 0 5 5
9	5

b. **Nico's Quiz Scores**

Stems (100s and 10s)	Leaves (1s)
5	5
6	5
7	5 5 5
8	5
9	5 5
10	0

3. Find each student's median score. Mia 80 Nico 75

4. What is the range of scores for each student? Mia 25 Nico 45

5. Which landmark, mean or median, is the better indicator of each student's overall performance? Explain.
Because Mia's mean and median scores are the same (80), either landmark is a good indicator for her. Nico's median score is the better indicator of his performance. His mean is not as good an indicator because of the range of his scores.

Practice

6. $4.57 + $1.25 = $5.82
7. $14.49 + $15.78 = $30.27
8. $19.99 − $5.75 = $14.24
9. $39.25 − $18.75 = $20.50

Math Masters, p. 13

Teaching Master

Name Date Time

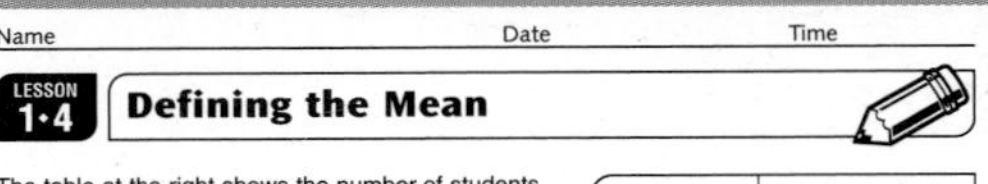
LESSON 1•4 **Defining the Mean**

The table at the right shows the number of students absent from gym class during the week.

1. Place unit cubes on the line below to show the number of absent students for each day.

Day	Students Absent
Monday	6
Tuesday	2
Wednesday	5
Thursday	4
Friday	8

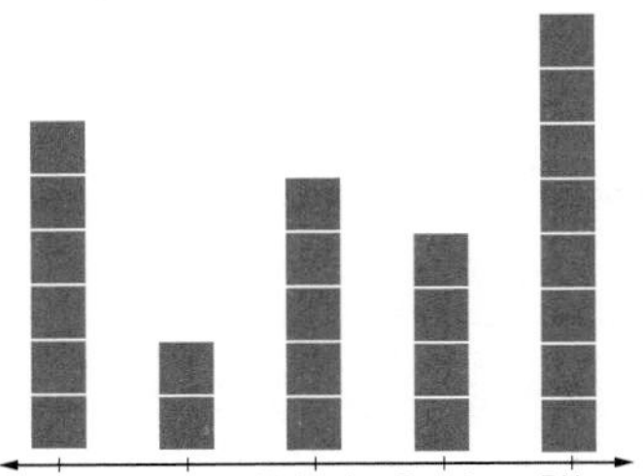

If you redistribute, or even out, the number of absent students so the number is the same for each day, you are finding the **mean.** The mean is a useful landmark when there are *not* one or two numbers that are far away from the rest of the data values (outliers).

2. Move the cubes on the line plot so that each day has the same number. After you've evened out the cubes, how many does each day have? 5

You can use a number sentence to model how you evened out the cubes. You started with 6 + 2 + 5 + 4 + 8 = 25 cubes. Then you redistributed the cubes so that the total number of cubes (25) was the same for each of the 5 days, or 25 ÷ 5 = 5.

3. Use the cubes to find the mean of the following number of absent students.
Monday: 5; Tuesday: 0; Wednesday: 6; Thursday: 2; Friday: 7

Then write a number sentence to model what you did. 20 ÷ 5 = 4

Math Masters, p. 14

Playing *Landmark Shark*

Objective To find the range, median, mode, and mean for sets of numbers.

1 Teaching the Lesson

Key Activities

Students play a new game, *Landmark Shark,* in which they score points based on the range, median, mode, and mean of their cards.

Key Concepts and Skills

- Mentally add, subtract, multiply, and divide whole numbers. [Operations and Computation Goals 1 and 2]
- Calculate landmarks (range, median, mean, mode) of a data set. [Data and Chance Goal 2]
- Predict how the landmarks of a data set change as the values of the data set change. [Data and Chance Goal 2]

materials

- ☐ *Student Reference Book,* pp. 325 and 326
- ☐ Study Link 1•4
- ☐ Game Masters (*Math Masters,* pp. 456 and 457)
- ☐ Per group: 4 each of number cards 0–10; 1 each of number cards 11–20 (from the Everything Math Deck, if available)

See **Advance Preparation**

2 Ongoing Learning & Practice

Students practice and maintain skills through Math Boxes and Study Link activities.

Ongoing Assessment: Recognizing Student Achievement Use journal page 17. [Data and Chance Goals 1 and 2]

materials

- ☐ *Math Journal 1,* p. 17
- ☐ Study Link Master (*Math Masters,* p. 15)

3 Differentiation Options

READINESS

Students practice calculating the range, median, and mean for a set of data and examine how these landmarks change as data are added to the existing set.

ENRICHMENT

Students apply mental-math strategies to calculate the mean of a data set containing five numbers.

EXTRA PRACTICE

Students calculate data landmarks for sets of numbers.

materials

- ☐ *Student Reference Book,* pp. 136 and 137
- ☐ Teaching Masters (*Math Masters,* pp. 16 and 17)
- ☐ 3" by 5" index cards, 10 per student
- ☐ markers
- ☐ *5-Minute Math,* pp. 119, 199, and 200

Additional Information

Advance Preparation For Part 1, make and cut apart copies of *Landmark Shark* cards (*Math Masters,* p. 456) so each student gets one set of the three cards—Range, Median, and Mode. Make one copy per group of the *Landmark Shark* score sheet (*Math Masters,* p. 457).

Technology

Assessment Management System
Math Boxes, Problem 1
See the **iTLG**.

Getting Started

Mental Math and Reflexes

Students write dictated numbers in standard form on their slates or dry-erase boards.

Suggestions:

●○○ twenty-three thousand one 23,001

seven million, four hundred thirty-two thousand, seventy-eight 7,432,078

●●○ thirty million, six hundred three thousand, twenty-four 30,603,024

seventeen and six hundredths 17.06

●●● three hundred ninety-eight and thirty-eight hundredths 398.38

twelve thousand, eight hundred three and eight tenths 12,803.8

Math Message

Mentally calculate the range and mean for each of the following data sets.

- 9, 6, 10, 5, 15 range: 10; mean: 9
- 20, 23, 10, 18, 19 range: 13; mean: 18
- 35, 28, 15, 27, 40 range: 25; mean: 29

Study Link 1•4 Follow-Up

Briefly review answers. Problem 5 encourages students to think about the shape of the data. The middles of the two plots are nearly the same, whether the median or the mean is used to characterize the middle. However, the shapes of the plots are very different. Mia's is compact and has a small range. Nico's appears stretched out and has a large range.

1 Teaching the Lesson

NOTE Some students may benefit from doing the Readiness activity before beginning Part 1 of the lesson. See Part 3 for details.

▶ Math Message Follow-Up

WHOLE-CLASS ACTIVITY

Review the answers. Ask students to share strategies for mentally calculating the range and mean for each data set. For example, in the first data set, use the Associative Property of Addition to find the sum of the five numbers:

$(9 + 6) + (10 + 5) + 15 = 3(15) = 45$. Divide 45 by 5 to find the mean (9).

For the second data set, subtract 3 from 23. Add 2 to 18 and 1 to 19 to get $20 + 20 + 10 + 20 + 20 = 90$. To mentally divide 90 by 5, divide 100 by 5 to get 20. Because $100 - 90 = 2$ sets of 5, subtract 2 from 20 to get 18.

Another way to mentally calculate the mean is to find the sum of the numbers, divide the sum by 10, and then multiply that number by 2. So, for the second set of data, divide 90 by 10 to get 9. Multiply 9 by 2 to get 18.

▶ Introducing *Landmark Shark*

WHOLE-CLASS DISCUSSION

(*Student Reference Book,* pp. 325 and 326; *Math Masters,* pp. 456 and 457)

Remind students that in previous lessons they learned to find the range, median, mode, and mean of a data set. Explain that in this lesson, students will apply what they have learned about these landmarks to play a game. They will also apply their mental computation skills.

Student Page

Games

Landmark Shark

Materials □ 1 complete deck of number cards
□ 1 each of Range, Median, and Mode *Landmark Shark* Cards for each player (*Math Masters,* p. 456)
□ 1 *Landmark Shark* Score Sheet (*Math Masters,* p. 457)

Players 2 or 3

Skill Finding the range, mode, median, and, mean

Object of the game To score the most points by finding data landmarks.

Directions

1. To play a round:
   - The dealer shuffles the number cards and deals 5 cards number-side down to each player.
   - Players put their cards in order from the smallest number to the largest.
   - There are 3 ways a player may score points using their five cards:

Range: The player's score is the range of the 5 numbers.

Example Brian's hand: 1 4 6 8 12

Range = 12 − 1 = 11 **points scored** = 11

Median: The player's score is the median of the 5 numbers.

Example Liz's hand: 4 9 13 14 15

Median = 13 **points scored** = 13

Mode: The player must have at least 2 cards with the same number. The player's score is found by multiplying the mode of the 5 numbers by the number of modal cards. If there is more than one mode, the player uses the mode that will produce the most points.

Example Caroline's hand: 1 2 8 8 10

Mode = 8 **points scored** = 2 ∗ 8 = 16

Student Reference Book, **p. 325**

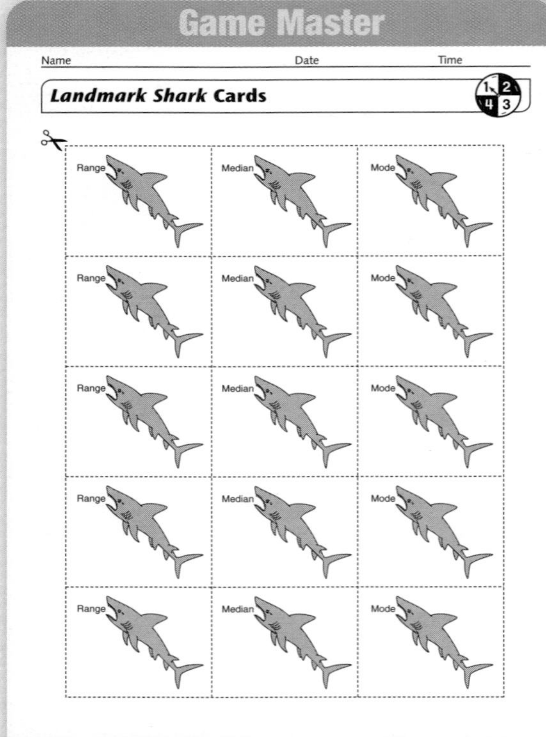
Game Master

Name Date Time

Landmark Shark Cards

Range	Median	Mode
Range	Median	Mode
Range	Median	Mode
Range	Median	Mode
Range	Median	Mode
Range	Median	Mode

***Math Masters,* p. 456**

Game Master

Name Date Time

Landmark Shark Score Sheet

SRB 325-326

		Player 1	Player 2	Player 3
Round 1:	Points Scored			
	Bonus Points			
	Round 1 Score			
Round 2:	Points Scored			
	Bonus Points			
	Round 2 Score			
Round 3:	Points Scored			
	Bonus Points			
	Round 3 Score			
Round 4:	Points Scored			
	Bonus Points			
	Round 4 Score			
Round 5:	Points Scored			
	Bonus Points			
	Round 5 Score			
Total Score for 5 Rounds				

***Math Masters,* p. 457**

NOTE Practice through games is an integral part of *Everyday Mathematics.* Games are an efficient way to build number skills that require frequent practice. Games are not boring, while drill often is. Games such as *Landmark Shark* should be played not only when they are introduced in Part 1 of a lesson, but also when they appear on a regular basis in Part 2 of lessons.

As a class, go over the directions for *Landmark Shark* on pages 325 and 326 of the *Student Reference Book.*

Play a few practice rounds with the class before students break into groups. While playing *Landmark Shark* with the class, encourage students to explain their reasoning for choosing the median, mode, or range card. Also ask students to explain why they decided to exchange certain cards for new cards.

Adjusting the Activity

Suggest that students play the game in teams until they clearly understand the rules and the strategies. Players can help one another decide which cards to put down and which ones to exchange to create the best solution.

AUDITORY ◆ KINESTHETIC ◆ TACTILE ◆ VISUAL

▶ Playing *Landmark Shark*

SMALL-GROUP ACTIVITY

(*Student Reference Book,* pp. 325 and 326; *Math Masters,* pp. 456 and 457)

After students have played several games, bring the class together to share strategies. Initially students will probably focus only on the points they can earn by finding ranges, medians, or modes. Eventually they will realize that they can improve their scores by paying attention to the mean when deciding whether or not to exchange cards.

Store the *Landmark Shark* cards for future use.

Landmark Shark cards

	Player 1	Player 2	Player 3
Points Scored			
Bonus Points			
Round 1 Score			

Landmark Shark score sheet

2 Ongoing Learning & Practice

▶ Math Boxes 1·5

INDEPENDENT ACTIVITY

(*Math Journal 1,* p. 17)

Mixed Practice Math Boxes in this lesson are paired with Math Boxes in Lesson 1-7. The skills in Problems 3 and 4 preview Unit 2 content.

Ongoing Assessment: Recognizing Student Achievement

Math Boxes Problem 1 

Use **Math Boxes, Problem 1** to assess students' ability to construct a line plot, as well as calculate the mean of a data set. Students are making adequate progress if they are able to accurately construct the line plot and calculate the mean. Some students may be able to calculate the mean without using a calculator.

[Data and Chance Goals 1 and 2]

Writing/Reasoning Have students write their responses to the following: *Explain the strategy you used in Problem 3 to convert between centimeters and meters.* Sample answer: Because a meter is 100 centimeters, I multiplied by 100 to convert meters to centimeters. A centimeter is $\frac{1}{100}$ meter, so I divided by 100 to convert centimeters to meters.

▶ Study Link 1·5

INDEPENDENT ACTIVITY

(*Math Masters,* p. 15)

Home Connection Students draw stem-and-leaf plots and find data landmarks for given data sets.

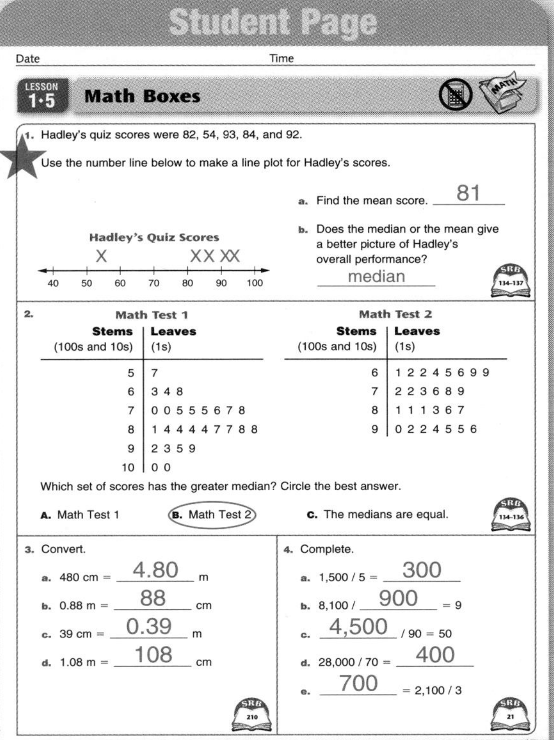

Student Page

Date Time

LESSON 1·5 **Math Boxes**

1. Hadley's quiz scores were 82, 54, 93, 84, and 92. Use the number line below to make a line plot for Hadley's scores.

a. Find the mean score. 81

b. Does the median or the mean give a better picture of Hadley's overall performance? median

2.

Math Test 1

Stems (100s and 10s)	Leaves (1s)
5	7
6	3 4 8
7	0 0 5 5 5 6 7 8
8	1 4 4 4 4 7 7 8 8
9	2 3 5 9
10	0 0

Math Test 2

Stems (100s and 10s)	Leaves (1s)
6	1 2 2 4 5 6 9 9
7	2 2 3 6 8 9
8	1 1 1 3 6 7
9	0 2 2 4 5 5 6

Which set of scores has the greater median? Circle the best answer.

A. Math Test 1 B. Math Test 2 (circled) C. The medians are equal.

3. Convert.

a. 480 cm = 4.80 m

b. 0.88 m = 88 cm

c. 39 cm = 0.39 m

d. 1.08 m = 108 cm

4. Complete.

a. 1,500 / 5 = 300

b. 8,100 / 900 = 9

c. 4,500 / 90 = 50

d. 28,000 / 70 = 400

e. 700 = 2,100 / 3

Math Journal 1, p. 17

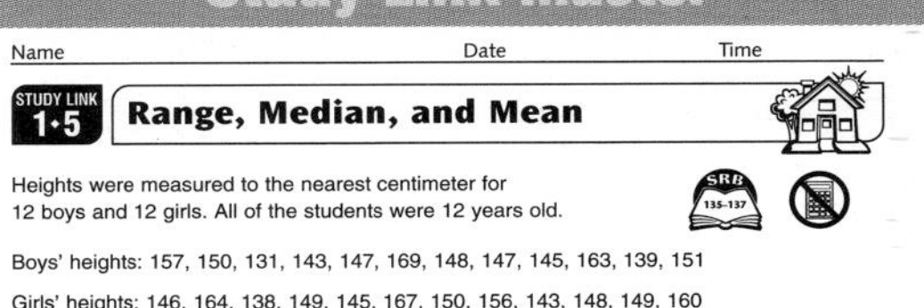

Study Link Master

Name Date Time

STUDY LINK 1·5 **Range, Median, and Mean**

Heights were measured to the nearest centimeter for 12 boys and 12 girls. All of the students were 12 years old.

Boys' heights: 157, 150, 131, 143, 147, 169, 148, 147, 145, 163, 139, 151

Girls' heights: 146, 164, 138, 149, 145, 167, 150, 156, 143, 148, 149, 160

1. Make a stem-and-leaf plot for the boys' data. Then find the range, median, and mean of the boys' heights.

a. range 38

b. median 147.5

c. mean 149.2

Boys' Heights (cm)

Stems (10s)	Leaves (1s)
13	1 9
14	3 5 7 7 8
15	0 1 7
16	3 9

2. Make a stem-and-leaf plot for the girls' data. Then find the range, median, and mean of the girls' heights.

a. range 29

b. median 149

c. mean 151.3

Girls' Heights (cm)

Stems (10s)	Leaves (1s)
13	8
14	3 5 6 8 9 9
15	0 6
16	0 4 7

Practice

3. \$5.86 + \$3.15 = \$9.01

4. \$221.17 + \$886.30 = \$1,107.47

5. \$75.37 − 29.50 = \$45.87

6. \$124.35 − \$88.68 = \$35.67

Math Masters, p. 15

3 Differentiation Options

READINESS

▶ Calculating and Analyzing Landmarks

(*Math Masters,* p. 16; *Student Reference Book,* pp. 136 and 137)

To provide students with experience analyzing landmarks, have them calculate the range, median, and mean of a data set prior to playing the *Landmark Shark* game in Part 1. Students record each of the last seven digits of their phone numbers on separate index cards. They use the cards to represent a data set for which they calculate the range, median, and mean. Students then add the three digits of their area code to the existing set and discuss how this affects the range, median, and mean.

ENRICHMENT

INDEPENDENT ACTIVITY

▶ Mentally Calculating a Mean

5–15 Min

(*Math Masters,* p. 17)

To extend students' knowledge of the mean, have them review and then apply the strategies on *Math Masters,* page 17 to mentally calculate the mean of five numbers.

EXTRA PRACTICE

SMALL-GROUP ACTIVITY

▶ *5-Minute Math*

To offer more practice with defining and calculating data landmarks, see *5-Minute Math,* pages 119, 199, and 200.

Teaching Master

Name Date Time

LESSON 1·5 **Calculating and Analyzing Landmarks**

1. Write your seven-digit home phone number in the boxes below.

□□□-□□□□ Answers vary.

2. Using a marker, write each digit on a separate index card. These digits will make up your data set.
3. Arrange the digits in order from least to greatest.
4. Find the following landmarks for your data set. If you need a reminder about how to find landmarks, review pages 136 and 137 of the *Student Reference Book.*

range ________

median ________

mode ________

mean ________

5. Explain how the range, median, and mean change if you add the three numbers of your area code to your data set.

Math Masters, p. 16

Teaching Master

Name Date Time

LESSON 1·5 **Mentally Calculating a Mean**

Consider some of these strategies when calculating the mean of a data set.

◆ Look for easy combinations of numbers and add them.

Example: 12 + 18 = 30
(10 + 2) + (10 + 8) =
(10 + 2) + (8 + 10) =
10 + (2 + 8) + 10 =
10 + 10 + 10 = 30

◆ If the data set has 5 numbers, you can divide the sum of the numbers by 10 and then multiply that number by 2.

Example: If the sum of 5 test scores is 80, then the mean is (80 ÷ 10) ∗ 2 = 8 ∗ 2 = 16.

◆ Multiply any mode(s) by the number of occurrences.

Example: For 20, 15, 20, 20, 10, the mode (20) occurs 3 times.
(20 ∗ 3) + 10 + 15 = (20 ∗ 3) + 25 = 85

1. Apply strategies like those above to mentally calculate the mean of the following temperatures: 43°F, 52°F, 37°F, 48°F, 40°F.
   a. Record the sum of the temperatures. 220°F
   b. Record the mean. 44°F
2. Mentally calculate the sum and mean for the following data sets. Then choose one of the data sets and write a number sentence to show the strategies you used to find your answers.
   a. **Data Set A:** Number of letters in first names: 6, 9, 10, 4, 6
   sum of letters = 35 mean number of letters = 7
   b. **Data Set B:** Lengths of standing long jumps (inches): 22, 31, 28, 20, 29
   sum of lengths = 130 mean length of jumps = 26
   c. For Data Set ________, I used the following number sentences:
   Answers vary.

Math Masters, p. 17

Broken-Line Graphs

Objective To create, read, and interpret broken-line graphs.

1 Teaching the Lesson

Key Activities

Students use broken-line graphs to examine variations in precipitation and temperature data.

Key Concepts and Skills

- Construct broken-line graphs. [Data and Chance Goal 1]
- Read and interpret broken-line and double broken-line graphs. [Data and Chance Goal 1]
- Describe and predict patterns and trends represented by broken-line graphs. [Data and Chance Goal 2]

Key Vocabulary line graph • broken-line graph • precipitation • graph key

Ongoing Assessment: Informing Instruction See page 45.

Ongoing Assessment: Recognizing Student Achievement Use journal page 19. [Data and Chance Goal 1]

materials

- ☐ *Math Journal 1,* pp. 18 and 19
- ☐ *Student Reference Book,* p. 140
- ☐ Study Link 1•5
- ☐ Transparency (*Math Masters,* p. 18; optional)
- ☐ straightedge

2 Ongoing Learning & Practice

Students practice finding and analyzing data landmarks by playing *Landmark Shark.*

Students practice and maintain skills through Math Boxes and Study Link activities.

materials

- ☐ *Math Journal 1,* p. 20
- ☐ *Student Reference Book,* pp. 325 and 326
- ☐ Study Link Master (*Math Masters,* p. 19)
- ☐ Game Masters (*Math Masters,* pp. 456 and 457)
- ☐ Per group: 4 each of number cards 0–10; 1 each of number cards 11–20
- ☐ straightedge

3 Differentiation Options

READINESS

Students practice reading and plotting points on a coordinate grid.

ENRICHMENT

Students use computer software to generate and analyze broken-line graphs.

ELL SUPPORT

Students use the Graphs Museum to develop fluency with graphing vocabulary.

materials

- ☐ *Student Reference Book,* p. 140
- ☐ Game Masters (*Math Masters,* pp. 465 and 466)
- ☐ Per partnership: 2 different-colored pencils; 2 six-sided dice; computer; spreadsheet/graphing software

Technology

Assessment Management System
Journal page 19, Problem 2
See the **iTLG.**

Getting Started

Mental Math and Reflexes

Students compare and order positive and negative numbers. Remind students that zero is neither positive nor negative. *Suggestions:*

●○○ Name two numbers between 3 and 4.
Sample answers: 3.009; 3.998

●●○ Name two numbers between −4 and −5.
Sample answers: $-4\frac{1}{8}$; −4.99

●●● Name five positive numbers less than 3.
Sample answers: 2, $2\frac{1}{4}$; $1\frac{3}{4}$; 1.3; 0.31

Math Message

Turn to page 140 in your Student Reference Book. *Use the graph in the example to answer the following questions:*

- *What do the horizontal and vertical axes show?*
- *What can you conclude from the graph?*

Study Link 1·5 Follow-Up

Twelve-year-old boys tend to be slightly shorter than twelve-year-old girls. The data samples in Study Link 1-5 support this conclusion. Discuss and compare the median and mean for each set of data.

NOTE Some students may benefit from doing the Readiness activity before beginning Part 1 of the lesson. See Part 3 for details.

NOTE *Math Masters,* page 18 is identical to journal page 18. You may want to use an overhead transparency of the master during your discussion.

1 Teaching the Lesson

▶ Math Message Follow-Up

WHOLE-CLASS DISCUSSION

(*Student Reference Book,* p. 140)

Review the information in the essay. The terms **line graph** and **broken-line graph** refer to graphs whose points are connected by a line or line segments to represent data. If the graph is one line or line segment, it is usually called a line graph. If the graph includes two or more line segments, it is usually called a broken-line graph.

Have students share their answers to the Math Message with a partner. Ask a few volunteers to share with the class. Help students understand how they can use graphs to analyze information and make predictions.

▶ Drawing and Interpreting a Broken-Line Graph

WHOLE-CLASS ACTIVITY

(*Math Journal 1,* p. 18; *Math Masters,* p. 18)

Science Link Broken-line graphs are often used to show trends and the results of scientific studies. Complete and discuss the broken-line graph with students. Call their attention to the title of the graph, the axes labels, and so on.

Student Page

Date Time

LESSON 1·6 The Climate in Omaha

SRB 140

Omaha, the largest city in Nebraska, is located on the eastern border of the state on the Missouri River.

Precipitation is moisture that falls as rain or snow. Rainfall is usually measured in inches; snowfall is usually translated into an equivalent amount of rain.

Average Number of Days in Omaha with At Least 0.01 Inch of Precipitation

	Jan	Feb	Mar	Apr	May	Jun	Jul	Aug	Sep	Oct	Nov	Dec
Number of days	7	6	7	10	12	11	9	9	9	7	5	7

These averages are the result of collecting data for more than 58 years.

1. Complete the following graph.
First make a dot for each month to represent the data in the table.
Then connect the dots with line segments. The result is called a **broken-line graph.**
This type of graph is often used to show trends.

Average Number of Days in Omaha with At Least 0.01 Inch of Precipitation

Number of Days: 0, 2, 4, 6, 8, 10, 12, 14

Month: Jan, Feb, Mar, Apr, May, Jun, Jul, Aug, Sep, Oct, Nov, Dec

Source: The Times Books World Weather Guide

***Math Journal 1,* p. 18**

Point out that the average number of days with a trace of **precipitation** (at least 0.01 inch) is shown with a dot for each month and that line segments connect consecutive dots. Discuss the meaning of *precipitation.* Ask students to give examples. Rain, sleet, snow, hail

Ask students to cover the table above the graph. Then ask the following questions:

- Which month has the greatest number of days with precipitation? May How can you tell? May shows the highest point on the graph.
- Which season has more days with precipitation—winter or summer? summer
- Which month has the least number of days with precipitation? November How can you tell? November shows the lowest point on the graph.
- Can you tell from the graph which month has the greatest amount of precipitation? No. May has the most days with precipitation, but it may rain less each day in May than in another month having fewer days with precipitation.
- Is there a period in which little change occurred? Yes; July to September
- How would you describe the pattern or trend shown by the graph? The number of days with at least 0.01 inch of precipitation generally increases until May and then decreases each month until November.

Ongoing Assessment: Informing Instruction

Watch for students who may not recognize the subtle difference between data in the form of a table and data in the form of a graph. A table is a collection of data, while a graph is a picture of the patterns or trends in the data set.

▶ Reading and Interpreting Broken-Line Graphs

INDEPENDENT ACTIVITY

(*Math Journal 1,* p. 19)

Introduce double-line graphs and explain that these graphs are often used to show comparative changes over time.

The graph on journal page 19 consists of two broken-line graphs on the same set of axes. The graphs can be analyzed separately or together for a comparison. Draw attention to the **graph key** and discuss its importance. To support English language learners, discuss and compare the mathematical uses of the word *key.*

Student Page

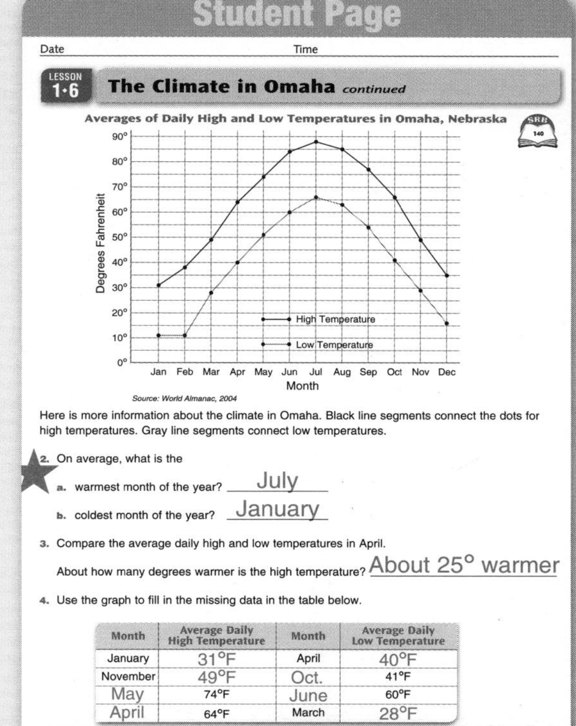

Date Time

LESSON 1·6 **The Climate in Omaha** *continued*

Here is more information about the climate in Omaha. Black line segments connect the dots for high temperatures. Gray line segments connect low temperatures.

2. On average, what is the
   a. warmest month of the year? July
   b. coldest month of the year? January
3. Compare the average daily high and low temperatures in April. About how many degrees warmer is the high temperature? About 25° warmer
4. Use the graph to fill in the missing data in the table below.

Month	Average Daily High Temperature	Month	Average Daily Low Temperature
January	31°F	April	40°F
November	49°F	Oct.	41°F
May	74°F	June	60°F
April	64°F	March	28°F

Math Journal 1, p. 19

Student Page

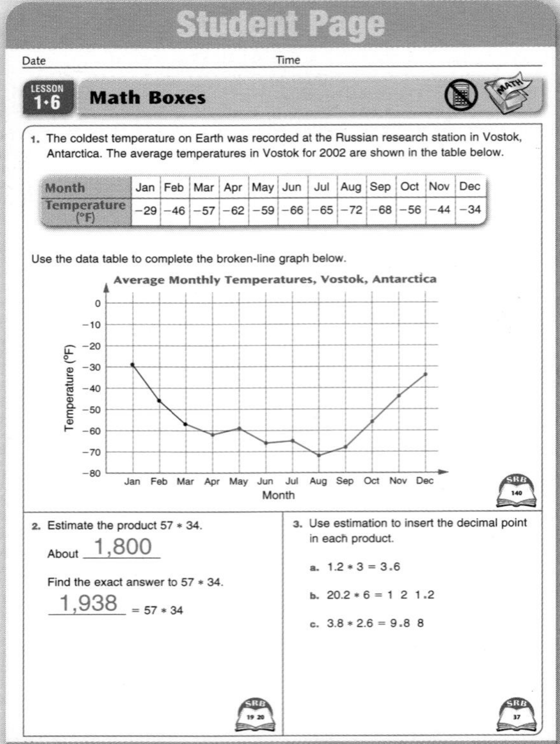

Date Time

LESSON 1·6 **Math Boxes**

1. The coldest temperature on Earth was recorded at the Russian research station in Vostok, Antarctica. The average temperatures in Vostok for 2002 are shown in the table below.

Month	Jan	Feb	Mar	Apr	May	Jun	Jul	Aug	Sep	Oct	Nov	Dec
Temperature (°F)	−29	−46	−57	−62	−59	−66	−65	−72	−68	−56	−44	−34

Use the data table to complete the broken-line graph below.

2. Estimate the product 57 ∗ 34.

About 1,800

Find the exact answer to 57 ∗ 34.

1,938 = 57 ∗ 34

3. Use estimation to insert the decimal point in each product.

a. 1.2 ∗ 3 = 3.6

b. 20.2 ∗ 6 = 1 2 1.2

c. 3.8 ∗ 2.6 = 9.8 8

Math Journal 1, p. 20

Links to the Future

The activities in this lesson are the first of several opportunities for students to recognize the value of line graphs as a tool for analyzing information and for making predictions. In Lesson 1-11, students will learn that graphs can be misleading, requiring that they think critically about how information is represented.

Study Link Master

Name Date Time

STUDY LINK 1·6 **Cooling Off**

The graph shows how a cup of hot tea cools as time passes.

1. Use the graph to fill in the missing data in the table.

Elapsed Time (minutes)	Temperature (°F)
0 (pour tea)	160
10	120
40	85
20	100
12.5	115
5	140

2. What is the tea's approximate temperature after 30 minutes? 90°F

3. About how many minutes does it take for the tea to cool to a temperature of 95°F? About 25 minutes

4. a. About how many minutes do you think it will take the tea to cool to room temperature (70°F)? Sample answers: About 100 minutes

b. Why do you think so? The rate of cooling levels off to $2\frac{1}{2}$°F every 10 min.

5. a. Does the tea cool at a constant rate? no

b. Explain your answer. The tea cools very quickly at first, but then the temperature drops slowly.

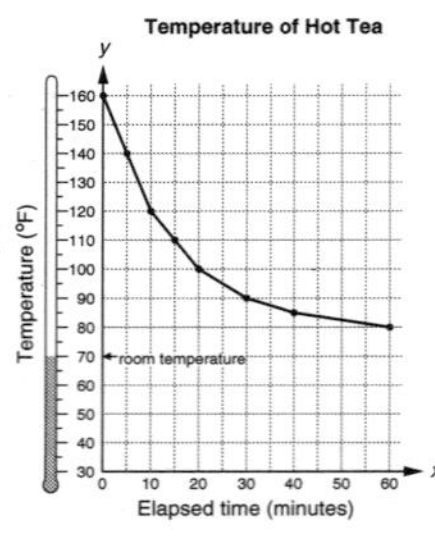

Practice

6. 32 ∗ 54 = 1,728

7. 3,306 = 87 ∗ 38

8. 59 ∗ 76 = 4,484

9. 2,538 = 94 ∗ 27

Math Masters, p. 19

Ask students to suggest data sets that could be displayed using double-line graphs. Sample answers: Average rainfall of two cities over a year; weekly or monthly sales of two different brands of peanut butter

Circulate and assist as students work on the journal page.

Ongoing Assessment: Recognizing Student Achievement

Journal Page 19 Problem 2

Use **journal page 19, Problem 2** to assess students' ability to read data values from a broken-line graph. Students are making adequate progress if they are able to identify the warmest and coldest months of the year. Some students may be able to interpret the relationship between the two graphs and apply this understanding to successfully complete Problems 3 and 4.

[Data and Chance Goal 1]

2 Ongoing Learning & Practice

▶ Playing *Landmark Shark*

SMALL-GROUP ACTIVITY

(*Student Reference Book,* pp. 325 and 326; *Math Masters,* pp. 456 and 457)

If necessary, have students review game directions on pages 325 and 326 in the *Student Reference Book.* Challenge them to find the mean of their five card numbers mentally. One way to do this is to add the five numbers, divide the total by 10, and then multiply that number by 2.

NOTE Consider spending the first or last 10 minutes of each math class playing *Landmark Shark* or any of the other games in this unit. Refer to the game section of the Unit Organizer for an overview of Unit 1 games.

▶ Math Boxes 1·6

INDEPENDENT ACTIVITY

(*Math Journal 1,* p. 20)

Mixed Practice Math Boxes in this lesson are paired with Math Boxes in Lesson 1-8. The skills in Problems 2 and 3 preview Unit 2 content.

Writing/Reasoning Have students write their responses to the following: *Explain why your estimate in Problem 2 may be greater or less than the exact answer.* Sample answer: It depends on how I round the factors.

▶ Study Link 1·6

INDEPENDENT ACTIVITY

(*Math Masters,* p. 19)

Home Connection Students interpret a broken-line graph that shows how a cup of hot tea cools over time.

3 Differentiation Options

READINESS

PARTNER ACTIVITY

▶ Playing *Over and Up Squares*

15–30 Min

(*Math Masters,* pp. 465 and 466)

To provide experience naming and plotting points on a coordinate grid, have students play *Over and Up Squares.* Review the game directions on *Math Masters,* page 465.

ENRICHMENT

SMALL-GROUP ACTIVITY

▶ Generating and Analyzing Broken-Line Graphs

5–15 Min

(*Student Reference Book,* p. 140)

To extend students' understanding of broken-line graphs, use graphing software and the Check Your Understanding data set (*Student Reference Book,* p. 140) to have students generate broken-line graphs.

ELL SUPPORT

SMALL-GROUP ACTIVITY

▶ Using the Graphs Museum

5–15 Min

Ask students to identify, compare, and describe the types of graphs displayed in the Graphs Museum. Encourage students to use terms related to graphs.

Examples:

▷ This is a bar graph. A bar graph makes it easy to read and compare data.

▷ This is a line plot. A line plot makes it easy to see how data are grouped.

▷ This is a circle graph. A circle graph makes it easy to see how parts make up a whole.

In this unit students will encounter various uses of the word *difference.* For example: "Find the difference between the highest and the shortest height." "What is the difference between a bar graph and a line plot?" Discuss these different meanings.

Planning Ahead

Consider using graphing software in Part 1 of Lesson 1-7 to extend students' knowledge of bar graphs. You will need a computer, spreadsheet/graphing software, and a large-screen display.

Game Master

Name Date Time

Over and Up Squares

Materials ☐ 1 *Over and Up Squares* gameboard and record sheet

☐ 1 color pencil per player (different color for each player)

☐ 2 six-sided dice

Players 2

Object of the game

To score the most points by connecting ordered pairs on a grid.

Directions

1. Player 1 rolls two dice and uses the numbers to make an ordered pair. Either number can be used to name the *x*-coordinate (over) of the ordered pair. The other number is used to name the *y*-coordinate (up) of the ordered pair. After deciding which ordered pair to use, the player uses a color pencil to plot the point.
2. Player 1 records the ordered pair and the score in the record sheet. A player earns 10 points each time an ordered pair is plotted correctly.
3. Player 2 rolls the dice and decides how to make an ordered pair. If both possible ordered pairs are already plotted, the player rolls the dice again. (Variation: If both possible ordered pairs are already plotted, the player can change one or both of the numbers to 0.)
4. Player 2 uses the other color pencil to plot the ordered pair and records his or her score on the record sheet.
5. Players continue to take turns rolling dice, plotting ordered pairs, and recording the results. If, on any player's turn, two plotted points are next to each other on the same side of one of the small grid squares, the player connects the points with a line segment. A player scores an additional 10 points for each line segment. Sometimes a player may draw more than one line segment in a single turn.
6. If a player draws a line segment that completes a grid square (so that all 4 sides of the square are drawn), that player shades in the square. A player earns an additional 50 points each time a square is completed.
7. The player with the most points after 10 rounds wins the game.

***Math Masters,* p. 465**

Game Master

Name Date Time

***Over and Up Squares* Gameboard and Record Sheet**

Player 1 ______

Round	Over (*x*-coordinate)	,	Up (*y*-coordinate)	Score
1				
2				
3				
4				
5				
6				
7				
8				
9				
10				
			Total Score	

Scoring	
Ordered pair	10 points
Line segment	10 points
Square	50 points

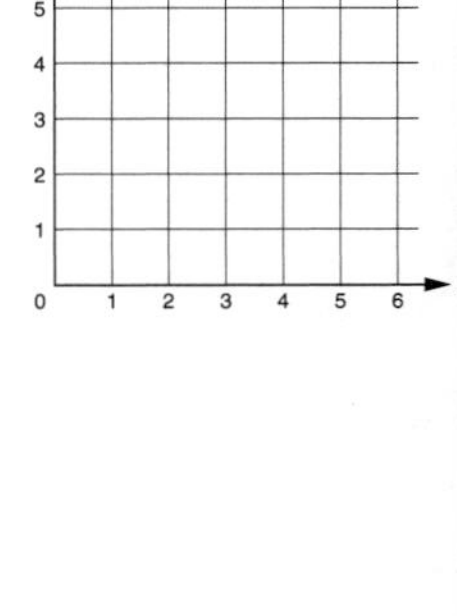

Player 2 ______

Round	Over (*x*-coordinate)	,	Up (*y*-coordinate)	Score
1				
2				
3				
4				
5				
6				
7				
8				
9				
10				
			Total Score	

***Math Masters,* p. 466**

Bar Graphs

Objective To create, read, and interpret bar graphs.

1 Teaching the Lesson

Key Activities

Students draw a bar graph. They use side-by-side bar graphs and stacked bar graphs to examine variations in snowfall and weather conditions for various locations.

Key Concepts and Skills

- Subtract multidigit whole numbers to find data ranges. [Operations and Computation Goal 1]
- Construct a bar graph to represent a description of data. [Data and Chance Goal 1]
- Read and interpret side-by-side and stacked bar graphs. [Data and Chance Goal 1]
- Use a graph key to distinguish represented data. [Data and Chance Goal 1]
- Use data ranges to read and interpret a stacked bar graph. [Data and Chance Goal 2]

Key Vocabulary

side-by-side bar graph • bar graph • stacked bar graph

Ongoing Assessment: Recognizing Student Achievement Use journal page 21. [Data and Chance Goal 1]

Ongoing Assessment: Informing Instruction See page 50.

materials

- ☐ *Math Journal 1,* pp. 21 and 22
- ☐ Study Link 1•6
- ☐ Transparency (*Math Masters,* p. 19; optional)
- ☐ straightedge

2 Ongoing Learning & Practice

Students practice reading and interpreting broken-line graphs.

Students practice and maintain skills through Math Boxes and Study Link activities.

materials

- ☐ *Math Journal 1,* pp. 23 and 24
- ☐ Study Link Master (*Math Masters,* p. 20)

3 Differentiation Options

READINESS

Students review how to read simple bar graphs.

ENRICHMENT

Students use graphing software to generate bar graphs from data sets.

EXTRA PRACTICE

Students find landmarks for a data set containing negative numbers.

materials

- ☐ Teaching Master (*Math Masters,* p. 21)
- ☐ computer
- ☐ spreadsheet/graphing software
- ☐ *5-Minute Math,* p. 201

See **Advance Preparation**

Additional Information

Advance Preparation Consider using a graphing program to generate the bar graphs for the optional Enrichment activity in Part 3.

Technology

Assessment Management System

Journal page 21, Problem 1

See the **iTLG**.

Getting Started

Mental Math and Reflexes

Students mentally calculate each difference. If time permits, have a volunteer share her or his strategy.

●○○ 225 − 75 150
165 − 53 112

●●○ 243 − 53 190
818 − 599 219
1,003 − 987 16

●●● 2,342 − 29 2,313

Math Message ★

Complete journal page 21.

Study Link 1·6 Follow-Up

Ask students to show how they obtained each answer. If possible, use a transparency of the Study Link. Students may have difficulty with Problem 5. Have them compare the temperature drop during the first 5 minutes with the temperature drop during the last 30 minutes shown on the graph. The temperature goes from 160° to 140°, a drop of 20°F, in the first 5 minutes. The temperature goes from 90° to 80°, a drop of 10°F, in the last 30 minutes.

1 Teaching the Lesson

▶ Math Message Follow-Up

WHOLE-CLASS DISCUSSION

(*Math Journal 1,* p. 21)

Review the answers. Note that there are two bars for each ski site in the January Snowfalls bar graph.

NOTE Although more recent snowfall data is available, the 1996 snowfall differs significantly from the average snowfall data. Such a difference is unlikely to occur again any time soon.

Bar graphs of this type are called **side-by-side bar graphs.** Write *side-by-side bar graph* on the board. Add a side-by-side bar graph to the Graphs Museum if you have not already done so. Be sure that students carefully read the questions and use the correct bar in each pair.

Remind students that **bar graphs** display numerical information in a way that allows readers to make easy comparisons. From the graph on journal page 21, readers can make two kinds of comparisons:

1. Compare January 1996 conditions to average conditions for every ski location.
2. Compare the different ski locations, using average conditions or January 1996 conditions.

NOTE Some students may benefit from doing the Readiness activity before beginning Part 1 of the lesson. See Part 3 for details.

NOTE If students successfully construct and interpret the bar graphs on journal page 21, consider demonstrating how to use computer software to revise a data set and generate bar graphs of the revised data. See the *Student Reference Book* for more information.

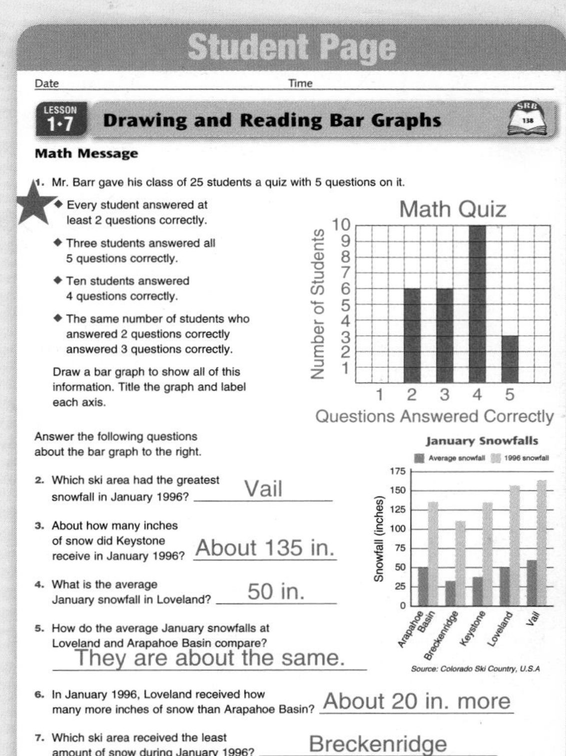

Student Page

Date Time

LESSON 1·7 **Drawing and Reading Bar Graphs** SRB 138

Math Message

1. Mr. Barr gave his class of 25 students a quiz with 5 questions on it.
   - Every student answered at least 2 questions correctly.
   - Three students answered all 5 questions correctly.
   - Ten students answered 4 questions correctly.
   - The same number of students who answered 2 questions correctly answered 3 questions correctly.

   Draw a bar graph to show all of this information. Title the graph and label each axis.

Answer the following questions about the bar graph to the right.

2. Which ski area had the greatest snowfall in January 1996? Vail
3. About how many inches of snow did Keystone receive in January 1996? About 135 in.
4. What is the average January snowfall in Loveland? 50 in.
5. How do the average January snowfalls at Loveland and Arapahoe Basin compare? They are about the same.
6. In January 1996, Loveland received how many more inches of snow than Arapahoe Basin? About 20 in. more
7. Which ski area received the least amount of snow during January 1996? Breckenridge

Math Journal 1, p. 21

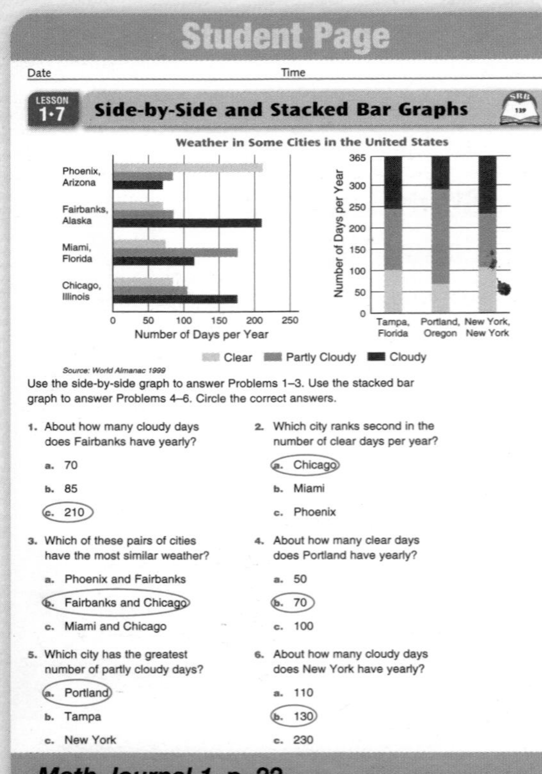

Student Page

Date Time

LESSON 1·7 **Side-by-Side and Stacked Bar Graphs** SRB 139

Source: World Almanac 1999

Use the side-by-side graph to answer Problems 1–3. Use the stacked bar graph to answer Problems 4–6. Circle the correct answers.

1. About how many cloudy days does Fairbanks have yearly?
   a. 70
   b. 85
   c. 210
2. Which city ranks second in the number of clear days per year?
   a. Chicago
   b. Miami
   c. Phoenix
3. Which of these pairs of cities have the most similar weather?
   a. Phoenix and Fairbanks
   b. Fairbanks and Chicago
   c. Miami and Chicago
4. About how many clear days does Portland have yearly?
   a. 50
   b. 70
   c. 100
5. Which city has the greatest number of partly cloudy days?
   a. Portland
   b. Tampa
   c. New York
6. About how many cloudy days does New York have yearly?
   a. 110
   b. 130
   c. 230

Math Journal 1, p. 22

Ongoing Assessment: Recognizing Student Achievement

Journal Page 21 Problem 1

Use **journal page 21, Problem 1** to assess students' ability to construct a bar graph from a description of data. Students are making adequate progress if they are able to represent a total of 25 data values in their bar graphs, as well as accurately label each axis and provide an appropriate title. Some students may be able to solve Problems 2–7 independently.

[Data and Chance Goal 1]

▶ Reading Side-by-Side and Stacked Bar Graphs

PARTNER ACTIVITY

(*Math Journal 1,* p. 22)

Science Link Remind students of how valuable graphs are for displaying data from scientific studies. Circulate and assist as students work on journal page 22. The first graph on the page is a side-by-side bar graph involving weather conditions.

Ongoing Assessment: Informing Instruction

Watch for students who are confused because the bars on the graph are horizontal. Most bar graphs are drawn with vertical bars, but horizontal bars are also correct.

Be sure that students correctly use the graph key. Point out that the lengths of the three bars for each city add up to 365.

The second graph is a **stacked bar graph** and may cause students more difficulty. Give them time on their own to see if they can figure out how this graph works. The stacked bar graph shows the same kind of information as the first graph, but it uses only a single bar to represent each city. The three bars from the side-by-side graph have been combined (stacked) to form a single bar. The vertical scale of the graph is marked in days, from 0 to 365. The same graph key is used to distinguish the clear, partly cloudy, and cloudy sections shown within each bar.

To find the number of days represented by any section of a bar in this stacked bar graph, students must first find where the top and bottom of that section align with the vertical axis. Then they subtract the smaller number from the larger number.

For example, the ends of the partly cloudy section for Tampa align with the axis at about 100 days and 240 days; $240 - 100 = 140$, so Tampa has about 140 partly cloudy days per year. Similarly, there are about $100 - 0 = 100$ clear days and $365 - 240 = 125$ cloudy days per year in Tampa.

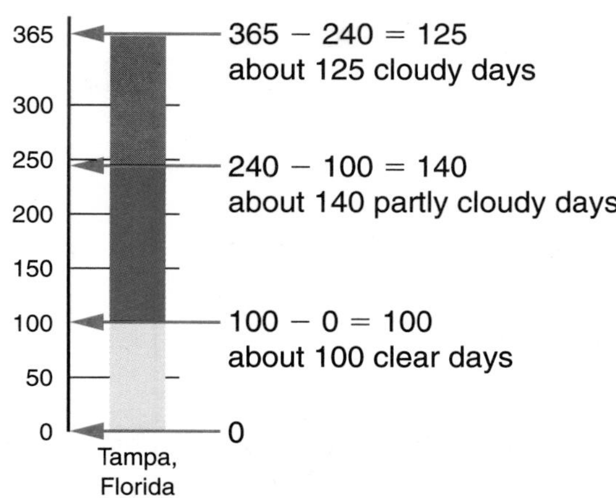

Adjusting the Activity

Comparison diagrams (introduced in *Third Grade Everyday Mathematics*) are used for problems involving two quantities and the difference between them. Consider having students draw comparison diagrams to organize their thinking.

Quantity
240

Quantity	
100	? Difference

AUDITORY ◆ KINESTHETIC ◆ TACTILE ◆ VISUAL

2 Ongoing Learning & Practice

▶ Reading and Interpreting Broken-Line Graphs

INDEPENDENT ACTIVITY

(*Math Journal 1,* p. 23)

The problems on journal page 23 provide practice creating and interpreting broken-line graphs.

Student Page

Date Time

LESSON 1•7 **Temperatures above Earth's Surface**

When you fly in a commercial airplane, you probably don't notice any large changes in temperature, because the cabin is temperature controlled. But if you are riding in a hot-air balloon, you feel the temperature drop as the balloon rises.

The table below shows temperatures at various heights above Omaha, Nebraska. The measurements were made on a January day when the temperature at ground level was 32°F. *Reminder:* 1 mile = 5,280 feet.

Height above Ground (miles)	Temperature (°F)
0 (ground level)	32°
1	25°
2	15°
3	−5°
4	−25°
4.5	−40°
5.5	−60°
10	−75°

Temperature above Ground Level

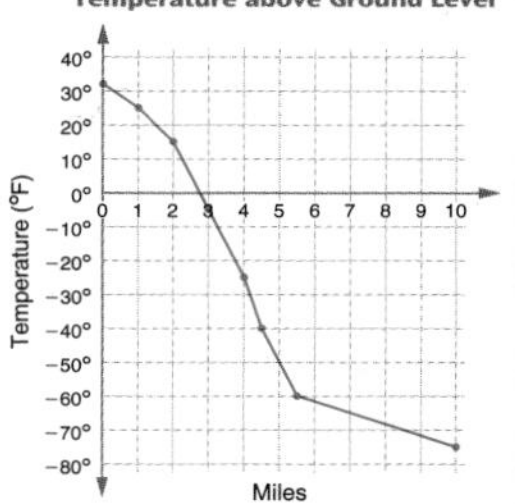

1. Make a broken-line graph of the data in the table.
2. At about what height above the ground was the temperature 0°F? About 2.75 miles
3. What was the approximate temperature 8 miles above Omaha? About −68°F
4. Suppose an airplane was about 26,000 feet above Omaha on the day recorded in the table.
   a. What was the approximate temperature at 26,000 feet? About −50°F
   b. How much colder was the temperature at 26,000 feet above ground than at ground level? About 82°F colder

***Math Journal 1,* p. 23**

Student Page

Date Time

LESSON 1•7 **Math Boxes**

1. Bigfoot is said to be a large, hairy, humanlike creature that lives in the wilderness areas of the United States and Canada. The following data are some footprint lengths reported by people who claim to have seen Bigfoot in California.

Reported Footprint Lengths (in cm)							
36	46	36	38	33	40	37	56

Use the number line to construct a line plot of the data in the table above.

Footprint Lengths

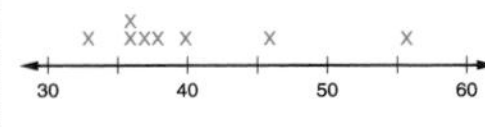

a. Find the mean length. 40.25 cm

b. Is the median or the mean a better representation of the recorded footprint lengths? Explain. median; Because the outlier 56 affects the mean, the median (37.5) is a better representation.

2. Average wind speeds for major U.S. cities are displayed in the table below.

City	State	Wind Speed (mph)
Anchorage	AK	7.1
Phoenix	AZ	6.2
Denver	CO	8.6
Washington	DC	9.4
Des Moines	IA	10.7
Chicago	IL	10.3
Boston	MA	12.4
Helena	MT	7.7
Memphis	TN	8.8
Salt Lake City	UT	8.8

Construct a stem-and-leaf plot of the wind-speed data.

Average Wind Speeds for U.S. Cities

Stems (10s and 1s)	Leaves (10ths)
6	2
7	1 7
8	6 8 8
9	4
10	3 7
11	
12	4

3. Convert.
   a. 18 cm = 180 mm
   b. 120 mm = 12 cm
   c. 254 cm = 2,540 mm
   d. 1,020 mm = 102 cm

4. 600,000 / 5,000 = ______

Circle the letter next to the best answer.

A 120,000 B 12,000
C 1,200 (D) 120

***Math Journal 1,* p. 24**

Study Link Master

Name Date Time

STUDY LINK 1•7 **Using Bar Graphs**

Every week, Ms. Penczar gives a math quiz to her class of 15 students. The table below shows the class's average scores for a six-week period.

1. Draw a bar graph that shows the same information. Give the graph a title and label each axis.

   Use the graph you drew to answer the following questions.

Week	Class Average
1	68
2	66
3	79
4	89
5	91
6	88

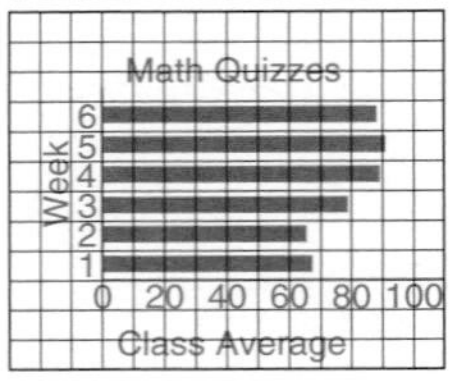

2. The highest average score occurred in Week 5.
3. The lowest average score occurred in Week 2.
4. How many times did scores improve from one week to the next? 3 times
5. How many times did scores decline from one week to the next? 2 times
6. The greatest one-week improvement occurred between Week 2 and Week 3.
7. Name a possible set of scores for Ms. Penczar's 15 students that would result in the class average given for Week 2. Sample answers:
   54 55 58 58 62 63 65 66
   67 67 69 72 76 78 80

Practice

8. 389 * 17 = 6,613
9. 8,448 = 176 * 48
10. 453 * 24 = 10,872
11. 9,711 = 249 * 39

***Math Masters,* p. 20**

Teaching Master

Name Date Time

LESSON 1•7 **Reviewing Bar Graphs**

A school board conducted a survey in which 70 ninth graders were asked how many hours they spend doing homework each day. The bar graph displays the survey results.

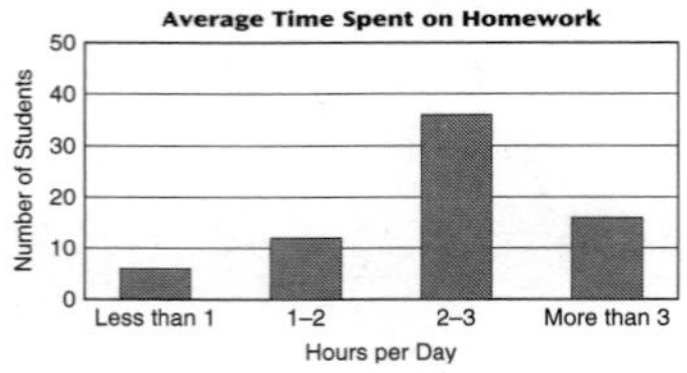

Decide whether each of the following statements about the survey results is true or false. If a statement is false, explain why.

1. All students spend some time each day doing homework. true
2. About half of the students spend more than 3 hours on homework. false
   About $\frac{1}{4}$ of the students spend more than 3 hours on homework.
3. More than 15 students spend 1–2 hours per day on homework. false
   Only about 12 students spend 1–2 hours per day on homework.
4. The number of students spending 2–3 hours on homework is about 3 times as many as the number of students who spend 1–2 hours on homework. true

***Math Masters,* p. 21**

▶ Math Boxes 1•7

INDEPENDENT ACTIVITY

(*Math Journal 1,* p. 24)

Mixed Practice Math Boxes in this lesson are paired with Math Boxes in Lesson 1-5. The skills in Problems 3 and 4 preview Unit 2 content.

▶ Study Link 1•7

INDEPENDENT ACTIVITY

(*Math Masters,* p. 20)

Home Connection Students draw and interpret a bar graph.

3 Differentiation Options

READINESS

INDEPENDENT ACTIVITY

▶ Reviewing Bar Graphs

15–30 Min

(*Math Masters,* p. 21)

Students prepare to work with the stacked and side-by-side bar graphs in this lesson by reviewing how to read and interpret a simple bar graph.

ENRICHMENT

SMALL-GROUP ACTIVITY

▶ Using Technology to Create and Analyze Bar Graphs

15–30 Min

To extend students' knowledge of graphs, have them use graphing software to generate bar graphs of data sets provided in the Data and Probability section of the *Student Reference Book.*

EXTRA PRACTICE

SMALL-GROUP ACTIVITY

▶ *5-Minute Math*

5–15 Min

To offer more practice with finding data ranges and other landmarks, see *5-Minute Math,* page 201.

1•8 Step Graphs

Objective To create, read, and interpret step graphs.

1 Teaching the Lesson

Key Activities

Students read and interpret step graphs involving time. They draw a step graph involving distance.

Key Concepts and Skills

- Read and interpret a data table and a step graph. [Data and Chance Goal 1]
- Construct a step graph to represent data from a table. [Data and Chance Goal 1]
- Compare the usefulness of various data representations. [Data and Chance Goal 2]

Key Vocabulary

step graph

Ongoing Assessment: Informing Instruction See page 56.

materials

- ☐ *Math Journal 1,* pp. 25–27
- ☐ Study Link 1•7
- ☐ straightedge
- ☐ jumbo paper clips ($1\frac{13}{16}$" by $\frac{3}{8}$")

2 Ongoing Learning & Practice

Students practice writing number sentences using order of operations by playing *Name That Number.*

Students practice and maintain skills through Math Boxes and Study Link activities.

Ongoing Assessment: Recognizing Student Achievement Use journal page 28. [Data and Chance Goal 1]

materials

- ☐ *Math Journal 1,* p. 28
- ☐ *Student Reference Book,* p. 329
- ☐ Study Link Masters (*Math Masters,* pp. 22 and 23)
- ☐ Game Master (*Math Masters,* p. 462)
- ☐ Per group: complete deck of number cards
- ☐ straightedge

3 Differentiation Options

READINESS

Students analyze a data table and identify the number and frequency of jumps in the data values.

EXTRA PRACTICE

Students construct and analyze a step graph.

EXTRA PRACTICE

Students complete teacher-generated Math Boxes.

materials

- ☐ Teaching Masters (*Math Masters,* pp. 24 and 25)
- ☐ Teaching Aid Master (*Math Masters,* p. 405)

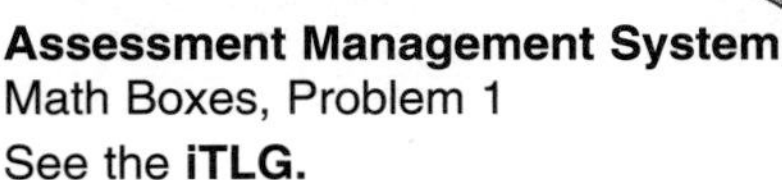

Technology

Assessment Management System
Math Boxes, Problem 1
See the **iTLG.**

Getting Started

Mental Math and Reflexes

Students signal thumbs-up for true statements and thumbs-down for false statements. *Suggestions:*

●○○ An inch is longer than a centimeter. Thumbs-up

●●○ A mile is longer than a kilometer. Thumbs-up
A yard is longer than a meter. Thumbs-down

●●● A kilogram is heavier than a pound. Thumbs-up
An ounce is about 1 gram. Thumbs-down

Math Message

Complete journal page 25.

Study Link 1·7 Follow-Up

Briefly review the answers.
Discuss how students might create a possible set of scores for Problem 7.

NOTE Some students may benefit from doing the Readiness activity before beginning Part 1 of the lesson. See Part 3 for details.

1 Teaching the Lesson

▶ Math Message Follow-Up

WHOLE-CLASS DISCUSSION

(*Math Journal 1,* p. 25)

This lesson involves working with graphs showing data changes that are not gradual, but occur in jumps. A **step graph** is a graph that looks like steps. Step graphs are particularly useful when the horizontal axis represents time or distance. Write *step graph* on the board. Add a step graph to the Graphs Museum if you haven't already done so.

The step graph on journal page 25 shows how the cost of mailing a letter weighing one ounce or less changed from 1905 to 2005. To give students an idea of how heavy an ounce is, distribute jumbo-size paper clips ($1\frac{13}{16}$" by $\frac{3}{8}$"), one per student.

Tell students that one paper clip weighs approximately one ounce. As you move from left to right along the horizontal axis (time), the cost stays the same for a while and then jumps to a new cost. Note that most jumps are up to a higher cost, but in 1919, there was a jump down to a lower cost.

Verify that students are correctly reading the graph and discuss their answers. Include the following points in your discussion:

▷ The height of each step shows the cost of mailing a letter during the years shown on the axis below the step. A move to a different step signals a change in the postal rate.

▷ The length of each step shows the length of time a price was in effect. A long step, such as the one between 1932 and 1958, indicates that the cost remained constant for a long time. A short step, such as the one between 1974 and 1975, indicates that the cost remained constant for only a short time.

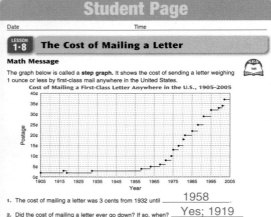

Student Page

Date Time

LESSON 1·8 **The Cost of Mailing a Letter**

Math Message

The graph below is called a **step graph.** It shows the cost of sending a letter weighing 1 ounce or less by first-class mail anywhere in the United States.

Cost of Mailing a First-Class Letter Anywhere in the U.S., 1905–2005

1. The cost of mailing a letter was 3 cents from 1932 until 1958.
2. Did the cost of mailing a letter ever go down? If so, when? Yes; 1919
3. How many rate increases were there between 1960 and 1970? Two; from 4¢ to 5¢ in 1963 and from 5¢ to 6¢ in 1967
4. In which year did the *greatest* increase occur? 1991
5. By how much did the cost of mailing a letter increase between 1960 and 1970? 2¢
6. Can you tell from the graph the cost of mailing a letter before 1900? No
7. In which year do you think the cost of mailing a letter will reach 50 cents? Explain. Sample answer: About 2015; The increase in cost has followed a steady pattern since 1970. Between 1980 and 2000, the cost rose 18 cents. The cost was 37 cents by 2002. All things being equal, the cost will likely rise another 15 cents by 2015, bringing the total to 52 cents.

Math Journal 1, p. 25

▷ The years have been rounded off. Postal rates do not always change on January 1. They often change during the year.

NOTE Students may think that before 1905 the cost of mailing a letter was only a few cents. In fact, the cost of sending a letter over 400 miles in 1799 was 31 cents and reached a high of 44 cents in 1815.

▶ Drawing a Step Graph for Taxicab Fares

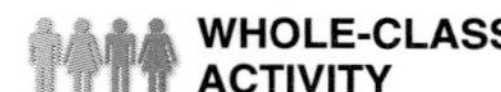

WHOLE-CLASS ACTIVITY

(*Math Journal 1,* p. 26)

The table on the journal page shows taxicab fares for various distances. The cost depends entirely on the distance covered by each trip.

Point out the dot at the end of each step. The dot shows which x-values are included in each step. Once the trip has begun, even if the taxi has moved only a few feet, the cost is \$2.00. For any distance up to and including 1 mile (the dot), the cost is still \$2.00. As soon as the taxi has traveled slightly more than 1 mile, the cost jumps to \$4.00. The cost remains at \$4.00 until the taxi has reached the 2-mile mark. If the distance traveled is exactly 2 miles, the cost is still \$4.00. But as soon as the taxi has traveled slightly more than 2 miles, the cost jumps to \$5.00. The cost then increases \$1 at each mile mark.

To ensure that students are correctly reading the table, name various trip distances and ask them for the cost. *Suggestions:*

$1\frac{1}{2}$ miles \$4.00	2.9 miles \$5.00	1 mile \$2.00
$\frac{1}{2}$ mile \$2.00	0.1 mile \$2.00	2 miles \$4.00

Students use the table on the journal page to complete the step graph. They then answer the questions at the bottom of the page using either the data table or the completed graph.

Point out the dot at the right end of each step. At an x-value where the step value jumps, the graph should indicate which y-value goes with the x-value. One way to construct a step graph is to first place a solid dot at every point at which a jump of the data values occurs. The one tricky part of making a step graph is to clearly indicate what happens at the points where the jumps occur. The dot at the right end of the first segment shows that at exactly 1 mile, the cost is still \$2.00. But the cost jumps to \$4.00 for a trip that is slightly longer than 1 mile.

Circulate and assist as needed. Be sure that students can answer the questions using both types of representations—the table and the graph.

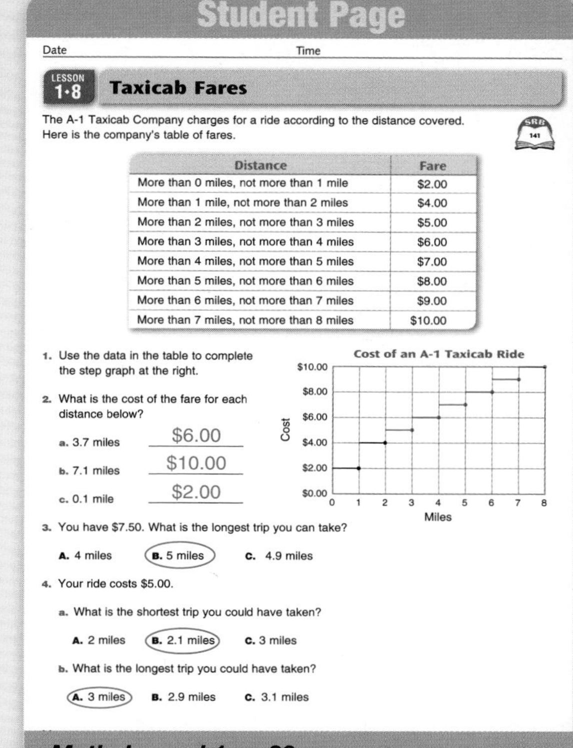

Student Page

Date Time

LESSON 1·8 **Taxicab Fares**

The A-1 Taxicab Company charges for a ride according to the distance covered. Here is the company's table of fares.

Distance	Fare
More than 0 miles, not more than 1 mile	\$2.00
More than 1 mile, not more than 2 miles	\$4.00
More than 2 miles, not more than 3 miles	\$5.00
More than 3 miles, not more than 4 miles	\$6.00
More than 4 miles, not more than 5 miles	\$7.00
More than 5 miles, not more than 6 miles	\$8.00
More than 6 miles, not more than 7 miles	\$9.00
More than 7 miles, not more than 8 miles	\$10.00

1. Use the data in the table to complete the step graph at the right.

2. What is the cost of the fare for each distance below?
   a. 3.7 miles \$6.00
   b. 7.1 miles \$10.00
   c. 0.1 mile \$2.00

3. You have \$7.50. What is the longest trip you can take?
   A. 4 miles (B. 5 miles) C. 4.9 miles

4. Your ride costs \$5.00.
   a. What is the shortest trip you could have taken?
   A. 2 miles (B. 2.1 miles) C. 3 miles
   b. What is the longest trip you could have taken?
   (A. 3 miles) B. 2.9 miles C. 3.1 miles

Math Journal 1, p. 26

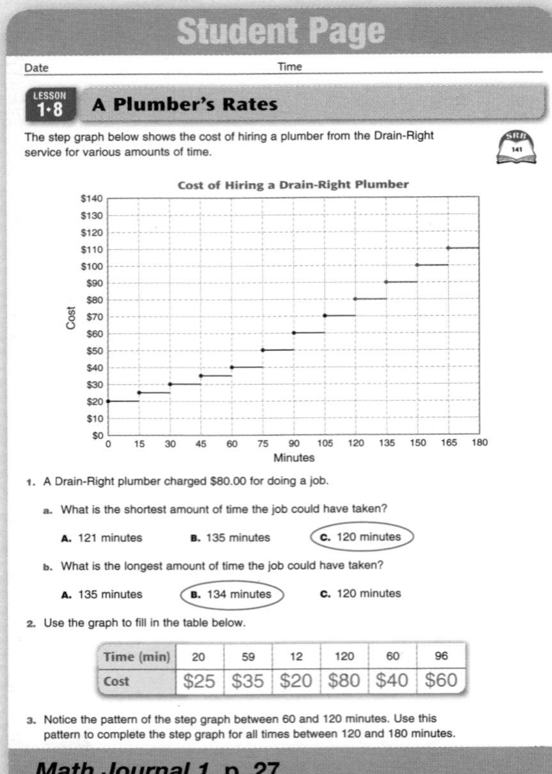

Student Page

Date Time

LESSON 1·8 **A Plumber's Rates**

The step graph below shows the cost of hiring a plumber from the Drain-Right service for various amounts of time.

SRB 141

Cost of Hiring a Drain-Right Plumber

Cost: $0, $10, $20, $30, $40, $50, $60, $70, $80, $90, $100, $110, $120, $130, $140

Minutes: 0, 15, 30, 45, 60, 75, 90, 105, 120, 135, 150, 165, 180

1. A Drain-Right plumber charged $80.00 for doing a job.
   a. What is the shortest amount of time the job could have taken?
      A. 121 minutes B. 135 minutes (C. 120 minutes)
   b. What is the longest amount of time the job could have taken?
      A. 135 minutes (B. 134 minutes) C. 120 minutes
2. Use the graph to fill in the table below.

Time (min)	20	59	12	120	60	96
Cost	$25	$35	$20	$80	$40	$60

3. Notice the pattern of the step graph between 60 and 120 minutes. Use this pattern to complete the step graph for all times between 120 and 180 minutes.

Math Journal 1, p. 27

Ongoing Assessment: Informing Instruction

Watch for students who have difficulty understanding the placement and meaning of the dot at the end of each line segment. Consider graphing the interval (2,3] on a line. Point out that because there is not a dot on 2, it is not included in the graph. However, any number greater than 2, up to and including 3, such as 2.01, is included in the graph. Ask students to list numbers that are included in the graph, for example, 2.1, $2\frac{1}{16}$, 2.999. To further clarify, an open dot can be placed at 2 to indicate that 2 is not included in the interval.

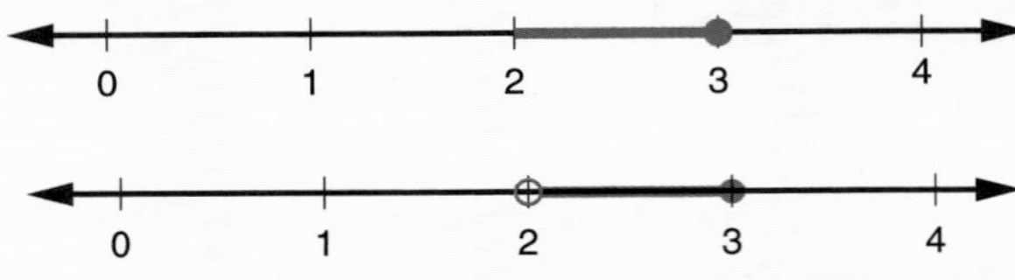

When most students have finished, discuss their work. Suggestions for questions:

- **Does the step graph show more information than the data table?** No. The step graph offers a visual display of the data in the table. It makes it easier to see the cost for various distances.

NOTE Taxi rates may include additional costs that are not considered here, such as costs for extra passengers, baggage, and waiting time.

- **Why would you not use a broken-line graph to display postal-rate or taxicab-rate data?** A broken-line graph would be misleading because the line segments connecting points imply that changes occur between connected points. For example, using the taxicab data, the cost for 1 mile is $2.00, and the cost for 2 miles is $4.00. If these two points were connected on the graph, it would appear that the cost steadily increases from $2.00 to $4.00 as the distance increases from 1 to 2 miles. But the cost does not steadily increase; the cost jumps after each exact mile.

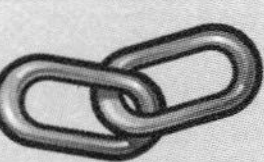

Links to the Future

The activities in this lesson are a first exposure to concepts that students will encounter when they graph solution sets of inequalities in Unit 6.

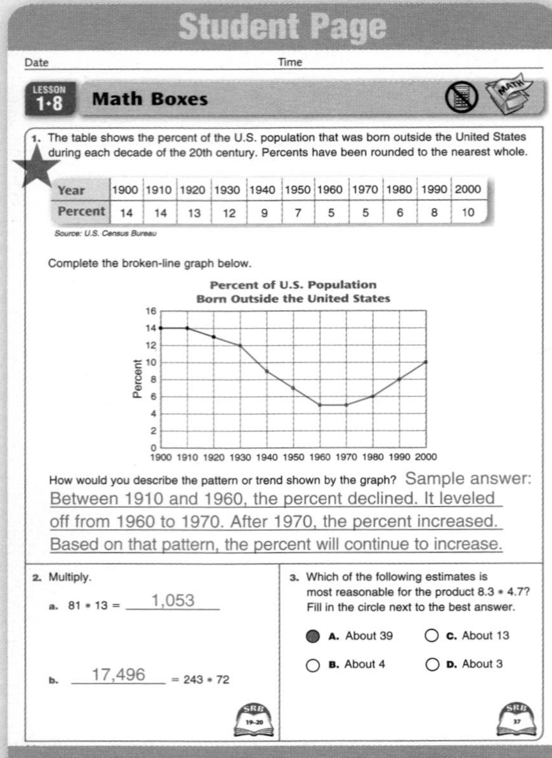

Student Page

Date Time

LESSON 1·8 **Math Boxes**

1. The table shows the percent of the U.S. population that was born outside the United States during each decade of the 20th century. Percents have been rounded to the nearest whole.

Year	1900	1910	1920	1930	1940	1950	1960	1970	1980	1990	2000
Percent	14	14	13	12	9	7	5	5	6	8	10

Source: U.S. Census Bureau

Complete the broken-line graph below.

Percent of U.S. Population Born Outside the United States

Percent: 0, 2, 4, 6, 8, 10, 12, 14, 16

1900 1910 1920 1930 1940 1950 1960 1970 1980 1990 2000

How would you describe the pattern or trend shown by the graph? Sample answer: Between 1910 and 1960, the percent declined. It leveled off from 1960 to 1970. After 1970, the percent increased. Based on that pattern, the percent will continue to increase.

2. Multiply.
   a. 81 * 13 = 1,053
   b. 17,496 = 243 * 72

   SRB 19–20

3. Which of the following estimates is most reasonable for the product 8.3 * 4.7? Fill in the circle next to the best answer.
   - (●) A. About 39
   - B. About 4
   - C. About 13
   - D. About 3

   SRB 37

Math Journal 1, p. 28

▶ Interpreting a Step Graph for a Plumber's Rates

INDEPENDENT ACTIVITY

(*Math Journal 1*, p. 27)

Circulate and assist as students work on the journal page.

Dots appear at the left end of each step in this graph. The dot at the left end of the first segment is directly above 0 on the horizontal (time) axis. It costs $20 to have the plumber show up, even if no work is done. The next dot, directly above 15 minutes, shows that after the plumber has worked for exactly 15 minutes, the cost jumps to $25.

2 Ongoing Learning & Practice

▶ Playing *Name That Number*

PARTNER ACTIVITY

(*Student Reference Book,* p. 329; *Math Masters,* p. 462)

Students practice writing number sentences that involve order of operations by playing *Name That Number.* Ask students to organize their number sentences to avoid using parentheses when possible. Game directions are in the *Student Reference Book.*

▶ Math Boxes 1•8

INDEPENDENT ACTIVITY

(*Math Journal 1,* p. 28)

Mixed Practice Math Boxes in this lesson are paired with Math Boxes in Lesson 1-6. The skills in Problems 2 and 3 preview Unit 2 content.

Ongoing Assessment: Recognizing Student Achievement

Math Boxes Problem 1 

Use **Math Boxes, Problem 1** to assess students' ability to draw a broken-line graph from a table of data values. Students are making adequate progress if they can draw a broken-line graph that accurately displays the values. Some students may be able to describe the pattern or the trend shown by the graph.

[Data and Chance Goal 1]

Game Master

Name Date Time

STUDY LINK 1•8 *Name That Number* Record Sheet

Round 1

Target Number: ______ My Cards: ____ ____ ____ ____ ____

My Solution (number sentence): ______________________

Number of cards used: ______

Round 2

Target Number: ______ My Cards: ____ ____ ____ ____ ____

My Solution (number sentence): ______________________

Number of cards used: ______

Name Date Time

***Name That Number* Record Sheet**

Round 1

Target Number: ______ My Cards: ____ ____ ____ ____ ____

My Solution (number sentence): ______________________

Number of cards used: ______

Round 2

Target Number: ______ My Cards: ____ ____ ____ ____ ____

My Solution (number sentence): ______________________

Number of cards used: ______

Math Masters, p. 462

Study Link Master

Name Date Time

STUDY LINK 1•8 The Cost of Mailing a Letter

The cost of mailing a first-class letter in the United States depends on how much the letter weighs. The table at the right shows first-class postal rates in 2004: 37 cents for a letter weighing 1 ounce or less; 60 cents for a letter weighing more than 1 ounce but not more than 2 ounces; and so on.

2004 First-Class Postal Rates	
Weight (oz)	Cost
1	$0.37
2	$0.60
3	$0.83
4	$1.06
5	$1.29
6	$1.52

A step graph for these data has been started on page 23. Notice the placement of dots in the graph. For example, on the step representing 60 cents, the dot at the right end, above the 2, shows that it costs 60 cents to mail a letter weighing exactly 2 ounces. There is no dot at the left end of the step—that is, at the intersection of 1 ounce and 60 cents—because the cost of mailing a 1-ounce letter is 37 cents, not 60 cents.

1. Continue the graph for letters weighing up to 6 ounces.
2. Using the rates shown in the table, how much would it cost to send a letter that weighs $4\frac{1}{2}$ ounces? $1.29

Try This

3. a. Using the rates shown in the table, how much would it cost to mail a letter that weighs $6\frac{1}{2}$ ounces? $1.75
   b. How did you determine your answer? Sample answer: The price difference per ounce is $0.23. The price jumps another $0.23 for every additional part of an ounce.
4. Continue the graph on page 23 to show the cost of mailing a first-class letter weighing more than 6 ounces, but not more than 7 ounces.

Practice

5. $\frac{252}{9}$ = 28
6. 45 = $8\overline{)360}$
7. $\frac{469}{7}$ = 67
8. 55 = $9\overline{)495}$

Math Masters, p. 22

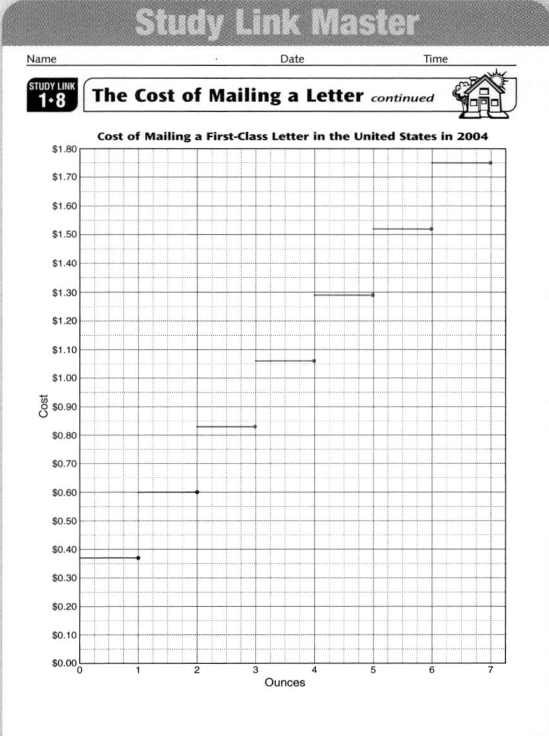

Math Masters, p. 23

Teaching Master

Name Date Time

LESSON 1·8 **Identifying Jumps in Data Values** 

Set by Congress, minimum wage is the minimum rate per hour that can be paid to workers. Some historical values of the U.S. minimum wage appear in the table below.

U.S. Minimum Wage, 1986–2003

Year	Minimum Wage	Year	Minimum Wage	Year	Minimum Wage
1986	$3.35	1992	$4.25	1998	$5.15
1987	$3.35	1993	$4.25	1999	$5.15
1988	$3.35	1994	$4.25	2000	$5.15
1989	$3.35	1995	$4.25	2001	$5.15
1990	$3.80	1996	$4.75	2002	$5.15
1991	$4.25	1997	$5.15	2003	$5.15

Source: Economic Policy Institute

Use the table above to answer the following questions.

1. Name the years at which a jump in the values occurs. 1990, 1991, 1996, 1997
2. Name the number of years for which the minimum wage is
   $3.35 4 $3.80 1 $4.25 5 $4.75 1 $5.15 7
3. Is the number of years between jumps the same? Explain.
   No. Answers vary.

Math Masters, p. 24

Teaching Master

Name Date Time

LESSON 1·8 **Parking Lot Charges** 

1. A parking lot charges $3.00 for the first hour or fraction of an hour and $2.00 for each additional hour or fraction of an hour.
   a. Complete the table at the right.
   b. What is the cost of parking for $2\frac{1}{2}$ hours? $7.00

Time	Cost
30 min	$3.00
1 hr	$3.00
$2\frac{1}{2}$ hr	$7.00
3 hr 59 min	$9.00
5 hr	$11.00
5 hr 15 min	$13.00

2. Draw a step graph of the parking lot charges. Remember: The parking lot charges $3.00 for the first hour or fraction of an hour and $2.00 for each additional hour or fraction of an hour.
3. What is the cost of parking for 1 hour and 15 minutes? $5.00
4. What is the cost of parking for 3 hours and 45 minutes? $9.00

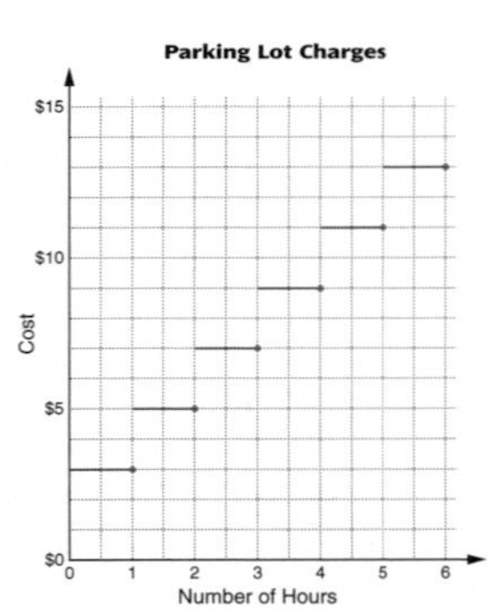

Math Masters, p. 25

▶ Study Link 1·8

INDEPENDENT ACTIVITY

(*Math Masters,* pp. 22 and 23)

Home Connection Students draw a step graph to represent the cost of mailing a first-class letter. Be sure that students notice the placement of dots in the graph.

NOTE The U.S. postal rates in the Study Link were accurate when this book went to press. You will need to make adjustments if they have changed.

3 Differentiation Options

READINESS

PARTNER ACTIVITY

▶ Identifying Jumps in Data Values

5–15 Min

(*Math Masters,* p. 24)

To provide experience with step graph concepts, have students analyze the data values in the table and identify the years at which jumps in the data occur and the number of years between jumps.

EXTRA PRACTICE

INDEPENDENT ACTIVITY

▶ Drawing a Step Graph

5–15 Min

(*Math Masters,* p. 25)

To provide extra practice with step graphs, have students complete a table of parking lot charges. Then have them use the data in the table to construct and interpret a step graph.

EXTRA PRACTICE

INDEPENDENT ACTIVITY

▶ Writing Custom-Made Math Boxes

5–15 Min

(*Math Masters,* page 405)

Use *Math Masters,* page 405 to generate Math Box questions that focus on a particular concept or skill for which students need extra practice.

The Percent Circle and Circle Graphs

Objectives To review the Percent Circle; and to interpret circle graphs.

1 Teaching the Lesson

Key Activities

Students review the markings on the Percent Circle. They interpret circle graphs and estimate percents on circle graphs.

Key Concepts and Skills

- Read and interpret circle graphs that have been constructed from survey data. [Data and Chance Goal 1]
- Estimate percents on circle graphs. [Data and Chance Goal 1]
- Use the Percent Circle to measure sectors to within ±2%. [Measurement and Reference Frames Goal 1]
- Review the meaning of *radius.* [Measurement and Reference Frames Goal 2]

Key Vocabulary

circle • interior of a circle • arc • sector • radius • Percent Circle • circle graph

Ongoing Assessment: Recognizing Student Achievement Use journal page 29. [Measurement and Reference Frames Goal 1]

materials

- ☐ *Math Journal 1,* pp. 29–31
- ☐ *Student Reference Book,* p. 145
- ☐ Study Link 1•8
- ☐ Teaching Master (*Math Masters,* p. 26)
- ☐ Transparencies (*Math Masters,* pp. 27 and 406; optional)
- ☐ Geometry Template

See **Advance Preparation**

2 Ongoing Learning & Practice

Students practice and maintain skills through Math Boxes and Study Link activities.

materials

- ☐ *Math Journal 1,* p. 32
- ☐ Study Link Masters (*Math Masters,* pp. 28 and 29)
- ☐ straightedge

3 Differentiation Options

READINESS

Students match percents with the shaded regions that represent them.

ENRICHMENT

Students use computer software to generate circle graphs of class data from the Math Message survey.

ELL SUPPORT

Students add *arc, sector, interior,* and *circle* to their Math Word Banks.

materials

- ☐ Game Masters (*Math Masters,* pp. 467–469)
- ☐ *Differentiation Handbook*
- ☐ scissors
- ☐ computer; spreadsheet/graphing software

See **Advance Preparation**

Additional Information

Advance Preparation Make enough copies of *Math Masters,* page 26 for each student to have one strip of survey questions.

For the optional Readiness activity, make one set of double-sided game tiles for each small group.

Technology

Assessment Management System
Journal page 29, Problems 2a–d
See the **iTLG.**

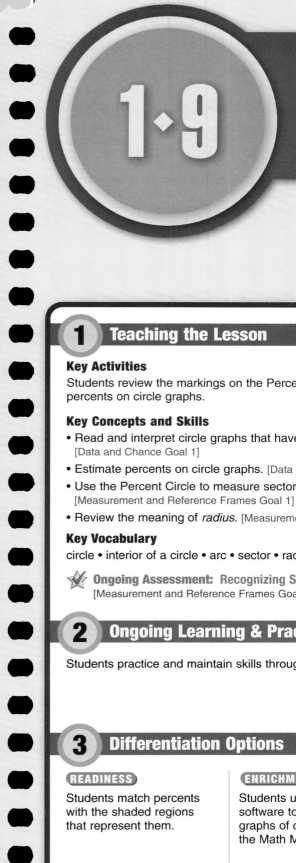

Getting Started

Mental Math and Reflexes

Students write each fraction as a percent. *Suggestions:*

●○○ $\frac{1}{2}$ 50%	●●○ $\frac{1}{4}$ 25%	●●● $\frac{3}{4}$ 75%
$\frac{1}{10}$ 10%	$\frac{7}{10}$ 70%	$\frac{1}{100}$ 1%
$\frac{1}{5}$ 20%	$\frac{3}{5}$ 60%	$\frac{4}{5}$ 80%

Math Message

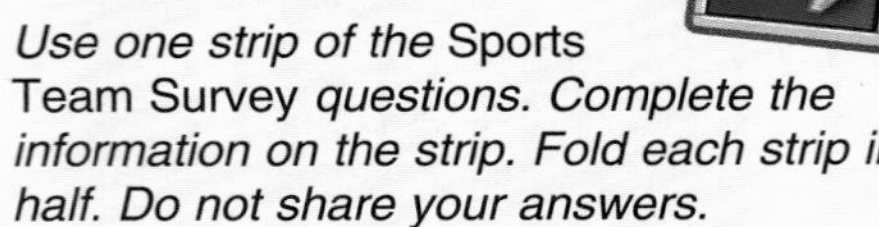

Use one strip of the Sports Team Survey *questions. Complete the information on the strip. Fold each strip in half. Do not share your answers.*

Study Link 1•8 Follow-Up

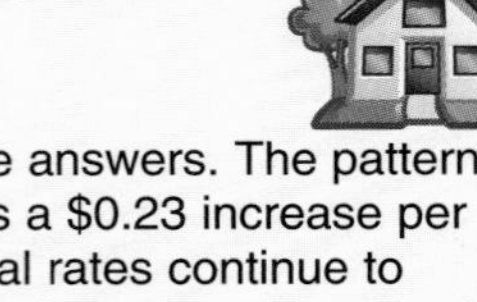

Briefly go over the answers. The pattern in the table shows a $0.23 increase per ounce. If the postal rates continue to follow this pattern, the postage required for a $6\frac{1}{2}$-ounce letter would be $1.52 + $0.23, or $1.75.

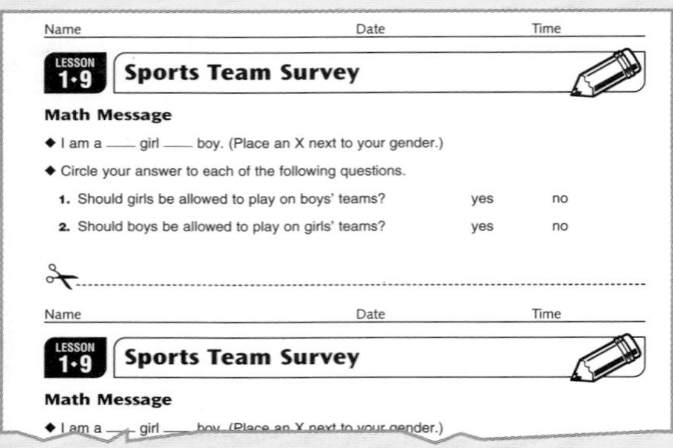

Name Date Time

LESSON 1•9 **Sports Team Survey**

Math Message

- I am a ___ girl ___ boy. (Place an X next to your gender.)
- Circle your answer to each of the following questions.

1. Should girls be allowed to play on boys' teams? yes no
2. Should boys be allowed to play on girls' teams? yes no

Name Date Time

LESSON 1•9 **Sports Team Survey**

Math Message

- I am a ___ girl ___ boy. (Place an X next to your gender.)

Student Page
Math Masters, page 26

NOTE The results of the Math Message survey are needed for the Enrichment activity. Consider leaving the charts up on the board or having a student record them.

Student Page

Data and Probability

How to Use the Percent Circle

A **compass** is a device for drawing circles. You can also use your **Geometry Template** to draw circles.

An **arc** is a piece of a circle. If you mark two points on a circle, these points and the part of the circle between them form an arc.

The region inside a circle is called its **interior.**

A **sector** is a wedge-shaped piece of a circle and its interior. A sector consists of two **radii** (singular: **radius**), one of the arcs determined by their endpoints, and the part of the interior of the circle bounded by the radii and the arc.

A **circle graph** is sometimes called a **pie graph** because it looks like a pie that has been cut into several pieces. Each "piece" is a sector of the circle.

You can use the **Percent Circle** on your Geometry Template to find what percent of the circle graph each sector represents. Here are two methods for using the Percent Circle.

sector
arc
interior

5th grade
1st grade
2nd grade
3rd grade
4th grade

The circle graph shows the distribution of students in grades 1 to 5 at Elm School.

Method 1: Direct Measure

- Place the center of the Percent Circle over the center of the circle graph.
- Rotate the template so that the 0% mark is aligned with one side (line segment) of the sector you are measuring.
- Read the percent at the mark on the Percent Circle located over the other side of the sector. This tells what percent the sector represents.

For example, the sector for first grade represents 20%.

20%

Method 2: Difference Comparison

- Place the center of the Percent Circle over the center of the circle graph.
- Note the percent reading for one side of the sector you are measuring.
- Find the percent reading for the other side of the sector.
- Find the difference between these readings.

The sector for second grade represents 45% – 20%, or 25%.

25%

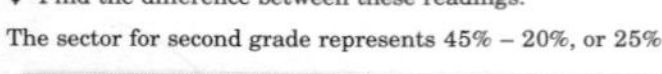

Check Your Understanding

What percents are represented by the other three sectors in the above circle graph?

Check your answers on page 419.

Student Reference Book, p. 145

NOTE Some students may benefit from doing the Readiness activity before beginning Part 1 of the lesson. See Part 3 for details.

1 Teaching the Lesson

▶ Math Message Follow-Up

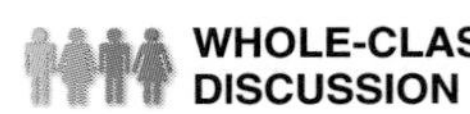

WHOLE-CLASS DISCUSSION

(*Math Masters,* p. 26)

Since some students will have strong opinions about the survey questions, remind them to keep their responses to themselves. Collect strips with students' responses. Tally yes or no responses to the two questions in charts according to gender.

Girls Allowed on Boys' Teams	
Girls' Responses	
Yes	**No**
卌 ////	///

Total Number of Girls Surveyed: 12

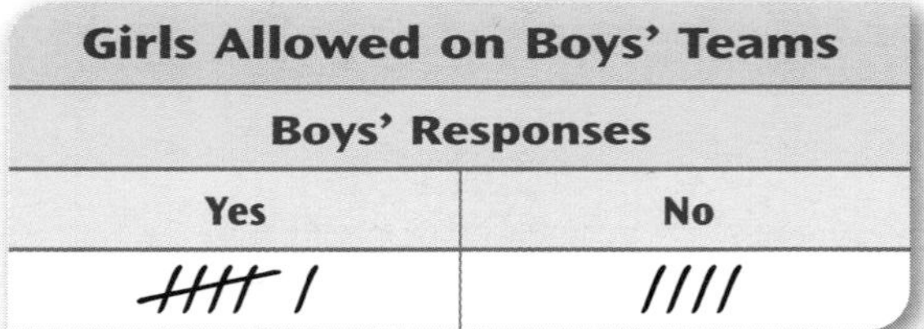

Girls Allowed on Boys' Teams	
Boys' Responses	
Yes	**No**
卌 /	////

Total Number of Boys Surveyed: 10

Ask students to write fractions and percents representing the survey results. Discuss their suggestions.

For example, if $\frac{9}{12}$ of the girls surveyed think that girls should be allowed on boys' teams, then

$$\frac{9}{12} = \frac{3}{4} = \frac{3 * 25}{4 * 25} = \frac{75}{100} = 75\%.$$

Because 75% said yes, 100% – 75%, or 25%, said no.

Similarly, if $\frac{6}{10}$ of the boys surveyed think that girls should be allowed on boys' teams, then $\frac{6}{10} = 0.6 = 60\%$.

Because 60% said yes, 100% – 60%, or 40%, said no.

Estimating Percents on Circle Graphs

WHOLE-CLASS DISCUSSION

(*Math Journal 1,* pp. 30 and 31)

Ask volunteers to explain how to estimate the shaded areas of circle graphs A–D. Compare the class survey results from the Math Message to those represented by graphs A–D.

Tell students to use Graph E to complete Problem 1 on journal page 31. Circulate and assist as needed. Have students share their responses to Problems 4 and 5.

Students should spend time interpreting circle graphs and estimating percents on circle graphs without using the Percent Circle on the Geometry Template. After students begin to use the Percent Circle, they tend to not think about the reasonableness of their answers. Encourage students to make quick estimates even when using the Percent Circle.

Reviewing Use of the Percent Circle

WHOLE-CLASS DISCUSSION

(*Math Journal 1,* p. 30; *Student Reference Book,* p. 145)

Discuss *Student Reference Book,* page 145. Be sure that students can distinguish between a circle and its interior as well as between an arc and a sector.

- ▷ A **circle** is a closed curve. The **interior of a circle** is not part of the circle. A circle together with its interior is called a *disk,* or a circular region.
- ▷ An **arc** is a part of a circle between and including two endpoints on a circle. A **sector** is a region bounded by, and including, an arc and two line segments (each a radius). A sector resembles a slice of pizza.

As you discuss each vocabulary term, write it on the board and draw a picture. Visually represent a sector and an arc on the board using one color to shade the sector and a different color to shade the arc. Write the words in the same color you used to shade each drawing.

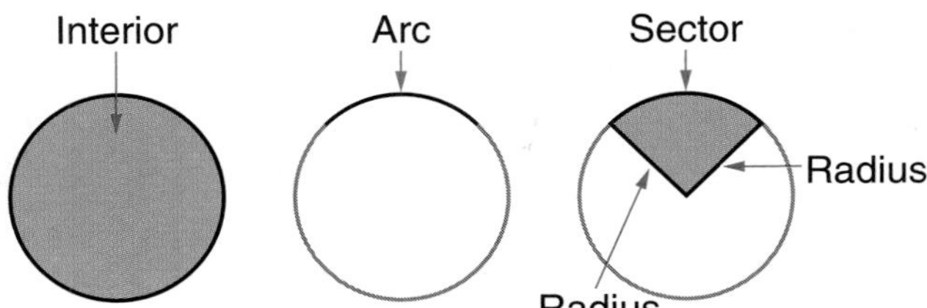

Student Page

Date Time

LESSON 1·9 A Magazine Survey

An issue of a sports magazine for kids featured a readers' survey. In the survey, readers were asked to respond to the following three questions:

1. Should girls be allowed to play on boys' teams?
2. Should boys be allowed to play on girls' teams?
3. On how many organized sports teams do you play during a year?

Readers' responses are represented by the circle graphs below.

Question 1: Should girls be allowed to play on boys' teams?

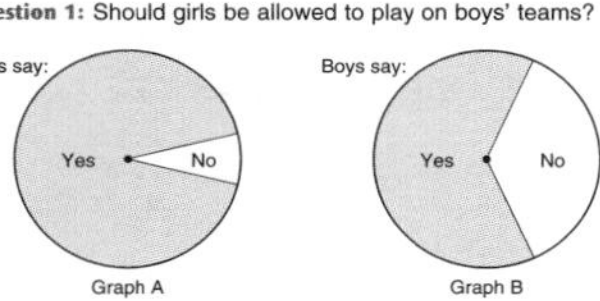

Question 2: Should boys be allowed to play on girls' teams?

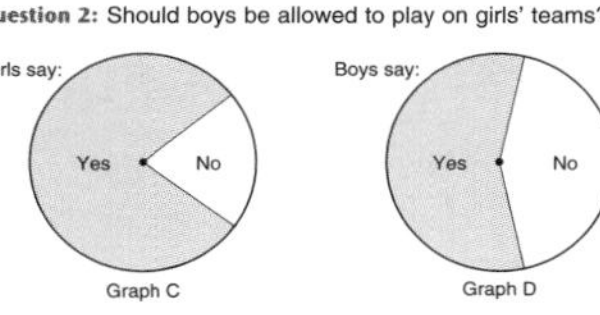

Question 3: On how many organized sports teams do you play during a year?

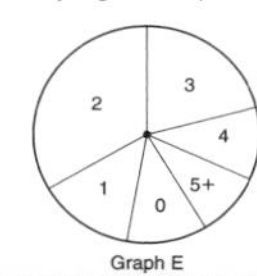

***Math Journal 1,* p. 30**

NOTE *Math Masters,* page 27 is identical to journal page 30. You may want to use the overhead transparency of the master when discussing the page.

Student Page

Date Time

LESSON 1·9 A Magazine Survey *continued*

Refer to the circle graphs on the preceding page to answer the following questions.

1. Estimate the percent of boys and girls who gave the following responses.
   a. Approximately 30 % play on 2 organized teams during a typical year.
   b. Approximately 75 % play on *at least* 2 organized teams during a year.
   c. Approximately 5 % of the girls think that girls should *not* be allowed to play on boys' teams.
2. Which graph (A, B, C, or D) shows almost everyone agreeing on an answer? A
3. Which graph (A, B, C, or D) shows opinions that are almost evenly divided between yes and no? D
4. Do you think that the readers of the sports magazine who responded to this survey play sports more often, less often, or about the same amount of time as the students in your school? Explain.
   Sample answers: More often; Kids who read a sports magazine might play sports more often than other kids. About the same; Kids at our school are very active in sports.
5. Circle graphs on journal page 30 show how boys and girls responded to a survey about boys playing on girls' teams and girls playing on boys' teams. Explain how girls' and boys' responses to the survey are alike and how they are different.
   Sample answer: A majority of both boys and girls thinks that the opposite gender should be allowed to play on boys' and girls' teams. However, more girls than boys think this way. Also, more kids agree that girls should be allowed to play on boys' teams than boys on girls' teams.

***Math Journal 1,* p. 31**

Student Page

Date Time

LESSON 1·9 Reading Circle Graphs

Use your estimation skills and your Percent Circle to answer the following questions.

1. The circle graph at the right shows people's preferences for preparing eggs.

Methods of Preparing Eggs

Source: American Egg Board

a. Which is the most popular method for preparing eggs? scrambled

b. Which is the least popular method for preparing eggs? poached

c. Which method is preferred by about 25% of the people surveyed? boiled

d. Which methods are preferred by less than 10% of the people surveyed? Omelettes, poached, and other

e. What percent of people surveyed prefer scrambled eggs? About 35 %

f. Is the percent greater for people favoring fried eggs or boiled eggs? fried

About how much greater? 8 %

g. How do you like your eggs prepared? Answers vary.

2. The circle graph at the right shows people's preferences for pizza crust.

Pizza Crust Preferences

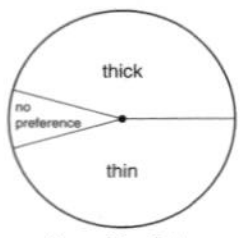

Source: Pizza Today

a. True or false: In this survey, the number of people who prefer thin-crust pizza is about the same as the number of people who prefer thick-crust pizza. true

b. What percent of people prefer thin-crust pizza? About 46 %

c. What percent prefer thick-crust pizza? About 46 %

d. What percent have no preference? About 8 %

e. What kind of crust do you prefer? Answers vary.

Math Journal 1, p. 29

Ask students to locate the **Percent Circle** on their Geometry Templates. You may want to display a transparency of the Geometry Template (*Math Masters,* p. 406). Guide students to make the following observations:

▷ There are 100 equally spaced marks around the Percent Circle.

▷ Line segments connect the center of the Percent Circle to its edge, dividing the Percent Circle and its interior into sectors. Each sector is 5% ($\frac{5}{100}$ or $\frac{1}{20}$) of the Percent Circle.

▷ If you were to connect each mark along the Percent Circle with the center of the circle, each sector would be equal to 1% ($\frac{1}{100}$) of the Percent Circle.

▷ The arc from 0% to 5% has marks halfway between whole-percent marks.

▷ There are several dotted line segments that indicate fractional parts (such as $\frac{1}{3}$) of the Percent Circle.

Discuss two ways to use the Percent Circle to interpret circle graphs, as described in the *Student Reference Book.* Students usually prefer the direct measure method.

For each **circle graph** on journal page 30, remind students of the estimates they made earlier in the lesson for Graphs A–D. Ask students to use the Percent Circle to find the percents for Graphs A–D.

You might want to use transparencies of *Math Masters,* pages 27 and 406 to demonstrate how to use the Percent Circle. Have students write each percent in or near the sector of the circle graph it describes.

Graph A: *Yes* is 92%; *No* is 8%. Graph B: *Yes* is 64%; *No* is 36%. Graph C: *Yes* is 80%; *No* is 20%. Graph D: *Yes* is 58%; *No* is 42%.

Adjusting the Activity

ELL

When measuring with the Percent Circle, encourage students to check their work by adding the percents. The sum of percents for each sector of the circle should be about 100 percent.

AUDITORY ◆ KINESTHETIC ◆ TACTILE ◆ VISUAL

Student Page

Date Time

LESSON 1·9 Math Boxes

1. Make a step graph from the data in the table.

Years	1969–1976	1977–1992	1993–1997	1998–2005
Number of Major League Teams	24	26	28	30

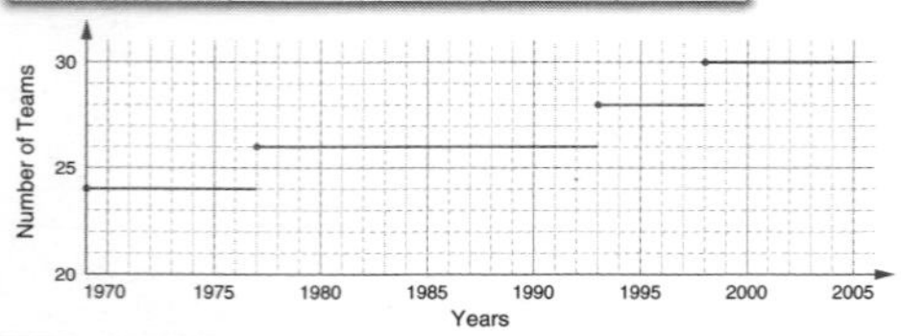

2. According to the circle graph at the right:

Peanut Butter Survey

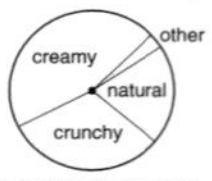

Source: Astounding Averages

a. Which kind of peanut butter do most Americans prefer? creamy

b. Which kind do about $\frac{1}{3}$ of Americans prefer? crunchy

c. About what percent of Americans prefer natural peanut butter? About 18%

3.

Tour Number	1	2	3	4	5	6
Number of People	10	9	40	12	14	5

Does the median or mean best describe the typical size of the tour groups shown in the table above? Explain.

Sample answer: median; The outlier 40 affects the mean, so the median 11 is a better representation.

4. Write the value of the digit 9 in each numeral below.

a. 401,297 9 tens

b. 1,927,387 9 hundred-thousands

c. 4.95 9 tenths

Math Journal 1, p. 32

▶ Practicing with the Percent Circle

INDEPENDENT ACTIVITY

(*Math Journal 1,* p. 29)

Students use the Percent Circle to complete the problems. Circulate and assist as needed. When students have finished, discuss any difficulties they encountered and any new strategies they discovered in solving the problems.

Ongoing Assessment: Recognizing Student Achievement

Journal Page 31 Problems 2a–d ★

Use **journal page 31, Problems 2a–d** to assess students' abilities to estimate and measure sector sizes using the Percent Circle of the Geometry Template. Students are making adequate progress if they are able to use the Percent Circle to measure sectors within ±2%. Some students may be able to measure sectors to the nearest 1%.

[Measurement and Reference Frames Goal 1]

2 Ongoing Learning & Practice

▶ Math Boxes 1·9

INDEPENDENT ACTIVITY

(*Math Journal 1,* p. 32)

Mixed Practice Math Boxes in this lesson are paired with Math Boxes in Lesson 1-11. The skill in Problem 4 previews Unit 2 content.

Writing/Reasoning Have students write a response for the following: *Explain what would happen to the median in Problem 3 if the number of people for Tour 3 changed from 40 to 22.* The median would stay the same.

▶ Study Link 1·9

INDEPENDENT ACTIVITY

(*Math Masters,* pp. 28 and 29)

Home Connection Students answer questions about circle graphs.

Study Link Master

Name Date Time

STUDY LINK 1·9 Analyzing Circle Graphs *continued*

Cut out the Percent Circle at the right and poke a hole in the center with a pencil. Use the Percent Circle to find the percent represented by each sector mentioned in the questions below.

3. According to the survey, are men or women more likely to alert strangers to an embarrassing situation? men

4. a. About what percent of men say they would tell strangers that they had food stuck between their teeth? 89%

b. About what percent of men would not be willing to tell? 11%

5. In the survey, how much greater is the percent of men who would be willing to alert strangers to smudges on their faces than the percent of women who would be willing to do so? 10% greater

6. How much greater is the percent of women who would be willing to tell strangers about food in their teeth than the percent of women who would tell strangers about dandruff? 60% greater

7. Why do you think people might be hesitant to alert strangers to such situations? Sample answer: Because they don't know the person, they don't know how the stranger will react.

Practice

8. $\frac{336}{14} =$ 24

9. 14 $= 50\overline{)700}$

10. $\frac{992}{31} =$ 32

11. 19 $= 29\overline{)551}$

Math Masters, p. 29

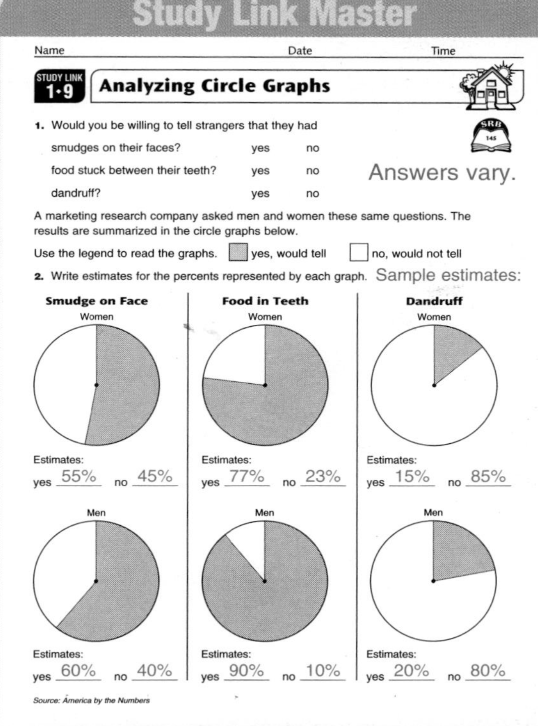

Study Link Master

Name Date Time

STUDY LINK 1·9 Analyzing Circle Graphs

1. Would you be willing to tell strangers that they had

smudges on their faces? yes no

food stuck between their teeth? yes no

dandruff? yes no

Answers vary.

A marketing research company asked men and women these same questions. The results are summarized in the circle graphs below.

Use the legend to read the graphs. yes, would tell; no, would not tell

2. Write estimates for the percents represented by each graph. Sample estimates:

	Smudge on Face	Food in Teeth	Dandruff
Women	yes 55% no 45%	yes 77% no 23%	yes 15% no 85%
Men	yes 60% no 40%	yes 90% no 10%	yes 20% no 80%

Source: *America by the Numbers*

Math Masters, p. 28

Game Master

Name Date Time

Percent/Sector Match Up

Materials ☐ 1 set of Percent/Sector tiles

Players 2 or 3

Object of the game

To match percents and the shaded sectors that represent them.

Directions

1. Shuffle the tiles and lay them facedown on a playing surface. The backs of the 12 percent tiles should have the percent symbol (%) showing. The backs of the sector tiles are blank. Arrange the tiles into a 6-row-by-4-column array, keeping them facedown.
2. Players take turns. At each turn, a player turns over a percent tile and a sector tile. If the tiles match, the player keeps the tiles. If the tiles do not match, the player turns the tiles facedown.
3. The game ends when all tiles have been taken. The player with the most tiles wins.

   (Variation: If the selected percent tile and sector tile add up to 100%, the player keeps the tiles.)

Math Masters, **p. 467**

3 Differentiation Options

READINESS

▶ Playing *Percent-Sector Match Up*

(*Math Masters,* pp. 467–469)

To provide experience with estimating percents, have students play *Percent-Sector Match Up.* After students have cut out the double-sided Percent/Sector tiles (made by copying *Math Masters*, pp. 468 and 469 back-to-back), have them read the game directions on page 467. Encourage students to play at least one round with the variation.

ENRICHMENT

▶ Using Technology to Generate Circle Graphs

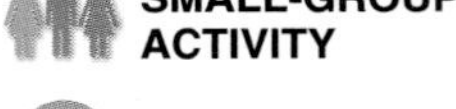

To extend students' knowledge of circle graphs, have them use computer software to generate a circle graph of the data collected from the Math Message survey. They also experiment with labeling sectors. After students complete their graphs, they compare them to the graphs on journal page 29.

ELL SUPPORT

▶ Building a Math Word Bank

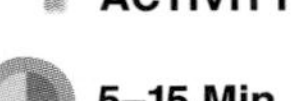

(*Differentiation Handbook*)

To provide language support for working with circles, have students use the Word Bank template found in the *Differentiation Handbook.* Ask them to write the terms *arc, sector, interior,* and *circle,* draw pictures relating to each term, and write other related words. See the *Differentiation Handbook* for more information.

Using a Graph to Investigate Perimeter and Area

Objectives To find the perimeter and area of a rectangle; and to describe relationships between perimeter and area.

1 Teaching the Lesson

Key Activities

Students find the dimensions of the rectangle with the largest area for a given perimeter. They use a graph to display data and to solve a problem.

Key Concepts and Skills

- Convert between fractions and decimals. [Number and Numeration Goal 5]
- Multiply decimal numbers. [Operations and Computation Goal 2]
- Calculate the area of rectangles. [Measurement and Reference Frames Goal 2]
- Use a graph to investigate the relationship between the perimeter and area of a rectangle. [Patterns, Functions, and Algebra Goal 1]

Key Vocabulary

perimeter • area

Ongoing Assessment: Informing Instruction See page 67.

materials

- ☐ *Math Journal 1,* pp. 34 and 35
- ☐ Study Link 1•9
- ☐ Teaching Aid Master (*Math Masters,* p. 407)
- ☐ Transparencies (*Math Masters,* pp. 407 and 30; optional)
- ☐ calculator
- ☐ *Student Reference Book,* pp. 212 and 215

2 Ongoing Learning & Practice

Students practice finding and analyzing data landmarks by playing *Landmark Shark.*
Students practice and maintain skills through Math Boxes and Study Link activities.

Ongoing Assessment: Recognizing Student Achievement Use an Exit Slip.
[Data and Chance Goal 2]

materials

- ☐ *Math Journal 1,* p. 33
- ☐ *Student Reference Book,* pp. 325 and 326
- ☐ Study Link Master (*Math Masters,* p. 31)
- ☐ Teaching Aid Masters (*Math Masters,* pp. 404 and 407)
- ☐ Game Masters (*Math Masters,* pp. 456 and 457)
- ☐ Per group: 4 each of number cards 0–10; 1 each of number cards 11–20

3 Differentiation Options

READINESS
Students draw rectangles on grid paper and determine the perimeters of these rectangles.

ENRICHMENT
Students solve area problems.

ELL SUPPORT
Students add terms to their Math Word Banks.

materials

- ☐ Teaching Masters (*Math Masters,* pp. 32 and 33)
- ☐ Teaching Aid Master (*Math Masters,* p. 408)
- ☐ *Differentiation Handbook*

Technology

Assessment Management System
Exit Slip
See the **iTLG.**

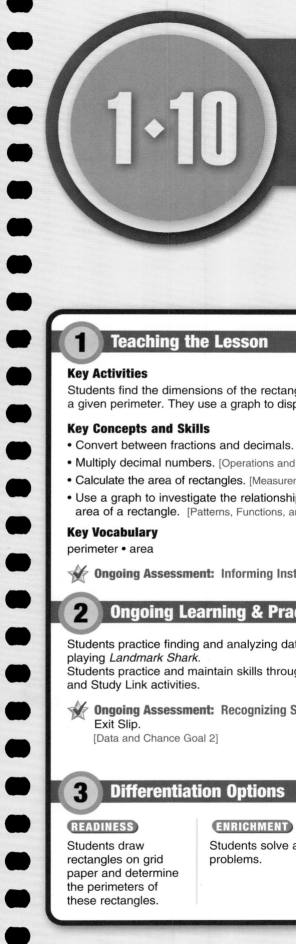

Getting Started

Mental Math and Reflexes

Students indicate on their slates whether they would need to find the area (A) or perimeter (P) in each of the following situations:

●○○ Carpeting the living room *A*
Finding the distance traveled around a lake *P*

●●○ Building a fence to put around a garden *P*
Determining the size of your waist *P*

●●● Buying a tablecloth *A*

Math Message

Use a sheet of $\frac{1}{4}$-inch Grid Paper (Math Masters, p. 407) to complete Problems 1 and 2 on journal page 34.

Study Link 1·9 Follow-Up

Briefly go over the answers. Ask students if they were surprised by any of the survey results.

NOTE Some students may benefit from doing the Readiness activity before beginning Part 1 of the lesson. See Part 3 for details.

1 Teaching the Lesson

▶ Math Message Follow-Up

WHOLE-CLASS ACTIVITY

(*Math Journal 1,* p. 34; *Math Masters,* p. 407; *Student Reference Book,* pp. 212 and 215)

Students share the width and area of each rectangle in the table. You might want to review pages 212 and 215 in the *Student Reference Book*.

NOTE You may want to use a transparency of $\frac{1}{4}$-inch Grid Paper (*Math Masters,* p. 407) for the Adjusting the Activity.

Adjusting the Activity

ELL

Show students how drawing pictures can help complete the table. For example, use a length of 4 ft and a perimeter of 22 ft. Draw one side of the rectangle 4 squares long on the grid paper. Explain that this represents a side measuring 4 feet. Ask questions such as the following:

- How long will the opposite side be when we draw it? 4 squares long
- How far below this first side do we draw it? You can't tell until you know how long the other pair of sides are.
- How much of the perimeter (22 ft) is taken up by these two sides? 4 ft + 4 ft = 8 ft
- How much of the perimeter remains? 22 ft − 8 ft = 14 ft
- How long is each of the other two sides? $\frac{1}{2}$ of 14 ft, or 7 ft

Complete the picture. Have students verify the area by counting the squares in the rectangle.

AUDITORY ◆ KINESTHETIC ◆ TACTILE ◆ VISUAL

Student Page

Date Time

LESSON 1·10 **Using a Graph to Find the Largest Area**

Math Message

Suppose you have enough material for 22 feet of fence. You want to enclose the largest possible rectangular region with this fence.

1. If you know the perimeter and length of a rectangle, how can you find its width?
Sample answer: Double the length, subtract the total from the perimeter, and then divide by 2.

2. The table below lists the lengths of some rectangles with a perimeter of 22 feet. Fill in the missing widths and areas. You may want to draw the rectangles on your grid paper. Let the side of each grid square represent 1 foot.

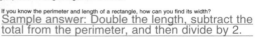

Length (ft)	1	2	3	4	5	6	7	8	9	10
Width (ft)	10	9	8	7	6	5	4	3	2	1
Perimeter (ft)	22	22	22	22	22	22	22	22	22	22
Area (ft^2)	10	18	24	28	30	30	28	24	18	10

3. If you have not already done so, draw each rectangle from the table above on your grid paper.

4. a. What are the length and width of the rectangle(s) in the table with the largest area? 5 ft 6 ft
   b. What is that area? 30 ft^2

5. On the graph on page 35, plot the length and area of each rectangle in the table. *Do not connect the plotted points yet.*

6. a. Find a rectangle whose perimeter is 22 feet and whose area is larger than the area of the rectangle in Problem 4 above. Use your graph to help you.
   What is the length? 5.5 ft Width? 5.5 ft Area? 30.25 ft^2
   b. Now plot the length and area of this rectangle on the grid on page 35. Then draw a curved line through all the plotted points.

Math Journal 1, p. 34

Ongoing Assessment: Informing Instruction

Watch for students who believe that the length of a rectangle is always the side with the greater dimension. While this is often the case, either side of a rectangle can be considered its length.

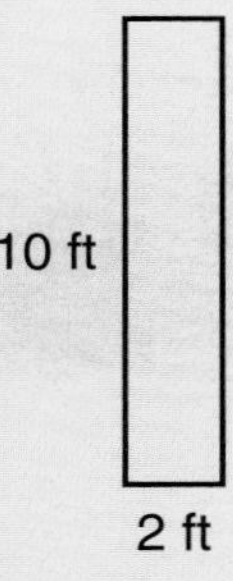

length = 10 ft, width = 2 ft

length = 2 ft, width = 10 ft

Some students may recognize and use patterns to complete the table. Ask them to calculate the **perimeter** and **area** of a rectangle that is not included in the table (for example, length = 7 ft, perimeter = 24 ft). width = 5 ft; area = 35 ft^2

▶ Finding the Largest Area for a Given Perimeter

PARTNER ACTIVITY

(*Math Journal 1,* pp. 34 and 35; *Math Masters,* p. 30)

Have students complete Problems 3–5 on journal page 34. If any students have not completed the table (Problem 2), they can do that as they complete Problem 3. Remind students not to connect the plotted points in their graphs (Problem 5). You may want to display a transparency of *Math Masters,* page 30 to assist students in completing the graph.

Circulate and assist as needed. Then discuss students' results. Ask the following questions:

- How many rectangles did you draw for Problem 3? Some students may notice that there are only five different rectangle shapes specified by the table: 1 × 10, 2 × 9, 3 × 8, 4 × 7, and 5 × 6. Most students, however, will probably draw 10 rectangles—one to represent each column of the table. Both approaches are correct.
- Which rectangle in the table has the largest area? The 5 ft × 6 ft or 6 ft × 5 ft rectangle (30 sq ft)

Read Problem 6 together as a class. Ask students to share possible solution strategies.

▷ The largest area plotted on the graph is for lengths of 5 and 6. Perhaps there is a length between 5 and 6 that will result in a rectangle with an even larger area. Try a length that is halfway between—$5\frac{1}{2}$, or 5.5.

▷ A square that is 5.5 ft on a side has a perimeter of 22 ft and an area of 5.5 ft × 5.5 ft = 30.25 ft^2. You might have students verify this by drawing a $5\frac{1}{2}$ in. × $5\frac{1}{2}$ in. square on grid paper and counting the whole, half, and quarter squares.

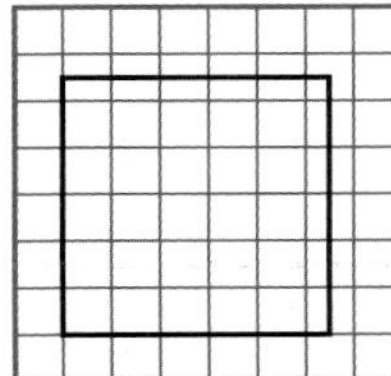

Area of a $5\frac{1}{2} \times 5\frac{1}{2}$ square is 25 full squares, 10 half-squares, and 1 quarter-square. 25 + 5 (from 10 ∗ 0.5) + 0.25 = 30.25

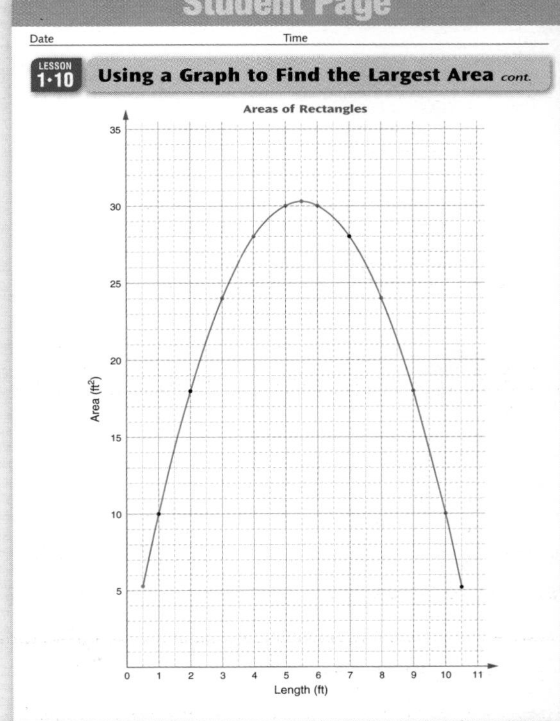

Math Journal 1, p. 35

Student Page

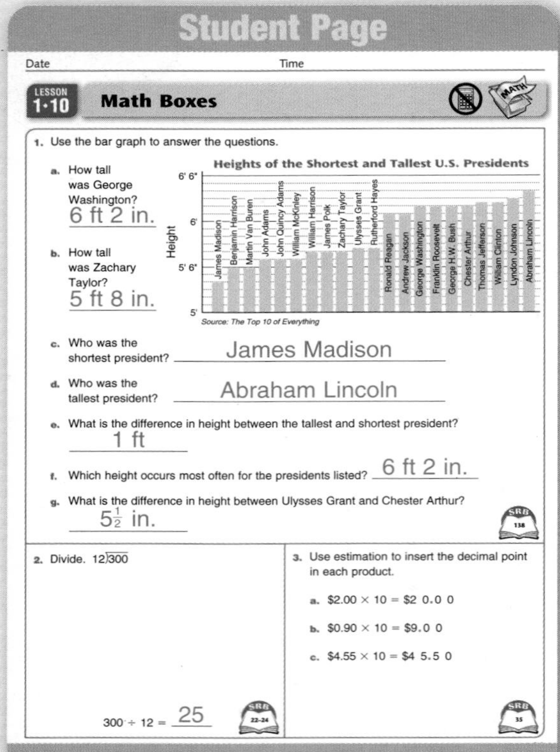

Date Time

LESSON 1·10 **Math Boxes**

1. Use the bar graph to answer the questions.

a. How tall was George Washington? 6 ft 2 in.

b. How tall was Zachary Taylor? 5 ft 8 in.

c. Who was the shortest president? James Madison

d. Who was the tallest president? Abraham Lincoln

e. What is the difference in height between the tallest and shortest president? 1 ft

f. Which height occurs most often for the presidents listed? 6 ft 2 in.

g. What is the difference in height between Ulysses Grant and Chester Arthur? $5\frac{1}{2}$ in.

SRB 138

2. Divide. $12\overline{)300}$

$300 \div 12 =$ 25

SRB 22-24

3. Use estimation to insert the decimal point in each product.

a. $2.00 × 10 = $2 0.0 0

b. $0.90 × 10 = $9.0 0

c. $4.55 × 10 = $4 5.5 0

SRB 35

Math Journal 1, p. 33

Study Link Master

Name Date Time

STUDY LINK 1·10 **Perimeter and Area**

The student council is preparing the gym floor for the annual talent show. They will use 24 feet of tape to mark the seating area for the judges.

SRB 212, 214 215

The table below lists the lengths of some rectangles with perimeters of 24 feet. Complete the table. You may want to draw the rectangles on grid paper. Let the side of each grid square represent 1 foot.

1.

Length (ft)	10	9	8	7	6	5	4	3	2	1
Width (ft)	2	3	4	5	6	7	8	9	10	11
Perimeter (ft)	24	24	24	24	24	24	24	24	24	24
Area (ft²)	20	27	32	35	36	35	32	27	20	11

2. How would you describe the rectangular region that will provide the largest seating area for the judges? square

The stage area for the talent show will be 48 square yards. The table below lists the lengths of some rectangles with areas of 48 yd². Complete the table.

3.

Length (yd)	48	24	16	12	8	6	4	3	2	1
Width (yd)	1	2	3	4	6	8	12	16	24	48
Perimeter (yd)	98	52	38	32	28	28	32	38	52	98
Area (yd²)	48	48	48	48	48	48	48	48	48	48

4. What is the length and width of the rectangular region that will take the least amount of tape to mark off?

a. length 6 yd or 8 yd b. width 8 yd or 6 yd

Practice

5. $0.01 ∗ 10 = $0.10
6. $0.40 ∗ 10 = $4.00
7. $48.50 ∗ 10 = $485.00
8. $205.00 ∗ 10 = $2,050.00

Math Masters, p. 31

To further verify that this square has the largest area, have students explore other rectangles whose sides are close to 5.5 feet. Encourage students to use their calculators. For example, a 5.4 ft × 5.6 ft rectangle has a perimeter of 22 ft and an area of 30.24 ft^2. A 5.45 ft × 5.55 ft rectangle has an area of 30.2475 ft^2.

Have students make dots on their individual graphs for the 5.5 ft × 5.5 ft square and then draw a curved line through all the dots. Discuss further. Include the following questions in your discussion:

- Look at the completed table. Can you use a shortcut to find the perimeter of a rectangle? Add one length and one width and multiply the result by 2. How would you use a formula to express this shortcut? $P = (l + w) * 2$
- What is the length of a rectangle whose width is 0.5 ft and whose perimeter is 22 ft? 10.5 ft; The sum of the length and width equals half the perimeter (11 ft). If the width is 0.5 ft, the length is 10.5 ft.
- What is the area of this rectangle? 5.25 ft^2; 0.5 ft ∗ 10.5 ft = 5.25 ft^2

$\frac{1}{2}$ ft

$10\frac{1}{2}$ ft

length = 10.5 ft, width = 0.5 ft
length = 0.5 ft, width = 10.5 ft
perimeter = 22 ft, area = 5.25 ft^2

- How would you add information for this 0.5 ft × 10.5 ft rectangle to your graph? Plot a point to represent length = 10.5 ft and area = 5.25 ft^2. Plot another point to represent length = 0.5 ft and area 5.25 ft^2. Extend the graph to include these points.

2 Ongoing Learning & Practice

▶ Playing *Landmark Shark*

SMALL-GROUP ACTIVITY

(*Math Masters,* pp. 456 and 457; *Student Reference Book,* pp. 325 and 326)

Students play *Landmark Shark*. Suggest the following variations:

▷ After exchanging up to three cards in their hand, players have the option of changing the landmarks on which the hand will be scored.

▷ Only the player with the highest score in his or her hand wins points for the hand. All players receive bonus points by calculating the means of the cards in their hand.

Ongoing Assessment: Recognizing Student Achievement

Exit Slip

Use an **Exit Slip** (*Math Masters,* p. 404) to assess students' understanding of how data landmarks change as data values change. Students list the cards in one hand of *Landmark Shark* and indicate what their score would be if they chose (1) the range, (2) the median, (3) the mode, and (4) the mean of the hand. Students list any cards they would exchange and why. Students are making adequate progress if they correctly calculate their scores for the landmarks. Some students may indicate that they can improve their scores by paying attention to the mean when deciding whether or not to exchange cards.

[Data and Chance Goal 2]

▶ Math Boxes 1•10

INDEPENDENT ACTIVITY

(*Math Journal 1,* p. 33)

Mixed Practice Math Boxes in this lesson are paired with Math Boxes in Lesson 1-12. The skills in Problems 2 and 3 preview Unit 2 content.

▶ Study Link 1•10

INDEPENDENT ACTIVITY

(*Math Masters,* p. 31 and 407)

Home Connection Students solve problems involving the relationship between perimeter and area.

3 Differentiation Options

READINESS

▶ Grid-Paper Perimeters

PARTNER ACTIVITY

15–30 Min

(*Math Masters,* pp. 32, 33, and 408)

To provide experience with perimeters, have students draw rectangles with perimeters of 12, 14, and 16 units and record the side lengths for each rectangle, as well as a number sentence for each perimeter. Help students find a systematic way to determine perimeters.

Teaching Master

Name Date Time

LESSON 1•10 **Grid-Paper Perimeters**

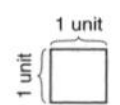

Work with a partner. Use page 408 for Problems 1 and 2.

Suppose one side of a centimeter square on the grid paper is 1 unit.

1 unit
1 unit

1. Use the lengths of the sides that appear in the first row of the table to draw a rectangle with a perimeter of 12 units.
2. Now make two different rectangles that also have perimeters of 12 units. Record the lengths of the sides for these rectangles. (*Remember:* A square is also a rectangle.)
3. Write a number sentence for the perimeter of the rectangle. For example, two possible number sentences for the first rectangle are 1 + 1 + 5 + 5 = 12 OR 2 ∗ (1 + 5) = 12.
4. Complete the table.

Perimeter	Shorter Side	Longer Side	Number Sentence
12 units	1 unit	5 units	1 + 5 + 1 + 5 = 12 OR 2 ∗ (1 + 5) = 12
12 units	2 units	4 units	2 + 4 + 2 + 4 = 12 OR 2 ∗ (2 + 4) = 12
12 units	3 units	3 units	3 + 3 + 3 + 3 = 12 OR 2 ∗ (3 + 3) = 12
14 units	1 units	6 units	1 + 6 + 1 + 6 = 14 OR 2 ∗ (1 + 6) = 14
14 units	2 units	5 units	2 + 5 + 2 + 5 = 14 OR 2 ∗ (2 + 5) = 14
14 units	3 units	4 units	3 + 4 + 3 + 4 = 14 OR 2 ∗ (3 + 4) = 14
16 units	1 units	7 units	1 + 7 + 1 + 7 = 16 OR 2 ∗ (1 + 7) = 16
16 units	2 units	6 units	2 + 6 + 2 + 6 = 16 OR 2 ∗ (2 + 6) = 16
16 units	3 units	5 units	3 + 5 + 3 + 5 = 16 OR 2 ∗ (3 + 5) = 16
16 units	4 units	4 units	4 + 4 + 4 + 4 = 16 OR 2 ∗ (4 + 4) = 16

Use your completed table to complete Problems 5 and 6 on page 33.

Math Masters, p. 32

Teaching Master

Name Date Time

LESSON 1•10 **Grid-Paper Perimeters** *continued*

5. Look for a pattern or rule in the results of your table. Then apply this rule to find the lengths of the sides of a rectangle with a perimeter of 20 units without using your grid paper. Record the lengths of the shorter and longer sides of this rectangle and a number sentence for its perimeter. Answers vary.

   shorter side ____ units longer side ____ units

   number sentence ____________________

6. What are the side lengths of the rectangle in your table that has the largest area?
   (*A* = shorter side ∗ longer side)

   shorter side 4 units longer side 4 units

Try This

7. Find the lengths of sides *x* and *y*. Then find the perimeter and area of the polygon.
   a. x = 9 cm
   b. y = 10 cm
   c. perimeter = 68 cm
   d. area = 198 cm^2

8 cm
16 cm
x
y
7 cm
18 cm

Math Masters, p. 33

ENRICHMENT

▶ Solving a Paint Problem

Students may record their answers to the following question on a separate sheet of paper.

Which requires more paint—a rectangular ceiling 30 feet by 40 feet, or a highway median strip 3 inches wide by 1 mile long?

The amount of paint used depends on the area of the surface, the type of surface, and the kind of paint. (A gallon of paint typically covers about 400 square ft.) Assume that the paints used for the median strip and the ceiling cover the same area per gallon.

The area of the ceiling is 30 ft $*$ 40 ft $=$ 1,200 ft^2. Think of the median strip as a long, thin rectangle with an area of 0.25 ft $*$ 5,280 ft $=$ 1,320 ft^2 (3 in. $= \frac{1}{4}$ ft $=$ 0.25 ft). The median strip has the larger area, so it needs more paint.

ELL SUPPORT

▶ Building a Math Word Bank

Explain that *area* is a word that has both everyday and mathematical meanings. It is used to measure the space inside a shape. As students discuss key ideas related to *area,* list them on the board. Using the Word Bank template in the *Differentiation Handbook,* have students write the words *area, perimeter, inch, feet,* and *square feet.* Because customary units may be unfamiliar to students new to the United States, clarify that the word *feet* in this context involves units of measure, not body parts.

Ask students to draw pictures representing the words *area* and *perimeter.* For the units *inch, feet,* and *square feet,* ask students to write the abbreviation for each unit and then draw pictures of objects that represent each one. See the *Differentiation Handbook* for more information.

Persuasive Data and Graphs

Objective To analyze data displays and explain ways in which data can be presented to misrepresent or mislead.

1 Teaching the Lesson

Key Activities

Students discuss how statistics can be presented in specific ways meant to astound the reader. They analyze a pictograph that displays incorrect and misleading information and compare broken-line graphs to decide which one is most persuasive.

Key Concepts and Skills

- Apply place-value concepts to read and round large numbers. [Number and Numeration Goal 1]
- Use a calculator to compute products and quotients of whole numbers. [Operations and Computation Goal 2]
- Interpret a pictograph and broken-line graph. [Data and Chance Goal 1]
- Analyze examples of inaccurate or misleading displays of data. [Data and Chance Goal 2]

Ongoing Assessment: Informing Instruction See page 74.

Ongoing Assessment: Recognizing Student Achievement Use journal page 38. [Data and Chance Goal 2]

materials

- ☐ *Math Journal 1,* pp. 36–38
- ☐ Study Link 1•10
- ☐ calculator

2 Ongoing Learning & Practice

Students preview Unit 2 skills of reading, writing, and comparing decimal numbers through thousandths by playing the decimal version of *High-Number Toss.*

Students practice and maintain skills through Math Boxes and Study Link activities.

materials

- ☐ *Math Journal 1,* p. 39
- ☐ *Student Reference Book,* p. 324
- ☐ Study Link Master (*Math Masters,* p. 34)
- ☐ Game Master (*Math Masters,* p. 455)
- ☐ 4 each of the number cards 0–9 per partnership
- ☐ calculator

3 Differentiation Options

ENRICHMENT

Students create persuasive graphs to make a point or advance a cause.

EXTRA PRACTICE

Students practice rounding numbers and estimating products.

materials

- ☐ Teaching Master (*Math Masters,* p. 35)
- ☐ *5-Minute Math,* pp. 18 and 95

Technology

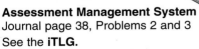

Assessment Management System
Journal page 38, Problems 2 and 3
See the **iTLG.**

Getting Started

Mental Math and Reflexes

Students write dictated numbers and then round them to a specified place.
Suggestions:

●○○ Write 95,938. Then round to the nearest thousand. 96,000

●●○ Write 584,378. Then round to the nearest ten thousand. 580,000

Write 7,806,215. Then round to the nearest million. 8,000,000

●●● Write 2,533,000,000. Then round to the nearest ten million. 2,530,000,000

Math Message

Estimate the following figures before looking at journal page 36. Answers vary.

- *the number of people living in the United States*
- *the number of pizzas the average person eats in one year*
- *the number of times each day that the average person drives his or her car*

Study Link 1·10 Follow-Up

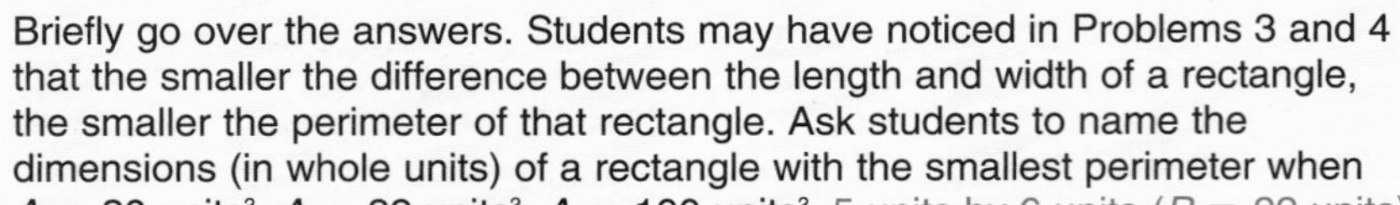

Briefly go over the answers. Students may have noticed in Problems 3 and 4 that the smaller the difference between the length and width of a rectangle, the smaller the perimeter of that rectangle. Ask students to name the dimensions (in whole units) of a rectangle with the smallest perimeter when $A = 30$ units^2; $A = 32$ units^2; $A = 100$ units^2. 5 units by 6 units ($P = 22$ units); 5 units by 8 units ($P = 26$); 10 units by 10 units ($P = 40$ units)

Links to the Future

Expect that some students will recognize the bar over the decimal number (*Math Journal,* p. 36) as a notation for a repeating decimal. Rational numbers are discussed in Unit 6. Although identification of numbers as rational or irrational is not a Grade 6 Goal, working with these numbers provides students a foundation for seventh- and eighth-grade Number and Numeration concepts.

Student Page

Date Time

LESSON 1·11 **Statistics Meant to Astound the Reader**

Americans Consume 90 Acres of Pizza per Day!
Each day we eat the equivalent of 90 football fields covered with pizza!
The National Association of Pizza Operators reported today that

Ninety acres may seem like a tremendous amount of pizza. The person who wrote this headline wants us to think so. However, let's look at this statistic more closely.

There are 43,560 square feet in an acre, so 90 acres is about 3,900,000 square feet of pizza.	90 * 43,560 = 3,920,400 Round to 3,900,000
If Americans eat 3,900,000 square feet of pizza each day for 365 days, that is about 1,420,000,000 square feet of pizza per year.	3,900,000 * 365 = 1,423,500,000 Round to 1,420,000,000
If 1,420,000,000 square feet of pizza is divided by **about** 270,000,000 people in the United States, then each person, on average, eats about 5 square feet of pizza per year.	1,420,000,000 / 270,000,000 = $5.\overline{259}$ Round to 5.

Suppose an average pizza is about 1 square foot in area. Then each person in the United States eats approximately 5 pizzas per year.

Here is a new headline based on the information above.

An Average American Eats 5 Pizzas per Year!
The National Association of Pizza Operators reported today that

1. Study the headline below.

An Average American Takes about 50,000 Automobile Trips in a Lifetime!

Write a new headline that gives the same information but will not astound the reader.
Sample answer: An Average American Takes 2 Car Trips per Day!

***Math Journal 1*, p. 36**

1 Teaching the Lesson

▶ Math Message Follow-Up

WHOLE-CLASS ACTIVITY

(*Math Journal 1,* p. 36)

The headline "Americans Consume 90 Acres of Pizza per Day!" is meant to convince the reader that Americans eat great quantities of pizza. Since some readers may not be able to visualize the size of an acre, the subhead is rephrased in terms of a football field (which has a surface area of about 1 acre) to ensure that all readers get the point.

Working as a class, read through the analysis of the headline on journal page 36. To support English language learners, write *acre* on the board and discuss its meaning.

1. Acres are converted to square feet. The headline can be converted to "Americans Consume 3,900,000 Square Feet of Pizza per Day!"
2. This quantity is multiplied by 365 to get a yearly consumption figure. The headline can be converted to "Americans Consume 1,420,000,000 Square Feet of Pizza per Year!"
3. This quantity is divided by the number of people in the United States. (about 270,000,000) to get yearly consumption per person. The headline can be converted to "Each American Consumes about 5 Square Feet of Pizza per Year!"
4. Square feet are converted to a number of pizzas, assuming that each pizza is about 1 square foot in area. The headline can finally be converted to "Each Person Eats about 5 Pizzas per Year!"

This final headline doesn't have the same effect as the original. Both provide the same information, but the way in which information is presented can make a big difference in how readers react.

Assign Problem 1 on the journal page. Have students work with partners or in groups for about 5 minutes. Allow them to use calculators. Regroup to discuss solution strategies and revised headlines. *Possible strategies:*

- ▷ Assume an average lifetime of about 70 years. Divide total lifetime trips by 70 to estimate the number of trips per year: 50,000 / 70 is about 714. Divide again by 365 to estimate the number of trips per day: 714 / 365 is about 1.96, or about 2 trips per day.
- ▷ Multiply 70 by 365 to find the number of days in a typical lifetime: $70 * 365 = 25{,}550$. Round to 25,000 days. Observe that 50,000 total trips in 25,000 days works out to be an average of 2 trips per day.

▶ Analyzing a Persuasive Pictograph

PARTNER ACTIVITY

(*Math Journal 1,* p. 37)

Graphs can present information in misleading ways. Some graphs are deliberately designed to support a point of view or a course of action. Many times, incorrect graphs are not intended to be misleading. Nevertheless, the reader should always be on the lookout. Discuss the meanings of *persuasive* and *misleading*. Be sure that students understand what a pictograph is.

The pictograph on journal page 37 is a good example of a graph that is both mathematically incorrect and misleading. Have students work in pairs to analyze the pictograph and find its errors. Circulate and assist as needed.

Health Link Follow up with a discussion:

- ▷ The large figure in the graph represents the number of deaths from cardiovascular disease. The smaller figures that stand one on top of another represent the number of deaths from other leading causes. To support English language learners, discuss the meanings of the words describing various causes of death, such as *cardiovascular disease* and *pneumonia.*
- ▷ Deaths from cancer (about half a million) are a little more than half the number of deaths resulting from cardiovascular disease (a little less than 1 million). The figure representing deaths from cancer should be a little more than half as tall as the large figure. The figure representing cancer deaths is much too small.
- ▷ Similarly, the figures representing deaths from other causes are much too large in relation to the figure representing deaths from cancer.

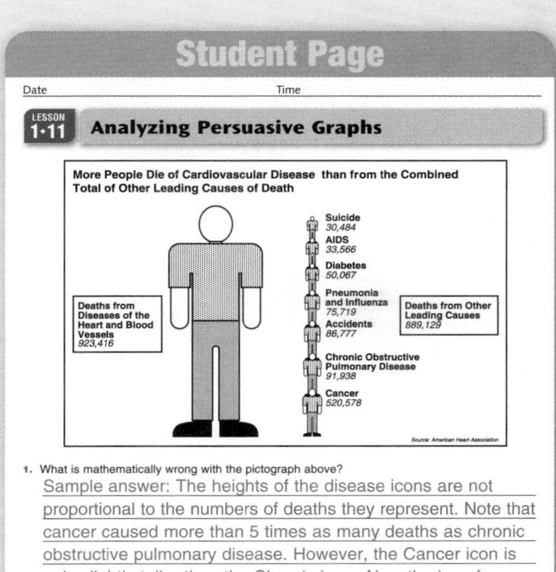

Student Page

Date Time

LESSON 1·11 **Analyzing Persuasive Graphs**

1. What is mathematically wrong with the pictograph above?
Sample answer: The heights of the disease icons are not proportional to the numbers of deaths they represent. Note that cancer caused more than 5 times as many deaths as chronic obstructive pulmonary disease. However, the Cancer icon is only slightly taller than the Chronic icon. Also, the icon for cardiovascular disease gives the impression that deaths caused by this disease total many times more than deaths caused by all other diseases and circumstances combined; actually, the total number of deaths caused by cardiovascular disease is only a little greater than the total number of deaths caused by all the other conditions and circumstances combined.

Math Journal 1, p. 37

Student Page

Date ______ Time ______

LESSON 1·11 Analyzing Persuasive Graphs *continued*

You are trying to convince your parents that you deserve an increase in your weekly allowance. You claim that over the past 10 weeks, you have spent more time doing jobs around the house, such as emptying the trash, mowing the lawn, and cleaning up after dinner. You have decided to present this information to your parents in the form of a graph. You have made two versions of the graph and need to decide which one to use.

Time Spent Doing Chores

Hours: 0, 1, 2, 3, 4, 5, 6, 7
Week: 1, 2, 3, 4, 5, 6, 7, 8, 9, 10

Graph A

Time Spent Doing Chores

Hours: 3:00, 3:05, 3:10, 3:15, 3:20, 3:25, 3:30, 3:35, 3:40, 3:45, 3:50, 3:55, 4:00
Week: 1, 2, 3, 4, 5, 6, 7, 8, 9, 10

Graph B

Sample answers:

2. How are Graph A and Graph B similar?
   Both graphs display the same basic information.
3. How are Graph A and Graph B different?
   The scales for the vertical axes are different.
4. Which graph, A or B, do you think will help you more as you try to convince your parents that you deserve a raise in your allowance? Why?
   Sample answer: Graph B will be more convincing because it is a more dramatic representation of the data.

Math Journal 1, p. 38

Student Page

Date ______ Time ______

LESSON 1·11 Math Boxes

1. From 1860 to 1861, 11 states seceded from the Union. All of them were reinstated between 1866 and 1870. Four new states joined the Union between 1860 and 1866. The table at the left shows the number of states in the United States from 1859 to 1870. Make a step graph to display this information.

Years	Number of States
1859	33
1860	32
1861–1862	23
1863	24
1864–1865	25
1866	26
1867	27
1868–1869	34
1870	37

Number of States: 20, 25, 30, 35, 40
Year: 1860, 1865, 1870

2. Use the circle graphs to answer the following questions.
   a. About what percent of the content of bread is water? 33%
   b. About what percent of the content of a ripe tomato is water? 95%

Percent of Water in Foods

water — Bread; water — Pineapple; water — Ripe Tomato

Source: Astounding Averages

SRB 145

3. Juan's mean score on three tests was 86. Two of his scores were 92 and 82. What was his third score? Circle the best answer.
   A. 76 B. 78 C. 80 (D. 84)

   SRB 137

4. Write the value of the digit 3 in each numeral below.
   8.43 hundredths
   24.35 tenths
   149.073 thousandths

   SRB 28

Math Journal 1, p. 39

The pictograph on the journal page actually appeared in a newspaper. Take this opportunity to reinforce the fact that readers should not automatically accept everything that appears in print as true. Encourage students to analyze and question representations of data, even if they appear to be authentic.

Ongoing Assessment: Informing Instruction

Watch for students who have difficulty recognizing the discrepancies in the heights of the figures shown in the pictograph. Some students may also not see that the areas of the figures are inaccurate. The area of the large figure representing cardiovascular disease deaths is more than 20 times the area of the figure representing cancer deaths. The graph gives the visual impression that the number of deaths from cardiovascular disease is far greater than the number of deaths from cancer.

▶ Selecting a Persuasive Broken-Line Graph

(*Math Journal 1,* p. 38)

Circulate and assist while students complete journal page 38. Discuss their responses. To support English language learners, discuss the meaning of the word *allowance.* Stress that both graphs on the journal page are correct, but the presentation of the data makes a significant difference.

Ongoing Assessment: Recognizing Student Achievement

Journal page 38 Problems 2 and 3 ★

Use **journal page 38, Problems 2 and 3** to assess students' ability to read and interpret a broken-line graph. Students are making adequate progress if they indicate that the graphs display the same basic information. Some students may be able to articulate that because the increments along the vertical axis of Graph B are smaller, the graph appears to rise faster.

[Data and Chance Goal 2]

2 Ongoing Learning & Practice

▶ Playing *High-Number Toss* (Decimal Version)

(*Student Reference Book,* p. 324; *Math Masters,* p. 455)

Students play the decimal version of *High-Number Toss* to preview Unit 2 skills of reading, writing, and comparing decimal numbers through thousandths.

▶ Math Boxes 1•11

INDEPENDENT ACTIVITY

(*Math Journal 1,* p. 39)

Mixed Practice Math Boxes in this lesson are paired with Math Boxes in Lesson 1-9. The skills in Problem 4 preview Unit 2 content.

▶ Study Link 1•11

INDEPENDENT ACTIVITY

(*Math Masters,* p. 34)

Home Connection Students analyze how data can be presented in such a way as to be misleading.

3 Differentiation Options

ENRICHMENT

INDEPENDENT ACTIVITY

▶ Creating Persuasive Graphs

15–30 Min

(*Math Masters,* p. 35)

Students create graphs that represent a given situation in the most favorable light without presenting false information. Provide time for students to share the graphs they created.

EXTRA PRACTICE

SMALL-GROUP ACTIVITY

▶ *5-Minute Math*

15–30 Min

To offer more practice with rounding numbers and estimating products, see *5-Minute Math,* pages 18 and 95.

Study Link Master

Name Date Time

STUDY LINK 1•11 **The Population of River City**

The way a graph is constructed affects how fairly the data are represented.

The mayor of River City is trying to convince the city council that the city needs more schools. She claims that the city's population has doubled since 1998. The mayor used the graph below to support her claim.

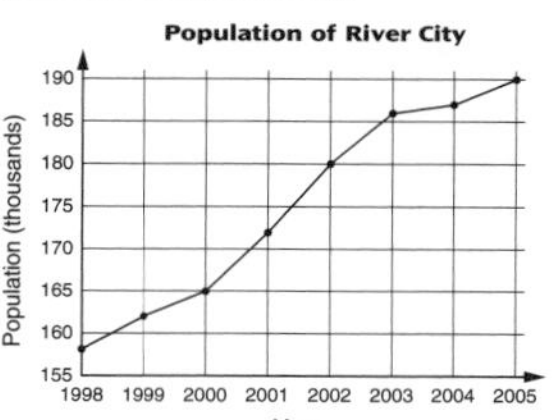

1. According to the graph, what was the population in 2000? 165,000
2. Between which 2 years was the increase in population the least? 2003 and 2004
3. Is the mayor's claim misleading? Explain. Sample answer: Yes. The population in 2005 would have to be 310,000 for the claim to be true.

Practice

4. $0.05 * 100 = $5.00
5. $0.90 * 100 = $90.00
6. $139.25 * 100 = $13,925.00
7. $0.89 * 100 = $8.90

Math Masters, p. 34

Teaching Master

Name Date Time

LESSON 1•11 **Persuasive Graphs**

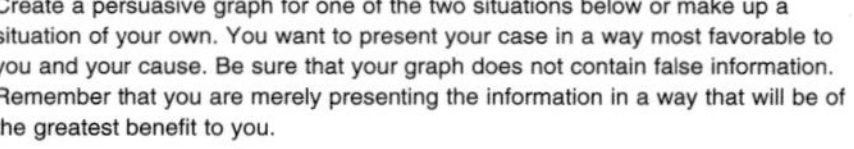

Create a persuasive graph for one of the two situations below or make up a situation of your own. You want to present your case in a way most favorable to you and your cause. Be sure that your graph does not contain false information. Remember that you are merely presenting the information in a way that will be of the greatest benefit to you.

- You have been in charge of sales at the school store this year. Each month profits have increased—from $10 in September to $18 in June. You would like to have the same job again next year and want to show your principal why you are the best candidate for the position.
- For health reasons, you have been encouraging your uncle to lose weight. Over the past 8 weeks, he has gone from 300 pounds to 291 pounds. You are proud of your uncle and want to show him how much progress he has made.

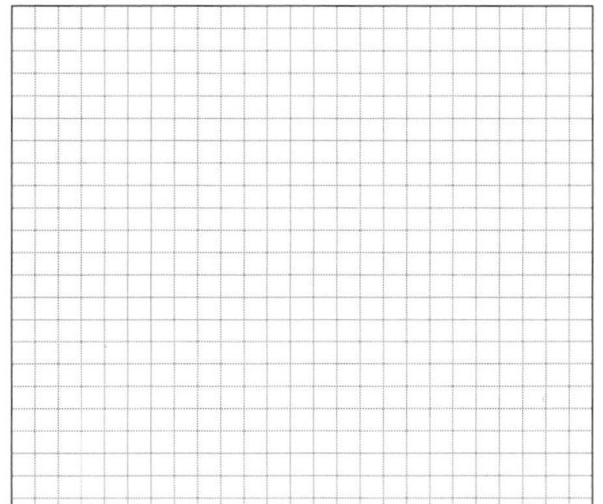

Math Masters, p. 35

1•12 Samples and Surveys

Objectives To determine whether a sample is random or biased; and to compare and analyze recall surveys.

1 Teaching the Lesson

Key Activities

Students identify samples as random or biased. They are introduced to a recall survey and analyze the responses and displays of the data gathered by such a survey.

Key Concepts and Skills

- Analyze, compare, and interpret side-by-side bar graphs. [Data and Chance Goal 1]
- Extract numerical data from text. [Data and Chance Goal 2]
- Examine the relationship between a sample and the population it represents. [Data and Chance Goal 3]

Key Vocabulary

sample • random sample • biased sample • recall survey

Ongoing Assessment: Recognizing Student Achievement Use journal page 41. [Data and Chance Goal 1]

materials

- ☐ *Math Journal 1,* pp. 40 and 41
- ☐ Study Link 1•11

2 Ongoing Learning & Practice

Students practice interpreting circle graphs. They also determine the median and mean of a data set and then decide which landmark best represents the data.

Students practice and maintain skills through Math Boxes and Study Link activities.

materials

- ☐ *Math Journal 1,* pp. 42 and 43
- ☐ Study Link Master (*Math Masters,* p. 36)

3 Differentiation Options

ENRICHMENT

Students survey their classmates, analyze the collected data, and then present their conclusions to the class.

ENRICHMENT

Students read about the opinion polls related to a presidential election.

EXTRA PRACTICE

Students practice estimating and calculating equivalent measures of capacity.

materials

- ☐ *Math Journal 1,* p. 41
- ☐ *5-Minute Math,* pp. 48, 132 and 214
- ☐ computer/graphing software

Technology

Assessment Management System
Journal page 41, Problems 1–3
See the **iTLG.**

Getting Started

Mental Math and Reflexes

Students make ballpark estimates for products. Volunteers share strategies if time permits.

Suggestions:

●○○ 26 ∗ 33 900 (30 ∗ 30) or 750 (25 ∗ 30)

●●○ 59 ∗ 94 5,400 (60 ∗ 90) or 6,000 (60 ∗ 100)

●●● 12 ∗ 224 2,400 (12 ∗ 200) or 2,250 (10 ∗ 225)

157 ∗ 319 45,000 (150 ∗ 300) or 60,000 (200 ∗ 300)

Math Message

Complete the Math Message on journal page 40 with a partner.

Study Link 1•11 Follow-Up

Briefly go over the answers.

1 Teaching the Lesson

▶ Math Message Follow-Up

WHOLE-CLASS ACTIVITY

(*Math Journal 1,* p. 40)

Have students share how they would find the percentage of cookie weight that is chocolate chips. Many students might suggest breaking up the cookies, removing the chocolate chips, and weighing the chips. Some students will need help taking the problem to the next step, which involves dividing the weight of the chips by the total weight of the cookies (20 ounces). Provide students with examples such as the following:

> If the weight of the chocolate chips in a 20-ounce bag of cookies is 13 ounces, then
>
> $$\frac{\text{weight of the chips}}{\text{weight of the sample}} = \frac{13}{20} = 0.65 * 100 = 65\%$$

Because a 20-ounce bag of cookies represents a part of all the chocolate chip cookies the manufacturer makes, the bag can be considered a **sample.** A sample is part of the population that is chosen to represent the whole population. In this case, the sample is the 20-ounce bag of cookies; the population is all the chocolate chip cookies the manufacturer makes.

Links to the Future

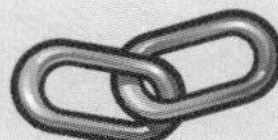

Converting between fractions, decimals, and percents is a Grade 5 Goal. Expect that students will recognize how to express a fraction as a percent (after some reminders). Students will review and apply fraction-decimal-percent equivalencies in Unit 4.

Student Page

Date ______ Time ______

LESSON 1•12 Samples and Surveys

Math Message

A cookie manufacturer that sells chocolate chip cookies uses the sales slogan "65% chips and 35% cookie." Suppose you have a 20-ounce bag of these cookies. Discuss with a partner how you could find what percent of the cookie weight is made up of chocolate chips.

Samples

SRB 132–133

A **random sample** is a sample that gives all members of the population the same chance of being selected. A **biased sample** is a sample that does not truly represent the total population. A sample is biased when the method used to collect the sample allows some members of the population to have a greater chance of being selected for the sample than others.

Random Sample	Biased Sample
Heights of boys in a sixth-grade class	Heights of boys on the basketball team
Math scores of sixth-grade students	Math scores of students in the math club
Batting average for an entire baseball team	Batting average for starting line-up of a baseball team
Door prize for 1 in every 10 people	Door prize for people who bought 5 or more tickets

For Problems 1–3, tell whether you think the sample is random or biased.

1. Every student whose home phone number ends in 5 was surveyed about plans for the new school library. Do you think this is a random or biased sample? Explain.
   random; All members have the same chance of being selected.

2. People living in Florida and California were surveyed to determine the percent of Americans who spend at least 1 week of the year at ocean beaches. Do you think this is a random or biased sample? Explain.
   biased; Only people living in two coastal states are represented.

3. The first 50 people standing in line for a football game were surveyed about how voters feel about a tax increase to build a new stadium. Do you think this is a random or biased sample?
   biased; Only people who attended this football game are represented.

Math Journal 1, p. 40

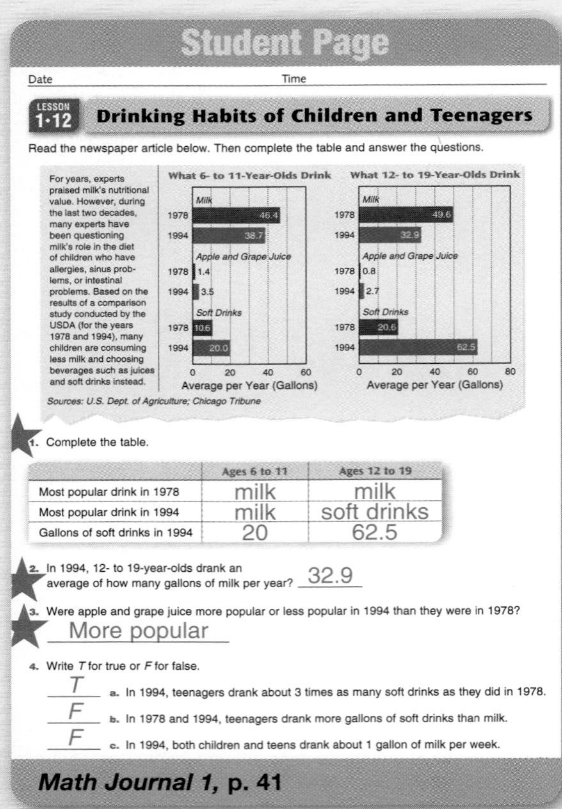

Student Page

Date Time

LESSON 1·12 Drinking Habits of Children and Teenagers

Read the newspaper article below. Then complete the table and answer the questions.

For years, experts praised milk's nutritional value. However, during the last two decades, many experts have been questioning milk's role in the diet of children who have allergies, sinus problems, or intestinal problems. Based on the results of a comparison study conducted by the USDA (for the years 1978 and 1994), many children are consuming less milk and choosing beverages such as juices and soft drinks instead.

What 6- to 11-Year-Olds Drink

	1978	1994
Milk	46.4	38.7
Apple and Grape Juice	1.4	3.5
Soft Drinks	10.6	20.0

Average per Year (Gallons)

What 12- to 19-Year-Olds Drink

	1978	1994
Milk	49.6	32.9
Apple and Grape Juice	0.8	2.7
Soft Drinks	20.6	62.5

Average per Year (Gallons)

Sources: U.S. Dept. of Agriculture; Chicago Tribune

1. Complete the table.

	Ages 6 to 11	Ages 12 to 19
Most popular drink in 1978	milk	milk
Most popular drink in 1994	milk	soft drinks
Gallons of soft drinks in 1994	20	62.5

2. In 1994, 12- to 19-year-olds drank an average of how many gallons of milk per year? 32.9
3. Were apple and grape juice more popular or less popular in 1994 than they were in 1978? More popular
4. Write *T* for true or *F* for false.
   T a. In 1994, teenagers drank about 3 times as many soft drinks as they did in 1978.
   F b. In 1978 and 1994, teenagers drank more gallons of soft drinks than milk.
   F c. In 1994, both children and teens drank about 1 gallon of milk per week.

***Math Journal 1*, p. 41**

Draw a Venn diagram to show the relationship between a sample and a population. Because the population is very large, it would be impractical to collect data about every chocolate chip cookie. Therefore, data are collected from a representative sample of the population. The data from the bag approximate the data from the entire population.

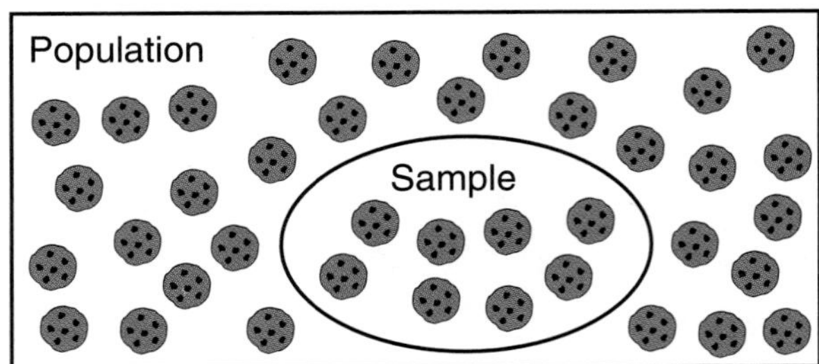

Determining Representative and Biased Samples

(*Math Journal 1,* p. 40)

A sample should always be examined to determine whether it is representative of the population. *Sample* is a word that has multiple meanings, including a mathematical meaning. To support English language learners, write *sample* on the board and discuss its meaning in this context. A representative sample can be provided by a random sample. A **random sample** gives all members of the population the same chance of being selected. The bag of cookies described in the Math Message is a random sample. It is assumed that the cookies in the bag were randomly selected. Cookies with few chips and those with many chips had an equal chance of being included.

A **biased sample** is a sample that does not truly represent the total population from which it was selected. A sample is biased if some members of the population have a greater chance of being selected than others. If the cookie manufacturer were to hand-select cookies for the sample, for example, it's likely that the manufacturer would select cookies with a generous amount of chips. To support English language learners, write *random sample* and *biased sample* on the board. Discuss the meanings and write some examples of each type of sample.

Circulate and assist as students work on journal page 40 to identify samples as random or biased. Discuss students' responses.

NOTE Biased samples are not always an attempt to mislead. In 1936, *Literary Digest* magazine dialed two million random telephone numbers, surveyed the people who answered, and used the results to predict that Franklin Roosevelt would lose the presidential election. In that year, however, many voters did not have phones. Therefore, telephone owners were not a representative sample of the voting population. Roosevelt won the election.

Analyzing a Newspaper Article

PARTNER ACTIVITY

(*Math Journal 1,* p. 41)

Surveys are often used to gather data from a sample of people. A **recall survey** is a survey used to collect information about past behaviors, habits, or activities. The individual pieces of information gathered in such a survey are usually not precise.

However, estimates based on combined survey data are often worthwhile. To support English language learners, write *recall survey* on the board. As you discuss examples of recall surveys, list them on the board.

The U.S. Department of Agriculture (USDA) conducts nationwide food consumption recall surveys. The data used in this activity are based on the USDA Continuing Survey of Food Intake by Individuals from 1977–1978 and 1994–1996. Data are collected by interviewing people who know a lot about the food that members of their households eat. A food list is used to help respondents recall kinds, quantities, and costs of foods used during the seven days prior to the interview.

To support English language learners, discuss the meaning of the words *consumption* and *preferences.* Have students read the newspaper article "What Kids Are Drinking" and answer the related questions.

Pose discussion questions such as the following:

- Why do you think side-by-side bar graphs were used in this article? They make it easy to see the changes in drinking habits between 1978 and 1994.
- Why are there separate data for children and teenagers? Their drinking habits are different.
- Why do you think there is a difference in data collected from 6- to 11-year-olds and from teenagers? Teenagers usually have more control over what they drink than young children.
- Why might milk consumption have decreased and juice and soft drink consumption have increased over the years? Sample answers: Soft drink and juice machines are in more places now. Juice is now available in juice boxes, which are convenient for lunches and snacks. Allergies and other medical problems are now associated with milk consumption.

Ongoing Assessment: Recognizing Student Achievement

Journal Page 41

Use **journal page 41, Problems 1–3** to assess students' ability to read and interpret a side-by-side bar graph. Students are making adequate progress if they are able to complete Problems 1–3. Some students may be able to apply estimation and computation strategies to solve Problem 4.

[Data and Chance Goal 1]

2 Ongoing Learning & Practice

▶ Interpreting Circle Graphs

INDEPENDENT ACTIVITY

(*Math Journal 1,* p. 42)

Students practice interpreting circle graphs. They also determine the median and mean of a data set and then decide which landmark best represents the data.

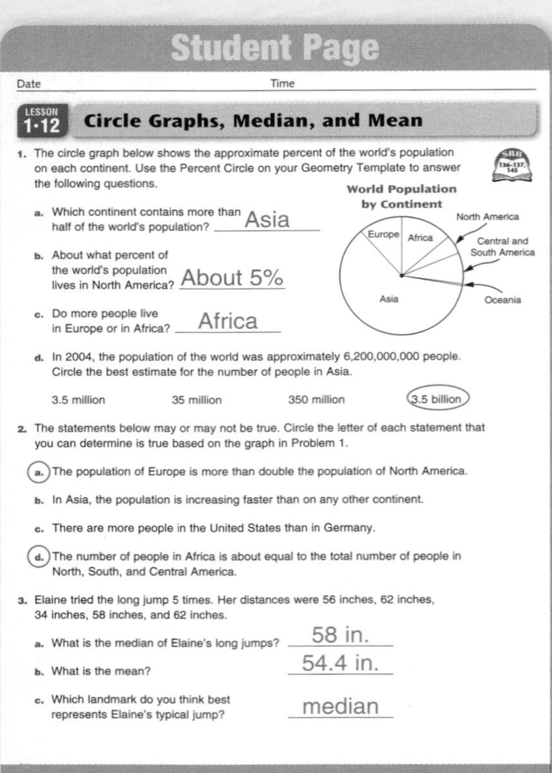

Student Page

Date Time

LESSON 1·12 **Circle Graphs, Median, and Mean**

1. The circle graph below shows the approximate percent of the world's population on each continent. Use the Percent Circle on your Geometry Template to answer the following questions.

a. Which continent contains more than half of the world's population? Asia

b. About what percent of the world's population lives in North America? About 5%

c. Do more people live in Europe or in Africa? Africa

d. In 2004, the population of the world was approximately 6,200,000,000 people. Circle the best estimate for the number of people in Asia.

3.5 million   35 million   350 million   (3.5 billion)

2. The statements below may or may not be true. Circle the letter of each statement that you can determine is true based on the graph in Problem 1.

(a.) The population of Europe is more than double the population of North America.

b. In Asia, the population is increasing faster than on any other continent.

c. There are more people in the United States than in Germany.

(d.) The number of people in Africa is about equal to the total number of people in North, South, and Central America.

3. Elaine tried the long jump 5 times. Her distances were 56 inches, 62 inches, 34 inches, 58 inches, and 62 inches.

a. What is the median of Elaine's long jumps? 58 in.

b. What is the mean? 54.4 in.

c. Which landmark do you think best represents Elaine's typical jump? median

Math Journal 1, p. 42

▶ Math Boxes 1·12

INDEPENDENT ACTIVITY

(*Math Journal 1,* p. 43)

Mixed Practice Math Boxes in this lesson are paired with Math Boxes in Lesson 1-10. The skills in Problems 2 and 3 preview Unit 2 content.

Student Page

Date Time

LESSON 1·12 **Math Boxes**

1. Use the bar graph to answer the questions below.

2004–05 Cost of Seats for the Chicago Bulls at the United Center

Seat Location: 100 Level (Rows 1–11, Rows 12–19); 200 Level (All Rows); 300 Level (Rows 1–7, Rows 8–12, Rows 13–17)

Ticket Price ($): 0 10 20 30 40 50 60 70 80 90 100

a. How much do the cheapest seats at the United Center cost? $26

b. What is the range of prices for seats? $69

c. What is the median price of a 300-level seat? $32

d. Mr. Harris wants to buy four 100-level seats. How much would he save if he bought the cheaper 100-level seats rather than the more expensive 100-level seats? $20

2. Divide. 15)405

405 ÷ 15 = 27

3. Which estimate is most reasonable for the product 10.7 * 4.6?

Choose the best answer.

- 0.5
- 5
- 50 (filled)
- 500

Math Journal 1, p. 43

▶ Study Link 1·12

INDEPENDENT ACTIVITY

(*Math Masters,* p. 36)

Home Connection Students interpret side-by-side bar graphs and distinguish between a random and biased sample.

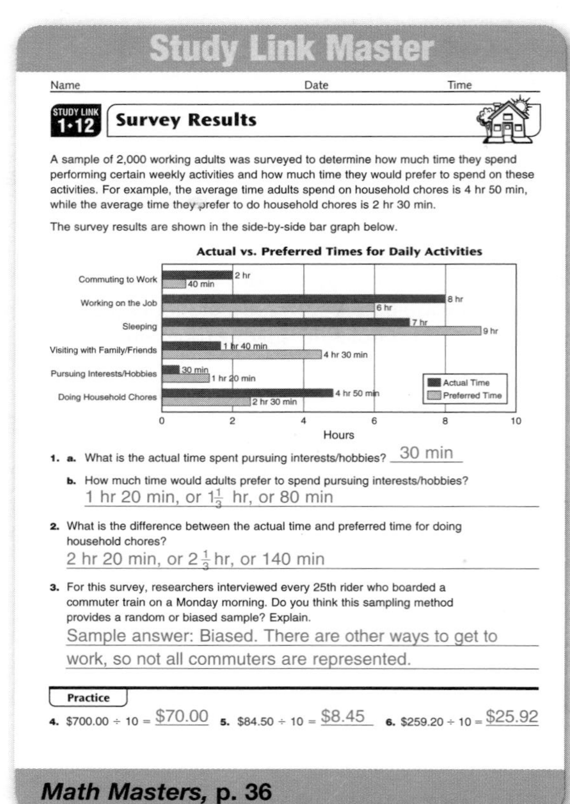

Study Link Master

Name Date Time

STUDY LINK 1·12 **Survey Results**

A sample of 2,000 working adults was surveyed to determine how much time they spend performing certain weekly activities and how much time they would prefer to spend on these activities. For example, the average time adults spend on household chores is 4 hr 50 min, while the average time they prefer to do household chores is 2 hr 30 min.

The survey results are shown in the side-by-side bar graph below.

1. a. What is the actual time spent pursuing interests/hobbies? 30 min

b. How much time would adults prefer to spend pursuing interests/hobbies? 1 hr 20 min, or $1\frac{1}{3}$ hr, or 80 min

2. What is the difference between the actual time and preferred time for doing household chores? 2 hr 20 min, or $2\frac{1}{3}$ hr, or 140 min

3. For this survey, researchers interviewed every 25th rider who boarded a commuter train on a Monday morning. Do you think this sampling method provides a random or biased sample? Explain.

Sample answer: Biased. There are other ways to get to work, so not all commuters are represented.

Practice

4. \$700.00 ÷ 10 = \$70.00 5. \$84.50 ÷ 10 = \$8.45 6. \$259.20 ÷ 10 = \$25.92

Math Masters, p. 36

3 Differentiation Options

ENRICHMENT

PARTNER ACTIVITY

▶ Collecting and Analyzing Data

5–15 Min

(*Math Journal 1,* p. 41)

To extend students' knowledge of representative samples and recall surveys, have them devise a survey about their classmates' drink preferences. Ask students to predict whether their results will be similar to those obtained by the USDA in 1994. Remind them to use the same drink choices and the same conversion factor to calculate the annual consumption of each choice. Encourage students to use computer software to construct any graphs.

ENRICHMENT

INDEPENDENT ACTIVITY

▶ Using Data—A Prediction from the Past

5–15 Min

History Link The 1948 U.S. presidential election is famous because the opinion polls predicted one candidate would win easily, when in fact that candidate lost.

Have students use reference materials to answer the following questions:

▷ Who were the two candidates? Harry S. Truman and Thomas Dewey

▷ Who won the election? Truman

▷ Why do you think the election results were different from what the opinion polls had predicted? The opinion polls used biased samples instead of random ones.

EXTRA PRACTICE

SMALL-GROUP ACTIVITY

▶ *5-Minute Math*

5–15 Min

To offer more practice with estimating and calculating capacity equivalents, see *5-Minute Math,* pages 48, 132, and 214.

Progress Check 1

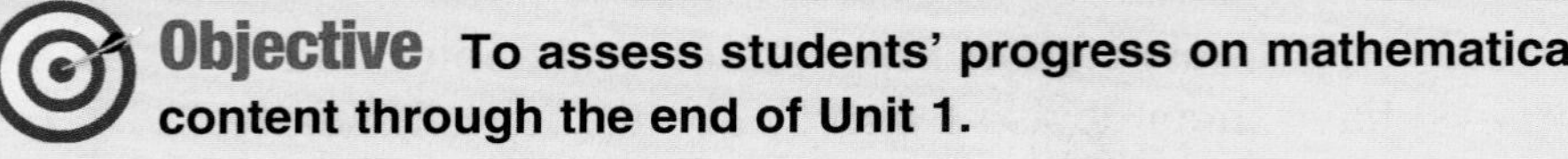

Objective To assess students' progress on mathematical content through the end of Unit 1.

1 Assessing Progress

Progress Check 1 is a cumulative assessment of concepts and skills taught in Unit 1.

See page 459 for a complete description of Grade 6 Goals.

materials

- ☐ Study Link 1•12
- ☐ Assessment Masters (*Assessment Handbook,* pp. 138–143)

CONTENT ASSESSED	LESSON(S)	ASSESSMENT ITEMS			
		SELF	ORAL/SLATE	WRITTEN	
				PART A	PART B
Read, write, and represent whole and decimal numbers. [Number and Numeration Goal 1]	1•3		5		
Create and use numerical expressions involving all four operations, parentheses, and order of operations to represent equivalent names for whole numbers. [Number and Numeration Goal 4]	1•8				10
Solve number stories involving addition and subtraction of whole numbers. [Operations and Computation Goal 1]	1•7			1–5	
Know multiplication and division facts. [Operations and Computation Goal 2]	1•4				9b, 12
Solve problems involving multiplication and division of whole and decimal numbers. [Operations and Computation Goal 2]	1•1, 1•11		3	3	9b
Create and interpret bar, line, and stem-and-leaf graphs for a set of data. [Data and Chance Goal 1]	1•2, 1•3, 1•6, 1•11	3–6		1a, 2a, 5–7	11
Find, compare, and use data landmarks to answer questions, draw conclusions, and make predictions. [Data and Chance Goal 2]	1•2, 1•4, 1•5	1, 2	1	1b, 2b, 3–5	
Estimate and measure circle graph sectors using the Percent Circle. [Measurement and Reference Frames Goal 1]	1•3, 1•9	7		8	
Use formulas to calculate perimeter and area. [Measurement and Reference Frames Goal 2]	1•10		2, 4		9

2 Building Background for Unit 2

Math Boxes 1•13 previews and practices skills for Unit 2.

The **Unit 2 Family Letter** introduces families to Unit 2 topics and terms.

materials

- ☐ *Math Journal 1,* p. 44
- ☐ Study Link Masters (*Math Masters,* pp. 37–40)

Additional Information

See *Assessment Handbook,* pages 52–59 for additional assessment information. For assessment checklists, see pages 226–229.

Technology

Assessment Management System
Written Assessment, Parts A and B
See the **iTLG.**

Getting Started

Math Message

*Complete the Self Assessment (*Assessment Handbook*, p. 138).*

Study Link 1·12 Follow-Up

Review answers. Discuss how students might change the sampling method described in Problem 3 to obtain a random sample.

1 Assessing Progress

▶ Math Message Follow-Up

INDEPENDENT ACTIVITY

(Self Assessment, *Assessment Handbook*, p. 138)

The Self Assessment offers students the opportunity to reflect upon their progress.

▶ Oral and Slate Assessments

WHOLE-CLASS ACTIVITY

Problems 1, 2, and 4 provid[illegible] used for grading purposes. I[illegible] information that can be use[illegible]

Oral Assessment

1. Baseball pitcher Nolan R[illegible] strikeouts—5,714. If you[illegible] strikeouts for major-leag[illegible] more accurate to use the [illegible] strikeouts? median Why? [illegible] outliers than the median [illegible]

2. Describe the difference be[illegible] of a rectangle. Perimeter i[illegible] 2-dimensional shape. Area[illegible] a closed boundary.

Slate Assessment

3. Convert 65 centimeters to meters; 1.9 meters to centimeters. 0.65 m; 190 cm

4. The length of a rectangle is 6 cm and the width is 9 cm. What is the perimeter of the rectangle? 30 cm What is the area of the rectangle? 54 cm^2

5. Write a number on the board. Ask students to round it to a specified place. *Suggestions:*

   ▷ Round 348,971 to the nearest ten thousand. 350,000

   ▷ Round 19.465 to the nearest tenth. 19.5

Assessment Master

Name ______ Date ______ Time ______

LESSON 1·13 Self Assessment — Progress Check 1

Think about each skill listed below. Assess your own progress by checking the most appropriate box.

Skills	I can do this on my own and explain how to do it.	I can do this on my own.	I can do this if I get help or look at an example.
1. Find the mean of a set of numbers.			
2. Find the median of a set of numbers.			
3. Make a line plot.			
4. Make a stem-and-leaf plot.			
5. Make a bar graph.			
6. Read a broken-line graph.			
7. Use the Percent Circle to measure sectors of a circle graph.			

Assessment Handbook, p. 138

Assessment Master

Name ______ Date ______ Time ______

LESSON 1·13 Written Assessment — Progress Check 1

Part A

1. Emperor penguins are the largest of all penguins. Some weights (in pounds) for these penguins are represented by the following data set.

   60, 59, 66, 64, 61, 64, 60, 59, 65, 64, 65, 60

   a. Construct a line plot to represent the penguin data.

   Weights of Emperor Penguins

59	60	61	62	63	64	65	66
X X	X X X	X			X X X	X X	X

   b. Use your line plot to find the following landmarks.

   maximum 66 minimum 59

   mode(s) 60, 64 range 7

2. The ages of some Nobel Peace Prize winners since 1990 appear in the following data set.

   56, 78, 62, 75, 61, 54, 47, 38, 46, 87, 65, 71, 72, 75, 57, 33, 46

   a. Construct a stem-and-leaf plot of the ages of prize winners.

   Ages of Nobel Peace Prize Winners since 1990

Stems (10s)	Leaves (1s)
3	3 8
4	6 6 7
5	4 6 7
6	1 2 5
7	1 2 5 5 8
8	7

   b. Use your stem-and-leaf plot to find the following landmarks.

   maximum 87

   minimum 33

   mode(s) 46, 75

   range 54

Assessment Handbook, p. 139

Name ______ Date ______ Time ______

LESSON 1·13 **Written Assessment** *continued*

3. The ages of the students in a Saturday art class are 14, 18, 43, 14, 15, 18, and 11.
   a. Find the median age and the mean age. median 15 mean 19
   b. Which landmark, the mean or median, is the better representation of the ages of students in the art class? Explain.
   median; The mean is greatly affected by the outlier 43, so the median (15) is the better representation of the age.

4. Suppose you are dealt the hand shown below in a game of *Landmark Shark*.
   Which landmark, the range, median, or mode, will show you the highest score for your hand? median

5. Study the double-line graph at the right. On average, what is the
   a. warmest month of the year? July
   b. coldest month of the year? January

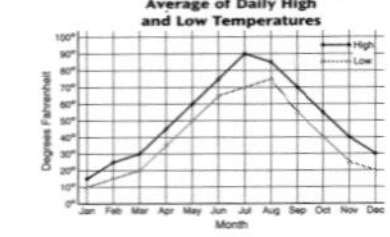

   c. Compare the average daily high and low temperatures in July. About how much warmer is the high temperature? About 20 degrees

6. Construct a bar graph to represent the data in the table below. Label each axis.

Friday Night Movie Ticket Sales	
Theater	Average Number of Tickets Sold
Theater A	2,250
Theater B	1,750
Theater C	1,500
Theater D	3,000

Assessment Handbook, p. 140

Assessment Master

Name ______ Date ______ Time ______

LESSON 1·13 **Written Assessment** *continued*

7. A small company produces video games. The marketing manager claims that sales fell 50% between the third and fourth quarters.
   a. According to the graph, what were the first quarter sales? $45,000
   b. Between which two quarters was the increase in sales the greatest? Between the 2nd and 3rd quarters
   c. Is the marketing manager's claim misleading? Explain.
   Yes. If sales had fallen 50%, the sales for the 4th quarter would be $32,500. If the scale of the vertical axis began at 0, the fall would not appear to be as dramatic.

End-of-Quarter Sales 2005

Dollar Amounts (thousands): 30, 35, 40, 45, 50, 55, 60, 65

Sales Quarter: 1, 2, 3, 4

8. Through a survey that used random sampling, 3,000 American adults were asked how much time they spend on various activities during an average day. The circle graph displays the results.
   Use your estimation skills and your Percent Circle to find the percent for the following activities.
   a. sleep: About 30%
   b. work: About 20%
   c. entertainment: About 18%
   d. other: About 18%

Assessment Handbook, p. 141

▶ Written Assessment

(*Assessment Handbook*, pp. 139–142)

Everyday Mathematics students are expected to master a variety of mathematical concepts and skills over time. The curriculum frequently revisits topics, concepts, and skills. For this reason, the written assessment includes items recently introduced as well as items that assess long-term retention and mastery.

The written assessment is only one part of a balanced assessment plan. Use it along with other assessment tools in the program. See the *Assessment Handbook* for additional information.

Part A Recognizing Student Achievement

The Recognizing Student Achievement, or *summative,* part of the written assessment is designed to help teachers assess students' progress toward Grade 6 Goals. The items in this section can be used for grading purposes since the curriculum to this point has provided multiple exposures to the content of the problems that appear in this part.

Problem(s)	Description
1–4	Analyze and compare data landmarks.
3–5	Use algorithms to add, subtract, multiply, and divide whole numbers.
5–8	Construct and interpret a graph.
8	Use the Percent Circle to measure sectors $\pm 2\%$.

Part B Informing Instruction

The Informing Instruction, or *formative,* part of the written assessment can help teachers make decisions about how best to approach concepts and skills the next time they appear. The items in this part of the written assessment are intended to inform future instruction.

Problem(s)	Description
9	Use algorithms to add and multiply numbers.
10	Represent equivalent names for numbers.
11	Interpret a step graph.
12	Apply multiplication and extended facts; estimate products of whole numbers.

▶ Open Response

INDEPENDENT ACTIVITY

(*Assessment Handbook,* p. 143)

Analyzing Jumping Jack Data

The open-response item requires students to apply skills and concepts from Unit 1 to solve a multistep problem. See *Assessment Handbook,* page 55–59 for rubrics and student work samples for this problem.

2 Building Background for Unit 2

▶ Math Boxes

INDEPENDENT ACTIVITY

(*Math Journal 1,* p. 44)

Mixed Practice This Math Boxes page previews Unit 2 content.

▶ Study Link 1•13: Unit 2 Family Letter

INDEPENDENT ACTIVITY

(*Math Masters,* pp. 37–40)

Home Connection The Unit 2 Family Letter provides parents and guardians with information and activities related to Unit 2 topics.

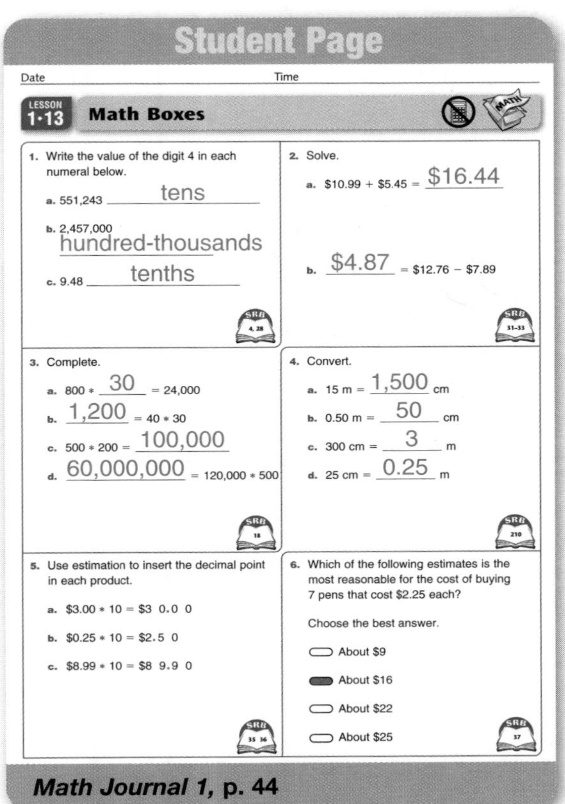

Student Page

Date Time

LESSON 1•13 **Math Boxes**

1. Write the value of the digit 4 in each numeral below.
   a. 551,243 tens
   b. 2,457,000 hundred-thousands
   c. 9.48 tenths

SRB 4, 28

2. Solve.
   a. $10.99 + $5.45 = $16.44
   b. $4.87 = $12.76 − $7.89

SRB 31–33

3. Complete.
   a. 800 ∗ 30 = 24,000
   b. 1,200 = 40 ∗ 30
   c. 500 ∗ 200 = 100,000
   d. 60,000,000 = 120,000 ∗ 500

SRB 18

4. Convert.
   a. 15 m = 1,500 cm
   b. 0.50 m = 50 cm
   c. 300 cm = 3 m
   d. 25 cm = 0.25 m

SRB 210

5. Use estimation to insert the decimal point in each product.
   a. $3.00 ∗ 10 = $3 0.0 0
   b. $0.25 ∗ 10 = $2.5 0
   c. $8.99 ∗ 10 = $8 9.9 0

SRB 35 36

6. Which of the following estimates is the most reasonable for the cost of buying 7 pens that cost $2.25 each?
   Choose the best answer.
   - ○ About $9
   - ● About $16
   - ○ About $22
   - ○ About $25

SRB 37

Math Journal 1, p. 44

Assessment Master

Name Date Time

LESSON 1•13 **Written Assessment** *continued*

Part B

9. The length of a rectangle is 6 cm and the width is 9 cm.
   a. Write a number sentence for the perimeter of the rectangle.
      Sample answers: 2 ∗ (6 + 9) or 6 + 6 + 9 + 9
   b. What is the area of the rectangle? Area = 54 cm²

10. Write four expressions for 25. Each must use a 7 and a 9. Sample answers:
    9 ∗ 2 + 7 7 + 9 + 9
    9 + (7 ∗ 2) + 2 (9 ∗ 5) − (7 ∗ 2) − 6

11. Use the step graph to answer the following questions.
    a. How much would it cost to rent a canoe for
       $1\frac{1}{2}$ hours? $15 3 hours? $20
       3 hours 5 minutes? $25
    b. Dimitri and his friends rent a canoe at 3:15 P.M. They don't want to pay more than $20. By what time do they need to return the canoe? 6:15 P.M.

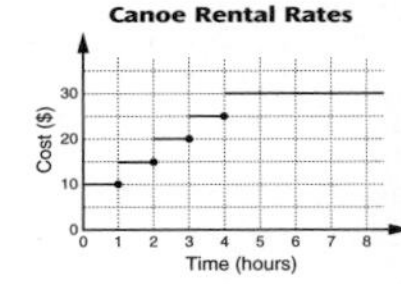

12. A pedestrian is a person who travels by walking. Consider the following statistic meant to astound the reader: "On average, a pedestrian is killed by a motor vehicle every 90 minutes. That is the equivalent of a plane crash in which 110 passengers are killed every week, year in and year out."
    a. About how many pedestrians are killed by motor vehicles each year?
       About 6,000; (24 ∗ 60) / 90 ∗ 7 ∗ 52 = 5,824
    b. The U.S. population is about 270 million people. About how many times as great is the estimated U.S. population than the number of pedestrians killed by motor vehicles each year?
       About 45,000 times

Assessment Handbook, p. 142

Planning Ahead

Review the calculator section of the *Student Reference Book* to familiarize yourself with the calculator students will use in Unit 2.

Assessment Master

Name Date Time

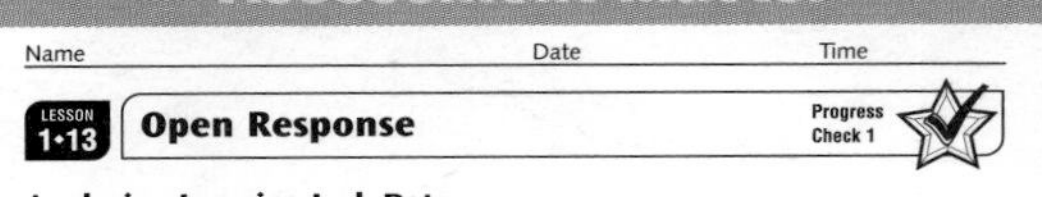

LESSON 1•13 **Open Response** Progress Check 1

Analyzing Jumping-Jack Data

Ms. Green's and Mr. Short's sixth-grade gym classes decided to hold a jumping-jack contest. Students did as many jumping jacks as they could in 1 minute. The results of the contest are shown below.

Ms. Green's Gym Class

Student #	Number of Jumping Jacks
1	87
2	101
3	62
4	102
5	85
6	114
7	89
8	89
9	149
10	67
11	100
12	73
13	90
14	82
15	79
16	81

Mr. Short's Gym Class

Student #	Number of Jumping Jacks
1	72
2	114
3	89
4	120
5	60
6	96
7	70
8	115
9	97
10	104
11	49
12	104
13	144
14	67
15	100
16	49

Ms. Green claims that her class was the best. Mr. Short claims that his class did better. With whom do you agree and why? Use data landmarks from both classes to support your reasoning. Show your work.

See the *Assessment Handbook* for sample answers and rubrics for this problem.

Assessment Handbook, p. 143

Unit 2 Organizer

Operations with Whole Numbers and Decimals

Overview

Unit 2 builds on students' conceptual understanding of place-value and whole-number operations to develop number sense and operational strategies for decimals. Unit 2 has five main areas of focus:

- To read, write, and interpret numbers written in standard, number-and-word, expanded, and scientific notations,
- To review adding and subtracting decimals,
- To develop power-of-ten strategies,
- To estimate products and quotients of decimal numbers, and
- To develop strategies for multiplying and dividing decimals.

Contents

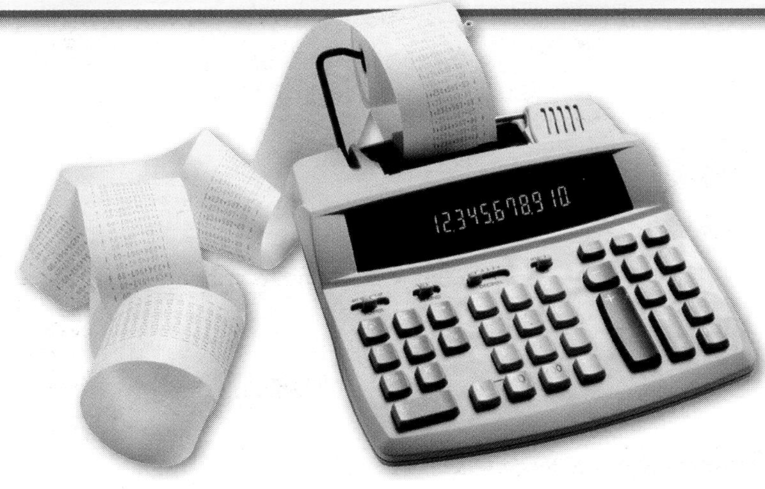

Unit 2 Organizer

Learning In Perspective

	Lesson Objectives	Links to the Past	Links to the Future
2•1	To read and write large numbers in standard, expanded, and number-and-word notations.	In Grade 5, students use standard, number-and-word, and expanded notations to represent and compare large numbers to billions.	In and after Grade 6, students develop a deeper understanding of very large and very small numbers and their various representations.
2•2	To read and write small numbers in standard and expanded notations.	In Grade 5, students review exponential notation and begin working with negative exponents.	In and after Grade 6, students develop a deeper understanding of very large and very small numbers and their various representations.
2•3	To add, subtract, and round decimal numbers.	In Grade 5, students extend addition and subtraction methods introduced in Grade 4 to decimal places beyond the hundredths.	Grade 6 and after: Applications and maintenance.
2•4	To develop and practice strategies for multiplying by powers of 10.	In Grade 5, students first use exponential notation to represent powers of 10 and round numbers to the nearest multiple of 10.	In Unit 4, students multiply by powers of 10 to convert between decimals and percents.
2•5	To develop an estimation strategy for multiplying decimals.	In Grade 5, students estimate the magnitude of products.	In and after Grade 6, students develop and use strategies to estimate the results of decimal-number computations and judge the reasonableness of the results.
2•6	To develop strategies for multiplying decimals.	In Grade 5, students extend the partial-products algorithm to decimals.	In Unit 9, students apply distributive strategies to multiply whole and decimal numbers. Grade 6 and after: Applications and maintenance.
2•7	To estimate quotients; and to use a paper-and-pencil division algorithm to divide whole numbers.	In Grade 5, students solve division problems with 1- and 2-digit divisors. They review and practice the partial-quotients algorithm and interpret remainders in context.	In and after Grade 6, students develop and use strategies to estimate the results of decimal-number computations and judge the reasonableness of the results.
2•8	To estimate and calculate quotients of whole-and decimal-number dividends; and to extend the partial-quotients division algorithm to include decimal-number quotients.	In Grade 5, students make magnitude estimates of quotients of whole and decimal numbers divided by 1- and 2-digit whole numbers.	In Units 6 and 8, students practice dividing by whole- and decimal-number divisors and finding quotients to a given number of decimal places.
2•9	To use scientific notation; and to convert between scientific and standard notations.	In Grade 5, students first use scientific notation to represent large numbers. They convert between scientific, standard, and number-and-word notations.	Grade 6 and after: Applications and maintenance. Students develop methods for finding products and quotients of numbers expressed in scientific notation.
2•10	To review and extend knowledge of exponential notation; and to use the power key on a calculator.	In Grade 5, students first use negative exponents to represent small numbers. They practice entering and interpreting exponential notation on a calculator.	In and after Grade 6, students select and apply appropriate methods and tools for computing with large and small numbers.
2•11	To use a calculator to convert between scientific and standard notations.	In Grade 5, students practice entering and interpreting decimal numbers and powers of 10 on a calculator.	In and after Grade 6, students select and apply appropriate methods and tools for computing with large and small numbers expressed in scientific notation.

Key Concepts and Skills

	Key Concepts and Skills	Grade 6 Goals*
2•1	Apply place-value concepts to read, write, and interpret large numbers.	Number and Numeration Goal 1
	Convert between standard and expanded notations.	Number and Numeration Goal 1
	Apply extended facts and order of operations to express the value of digits in a number.	Operations and Computation Goal 2
2•2	Apply place-value concepts to read, write, and interpret numbers less than 1.	Number and Numeration Goal 1
	Convert between standard and expanded notations.	Number and Numeration Goal 1
	Apply extended facts and order of operations to express the value of digits in a number.	Operations and Computation Goal 2
2•3	Apply place-value concepts to round decimals to a given place.	Number and Numeration Goal 1
	Adapt whole-number algorithms to add and subtract decimals.	Operations and Computation Goal 1
	Use extended multiplication and division facts to convert between metric units.	Operations and Computation Goal 2
	Estimate sums and differences of decimals.	Operations and Computation Goal 5
2•4	Apply place-value concepts to find values 10, 100, and 1,000 times as great.	Number and Numeration Goal 1
	Use a multiplication-by-power-of-10 strategy to convert between percents and decimals.	Number and Numeration Goal 5
	Estimate the product of a decimal and a power of 10.	Operations and Computation Goal 5
	Extend a pattern to develop a rule for multiplying by powers of 10.	Patterns, Functions, and Algebra Goal 1
2•5	Write equivalent names for numbers to calculate products and make estimates.	Number and Numeration Goal 4
	Apply multiplication facts and extended-fact strategies to multiply decimals.	Operations and Computation Goal 2
	Make reasonable estimates for products of decimal factors.	Operations and Computation Goal 5
2•6	Use place-value concepts to place the decimal point in products.	Number and Numeration Goal 1
	Multiply decimals using the lattice and traditional methods.	Operations and Computation Goal 2
	Make reasonable estimates for products of decimal factors.	Operations and Computation Goal 5
2•7	Find differences of partial quotients.	Operations and Computation Goal 1
	Use multiplication and extended facts to compute partial quotients.	Operations and Computation Goal 2
	Divide multidigit whole numbers.	Operations and Computation Goal 2
2•8	Apply place-value concepts to attach zeros to a dividend.	Number and Numeration Goal 1
	Find differences of partial quotients.	Operations and Computation Goal 1
	Use multiplication and extended facts to compute partial quotients.	Operations and Computation Goal 2
	Divide a decimal number by a whole number.	Operations and Computation Goal 2
	Use an estimate to place the decimal point in a quotient.	Operations and Computation Goal 5
2•9	Convert between scientific and standard notations.	Number and Numeration Goal 1
	Use extended facts to find products of very large and very small numbers.	Operations and Computation Goal 2
	Multiply a decimal number by a power of 10.	Operations and Computation Goal 2
2•10	Apply place-value concepts to convert between exponential and standard notations.	Number and Numeration Goal 1
	Interpret and evaluate numerical expressions involving exponents.	Number and Numeration Goal 4
	Use a calculator to find the product of repeated factors.	Operations and Computation Goal 2
2•11	Read and write numbers to trillions in standard and number-and-word notations.	Number and Numeration Goal 1
	Convert between scientific and standard notations with or without a calculator.	Number and Numeration Goal 1
	Use extended facts to find products of very large and very small numbers.	Operations and Computation Goal 2
	Multiply a decimal number by a power of 10.	Operations and Computation Goal 2

* For a detailed listing of all Grade 6 Goals, see the Appendix.

Ongoing Learning and Practice

Math Boxes

Math Boxes are paired across lessons as shown in the brackets below. This makes them useful as assessment tools. Math Boxes also preview content of the next unit.

Mixed practice	[2•1, 2•3], [2•2, 2•4], [2•5, 2•7], [2•6, 2•8, 2•10]
Mixed practice with multiple choice	2•1, 2•2, 2•5, 2•9, 2•10, 2•11
Mixed practice with writing/reasoning opportunity	2•1, 2•2, 2•5, 2•6, 2•9, 2•10

Practice through Games

Games are an essential component of practice in the *Everyday Mathematics* program. Games offer skills practice and promote strategic thinking.

Lesson	Game	Skill Practiced
2•1	*Number Top-It*	**Reading, writing, and comparing decimals** Numbers and Numeration Goal 1
2•2	*High-Number Toss* (Decimal Version)	**Reading, writing, and comparing decimals through thousandths** Numbers and Numeration Goal 1
2•4, 2•11	*Doggone Decimal*	**Estimating products of whole and decimal numbers** Operations and Computation Goal 5
2•5	*Multiplication Bull's-Eye*	**Estimating products of multidigit numbers** Operations and Computation Goal 5
2•6	*Divisibility Dash*	**Applying rules of divisibility** Numbers and Numeration Goal 3
2•7	*Division Top-It* (Advanced Version)	**Practicing whole-number division** Operations and Computation Goal 2
2•9	*Scientific Notation Toss*	**Translating between scientific and standard notations** Numbers and Numeration Goal 1
2•10, 2•11	*Exponent Ball*	**Converting between exponential and standard notations** Numbers and Numeration Goal 1

See the *Differentiation Handbook* for ways to adapt games to meet students' needs.

Home Communication

Study Links provide homework and home communication.

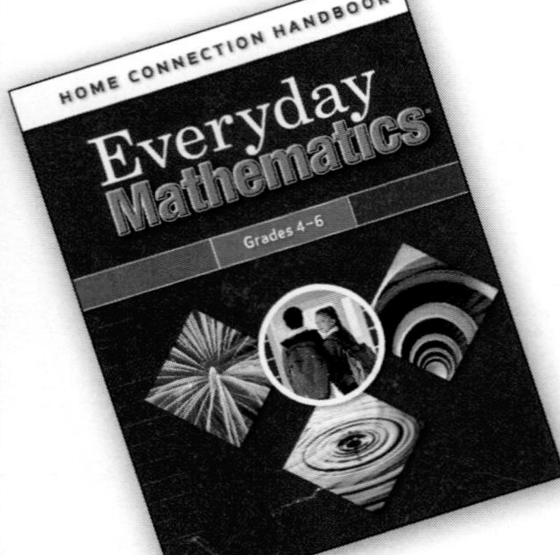

◀ ***Home Connection Handbook*** provides more ideas to communicate effectively with parents.

Unit 2 Family Letter provides families with an overview, Do-Anytime Activities, Building Skills Through Games, and a list of vocabulary.

Problem Solving

Encourage students to use a variety of strategies to solve problems and to explain those strategies. Strategies that students might use in this unit:

- Finding and using a pattern
- Using computation
- Using estimation
- Making and interpreting a graph
- Writing a number sentence
- Using logical reasoning

Lessons that teach *through* problem solving, not just *about* problem solving

Lesson	Activity
2•1, 2•2, 2•4	Use a pattern to develop a rule for writing numbers in exponential notation and multiplying by powers of 10.
2•3	Solve number stories by rounding measures to the same precision and computing sums and differences of decimal numbers.
2•3	Solve number stories involving sports records.
2•3	Make and interpret a step graph to calculate phone-call costs.
2•5, 2•7, 2•11	Write equivalent names for numbers to estimate and mentally compute products and quotients of whole and decimal numbers.
2•8	Use logical reasoning to interpret remainders of division number stories.

See Chapter 18 in the *Teacher's Reference Manual* for more information about problem solving.

Planning Tips

Pacing

Pacing depends on a number of factors, such as students' individual needs and how long your school has been using *Everyday Mathematics*. At the beginning of Unit 2, review your *Content by Strand* Poster to help you set a monthly pace.

SEPTEMBER	OCTOBER	NOVENBER
	← MOST CLASSROOMS →	

NCTM Standards

Unit 2 Lessons	2•1	2•2	2•3	2•4	2•5	2•6	2•7	2•8	2•9	2•10	2•11
NCTM Standards	1, 5–8	1, 6–8	1, 4, 5–10	1, 2, 6–8	1, 6–10	1, 6–10	1, 6–8	1, 6–8	1, 4, 6–10	1, 6–10	1, 6–10

Content Standards: 1 Number and Operations, **2** Algebra, **3** Geometry, **4** Measurement, **5** Data Analysis and Probability
Process Standards: 6 Problem Solving, **7** Reasoning and Proof, **8** Communication, **9** Connections, **10** Representation

Balanced Assessment

Ongoing Assessment

Recognizing Student Achievement

Opportunities to assess students' progress toward Grade 6 Goals:

Lesson	Content Assessed
2•1	Write whole numbers to billions. [Number and Numeration Goal 1]
2•2	Compare decimal numbers through thousandths. [Number and Numeration Goal 6]
2•3	Align digits of whole and decimal numbers by place value. [Number and Numeration Goal 1]
2•4	Write decimals to thousandths. [Number and Numeration Goal 1]
2•5	Estimate products of decimals. [Operations and Computation Goal 5]
2•6	Make reasonable estimates for products and use a reliable algorithm to mulitply decimals. [Operations and Computation Goal 2]
2•7	Estimate partial quotients and choose a reliable algorithm to divide by a multidigit divisor. [Operations and Computation Goal 2]
2•8	Make a reasonable estimate for a quotient and use a reliable algorithm to solve a division problem. [Operations and Computation Goal 2]
2•9	Determine the power of 10 needed to move the decimal point in the other factor to the right or left. [Number and Numeration Goal 1]
2•10	Interpret exponential notation and use the power key on the calculator. [Number and Numeration Goal 4]
2•11	Translate from scientific notation to standard notation. [Number and Numeration Goal 1]

Use the **Assessment Management System** to collect and analyze data about students' progress throughout the year.

Informing Instruction

To anticipate common student errors and to highlight problem-solving strategies:

Lesson 2•1 Use a strategy to enter numbers into the place-value template

Lesson 2•4 Know the meaning and position of the decimal point in whole numbers

Lesson 2•7 Use easy numbers to make partial quotients

Lesson 2•9 Recognize the relationship between the exponent and decimal-point placement in a number

Periodic Assessment

2•12 Progress Check 2

CONTENT ASSESSED	ASSESSMENT ITEMS			
	Self	Oral/Slate	Written	Open Response
Apply place-value concepts to identify digits in numbers and express their values. [Number and Numeration Goal 1]			✔	
Translate between standard, expanded, scientific and number-and-word notations with or without a calculator. [Number and Numeration Goal 1]	✔	✔	✔	
Compare and order rational numbers. [Number and Numeration Goal 6]		✔	✔	
Add and subtract decimals. [Operations and Computation Goal 1]	✔	✔	✔	
Multiply by positive and negative powers of 10. [Operations and Computation Goal 2]	✔	✔	✔	
Multiply and divide whole and decimal numbers. [Operations and Computation Goal 2]	✔		✔	✔
Estimate differences, products, and quotients of whole numbers and decimals. [Operations and Computation Goal 5]	✔	✔		✔
Construct and interpret a graph. [Data and Chance Goal 1]			✔	
Compare the median and mean of a data set. [Data and Chance Goal 2]			✔	

Portfolio Opportunities

Opportunities to gather samples of students' mathematical writings, drawings, and creations to add balance to the assessment process:

- Solving a multistep multiplication/division problem, **Lesson 2•1**
- Interpreting a line graph, **Lesson 2•2**
- Using the Product of Powers Rule, **Lesson 2•4**
- Comparing products and factors, **Lesson 2•5**
- Applying estimation skills, **Lesson 2•5**
- Exploring mental multiplication, **Lesson 2•6**
- Placing the decimal point in products, **Lesson 2•9**

Assessment Handbook

Unit 2 Assessment Support

- Grade 6 Goals, pp. 37–50
- Unit 2 Assessment Overview, pp. 60–67
- Unit 2 Open Response
  - Detailed rubric, p. 64
  - Sample student responses, pp. 65–67

Unit 2 Assessment Masters

- Unit 2 Self-Assessment, p. 144
- Unit 2 Written Assessment, pp. 145–148
- Unit 2 Open Response, p. 149
- Unit 2 Class Checklist, pp. 232, 233, and 275
- Unit 2 Individual Profile of Progress, pp. 230, 231, and 274
- Exit Slip, p. 283
- Math Logs, pp. 278–280
- Other Student Assessment Forms, pp. 276, 277, 281, and 282

Unit 2 Organizer

Differentiated Instruction

Daily Lesson Support

ENGLISH LANGUAGE LEARNERS

- **2•1** Building a Math Word Bank
- **2•4** Building a Math Word Bank
- **2•6** Displaying a method for multiplying decimals
- **2•7** Building a Math Word Bank
- **2•11** Building a Math Word Bank

EXTRA PRACTICE

- **2•5** Multiplying multidigit whole numbers
- **2•11** Converting between notations

5-Minute Math **2•3** Rounding decimals; **2•4** Multiplying and dividing numbers by powers of 10; **2•9** Writing powers of 10

READINESS

- **2•1** Reading, writing, and comparing numbers through billions
- **2•2** Modeling and comparing decimals through thousandths
- **2•3** Modeling subtraction of decimals
- **2•4** Reviewing multiplying and dividing by 10
- **2•5** Reviewing multiplication facts
- **2•6** Using an area model to visualize decimal multiplication
- **2•8** Using bills and coins to model problems with decimal remainders
- **2•9** Reviewing positive and negative powers of 10

ENRICHMENT

- **2•1** Solving a multistep problem
- **2•2** Exploring the density of rational numbers
- **2•3** Exploring meaningful zeros
- **2•4** Exploring the Product of Powers Rule
- **2•5** Applying estimation skills and strategies
- **2•6** Using a doubling and halving strategy
- **2•7** Testing for divisibility by 7
- **2•7** Exploring the column division algorithm
- **2•8** Finding patterns in quotients
- **2•9** Converting between notations
- **2•10** Exploring binary numbers
- **2•10** Finding examples of facts
- **2•11** Exploring a Quotient Rule

Adjusting the Activity

- **2•1** Using place-value templates
- **2•2** Discussing the meanings of *tenth* **ELL**
- **2•2** Using place-value templates
- **2•3** Using money to model problems with whole numbers, tenths, and hundredths
- **2•5** Applying a rule to place the decimal point
- **2•6** Using colors to differentiate factors and partial products **ELL**
- **2•6** Using a computation or lattice grid
- **2•7** Labeling division problem parts **ELL**
- **2•7** Making a list of "easy" multiples
- **2•8** Applying a method to round a quotient

AUDITORY • KINESTHETIC • TACTILE • VISUAL

Cross-Curricular Links

Consumer Education

Lesson 2•3 Students use phone-call cost data to draw and interpret a graph.

Social Studies

Lesson 2•9 Students convert the ground areas of famous buildings from scientific to standard notations.

Science

Lesson 2•10 Students look for facts expressed in exponential or scientific notations.

Using the Projects

Projects 1 through 5 provide opportunities for students to apply whole and decimal number notation and computation skills as they learn about our solar system. These projects can be used during or after Unit 2. See the *Differentiation Handbook* for modifications to Projects 1–5.

Differentiation Handbook

See the *Differentiation Handbook* for materials on Unit 2.

Language Support

Everyday Mathematics provides lesson-specific suggestions to help all students, including non-native English speakers, to acquire, process, and express mathematical ideas.

Unit 2 Vocabulary

base
dividend
divisor
expanded notation
exponent
exponential notation
factor
negative power of 10
number-and-word notation
partial-quotients division algorithm
positive power of 10
power key
powers of 10
precise
quotient
remainder
scientific notation
standard notation
truncated (teacher)

Connecting Math and Literacy

Arithme-Tickle, by J. Patrick Lewis, Harcourt, Inc., 2002
The Best of Times, by Greg Tang, Scholastic Press, 2002
The King's Chessboard, by David Birch, Puffin Books, 1988
How Much Is a Million?, by David Schwartz, Lothrop, Lee & Shepard Books, 1993
Can You Count to a Googol?, by Robert E. Wells, Albert Whitman & Co., 2000
On Beyond a Million: An Amazing Math Journey, by David Schwartz, Random House, Inc., 1999

Student Reference Book

pp. 6–8, 11, 20, 22–24, 31–35, 37–39, 285–289, 309–311, 324, 328, 331, and 336

Multiage Classroom ◆ Companion Lessons

Companion Lessons from Grade 5 can help you meet instructional needs of a multiage classroom. The full Scope and Sequence can be found in the Appendix.

Grade 5	2•8	2•8	2•10			2•2 2•3	7•1 7•2	7•3	4•4	4•1 4•2	7•3	
Grade 6	**2•1**	**2•2**	**2•3**	**2•4**	**2•5**	**2•6**	**2•7**	**2•8**	**2•9**	**2•10**	**2•11**	**2•12**

Professional Development

Teacher's Reference Manual Links

Lesson	Topic	Section
2•1, 2•2	Scientific and Other Notations	10.1.2
2•4	Multiplying by Powers of 10	10.1.2
2•5, 2•6	Multiplication of Decimals	11.2.3
2•7, 2•8	Division of Whole and Decimal Numbers	11.2.4
2•9–2•11	Scientific and Exponential Notations	10.1.2

Materials

Lesson	Masters	Manipulative Kit Items	Other Items
2◆1	Teaching Aid Master, p. 409 transparency of *Math Masters,* p. 409 Study Link Masters, pp. 41 and 42 Teaching Master, p. 43 Game Masters, pp. 463, 464, and 478	per group: 4 each of number cards 0–9	scissors; tape
2◆2	Study Link 2◆1 Teaching Aid Masters, pp. 410–413 transparency of *Math Masters,* p. 410 Study Link Masters, pp. 44 and 45 Game Master, p. 455 Teaching Master, p. 46	per group: 4 each of number cards 0–9 calculator	scissors
2◆3	Study Link 2◆2 Teaching Aid Masters, pp. 411–413 and 414* Study Link Master, p. 47 Teaching Master, p. 48		scissors
2◆4	Study Link 2◆3 Study Link Master, p. 49 Game Master, p. 433 Teaching Master, p. 50	per group: 4 each of number cards 0–9 calculator	per group: index cards labeled 0.1, 1, 10, and 100; 4 counters or coins
2◆5	Study Link 2◆4 Study Link Master, p. 51 Game Master, p. 478 Teaching Masters, pp. 52 and 53	per group: number cards 0–10, 6-sided die calculator	
2◆6	Study Link 2◆5 Teaching Aid Masters, pp. 414 and 415*; Study Link Master, p. 54 Game Master, p. 432 Teaching Masters, pp. 55 and 56	per group: 2 decks of number cards 0–10 calculator	posterboard; markers
2◆7	Study Link 2◆6 Teaching Aid Master, p. 414 Study Link Master, p. 57 Game Master, p. 478	per group: 4 each of number cards 1–9	
2◆8	Study Link 2◆7 Teaching Aid Master, p. 414 Study Link Master, p. 58		bills and coins of various denominations
2◆9	Study Link 2◆8 Study Link Master, p. 59 Game Master, p. 472 Teaching Masters, pp. 60–62	per group: two 6-sided dice	
2◆10	Study Link 2◆9 Teaching Aid Master, p. 404 Game Master, p. 436 Study Link Master, p. 63 Teaching Master, p. 64	per group: 6-sided die calculator	per group: one penny or counter
2◆11	Study Link 2◆10 Study Link Master, p. 65 Game Masters, pp. 433 and 436 Teaching Master, p. 66	calculator	
2◆12	Study Link 2◆11 Assessment Masters, pp. 144–149 Study Link Masters, pp. 67–70	dry-erase board/slate	

Technology

Assessment Management System, Unit 2
iTLG, Unit 2

* Denotes optional materials

Mathematical Background

The discussion below highlights the major content ideas presented in Unit 2 and helps establish instructional priorities.

Powers of 10 and Scientific Notation (Lessons 2•1, 2•2, and 2•9)

The existence of equivalent names for the same number is a consistent theme of *Everyday Mathematics.* It can be argued that most of arithmetic is concerned with expressing numbers in equivalent forms. For example, 2 * 40, 100 − 20, 320 ÷ 4, 8 * 10, 60 + 20, 0.8 * 100, 1,070 − 990, and many others are all expressions for 80; each one might be useful as a number sentence in a particular problem.

The diameter of a typical human red blood cell is 6–8 micrometers. One micrometer is about 0.001 millimeters long.

In the world outside of school, large numbers are often written with words such as *million* or *billion* substituted for digits. Huge numbers, such as those astronomers use to describe the universe, are usually shown with the help of positive powers of 10. Very small numbers, which are common in other sciences, are given in terms of units such as the nanometer (one billionth of a meter) or with negative powers of 10. Notations with powers of 10 are especially helpful in estimating and calculating with very large and very small numbers.

The term **standard notation** is used for the usual base-ten numerals, such as 1,000,000. When a number is written in **expanded notation,** each digit is multiplied by the power of 10 in which its place value holds. For example, 0.374 is written as (3 * 0.1) + (7 * 0.01) + (4 * 0.001). Strictly defined, a number in **scientific notation** is written as the product of a power of 10 and a number that is at least 1 but less than 10 (for example, $4.7 * 10^9$).

Standard Notation	Expanded Notation	Scientific Notation
2,500,000	(2 * 1,000,000) + (5 * 100,000)	$2.5 * 10^6$
54,000,000	(5 * 10,000,000) + (4 * 1,000,000)	$5.4 * 10^7$
0.00038	(3 * 0.0001) + (8 * 0.00001)	$3.8 * 10^{-4}$

Most people have a poor concept of the magnitude of large numbers. For example, it is not uncommon for students and adults to view 1 billion as roughly twice as much as 1 million. Few people comprehend what "1,000 times as much" means. To help students grasp the concept of 1,000 times as much, you might provide additional examples by asking such questions as the following:

- How long might it take you to run 1 mile? 1,000 miles?
- What can you buy with \$5 versus \$5,000? \$50 versus \$50,000?

These lessons deal with skills that are essential to learning science and to functioning in a world where calculators and computer skills are more important than paper-and-pencil skills for multiplying or dividing with large numbers or small decimals.

Unit 2 Organizer

Addition and Subtraction of Decimals (Lesson 2◆3)

Students review decimal computation skills developed in earlier grades of *Everyday Mathematics.* Two important topics are considered: adding and subtracting numbers with differing numbers of decimal places and ensuring that measurements being added or subtracted have the same unit.

For more information about the addition and subtraction of decimals, refer to the *Teacher's Reference Manual,* Sections 11.2.1 and 11.2.2.

Note

The TI-15 and Casio *fx*-55 calculators allow the user to "fix" the number of decimal places that will be displayed. This feature can be used to suppress the display of decimal places beyond those in the least accurate number used in computation. See pages 282 and 283 of the *Student Reference Book.*

Multiplying by Powers of 10 (Lesson 2◆4)

For several years, students of *Everyday Mathematics* have practiced "extended multiplication facts." For example, the basic fact 4 ∗ 5 = 20 can help in finding answers to 4 ∗ 50, 400 ∗ 5, 40 ∗ 50, and so on. In keeping with the intention of *Sixth Grade Everyday Mathematics* to consolidate ideas and teach useful algorithmic shortcuts, Lesson 2-4 invites students to formulate routine ways of dealing with such products and to extend those to products like 12.4 ∗ 1,000 and 0.1 ∗ 0.53. Since the preferred shortcut involves shifting decimal points, students also need to know that any whole number can be followed by a decimal point and that zeros can be attached after decimal parts of numbers to provide places for decimal shifts.

Refer to the *Teacher's Reference Manual,* Section 10.1.2, to learn more about multiplying powers of 10.

The international measuring system is based on the meter (39.37 inches) as the unit of length. Metric bicycle parts and dimensions are usually given in millimeters (0.001 meter) or centimeters (0.01 meter). Most wrenches used on bicycles have sizes in millimeters.

Multiplication of Decimals (Lessons 2◆5 and 2◆6)

There are several methods for locating the decimal point in products of decimals.

- Estimate the size of the product. For example, 0.23 ∗ 17.56 is about twice as much as 0.1 ∗ 17.56, which equals 1.756. So 0.23 ∗ 17.56 is about 4. Ignore the decimal points in the factors, use whichever whole-number multiplication method you prefer, and get the result. Then insert the decimal point to make the product the right size.
- Use a calculator, but be sure to verify the size of the "answer" in the display, because even experienced users of calculators often make mistakes keying in numbers.
- Use nearby fraction equivalents in size estimates. For example, 0.23 ∗ 17.56 is about $\frac{1}{4}$ of 16 or $\frac{1}{5}$ of 20, either of which suggests that the answer is somewhere near 4.
- Multiply as if the factors were whole numbers, and use a rule for placing the decimal point in the answer. For example, many of us were taught to count the numbers of decimal places in the factors, add them, and mark off that many decimal places in the answer.

The last method has the same advantages and disadvantages as many other computation algorithms—automatic processing on the one hand, with the potential for misapplication on the other hand. In each of the first three methods above, students are using estimation skills to judge the reasonableness of their answers, and the habit of estimating avoids bad mistakes even when using relatively automatic procedures. The first method is covered in Lesson 2-5 and the last method is offered as an option in Lesson 2-6.

To learn more about multiplication of decimals, refer to the *Teacher's Reference Manual,* Section 11.2.3.

The Lattice Method of Multiplication (Lesson 2•6)

The lattice method was introduced previously in *Everyday Mathematics* for multiplying whole numbers. This "low stress" algorithm has proven to be popular with students. In Lesson 2-6, the lattice method is extended to multiplication of decimals.

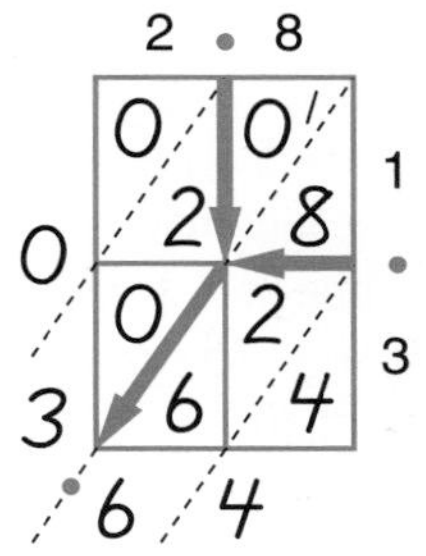

Refer to the *Teacher's Reference Manual,* Section 11.2.3, for more information about the lattice method of multiplication.

Division of Whole Numbers and Decimals (Lessons 2•7 and 2•8)

In the adult world, the usual procedure for solving any moderately complicated division problem is to reach for a calculator, and the authors of *Everyday Mathematics* believe that this is sensible. But school expectations still include being able to solve some division problems without a calculator, and there is also some understanding of division to be gained by learning paper-and-pencil computation procedures.

Lesson 2-7 reviews the partial-quotients division algorithm, a paper-and-pencil procedure for dividing whole numbers that was introduced in *Fourth* and *Fifth Grade Everyday Mathematics.* This algorithm takes much of the mystery out of "long division." It is offered as a "low stress" and conceptually revealing alternative to the traditional U.S. long division algorithm that, according to research, is difficult for many students to learn and apply.

Division is a way of answering the question, "How many of these are there in that?" or "How many n's are there in m?" The algorithm taught here encourages successive estimates of "How many. . .?" without penalizing students for inexact estimates. Each estimate is checked. If not enough n's have been taken from the m, more are taken. When all possible n's have been taken, the interim estimates are added. For example, 158 ÷ 12 can be thought of as "How may 12s are there in 158?" How this question is answered with the algorithm reviewed in Lesson 2-7 is shown in the margin.

12)158	
− 120	10
38	
− 36	3
2	13

"Easy" Multiples of 12

10 * 12 = 120
5 * 12 = 60
2 * 12 = 24
1 * 12 = 12

Unit 2 Organizer

One advantage of the partial-quotients division algorithm is that students can work with "easy" numbers. Students who are good estimators and confident with extended multiplication facts will make only a few estimates to arrive at a quotient while others will be more comfortable taking smaller steps. In the example above, a student might use 2 as a second estimate, taking just two 12s and leaving 14 still unaccounted for. The student will reach the final answer in three steps rather than two. One way is not better than another. More important than the number of steps a student takes is that the student understands the algorithm and can use it to get an accurate answer.

Note

While a diagram may be useful in solving a particular number story, there are usually many ways of thinking about a problem. It is important for students to understand that problem solving is a creative activity that requires ingenuity and cannot be performed according to a preset prescription.

The partial-quotients division algorithm is the focus algorithm for division in *Everyday Mathematics.* The authors recommend that all students learn it. If, however, students know another algorithm and prefer it to the one in the lesson, they should feel free to use it. If parents or siblings insist on the superiority of the algorithm they learned, it can be easily accommodated as an alternative. If you want to teach another algorithm, please feel free to do so. Some students enjoy figuring out algorithms for long division and may need only a little help to move on to more difficult problems.

In giving answers for division problems with a remainder or posing division problems for which there might be a remainder, *Everyday Mathematics* uses an arrow rather than an equal sign ($492 \div 24 \rightarrow 20$ R12). Using this convention shows that $492 \div 24 = 20$ R12 is not a proper number sentence because the right-hand side (20 R12) is not actually a number. If you want students to write the solution as a number sentence, have them express the remainder as a fraction: $492 \div 24 = 20\frac{12}{24}$ or $20\frac{1}{2}$. Students worked with expressing remainders as fractions in *Fifth Grade Everyday Mathematics.*

Lesson 2-8 focuses on how to answer whole-number division problems with decimals to a specified number of decimal places. For example, if seven people share the cost of a $29 meal, what is each person's share in dollars and cents? In this lesson, the dividend is larger than the divisor. Students also learn how to extend the partial-quotients division algorithm to problems in which the dividend is a decimal. Other division cases—decimals divided by decimals and dividends smaller than divisors—are covered in Unit 8.

Note

An open sentence can have more than one solution; for example, 1, 2, and 3 are all solutions of the *inequality* $x < 4$. However, any open sentence in this unit contains an = sign and has only one solution.

$3 + x = 13$

$5 = 12 - x$

$25 - x = 15$

Section 11.2.4 in the *Teacher's Reference Manual* contain more information on division of whole numbers and decimals.

Exponential Notation, Scientific Notation, and the Power Key on a Calculator (Lessons 2•10 and 2•11)

Some calculators have a square key, $\boxed{x^2}$, for finding the second power of the number in the display. The power key, $\boxed{\wedge}$ on the TI-15 and $\boxed{x^y}$ on the Casio *fx*-55 calculator, enables the user to find any power of a given number. It is a faster method than using repeated multiplication.

It is difficult to work with very large or very small numbers in their full written form, and it is seldom necessary or sensible to do so. Calculators that perform only the basic operations with whole numbers allow the user to enter a limited number of digits (usually eight); they display an error message when the result of a calculation is too large for the display. For this reason, the authors recommend that students in *Sixth Grade Everyday Mathematics* have access to a scientific calculator.

When the result of a calculation is too large to display in standard notation, a scientific calculator displays it in scientific notation. For example, if the user enters 35,000,000 $\boxed{\times}$ 1,200 $\boxed{=}$, the display on the TI-15 shows 4.2 × 10^10, the display on the Casio *fx*-55 shows 4.2 10.

Refer to the *Teacher's Reference Manual,* Section 10.1.2, for more information about exponential notation, scientific notation, and the power key on a calculator.

Prefixes for very large and very small numbers

yotta-	10^{24}
zetta-	10^{21}
exa-	10^{18}
peta-	10^{15}
tera-	10^{12}
giga-	10^{9}
mega-	10^{6}
kilo-	10^{3}
hecto-	10^{2}
deca-	10^{1}
deci-	10^{-1}
centi-	10^{-2}
milli-	10^{-3}
micro-	10^{-6}
nano-	10^{-9}
pico-	10^{-12}
femto-	10^{-15}
atto-	10^{-18}
zepto-	10^{-21}
yocto-	10^{-24}

Reading and Writing Large Numbers

Objective To read and write large numbers in standard, expanded, and number-and-word notations.

1 Teaching the Lesson

Key Activities

Students read and write numbers to trillions in standard notation, expanded notation, and number-and-word notation and convert between these notations.

Key Concepts and Skills

- Apply place-value concepts to read, write, and interpret large numbers. [Number and Numeration Goal 1]
- Convert between standard and expanded notations. [Number and Numeration Goal 1]
- Apply extended facts and order of operations to express the value of digits in a number. [Operations and Computation Goal 2]

Key Vocabulary

standard notation • expanded notation • number-and-word notation

Ongoing Assessment: Recognizing Student Achievement Use journal page 45. [Number and Numeration Goal 1]

Ongoing Assessment: Informing Instruction See page 106.

materials

- ☐ *Math Journal 1,* pp. 45 and 46
- ☐ Teaching Aid Master (*Math Masters,* p. 409)
- ☐ Transparency (*Math Masters,* p. 409)

See **Advance Preparation**

2 Ongoing Learning & Practice

Students practice and maintain skills through Math Boxes and Study Link activities.

materials

- ☐ *Math Journal 1,* p. 47
- ☐ Study Link Masters (*Math Masters,* pp. 41 and 42)

3 Differentiation Options

READINESS

Students apply place-value concepts to read, write, and compare numbers through billions.

ENRICHMENT

Students apply place-value concepts and extended multiplication and division facts to solve a multistep problem.

ELL SUPPORT

Students add *expanded notation, standard notation,* and *number-and-word notation* to their Math Word Banks.

materials

- ☐ Teaching Master (*Math Masters,* p. 43)
- ☐ Game Masters (*Math Masters,* pp. 463, 464, and 478)
- ☐ *Differentiation Handbook*

per partnership:

- ☐ 4 each of number cards 0–9 (from the Everything Math Deck, if available)
- ☐ scissors, tape

Additional Information

Advance Preparation Allow three days to complete Lessons 2•1 and 2•2. Make at least one copy of *Math Masters,* page 409 per student.

Technology

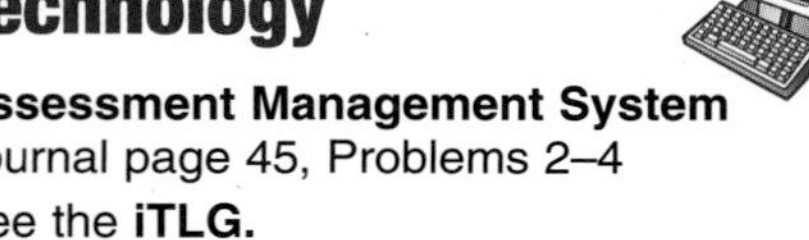

Assessment Management System
Journal page 45, Problems 2–4
See the **iTLG.**

Getting Started

Mental Math and Reflexes

Students write numbers from dictation and record numbers that are 10 times as great.

Suggestions:

●○○ Write 9,010. Write the number that is 10 times as great. 90,100

●●○ Write 150,100. Write the number that is 10 times as great. 1,501,000

Write 30,010,000. Write the number that is 10 times as great. 300,100,000

●●● Write 701,010,100. Write the number that is 10 times as great. 7,010,101,000

Refer back to the above problems during discussions of place-value chart patterns.

Math Message

Complete the Math Message on journal page 45.

1 Teaching the Lesson

▶ Math Message Follow-Up

WHOLE-CLASS DISCUSSION

(*Math Journal 1,* p. 45)

Ask students to share the methods they used to record the number 9,500,000,000,000 in the place-value chart. Some students may have entered digits from right to left, moving from ones to trillions. Others may have used the commas to organize their digit entries.

The number 9,500,000,000,000 is written in **standard notation**—the most familiar way of representing whole numbers and decimal numbers. In standard notation, digits are written in specified places. Most students should be able to read and write large numbers in standard notation.

Have pairs of students look for patterns in the place-value chart and share the patterns they find. Patterns include:

▷ Each place is 10 times the place to its right.

▷ Each period or group is divided into three places—ones, tens, and hundreds.

▷ Each period or group is separated by a comma.

Ask students to write on their slates or on the board the number that is:

▷ 10 times as great as 9,500,000,000,000. 90,500,000,000,000

▷ $\frac{1}{10}$ times as great as 9,500,000,000,000. 950,000,000,000

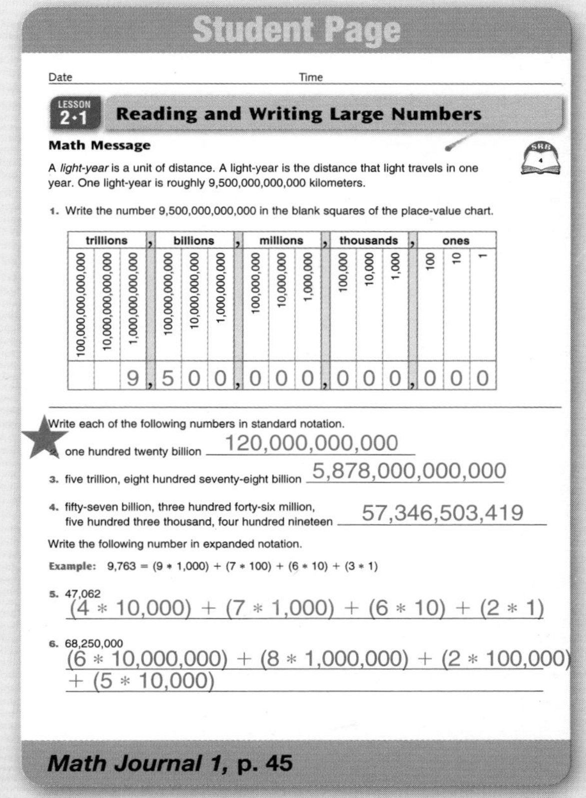

Student Page

Date ______ Time ______

LESSON 2·1 **Reading and Writing Large Numbers**

Math Message

A *light-year* is a unit of distance. A light-year is the distance that light travels in one year. One light-year is roughly 9,500,000,000,000 kilometers.

1. Write the number 9,500,000,000,000 in the blank squares of the place-value chart.

trillions			billions			millions			thousands			ones		
100,000,000,000,000	10,000,000,000,000	1,000,000,000,000	100,000,000,000	10,000,000,000	1,000,000,000	100,000,000	10,000,000	1,000,000	100,000	10,000	1,000	100	10	1
		9	5	0	0	0	0	0	0	0	0	0	0	0

Write each of the following numbers in standard notation.

2. one hundred twenty billion 120,000,000,000
3. five trillion, eight hundred seventy-eight billion 5,878,000,000,000
4. fifty-seven billion, three hundred forty-six million, five hundred three thousand, four hundred nineteen 57,346,503,419

Write the following number in expanded notation.

Example: 9,763 = (9 * 1,000) + (7 * 100) + (6 * 10) + (3 * 1)

5. 47,062
(4 * 10,000) + (7 * 1,000) + (6 * 10) + (2 * 1)
6. 68,250,000
(6 * 10,000,000) + (8 * 1,000,000) + (2 * 100,000) + (5 * 10,000)

Math Journal 1, p. 45

▶ Interpreting Expanded Notation for Large Numbers

(*Math Journal 1,* p. 45; *Math Masters,* p. 409; Transparency of *Math Masters,* p. 409)

trillions			,	billions			,	millions			,	thousands			,	ones		
100,000,000,000,000	10,000,000,000,000	1,000,000,000,000		100,000,000,000	10,000,000,000	1,000,000,000		100,000,000	10,000,000	1,000,000		100,000	10,000	1,000		100	10	1

Display a transparency of *Math Masters,* page 409 and give one copy of the same page to each student. Ask students to write the number 235 in the place-value chart at the top half of the page. They will convert this number from standard notation into **expanded notation.** In expanded notation, a number is written as the sum of the values of its digits. For example, in the number 235, the place of the digit 2 is hundreds, so its value is 2 ∗ 100. The value of the digit 3 is 3 ∗ 10. The value of the digit 5 is 5 ∗ 1. So, in expanded notation, 235 is written as:

$$(2 * 100) + (3 * 10) + (5 * 1).$$

Help students see how they can apply their extended multiplication facts to write numbers in expanded notation.

The diameter of the Sun is about 863,706 miles. Ask students to record this number in their place-value charts. Suggest they use the place-value chart to convert this number from standard notation to expanded notation. When students have finished, ask a volunteer to share his or her work.

863,706 = (8 ∗ 100,000) + (6 ∗ 10,000) + (3 ∗ 1,000) + (7 ∗ 100) + (6 ∗ 1)

Pose additional problems such as the following:

▷ Write 68,250,000 in expanded notation. (6 ∗ 10,000,000) + (8 ∗ 1,000,000) + (2 ∗ 100,000) + (5 ∗ 10,000)

▷ Write 2,703,109 in expanded notation. (2 ∗ 1,000,000) + (7 ∗ 100,000) + (3 ∗ 1,000) + (1 ∗ 100) + (9 ∗ 1)

Have students work independently to complete journal page 45. When most students have finished, go over the answers.

Ongoing Assessment: Recognizing Student Achievement

Journal Page 45 Problems 2–4 ★

Use **journal page 45, Problems 2–4** to assess students' ability to write whole numbers to billions. Students are making adequate progress if they are able to successfully complete Problems 2–4. Some students may be able to complete Problem 5.

[Number and Numeration Goal 1]

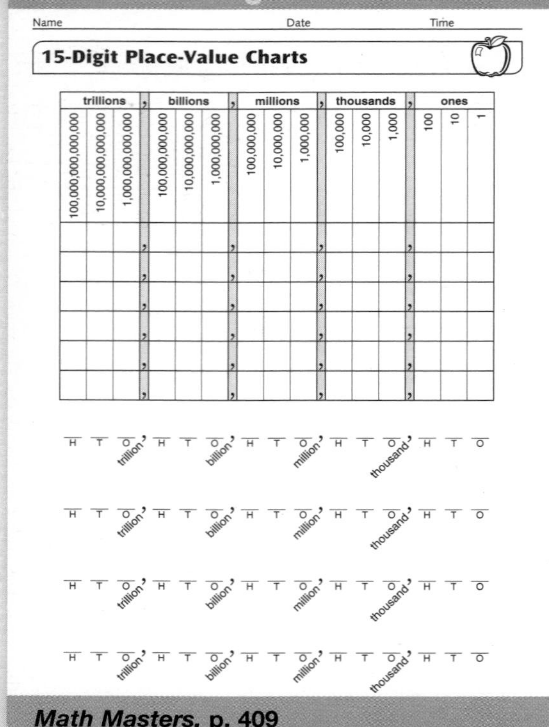

Teaching Aid Master

Name Date Time

15-Digit Place-Value Charts

trillions			,	billions			,	millions			,	thousands			,	ones		
100,000,000,000,000	10,000,000,000,000	1,000,000,000,000		100,000,000,000	10,000,000,000	1,000,000,000		100,000,000	10,000,000	1,000,000		100,000	10,000	1,000		100	10	1
			,				,				,				,			
			,				,				,				,			
			,				,				,				,			
			,				,				,				,			
			,				,				,				,			
			,				,				,				,			

H T O trillion, H T O billion, H T O million, H T O thousand, H T O

H T O trillion, H T O billion, H T O million, H T O thousand, H T O

H T O trillion, H T O billion, H T O million, H T O thousand, H T O

H T O trillion, H T O billion, H T O million, H T O thousand, H T O

Math Masters, p. 409

▶ Interpreting Number-and-Word Notation for Large Numbers

WHOLE-CLASS ACTIVITY

(*Math Journal 1,* p. 46; *Math Masters,* p. 409; Transparency of *Math Masters,* p. 409)

On the board, draw and label five sets of three dashed lines, separated by commas, or use an overhead and show the transparency of *Math Masters,* page 409.

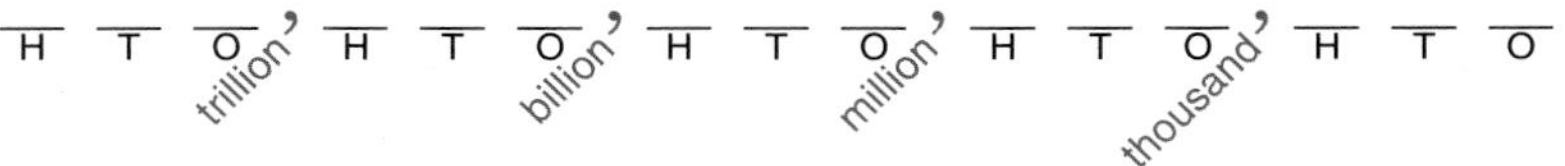

Number-and-word notation consists of the significant digits of a large number followed by a word for the place value. Examples include 27 million and 8.5 billion. Use the template to practice converting between standard and number-and-word notations.

1. Convert standard notation to number-and-word notation.

   Write 27,000,000 on the place-value template.

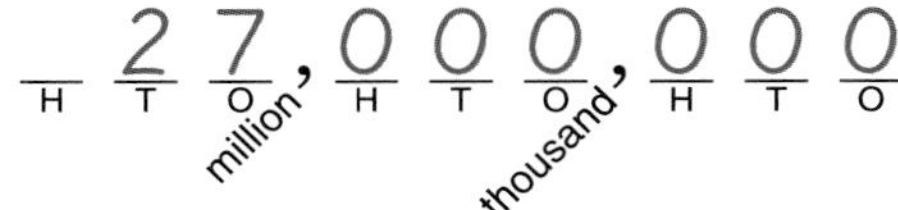

27 million

Number-and-word notation depends on the largest period. Because the digits 2 and 7 are in the millions period, the number-and-word notation of 27,000,000 is 27 million.

Now write 8,500,000,000 on the place-value template.

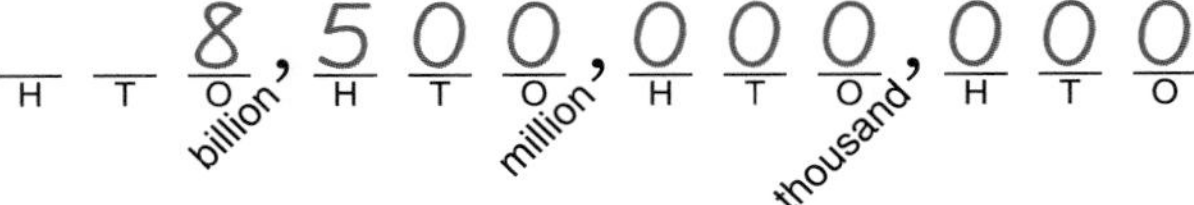

8.5 billion

The digit 8 is in the billions period and 5 is in the millions period. Billions is the largest period, so the number-and-word notation should be in terms of billions. Since 500,000,000 is 0.5 billion, 8 billion + 0.5 billion = 8.5 billion.

Pose additional problems such as the following:

▷ Convert 46,750,000 to number-and-word notation.
46.75 million

▷ Convert 203,600,000,000 to number-and-word notation.
203.6 billion

▷ Convert 900,000 to number-and-word notation.
900 thousand, or 0.9 million

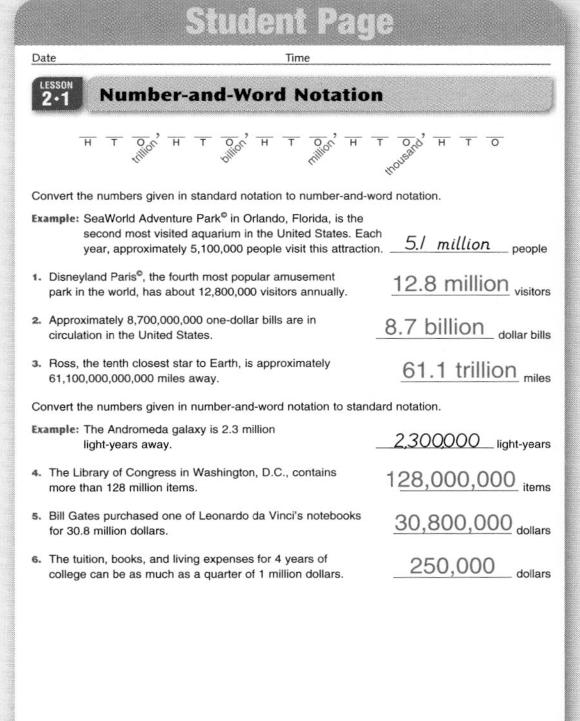

Student Page

Date Time

LESSON 2·1 **Number-and-Word Notation**

H T O, H T O, H T O, H T O, H T O (trillion, billion, million, thousand)

Convert the numbers given in standard notation to number-and-word notation.

Example: SeaWorld Adventure Park© in Orlando, Florida, is the second most visited aquarium in the United States. Each year, approximately 5,100,000 people visit this attraction. 5.1 million people

1. Disneyland Paris©, the fourth most popular amusement park in the world, has about 12,800,000 visitors annually. 12.8 million visitors
2. Approximately 8,700,000,000 one-dollar bills are in circulation in the United States. 8.7 billion dollar bills
3. Ross, the tenth closest star to Earth, is approximately 61,100,000,000,000 miles away. 61.1 trillion miles

Convert the numbers given in number-and-word notation to standard notation.

Example: The Andromeda galaxy is 2.3 million light-years away. 2,300,000 light-years

4. The Library of Congress in Washington, D.C., contains more than 128 million items. 128,000,000 items
5. Bill Gates purchased one of Leonardo da Vinci's notebooks for 30.8 million dollars. 30,800,000 dollars
6. The tuition, books, and living expenses for 4 years of college can be as much as a quarter of 1 million dollars. 250,000 dollars

Math Journal 1, p. 46

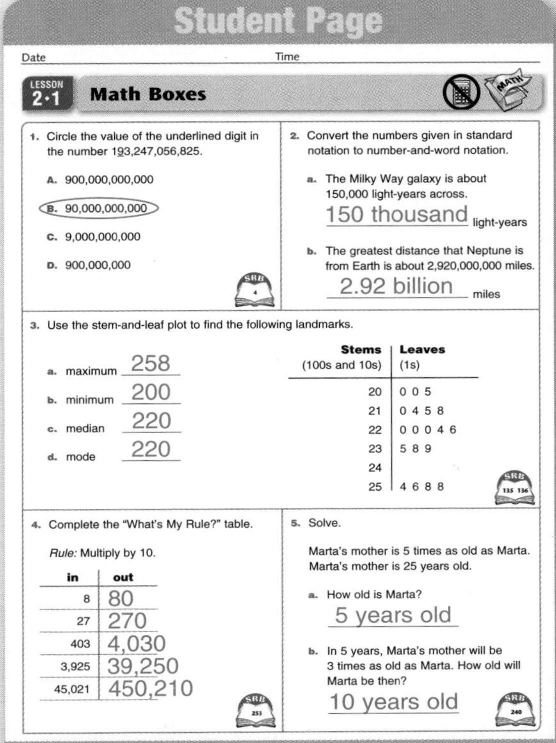

Student Page

Date Time

LESSON 2·1 **Math Boxes**

1. Circle the value of the underlined digit in the number 193,247,056,825.
   - A. 900,000,000,000
   - B. 90,000,000,000 (circled)
   - C. 9,000,000,000
   - D. 900,000,000

2. Convert the numbers given in standard notation to number-and-word notation.
   - a. The Milky Way galaxy is about 150,000 light-years across. 150 thousand light-years
   - b. The greatest distance that Neptune is from Earth is about 2,920,000,000 miles. 2.92 billion miles

3. Use the stem-and-leaf plot to find the following landmarks.
   - a. maximum 258
   - b. minimum 200
   - c. median 220
   - d. mode 220

Stems (100s and 10s)	Leaves (1s)
20	0 0 5
21	0 4 5 8
22	0 0 0 4 6
23	5 8 9
24	
25	4 6 8 8

4. Complete the "What's My Rule?" table.

   Rule: Multiply by 10.

in	out
8	80
27	270
403	4,030
3,925	39,250
45,021	450,210

5. Solve.

   Marta's mother is 5 times as old as Marta. Marta's mother is 25 years old.
   - a. How old is Marta? 5 years old
   - b. In 5 years, Marta's mother will be 3 times as old as Marta. How old will Marta be then? 10 years old

Math Journal 1, p. 47

decimal point in number-and-word notation

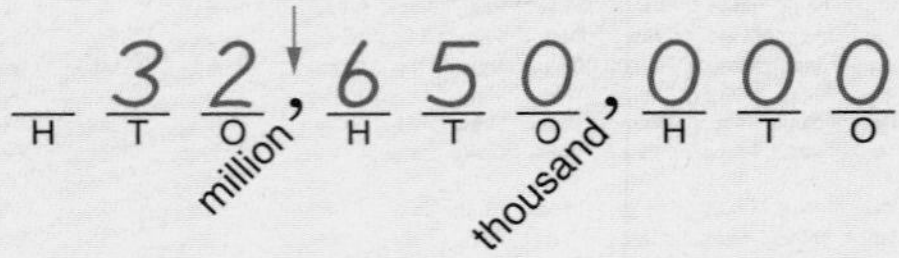

32.65 million

decimal point in number-and-word notation

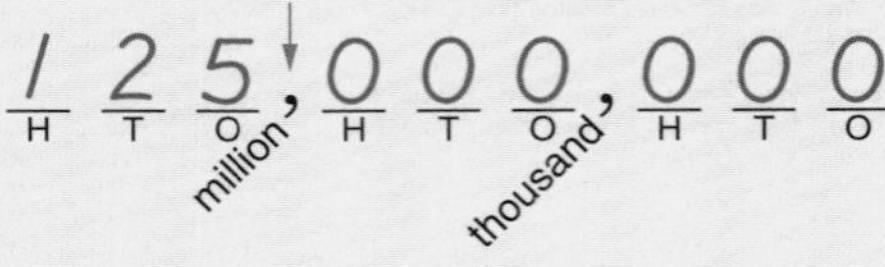

125 million

Study Link Master

Name Date Time

STUDY LINK 2·1 Large Numbers

trillions			billions			millions			thousands			ones		
100,000,000,000,000	10,000,000,000,000	1,000,000,000,000	100,000,000,000	10,000,000,000	1,000,000,000	100,000,000	10,000,000	1,000,000	100,000	10,000	1,000	100	10	1

1. Write the digit in each place of the number 6,812,507,439.
   a. millions 2 b. hundred thousands 5 c. ten millions 1
   d. billions 6 e. hundred millions 8 f. ten thousands 0
2. Write each of the following numbers in standard form.
   a. four hundred thirty thousand 430,000
   b. ninety million, one hundred five thousand 90,105,000
   c. one hundred seventy million, sixty-five 170,000,065
   d. nine billion, five hundred million, two hundred forty-three thousand 9,500,243,000
3. Write each number in expanded form. **Example:** 235 = (2 ∗ 100) + (3 ∗ 10) + (5 ∗ 1)
   a. 321,000
   (3 ∗ 100,000) + (2 ∗ 10,000) + (1 ∗ 1,000)
   b. 7,300,000,000,000
   (7 ∗ 1,000,000,000,000) + (3 ∗ 100,000,000,000)
   c. 2,510,709
   (2 ∗ 1,000,000) + (5 ∗ 100,000) + (1 ∗ 10,000) + (7 ∗ 100) + (9 ∗ 1)
4. Use extended facts to complete the following.
   a. 1 million = 1,000 ∗ 1,000
   b. 1 billion = 1,000 ∗ 1,000,000
   c. 1 trillion = 1,000 ∗ 1,000,000,000

Math Masters, p. 41

Ongoing Assessment: Informing Instruction

Watch for students who have not developed an effective strategy for entering numbers into the place-value template. Encourage those students to enter digits from right to left.

2. Convert number-and-word notation to standard notation.

Write 32.65 million on the board. Point out that the decimal point represents the comma named by the word. So, in 32.65 million, the decimal point represents the millions comma. Show students how to use the comma to position the nonzero digits. Then insert zeros to complete the conversion to standard notation. (*See margin.*)

Pose additional problems such as the following:

▷ Convert 125 million to standard notation. 125,000,000

▷ Convert 27.5 thousand to standard notation. 27,500

▷ Convert 140 billion to standard notation. 140,000,000,000

Have students complete journal page 46.

Adjusting the Activity

Have students use the place-value templates (*Math Masters,* p. 409) as they work on the journal pages, Math Boxes, and Study Link for this lesson.

AUDITORY ◆ KINESTHETIC ◆ TACTILE ◆ VISUAL

2 Ongoing Learning & Practice

▶ Math Boxes 2·1

INDEPENDENT ACTIVITY

(*Math Journal 1,* p. 47)

Mixed Practice Math Boxes in this lesson are paired with Math Boxes in Lesson 2-3. The skills in Problems 4 and 5 preview Unit 3 content.

Writing/Reasoning Have students write a response to the following: *Explain how you solved Problem 5a.* Sample answer: I divided Marta's mother's age by 5 to get Marta's age.

▶ Study Link 2•1

(*Math Masters,* pp. 41 and 42)

Home Connection Students apply place-value concepts to convert between standard notation and number-and-word notation.

3 Differentiation Options

READINESS

▶ Playing *Number Top-It*

15–30 Min

(*Math Masters,* pp. 463, 464, and 478)

To provide experience applying place-value concepts, have students play *Number Top-It.* Give each pair of players a copy of *Math Masters,* pages 463, 464, and 478, scissors, tape, and number cards. After students have assembled their place-value mats, have them read the game directions. Ask them to record the results for each round of play on page 478.

ENRICHMENT

▶ Walking Away with a Billion Dollars

5–15 Min

(*Math Masters,* p. 43)

Students apply their knowledge of place-value concepts and extended multiplication and division facts to solve a multistep problem and explain their solution strategies.

ELL SUPPORT

▶ Building a Math Word Bank

5–15 Min

(*Differentiation Handbook*)

To provide language support for number notations, have students use the Word Bank template in the *Differentiation Handbook.* Ask students to write the terms *expanded notation, standard notation,* and *number-and-word notation,* draw pictures representing each term, and write other related words. See the *Differentiation Handbook* for more information.

Study Link Master

Name Date Time

STUDY LINK 2•1 **Large Numbers** *continued*

___ ___ ___ , ___ ___ ___ , ___ ___ ___ , ___ ___ ___ , ___ ___ ___
trillion billion million thousand

Because the orbits of the planets are elliptical in shape, the distance between two planets changes over time. The least distances of Mercury, Venus, Saturn, and Neptune from Earth appear in the table at the right. The distances are approximations.

Least Distance from Earth	
Planet	**Distance (in miles)**
Mercury	48,000,000
Venus	25,700,000
Saturn	850,000,000
Neptune	2,680,000,000

5. Write each planet's least distance from Earth in number-and-word notation.
   a. Mercury 48 million miles
   b. Venus 25.7 million miles
   c. Saturn 850 million miles
   d. Neptune 2.68 billion miles

6. Write the following numbers in standard notation.
   a. 44.3 billion 44,300,000,000
   b. 6.5 trillion 6,500,000,000,000
   c. 0.9 million 900,000
   d. 0.7 hundred 70

Practice

Round each number to the given place.

7. 416,254; hundreds 416,300
8. 234,989; ten thousands 230,000
9. 1,857,000; hundred thousands 1,900,000
10. 6,593,278; millions 7,000,000

Math Masters, p. 42

Teaching Master

Name Date Time

LESSON 2•1 **Walking Away with a Billion Dollars**

Suppose you inherit one billion dollars. The bank pays you the entire amount of money in $100 bills. About how much will your payment weigh in tons?

Use the information below to solve the problem.

- You can cover a sheet of paper with about six $100 bills.
- There are 500 sheets in a ream of paper.
- There are 10 reams in 1 carton of paper.
- One ream of paper weighs about 5 pounds.
- One ton equals 2,000 pounds.

Show all your work. Write an explanation that is clear and easy to follow.

Sample answer: One sheet of paper is worth about $600, so one ream of paper is worth about $600 ∗ 500, or $300,000. One carton of paper is worth 10 ∗ $300,000, or $3,000,000, and weighs 50 pounds. So, every 3 million dollars weighs about 50 pounds. There are about 333 sets of 3 million dollars in 1 billion dollars, so 1 billion dollars will weigh about 333 ∗ 50 = 16,650 pounds. 16,650 / 2,000 = 8.3 tons. My payment will weigh about 8 tons.

Math Masters, p. 43

2•2 Reading and Writing Small Numbers

Objective To read and write small numbers in standard and expanded notations.

1 Teaching the Lesson

Key Activities

Students read and write numbers to thousandths in standard notation and expanded notation. They also convert between these notations.

Key Concepts and Skills

- Apply place-value concepts to read, write, and interpret numbers less than 1. [Number and Numeration Goal 1]
- Convert between standard and expanded notations. [Number and Numeration Goal 1]
- Apply extended facts and order of operations to express the value of digits in a number. [Operations and Computation Goal 2]

Key Vocabulary

standard notation • expanded notation

materials

- ☐ *Math Journal 1,* pp. 48–50
- ☐ Study Link 2•1
- ☐ Teaching Aid Master (*Math Masters,* p. 410)
- ☐ Transparency (*Math Masters,* p. 410)

***See* Advance Preparation**

2 Ongoing Learning & Practice

Students practice reading, writing, and comparing numbers through thousandths by playing the decimal version of *High-Number Toss.*

Students practice and maintain skills through Math Boxes and Study Link activities.

Ongoing Assessment: Recognizing Student Achievement Use *Math Masters,* page 455. [Number and Numeration Goal 6]

materials

- ☐ *Math Journal 1,* p. 51
- ☐ *Student Reference Book,* p. 324
- ☐ Study Link Masters (*Math Masters,* pp. 44 and 45)
- ☐ Game Master (*Math Masters,* p. 455)

Per partnership:

- ☐ 4 each of number cards 0–9 (from the Everything Math Deck, if available)
- ☐ calculator

3 Differentiation Options

READINESS

Students use base-10 grids to model and compare decimals through thousandths.

ENRICHMENT

Students explore the infinite number of decimals between any two given decimal numbers.

materials

- ☐ Teaching Master (*Math Masters,* p. 46)
- ☐ Teaching Aid Masters (*Math Masters,* pp. 411–413)
- ☐ scissors

Additional Information

Advance Preparation Allow three days for Lessons 2•1 and 2•2. Make at least one copy of *Math Masters,* page 410 per student.

Technology

Assessment Management System
Math Masters, page 455
See the **iTLG.**

Getting Started

Mental Math and Reflexes

Students divide numbers by 10 and record their answers on slates or dry-erase boards.

●○○ \$10.00 / 10 \$1.00
\$1.00 / 10 \$0.10

●●○ \$0.30 / 10 \$0.03
0.01 / 10 0.001

●●● 0.001 / 10 0.0001
0.0001 / 10 0.00001

Refer to the above problems during discussions of place-value chart patterns.

Math Message

Complete the Math Message on journal page 48.

Study Link 2•1 Follow-Up

Briefly review answers.

1 Teaching the Lesson

▶ Math Message Follow-Up

(*Math Journal 1,* pp. 48 and 49)

In the previous lesson, students used their knowledge of place-value concepts to read and write whole numbers. In this lesson, they will apply similar place-value concepts to read and write fractional quantities.

The number 0.1016 that students recorded in the chart is written in **standard notation.** Standard notation is a base-ten place-value numeration.

Ask students to look at 0.1016 and identify the digits in the following places:

tenths 1 hundredths 0

thousandths 1 ten-thousandths 6

Ask students to generate a few sentences using the different meanings of *tenth.* For example, *Mary finished in tenth place; A dime is a tenth of a dollar.*

Have students work in pairs to look for patterns in the place-value chart. Then ask them to share the patterns they found. Patterns include:

▷ Each place is $\frac{1}{10}$ the value of the place to its left and 10 times the value of the place to its right.

▷ The value of each place in the place-value chart is a power of 10. The value of each place to the left of the decimal point is a product of 10s, for example, $1{,}000 = 10 * 10 * 10$. The value of each place to the right of the decimal point is a product of $\frac{1}{10}$s (or 0.1s), for example, $0.01 = \frac{1}{10} * \frac{1}{10} = 0.1 * 0.1$.

NOTE Multiplying a number by $\frac{1}{10}$ is the same as dividing the number by 10.

Adjusting the Activity

ELL

Have students highlight each *th* ending in the place-value chart on journal page 48. Discuss the difference between *tenth* as an ordinal number and *tenth* as a fractional part.

AUDITORY ◆ KINESTHETIC ◆ TACTILE ◆ VISUAL

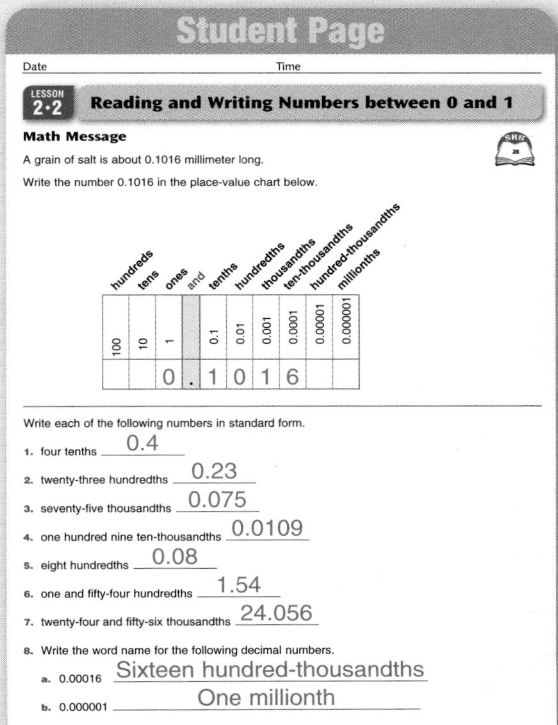

Student Page

Date Time

LESSON 2•2 **Reading and Writing Numbers between 0 and 1**

Math Message

A grain of salt is about 0.1016 millimeter long.

Write the number 0.1016 in the place-value chart below.

hundreds	tens	ones	and	tenths	hundredths	thousandths	ten-thousandths	hundred-thousandths	millionths
100	10	1		0.1	0.01	0.001	0.0001	0.00001	0.000001
		0	.	1	0	1	6		

Write each of the following numbers in standard form.

1. four tenths 0.4
2. twenty-three hundredths 0.23
3. seventy-five thousandths 0.075
4. one hundred nine ten-thousandths 0.0109
5. eight hundredths 0.08
6. one and fifty-four hundredths 1.54
7. twenty-four and fifty-six thousandths 24.056
8. Write the word name for the following decimal numbers.
   a. 0.00016 Sixteen hundred-thousandths
   b. 0.000001 One millionth

Math Journal 1, p. 48

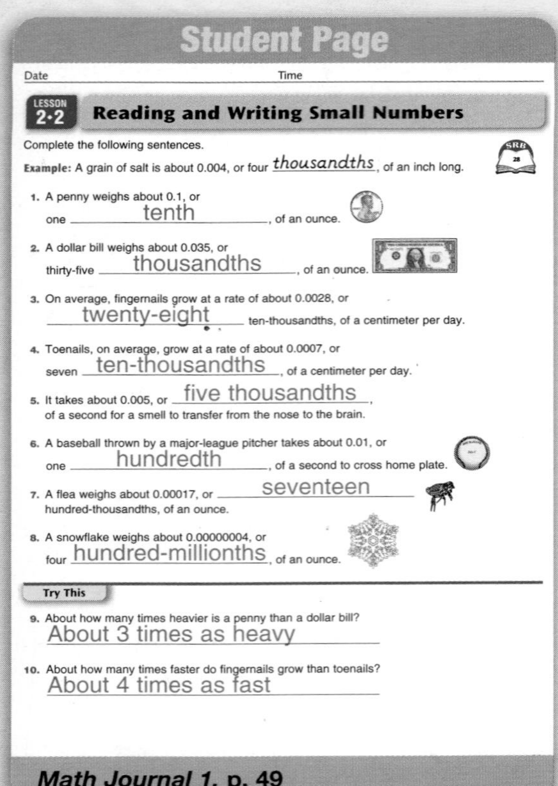

Student Page

Date Time

LESSON 2·2 **Reading and Writing Small Numbers**

Complete the following sentences.

Example: A grain of salt is about 0.004, or four *thousandths* of an inch long.

1. A penny weighs about 0.1, or one tenth, of an ounce.
2. A dollar bill weighs about 0.035, or thirty-five thousandths, of an ounce.
3. On average, fingernails grow at a rate of about 0.0028, or twenty-eight ten-thousandths, of a centimeter per day.
4. Toenails, on average, grow at a rate of about 0.0007, or seven ten-thousandths, of a centimeter per day.
5. It takes about 0.005, or five thousandths, of a second for a smell to transfer from the nose to the brain.
6. A baseball thrown by a major-league pitcher takes about 0.01, or one hundredth, of a second to cross home plate.
7. A flea weighs about 0.00017, or seventeen hundred-thousandths, of an ounce.
8. A snowflake weighs about 0.00000004, or four hundred-millionths, of an ounce.

Try This

9. About how many times heavier is a penny than a dollar bill? About 3 times as heavy
10. About how many times faster do fingernails grow than toenails? About 4 times as fast

Math Journal 1, p. 49

6	.	7	3	8
ones		$\frac{1}{10}$	$\frac{1}{100}$	$\frac{1}{1,000}$

Six and seven hundred thirty-eight thousandths

0	.	0	3	5	9
ones		tenths	hundredths	thousandths	ten-thousandths

Three hundred fifty-nine ten thousandths

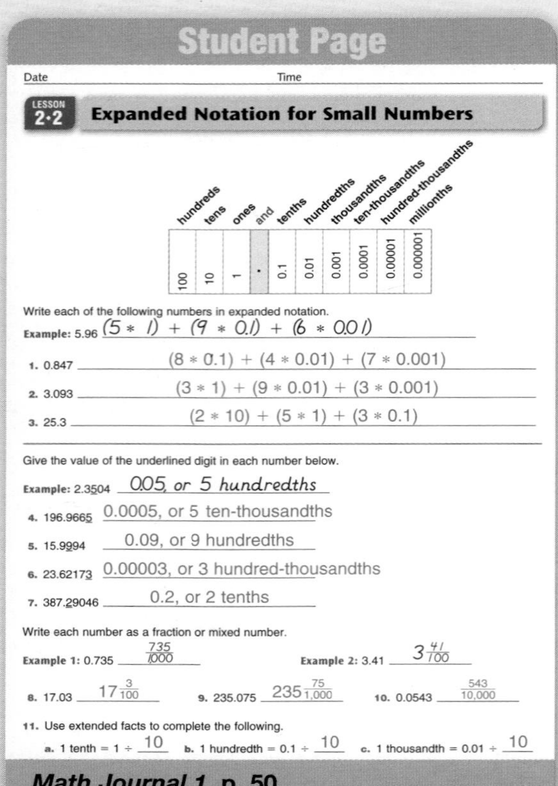

Student Page

Date Time

LESSON 2·2 **Expanded Notation for Small Numbers**

hundreds	tens	ones	and	tenths	hundredths	thousandths	ten-thousandths	hundred-thousandths	millionths
100	10	1	.	0.1	0.01	0.001	0.0001	0.00001	0.000001

Write each of the following numbers in expanded notation.

Example: 5.96 (5 * 1) + (9 * 0.1) + (6 * 0.01)

1. 0.847 (8 * 0.1) + (4 * 0.01) + (7 * 0.001)
2. 3.093 (3 * 1) + (9 * 0.01) + (3 * 0.001)
3. 25.3 (2 * 10) + (5 * 1) + (3 * 0.1)

Give the value of the underlined digit in each number below.

Example: 2.3504 .005, or 5 hundredths

4. 196.9665 0.0005, or 5 ten-thousandths
5. 15.9994 0.09, or 9 hundredths
6. 23.62173 0.00003, or 3 hundred-thousandths
7. 387.29046 0.2, or 2 tenths

Write each number as a fraction or mixed number.

Example 1: 0.735 $\frac{735}{1000}$ **Example 2:** 3.41 $3\frac{41}{100}$

8. 17.03 $17\frac{3}{100}$ 9. 235.075 $235\frac{75}{1,000}$ 10. 0.0543 $\frac{543}{10,000}$

11. Use extended facts to complete the following.
a. 1 tenth = 1 ÷ 10 b. 1 hundredth = 0.1 ÷ 10 c. 1 thousandth = 0.01 ÷ 10

Math Journal 1, p. 50

To read a small number such as 0.1016, underline the final digit and identify its place value. 0.1016, ten-thousandths Then read the number (ignoring the decimal point and any leading zeros) followed by the place value. One thousand sixteen ten-thousandths

Writing the number as a fraction or a mixed number can also help students read it. For example, 6.738 as a mixed number is $6\frac{738}{1,000}$ and is read *six and seven hundred thirty-eight thousandths.*

To write a small number, such as three hundred fifty-nine ten-thousandths, in standard notation, the last digit of the decimal number should be in the place value named. Ten-thousandths Draw a decimal point and mark spaces up to and including the place identified. 0._ _ _ _ Write the number in the spaces so the final digit is written in the last space at the right. 0._ 3 5 9 Fill any blank spaces with zeros. 0.0 3 5 9

NOTE In *Everyday Mathematics,* a zero appears to the left of the decimal point in any number greater than 0 and less than 1. This makes it easier to order decimal numbers, to draw attention to the decimal point, and to correspond with the display on most calculators.

Have students complete journal pages 48 and 49.

Adjusting the Activity

Have students use the place-value template (*Math Masters,* p. 410) as they work on the journal pages, Math Boxes, and Study Link for this lesson.

AUDITORY ◆ KINESTHETIC ◆ TACTILE ◆ VISUAL

▶ Interpreting Expanded Notation for Small Numbers

(*Math Journal,* p. 50; *Math Masters,* p. 410; Transparency of *Math Masters,* p. 410)

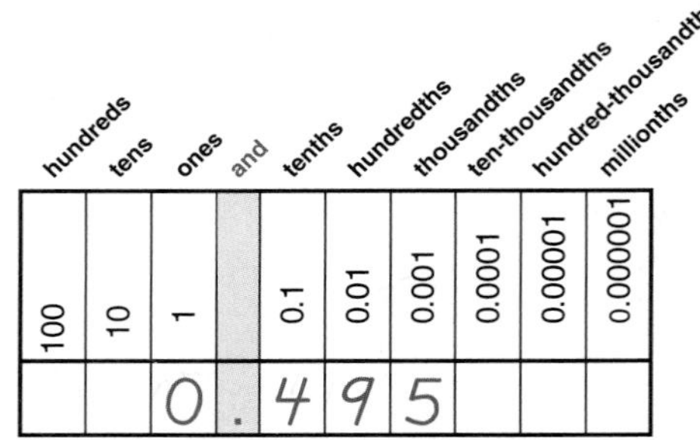

hundreds	tens	ones	and	tenths	hundredths	thousandths	ten-thousandths	hundred-thousandths	millionths
100	10	1		0.1	0.01	0.001	0.0001	0.00001	0.000001
		0	.	4	9	5			

Display a transparency of *Math Masters,* page 410 and distribute one copy of the same page to each student. Ask students to write the number 0.495 in the place-value chart. Students will apply skills they used in the previous lesson to write this decimal number in **expanded notation.**
(4 * 0.10) + (9 * 0.01) + (5 * 0.001)

Have students work independently to complete journal page 50.

2 Ongoing Learning & Practice

▶ Playing *High-Number Toss* (Decimal Version)

PARTNER ACTIVITY

(*Student Reference Book,* p. 324; *Math Masters,* p. 455)

Divide the class into pairs and distribute four each of number cards 0–9 to each pair, as well as a game record sheet (*Math Masters,* p. 455). Students may need to play a practice game.

Ongoing Assessment: Recognizing Student Achievement

Math Masters Page 455 

Use ***Math Masters,* page 455** to assess students' ability to compare decimals through thousandths. Students are making adequate progress if they are able to identify the larger number. Some students may not need a calculator to find the difference between scores.

[Number and Numeration Goal 6]

▶ Math Boxes 2•2

INDEPENDENT ACTIVITY

(*Math Journal 1,* p. 51)

Mixed Practice Math Boxes in this lesson are paired with Math Boxes in Lesson 2-4. The skills in Problems 4 and 5 preview Unit 3 content.

Writing/Reasoning Have students write a response to the following: *Explain why each of the other three answers for Problem 3 is not the best choice.* Sample answer: **A** is not correct because only 5 months have an average rainfall less than 3.5 inches. **B** is incorrect because the average rainfall is very low from October to December. **D** is not correct because there is no way to know what the average rainfall is for Tampa.

▶ Study Link 2•2

INDEPENDENT ACTIVITY

(*Math Masters,* pp. 44 and 45)

Home Connection Students practice place-value skills and write small numbers in standard and expanded notations.

Game Master

Name ______ Date ______ Time ______

***High-Number Toss* (Decimal Version) Record Sheet**

Circle the winning number for each round. Fill in the Score column each time you have the winning number.

Player 1 ______ (Name) Player 2 ______ (Name)

Round	Player 1	Player 2	Score
Sample	0.6 5 4	0.7 5 3	0.753 − 0.654 = 0.099
1	0.___ ___ ___	0.___ ___ ___	
2	0.___ ___ ___	0.___ ___ ___	
3	0.___ ___ ___	0.___ ___ ___	
4	0.___ ___ ___	0.___ ___ ___	
5	0.___ ___ ___	0.___ ___ ___	
		Total Score	

Math Masters, p. 455

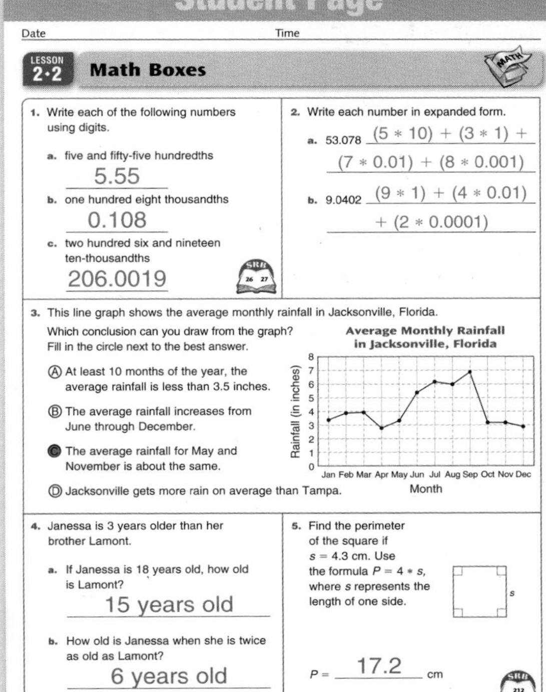

Student Page

Date ______ Time ______

LESSON 2•2 **Math Boxes**

1. Write each of the following numbers using digits.
   a. five and fifty-five hundredths 5.55
   b. one hundred eight thousandths 0.108
   c. two hundred six and nineteen ten-thousandths 206.0019

2. Write each number in expanded form.
   a. 53.078 $(5 * 10) + (3 * 1) + (7 * 0.01) + (8 * 0.001)$
   b. 9.0402 $(9 * 1) + (4 * 0.01) + (2 * 0.0001)$

3. This line graph shows the average monthly rainfall in Jacksonville, Florida. Which conclusion can you draw from the graph? Fill in the circle next to the best answer.
   - Ⓐ At least 10 months of the year, the average rainfall is less than 3.5 inches.
   - Ⓑ The average rainfall increases from June through December.
   - ● The average rainfall for May and November is about the same.
   - Ⓓ Jacksonville gets more rain on average than Tampa.

4. Janessa is 3 years older than her brother Lamont.
   a. If Janessa is 18 years old, how old is Lamont? 15 years old
   b. How old is Janessa when she is twice as old as Lamont? 6 years old

5. Find the perimeter of the square if $s = 4.3$ cm. Use the formula $P = 4 * s$, where s represents the length of one side.
   $P =$ 17.2 cm

Math Journal 1, p. 51

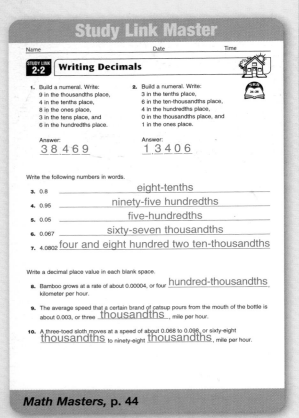

Study Link Master

Name Date Time

STUDY LINK 2·2 Writing Decimals

1. Build a numeral. Write:
   9 in the thousandths place,
   4 in the tenths place,
   8 in the ones place,
   3 in the tens place, and
   6 in the hundredths place.

   Answer: 38.469

2. Build a numeral. Write:
   3 in the tenths place,
   6 in the ten-thousandths place,
   4 in the hundredths place,
   0 in the thousandths place, and
   1 in the ones place.

   Answer: 1.3406

Write the following numbers in words.

3. 0.8 eight-tenths
4. 0.95 ninety-five hundredths
5. 0.05 five-hundredths
6. 0.067 sixty-seven thousandths
7. 4.0802 four and eight hundred two ten-thousandths

Write a decimal place value in each blank space.

8. Bamboo grows at a rate of about 0.00004, or four hundred-thousandths, kilometer per hour.
9. The average speed that a certain brand of catsup pours from the mouth of the bottle is about 0.003, or three thousandths, mile per hour.
10. A three-toed sloth moves at a speed of about 0.068 to 0.098, or sixty-eight thousandths to ninety-eight thousandths, mile per hour.

Math Masters, p. 44

NOTE Collect and store students' base-10 grids for future use.

Study Link Master

Name Date Time

STUDY LINK 2·2 Writing Decimals *continued*

hundreds	tens	ones	and	tenths	hundredths	thousandths	ten-thousandths	hundred-thousandths	millionths
100	10	1	.	0.1	0.01	0.001	0.0001	0.00001	0.000001

Write each of the following numbers in expanded notation.

Example: $2.756 = (2 * 1) + (7 * 0.1) + (5 * 0.01) + (6 * 0.001)$

11. 0.013 $(1 * 0.01) + (3 * 0.001)$
12. 109.3527 $(1 * 100) + (9 * 1) + (3 * 0.1) + (5 * 0.01) + (2 * 0.001) + (7 * 0.0001)$
13. Using the digits 0, 3, 6, and 8, write the greatest decimal number possible. 8.630
14. Using the digits 0, 3, 6, and 8, write the least decimal number possible. 0.368

Try This

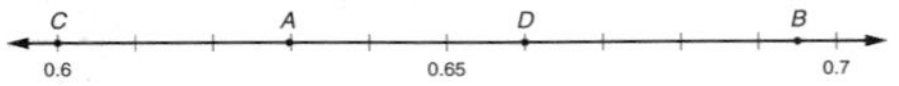

Name the point on the number line that represents each of the following numbers.

15. 0.66 D 16. 0.6299 A 17. 0.6 C 18. 0.695 B
19. Refer to the number line above. Round 0.6299 to the nearest hundredth. 0.63

Practice

20. $0.01 + 0.006 + 0.0008 =$ 0.0168
21. $0.7 + 0.04 + 0.0002 =$ 0.7402
22. 45.009 $= 40 + 5 + 0.009$
23. 0.5801 $= 0.50 + 0.080 + 0.00010$

Math Masters, p. 45

3 Differentiation Options

READINESS

PARTNER ACTIVITY

5–15 Min

▶ Modeling and Comparing Decimals

(*Math Masters,* pp. 46, 411–413)

To provide experience comparing decimals, have students use base-10 grids. Provide each pair with one copy of *Math Masters,* page 46, two copies of page 411, one copy of page 412, and scissors. Review the worth of the flat, long, unit, and fractional parts of the unit, as shown on *Math Masters,* page 46. After students have prepared their base-10 grids, ask them to record their models and compare the given decimal numbers using <, >, or =.

ENRICHMENT

PARTNER ACTIVITY

5–15 Min

▶ Decimals between Decimals

Between any two decimal numbers, there is always another decimal number. Help students explore this concept by asking them to list 20 or more decimal numbers between a given pair of decimals. Suggested decimal pairs include:

0.1 and 0.2; 0.33 and 0.34; 2.561 and 2.562.

Have students describe any patterns or strategies they used to generate their lists.

Teaching Master

Name Date Time

LESSON 2·2 Modeling and Comparing Decimals

One way to compare decimals is to model them with base-10 grids.

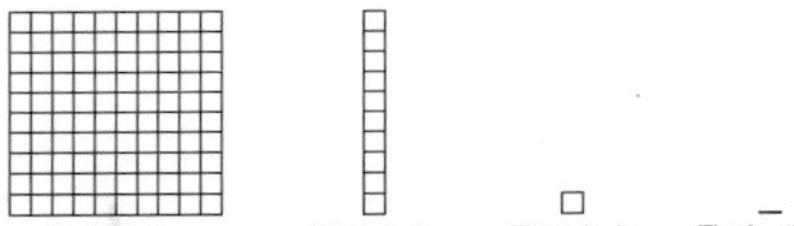

The flat is the whole, or 1.0. The long is worth 0.1. The cube is worth 0.01. The fractional part of the cube is worth 0.001.

Another way to compare decimals is to draw pictures.

The flat is the whole, or 1.0. The long is worth 0.1. The cube is worth 0.01. The fractional part of the cube is worth 0.001.

1. Use decimal models to complete the following.
   $1.0 = 0.10 *$ 10 $0.10 = 0.01 *$ 10 $0.01 = 0.001 *$ 10

Model the decimal numbers in each pair. Draw a picture to record each model. Then compare the decimal numbers using <, >, or =.

2. 
   0.3 > 0.14
3. 
   1.56 < 1.562
4. 
   0.2 > 0.025
5. Model and record a decimal number that is between 0.41 and 0.42. Sample answer:

   0.41 < 0.418 < 0.42

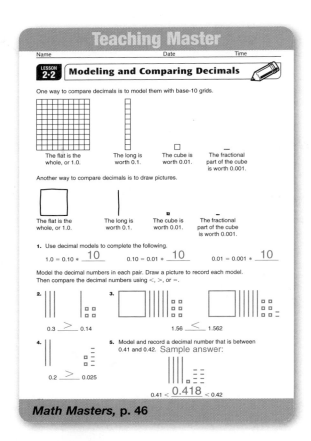

Math Masters, p. 46

Addition and Subtraction of Decimals

Objective To add, subtract, and round decimals.

1 Teaching the Lesson

Key Activities

Students add and subtract decimals. They also round decimals and convert metric units.

Key Concepts and Skills

- Apply place-value concepts to round decimals to a given place.
  [Number and Numeration Goal 1]
- Adapt whole-number algorithms to add and subtract decimals.
  [Operations and Computation Goal 1]
- Use extended multiplication and division facts to convert between metric units.
  [Operations and Computation Goal 2]
- Estimate sums and differences of decimals.
  [Operations and Computation Goal 5]

Key Vocabulary

precise

Ongoing Assessment: Recognizing Student Achievement Use the Math Message.
[Number and Numeration Goal 1]

materials

- ☐ *Math Journal 1,* pp. 52 and 53
- ☐ *Student Reference Book,* pp. 31–34
- ☐ Study Link 2•2
- ☐ Teaching Aid Master (*Math Masters,* p. 414; optional)

***See* Advance Preparation**

2 Ongoing Learning & Practice

Students practice drawing and interpreting a step graph.

Students practice and maintain skills through Math Boxes and Study Link activities.

materials

- ☐ *Math Journal 1,* pp. 54 and 55
- ☐ Study Link Master (*Math Masters,* p. 47)

3 Differentiation Options

READINESS

Students model subtraction of decimals using base-10 grids or pictures.

ENRICHMENT

Students explore how rounding increases the possible variations in the amounts represented.

EXTRA PRACTICE

Students practice rounding decimals.

materials

- ☐ Teaching Master (*Math Masters,* p. 48)
- ☐ Teaching Aid Masters (*Math Masters,* pp. 411–413)
- ☐ *5-Minute Math,* pp. 89 and 178
- ☐ scissors

Additional Information

Advance Preparation Consider having some students use a place-value chart from Lesson 2•2 when completing the Math Message.

Technology

Assessment Management System
Math Message
See the **iTLG.**

Getting Started

Mental Math and Reflexes

Students write numbers from dictation and record numbers that are 0.1 more than the dictated number.

Suggestions:

●○○ 0.9 1.0
19.08 19.18

●●○ 1.742 1.842
382.15 382.25

●●● 1,019.904 1,020.004
46,099.9 46,100

Math Message ★

List the following decimals in a column so the digits are lined up by place value.

70.5; 501; 109.4; 9.892; 0.29; 354.399; 3,897.0041

70.5
501.0
109.4
9.892
0.29
354.399
3,897.0041

Study Link 2·2 Follow-Up

Briefly go over the answers.
For Problems 15–19, ask students to explain their strategies for identifying points on the number line.

1 Teaching the Lesson

▶ Math Message Follow-Up

WHOLE-CLASS DISCUSSION

(*Student Reference Book,* pp. 31 and 32)

Ask a volunteer to present his or her list of numbers and share the strategy used to align the numbers. Encourage students to share alternate strategies. Discuss the advantage of attaching zeros when aligning decimals by place value.

Select two decimals from the list of numbers, for example, 109.4 and 9.892. Ask students to first add them 119.292 and then subtract them. 99.508 Remind students to estimate before adding or subtracting. Discuss their estimation strategies, preferred algorithms, solutions, and checks for reasonableness. Expect that virtually all students will have mastered one algorithm for addition and one for subtraction. If necessary, encourage students to review the algorithms shown on pages 31 and 32 of the *Student Reference Book.*

Ongoing Assessment: Recognizing Student Achievement

Math Message ★

Use the **Math Message** to assess students' ability to align the digits of whole and decimal numbers by place value. Students are making adequate progress if they correctly align the numbers containing decimal points. Some students might recognize that 501 is equivalent to 501.0 and align this number accordingly.

[Number and Numeration Goal 1]

▶ Renaming or Rounding to the Same Number of Decimal Places

(*Student Reference Book,* pp. 33 and 34)

Discuss situations in which numbers to be added or subtracted do not have the same number of decimal places.

Example 1:

A ribbon is 8 meters long. If you cut off a piece 1.68 meters long, what length of ribbon remains?

▷ One approach is to convert meters to centimeters.

8 m = 800 cm and 1.68 m = 168 cm

800 cm − 168 cm = 632 cm, or 6.32 m

6.32 m of ribbon remain.

▷ A second approach is to solve 8 − 1.68 = ?

The number 1.68 has two decimal places. Put a decimal point and two zeros to the right of 8 so it also has two decimal places.

8 m = 8.00 m

8.00 m − 1.68 m = 6.32 m

6.32 m of ribbon remain.

The smaller the unit of measure you use, the more **precise** the measurement will be. Measurements should be rounded so they all have the same precision—that of the less precise measurement.

Example 2:

Aaron has a physical exam each year, just before school begins. Aaron's height in August was 1.38 meters. His height one year later was 1.424 meters. How much had Aaron grown during the year?

In August, Aaron's height was measured to the nearest centimeter (hundredth of a meter). One year later, Aaron's height was measured to the nearest millimeter (thousandth of a meter). Because a centimeter is a larger unit than a millimeter, the measure in centimeters is the less precise measurement. Before finding the difference between the two heights, round the more precise measurement (1.424 m) to match the less precise measurement (1.38 m).

Round 1.424 m to 1.42 m

1.42 m − 1.38 m = 0.04 m

Aaron grew about 0.04 m, or 4 cm, during the year.

For additional practice in renaming or rounding to equalize the number of decimal places, discuss the examples on page 34 of the *Student Reference Book.*

Student Page

Date ______ Time ______

LESSON 2·3 **Adding and Subtracting Decimals**

Estimate each sum or difference. Then solve. Sample estimates given.

1. 32.5 + 19.6 Estimate 53 32.5 + 19.6 = 52.1	**2.** 5.67 − 1.84 Estimate 4 5.67 − 1.84 = 3.83
3. 10.89 − 3.5 Estimate 7 10.89 − 3.5 = 7.39	**4.** 4.07 + 9.38 Estimate 13 4.07 + 9.38 = 13.45
5. 0.671 + 8.935 Estimate 10 0.671 + 8.935 = 9.606	**6.** 115.97 + 257.49 + 19.95 Estimate 393 115.97 + 257.49 + 19.95 = 393.41
7. 49.2 − 27.6 Estimate 22 49.2 − 27.6 = 21.6	**8.** 5.006 − 0.392 Estimate 4.5 5.006 − 0.392 = 4.614
9. 8.03 − 4.715 Estimate 3 8.03 − 4.715 = 3.315	**10.** 13.9 − 0.38 Estimate 13.5 13.9 − 0.38 = 13.52

Math Journal 1, p. 52

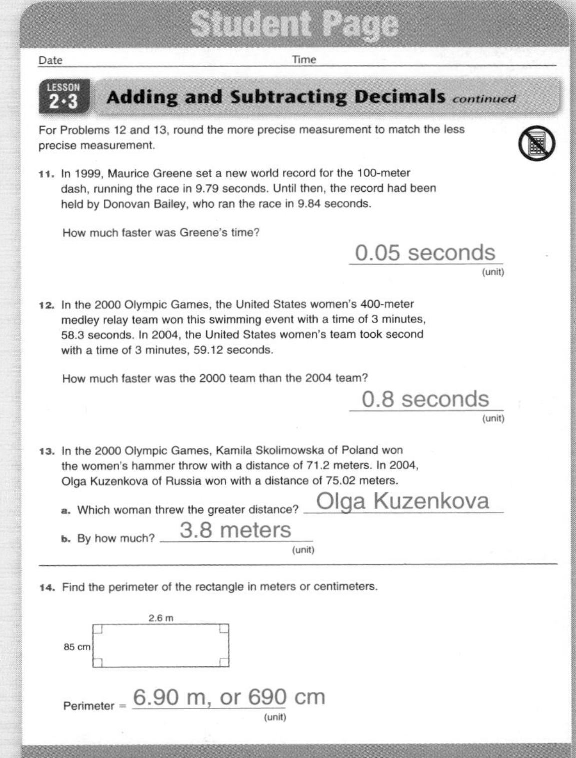

Student Page

Date ______ Time ______

LESSON 2·3 **Adding and Subtracting Decimals** *continued*

For Problems 12 and 13, round the more precise measurement to match the less precise measurement.

11. In 1999, Maurice Greene set a new world record for the 100-meter dash, running the race in 9.79 seconds. Until then, the record had been held by Donovan Bailey, who ran the race in 9.84 seconds.

How much faster was Greene's time? 0.05 seconds (unit)

12. In the 2000 Olympic Games, the United States women's 400-meter medley relay team won this swimming event with a time of 3 minutes, 58.3 seconds. In 2004, the United States women's team took second with a time of 3 minutes, 59.12 seconds.

How much faster was the 2000 team than the 2004 team? 0.8 seconds (unit)

13. In the 2000 Olympic Games, Kamila Skolimowska of Poland won the women's hammer throw with a distance of 71.2 meters. In 2004, Olga Kuzenkova of Russia won with a distance of 75.02 meters.

a. Which woman threw the greater distance? Olga Kuzenkova

b. By how much? 3.8 meters (unit)

14. Find the perimeter of the rectangle in meters or centimeters.

2.6 m
85 cm

Perimeter = 6.90 m, or 690 cm (unit)

Math Journal 1, p. 53

Student Page

Date ______ Time ______

LESSON 2·3 **Drawing and Interpreting a Step Graph**

The cost of a telephone call usually depends on how long the call lasts. The calling costs for one phone company appear in the table at the right.

Length of Call	Cost
More than **0** minutes, but not more than **20** minutes	$5.00
More than **20** minutes, but not more than **21** minutes	$5.10
More than **21** minutes, but not more than **22** minutes	$5.20
More than **22** minutes, but not more than **23** minutes	$5.30
More than **23** minutes, but not more than **24** minutes	$5.40

1. Use the data in the table to complete the step graph below.

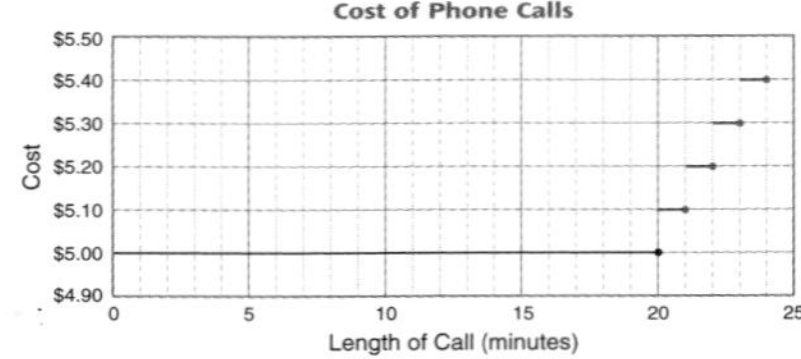

Give the cost for each phone call.

2. 1 minute costs $ 5.00
3. 12 minutes cost $ 5.00
4. 20 minutes cost $ 5.00

5. A phone call costs $5.40. Choose the best answer for each of the following questions.
   a. What is the shortest amount of time the phone call can last?
      ○ 23 minutes ● between 23 and 24 minutes ○ 24 minutes
   b. What is the longest amount of time the phone call can last?
      ○ 23 minutes ○ between 23 and 24 minutes ● 24 minutes

6. If you make a 4-minute call, what is the cost per minute? $ 1.25

Math Journal 1, **p. 55**

NOTE You can use the FIX function of some calculators to round numbers to ten-millionths. See the calculator section of the *Student Reference Book.*

Student Page

Date ______ Time ______

LESSON 2·3 **Math Boxes**

1. Write each number in expanded form.
   a. 346.52
      (3 * 100) + (4 * 10) + (6 * 1) + (5 * 0.1) + (2 * 0.01)
   b. 70.039
      (7 * 10) + (3 * 0.01) + (9 * 0.001)

2. Convert the numbers given in number-and-word notation to standard notation.
   a. The least distance that Pluto is from Earth is about 2.7 billion miles.
      2,700,000,000 miles
   b. Earth is about 150 million kilometers from the Sun.
      150,000,000 kilometers

3. Make a double-stem plot for the data below.

Inauguration Age of U.S. Presidents Since 1861						
52	56	46	54	49	50	47
55	55	54	42	51	56	55
51	54	51	60	62	43	55
56	61	52	69	62	46	54

Stems (10s)	Leaves (1s)
4	2 3
4	6 6 7 9
5	0 1 1 1 2 2 4 4 4 4
5	5 5 5 5 6 6 6
6	0 1 2 2
6	9

Use your double-stem plot to find the following landmarks.

a. range 27 b. median 54 c. mode(s) 54 and 55

4. Complete the "What's My Rule?" table.

   Rule: Multiply by 10.

in	out
7	70
80	800
0.4	4
9.2	92
32.6	326

5. Solve.

   Alma is $\frac{1}{4}$ the age of her father. Alma's father is 60 years old.
   a. How old is Alma?
      15 years old
   b. Alma's brother Luke is $\frac{1}{5}$ his father's age. How old is Luke?
      12 years old

Math Journal 1, **p. 54**

▶ Adding and Subtracting Decimals

INDEPENDENT ACTIVITY

(*Math Journal 1,* pp. 52 and 53; *Math Masters,* p. 414)

Assign the problems on journal pages 52 and 53. Circulate and assist as needed.

Reserve some time for students to discuss their solutions. Problems 12–14 include numbers that do not have the same units. Remind students that for addition or subtraction of measurements all the numbers must have the same unit.

Adjusting the Activity

Have students use a computation grid (*Math Masters,* p. 414) when adding and subtracting decimals. Use money to model those problems dealing with whole numbers, tenths, and hundredths.

AUDITORY ◆ KINESTHETIC ◆ TACTILE ◆ VISUAL

2 Ongoing Learning & Practice

▶ Drawing and Interpreting a Step Graph

INDEPENDENT ACTIVITY

(*Math Journal 1,* p. 55)

Consumer Education Link Students use phone-call cost data to draw and interpret a step graph.

▶ Math Boxes 2·3

INDEPENDENT ACTIVITY

(*Math Journal 1,* p. 54)

Mixed Practice Math Boxes in this lesson are paired with Math Boxes in Lesson 2-1. The skills in Problems 4 and 5 preview Unit 3 content.

▶ Study Link 2·3

INDEPENDENT ACTIVITY

(*Math Masters,* p. 47)

Home Connection Students practice estimating and finding sums and differences of decimals.

3 Differentiation Options

READINESS

 PARTNER ACTIVITY

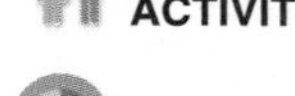 5–15 Min

▶ Modeling Subtraction of Decimals

(*Math Masters,* pp. 48, 411–413)

Students use modeling to gain experience with subtraction of decimal numbers. Provide each pair with one copy of *Math Masters,* page 48, at least two copies each of *Math Masters,* pages 411–413, and scissors. Students should think of the flat as the ONE, the longs as tenths, the units as hundredths, and the fractional parts of the units as thousandths. They can then use the cut-apart grids when completing journal pages in Part 1 or the Study Link in Part 2 of the lesson.

ENRICHMENT

 SMALL-GROUP ACTIVITY

 5–15 Min

▶ Exploring Meaningful Zeros

Many tools, such as Allen wrenches, are sized as 2.0 mm, 3.0 mm, and 4.0 mm. Most students would drop the zeros and report these sizes as 2 mm, 3 mm, and 4 mm. However, a measurement of 3.0 mm is not necessarily the same as 3 mm. The zero(s) at the end of decimal numbers such as 3.0 and 3.00 are meaningful in expressing precision.

To extend their knowledge of place-value concepts, have students identify and compare the range of numbers that can be rounded

to 3. Numbers greater than 2.5 and less than 3.5; range: 1

to 3.0. Numbers greater than 2.95 and less than 3.05; range: 0.1

to 3.00. Numbers greater than 2.995 and less than 3.005; range: 0.01

EXTRA PRACTICE

 SMALL-GROUP ACTIVITY

 5–15 Min

▶ *5-Minute Math*

To offer more practice with rounding decimals, see *5-Minute Math,* pages 89 and 178.

Study Link Master

Name Date Time

STUDY LINK 2·3 **Sports Records**

Solve.

1. The fastest winning time for the New York Marathon (Tesfay Jifar of Ethiopia, 2001) is 2 hours, 7.72 minutes. The second fastest time is 2 hours, 8.017 minutes (Juma Ikangaa of Tanzania, 1989).
   How much faster was Jifar's time than Ikangaa's? 0.297 minutes
2. In the 1908 Olympic Games, Erik Lemming of Sweden won the javelin throw with a distance of 54.825 meters. He won again in 1912 with a distance of 60.64 meters.
   How much longer was his 1912 throw than his 1908 throw? 5.815 meters
3. Driver Buddy Baker (Oldsmobile, 1980) holds the record for the fastest winning speed in the Daytona 500 at 177.602 miles per hour. Bill Elliott (Ford, 1987) has the second fastest speed at 176.263 miles per hour.
   How much faster is Baker's speed than Elliott's? 1.339 miles per hour
4. The highest scoring World Cup Soccer Final was in 1954. Teams played 26 games and scored 140 goals for an average of 5.38 goals per game. In 1950, teams played 22 games and scored 88 goals for an average of 4 goals per game.
   What is the difference between the 1954 and the 1950 average goals per game? 1.38 goals

Sample estimates given.

5. 46.09 + 123.047 Estimate 170
   46.09 + 123.047 = 169.137
6. 0.172 + 4.5 Estimate 4.6
   0.172 + 4.5 = 4.672

Practice

Solve mentally.

7. \$0.36 + \$0.29 + \$0.64 + \$0.71 = \$2.00
8. 7.03 + 0.85 + 14.05 + 13.07 = 35
9. 9.225 + 8.5 + 5.775 + 1.5 = 25
10. \$3.69 + \$6.75 + \$8.31 + \$6.25 = \$25

Math Masters, p. 47

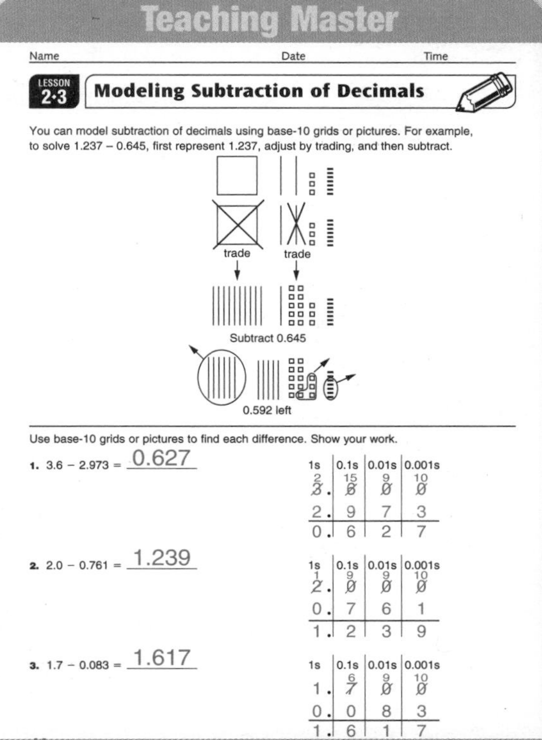

Teaching Master

Name Date Time

LESSON 2·3 **Modeling Subtraction of Decimals**

You can model subtraction of decimals using base-10 grids or pictures. For example, to solve 1.237 − 0.645, first represent 1.237, adjust by trading, and then subtract.

Use base-10 grids or pictures to find each difference. Show your work.

1. 3.6 − 2.973 = 0.627

1s	0.1s	0.01s	0.001s
2 3.	15 6	9 0	10 0
2.	9	7	3
0.	6	2	7

2. 2.0 − 0.761 = 1.239

1s	0.1s	0.01s	0.001s
1 2.	9 0	9 0	10 0
0.	7	6	1
1.	2	3	9

3. 1.7 − 0.083 = 1.617

1s	0.1s	0.01s	0.001s
1.	6 7	9 0	10 0
0.	0	8	3
1.	6	1	7

Math Masters, p. 48

2·4 Multiplying by Powers of 10

Objective To develop and practice strategies for multiplying by powers of 10.

1 Teaching the Lesson

Key Activities

Students develop strategies for multiplying by positive and negative powers of 10.

Key Concepts and Skills

- Apply place-value concepts to find values 10, 100, and 1,000 times as great. [Number and Numeration Goal 1]
- Use a multiplication-by-power-of-10 strategy to convert between percents and decimals. [Number and Numeration Goal 5]
- Estimate the product of a decimal and a power of 10. [Operations and Computation Goal 5]
- Extend a pattern to develop a rule for multiplying by powers of 10. [Patterns, Functions, and Algebra Goal 1]

Key Vocabulary powers of 10 • exponential notation

Ongoing Assessment: Informing Instruction See page 120.

materials

- ☐ *Math Journal 1,* pp. 56 and 57
- ☐ *Student Reference Book,* p. 35
- ☐ Study Link 2•3

2 Ongoing Learning & Practice

Students practice estimating products of whole and decimal numbers by playing *Doggone Decimal.*

Students practice and maintain skills through Math Boxes and Study Link activities.

Ongoing Assessment: Recognizing Student Achievement Use journal page 58. [Number and Numeration Goal 1]

materials

- ☐ *Math Journal 1,* p. 58
- ☐ *Student Reference Book,* p. 310
- ☐ Study Link Master (*Math Masters,* p. 49)
- ☐ Game Master (*Math Masters,* p. 433)

Per partnership:

- ☐ 4 each of number cards 0–9
- ☐ index cards labeled 0.1, 1, 10, and 100
- ☐ 4 counters or coins

3 Differentiation Options

READINESS

Students review multiplying and dividing by 10.

ENRICHMENT

Students extend a pattern to develop a rule for products of power-of-10 factors.

EXTRA PRACTICE

Students practice multiplying and dividing numbers by powers of 10.

ELL SUPPORT

Students add *powers of 10* and *exponential notation* to their Math Word Banks.

materials

- ☐ Teaching Master (*Math Masters,* p. 50)
- ☐ *Student Reference Book,* p. 285
- ☐ *5-Minute Math,* pp. 2, 3, and 80
- ☐ *Differentiation Handbook*
- ☐ calculator

Technology

Assessment Management System
Math Boxes, Problem 1
See the **iTLG.**

Getting Started

Mental Math and Reflexes

Students write each fraction as a decimal.

●○○ $\frac{3}{10}$ 0.3 ●●○ $\frac{35}{100}$ 0.35 ●●● $\frac{7}{1,000}$ 0.007

$\frac{4}{100}$ 0.04 $\frac{600}{100}$ 6.00 $\frac{921}{1,000}$ 0.921

Math Message

Complete Problems 1–3 on journal page 56.

Study Link 2·3 Follow-Up

Review answers. For Problems 5 and 6, ask students to explain their estimation strategies.

1 Teaching the Lesson

▶ Math Message Follow-Up

(*Math Journal 1,* p. 56; *Student Reference Book,* p. 35)

Encourage students to share the patterns they found in the table in the Math Message. Numbers such as 10; 100; 1,000; 0.1; 0.01; and 0.001 are called **powers of 10.** Powers of 10 are numbers that can be written using only 10s and $\frac{1}{10}$s as factors. To support English language learners, discuss the different uses of *power* as well as its meaning in this context. Numbers that are written with an exponent, such as the powers of 10 shown in the table, are in **exponential notation.**

Ask students to rewrite the following multiplication problems to express 10, 100, and 1,000 in exponential notation. Then have them apply extended multiplication facts to solve each problem.

$5 * 10 = 5 *$ _______ $= ?$ 10^1; 50

$5 * 100 = 5 *$ _______ $= ?$ 10^2; 500

$5 * 1,000 = 5 *$ _______ $= ?$ 10^3; 5,000

Have students look for a pattern and develop a strategy for multiplying by powers of 10 that are greater than 1. Discuss their strategies and record key ideas on the board. Move the decimal point to the right for each power of 10 or the same number of places as the exponent. Have students complete journal page 56.

Student Page

Date Time

LESSON 2·4 **Multiplying by Powers of 10**

Math Message

Some Powers of 10

10^4	10^3	10^2	10^1	10^0	.	10^{-1}	10^{-2}	10^{-3}	10^{-4}
$10 * 10 * 10 * 10$	$10 * 10 * 10$	$10 * 10$	10	1	.	$\frac{1}{10}$	$\frac{1}{10} * \frac{1}{10}$	$\frac{1}{10} * \frac{1}{10} * \frac{1}{10}$	$\frac{1}{10} * \frac{1}{10} * \frac{1}{10} * \frac{1}{10}$
10,000	1,000	100	10	1	.	0.1	0.01	0.001	0.0001

Work with a partner. Study the table above and then discuss the following questions.

1. What is the relationship between the exponent (Row 1) and the number of zeros in the positive powers of 10 (Row 3)?
   The exponent and number of zeros are equal.
2. What is the relationship between the exponent (Row 1) and the number of digits after the decimal point in the negative powers of 10 (Row 3)?
   The exponent and number of digits are equal.
3. In Lesson 2-1, you learned that each place on the place-value chart is 10 times the value of the place to its right and $\frac{1}{10}$ the value of the place to its left.
   a. What happens to the decimal point when you multiply 1.0 by 10; 10.0 by 10; 100.0 by 10; and so on?
      It moves one place to the right.
   b. What happens to the decimal point when you multiply 1.0 by $\frac{1}{10}$; 10.0 by $\frac{1}{10}$; 100.0 by $\frac{1}{10}$; and so on?
      It moves one place to the left.

Use extended multiplication facts and any strategies you have developed through your study and discussion of patterns to complete the following.

4. $0.2 * 10^3 =$ 200.0
5. $70 = 0.07 *$ 10^3
6. $0.5 = 0.005 *$ 10^2

Math Journal 1, p. 56

Student Page

Time

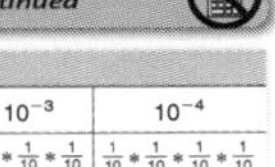

LESSON 2·4 **Multiplying by Powers of 10** *continued*

Some Powers of 10

10^4	10^3	10^2	10^1	10^0	.	10^{-1}	10^{-2}	10^{-3}	10^{-4}
10 * 10 * 10 * 10	10 * 10 * 10	10 * 10	10	1	.	$\frac{1}{10}$	$\frac{1}{10} * \frac{1}{10}$	$\frac{1}{10} * \frac{1}{10} * \frac{1}{10}$	$\frac{1}{10} * \frac{1}{10} * \frac{1}{10} * \frac{1}{10}$
10,000	1,000	100	10	1	.	0.1	0.01	0.001	0.0001

Use extended multiplication facts and any strategies you have developed through your study and discussion of patterns to complete the following.

7. $50 * 0.1 =$ 5.0
8. $5 * 10^{-1} =$ 0.5
9. $0.4 * 10^{-1} =$ 0.04
10. $0.4 * 10^{-2} =$ 0.004
11. $0.4 * 10^{-3} =$ 0.0004
12. $3.2 * 0.001 =$ 0.0032
13. $0.32 = 3.2 *$ 10^{-1}
14. $0.032 =$ 3.2 $* 10^{-2}$
15. In Expanded notation, $5.26 = (5 * 1.0) + (2 * 0.1) + (6 * 0.01)$. Exponential notation can be used to write numbers in expanded notation. Using exponential notation, $5.26 = (5 * 10^0) + (2 * 10^{-1}) + (6 * 10^{-2})$.

    Write each number in expanded notation using exponential notation.

    a. $0.384 =$ $(3 * 10^{-1}) + (8 * 10^{-2}) + (4 * 10^{-3})$

    b. $71.0295 =$ $(7 * 10^1) + (1 * 10^0) + (2 * 10^{-2}) + (9 * 10^{-3}) + (5 * 10^{-4})$

Recall that percents are parts of 100. You can think of the percent symbol, %, as meaning *times* $\frac{1}{100}$, *times 0.01, or times* 10^{-2}.

Example: $25\% = 25 * 10^{-2} = 0.25$

Use your power-of-10 strategy to rewrite each percent as an equivalent decimal number.

16. 5% = 0.05
17. 50% = 0.50
18. 500% = 5.00
19. 125% = 1.25
20. 12.5% = 0.125
21. $1\frac{1}{4}$% = 0.0125
22. 3% = 0.03
23. 0.3% = 0.003
24. 0.03% = 0.0003

Math Journal 1, p. 57

Ongoing Assessment: Informing Instruction

Watch for students who do not recognize that they can write any whole number with a decimal point following the last digit. Suggest that they rewrite whole numbers to include the decimal, for example, rewrite 8 as 8.0.

Next, have students rewrite the following multiplication problems to express $\frac{1}{10}$, $\frac{1}{100}$, and $\frac{1}{1,000}$ in exponential notation. Have students solve each problem.

$1 * \frac{1}{10} = 1 * 0.1 = 1 *$ ______ $= ?$ 10^{-1}; 0.1

$1 * \frac{1}{100} = 1 * 0.01 = 1 *$ ______ $= ?$ 10^{-2}; 0.01

$1 * \frac{1}{1,000} = 1 * 0.001 = 1 *$ ______ $= ?$ 10^{-3}; 0.001

Have students demonstrate and discuss their strategies for multiplying by a power of 10 less than 1. Move the decimal point to the left for each power of 10 or the same number of places as the exponent. If necessary, model the strategy that appears on page 35 in the *Student Reference Book.*

Students can use their knowledge of extended multiplication facts to confirm the product of a number and a power of 10. For example, students might estimate 1,000 * 45.6 as 1,000 * 40 40,000; as 1,000 * 45 45,000; or as 1,000 * 50 50,000. Any of these estimates can help students place the decimal point in the answer.

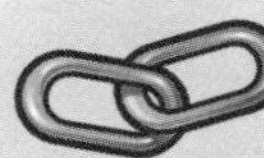

Links to the Future

Students will apply their knowledge of exponential notation, such as $n^{-1} = \frac{1}{n}$ when they use their calculators to find reciprocals of numbers in Lesson 6-1.

Student Page

Games

Doggone Decimal

Materials
- number cards 0–9 (4 of each)
- 4 index cards labeled 0.1, 1, 10, and 100
- 2 counters per player (to use as decimal points)
- 1 calculator for each player

Players 2

Skill Estimating products of whole numbers and decimals

Object of the game To collect more number cards.

Directions

1. One player shuffles the number cards and deals 4 cards to each player.
2. The other player shuffles the index cards, places them number-side down, and turns over the top card. The number that appears (0.1, 1, 10, or 100) is the **target number.**
3. Using 4 number cards and 2 decimal-point counters, each player forms 2 numbers. Each number must have 2 digits and a decimal point.
   - Players try to form 2 numbers whose product is as close as possible to the target number.
   - The decimal point can go anywhere in a number—for example: .48 4.8 48.
4. Each player computes the product of their numbers using a calculator.
5. The player whose product is closer to the target number takes all 8 number cards.
6. Four new number cards are dealt to each player and a new target number is turned over. Repeat Steps 3–5 using the new target number.
7. The game ends when all the target numbers have been used.
8. The player with more number cards wins the game. In the case of a tie, reshuffle the index cards and turn over a target number. Play one tie-breaking round.

Example The target number is 10.

Briana is dealt 1, 4, 8, and 8. She forms the numbers 8.8 and 1.4.
Evelyn is dealt 2, 3, 6, and 9. She forms the numbers 2.6 and 3.9.

Briana's product is 12.32 and Evelyn's is 10.14.
Evelyn's product is closer to 10. She wins the round and takes all 8 cards.

Student Reference Book, p. 310

▶ Multiplying Decimals by Powers of 10

INDEPENDENT ACTIVITY

(*Math Journal 1,* p. 57; *Student Reference Book,* p. 35)

Have students complete journal page 57. Circulate and assist. When most students have finished, go over the answers.

For Problem 26, remind students that before changing $1\frac{1}{4}\%$ to a decimal, they could write it as 1.25% and that they can include zeros at either end of a number to provide places for decimal point shifts.

2 Ongoing Learning & Practice

▶ Playing *Doggone Decimal*

PARTNER ACTIVITY

(*Student Reference Book,* p. 310; *Math Masters,* p. 433)

Review the directions for *Doggone Decimal* on page 310 in the *Student Reference Book.* Play one or two rounds with the class. Make the following points:

▷ If one factor is less than 1, the product will be less than the other factor.

▷ One way to quickly estimate a product is to round each factor to its greatest place value. For example, you can estimate 5.3 ∗ 0.64 as 5.0 ∗ 0.60. 3

▶ Math Boxes 2•4

INDEPENDENT ACTIVITY

(*Math Journal 1,* p. 58)

Mixed Practice Math Boxes in this lesson are paired with Math Boxes in Lesson 2-2. The skills in Problems 4 and 5 preview Unit 3 content.

Ongoing Assessment: Recognizing Student Achievement

Math Boxes Problem 1

Use **Math Boxes, Problem 1** to assess students' ability to write decimals to thousandths. Students are making adequate progress if they are able to successfully complete parts a–c. Some students may be able to convert from expanded to standard notation as in Problem 2.

[Number and Numeration Goal 1]

▶ Study Link 2•4

INDEPENDENT ACTIVITY

(*Math Masters,* p. 49)

Home Connection Students use estimation or a power-of-10 strategy to multiply and place decimal points in products.

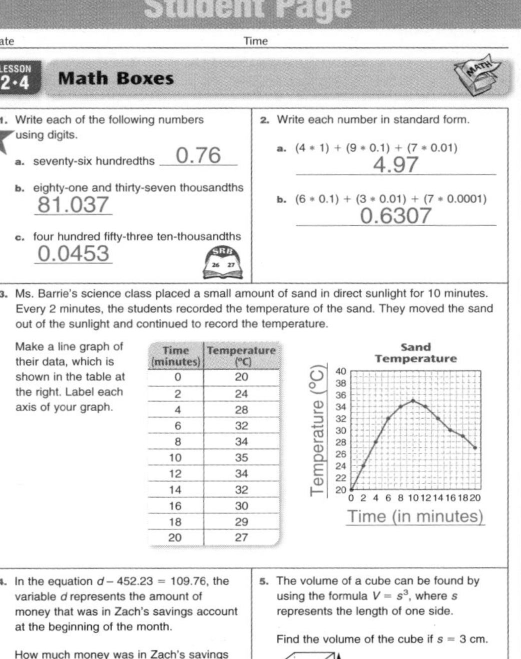

Student Page

Date ____ Time ____

LESSON 2•4 **Math Boxes**

1. Write each of the following numbers using digits.
   a. seventy-six hundredths 0.76
   b. eighty-one and thirty-seven thousandths 81.037
   c. four hundred fifty-three ten-thousandths 0.0453

SRB 26 27

2. Write each number in standard form.
   a. (4 ∗ 1) + (9 ∗ 0.1) + (7 ∗ 0.01) 4.97
   b. (6 ∗ 0.1) + (3 ∗ 0.01) + (7 ∗ 0.0001) 0.6307

3. Ms. Barrie's science class placed a small amount of sand in direct sunlight for 10 minutes. Every 2 minutes, the students recorded the temperature of the sand. They moved the sand out of the sunlight and continued to record the temperature.

Make a line graph of their data, which is shown in the table at the right. Label each axis of your graph.

Time (minutes)	Temperature (°C)
0	20
2	24
4	28
6	32
8	34
10	35
12	34
14	32
16	30
18	29
20	27

4. In the equation $d - 452.23 = 109.76$, the variable d represents the amount of money that was in Zach's savings account at the beginning of the month.

   How much money was in Zach's savings account at the beginning of the month? $561.99

SRB 250 251

5. The volume of a cube can be found by using the formula $V = s^3$, where s represents the length of one side.

   Find the volume of the cube if $s = 3$ cm.

   $V =$ 27 cm³

SRB 6 221

Math Journal 1, **p. 58**

Study Link Master

Name ____ Date ____ Time ____

STUDY LINK 2•4 **Multiplying by Powers of 10**

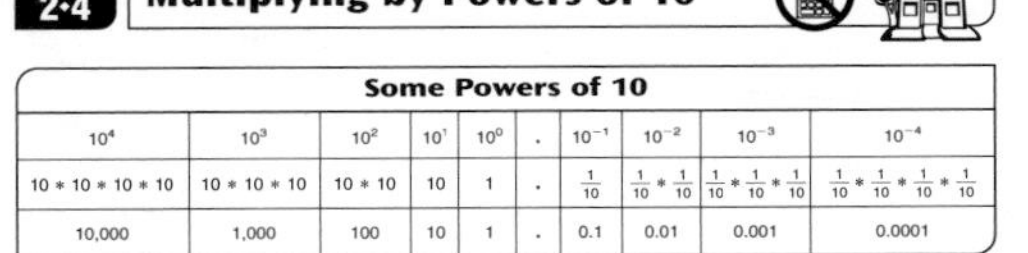

Some Powers of 10

10^4	10^3	10^2	10^1	10^0	.	10^{-1}	10^{-2}	10^{-3}	10^{-4}
10 ∗ 10 ∗ 10 ∗ 10	10 ∗ 10 ∗ 10	10 ∗ 10	10	1	.	$\frac{1}{10}$	$\frac{1}{10} * \frac{1}{10}$	$\frac{1}{10} * \frac{1}{10} * \frac{1}{10}$	$\frac{1}{10} * \frac{1}{10} * \frac{1}{10} * \frac{1}{10}$
10,000	1,000	100	10	1	.	0.1	0.01	0.001	0.0001

Multiply.

1. 4.9 ∗ 0.001 = 0.0049
2. 0.078 = 7.8 ∗ 0.01
3. $30 * 10^{-1}$ = 3.0
4. 0.07 = $7 * 10^{-2}$
5. $0.15 * 10^3$ = 150.0
6. 190 = 1.9 ∗ 100
7. $37.6 * 10^2$ = 3,760
8. $42.8 * 10^{-3}$ = 0.0428
9. Mathematician Edward Kasner asked his 9-year-old nephew to invent a name for the number represented by 10^{100}. The boy named it a *googol.* Later, an even larger number was named—a *googolplex.* This number is represented by 10^{googol}, or $10^{10^{100}}$.
   a. How many zeros are in the standard form of a googol, or 10^{100}? 100
   b. One googolplex is 1 followed by how many zeros? 10^{100}
10. The speed of computer memory and logic chips is measured in nanoseconds. A nanosecond is one-billionth of a second, or 10^{-9} second. Write this number in standard form. 0.000000001
11. Light travels about 1 mile in 0.000005 seconds. If a spacecraft could travel at this speed, it would travel almost 10^6 miles in 5 seconds. About how far would this spacecraft travel in 50 seconds? 10^7 miles

Practice

Mentally calculate your change from $10.

12. Cost: $4.75; Change: $5.25
13. Cost: $3.98; Change: $6.02
14. Cost: $0.89; Change: $9.11
15. Cost: $8.46; Change: $1.54

Math Masters, **p. 49**

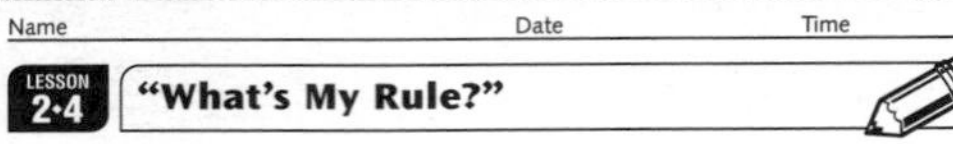

For each problem, complete the table and find the rule. Use Problem 4 to write your own "What's My Rule?" problem.

1. *Rule:* Multiply the in number by 10.

in	out
$10	$100
$25	$250
$145	$1,450
$7,985	$79,850
$230,000	$2,300,000

2. *Rule:* Multiply the in number by 10.

in	out
$0.10	$1.00
$3.00	$30.00
$50.00	$500.00
$88.50	$885.00
$235.75	$2,357.50

3. *Rule:* Divide the in number by 10.

in	out
$0.90	$0.09
$5.00	$0.50
$20.00	$2.00
$760	$76
$1,000	$100

4. *Rule:* Answers vary.

in	out

***Math Masters*, p. 50**

NOTE Depending on the calculator, the key sequence for entering a power of 10, such as 10^5, is:

TI-15: 10 [^] 5 [Enter]

Casio *fx*-55: 10 [x^y] 5 [=]

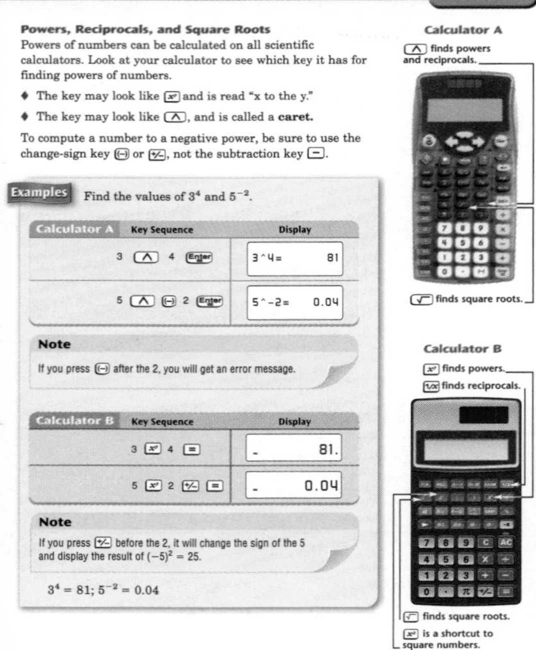
Student Page

Calculators

Powers, Reciprocals, and Square Roots

Powers of numbers can be calculated on all scientific calculators. Look at your calculator to see which key it has for finding powers of numbers.

- The key may look like [x^y] and is read "x to the y."
- The key may look like [^], and is called a **caret.**

To compute a number to a negative power, be sure to use the change-sign key [(−)] or [+/−], not the subtraction key [−].

Examples Find the values of 3^4 and 5^{-2}.

Calculator A	Key Sequence	Display
	3 [^] 4 [Enter]	3^4= 81
	5 [^] [(−)] 2 [Enter]	5^-2= 0.04

Note

If you press [(−)] after the 2, you will get an error message.

Calculator B	Key Sequence	Display
	3 [x^y] 4 [=]	81.
	5 [x^y] 2 [+/−] [=]	0.04

Note

If you press [+/−] before the 2, it will change the sign of the 5 and display the result of $(-5)^2 = 25$.

$3^4 = 81$; $5^{-2} = 0.04$

***Student Reference Book*, p. 285**

3 Differentiation Options

READINESS

▶ Solving "What's My Rule?" Problems

5–15 Min

(*Math Masters,* p. 50)

Students complete tables and find rules for "What's My Rule?" problems to gain experience multiplying and dividing whole and decimal numbers by 10.

ENRICHMENT

▶ Finding Patterns with Powers of 10

15–30 Min

(*Student Reference Book,* p. 285)

The Product of Powers Rule says that when you multiply powers having the same base, you add the exponents ($a^m * a^n = a^{m+n}$). Students explore this rule by using a calculator to find the first row of the following products.

$10^2 * 10^4$ 10^6	$10^3 * 10^3$ 10^6	$10^5 * 10^1$ 10^6	$10^7 * 10^{-1}$ 10^6
$10^{-4} * 10^{-4}$ 10^{-8}	$10^{-2} * 10^{-6}$ 10^{-8}	$10^{-3} * 10^{-5}$ 10^{-8}	$10^{-1} * 10^{-7}$ 10^{-8}
$10^{-6} * 10^6$ 10^0	$10^{-5} * 10^5$ 10^0	$10^{-4} * 10^4$ 10^0	$10^{-3} * 10^3$ 10^0

For each problem, ask students to compare the power of 10 in the factors to the power of 10 in the product. Students should use any patterns they notice to predict the power of 10 in the remaining products. The power of 10 in the product is equal to the sum of the powers of 10 in the factors: $a^m * a^n = a^{m+n}$. Have students use a calculator to check their predictions.

EXTRA PRACTICE

▶ *5-Minute Math*

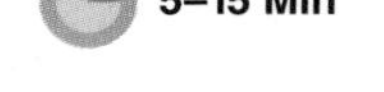

To provide more practice multiplying and dividing numbers by powers of 10, see *5-Minute Math,* pages 2, 3, and 80.

ELL SUPPORT

▶ Building a Math Word Bank

(*Differentiation Handbook*)

To provide language support for exponents, have students use the Word Bank template found in the *Differentiation Handbook.* Ask students to write the terms *powers of 10* and *exponential notation,* draw pictures representing each term, and write other related words. See the *Differentiation Handbook* for more information.

2•5 Multiplication of Decimals: Part 1

Objective To develop an estimation strategy for multiplying decimals.

1 Teaching the Lesson

Key Activities

Students find products of decimals and locate the decimal point in an answer by estimating the product.

Key Concepts and Skills

- Write equivalent names for numbers to calculate products and make estimates. [Number and Numeration Goal 4]
- Apply multiplication facts and extended-fact strategies to multiply decimals. [Operations and Computation Goal 2]
- Make reasonable estimates for products of decimal factors. [Operations and Computation Goal 5]

Ongoing Assessment: Recognizing Student Achievement Use journal page 60. [Operations and Computation Goal 6]

materials

- ☐ *Math Journal 1,* pp. 59 and 60
- ☐ *Student Reference Book,* pp. 37 and 38
- ☐ Study Link 2•4

2 Ongoing Learning & Practice

Students practice estimating products of multidigit factors by playing *Multiplication Bull's-Eye.*

Students practice and maintain skills through Math Boxes and Study Link activities.

materials

- ☐ *Math Journal 1,* p. 61
- ☐ *Student Reference Book,* p. 328
- ☐ Study Link Master (*Math Masters,* p. 51)

Per partnership:

- ☐ 4 each of number cards 0–9 (from the Everything Math Deck, if available)
- ☐ 6-sided die; calculator

3 Differentiation Options

READINESS

Students review whole-number multiplication facts.

ENRICHMENT

Students apply estimation and computation skills to solve a real-world problem.

EXTRA PRACTICE

Students practice multiplying multidigit whole numbers.

materials

- ☐ *Student Reference Book,* p. 336
- ☐ Game Master (*Math Masters,* p. 478)
- ☐ Teaching Masters (*Math Masters,* pp. 52 and 53)
- ☐ 4 each of number cards 1–10

Technology

Assessment Management System
Journal page 60, Problems 5–8
See the **iTLG.**

Getting Started

Mental Math and Reflexes

Students multiply by powers of 10.

Suggestions:

●○○	●●○	●●●
13.8 ∗ 10 138	9,905 ∗ 0.01 99.05	$0.297 * \frac{1}{100}$ 0.00297
321 ∗ 0.1 32.1	0.228 ∗ 100 22.8	$4005.5 * \frac{1}{1000}$ 4.0055
$49.7 * 10^{-1}$ 4.97	$0.6 * 10^{-2}$ 0.006	$13.4 * 10^{-3}$ 0.0134

Math Message

Complete Problems 1a and 1b at the top of journal page 59.

Study Link 2·4 Follow-Up

Review answers. Have students share their strategies for mentally calculating the change from $10.

1 Teaching the Lesson

▶ Math Message Follow-Up

WHOLE-CLASS DISCUSSION

(*Math Journal 1,* p. 59)

Ask students to share strategies for solving Problem 1a. Strategies may include:

▷ If $1.75 * 2 = 3.50$, then $1.75 * 4$ is double that, or 7; $1.75 * 8 = (1.75 * 4) * 2 = 7 * 2 = 14$.

▷ $1.75 * 8 = 1.75 * (10 - 2) = (1.75 * 10) - (1.75 * 2) = 17.50 - 3.50 = 14.00$

▷ $8 * 1.75 = 8 * (1 + 0.75) = 8 * (1 + \frac{3}{4}) = (8 * 1) + (8 * \frac{3}{4}) = 8 + 6 = 14$

Draw attention to how students can apply the strategies they developed in the previous lesson to convert their answer from millimeters to centimeters. Because 1 millimeter equals $\frac{1}{10}$ centimeter, 14 mm = 14 ∗ 0.1, or 1.4 cm.

Pose additional conversion problems such as the following:

2,000 mm = __200__ cm   5 mm = __0.5__ cm

100 cm = __1,000__ mm   0.09 cm = __0.9__ mm

Have students complete journal page 59. They should estimate each product before solving the problem. Bring the class together to check answers.

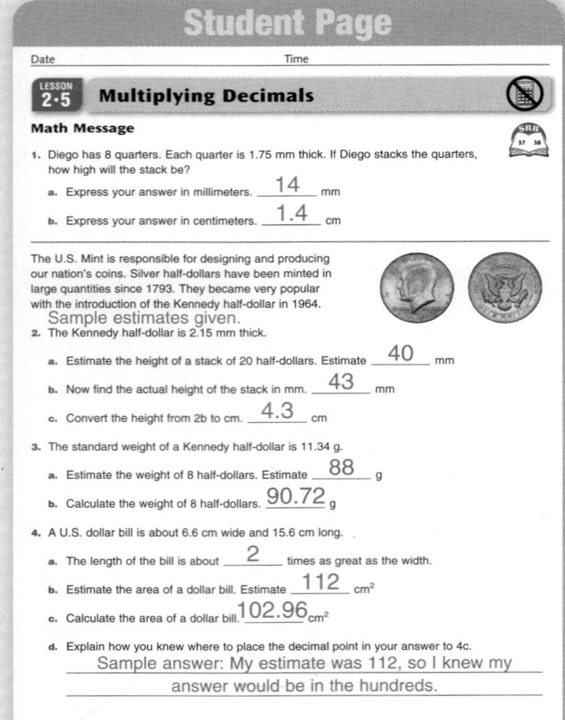

Student Page

Date ______ Time ______

LESSON 2·5 **Multiplying Decimals**

Math Message

1. Diego has 8 quarters. Each quarter is 1.75 mm thick. If Diego stacks the quarters, how high will the stack be?
   a. Express your answer in millimeters. __14__ mm
   b. Express your answer in centimeters. __1.4__ cm

The U.S. Mint is responsible for designing and producing our nation's coins. Silver half-dollars have been minted in large quantities since 1793. They became very popular with the introduction of the Kennedy half-dollar in 1964.

Sample estimates given.

2. The Kennedy half-dollar is 2.15 mm thick.
   a. Estimate the height of a stack of 20 half-dollars. Estimate __40__ mm
   b. Now find the actual height of the stack in mm. __43__ mm
   c. Convert the height from 2b to cm. __4.3__ cm
3. The standard weight of a Kennedy half-dollar is 11.34 g.
   a. Estimate the weight of 8 half-dollars. Estimate __88__ g
   b. Calculate the weight of 8 half-dollars. __90.72__ g
4. A U.S. dollar bill is about 6.6 cm wide and 15.6 cm long.
   a. The length of the bill is about __2__ times as great as the width.
   b. Estimate the area of a dollar bill. Estimate __112__ cm^2
   c. Calculate the area of a dollar bill. __102.96__ cm^2
   d. Explain how you knew where to place the decimal point in your answer to 4c.
   Sample answer: My estimate was 112, so I knew my answer would be in the hundreds.

Math Journal 1, p. 59

▶ Estimating Products of Decimals

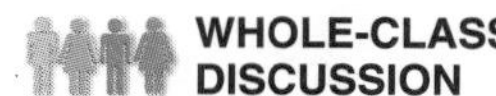

WHOLE-CLASS DISCUSSION

Whenever students are given a multiplication or division problem, they should first make an estimate, even if they will be using a calculator.

Write the following problems on the board or overhead projector:

2.8 ∗ 1.3 = ?   2.8 ∗ 13.0 = ?   0.28 ∗ 1.3 = ?

Encourage students to read decimals such as 2.8 as *two and eight-tenths,* rather than as *two point eight.*

Have students estimate each product. Record estimates next to the appropriate problem.

Discuss students' estimates. Some students might round 2.8 ∗ 1.3 3 ∗ 1 and find the product of the rounded numbers. 3.0 Others might use "friendly" numbers that are close to the numbers being multiplied and easy to work with, such as 3 ∗ 1.5. 4.5 Either estimate is satisfactory. The purpose of estimating is to help place the decimal point in the product. Consider using the following set of questions to guide discussion.

- Which problem is most likely to have the answer 3.64? 2.8 ∗ 1.3 How do you know? The estimate for this problem was about 2 or 3. The estimates for the other problems were much greater or less.
- Write the number 364 next to the second problem, 2.8 ∗ 13.0. Where should you place the decimal point? Between the 6 and the 4 How do you know? One strategy: Multiplying by a power of 10, $2.8 * 10 = 2.8 * 10^1 = 28.0$.
- Will the product 0.28 ∗ 1.3 be greater than or less than 1.3? Less than How do you know? One strategy: The factor 0.28 is less than 1, so the answer is less than 1 ∗ 1.3, or 1.3. Another strategy: 0.10 ∗ 1.3 = 0.13, so 0.28 is about 3 ∗ 0.13, or 0.39.

Ask a volunteer to summarize how to use estimation to place the decimal point when multiplying decimals. The explanation for 2.8 ∗ 1.3 should resemble the following:

1. Estimate the product.	2.8 ∗ 1.3 is about 3 ∗ 1, or 3.
2. Multiply the factors as though they were whole numbers.	28 ∗ 13 = 364
3. Use the estimate to place the decimal point.	3.64 is close to 3.

Student Page

Decimals and Percents

Multiplication of Decimals

You can use the same procedures for multiplying decimals as you use for whole numbers. The main difference is that with decimals you have to decide where to place the decimal point in the product.

Here is one way to multiply with decimals.

Step 1: Make a magnitude estimate of the product.

Step 2: Multiply the factors as if they were whole numbers, ignoring any decimal points. Use a multiplication method you would use for whole numbers. The answer will be a whole number.

Step 3: Use your estimate of the product from Step 1 to place the decimal point in the answer.

Note A *magnitude estimate* is a very rough estimate that answers questions like: *Is the solution in the ones? Tens? Hundreds? Thousands?*

Example 16.3 ∗ 4.7 = ?

Step 1: Estimate the product. Round 16.3 to 16 and 4.7 to 5. Since 16 ∗ 5 = 80, the product will be in the tens. (*In the tens* means between 10 and 100.)

Step 2: Multiply. Ignore the decimal points.

		163
		∗ 47
40 ∗ 100	→	4000
40 ∗ 60	→	2400
40 ∗ 3	→	120
7 ∗ 100	→	700
7 ∗ 60	→	420
7 ∗ 3	→	+ 21
		7661

Step 3: Use the estimate to place the decimal point in the product. Since the magnitude estimate is in the tens, the product must be in the tens. Place the decimal point between the 6s in 7661.

So, 16.3 ∗ 4.7 = 76.61.

Did You Know? In 1674, Gottfried Leibniz invented one of the first mechanical calculating machines that could multiply numbers. None of these machines have survived. The photograph below shows a reproduction that was built using Leibniz's plans.

Student Reference Book, **p. 37**

NOTE The partial-products and lattice methods of multiplication were introduced in *Third Grade Everyday Mathematics.* Refer students to pages 37 and 38 in the *Student Reference Book.* They will review the lattice method in Lesson 2-6.

Student Page

Decimals and Percents

Example 3.27 ∗ 0.8 = ?

Step 1: Make a magnitude estimate. Round 3.27 to 3 and 0.8 to 1. Since 3 ∗ 1 = 3, the product will be in the ones. (*In the ones* means between 1 and 10.)

Step 2: Multiply as you would with whole numbers. Ignore the decimal points. 327 ∗ 8 = 2616

Step 3: Place the decimal point correctly in the answer. Since the magnitude estimate is in the ones, the product must be in the ones. Place the decimal point between the 2 and the 6 in 2616.

So, 3.27 ∗ 0.8 = 2.616.

Note A magnitude estimate may be on the "borderline" and you need to be more careful. For example, a magnitude estimate for 3.4 ∗ 3.4 is 3 ∗ 3 = 9. This estimate is "in the 1s." But 9 is close to 10, so that the exact answer may be "in the 10s." You should place the decimal point so that the answer is close to 10. Since 34 ∗ 34 = 1156, the exact answer must be 3.4 ∗ 3.4 = 11.56.

There is another way to find where to place the decimal point in the product. This method is especially useful when the factors are less than 1 and have many decimal places.

Example 0.05 ∗ 0.0062 = ?

Step 1: Count the decimal places to the right of the decimal point in each factor. 2 decimal places in 0.05; 4 decimal places in 0.0062

Step 2: Add the number of decimal places. 2 + 4 = 6

Step 3: Multiply the factors as if they were whole numbers. 5 ∗ 62 = 310

Step 4: Start at the right of the product. Move the decimal point LEFT by the number of decimal places found in Step 2. 0.0 0 0 3 1 0.

Note that when these two numbers are multiplied as if they were whole numbers, there are only 3 digits in the product (5 ∗ 62 = 310). It is necessary to insert 3 zeros in front of 310 in order to move the decimal point 6 times.

0.05 ∗ 0.0062 = 0.000310

Check Your Understanding

Multiply.

1. 2.8 ∗ 4.6   2. 3.05 ∗ 6.5   3. 0.52 ∗ 3.03   4. 0.2 ∗ 0.022

Check your answers on page 415.

Student Reference Book, **p. 38**

Student Page

Date ______ Time ______

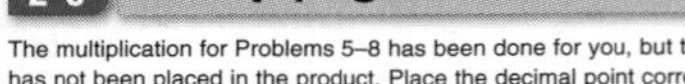

LESSON 2·5 Multiplying Decimals *continued*

The multiplication for Problems 5–8 has been done for you, but the decimal point has not been placed in the product. Place the decimal point correctly.

5. 2.3 ∗ 7.3 = 1 6.7 9
6. 51 ∗ 3.8 = 1 9 3.8
7. 6.91 ∗ 8.2 = 5 6.6 6 2
8. 0.2 ∗ 5.777 = 1.1 5 5 4

9. Explain how you decided where to place the decimal point in Problem 8.
Sample answer: I knew my product would be less than 11, but greater than 1.

10. Masumi used her calculator to multiply 9.1 ∗ 2.3. She got the answer 209.3.

a. Explain why this is not a reasonable answer.
Sample answer: An estimate for 9.1 ∗ 2.3 would be 18. 20 is close to 18, so the answer 20.93 seems reasonable.

b. What do you think Masumi might have done wrong?
Sample answer: She might have missed the decimal point in 9.1 and keyed 91 in the calculator instead.

Without using a calculator, estimate, and then find each of the following products. Use your estimation skills to help you place each decimal point. Show your work. Sample estimates given.

11. 2.7 ∗ 4.5 Estimate 15
2.7 ∗ 4.5 = 12.15

12. 24 ∗ 5.1 Estimate 125
24 ∗ 5.1 = 122.4

13. 5.4 ∗ 0.2 Estimate 1
5.4 ∗ 0.2 = 1.08

14. 9.8 ∗ 16 Estimate 160
9.8 ∗ 16 = 156.8

Math Journal 1, p. 60

Adjusting the Activity

Provide students with a rule for placing the decimal point. Have them first identify the leftmost digit in each factor that is different from zero and then change all the remaining digits to zeros. The resulting estimates will be sufficient for guiding the placement of the decimal point in the product. Using this method, 3.7 ∗ 8.2 is estimated as 3.0 ∗ 8.0 = 24, and 14.25 ∗ 2.6 is estimated as 10.00 ∗ 2.0 = 20.

AUDITORY ◆ KINESTHETIC ◆ TACTILE ◆ VISUAL

▶ Practicing Decimal Multiplication

PARTNER ACTIVITY

(*Math Journal 1,* p. 60)

Have students work in pairs to complete journal page 60. When most students have completed the page, bring the class together to share estimation strategies and solutions.

Ongoing Assessment: Recognizing Student Achievement

Journal Page 60 Problems 5–8

Use **journal page 60, Problems 5–8** to assess students' ability to estimate products of decimals. Students are making adequate progress if they are able to correctly place the decimal point in Problems 5–8. Some students might be able to articulate the discrepancies described in Problem 10.

[Operations and Computation Goal 5]

NOTE The traditional method for determining where to place the decimal in the answer will be offered as an alternative in the next lesson.

Student Page

Games

Multiplication Bull's-Eye

Materials □ number cards 0–9 (4 of each)
□ 1 six-sided die
□ 1 calculator

Players 2

Skill Estimating products of 2- and 3-digit numbers

Object of the game To score more points.

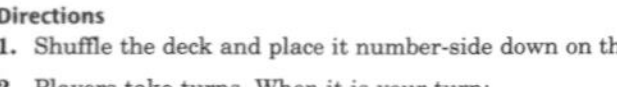

Directions

1. Shuffle the deck and place it number-side down on the table.
2. Players take turns. When it is your turn:
   - Roll the die. Look up the target range of the product in the table at the right.
   - Take 4 cards from the top of the deck.
   - Use the cards to try to form 2 numbers whose product falls within the target range. **Do not use a calculator.**
   - Multiply the 2 numbers on your calculator to determine whether the product falls within the target range. If it does, you have hit the bull's-eye and score 1 point. If it doesn't, you score 0 points.
   - Sometimes it is impossible to form 2 numbers whose product falls within the target range. If this happens, you score 0 points for that turn.
3. The game ends when each player has had 5 turns.
4. The player scoring more points wins the game.

Number on Die	Target Range of Product
1	500 or less
2	501–1,000
3	1,001–3,000
4	3,001–5,000
5	5,001–7,000
6	more than 7,000

Example Tom rolls a 3, so the target range of the product is from 1,001 to 3,000. He turns over a 5, a 7, a 2, and a 9.

Tom uses estimation to try to form 2 numbers whose product falls within the target range—for example, 97 and 25.

He then finds the product on the calculator: 97 ∗ 25 = 2,425.

Since the product is between 1,001 and 3,000, Tom has hit the bull's-eye and scores 1 point.

Some other possible winning products from the 5, 7, 2, and 9 cards are: 25 ∗ 79, 27 ∗ 59, 9 ∗ 257, and 2 ∗ 579.

Student Reference Book, p. 328

2 Ongoing Learning & Practice

▶ Playing *Multiplication Bull's-Eye*

PARTNER ACTIVITY

(*Student Reference Book,* p. 328)

Review the game directions on page 328 in the *Student Reference Book.* Play a few rounds with the class. Although the directions call for two players, the game can be adjusted for a student to play alone. If a student plays alone, the game ends after 10 turns, and the goal of the game is to top previous scores.

▶ Math Boxes 2•5

INDEPENDENT ACTIVITY

(*Math Journal 1,* p. 61)

Mixed Practice Math Boxes in this lesson are paired with Math Boxes in Lesson 2-7. The skills in Problems 4 and 5 preview Unit 3 content.

Writing/Reasoning Have students write a response to the following: *Explain why the product 77 ∗ 0.1 (Problem 1b) is less than 77.* Sample answer: Multiplying 77 by 0.1 is the same as finding $\frac{1}{10}$ of 77; $\frac{1}{10}$ of 77 is less than 77.

▶ Study Link 2•5

INDEPENDENT ACTIVITY

(*Math Masters,* p. 51)

Home Connection Students use estimation to locate the decimal point in the product of decimal factors.

3 Differentiation Options

READINESS

PARTNER ACTIVITY

▶ Playing *Multiplication Top-It*

5–15 Min

(*Student Reference Book,* p. 336; *Math Masters,* p. 478)

To provide students an opportunity to review multiplication facts, have students play *Multiplication Top-It.* Provide each pair with four each of number cards 1–10. Have students read the game directions on page 336 of the *Student Reference Book* and record their number sentences on the game record sheet (*Math Masters,* p. 478). Most students will be familiar with this game from previous grades. Consider using the variation described on page 336 to provide practice with finding products of multidigit whole numbers.

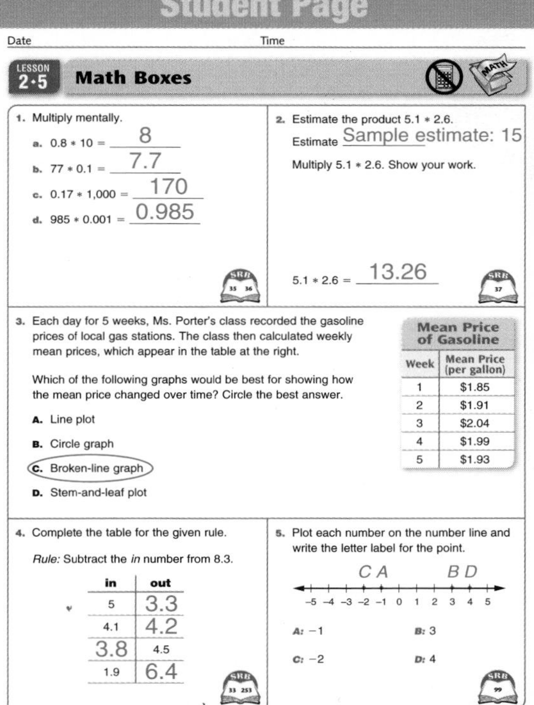

Student Page

Date Time

LESSON 2•5 **Math Boxes**

1. Multiply mentally.
a. 0.8 ∗ 10 = 8
b. 77 ∗ 0.1 = 7.7
c. 0.17 ∗ 1,000 = 170
d. 985 ∗ 0.001 = 0.985

2. Estimate the product 5.1 ∗ 2.6.
Estimate Sample estimate: 15
Multiply 5.1 ∗ 2.6. Show your work.
5.1 ∗ 2.6 = 13.26

3. Each day for 5 weeks, Ms. Porter's class recorded the gasoline prices of local gas stations. The class then calculated weekly mean prices, which appear in the table at the right.

Which of the following graphs would be best for showing how the mean price changed over time? Circle the best answer.

A. Line plot
B. Circle graph
C. Broken-line graph (circled)
D. Stem-and-leaf plot

Mean Price of Gasoline

Week	Mean Price (per gallon)
1	$1.85
2	$1.91
3	$2.04
4	$1.99
5	$1.93

4. Complete the table for the given rule.
Rule: Subtract the *in* number from 8.3.

in	out
5	3.3
4.1	4.2
3.8	4.5
1.9	6.4

5. Plot each number on the number line and write the letter label for the point.
C A B D
–5 –4 –3 –2 –1 0 1 2 3 4 5
A: –1 B: 3
C: –2 D: 4

Math Journal 1, **p. 61**

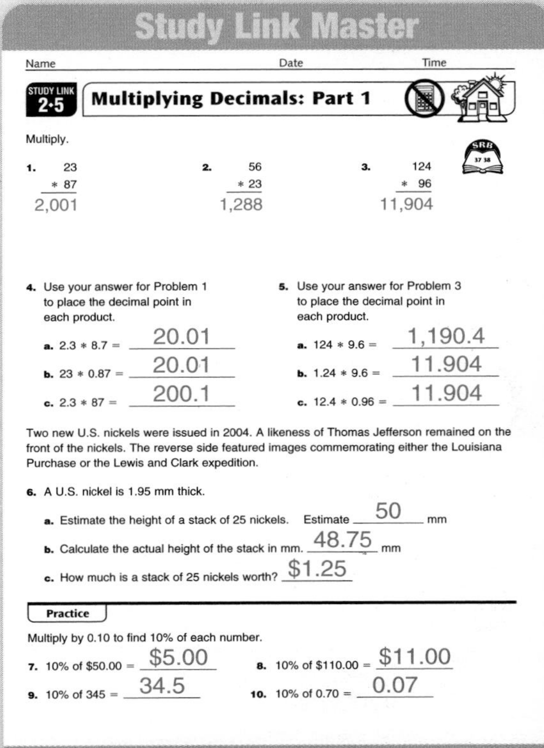

Study Link Master

Name Date Time

STUDY LINK 2•5 **Multiplying Decimals: Part 1**

Multiply.

1. 23 ∗ 87 = 2,001
2. 56 ∗ 23 = 1,288
3. 124 ∗ 96 = 11,904

4. Use your answer for Problem 1 to place the decimal point in each product.
a. 2.3 ∗ 8.7 = 20.01
b. 23 ∗ 0.87 = 20.01
c. 2.3 ∗ 87 = 200.1

5. Use your answer for Problem 3 to place the decimal point in each product.
a. 124 ∗ 9.6 = 1,190.4
b. 1.24 ∗ 9.6 = 11.904
c. 12.4 ∗ 0.96 = 11.904

Two new U.S. nickels were issued in 2004. A likeness of Thomas Jefferson remained on the front of the nickels. The reverse side featured images commemorating either the Louisiana Purchase or the Lewis and Clark expedition.

6. A U.S. nickel is 1.95 mm thick.
a. Estimate the height of a stack of 25 nickels. Estimate 50 mm
b. Calculate the actual height of the stack in mm. 48.75 mm
c. How much is a stack of 25 nickels worth? $1.25

Practice

Multiply by 0.10 to find 10% of each number.

7. 10% of $50.00 = $5.00
8. 10% of $110.00 = $11.00
9. 10% of 345 = 34.5
10. 10% of 0.70 = 0.07

Math Masters, **p. 51**

Name Date Time

LESSON 2·5 **Estimating and Calculating Cost**

Suppose you have $25.00 to spend on snacks for your basketball team. You need to purchase 25 pieces of fruit and 25 beverages. The table below shows the food items available and the cost of each item.

Fruit	Cost	Beverages	Cost
Banana	$0.42	Fruit punch	$0.65
Apple	$0.28	Orange juice	$0.50
Orange	$0.41	Bottled water	$0.75

1. Make a table of the items you will buy, how many of each item, and the cost. Remember that you can spend up to $25.00 but not more than $25.00. Your table might have four columns with these headings: Food Item, Number of Items, Cost per Item, and Subtotals. Sample answer:

Food Item	Number of Items	Cost per Item	Subtotals
Banana	6	$0.42	$2.52
Apple	12	$0.28	$3.36
Orange	7	$0.41	$2.87
Fruit punch	9	$0.65	$5.85
Orange juice	8	$0.50	$4.00
Bottled water	8	$0.75	$6.00
TOTAL	Fruit: 25 Beverages: 25		$24.60

2. Explain how you decided which items to buy and how many of each item.
Answers vary.

Math Masters, p. 52

ENRICHMENT

▶ Estimating and Calculating Total Cost

5–15 Min

(*Math Masters*, p. 52)

Portfolio Ideas

To apply estimation skills and strategies, students plan how many food items they can buy with $25. They construct a table to organize their plan and calculate costs. Students then explain how they decided which items and how many of each item to buy.

EXTRA PRACTICE

▶ Multiplying Whole Numbers

15–30 Min

(*Math Masters*, p. 53)

To provide extra practice multiplying decimals, have students review and apply algorithms for multiplying multidigit whole numbers.

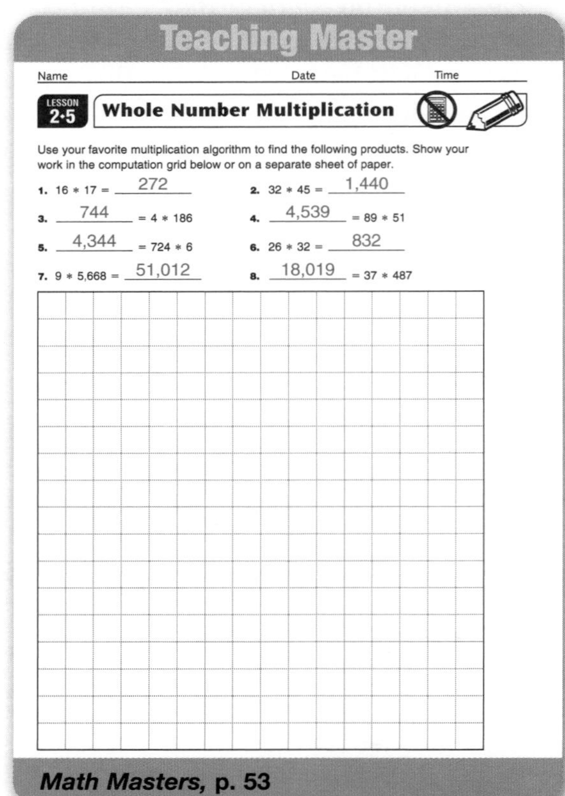

Teaching Master

Name Date Time

LESSON 2·5 **Whole Number Multiplication**

Use your favorite multiplication algorithm to find the following products. Show your work in the computation grid below or on a separate sheet of paper.

1. 16 * 17 = 272
2. 32 * 45 = 1,440
3. 744 = 4 * 186
4. 4,539 = 89 * 51
5. 4,344 = 724 * 6
6. 26 * 32 = 832
7. 9 * 5,668 = 51,012
8. 18,019 = 37 * 487

Math Masters, p. 53

Multiplication of Decimals: Part 2

Objective To develop strategies for multiplying decimals.

1 Teaching the Lesson

Key Activities

Students practice the lattice method of multiplication, which has been modified to find products of decimals. They also discuss a traditional method for locating the decimal point in a product.

Key Concepts and Skills

- Use place-value concepts to place the decimal point in products. [Number and Numeration Goal 1]
- Multiply decimals using the lattice and traditional methods. [Operations and Computation Goal 2]
- Make reasonable estimates for products of decimal factors. [Operations and Computation Goal 5]

materials

- ☐ *Math Journal 1,* pp. 62 and 63
- ☐ *Student Reference Book,* pp. 20 and 39
- ☐ Study Link 2•5
- ☐ Teaching Aid Masters (*Math Masters,* pp. 414 and 415; optional)

***See* Advance Preparation**

2 Ongoing Learning & Practice

Students practice rules of divisibility by playing *Divisibility Dash*.

Students practice and maintain skills through Math Boxes and Study Link activities.

Ongoing Assessment: Recognizing Student Achievement Use journal page 64. [Operations and Computation Goal 2]

materials

- ☐ *Math Journal 1,* p. 64
- ☐ *Student Reference Book,* pp. 309 and 11
- ☐ Study Link Master (*Math Masters,* p. 54)
- ☐ Game Master (*Math Masters,* p. 432)

Per partnership:

- ☐ 4 each of number cards 0–9 (from the Everything Math Deck, if available)
- ☐ 2 each of number cards 2, 3, 5, 6, 9, and 10 (from another Everything Math Deck, if available)

***See* Advance Preparation**

3 Differentiation Options

READINESS

Students use an area model to visualize decimal multiplication.

ENRICHMENT

Students use doubling and halving strategies to mentally multiply decimals.

ELL SUPPORT

Students display a method for multiplying decimals.

materials

- ☐ Teaching Masters (*Math Masters,* pp. 55 and 56)
- ☐ calculator
- ☐ markers; posterboard

Additional Information

Advance Preparation Consider making at least one copy of *Math Masters,* pages 414 and 415 for each student.

For Part 2, familiarize yourself with the directions for *Divisibility Dash* on page 309 of the *Student Reference Book.*

Technology

Assessment Management System
Math Boxes, Problem 2
See the **iTLG.**

Getting Started

Mental Math and Reflexes

Students signal thumbs-up for products greater than the first factor and thumbs-down for products less than the first factor.

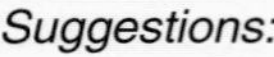

Suggestions:

●○○ 2.03 * 10 thumbs-up
62.3 * 0.1 thumbs-down

●●○ 1,538 * 0.19 thumbs-down
0.506 * 1.03 thumbs-up

●●● 849 * 0.993 thumbs-down
704 * 1.005 thumbs-up

Math Message

Complete Problems 1 and 2 at the top of journal page 62.

Study Link 2·5 Follow-Up

Briefly go over the answers. Draw attention to the factors in problems where multiplication makes smaller (4b and 5c). If time permits, ask students to convert their answer for 6b to centimeters.

1 Teaching the Lesson

▶ Math Message Follow-Up

WHOLE-CLASS DISCUSSION

(*Math Journal 1,* p. 62; *Student Reference Book,* p. 20)

Students used lattice multiplication in *Fifth Grade Everyday Mathematics* to find products of whole numbers. With some review, most students should be able to use the lattice method. If necessary, refer them to page 20 of the *Student Reference Book,* and have them solve several of the Check Your Understanding problems.

Ask volunteers to show how they found the product 28 * 13 using lattice multiplication.

Use 2.8 * 1.3 to show the lattice method using decimal factors. Ask students to explain how they located the decimal point in the answer. Answers vary. Draw attention to the arrows on the lattice grid and how students can use them to help locate the decimal point in the product. Demonstrate the procedure at the board or overhead projector. See procedure on the following page.

Adjusting the Activity

ELL

Use one color to write the original factors and another color to write the partial products inside the lattice.

AUDITORY ◆ KINESTHETIC ◆ TACTILE ◆ VISUAL

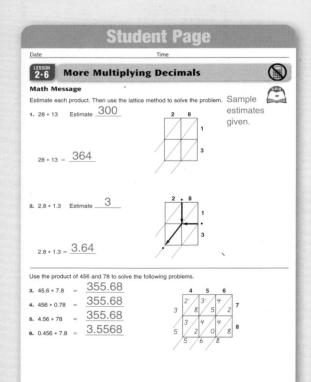

Student Page

Date Time

LESSON 2·6 **More Multiplying Decimals**

Math Message

Estimate each product. Then use the lattice method to solve the problem. Sample estimates given.

1. 28 * 13 Estimate 300

28 * 13 = 364

2. 2.8 * 1.3 Estimate 3

2.8 * 1.3 = 3.64

Use the product of 456 and 78 to solve the following problems.

3. 45.6 * 7.8 = 355.68
4. 456 * 0.78 = 355.68
5. 4.56 * 78 = 355.68
6. 0.456 * 7.8 = 3.5568

Math Journal 1, p. 62

1. Record the factors on a lattice grid. Mark the decimal point for each factor above or beside the appropriate grid line.

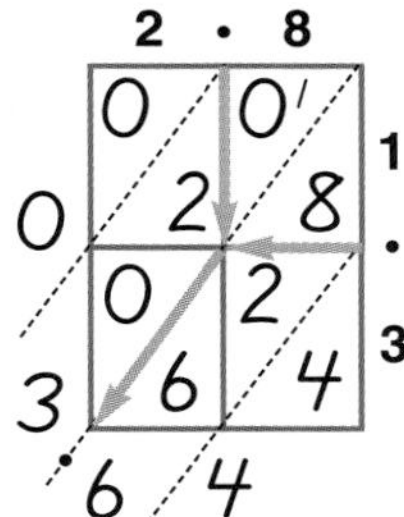

2. Follow the grid lines below and beside the two decimal points to the point at which they meet on the lattice grid. Then follow the diagonal down to the end of the grid and place a decimal point there. This procedure locates the decimal point in the answer.

Adjusting the Activity

Have students use a computation grid (*Math Masters,* p. 414) or a lattice multiplication grid (*Math Masters,* p. 415). If they need to use a facts table, refer them to page 370 of the *Student Reference Book.*

AUDITORY ◆ KINESTHETIC ◆ TACTILE ◆ VISUAL

Continue with related examples, such as the following:

0.28 * 1.3 = 0.364

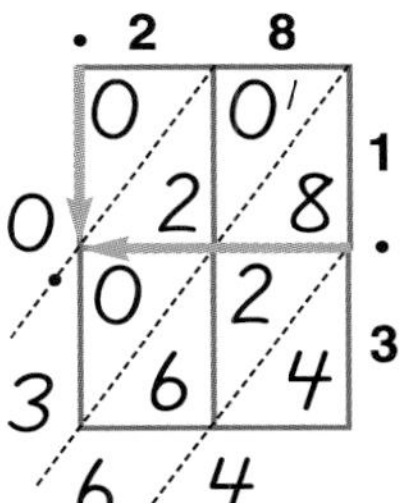

28 * 1.3 = 36.4

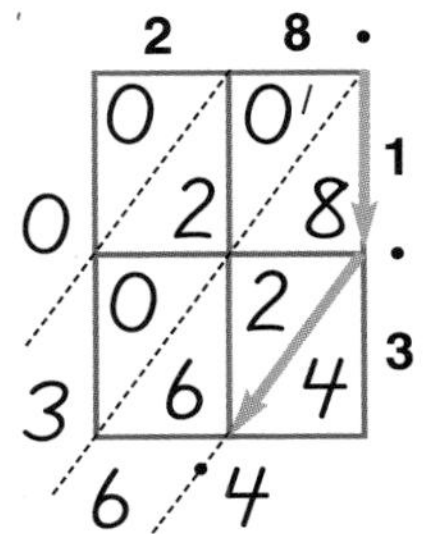

0.28 * 13 = 3.64

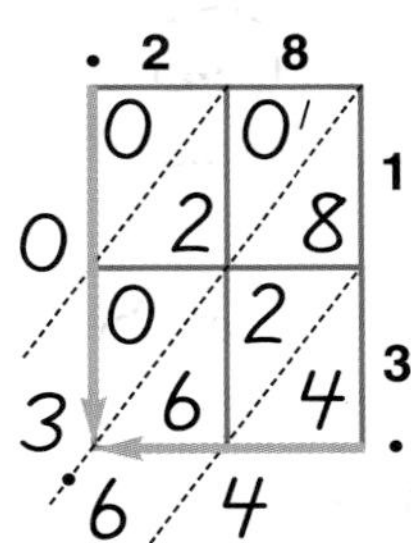

0.28 * 0.13 = 0.0364

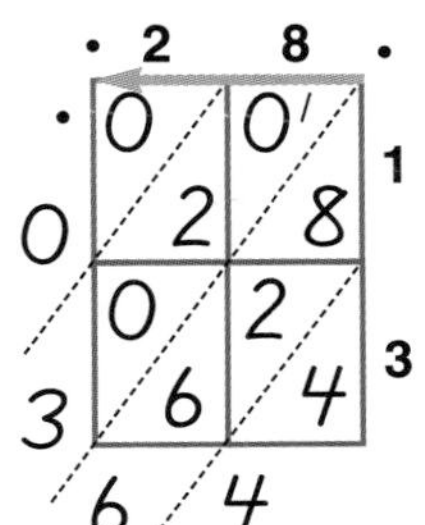

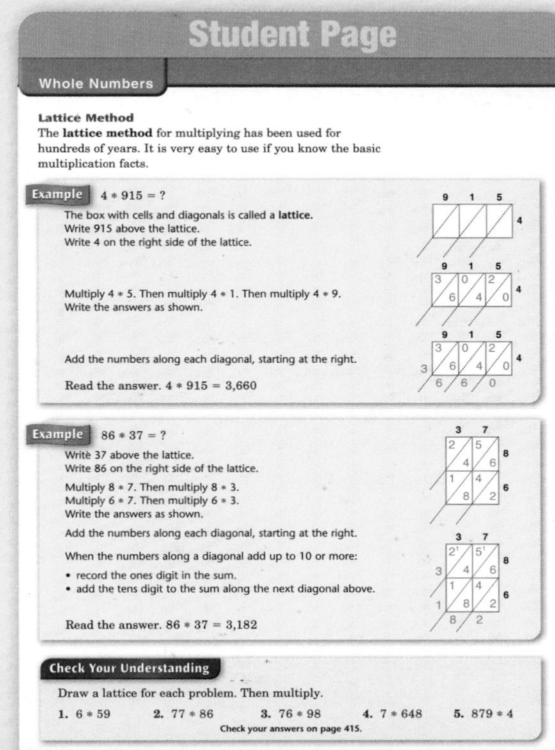

Student Page

Whole Numbers

Lattice Method

The **lattice method** for multiplying has been used for hundreds of years. It is very easy to use if you know the basic multiplication facts.

Example 4 * 915 = ?

The box with cells and diagonals is called a **lattice.**
Write 915 above the lattice.
Write 4 on the right side of the lattice.

Multiply 4 * 5. Then multiply 4 * 1. Then multiply 4 * 9.
Write the answers as shown.

Add the numbers along each diagonal, starting at the right.

Read the answer. 4 * 915 = 3,660

Example 86 * 37 = ?

Write 37 above the lattice.
Write 86 on the right side of the lattice.

Multiply 8 * 7. Then multiply 8 * 3.
Multiply 6 * 7. Then multiply 6 * 3.
Write the answers as shown.

Add the numbers along each diagonal, starting at the right.

When the numbers along a diagonal add up to 10 or more:

- record the ones digit in the sum.
- add the tens digit to the sum along the next diagonal above.

Read the answer. 86 * 37 = 3,182

Check Your Understanding

Draw a lattice for each problem. Then multiply.

1. 6 * 59 2. 77 * 86 3. 76 * 98 4. 7 * 648 5. 879 * 4

Check your answers on page 415.

***Student Reference Book,* p. 20**

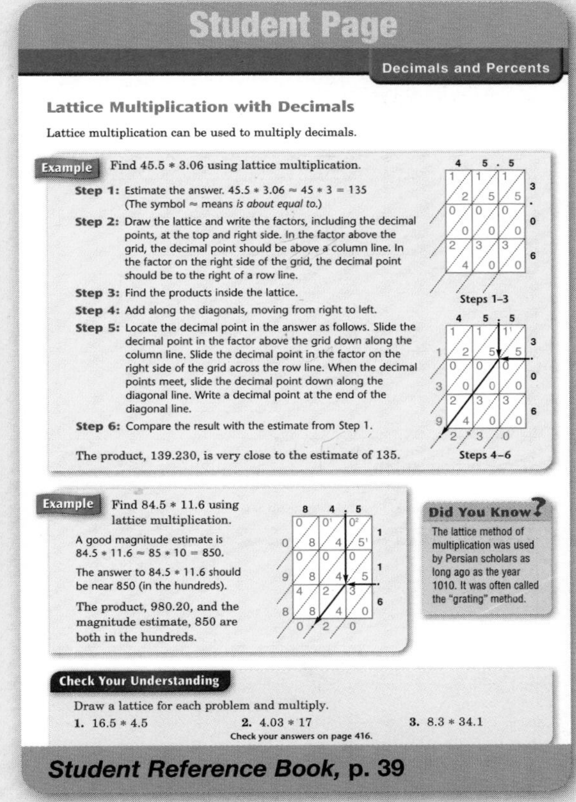

Student Page

Decimals and Percents

Lattice Multiplication with Decimals

Lattice multiplication can be used to multiply decimals.

Example Find 45.5 * 3.06 using lattice multiplication.

Step 1: Estimate the answer. 45.5 * 3.06 ≈ 45 * 3 = 135
(The symbol ≈ means *is about equal to.*)

Step 2: Draw the lattice and write the factors, including the decimal points, at the top and right side. In the factor above the grid, the decimal point should be above a column line. In the factor on the right side of the grid, the decimal point should be to the right of a row line.

Step 3: Find the products inside the lattice.

Step 4: Add along the diagonals, moving from right to left.

Step 5: Locate the decimal point in the answer as follows. Slide the decimal point in the factor above the grid down along the column line. Slide the decimal point in the factor on the right side of the grid across the row line. When the decimal points meet, slide the decimal point down along the diagonal line. Write a decimal point at the end of the diagonal line.

Step 6: Compare the result with the estimate from Step 1.

Steps 1–3

Steps 4–6

The product, 139.230, is very close to the estimate of 135.

Example Find 84.5 * 11.6 using lattice multiplication.

A good magnitude estimate is 84.5 * 11.6 ≈ 85 * 10 = 850.

The answer to 84.5 * 11.6 should be near 850 (in the hundreds).

The product, 980.20, and the magnitude estimate, 850 are both in the hundreds.

Did You Know?

The lattice method of multiplication was used by Persian scholars as long ago as the year 1010. It was often called the "grating" method.

Check Your Understanding

Draw a lattice for each problem and multiply.

1. 16.5 * 4.5 2. 4.03 * 17 3. 8.3 * 34.1

Check your answers on page 416.

***Student Reference Book,* p. 39**

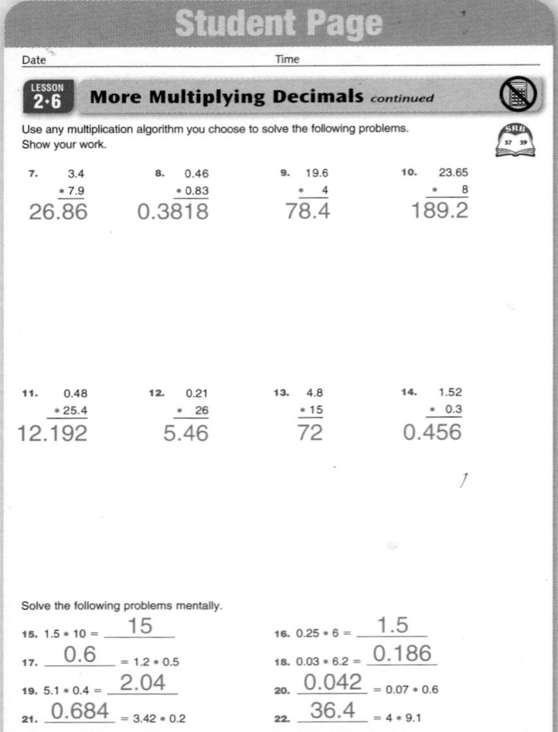

Student Page

Date Time

LESSON 2·6 **More Multiplying Decimals** *continued*

Use any multiplication algorithm you choose to solve the following problems. Show your work.

7. 3.4 * 7.9 = 26.86
8. 0.46 * 0.83 = 0.3818
9. 19.6 * 4 = 78.4
10. 23.65 * 8 = 189.2
11. 0.48 * 25.4 = 12.192
12. 0.21 * 26 = 5.46
13. 4.8 * 15 = 72
14. 1.52 * 0.3 = 0.456

Solve the following problems mentally.

15. 1.5 * 10 = 15
16. 0.25 * 6 = 1.5
17. 0.6 = 1.2 * 0.5
18. 0.03 * 6.2 = 0.186
19. 5.1 * 0.4 = 2.04
20. 0.042 = 0.07 * 0.6
21. 0.684 = 3.42 * 0.2
22. 36.4 = 4 * 9.1

Math Journal 1, p. 63

▶ Locating Decimal Points in Products

Some students may propose the following traditional method, or you may want to teach it as an alternative.
For example, $2.8 * 1.3 = ?$

1. Count the number of decimal places in each factor. — 1 decimal place in 2.8; 1 decimal place in 1.3
2. Add the number of decimal places. — $1 + 1 = 2$
3. Multiply the factors as if they were whole numbers. — $28 * 13 = 364$
4. To place the decimal point, start at the right of the product and move left the number of decimal places determined in Step 2. — 3.64

Students know from a previous lesson that tenths times tenths equals hundredths ($0.1 * 0.1 = 0.01$). Ask students how this relates to moving two decimal places in Step 4. Sample answer: When you multiply a number by 0.01 (or 10^{-2}) you move the decimal point 2 places to the left.

▶ Multiplying Decimals

(*Math Journal 1,* pp. 62 and 63; *Student Reference Book,* p. 39)

Students work in pairs to complete journal pages 62 and 63. When most students have completed the pages, briefly go over the answers.

2 Ongoing Learning & Practice

▶ Playing *Divisibility Dash*

(*Student Reference Book,* pp. 309 and 11; *Math Masters,* p. 432)

Distribute four each of the number cards 0–9 from 1 deck and two each of the number cards 2, 3, 5, 6, 9, and 10 from a second deck to each group of two or three players, as well as a game record sheet (*Math Masters,* p. 432). If necessary, have students read page 11 of the *Student Reference Book* to review divisibility rules.

Game Master

Name Date Time

Divisibility Dash

Record Sheet

Player 1

Round	Cards in your hand	Divisor	2-digit or 3-digit multiples
1			
2			
3			
4			
6			
7			
8			
9			
10			

Name Date Time

Divisibility Dash

Record Sheet

Player 2

Round	Cards in your hand	Divisor	2-digit or 3-digit multiples
1			
2			
3			
4			
6			
7			
8			
9			
10			

Math Masters, p. 432

▶ Math Boxes 2·6

INDEPENDENT ACTIVITY

(*Math Journal 1,* p. 64)

Mixed Practice Math Boxes in this lesson are paired with Math Boxes in Lessons 2-8 and 2-10. The skill in Problem 5 previews Unit 3 content.

Writing/Reasoning Have students write a response to the following: *When you multiply two factors, each of which is less than 1, the product is always less than either of the factors. Explain why, using two examples from Problem 3.* Sample answer: In Problem **3a** and **3c,** you are taking a part of a number that is less than 1. Therefore, the product will be less than 1.

Ongoing Assessment: Recognizing Student Achievement

Math Boxes Problem 2

Use **Math Boxes, Problem 2** to assess students' abilities to estimate a product and to use an algorithm to multiply decimal numbers. Students are making adequate progress if they are able to make a reasonable estimate and choose a reliable algorithm to solve Problem 2. Some students may recognize that the product $0.53 * 29.6$ will be close to $\frac{1}{2}$ of 30, or 15.

[Operations and Computation Goal 2]

▶ Study Link 2·6

INDEPENDENT ACTIVITY

(*Math Masters,* p. 54)

Home Connection Students use estimation to multiply decimals and place decimal points. They also use "easy" fraction-decimal conversions to solve decimal-multiplication number stories.

Student Page

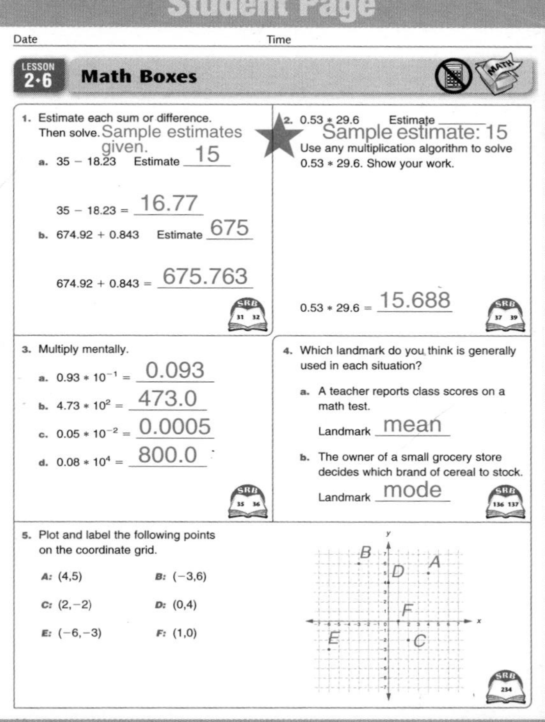

Date Time

LESSON 2·6 **Math Boxes**

1. Estimate each sum or difference. Then solve. Sample estimates given.
   a. 35 − 18.23 Estimate 15
   35 − 18.23 = 16.77
   b. 674.92 + 0.843 Estimate 675
   674.92 + 0.843 = 675.763

2. 0.53 ∗ 29.6 Estimate Sample estimate: 15
   Use any multiplication algorithm to solve 0.53 ∗ 29.6. Show your work.
   0.53 ∗ 29.6 = 15.688

3. Multiply mentally.
   a. $0.93 * 10^{-1}$ = 0.093
   b. $4.73 * 10^{2}$ = 473.0
   c. $0.05 * 10^{-2}$ = 0.0005
   d. $0.08 * 10^{4}$ = 800.0

4. Which landmark do you think is generally used in each situation?
   a. A teacher reports class scores on a math test. Landmark mean
   b. The owner of a small grocery store decides which brand of cereal to stock. Landmark mode

5. Plot and label the following points on the coordinate grid.
   A: (4,5) B: (−3,6)
   C: (2,−2) D: (0,4)
   E: (−6,−3) F: (1,0)

Math Journal 1, p. 64

Study Link Master

Name Date Time

STUDY LINK 2·6 **Multiplying Decimals: Part 2**

Place a decimal point in each problem.

1. 2 4.3 ∗ 7.06 = 171.558
2. 16.4 ∗ 0.7 = 1 1.4 8
3. .8 2 7 ∗ 9.5 = 7.8565
4. 7 5 6.3 ∗ 5.1 = 3,857.13

Multiply. Show your work on a separate sheet of paper or on the back of this page.

5. 18.012 = 2.28 ∗ 7.9
6. 29.82 = 49.7 ∗ 0.6
7. 49.92 = 3.84 ∗ 13
8. 10.241 = 0.19 ∗ 53.9

Solve each problem. Then write a number model. (*Hint: Change fractions to decimals.*)

9. Janine rides her bike at an average speed of 11.8 miles per hour. At that speed, about how many miles can she ride in $6\frac{1}{2}$ hours? 76.7 miles
   Number Model 11.8 ∗ 6.5 = 76.7

10. Kate types at an average rate of 1.25 pages per quarter hour. If she types for $2\frac{3}{4}$ hours, about how many pages can she type? 13.75 pages
    Number Model (1.25 ∗ 4) ∗ 2.75 = 13.75

11. Find the area in square meters of a rectangle with length 1.4 m and width 2.9 m. 4.06 sq m
    Number Model 1.4 ∗ 2.9 = 4.06

Practice

Multiply mentally by 0.10 to find 10%. Then mentally calculate the percent that has been assigned to each number.

12. 20% of \$80.00 = \$16.00
13. 5% of \$220.00 = \$11.00
14. 15% of 640 = 96
15. 30% of 80 = 24

Math Masters, p. 54

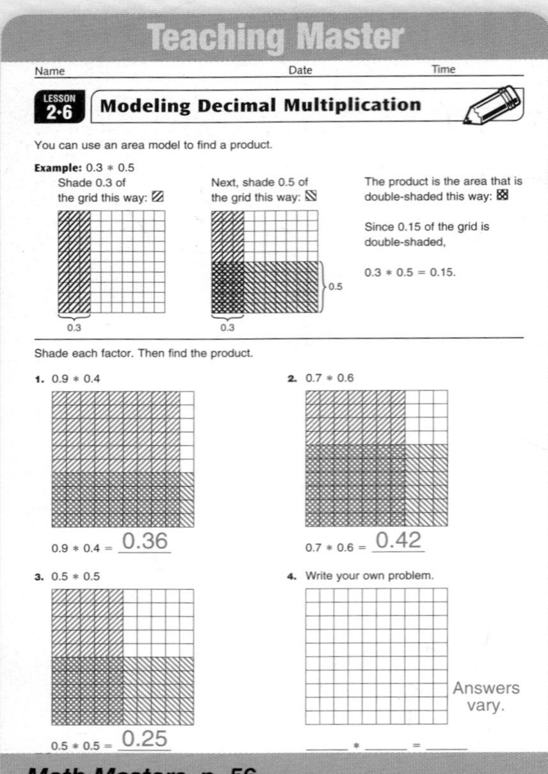
Teaching Master

Name Date Time

LESSON 2·6 **Modeling Decimal Multiplication**

You can use an area model to find a product.

Example: 0.3 * 0.5

Shade 0.3 of the grid this way: ▨ — Next, shade 0.5 of the grid this way: ▧ — The product is the area that is double-shaded this way: ▩

Since 0.15 of the grid is double-shaded, 0.3 * 0.5 = 0.15.

Shade each factor. Then find the product.

1. 0.9 * 0.4 — 0.9 * 0.4 = 0.36
2. 0.7 * 0.6 — 0.7 * 0.6 = 0.42
3. 0.5 * 0.5 — 0.5 * 0.5 = 0.25
4. Write your own problem. Answers vary. ____ * ____ = ____

Math Masters, p. 56

Teaching Master

Name Date Time

LESSON 2·6 **A Mental Multiplication Strategy**

The same strategy was used to solve both example problems below. This strategy can also be used to multiply numbers mentally.

Example 1:	Example 2:
16 * 2.5 16 / 2 2.5 * 2 8 * 5 16 * 2.5 = 8 * 5 = 40	72 * 0.125 72 / 2 0.125 * 2 36 * 0.25 36 / 2 0.25 * 2 18 * 0.50 72 * 0.125 = 18 * 0.50 = 9

1. Explain the strategy. Sample answer: Divide the whole number by 2 and multiply the decimal by 2 until you can multiply mentally.
2. Use the strategy to solve the problems below. Show your work.
   a. 16 * 1.5 = 24
   b. 18 * 3.5 = 63
   c. 20 * 0.75 = 15
   d. 0.125 * 16 = 2
3. Solve these problems mentally.
   a. 8 * 7.5 = 60
   b. 24 * 1.25 = 30
4. Make up two problems that can be solved using a mental multiplication strategy.
   a. Answers vary.
   b. ________

Math Masters, p. 55

3 Differentiation Options

READINESS

INDEPENDENT ACTIVITY

15–30 Min

▶ Modeling Decimal-Number Multiplication

(*Math Masters,* p. 56)

Students shade grids to provide a visual model of decimal-number multiplication. They begin by reviewing the example on *Math Masters,* page 56. Students use different-colored pencils or markers, such as red and blue, to shade the areas representing factors and then find the intersection of those shaded areas. Have students compare the sizes of factor and product areas to better understand how multiplication can make smaller.

ENRICHMENT

INDEPENDENT ACTIVITY

5–15 Min

▶ A Mental Multiplication Strategy

(*Math Masters,* p. 55)

To further explore multiplying decimals, students review examples of a halving-and-doubling strategy and use this strategy to mentally compute products. They check their answers with a calculator.

ELL SUPPORT

INDEPENDENT ACTIVITY

15–30 Min

▶ Creating Decimal Multiplication Posters

To provide language support for multiplication algorithms, have students create a poster that features their preferred method for multiplying decimals. Posters should include labeled factors and products, as well as brief descriptions of the steps involved.

Some students from other countries may have learned algorithms that involve unusual steps or procedures. Encourage volunteers to present these algorithms to the class. Work with students to identify similarities and differences between algorithms.

Division of Whole Numbers

Objectives **To estimate quotients; and to use a paper-and-pencil division algorithm to divide whole numbers.**

1 Teaching the Lesson

Key Activities

Students estimate quotients and practice the partial-quotients division algorithm for whole numbers.

Key Concepts and Skills

- Find differences of partial quotients. [Operations and Computation Goal 1]
- Use multiplication and extended facts to compute partial quotients. [Operations and Computation Goal 2]
- Divide multidigit whole numbers. [Operations and Computation Goal 2]

Key Vocabulary

partial-quotients division algorithm • dividend • divisor • quotient • remainder

 **Ongoing Assessment: Informing Instruction** See page 138.

 **Ongoing Assessment: Recognizing Student Achievement** Use journal page 66. [Operations and Computation Goal 2]

materials

- ☐ *Math Journal 1,* pp. 66 and 67
- ☐ *Student Reference Book,* pp. 22 and 23
- ☐ Study Link 2•6
- ☐ Teaching Aid Master (*Math Masters,* p. 414)

***See* Advance Preparation**

2 Ongoing Learning & Practice

Students practice whole-number division by playing the advanced version of *Division Top-It.*

Students practice and maintain skills through Math Boxes and Study Link activities.

materials

- ☐ *Math Journal 1,* p. 65
- ☐ *Student Reference Book,* p. 336
- ☐ Study Link Master (*Math Masters,* p. 57)
- ☐ Game Master *(Math Masters,* 478)

Per partnership:

- ☐ 4 each of number cards 1–9 (from the Everything Math Deck, if available)

3 Differentiation Options

ENRICHMENT

Students use a little-known rule to test for divisibility by 7.

ENRICHMENT

Students explore the column division algorithm.

ELL SUPPORT

Students add *divisor, dividend, quotient,* and *remainder* to their Math Word Banks.

materials

- ☐ *Student Reference Book,* p. 24
- ☐ *Differentiation Handbook*

Additional Information

Advance Preparation Make one or two copies of the computation grid (*Math Masters,* p. 414) for each student.

Technology

Assessment Management System
Journal page 66, Problems 1–3
See the **iTLG.**

Getting Started

Mental Math and Reflexes

Pose problems such as the following:

●○○ How many 5s are in 45? 9
Which number multiplied by 9 equals 27? 3
Multiply 3 by 120. 360

●●○ How many 4s are in 32? 8
Which number multiplied by 8 equals 40? 5
Multiply 5 by 80. 400

●●● Which number multiplied by 50 equals 600? 12
How many 12s are in 132? 11
Multiply 3 by 55. 165

Math Message

Josie has 327 photographs. She can put 12 photos on each page of her scrapbook. Estimate the number of scrapbook pages she will need.

Study Link 2·6 Follow-Up

Review answers. Ask students to explain their strategies for placing the decimal point in Problems 1–4.

NOTE When expressing the result of a division problem in terms of a quotient and a remainder, *Everyday Mathematics* uses an arrow rather than an equal sign. For example, 157 / 12 = 13 R1 is not a proper number sentence because the right side (13 R1) is not an actual number. To write the solution as a number sentence, express the remainder as a fraction: $157 / 12 = 13\frac{1}{12}$. Students learned to express remainders as fractions in *Fifth Grade Everyday Mathematics.*

1 Teaching the Lesson

▶ Math Message Follow-Up

WHOLE-CLASS DISCUSSION

This is an equal-grouping problem. The total number of photos is divided into groups of 12. The number of pages or groups Josie needs can be found by dividing the number of photographs (327) by 12.

Discuss students' strategies for estimating the quotient. *For example:*

▷ 10 [12s] = 120; 20 [12s] = 240; 30 [12s] = 360
Josie would need 30 pages for 360 photos, so she will need fewer than 30 pages for 327 photos.

▷ Use close numbers that are easy to divide. 327 is close to 300, and 12 is close to 10. Because 300 divided by 10 is 30, Josie needs about 30 pages.

▶ Reviewing the Partial-Quotients Division Algorithm

WHOLE-CLASS ACTIVITY

(*Math Masters,* p. 414)

Continue with the Math Message problem. To answer this question exactly, students need to figure out how many 12s are in 327.

Model the **partial-quotients division algorithm** while students follow along using paper and pencil on a computation grid (*Math Masters,* p. 414).

Adjusting the Activity

ELL

Write a division problem on the board. Label the **dividend, divisor, quotient**, and **remainder.**

Example:

remainder
↓
27R3 ← quotient
12)327 ← dividend
↑
divisor

AUDITORY ◆ KINESTHETIC ◆ TACTILE ◆ VISUAL

Write the problem in this form: 12)327

1. A good strategy is to start with multiples of 10 because they are "easy" numbers with which to work. Ask: *Are there at least 20 [12s]?* Yes, because 20 ∗ 12 = 240 *Are there more than 30 [12s]?* No, because 30 ∗ 12 = 360 So, the answer is at least 20 but not more than 30. Try 20, because 20 is the first partial quotient. Partial quotients will be used to build up to the final quotient.

12)327		
240	20	←(The first partial quotient) 20 ∗ 12 = 240

2. The next step is to find out how much is left to divide. Subtract 240 from 327.

12)327		
− 240	20	←Estimate. Write 20 ∗ 12.
87		←Subtract.

3. Now find the number of 12s in 87. There are two ways to do this:

▷ Use a fact family to find the number of 12s in 8. There are 7, since 7 ∗ 12 = 84. Record as follows:

12)327		
− 240	20	←(The first partial quotient) 20 ∗ 12 = 240
87		←Subtract. 87 is left to divide.
− 84	7	←(The second partial quotient) 7 ∗ 12 = 84
3		←Subtract.

▷ Use *at least/not more than* estimates with numbers that are easy to multiply. Ask: *Are there at least 10 [12s] in 7?* No, because 10 ∗ 12 = 120 *Are there at least 5 [12s]?* Yes, because 5 ∗ 12 = 60 Next, subtract 60 from 87 and continue by asking, *How many 12s are in 27?*

12)327		
− 240	20	←(The first partial quotient) 20 ∗ 12 = 240
87		←Subtract. 87 is left to divide.
− 60	5	←(The second partial quotient) 5 ∗ 12 = 60
27		←Subtract. 27 is left to divide.
− 24	2	←(The third partial quotient) 2 ∗ 12 = 24
3		←Subtract.

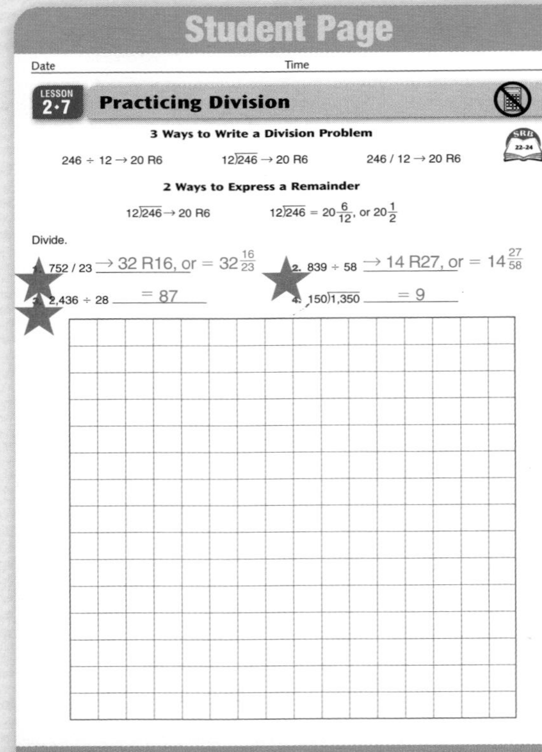

Student Page

Date Time

LESSON 2·7 **Practicing Division**

3 Ways to Write a Division Problem

SRB 22-24

246 ÷ 12 → 20 R6   12)246 → 20 R6   246 / 12 → 20 R6

2 Ways to Express a Remainder

12)246 → 20 R6   12)246 = $20\frac{6}{12}$, or $20\frac{1}{2}$

Divide.

1. 752 / 23 → 32 R16, or = $32\frac{16}{23}$
2. 839 ÷ 58 → 14 R27, or = $14\frac{27}{58}$
3. 2,436 ÷ 28 = 87
4. 150)1,350 = 9

Math Journal 1, p. 66

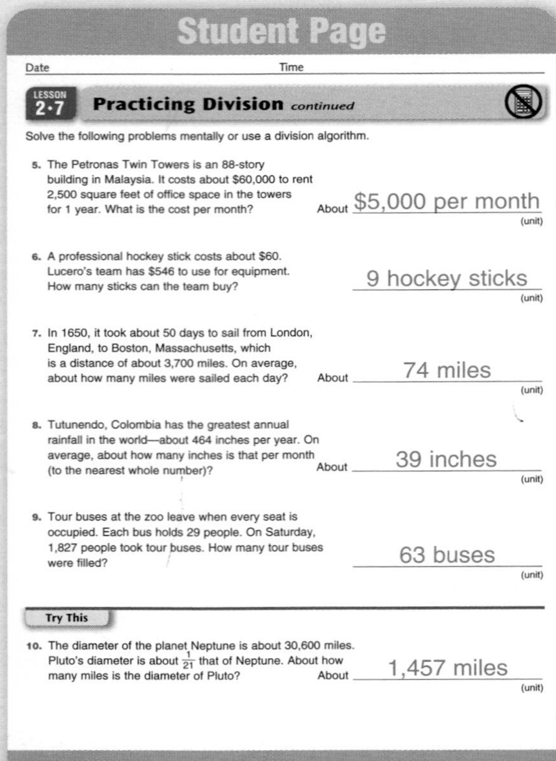

Student Page

Date Time

LESSON 2·7 **Practicing Division** *continued*

Solve the following problems mentally or use a division algorithm.

5. The Petronas Twin Towers is an 88-story building in Malaysia. It costs about $60,000 to rent 2,500 square feet of office space in the towers for 1 year. What is the cost per month? About $5,000 per month (unit)
6. A professional hockey stick costs about $60. Lucero's team has $546 to use for equipment. How many sticks can the team buy? 9 hockey sticks (unit)
7. In 1650, it took about 50 days to sail from London, England, to Boston, Massachusetts, which is a distance of about 3,700 miles. On average, about how many miles were sailed each day? About 74 miles (unit)
8. Tutunendo, Colombia has the greatest annual rainfall in the world—about 464 inches per year. On average, about how many inches is that per month (to the nearest whole number)? About 39 inches (unit)
9. Tour buses at the zoo leave when every seat is occupied. Each bus holds 29 people. On Saturday, 1,827 people took tour buses. How many tour buses were filled? 63 buses (unit)

Try This

10. The diameter of the planet Neptune is about 30,600 miles. Pluto's diameter is about $\frac{1}{21}$ that of Neptune. About how many miles is the diameter of Pluto? About 1,457 miles (unit)

Math Journal 1, p. 67

Ongoing Assessment: Informing Instruction

Encourage students to use numbers that are easy for them to work with. Using easy numbers to make partial quotients may require more steps, but it makes the work go faster.

4. With either strategy, the division is complete when the subtraction results in a number less than 12 (the **divisor,** or the number by which you are dividing). The final step is to add the partial quotients.

12)327	
− 240	20
87	
− 84	+ 7
3	27

12)327	
− 240	20
87	
− 60	5
27	
− 24	+ 2
3	27

5. Because the work shows that there are 27 [12s] in 327, 27 is the **quotient.** The work also shows 3 left, which is the **remainder.** Josie needs 27 full pages, as well as part of another page, to include all 327 photos. Josie needs a total of 28 pages.

▶ Practicing the Partial-Quotients Division Algorithm

WHOLE-CLASS ACTIVITY

(*Student Reference Book,* pp. 22 and 23)

For additional whole-class practice, pose problems similar to the ones below. Have students estimate the quotients using "close" numbers. They can use the estimates to check answers.

▷ 866 / 27 Sample answer: 900 / 30 = 30; solution: → 32 R2, or = $32\frac{2}{27}$

▷ 791 / 33 Sample answer: 750 / 25 = 30; solution: → 23 R32, or = $23\frac{32}{33}$

Adjusting the Activity

Have students use doubles and halves to construct a list of easy multiples. For example, if the divisor is 36, students would make the following list:

200 ∗ 36 = 7,200
100 ∗ 36 = 3,600
50 ∗ 36 = 1,800
25 ∗ 36 = 900
20 ∗ 36 = 720
10 ∗ 36 = 360
5 ∗ 36 = 180
2 ∗ 36 = 72

AUDITORY ◆ KINESTHETIC ◆ TACTILE ◆ VISUAL

▶ Using the Partial-Quotients Division Algorithm

INDEPENDENT ACTIVITY

(*Math Journal 1,* pp. 66 and 67)

Have students solve the problems on journal pages 66 and 67. After students have completed the pages, ask volunteers to discuss their solutions. Encourage those students who used different estimates to share their work.

Ongoing Assessment: Recognizing Student Achievement

Journal Page 66 Problems 1–3 ★

Use **journal page 66, Problems 1–3** to assess students' abilities to estimate quotients and to use an algorithm to divide whole numbers by 2-digit divisors. Students are making adequate progress if they give reasonable estimates for partial quotients and choose a reliable algorithm to solve Problems 1–3. Some students may be able to divide by a 3-digit divisor to solve Problem 4.

[Operations and Computation Goal 2]

2 Ongoing Learning & Practice

▶ Playing *Division Top-It* (Advanced Version)

PARTNER ACTIVITY

(*Student Reference Book,* p. 336; *Math Masters,* p. 478)

Divide the class into pairs and distribute 4 each of number cards 1–9 to each partnership, as well as a game record sheet. Students may need to play a practice game.

▶ Math Boxes 2·7

INDEPENDENT ACTIVITY

(*Math Journal 1,* p. 65)

Mixed Practice Math Boxes in this lesson are paired with Math Boxes in Lesson 2-5. The skills in Problems 4 and 5 preview Unit 3 content.

Student Page

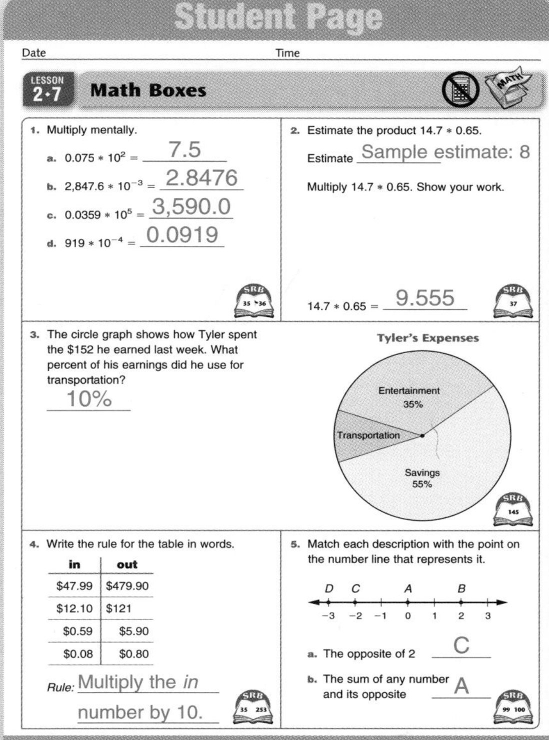

Date Time

LESSON 2·7 **Math Boxes**

1. Multiply mentally.
   a. $0.075 * 10^2 =$ 7.5
   b. $2{,}847.6 * 10^{-3} =$ 2.8476
   c. $0.0359 * 10^5 =$ 3,590.0
   d. $919 * 10^{-4} =$ 0.0919

2. Estimate the product 14.7 ∗ 0.65.
   Estimate Sample estimate: 8
   Multiply 14.7 ∗ 0.65. Show your work.
   14.7 ∗ 0.65 = 9.555

3. The circle graph shows how Tyler spent the $152 he earned last week. What percent of his earnings did he use for transportation?
   10%

4. Write the rule for the table in words.

in	out
$47.99	$479.90
$12.10	$121
$0.59	$5.90
$0.08	$0.80

Rule: Multiply the *in* number by 10.

5. Match each description with the point on the number line that represents it.

   a. The opposite of 2 C
   b. The sum of any number and its opposite A

Math Journal 1, p. 65

Study Link Master

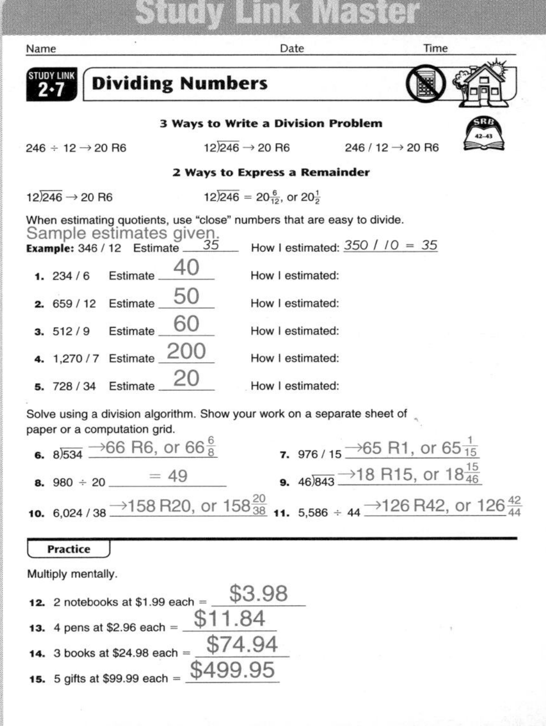

Name Date Time

STUDY LINK 2·7 **Dividing Numbers**

3 Ways to Write a Division Problem

246 ÷ 12 → 20 R6   12)246 → 20 R6   246 / 12 → 20 R6

2 Ways to Express a Remainder

12)246 → 20 R6   12)246 = $20\frac{6}{12}$, or $20\frac{1}{2}$

When estimating quotients, use "close" numbers that are easy to divide.

Sample estimates given.

Example: 346 / 12 Estimate 35 How I estimated: 350 / 10 = 35

1. 234 / 6 Estimate 40 How I estimated:
2. 659 / 12 Estimate 50 How I estimated:
3. 512 / 9 Estimate 60 How I estimated:
4. 1,270 / 7 Estimate 200 How I estimated:
5. 728 / 34 Estimate 20 How I estimated:

Solve using a division algorithm. Show your work on a separate sheet of paper or a computation grid.

6. 8)534 → 66 R6, or $66\frac{6}{8}$
7. 976 / 15 → 65 R1, or $65\frac{1}{15}$
8. 980 ÷ 20 = 49
9. 46)843 → 18 R15, or $18\frac{15}{46}$
10. 6,024 / 38 → 158 R20, or $158\frac{20}{38}$
11. 5,586 ÷ 44 → 126 R42, or $126\frac{42}{44}$

Practice

Multiply mentally.

12. 2 notebooks at $1.99 each = $3.98
13. 4 pens at $2.96 each = $11.84
14. 3 books at $24.98 each = $74.94
15. 5 gifts at $99.99 each = $499.95

Math Masters, p. 57

Divisibility Rules For 7

Example 1: Is 2,758 divisible by 7?

Step 1: Isolate the ones digit. Multiply by 2. **(8 * 2 = 16)**

```
  2,75|8
–   16|
  25|9
– 18|
    7
```

Step 2: Subtract the product **(16)** from the remaining digits.

Repeat Steps 1 and 2 until you get 0 or another multiple of 7. If the result is 0 or another number divisible by 7, then the original number is divisible by 7.

7 is divisible by 7, so 2,758 is also divisible by 7.

Example 2: Is 1,667 divisible by 7?

Step 1: Isolate the ones digit. Multiply by 2. **(7 * 2 = 14)**

```
  1,66|7
–   14|
  15|2
–  4|
  11
```

Step 2: Subtract the product **(14)** from the remaining digits.

11 is not divisible by 7, so 1,667 is not divisible by 7.

Student Page

Whole Numbers

Column-Division Method

The best way to understand column division is to think of a division problem as a money-sharing problem. In the example below, think of sharing $863 equally among 5 people.

Example $5\overline{)863} = ?$

1. Draw lines to separate the digits in the dividend (the number being divided). Work left to right. Begin in the left column.
2. Think of the 8 in the hundreds column as 8 $100 bills to be shared by 5 people. Each person gets 1 $100 bill. There are 3 $100 bills remaining.
3. Trade the 3 $100 bills for 30 $10 bills. Think of the 6 in the tens column as 6 $10 bills. That makes 30 + 6 = 36 $10 bills.
4. If 5 people share 36 $10 bills, each person gets 7 $10 bills. There is 1 $10 bill remaining.
5. Trade the 1 $10 bill for 10 $1 bills. Think of the 3 in the ones column as 3 $1 bills. That makes 10 + 3 = 13 $1 bills.
6. If 5 people share 13 $1 bills, each person gets 2 $1 bills. There are 3 $1 bills remaining.

```
     1 | 7 | 2
 5 ) 8 | 6 | 3
   – 5 |36 |13
     3 |–35|–10
       | 1 |  3
```

Record the answer as 172 R3.
Each person receives $172 and $3 are left over.

Student Reference Book, p. 24

▶ Study Link 2•7

INDEPENDENT ACTIVITY

(*Math Masters,* p. 57)

Home Connection Students use close numbers to estimate quotients. They use a paper-and-pencil division algorithm to solve division problems.

3 Differentiation Options

ENRICHMENT

INDEPENDENT ACTIVITY

▶ Divisibility by 7

5–15 Min

None of the simple divisibility rules apply to the prime number 7. To extend students' knowledge of divisibility rules, consider introducing them to the divisibility rule for 7. (*See margin.*)

To support English language learners, discuss the meaning of the terms *divisibility rule* and *isolate*. Have students test the following numbers for divisibility by 7. *Suggestions:*

343 Yes 1,372 Yes 5,527 No 17,276 Yes

ENRICHMENT

INDEPENDENT ACTIVITY

▶ Exploring an Alternative Division Algorithm

15–30 Min

(*Student Reference Book,* p. 24)

Students begin by reviewing the column division algorithm on page 24 of the *Student Reference Book*. They extend and explore this algorithm to solve a problem with a 2-digit divisor, such as $15\overline{)2,589}$.

ELL SUPPORT

INDEPENDENT ACTIVITY

▶ Building a Math Word Bank

5–15 Min

(*Differentiation Handbook*)

To provide language support for division, have students use the Word Bank template found in the *Differentiation Handbook.* Ask them to write the terms *divisor, dividend, quotient,* and *remainder,* record examples representing each term, and write other related words. See the *Differentiation Handbook* for more information.

2·8 Division of Decimals

Objectives To estimate and calculate quotients of whole- and decimal-number dividends; and to extend the partial-quotients division algorithm to include decimal-number quotients.

1 Teaching the Lesson

Key Activities

Students estimate quotients and use the estimates to insert the decimal point into quotients. They rewrite whole-number division problems to obtain quotients to a specified number of decimal places.

Key Concepts and Skills

- Apply place-value concepts to attach zeros to a dividend. [Number and Numeration Goal 1]
- Find differences of partial quotients. [Operations and Computation Goal 1]
- Use multiplication and extended facts to compute partial quotients. [Operations and Computation Goal 2]
- Divide a decimal number by a whole number. [Operations and Computation Goal 2]
- Use an estimate to place the decimal point in a quotient. [Operations and Computation Goal 5]

Key Vocabulary (teacher)

truncated

materials

- ☐ *Math Journal 1,* pp. 68 and 69
- ☐ Study Link 2•7
- ☐ Teaching Aid Master (*Math Masters,* p. 414)

2 Ongoing Learning & Practice

Students practice interpreting remainders of division problems.

Students practice and maintain skills through Math Boxes and Study Link activities.

Ongoing Assessment: Recognizing Student Achievement Use journal page 70. [Operations and Computation Goal 2]

materials

- ☐ *Math Journal 1,* pp. 70 and 71
- ☐ Study Link Master (*Math Masters,* p. 58)
- ☐ Teaching Aid Master (*Math Masters,* p. 414; optional)

3 Differentiation Options

READINESS

Students use bills and coins to model problems with decimal remainders.

ENRICHMENT

Students study patterns that involve multiplying the dividend and divisor by the same number.

materials

- ☐ bills and coins of various denominations

Technology

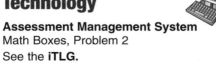

Assessment Management System
Math Boxes, Problem 2
See the **iTLG.**

Getting Started

Mental Math and Reflexes

Students estimate quotients by using "close" numbers that are easy to divide. *Suggestions:*

●○○ 96 / 8 100 / 10 = 10

●●○ 482 / 6 480 / 6 = 80; 500 / 5 = 100

●●● 774 / 27 775 / 25 = 31; 800 / 25 = 32

Math Message

A spool contains 96.2 yards of ribbon. You want to cut the ribbon into 13 pieces, all the same length. About how long should each piece be? Do not calculate the exact answer.

Study Link 2·7 Follow-Up

Have students share strategies they used to estimate quotients and solve the division problems.

Links to the Future

This lesson does not cover all types of decimal division. On journal page 68, decimal numbers are divided by whole numbers. All answers come out even—no zeros need to be attached, and the remainder is zero. On journal page 69, whole numbers are divided by smaller whole numbers, zeros are attached, and answers are found to a specified number of decimal places. Unit 8 will cover division of decimals by decimals.

Student Page

Date Time

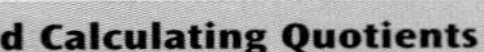

LESSON 2·8 **Estimating and Calculating Quotients**

For each problem, follow the steps below. Show your work on a separate sheet of paper or a computation grid.

- Estimate the quotient by using numbers that are "close" to the numbers given and that are easy to divide. Write your estimate. Then write a number sentence showing how you estimated.
- Ignore any decimal points. Divide as if the numbers were whole numbers.
- Use your estimate to insert a decimal point in the final answer.

Sample estimates given.

1. 16)54.4 Estimate 3; How I estimated 54 ÷ 18 = 3; Answer 3.4
2. 12)206.4 Estimate 20; How I estimated 200 ÷ 10 = 20; Answer 17.2
3. $37.10 ÷ 14 Estimate 3; How I estimated 39 ÷ 13 = 3; Answer $2.65
4. 39.27 ÷ 21 Estimate 2; How I estimated 42 ÷ 21 = 2; Answer 1.87
5. 32)120 Estimate 4; How I estimated 120 ÷ 30 = 4; Answer 3.75
6. 28)232.4 Estimate 7; How I estimated 210 ÷ 30 = 7; Answer 8.3

Math Journal 1, p. 68

1 Teaching the Lesson

▶ Math Message Follow-Up

WHOLE-CLASS DISCUSSION

Discuss students' strategies for estimating the quotient 96.2 / 13.

Example:

▷ If there were 130 yards of ribbon, the length of each piece would be 130 yards divided by 13 pieces, or 10 yards. So, the answer is less than 10 yards.

▷ 2 ∗ 13 = 26. Double this: 4 ∗ 13 = 52. Double again: 8 ∗ 13 = 104, which is a little more than 96.2. Each piece is about 7 or 8 yards long.

▶ Dividing Decimals

WHOLE-CLASS ACTIVITY

(*Math Journal 1,* p. 68; *Math Masters,* p. 414)

Ask students to ignore the decimal point in the Math Message problem and divide 962 by 13, using the partial-quotients division algorithm they reviewed in the previous lesson. Students can work on a computation grid (*Math Masters*, p. 414). As an aid, they might want to develop a list of multiples of 13. (*See margin of page 143.*)

Ask: *Can 74 be the answer to the problem?* No. Estimated answers were in the range of 7 to 10 yards. Ask students to use their estimates to insert a decimal point in 74 so they get a correct answer. 7.4 Have students check their answers with a calculator. 13 ∗ 7.4 = 96.2

Work as a class to solve Problem 1 on journal page 68.

1. First, have students estimate the quotient. 54 / 18 = 3 or 60 / 15 = 4 are both reasonable estimates using close numbers that are easy to divide.
2. Next, have them ignore the decimal point and divide 544 by 16, using the partial-quotients division algorithm. (*See margin.*)
3. Finally, have students use their estimates to insert a decimal point so that they get a correct answer. 54.4 / 16 = 3.4; Estimated answers were in the range of 3 to 4, so 3.4 seems reasonable.

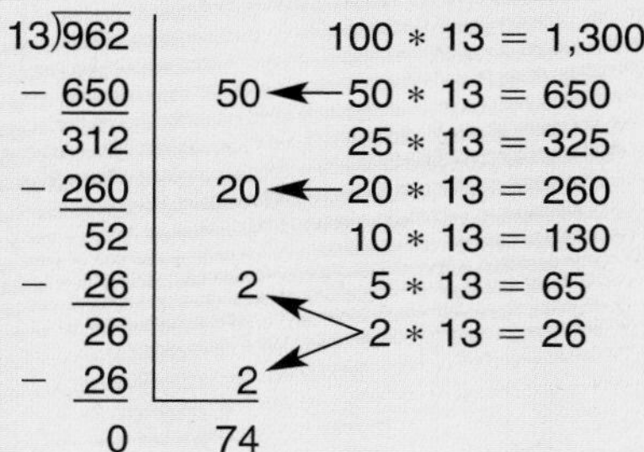

Students use the same routine to solve the rest of the problems on their own.

When most students have completed the page, have volunteers show how they solved the problems. Discuss solution strategies.

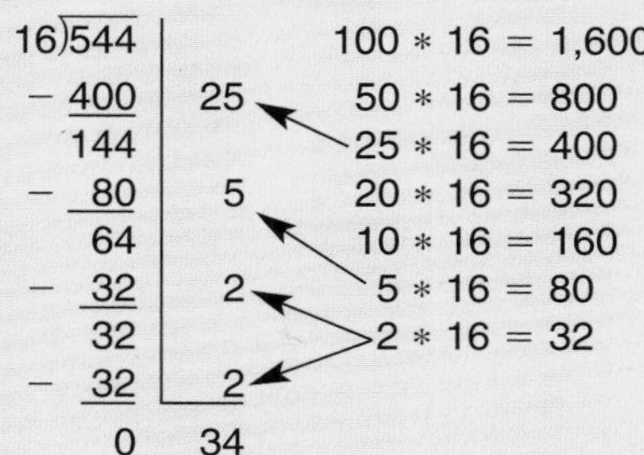

▶ Finding Decimal Solutions to Whole-Number Division Problems

WHOLE-CLASS ACTIVITY

(*Math Journal 1,* p. 69; *Math Masters,* p. 414)

Solve Problem 1 on journal page 69 as a class. Calculate the quotient and remainder. Each share is $4, but $1 remains to be shared by the 7 diners.

```
7)29  |
- 28  |_4
   1   4
```

A better solution would give the amount of each share in dollars and cents, requiring an answer with two decimal places.

Ask students to do the following:

1. Rewrite the dividend (the number being divided), 29, as 29.00.
2. Divide 29.00 by 7, using the partial-quotients division algorithm. Ignore the decimal point and divide 2,900 by 7. The answer is 414 with remainder 2.

```
7)2,900
- 2,800  |400
    100  |
   - 70  | 10
     30  |
   - 28  |  4
      2  |414
```

3. Insert the decimal point. The estimate was about 4, so the correct answer is 4.14.
4. Check the answer: 7 ∗ 4.14 = 28.98. The remainder of 2 corresponds to 2 cents of the original $29.00. Seven people cannot share 2 cents.

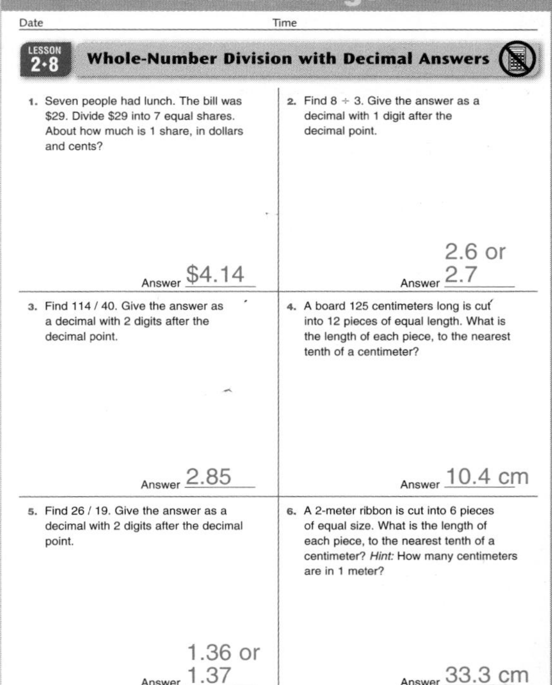
Student Page

Date Time

LESSON 2•8 Whole-Number Division with Decimal Answers

1. Seven people had lunch. The bill was $29. Divide $29 into 7 equal shares. About how much is 1 share, in dollars and cents?
Answer $4.14

2. Find 8 ÷ 3. Give the answer as a decimal with 1 digit after the decimal point.
Answer 2.6 or 2.7

3. Find 114 / 40. Give the answer as a decimal with 2 digits after the decimal point.
Answer 2.85

4. A board 125 centimeters long is cut into 12 pieces of equal length. What is the length of each piece, to the nearest tenth of a centimeter?
Answer 10.4 cm

5. Find 26 / 19. Give the answer as a decimal with 2 digits after the decimal point.
Answer 1.36 or 1.37

6. A 2-meter ribbon is cut into 6 pieces of equal size. What is the length of each piece, to the nearest tenth of a centimeter? *Hint:* How many centimeters are in 1 meter?
Answer 33.3 cm

Math Journal 1, p. 69

Continue by working Problem 2 on journal page 69 as a class. Have students divide 8 by 3 in the usual way. 8 / 3 → 2 R2, or $2\frac{2}{3}$ Ask them how they might rewrite the problem so the answer is a decimal number to the tenths place. Rewrite 8 as 8.0. Ignore the decimal point. 80 / 3 → 26 R2, or = $26\frac{2}{3}$. Insert the decimal point between the 2 and the 6, because the estimated answer is about 2. Ignoring the remainder yields a **truncated** quotient, for example, 2.6 for 8 / 3. The final answer is about 2.6, ignoring the remainder of 2.

Adjusting the Activity

Have students consider whether the remainder is at least half of the divisor. If it is, then they should increase the digit in the last decimal place by 1 to give a rounded quotient (for example, 2.7 for 8 / 3).

AUDITORY ◆ KINESTHETIC ◆ TACTILE ◆ VISUAL

Help students summarize:

▷ Dividing a greater whole number by a lesser whole number will give a whole-number quotient and might result in a nonzero remainder.

▷ If you want a 1-place decimal answer, rewrite the dividend as a decimal with 0 in the tenths place. If you want a 2-place decimal answer, rewrite the dividend as a decimal with zeros in the tenths and hundredths places, and so on. (For all the problems on journal page 69, the number of decimal places required in the answer is specified.)

▷ Estimate the quotient. Ignore the decimal point in the dividend and divide; disregard any remainder. Then use the estimate to place the decimal point in the answer.

Students solve the remaining problems on journal page 69. Circulate and assist as needed.

Student Page

Date Time

LESSON 2·8 **Interpreting Remainders**

Use any division algorithm to find each quotient. Then use the information in the problem to make sense of the remainder.

1. Mr. Jacobson has a can of Mancala beans. He asks Bill to divide the beans into sets of 48 beans each. There are 389 beans in the can. How many sets of 48 can Bill make?
   8 sets

2. Sharon is organizing her CD collection. She has 68 CDs in all. Each CD rack holds 25 CDs. How many racks does she need to hold her entire collection?
   3 racks

3. Jesse is making cookies for the class bake sale. He plans to charge 25 cents per cookie. He wants to make at least 342 cookies (one for each student in the school). Each batch makes about 25 cookies. How many batches should he make?
   14 batches

4. Mrs. Hanley's sixth-grade class is putting on a play for the rest of the school. They will set up rows of chairs in the gymnasium. If there are 21 chairs in each row, how many rows are needed for the 297 people who are expected to come?
   15 rows

5. Nestor's favorite sport is baseball. He went to 18 games last year. Nestor usually sits in the upper boxes, where tickets cost $15. This year, he's saved $238 for tickets. How many tickets will he be able to buy?
   15 tickets

6. Regina, Ruth, Stanley, and Sam sold lemonade. They charged $0.20 per glass. They collected a total of $29.60. They paid $8.00 for supplies and evenly split the money that was left. How much did each of them receive?
   $5.40

Math Journal 1, p. 71

2 Ongoing Learning & Practice

▶ Interpreting Remainders

INDEPENDENT ACTIVITY

(*Math Journal 1,* p. 71)

Students practice solving division problems and interpreting remainders.

▶ Math Boxes 2•8

INDEPENDENT ACTIVITY

(*Math Journal 1,* p. 70)

Mixed Practice Math Boxes in this lesson are paired with Math Boxes in Lessons 2-6 and 2-10. The skill in Problem 5 previews Unit 3 content.

Ongoing Assessment: Recognizing Student Achievement

Math Boxes Problem 2 

Use **Math Boxes, Problem 2** to assess students' abilities to estimate a quotient and to use an algorithm to divide a multidigit number. Students are making adequate progress if they are able to make a reasonable estimate and choose a reliable algorithm to solve Problem 2. Some students may be able to use their estimate to insert the decimal point.

[Operations and Computation Goal 2]

▶ Study Link 2•8

INDEPENDENT ACTIVITY

(*Math Masters,* p. 58; p. 414 optional)

Home Connection Students practice division with decimals.

Student Page

Date Time

LESSON 2•8 **Math Boxes**

1. Estimate each sum or difference. Then solve. Sample estimates given.
 a. 5.6 − 2.983 Estimate 3
 5.6 − 2.983 = 2.617
 b. 5.83 + 6.025 + 12.7 Estimate 24
 5.83 + 6.025 + 12.7 = 24.555

2. 43.2 / 16 Estimate Sample estimate: 2.5
 Use any division algorithm to solve 43.2 / 16. Show your work.
 43.2 / 16 = 2.7

3. Multiply mentally.
 a. $27.8 * \frac{1}{10}$ = 2.78
 b. 3.0078 ∗ 100 = 300.78
 c. $45.6 * \frac{1}{100}$ = 0.456
 d. 0.001 ∗ 10,000 = 10.0

4. The hourly wages of 5 employees are $9.25, $10.50, $11.60, $11.75, and $12.20.
 Explain how the median and mean would change if $9.25 were removed from the set of wages.
 Both the median and the mean would increase.

5. Write the number pair for each of the following points shown on the coordinate grid.
 A: (4, 2)
 B: (2, 0)
 C: (−5, 1)
 D: (3, −5)
 E: (0, −4)
 F: (−2, −3)

Math Journal 1, p. 70

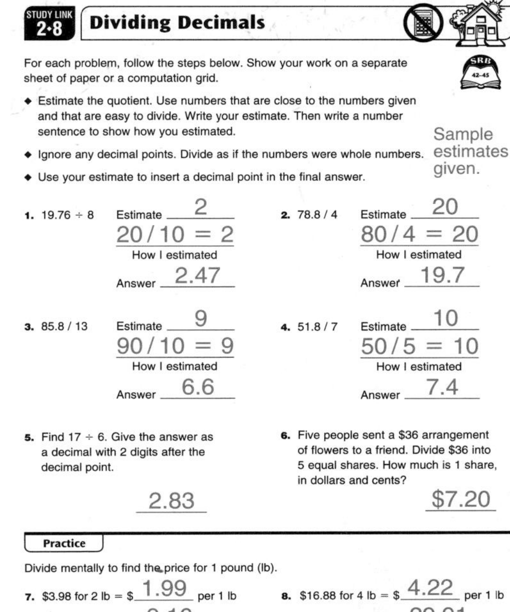

Study Link Master

Name Date Time

STUDY LINK 2•8 **Dividing Decimals**

For each problem, follow the steps below. Show your work on a separate sheet of paper or a computation grid.

- Estimate the quotient. Use numbers that are close to the numbers given and that are easy to divide. Write your estimate. Then write a number sentence to show how you estimated.
- Ignore any decimal points. Divide as if the numbers were whole numbers.
- Use your estimate to insert a decimal point in the final answer.

Sample estimates given.

1. 19.76 ÷ 8 Estimate 2
 20 / 10 = 2 How I estimated
 Answer 2.47

2. 78.8 / 4 Estimate 20
 80 / 4 = 20 How I estimated
 Answer 19.7

3. 85.8 / 13 Estimate 9
 90 / 10 = 9 How I estimated
 Answer 6.6

4. 51.8 / 7 Estimate 10
 50 / 5 = 10 How I estimated
 Answer 7.4

5. Find 17 ÷ 6. Give the answer as a decimal with 2 digits after the decimal point. 2.83

6. Five people sent a $36 arrangement of flowers to a friend. Divide $36 into 5 equal shares. How much is 1 share, in dollars and cents? $7.20

Practice

Divide mentally to find the price for 1 pound (lb).

7. $3.98 for 2 lb = $1.99 per 1 lb
8. $16.88 for 4 lb = $4.22 per 1 lb
9. $45.80 for 5 lb = $9.16 per 1 lb
10. $299.10 for 10 lb = $29.91 per 1 lb

Math Masters, p. 58

3 Differentiation Options

READINESS

SMALL-GROUP ACTIVITY

▶ Modeling Decimal Remainders

5–15 Min

To provide experience with remainders, have students use bills and coins to model division problems.

Suggestions:

▷ Cost of $27 shared equally by 2 friends $13.50

▷ Cost of $69 shared equally by 5 people $13.80

▷ Cost of $122 shared equally by 8 students $15.25

Have students describe how they solved each problem. Encourage them to use the mathematical words *share, equal, divide,* and *remainder.*

ENRICHMENT

INDEPENDENT ACTIVITY

▶ Finding Patterns in Quotients

5–15 Min

Students explore how to maintain the value of the quotient by studying and comparing the first and second columns in the table below.

Division Problem	Division Problem after Multiplying Dividend and Divisor by 10
60 / 0.3 = 200	600 / 3 = 200
6 / 0.3 = 20	60 / 3 = 20
0.6 / 0.3 = 2	6 / 3 = 2
0.06 / 0.3 = 0.2	0.6 / 3 = 0.2

Then students share observations about what happens to the quotient when they multiply both the dividend and divisor by 10.

Finally, students apply patterns to complete the table below.

Dividend	Divisor	Multiply Dividend and Divisor by:	Quotient
3.5	0.007	1,000	500
3.5	0.07	100	50
3.5	0.7	10	5

Scientific Notation for Large and Small Numbers

Objectives To use scientific notation; and to convert between scientific and standard notations.

1 Teaching the Lesson

Key Activities

Students discuss how scientific notation is used to represent large and small numbers. They practice translating between scientific and standard notations.

Key Concepts and Skills

- Convert between scientific and standard notations. [Number and Numeration Goal 1]
- Use extended facts to find products of very large and very small numbers. [Operations and Computation Goal 2]
- Multiply a decimal number by a power of 10. [Operations and Computation Goal 2]

Key Vocabulary

positive power of 10 • negative power of 10 • scientific notation

Ongoing Assessment: Recognizing Student Achievement Use journal page 72. [Number and Numeration Goal 1]

Ongoing Assessment: Informing Instruction See page 149.

materials

- ☐ *Math Journal 1,* pp. 72 and 73
- ☐ *Student Reference Book,* pp. 7 and 8
- ☐ Study Link 2•8

2 Ongoing Learning & Practice

Students practice translating between scientific and standard notations by playing *Scientific Notation Toss.*

Students practice and maintain skills through Math Boxes and Study Link activities.

materials

- ☐ *Math Journal 1,* p. 74
- ☐ *Student Reference Book,* p. 331
- ☐ Study Link Master (*Math Masters,* p. 59)
- ☐ Game Master (*Math Masters,* p. 472)
- ☐ 2 six-sided dice

3 Differentiation Options

READINESS

Students review positive and negative powers of 10.

ENRICHMENT

Students convert ground areas of famous buildings from scientific to standard notation.

EXTRA PRACTICE

Students write powers of 10 for numbers less than 1.

materials

- ☐ Teaching Masters (*Math Masters,* pp. 60–62)
- ☐ *5-Minute Math*, pp. 166 and 167

See **Advance Preparation**

Additional Information

Advance Preparation For the optional Enrichment activity, determine the ground area (square footage) of your school.

Technology

Assessment Management System
Journal page 72, Problems 15–20
See the **iTLG.**

Getting Started

Mental Math and Reflexes

Students convert number-and-word notation to standard notation.

Pose problems such as the following:

●○○ 4.6 million 4,600,000

●●○ 0.8 million 800,000

5.6 billion 5,600,000,000

●●● 36.1 billion 36,100,000,000

Math Message

In Lesson 2-4, you multiplied numbers by powers of 10. Review your answers to Problems 1–3 on journal page 56. Then find the following products:

$5 * 10^6$ $4 * 10^{-3}$ $9 * 10^9$ $3 * 10^{-6}$

Study Link 2·8 Follow-Up

Review answers.

1 Teaching the Lesson

▶ Math Message Follow-Up

WHOLE-CLASS DISCUSSION

(*Math Journal 1,* p. 72)

Ask students to explain how they used their answers to Problems 1–3 on journal page 56 to find the following products:

$5 * 10^6$	$4 * 10^{-3}$	$9 * 10^9$	$3 * 10^{-6}$
5,000,000	0.004	9,000,000,000	0.000003

Discuss the strategy students used in Lesson 2-4 to multiply numbers by powers of 10. In this lesson, students will apply their power-of-10 strategy to write numbers in scientific notation.

A **positive power of 10** is a number that can be represented as a product whose only factors are 10s. A **negative power of 10** is a number that can be represented as a product whose only factors are $\frac{1}{10}$s (or 0.1s). Zero is neither positive nor negative. To support English language learners, write *positive power of 10* along with its definition and some examples on the board. Repeat with *negative power of 10* and *zero power.* Ask students how they would write 10^0 in standard notation. 1 Emphasize that the zero power of any nonzero number is equal to 1, for example, $2^0 = 1$; $25^0 = 1$; $8{,}156{,}293^0 = 1$; and so on.

Have students complete journal page 72. When most students have completed the page, briefly go over the answers.

Ongoing Assessment: Recognizing Student Achievement

Journal Page 72 Problems 15–20 ★

Use **journal page 72, Problems 15–20** to assess students' ability to determine the power of 10 needed to move the decimal point in the other factor to the right or left. Students are making adequate progress if they can solve Problems 15–20.

[Number and Numeration Goal 1]

Student Page

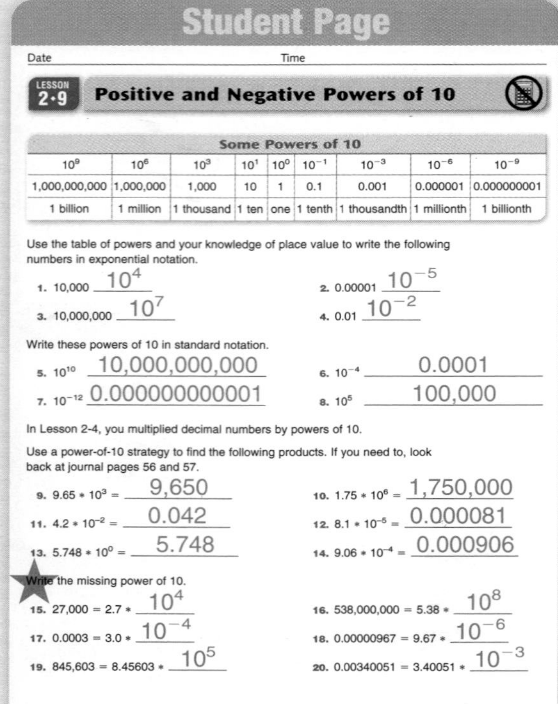

Date Time

LESSON 2·9 **Positive and Negative Powers of 10**

Some Powers of 10

10^9	10^6	10^3	10^1	10^0	10^{-1}	10^{-3}	10^{-6}	10^{-9}
1,000,000,000	1,000,000	1,000	10	1	0.1	0.001	0.000001	0.000000001
1 billion	1 million	1 thousand	1 ten	one	1 tenth	1 thousandth	1 millionth	1 billionth

Use the table of powers and your knowledge of place value to write the following numbers in exponential notation.

1. 10,000 10^4
2. 0.00001 10^{-5}
3. 10,000,000 10^7
4. 0.01 10^{-2}

Write these powers of 10 in standard notation.

5. 10^{10} 10,000,000,000
6. 10^{-4} 0.0001
7. 10^{-12} 0.000000000001
8. 10^5 100,000

In Lesson 2-4, you multiplied decimal numbers by powers of 10.

Use a power-of-10 strategy to find the following products. If you need to, look back at journal pages 56 and 57.

9. $9.65 * 10^3 =$ 9,650
10. $1.75 * 10^6 =$ 1,750,000
11. $4.2 * 10^{-2} =$ 0.042
12. $8.1 * 10^{-5} =$ 0.000081
13. $5.748 * 10^0 =$ 5.748
14. $9.06 * 10^{-4} =$ 0.000906

★ Write the missing power of 10.

15. $27{,}000 = 2.7 *$ 10^4
16. $538{,}000{,}000 = 5.38 *$ 10^8
17. $0.0003 = 3.0 *$ 10^{-4}
18. $0.00000967 = 9.67 *$ 10^{-6}
19. $845{,}603 = 8.45603 *$ 10^5
20. $0.00340051 = 3.40051 *$ 10^{-3}

Math Journal 1, p. 72

▶ Discussing the Advantages of Scientific Notation

(*Student Reference Book,* pp. 7 and 8)

As a class, read and work through the examples on *Student Reference Book,* page 7. Be sure students recognize that a number in strict **scientific notation** is written as the product of two factors:

▷ The first factor is at least 1 but less than 10.

▷ The second factor is a power of 10, either positive or negative.

Page 8 of the *Student Reference Book* shows how to convert between scientific notation and standard notation. Work through the examples with the class. Provide time for students to try the Check Your Understanding problems. If necessary, pose additional problems.

NOTE It is possible to perform operations with numbers in scientific notation, but it is not necessary to discuss this now. The procedure will be introduced in Lesson 2-11.

▶ Translating between Scientific and Standard Notations

(*Math Journal 1,* p. 73)

Have students complete journal page 73. When most students have completed the page, briefly go over the answers.

The Try This problem is quite difficult. One approach for Problem 8a is to recognize that 10^9 equals 1 billion and convert the numbers to number-and-word notation using billions. A CD holds $6 * 10^9$, or 6 billion, bits of information. An average person's memory holds $100 * 10^9$, or 100 billion, bits of information. Divide 100 billion by 6 billion: 100 billion / 6 billion. Dividing both the dividend and divisor by 1 billion yields the equivalent division 100 / 6, which equals $16.\overline{6}$ and rounds to 16.7.

For Problem 8b, multiply 16.7 CDs by 400,000 $(4 * 10^5)$ pages of text per CD. The answer is about 6,680,000 pages of text, or $6.68 * 10^6$.

Ongoing Assessment: Informing Instruction

Watch for students who assume that the exponent always matches the number of zeros in the number. Some students might think $3.5 * 10^8$ will have eight zeros, or that $1.4 * 10^{-4}$ will have four zeros. Stress that the exponent matches the number of places the decimal point will move.

Student Page

Date ______ Time ______

LESSON 2·9 **Translating Standard & Scientific Notation**

Scientific notation is used in the following facts. Rewrite each number in standard notation. Study the example.

Example: The number of taste buds in an average human mouth is about $9 * 10^3$, or 9,000, taste buds.

1. The number of hairs on an average human body is about $5 * 10^6$, or 5,000,000, hairs.
2. The width of a hair is between $2 * 10^{-7}$ and $3 * 10^{-7}$, or 0.0000002 and 0.0000003, inches.
3. The length of a grain of salt is about $1 * 10^{-5}$, or 0.00001, meter.
4. The time for a flea to take off on a vertical jump is $7.9 * 10^{-5}$, or 0.000079, second.

Standard notation is used in the following facts. Rewrite each number in scientific notation. Study the example.

Example: The approximate cost of fuel for a space shuttle mission is \$2,000,000, or $2 * 10^6$ dollars.

5. A Stradivarius violin in perfect condition sells for approximately \$3,000,000, or $3 * 10^6$ dollars.
6. The average growth rate of a child between birth and the age of 18 years is 0.007, or $7 * 10^{-3}$, inch per day.
7. The weight of a bee's brain is approximately 0.00004, or $4 * 10^{-5}$, ounce.

Try This

8. A CD (compact disc) holds about $6 * 10^9$ bits of information. This equals about $4 * 10^5$ pages of text. A person's memory can hold about $1 * 10^{11}$ bits of information.
   a. About how many CDs' worth of information can one person's memory hold? About 16.7 CDs (unit)
   b. About how many pages of text can one person's memory hold? About $6.68 * 10^6$ pages (unit)

Sources: The Sizesaurus; The Compass in Your Nose and Other Astonishing Facts about Humans; and Everything Has Its Price

***Math Journal 1,* p. 73**

Student Page

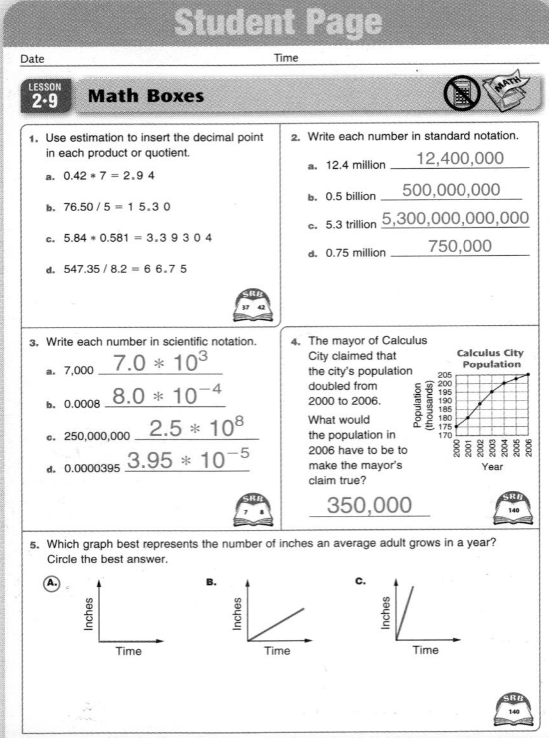

Date Time

LESSON 2·9 **Math Boxes**

1. Use estimation to insert the decimal point in each product or quotient.
   a. $0.42 * 7 = 2.9\ 4$
   b. $76.50 / 5 = 1\ 5.3\ 0$
   c. $5.84 * 0.581 = 3.3\ 9\ 3\ 0\ 4$
   d. $547.35 / 8.2 = 6\ 6.7\ 5$

2. Write each number in standard notation.
   a. 12.4 million 12,400,000
   b. 0.5 billion 500,000,000
   c. 5.3 trillion 5,300,000,000,000
   d. 0.75 million 750,000

3. Write each number in scientific notation.
   a. 7,000 $7.0 * 10^3$
   b. 0.0008 $8.0 * 10^{-4}$
   c. 250,000,000 $2.5 * 10^8$
   d. 0.0000395 $3.95 * 10^{-5}$

4. The mayor of Calculus City claimed that the city's population doubled from 2000 to 2006. What would the population in 2006 have to be to make the mayor's claim true?
   350,000

5. Which graph best represents the number of inches an average adult grows in a year? Circle the best answer.

Math Journal 1, p. 74

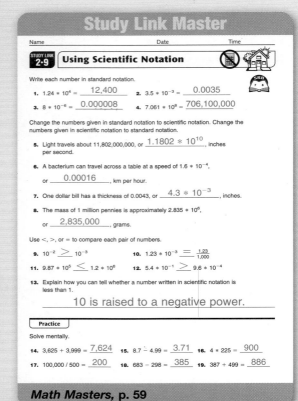

Study Link Master

Name Date Time

STUDY LINK 2·9 **Using Scientific Notation**

Write each number in standard notation.

1. $1.24 * 10^4 =$ 12,400
2. $3.5 * 10^{-3} =$ 0.0035
3. $8 * 10^{-6} =$ 0.000008
4. $7.061 * 10^8 =$ 706,100,000

Change the numbers given in standard notation to scientific notation. Change the numbers given in scientific notation to standard notation.

5. Light travels about 11,802,000,000, or $1.1802 * 10^{10}$, inches per second.
6. A bacterium can travel across a table at a speed of $1.6 * 10^{-4}$, or 0.00016, km per hour.
7. One dollar bill has a thickness of 0.0043, or $4.3 * 10^{-3}$, inches.
8. The mass of 1 million pennies is approximately $2.835 * 10^6$, or 2,835,000, grams.

Use $<$, $>$, or $=$ to compare each pair of numbers.

9. $10^{-2} > 10^{-3}$
10. $1.23 * 10^{-3} = \frac{1.23}{1,000}$
11. $9.87 * 10^5 < 1.2 * 10^6$
12. $5.4 * 10^{-1} > 9.6 * 10^{-4}$
13. Explain how you can tell whether a number written in scientific notation is less than 1.
    10 is raised to a negative power.

Practice

Solve mentally.

14. $3,625 + 3,999 =$ 7,624
15. $8.7 - 4.99 =$ 3.71
16. $4 * 225 =$ 900
17. $100,000 / 500 =$ 200
18. $683 - 298 =$ 385
19. $387 + 499 =$ 886

Math Masters, p. 59

2 Ongoing Learning & Practice

▶ Playing *Scientific Notation Toss*

PARTNER ACTIVITY

(*Student Reference Book,* p. 331; *Math Masters,* p. 472)

Divide the class into pairs and distribute two 6-sided dice to each, as well as a game record sheet. Students read the directions on page 331 in the *Student Reference Book*. Have a volunteer demonstrate how to play the game. Students may need to play a practice game.

▶ Math Boxes 2·9

INDEPENDENT ACTIVITY

(*Math Journal 1,* p. 74)

Mixed Practice Math Boxes in this lesson are paired with Math Boxes in Lesson 2-11. The skill in Problem 5 previews Unit 3 content.

Writing/Reasoning Have students write a response to the following: *Explain how you decided where to place the decimal point in Problems 1c and 1d.* Sample answer: For Problem 1c, I counted the number of decimal places in each factor (2 and 3) and added the number of decimal places (5). Then I multiplied the factors as if they were whole numbers. Starting at the right of the product, I moved left 5 places and inserted the decimal point to get 3.39304. For Problem 1d, I used "close" numbers (560 and 8) to estimate the quotient. $560 \div 8$ is 70, so I inserted the decimal point to get 66.75, which is about 70.

▶ Study Link 2·9

INDEPENDENT ACTIVITY

(*Math Masters,* p. 59)

Home Connection Students practice converting between standard and scientific notations.

3 Differentiation Options

READINESS

INDEPENDENT ACTIVITY

▶ Reviewing Powers of 10

5–15 Min

(*Math Masters,* p. 62)

Students use patterns to write positive and negative powers of 10 in exponential and standard notations.

ENRICHMENT

INDEPENDENT ACTIVITY

▶ Comparing Ground Areas of Famous Buildings

15–30 Min

(*Math Masters,* pp. 60 and 61)

Social Studies Students convert the ground areas of famous buildings from scientific to standard notation. Then they use this information to make ratio and difference comparisons. Encourage students to find ground areas of other buildings (famous or local) and to use this data to make more comparisons. Consider supplying the class with the ground area for your school building to further explore area relationships.

EXTRA PRACTICE

SMALL-GROUP ACTIVITY

▶ *5-Minute Math*

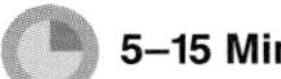

5–15 Min

To offer more practice with writing powers of 10 for numbers less than 1, see *5-Minute Math,* pages 166 and 167.

Teaching Master

Name Date Time

LESSON 2·9 **Patterns and Powers of 10**

Use any patterns you notice to fill in the blanks.

10^5 = 100,000	10^0 = 1
10^{4} = 10,000	10^{-1} = 0.1
10^3 = 1,000	10^{-2} = 0.01
10^{2} = 100	10^{-3} = 0.001
10^1 = 10	10^{-4} = 0.0001

What do you notice about the number of digits after the decimal point and the negative powers of 10?

The number of digits and the digit of the exponent are the same.

Name Date Time

LESSON 2·9 **Patterns and Powers of 10**

Use any patterns you notice to fill in the blanks.

10^5 = ______	10^0 = 1
$10^{\square}$ = 10,000	10^{-1} = 0.1
10^3 = 1,000	$10^{\square}$ = 0.01
$10^{\square}$ = 100	10^{-3} = ______
10^1 = ______	$10^{\square}$ = 0.0001

What do you notice about the number of digits after the decimal point and the negative powers of 10?

Math Masters, p. 62

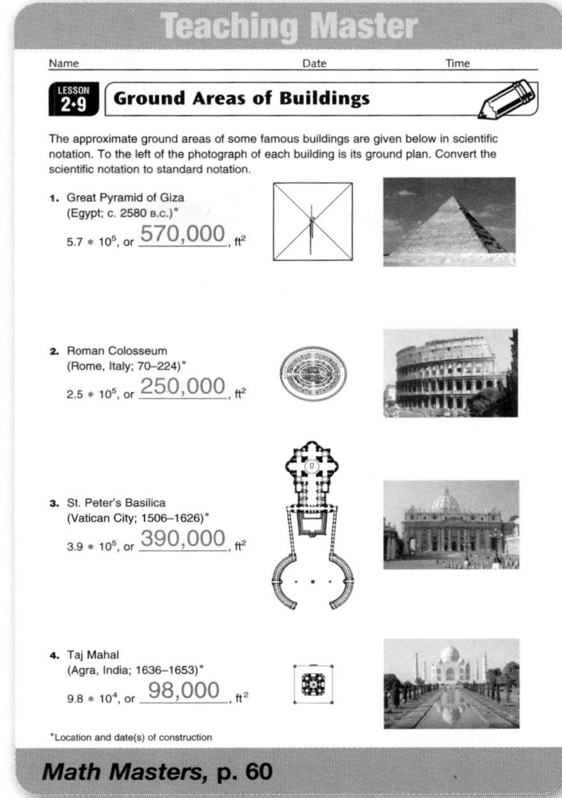

Teaching Master

Name Date Time

LESSON 2·9 **Ground Areas of Buildings**

The approximate ground areas of some famous buildings are given below in scientific notation. To the left of the photograph of each building is its ground plan. Convert the scientific notation to standard notation.

1. Great Pyramid of Giza (Egypt; c. 2580 B.C.)*
   $5.7 * 10^5$, or 570,000 ft²
2. Roman Colosseum (Rome, Italy; 70–224)*
   $2.5 * 10^5$, or 250,000 ft²
3. St. Peter's Basilica (Vatican City; 1506–1626)*
   $3.9 * 10^5$, or 390,000 ft²
4. Taj Mahal (Agra, India; 1636–1653)*
   $9.8 * 10^4$, or 98,000 ft²

*Location and date(s) of construction

Math Masters, p. 60

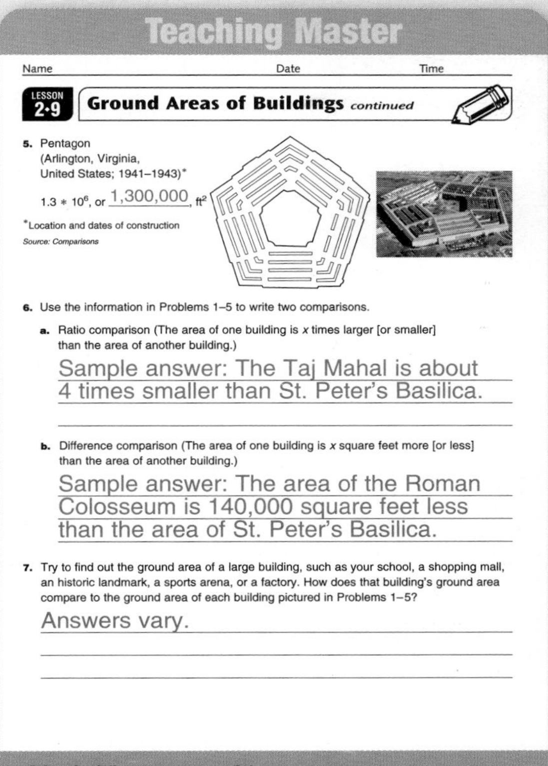

Teaching Master

Name Date Time

LESSON 2·9 **Ground Areas of Buildings** *continued*

5. Pentagon (Arlington, Virginia, United States; 1941–1943)*
   $1.3 * 10^6$, or 1,300,000 ft²

*Location and dates of construction

Source: Comparisons

6. Use the information in Problems 1–5 to write two comparisons.
   a. Ratio comparison (The area of one building is *x* times larger [or smaller] than the area of another building.)
      Sample answer: The Taj Mahal is about 4 times smaller than St. Peter's Basilica.
   b. Difference comparison (The area of one building is *x* square feet more [or less] than the area of another building.)
      Sample answer: The area of the Roman Colosseum is 140,000 square feet less than the area of St. Peter's Basilica.
7. Try to find out the ground area of a large building, such as your school, a shopping mall, an historic landmark, a sports arena, or a factory. How does that building's ground area compare to the ground area of each building pictured in Problems 1–5?
   Answers vary.

Math Masters, p. 61

2•10 Exponential Notation and the Power Key on a Calculator

Objectives To review and extend knowledge of exponential notation; and to use the power key on a calculator.

1 Teaching the Lesson

Key Activities

Students read and write numbers in exponential notation. They convert between exponential and standard notations, with and without a calculator. Students also play *Exponent Ball.*

Key Concepts and Skills

- Apply place-value concepts to convert between exponential and standard notations. [Number and Numeration Goal 1]
- Interpret and evaluate numerical expressions involving exponents. [Number and Numeration Goal 4]
- Use a calculator to find the product of repeated factors. [Operations and Computation Goal 2]

Key Vocabulary

power key • exponential notation • factor • base • exponent

Ongoing Assessment: Recognizing Student Achievement Use an Exit Slip. [Number and Numeration Goal 4]

materials

- ☐ *Math Journal 1,* p. 75
- ☐ *Student Reference Book,* pp. 6, 285–286, and 311
- ☐ Study Link 2•9
- ☐ Teaching Aid Master (*Math Masters,* p. 404)
- ☐ Game Master (*Math Masters,* p. 436)

Per partnership:

- ☐ calculator
- ☐ 6-sided die
- ☐ one penny or counter

See **Advance Preparation**

2 Ongoing Learning & Practice

Students practice multiplication and division of decimals.

Students practice and maintain skills through Math Boxes and Study Link activities.

materials

- ☐ *Math Journal 1,* pp. 76 and 77
- ☐ Study Link Master (*Math Masters,* p. 63)
- ☐ calculator

3 Differentiation Options

ENRICHMENT

Students use powers of 2, as well as expanded and exponential notations, to convert between binary and base-10 numbers.

ENRICHMENT

Students find examples of facts that are given in exponential or scientific notation.

materials

- ☐ Teaching Master (*Math Masters,* p. 64)
- ☐ calculator

Additional Information

Advance Preparation Review how to use the power key on the calculator that students will be using. Copy the second table from journal page 75 onto the board.

Technology

Assessment Management System
Exit Slip
See the **iTLG.**

Getting Started

Mental Math and Reflexes

Students mentally solve problems such as the following:

●○○ 5^3 125

●●○ 3^4 81

10^{-1} 0.1 or $\frac{1}{10}$

●●● $4 * 10^{-2}$ 0.04 or $\frac{4}{100}$

$6 * 10^3$ 6,000

Math Message

Work with a partner to find a way to use the keys on your calculator to find the values of 18^3 and 6^7.

Study Link 2•9 Follow-Up

Review answers.

1 Teaching the Lesson

▶ Math Message Follow-Up

(*Student Reference Book,* pp. 285 and 286)

Have students share the key sequences they used to find the values. Enter the key sequences into the table you copied on the board. Verify that students followed the correct sequences. Depending on the calculator, key sequences may be as follows:

18 [^] 3 [Enter] Display: 5,832

18 [x^y] 3 [=] Display: 5,832

Tell students that the [^] or [x^y] key is called the **power key.**

Some students may believe that keying a [^] b or a [x^y] b simply results in the multiplication of a and b. Have students calculate a [^] b or a [x^y] b and $a * b$ for several pairs of numbers a and b to verify that the power key does not simply multiply the numbers keyed in.

▶ Reviewing Exponential Notation and the Power Key

WHOLE-CLASS ACTIVITY

(*Student Reference Book,* p. 6)

As a class, read and discuss page 6, Exponential Notation, in the *Student Reference Book.* Be sure to cover the following points:

▷ Standard notation can be a cumbersome way to represent extremely large or small numbers.

▷ **Exponential notation** is a shorthand way to write multiplication in which a **factor** is repeated. The factor is called the **base,** and the **exponent** indicates the number of times the base is repeated. To support English language learners, discuss the meaning of *base* in this context. Write some examples on the board.

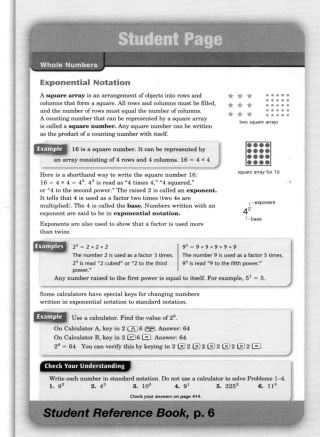

Student Page

Whole Numbers

Exponential Notation

A **square array** is an arrangement of objects into rows and columns that form a square. All rows and columns must be filled, and the number of rows must equal the number of columns. A counting number that can be represented by a square array is called a **square number.** Any square number can be written as the product of a counting number with itself.

two square arrays

Example 16 is a square number. It can be represented by an array consisting of 4 rows and 4 columns. $16 = 4 * 4$

square array for 16

Here is a shorthand way to write the square number 16: $16 = 4 * 4 = 4^2$. 4^2 is read as "4 times 4," "4 squared," or "4 to the second power." The raised 2 is called an **exponent.** It tells that 4 is used as a factor two times (two 4s are multiplied). The 4 is called the **base.** Numbers written with an exponent are said to be in **exponential notation.**

4^2 exponent; base

Exponents are also used to show that a factor is used more than twice.

Examples $2^3 = 2 * 2 * 2$
The number 2 is used as a factor 3 times. 2^3 is read "2 cubed" or "2 to the third power."

$9^5 = 9 * 9 * 9 * 9 * 9$
The number 9 is used as a factor 5 times. 9^5 is read "9 to the fifth power."

Any number raised to the first power is equal to itself. For example, $5^1 = 5$.

Some calculators have special keys for changing numbers written in exponential notation to standard notation.

Example Use a calculator. Find the value of 2^6.

On Calculator A, key in 2 [^] 6 [Enter]. Answer: 64

On Calculator B, key in 2 [x^y] 6 [=]. Answer: 64

$2^6 = 64$ You can verify this by keying in 2 [×] 2 [×] 2 [×] 2 [×] 2 [×] 2 [=].

Check Your Understanding

Write each number in standard notation. Do not use a calculator to solve Problems 1–4.

1. 6^2 **2.** 4^3 **3.** 10^5 **4.** 9^1 **5.** 225^2 **6.** 11^5

Check your answers on page 414.

Student Reference Book, p. 6

Student Page

Date Time

LESSON 2·10 **Exponential Notation and the Power Key**

1. Complete the following table.

Words	Exponential Notation	Base	Exponent	Repeated Factors	Standard Notation
three to the fifth power	3^5	3	5	3 * 3 * 3 * 3 * 3	243
seven to the fourth power	7^4	7	4	7 * 7 * 7 * 7	2,401
twenty to the third power	20^3	20	3	20 * 20 * 20	8,000
five to the sixth power	5^6	5	6	5 * 5 * 5 * 5 * 5 * 5	15,625
ten to the negative fourth power	10^{-4}	10	−4	0.1 * 0.1 * 0.1 * 0.1	0.0001

2. Complete the following table. Two possible key sequences are shown below.

Words	Exponential Notation	Base	Exponent	Calculator Key Sequence	Standard Notation
eight to the seventh power	8^7	8	7	8 [^] 7 [Enter] 8 [x^y] 7 [=]	2,097,152
ten to the sixth power	10^6	10	6	10 [^] 6 [Enter] 10 [x^y] 6 [=]	1,000,000
nine to the fourth power	9^4	9	4	9 [^] 4 [Enter] 9 [x^y] 4 [=]	6,561
two to the twenty-fifth power	2^{25}	2	25	2 [^] 20 [Enter] 2 [x^y] 20 [=]	33,554,432
ten to the negative third power	10^{-3}	10	−3	10 [^] [(−)] 3 [Enter] 10 [x^y] 3 [+/−] [=]	0.001
five to the negative second power	5^{-2}	5	−2	5 [^] [(−)] 2 [Enter] 5 [x^y] 2 [+/−] [=]	0.04

Math Journal 1, p. 75

NOTE The key sequences shown are for the Texas Instruments TI-15 and the Casio *fx*-55. The Casio *fx*-55 has the [x^2] key, which is used to square a number.

Some calculators have only [x^y] as the power key.

Student Page

Date Time

LESSON 2·10 **Math Boxes**

1. Using each of the digits 8, 4, 3, 2, 1, and 0 exactly once, make 2 decimal numbers whose difference is between 50 and 52.

   82.4 - 31.0 = 51.4

   SRB 31 32

2. Without using a calculator, decide which of the following has the greatest quotient. Circle the best answer.

   (A.) 23 / 0.04 B. 23 / 0.4
   C. 23 / 4 D. 23 / 40

   SRB 42

3. Use your calculator to help you convert the numbers written in exponential notation to standard notation.

   a. 2^8 = 256
   b. 15^5 = 759,375
   c. 3^{-4} = 0.012345679
   d. 2^{-3} = 0.125

   SRB 285 286

4. In 1 week, the hours worked by the 6 cashiers at *Buy and Fly* were 20, 20, 29, 48, 52, and 56.

   Would using the mean or the median number of hours encourage a person who wants to work at least 35 hours per week to apply for a job at *Buy and Fly*? Explain.

   Sample answer: Since both are more than 35, either would encourage the person to apply.

   SRB 136 137

5. Write the number pair for each of the following points on the line graph.

   P: (−1, −4)
   Q: (0, −2)
   R: (1, 0)

   SRB 234

Math Journal 1, p. 76

▷ Depending on the calculator, the [^] or [x^y] key can be used to rename numbers in exponential notation as numbers in standard notation.

▷ The calculator display should always be cleared before entering a problem.

Have students solve the Check Your Understanding problems before continuing with the next activity.

▶ Working with Exponents on a Calculator

WHOLE-CLASS ACTIVITY

(*Math Journal 1*, p. 75; *Student Reference Book*, pp. 285 and 286)

Copy the top row of the table. Have students use the power key to convert each number written in exponential notation to standard notation. Fill in the table as students report their answers. After completing the table, ask students to identify patterns.

5^4	5^3	5^2	5^1	5^0	5^{-1}	5^{-2}	5^{-3}	5^{-4}
625	125	25	5	1	0.20	0.04	0.008	0.0016

Students should not have difficulty when the exponent is positive. Depending on the calculator, to rename 5^4, they should press 5 [^] 4 [Enter] or 5 [x^y] 4 [=]. The display will read 625. To rename 5^0, students press 5 [^] 0 [Enter] or 5 [x^y] 0 [=]. The display will read 1.

Expect that most students will not know how to use the power key when the exponent is negative. Suggest the following key sequence, and work several examples to get them started. For example, to rename 5^{-1}, press 5 [^] [(−)] 1 [Enter] or 5 [x^y] 1 [+/−] [=]. The display will read 0.2. To rename 5^{-2}, press 5 [^] [(−)] 2 [Enter] or 5 [x^y] 2 [+/−] [=]. The display will read 0.04.

Links to the Future

Some students might observe that $5^{-1} = \frac{1}{5}$, or 0.2, and wonder whether $a^{-1} = \frac{1}{a}$ is true for all numbers. Suggest that they compare a^{-1} and $\frac{1}{a}$ for different values of *a*. They should conclude that $a^{-1} = \frac{1}{a}$ is true for any number except 0. This will provide students with early exposure to one of the laws of exponents that they will encounter in seventh and eighth grades.

Students work in partnerships to complete journal page 75. Circulate and assist as needed.

NOTE Some students may confuse [(−)] and [−] on the TI-15. [(−)] is for entering negative numbers and [−] is for subtraction. With the Casio *fx*-55, they must enter the number before pressing the [+/−] key.

▶ Playing *Exponent Ball*

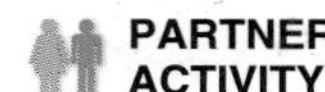
PARTNER ACTIVITY

(*Student Reference Book,* p. 311; *Math Masters,* pp. 404 and 436)

Provide each pair of students with a gameboard (*Math Masters,* p. 436). Lead the class through a demonstration game. Point out the odds tables on the gameboard that players use to decide whether to run or kick. Have students compare the odds of moving the ball at least 20 yards on the ground to the odds of kicking it at least 20 yards.

Ongoing Assessment: Recognizing Student Achievement

Exit Slip 

Ask students to respond to one of the following questions on an Exit Slip (*Math Masters,* p. 404).

- ▷ Name several combinations of base and exponent that would result in a 20-yard gain.
- ▷ Would you rather roll a 2^6 or a 4^3? Explain.

Use students' responses to assess their knowledge of exponential notation and their ability to use the power key on a calculator. Students are making adequate progress if they can use a calculator to compute scores. Some students may be able to mentally calculate scores.

[Number and Numeration Goal 4]

Student Page

Exponent Ball

Materials ☐ 1 *Exponent Ball* Gameboard (*Math Masters,* p. 436)
☐ 1 six-sided die
☐ 1 counter
☐ 1 calculator

Players 2

Skill Converting exponential notation to standard notation, comparing probabilities

Object of the game To score more points in 4 turns.

Directions

1. The game is similar to U.S. football. Player 1 first puts the ball (counter) on one of the 20-yard lines. The objective is to reach the opposite goal line, 80 yards away. A turn consists of 4 chances to advance the counter to the goal line and score.
2. The first 3 chances must be runs on the ground. To run, Player 1 rolls the die twice. The first roll names the **base,** the second roll names the **exponent.** For example, rolls of 5 and 4 name the number $5^4 = 625$.
3. Player 1 calculates the value of the roll and uses Table 1 on the gameboard page to find how far to move the ball forward (+) or backward (−).
4. If Player 1 does not score in the first 3 chances, he or she may choose to run or kick on the fourth chance. To kick, the player rolls the die once and multiplies the number shown by 10. The result is the distance the ball travels (Table 2 on the gameboard).
5. If the ball reaches the goal line on a run, the player scores 7 points. If the ball reaches the goal line on a kick, the player scores 3 points.
6. If the ball does not reach the goal line in 4 chances, Player 1's turn ends. Player 2 starts where Player 1 stopped and moves toward the opposite goal line.
7. If Player 1 scores, Player 2 puts the ball on one of the 20-yard lines and follows the directions above.
8. Players take turns. A round consists of 4 turns for each player. The player with more points wins.

***Exponent Ball* Gameboard**

Table 1: Runs

Value of Roll	Move Ball	Chances of Gaining on the Ground
1	−15 yd	−15 yards: 1 out of 6 or about 17%
2 to 6	+10 yd	10 yards or more: 5 out of 6 or about 83%
8 to 81	+20 yd	20 yards or more: 4 out of 6 or about 67%
in the 100s	+30 yd	30 yards or more: 13 out of 36 or about 36%
in the 1,000s	+40 yd	40 yards or more: 7 out of 36 or about 19%
in the 10,000s	+50 yd	50 yards: 1 out of 18 or about 6%

Table 2: Kicks

Value of Roll	Move Ball	Chances of Kicking
1	+10 yd	10 yards or more: 6 out of 6 or 100%
2	+20 yd	20 yards or more: 5 out of 6 or about 83%
3	+30 yd	30 yards or more: 4 out of 6 or about 67%
4	+40 yd	40 yards or more: 3 out of 6 or about 50%
5	+50 yd	50 yards or more: 2 out of 6 or about 33%
6	+60 yd	60 yards: 1 out of 6 or about 17%

Note
If a backward move should carry the ball behind the goal line, the ball (counter) is put on the goal line.

***Student Reference Book,* p. 311**

2 Ongoing Learning & Practice

▶ Multiplying and Dividing with Decimals

INDEPENDENT ACTIVITY

(*Math Journal 1,* p. 77)

Students practice solving word problems involving the multiplication and division of decimal numbers.

Student Page

Date Time

LESSON 2·10 **Multiplying and Dividing Decimals**

Sample estimates given:

1. A ticket for the school play costs $7.50. If 846 tickets are sold, what is the total for ticket sales?
   Estimate $6,400
   Answer $6,345
2. Brooke earns $450 per week before taxes. If she works 40 hours each week, what is Brooke's hourly rate of pay?
   Estimate $10.00
   Answer $11.25
3. You and 11 team members go out for lunch. The total, including tip, comes to $42.75. If you split the bill evenly, about how much should each person pay?
   Estimate $3.50
   Answer $3.56
4. In 1967, a 30-second commercial during the Super Bowl cost $42,000. In 2004, the cost was $2.5 million. About how many times as great was the cost in 2004 as in 1967?
   About 60 times

The table below shows customary and metric unit equivalents. Only the equivalent for inches and centimeters is exact. All the other equivalents are approximate.

Metric and Customary Unit Equivalents

Length	Mass/Weight	Capacity
1 in. = 2.54 cm	1 oz is about 28.35 g	1 L is about 1.06 qt
1 m is about 3.28 ft	1 kg is about 2.2 lb	1 gal is about 3.79 L

Complete.

5. 76.2 cm = 30 in.
6. 500 m is about 1,640 ft.
7. 55 lb is about 25 kg.
8. 5 gal is about 18.95 L.

***Math Journal 1,* p. 77**

▶ Math Boxes 2·10

INDEPENDENT ACTIVITY

(*Math Journal 1,* p. 76)

Mixed Practice Math Boxes in this lesson are paired with Math Boxes in Lessons 2-6 and 2-8. The skill in Problem 5 previews Unit 3 content.

Writing/Reasoning Have students write a response to the following: *Describe any patterns in the ordered pairs as you move from* P *to* Q *on the line graph in Problem 5.* Sample answer: As you move from P to Q, the y-value increases by 2 while the x-value increases by 1.

Study Link Master

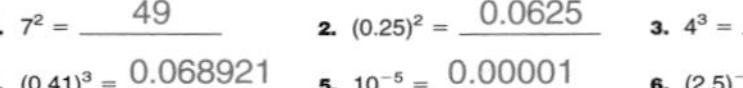

Name ______ Date ______ Time ______

STUDY LINK 2·10 Exponential Notation

Use your calculator to write each number in standard notation.

1. $7^2 =$ 49
2. $(0.25)^2 =$ 0.0625
3. $4^3 =$ 64
4. $(0.41)^3 =$ 0.068921
5. $10^{-5} =$ 0.00001
6. $(2.5)^{-3} =$ 0.064

Use digits to write each number in exponential notation.

7. three to the ninth power 3^9
8. eight to the seventh power 8^7
9. eleven to the negative third power 11^{-3}
10. five-tenths to the negative sixth power $(0.5)^{-6}$

Write each number as a product of repeated factors.

Example: $5^3 = 5 * 5 * 5$

11. $(\frac{1}{2})^5 =$ $\frac{1}{2} * \frac{1}{2} * \frac{1}{2} * \frac{1}{2} * \frac{1}{2}$
12. $10^{-2} =$ $0.1 * 0.1$, or $\frac{1}{10} * \frac{1}{10}$
13. $10^{-6} =$ $0.1 * 0.1 * 0.1 * 0.1 * 0.1 * 0.1$, or $\frac{1}{10} * \frac{1}{10} * \frac{1}{10} * \frac{1}{10} * \frac{1}{10} * \frac{1}{10}$
14. You can find the total number of different 4-digit numbers that can be made using the digits 1 through 9 by raising the number of choices for each digit (9) to the number of digits (4), or 9^4.

    Based on this pattern, how many different 5-digit numbers could you make from the digits 1 through 8? $8^5 = 32{,}768$

Practice

Solve mentally.

15. $15.32 - 1.88 =$ 13.44
16. $7{,}200 / 90 =$ 80
17. $4.98 + 3.99 =$ 8.97
18. $8 * 525 =$ 4,200

Math Masters, p. 63

Teaching Master

Name ______ Date ______ Time ______

LESSON 2·10 Binary Numbers

The table below shows how to write whole numbers 1 through 10 as binary numbers. A binary number is written with a subscripted *two* to distinguish it from a base-ten number.

		Powers of 2						
		2^6	2^5	2^4	2^3	2^2	2^1	2^0
Base-Ten Number	**Binary Number**	64	32	16	8	4	2	1
1	1_{two}							$1 * 2^0$
2	10_{two}						$1 * 2^1$	$0 * 2^0$
3	11_{two}						$1 * 2^1$	$1 * 2^0$
4	100_{two}					$1 * 2^2$	$0 * 2^1$	$0 * 2^0$
5	101_{two}					$1 * 2^2$	$0 * 2^1$	$1 * 2^0$
6	110_{two}					$1 * 2^2$	$1 * 2^1$	$0 * 2^0$
7	111_{two}					$1 * 2^2$	$1 * 2^1$	$1 * 2^0$
8	1000_{two}				$1 * 2^3$	$0 * 2^2$	$0 * 2^1$	$0 * 2^0$
9	1001_{two}				$1 * 2^3$	$0 * 2^2$	$0 * 2^1$	$1 * 2^0$
10	1010_{two}				$1 * 2^3$	$0 * 2^2$	$1 * 2^1$	$0 * 2^0$

To write a binary number as a base-ten number, first write the binary number in expanded notation. Then convert to standard form.

Example:

$$\begin{aligned} 11111_{two} &= (1 * 2^4) + (1 * 2^3) + (1 * 2^2) + (1 * 2^1) + (1 * 2^0) \\ &= (1 * 16) + (1 * 8) + (1 * 4) + (1 * 2) + (1 * 1) \\ &= 16 + 8 + 4 + 2 + 1 \\ &= 31 \end{aligned}$$

Use the table and example above to write each binary number as a base-ten number.

1. $1011_{two} =$ 11
2. $101110_{two} =$ 46
3. $1110101_{two} =$ 117
4. $111101_{two} =$ 61
5. $1000001_{two} =$ 65
6. $1111111_{two} =$ 127

Try This

Use patterns in the table to write the binary number for each number.

7. $21 =$ 10101_{two}
8. $68 =$ 1000100_{two}
9. $100 =$ 1100100_{two}

Math Masters, p. 64

▶ Study Link 2·10

INDEPENDENT ACTIVITY

(*Math Masters,* p. 63)

Home Connection Students practice using exponential notation.

3 Differentiation Options

ENRICHMENT

INDEPENDENT ACTIVITY

▶ Converting between Binary and Base-10 Numbers

15–30 Min

(*Math Masters,* p. 64)

Computers are internally limited to using binary digits. A binary digit is either 0 or 1. A binary number consists of a string of binary digits. For example, 1101_{two} is a 4-digit binary number. The binary number 1101_{two} is equal to the base-10 number 13.

Provide students with one copy of *Math Masters,* page 64. Encourage students to carefully study the table and example before trying to convert between binary and base-10 numbers.

ENRICHMENT

INDEPENDENT ACTIVITY

▶ Finding Facts

30+ Min

Science Link Students look through newspapers, magazines, textbooks, and Internet sites to find examples of facts that are given in exponential notation or scientific notation.

Examples:

▷ The speed of light is about $6.706 * 10^8$ miles per hour.

▷ The wavelength of an X-ray is about 10^{-11} meters.

▷ The mass of Earth is about $5.972 * 10^{21}$ metric tons.

▷ A nanosecond is equal to 10^{-9} seconds.

Scientific Notation on a Calculator

Objective To use a calculator to convert between scientific and standard notations.

1 Teaching the Lesson

Key Activities

Students interpret scientific notation displays on a calculator. They convert numbers from standard notation to scientific notation.

Key Concepts and Skills

- Read and write numbers to trillions in standard and number-and-word notations. [Number and Numeration Goal 1]
- Convert between scientific and standard notations with or without a calculator. [Number and Numeration Goal 1]
- Use extended facts to find products of very large and very small numbers. [Operations and Computation Goal 2]
- Multiply a decimal number by a power of 10. [Operations and Computation Goal 2]

materials

- ☐ *Math Journal 1,* pp. 78 and 79
- ☐ *Student Reference Book,* pp. 287–289
- ☐ Study Link 2•10
- ☐ calculator

***See* Advance Preparation**

2 Ongoing Learning & Practice

Students estimate and multiply decimal numbers by playing *Doggone Decimal.* They convert between exponential and standard notations by playing *Exponent Ball.*

Students practice and maintain skills through Math Boxes and Study Link activities.

Ongoing Assessment: Recognizing Student Achievement Use journal page 80. [Number and Numeration Goal 1]

materials

- ☐ *Math Journal 1,* p. 80
- ☐ *Student Reference Book,* pp. 310 and 311
- ☐ Study Link Master (*Math Masters,* p. 65)
- ☐ Game Masters (*Math Masters,* pp. 433 and 436)
- ☐ calculator

3 Differentiation Options

ENRICHMENT

Students extend a pattern to develop a rule for quotients of power-of-10 dividends and divisors.

EXTRA PRACTICE

Students use calculators to convert from exponential notation to scientific and standard notations.

ELL SUPPORT

Students add *scientific notation* to their Math Word Banks.

materials

- ☐ Teaching Master (*Math Masters,* p. 66)
- ☐ *Student Reference Book,* p. 285
- ☐ *Differentiation Handbook*
- ☐ calculator

Additional Information

Advance Preparation Familiarize yourself with the keystrokes and display of the calculator that students will be using.

Technology

Assessment Management System
Math Boxes, Problem 3
See the **iTLG.**

Getting Started

Mental Math and Reflexes

Students record and then round dictated numbers in standard notation on their slates or dry-erase boards.

●○○ *Write forty-five million, nine thousand, three hundred twenty-one. Then round to the nearest ten million.* 45,009,321; 50,000,000

●●○ *Write one billion, sixty-seven million, eight hundred eighty-eight thousand, four hundred six. Then round to the nearest hundred million.* 1,067,888,406; 1,100,000,000

●●● *Write seven trillion, four hundred nine billion, five hundred million, four hundred fifty-eight thousand, five hundred thirty-two. Then round to the nearest ten billion.* 7,409,500,458,532; 7,410,000,000,000

Math Message

Use your calculator to multiply 87,500 ∗ 10,000,000.

What answer does the calculator display? 8.75 × 10^11

Study Link 2•10 Follow-Up

Briefly review answers.

1 Teaching the Lesson

▶ Math Message Follow-Up

The product 87,500 ∗ 10,000,000 is 875 billion (875,000,000,000). Some calculators display extremely large and small numbers in scientific notation. For 875,000,000,000, you might see any of the displays below.

8.75   11

8.75 × 10^11

8.75×10^{11}

8.75   E11

8.75   E+11

8.75   EE11

Ask students why the calculator does not display the answer in standard notation. Sample answer: There are not enough digit spaces in the calculator's display window to show the entire 12-digit answer.

Point out that the first part of the calculator display (8.75) is a number between 1 and 10. Remind students that a number in scientific notation is written as the product of two factors.

▷ The first factor is at least 1 but less than 10.

▷ The second factor is a power of 10, either positive or negative.

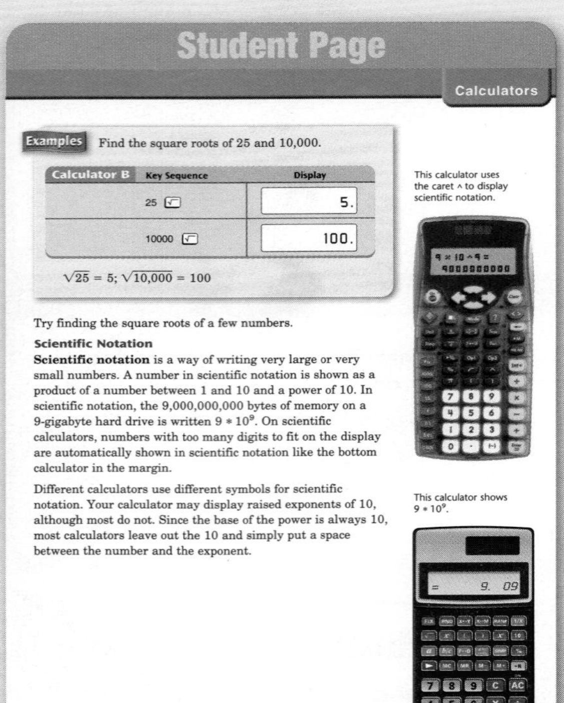

Student Page

Calculators

Examples Find the square roots of 25 and 10,000.

Calculator B Key Sequence	Display
25 [√]	5.
10000 [√]	100.

$\sqrt{25} = 5$; $\sqrt{10,000} = 100$

This calculator uses the caret ^ to display scientific notation.

Try finding the square roots of a few numbers.

Scientific Notation

Scientific notation is a way of writing very large or very small numbers. A number in scientific notation is shown as a product of a number between 1 and 10 and a power of 10. In scientific notation, the 9,000,000,000 bytes of memory on a 9-gigabyte hard drive is written $9 * 10^9$. On scientific calculators, numbers with too many digits to fit on the display are automatically shown in scientific notation like the bottom calculator in the margin.

Different calculators use different symbols for scientific notation. Your calculator may display raised exponents of 10, although most do not. Since the base of the power is always 10, most calculators leave out the 10 and simply put a space between the number and the exponent.

This calculator shows $9 * 10^9$.

Student Reference Book, p. 287

▶ Using Scientific Notation on a Calculator

WHOLE-CLASS ACTIVITY

(*Student Reference Book,* pp. 287–289)

Read and work through the three examples on pages 287–289 in the *Student Reference Book* as a class. These examples cover three different situations. Pose additional problems as necessary. If you have a scientific calculator for the overhead projector, model the keystrokes on the overhead while students work with calculators. Remind students to clear the calculator display before entering a problem.

▶ Practicing Calculator Skills with Scientific Notation

PARTNER ACTIVITY

(*Math Journal 1,* pp. 78 and 79)

Have students use their calculators to complete journal pages 78 and 79. If students are having difficulty, refer them to pages 287–289 in the *Student Reference Book.* Discuss any difficulties they encountered or strategies they discovered while completing the problems.

2 Ongoing Learning & Practice

▶ Playing *Doggone Decimal* or *Exponent Ball*

PARTNER ACTIVITY

(*Student Reference Book,* pp. 310 and 311; *Math Masters,* pp. 433 and 436)

Depending on whether students need practice multiplying decimal numbers or converting between exponential and standard notations, have them play *Doggone Decimal* or *Exponent Ball.* If needed, have students review instructions on pages 310 and 311 in the *Student Reference Book.*

▶ Math Boxes 2•11

INDEPENDENT ACTIVITY

(*Math Journal 1,* p. 80)

Mixed Practice Math Boxes in this lesson are paired with Math Boxes in Lesson 2-9. The skill in Problem 5 previews Unit 3 content.

Student Page

LESSON 2•11 **Scientific Notation on a Calculator**

Use your calculator to help you fill in Column 2 first. Then fill in Columns 3 and 4 without using your calculator. Sample answers:

Exponential Notation	Calculator Display	Scientific Notation	Number-and-Word Notation
1. $1{,}000{,}000^2$	1 × 10 ∧ 12	$1 * 10^{12}$	1 trillion
2. $10{,}000^3$	1 × 10 ∧ 12	$1 * 10^{12}$	1 trillion
3. $2{,}000{,}000^2$	4 × 10 ∧ 12	$4 * 10^{12}$	4 trillion
4. $20{,}000^3$	8 × 10 ∧ 12	$8 * 10^{12}$	8 trillion
5. $3{,}000{,}000^2$	9 × 10 ∧ 12	$9 * 10^{12}$	9 trillion
6. $30{,}000^3$	2.7 × 10 ∧ 13	$2.7 * 10^{13}$	27 trillion

Rewrite each of the following numbers in standard notation. Enter each number into your calculator and press the [Enter] key. Then write each number in scientific notation.

	Standard Notation	Scientific Notation
7. 456 million	456,000,000	$4.56 * 10^8$
8. 3.2 trillion	3,200,000,000,000	$3.2 * 10^{12}$
9. 23.4 billion	23,400,000,000	$2.34 * 10^{10}$
10. 78 trillionths	0.000000000078	$7.8 * 10^{-11}$

Solve each problem. Write each answer in standard and scientific notations.

11. 3,200,000 * 145,000 — 464,000,000,000 — $4.64 * 10^{11}$
12. 10 billion / 2.5 million — 4,000 — $4 * 10^3$
13. $(5 * 10^4) - 10^2$ — 49,900 — $4.99 * 10^4$
14. $10^2 + (3 * 10^3)$ — 3,100 — $3.1 * 10^3$
15. $(8 * 10^{-1}) - 0.3$ — 0.5 — $5 * 10^{-1}$
16. $(4.1 * 10^8) - (3.6 * 10^6)$ — 406,400,000 — $4.064 * 10^8$
17. $(17 * 10^{12}) / (4.25 * 10^6)$ — 4,000,000 — $4 * 10^6$
18. $(6 * 10^{11}) + (7 * 10^9)$ — 607,000,000,000 — $6.07 * 10^{11}$

Math Journal 1, p. 78

Student Page

LESSON 2•11 **Scientific Notation on a Calculator** *continued*

Solve the number stories. Use a calculator and scientific notation to help you.

19. There are approximately 40 million students in the United States in Kindergarten through eighth grade. If, on average, each student goes to school for about 1,000 hours per year, about how many total hours do all of the students in Grades K–8 spend in school each year?

Answer: About 40 billion hours

Number Model: $(4.0 * 10^7) * (1 * 10^3) = 4 * 10^{10}$

20. The distance from Earth to the Sun is about 93 million miles. The distance from Jupiter to the Sun is about 483.6 million miles. About how many times as great is the distance from the Sun to Jupiter as the Sun to Earth?

Answer: About 5.2 times as great

Number Model: $(483.6 * 10^6) / (93 * 10^6) = 5.2$

21. Light travels at a speed of about 186,300 miles per second.

a. About how many miles does light travel in 1 minute?

Answer: About 11,178,000 miles

Number Model: 186,300 * 60 = 11,178,000

b. About how many miles does light travel in 1 hour?

Answer: About 670,680,000 miles

Number Model: 11,780,000 * 60 = 670,680,000

c. About how many miles does light travel in 1 day?

Answer: About 16,100,000,000 miles

Number Model: $670{,}680{,}000 * 24 = 1.61 * 10^{10} = 16{,}100{,}000{,}000$

22. The average distance from the Sun to Earth is about $9.3 * 10^7$ miles and from the Sun to Mars is about $1.4 * 10^8$ miles. What is the average distance from Earth to Mars?

Answer: About 233,000,000 miles

Number Model: $(9.3 * 10^7) + (1.4 * 10^8) = 233{,}000{,}000$

Math Journal 1, p. 79

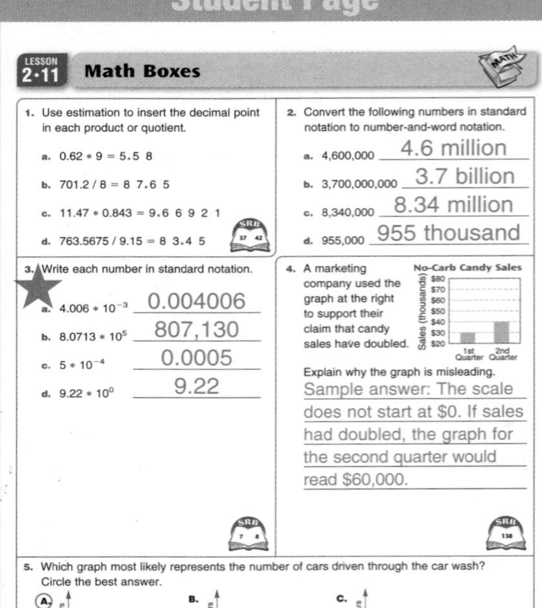

Student Page

LESSON 2·11 **Math Boxes**

1. Use estimation to insert the decimal point in each product or quotient.
   a. 0.62 * 9 = 5.5 8
   b. 701.2 / 8 = 8 7.6 5
   c. 11.47 * 0.843 = 9.6 6 9 2 1
   d. 763.5675 / 9.15 = 8 3.4 5

2. Convert the following numbers in standard notation to number-and-word notation.
   a. 4,600,000 4.6 million
   b. 3,700,000,000 3.7 billion
   c. 8,340,000 8.34 million
   d. 955,000 955 thousand

3. Write each number in standard notation.
   a. $4.006 * 10^{-3}$ 0.004006
   b. $8.0713 * 10^{5}$ 807,130
   c. $5 * 10^{-4}$ 0.0005
   d. $9.22 * 10^{0}$ 9.22

4. A marketing company used the graph at the right to support their claim that candy sales have doubled.

Explain why the graph is misleading.
Sample answer: The scale does not start at $0. If sales had doubled, the graph for the second quarter would read $60,000.

5. Which graph most likely represents the number of cars driven through the car wash? Circle the best answer.

(A) B. C.

Math Journal 1, p. 80

NOTE Have students experiment with their calculators to find a key sequence for entering a power of 10, such as 10^{-4}.

Study Link Master

Name Date Time

STUDY LINK 2·11 **Scientific Notation**

Write the following numbers in scientific notation.

1. 0.0036 $3.6 * 10^{-3}$
2. 0.0007 $7.0 * 10^{-4}$
3. 80,000 $8 * 10^{4}$
4. 600 thousand $6 * 10^{5}$

Write the following numbers in standard notation.

5. $5 * 10^{4}$ 50,000
6. $4.73 * 10^{9}$ 4,730,000,000
7. $4.81 * 10^{7}$ 48,100,000
8. $8.04 * 10^{-2}$ 0.0804

Write the next two numbers in each pattern.

9. $1 * 10^{-1}$; 0.1; $1 * 10^{-2}$; 0.01; $1 * 10^{-3}$; 0.001
10. 0.01, 0.002, 0.0003, 0.00004, 0.000005

Solve the following problems. Write each answer in scientific notation.

11. $(4 * 10^{3}) - 10^{2} =$ $3.9 * 10^{3}$
12. $10^{3} - (2 * 10^{1}) =$ $9.8 * 10^{2}$
13. $(5 * 10^{-1}) + 0.02 =$ $5.2 * 10^{-1}$
14. $(7 * 10^{4}) - 10^{3} =$ $6.9 * 10^{4}$
15. Use a calculator to complete the table. Sample answers given for calculator display.

Problem	Calculator Display	Scientific Notation	Standard Notation
$5{,}000{,}000^2$	2.5 × 10^13	$2.5 * 10^{13}$	25,000,000,000,000
$90^4 - 300^2$	65520000	$6.552 * 10^{7}$	65,520,000
$20^3 + 30^2$	8900	$8.9 * 10^{3}$	8,900
$10^4 * 10^4$	100000000	$1 * 10^{8}$	100,000,000
$5^{20} / 5^{16}$	625	$625 * 10^{2}$	625

Practice

Find the missing digits to complete each number sentence.

16. [6][7]63 − 3,9[2]9 = 2,83[4]
17. 71,[1]4[6] − 4,8[7]6 = 6[6],270

Math Masters, p. 65

Ongoing Assessment: Recognizing Student Achievement

Math Boxes Problem 3 

Use **Math Boxes, Problem 3** to assess students' ability to translate from scientific notation to standard notation. Students are making adequate progress if they are able to complete Problems 3a–3c. Some students may recognize that multiplying a number by 10^{0} (Problem 3d) is the same as multiplying the number by 1.

[Number and Numeration Goal 1]

Study Link 2·11

INDEPENDENT ACTIVITY

(*Math Masters,* p. 65)

Home Connection Students practice converting between scientific and standard notations. They interpret scientific notation displays on a calculator.

3 Differentiation Options

ENRICHMENT

PARTNER ACTIVITY

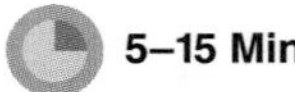

5–15 Min

Finding Patterns with Powers of 10

(*Student Reference Book,* p. 285)

The Quotient Rule for Exponents says that when you divide powers having the same base, you subtract the exponents. Help students explore this rule by first having them use their calculator to find the following quotients.

$10^5 / 10^1$ $10^4 = 10{,}000$	$10^{12} / 10^{11}$ $10^1 = 10$	$10^8 / 10^{10}$ $10^{-2} = \frac{1}{100} = 0.01$
$10^6 / 10^2$ $10^4 = 10{,}000$	$10^7 / 10^6$ $10^1 = 10$	$10^0 / 10^2$ $10^{-2} = \frac{1}{100} = 0.01$
$10^9 / 10^5$ $10^4 = 10{,}000$	$10^4 / 10^3$ $10^1 = 10$	$10^{-1} / 10^1$ $10^{-2} = \frac{1}{100} = 0.01$
$10^{10} / 10^6$ $10^4 = 10{,}000$	$10^{-2} / 10^{-3}$ $10^1 = 10$	$10^{-4} / 10^{-2}$ $10^{-2} = \frac{1}{100} = 0.01$

Ask students to compare the power of 10 in each dividend and divisor to the power of 10 in each quotient. Students then use patterns to predict the power of 10 in quotients such as $10^9 / 10^6$, $10^{13} / 10^{10}$, and $10^{-8} / 10^{-11}$. 10^3, 10^3, 10^3; The power of 10 in the quotient is equal to the difference of the powers of 10 in the dividend and the divisor; $a^m / a^n = a^{m-n}$. Have students use a calculator to check their predictions.

EXTRA PRACTICE

▶ Practicing Calculator Skills

INDEPENDENT ACTIVITY

5–15 Min

(*Math Masters*, p. 66)

Students practice using the [^] or [x^y] key. They enter numbers written in exponential notation and convert what appears in the calculator display to scientific and standard notations.

ELL SUPPORT

▶ Building a Math Word Bank

INDEPENDENT ACTIVITY

5–15 Min

(*Differentiation Handbook*)

To provide language support for scientific notation, have students use the Word Bank template found in the *Differentiation Handbook.* Ask students to write the term *scientific notation,* draw pictures or examples representing the term, and write other related words. See the *Differentiation Handbook* for more information.

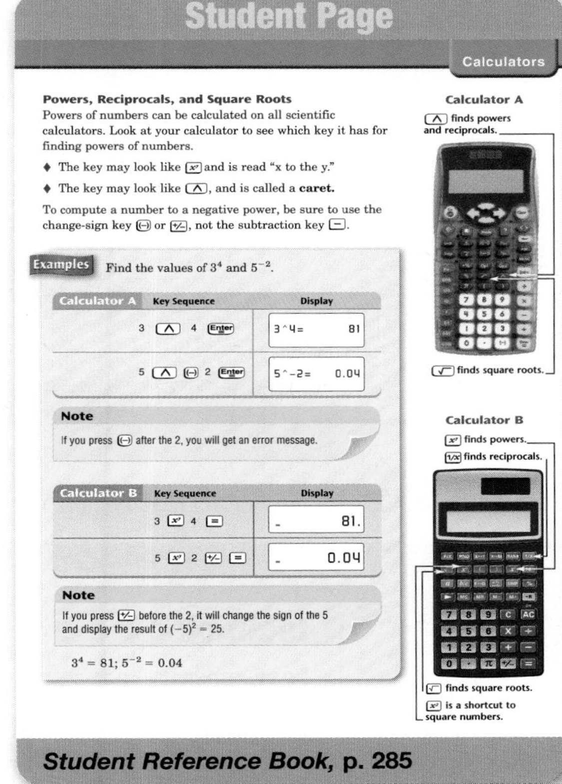

Student Page

Calculators

Powers, Reciprocals, and Square Roots

Powers of numbers can be calculated on all scientific calculators. Look at your calculator to see which key it has for finding powers of numbers.

- The key may look like [x^y] and is read "x to the y."
- The key may look like [^], and is called a **caret.**

To compute a number to a negative power, be sure to use the change-sign key [(-)] or [+/-], not the subtraction key [-].

Examples Find the values of 3^4 and 5^{-2}.

Calculator A Key Sequence	Display
3 [^] 4 [Enter]	3^4= 81
5 [^] [(-)] 2 [Enter]	5^-2= 0.04

Note

If you press [(-)] after the 2, you will get an error message.

Calculator B Key Sequence	Display
3 [x^y] 4 [=]	81.
5 [x^y] 2 [+/-] [=]	0.04

Note

If you press [+/-] before the 2, it will change the sign of the 5 and display the result of $(-5)^2 = 25$.

$3^4 = 81$; $5^{-2} = 0.04$

Calculator A
[^] finds powers and reciprocals.
[√] finds square roots.
Calculator B
[x^y] finds powers.
[1/x] finds reciprocals.
[√] finds square roots.
[x^2] is a shortcut to square numbers.

Student Reference Book, p. 285

Teaching Master

Name Date Time

LESSON 2·11 **Practicing Calculator Skills**

Use your calculator to complete the table.

Problem	Scientific Notation	Standard Notation
$100{,}000^3$	$1 * 10^{15}$	1,000,000,000,000,000
$20{,}000^5$	$3.2 * 10^{21}$	3,200,000,000,000,000,000,000
$30^8 + 30^8$	$1.3122 * 10^{12}$	1,312,200,000,000
$800^4 - 400^2$	$4.0959 * 10^{11}$	409,590,000,000
$10^7 * 10^7$	$1 * 10^{14}$	100,000,000,000,000
$\frac{70^{12}}{70^4}$	$5.7648 * 10^{14}$	576,480,000,000,000

Name Date Time

LESSON 2·11 **Practicing Calculator Skills**

Use your calculator to complete the table.

Problem	Scientific Notation	Standard Notation
$100{,}000^3$	$1 * 10^{15}$	1,000,000,000,000,000
$20{,}000^5$		
$30^8 + 30^8$		
$800^4 - 400^2$		
$10^7 * 10^7$		
$\frac{70^{12}}{70^4}$		

Math Masters, p. 66

2•12 Progress Check 2

Objective **To assess students' progress on mathematical content through the end of Unit 2.**

1 Assessing Progress

Progress Check 2 is a cumulative assessment of concepts and skills taught in Unit 2 and in previous units.

See the Appendix for a complete list of Grade 6 Goals.

materials

- ☐ Assessment Masters (*Assessment Handbook,* pp. 144–149)
- ☐ Study Link 2•11 ☐ slate

CONTENT ASSESSED	LESSON(S)	ASSESSMENT ITEMS			
		SELF	ORAL/SLATE	WRITTEN PART A	WRITTEN PART B
Apply place-value concepts to identify digits in numbers and express their values. [Number and Numeration Goal 1]	2•1, 2•2			1	
Translate between standard, expanded, scientific, and number-and-word notations with or without a calculator. [Number and Numeration Goal 1]	2•1, 2•2, 2•9–2•11	1–3	1	2–7	12, 13
Compare and order rational numbers. [Number and Numeration Goal 6]	2•5, 2•7		2		15–18
Add and subtract decimals. [Operations and Computation Goal 1]	2•3	4	4	8, 9	
Multiply by positive and negative powers of 10. [Operations and Computation Goal 2]	2•4, 2•9	5	1	5	14
Multiply and divide whole and decimal numbers. [Operations and Computation Goal 2]	2•5–2•8	6, 7		10, 11	
Estimate differences, products, and quotients of whole numbers and decimals. [Operations and Computation Goal 5]	2•3, 2•5, 2•8	8	3		
Construct and interpret a graph. [Data and Chance Goal 1]	2•7				19a, 20
Compare the median and mean of a data set. [Data and Chance Goal 2]	2•8, 2•10				19b, 19c

2 Building Background for Unit 3

Math Boxes 2•12 previews and practices skills for Unit 3.

The **Unit 3 Family Letter** introduces families to Unit 3 topics and terms.

materials

- ☐ *Math Journal 1,* p. 81
- ☐ Study Link Masters (*Math Masters,* pp. 67–70)

Additional Information

See *Assessment Handbook,* pages 60–67 for additional assessment information. For assessment checklists, see pages 230–233.

Technology

Assessment Management System
Written Assessment, Parts A and B
See the **iTLG.**

Getting Started

Math Message • Self Assessment

Complete the Self Assessment page (Assessment Handbook, *p. 144).*

Study Link 2·11 Follow-Up

Briefly review answers.

1 Assessing Progress

▶ Math Message Follow-Up

INDEPENDENT ACTIVITY

(Self Assessment, *Assessment Handbook,* p. 144)

The Self Assessment offers students the opportunity to reflect upon their progress.

▶ Oral and Slate Assessments

WHOLE-CLASS ACTIVITY

Problems 1 and 3 provide summative information and can be used for grading purposes. Problems 2 and 4 provide formative information that can be useful in planning future instruction.

Oral Assessment

1. Students use a calculator to solve the problems and then explain the calculator display.
   - 45,800,000 ∗ 300,000 $1.374 * 10^{13}$
   - 39,186,000 ∗ 52,946 $2.0747 * 10^{12}$
   - $784 * 10^8$ $7.84 * 10^{10}$
   - $2{,}301 * 10^{-15}$ $2.301 * 10^{-12}$
2. Students compare numbers using <, >, or =.
   - 8.43099 ___<___ 8.431
   - $\frac{7}{8}$ ___>___ 0.78
   - $\frac{1}{2}$ ___>___ $\frac{4}{9}$
   - 0.625 ___=___ $\frac{5}{8}$

Slate Assessment

3. Students estimate products and quotients by using "close" numbers and record a number sentence. Sample estimates:
   - 21.2 ∗ 7.9 = ? 20 ∗ 8 = 160
   - 0.83 ∗ 13.6 = ? 1 ∗ 14 = 14
   - 56.7 / 2.8 = ? 60 / 3 = 20
   - 27.1 / 8.65 = ? 27 / 9 = 3
4. Students mentally calculate sums and differences.
   - 37.8 + 11.2 = ? 49
   - 6.5 − 1.75 = ? 4.75
   - 33.6 + 12.5 = ? 46.1
   - 59.1 − 7.6 = ? 51.5

Assessment Master

Name ______ Date ______ Time ______

LESSON 2·12 **Self Assessment** Progress Check 2

Think about each skill listed below. Assess your own progress by checking the most appropriate box.

Skills	I can do this on my own and explain how to do it.	I can do this on my own.	I can do this if I get help or look at an example.
1. Read and write numbers to trillions.			
2. Read and write numbers to thousandths.			
3. Write numbers in scientific notation.			
4. Add and subtract decimals.			
5. Multiply by positive and negative powers of 10.			
6. Multiply decimals.			
7. Divide whole numbers.			
8. Estimate products and quotients of decimal numbers.			

Assessment Handbook, **p. 144**

Assessment Master

Name ______ Date ______ Time ______

LESSON 2·12 **Written Assessment** Progress Check 2

Part A

1. Write the digit in each place of the number below.

   5,146,702,897,352.6138

   a. ten billions 4 b. hundredths 1 c. hundred millions 7
   d. thousandths 3 e. trillions 5 f. tenths 6

2. Write the following numbers in standard notation.

   a. 4.6 million 4,600,000 b. 32.1 trillion 32,100,000,000

3. Write each number in number-and-word notation.

   a. 5,600,000,000 5.6 billion
   b. 462,800,000,000,000 462.8 trillion

4. Write the exponent for each of the following numbers.

   a. $0.001 = 10^{-3}$ b. $1 \text{ billion} = 10^{9}$
   c. $10 * 10 * 10 * 10 = 10^{4}$ d. $\frac{1}{10} = 10^{-1}$

5. Complete.

   a. 76,541 ∗ 0.0001 = 7.6541 b. 0.421 ∗ 10,000 = 4,210
   c. $45.7 * 10^{-3}$ = 0.0457 d. 85 = 0.0085 ∗ 10,000, or 10^4
   e. $2.9 * 10^5$ = 290,000 f. 0.7 = 0.007 ∗ 100, or 10^2

Assessment Handbook, **p. 145**

▶ Written Assessment

INDEPENDENT ACTIVITY

(*Assessment Handbook,* pp. 145–148)

Part A Recognizing Student Achievement

Problems 1–11 provide summative information and may be used for grading purposes.

Problem(s)	Description
1–3	Translate between standard and number-and-word notations.
4, 6, 7	Translate between standard, exponential, and scientific notations.
5	Multiply by positive and negative powers of 10.
8–11	Add, subtract, multiply, and divide decimals.

Part B Informing Instruction

Problems 12–20 provide formative information that can be useful in planning future instruction.

Problem(s)	Description
12	Write numbers in expanded notation.
13	Translate between exponential and standard notations.
14	Convert between metric units of measure.
15–18	Order and round decimals.
19, 20	Construct and interpret a graph.

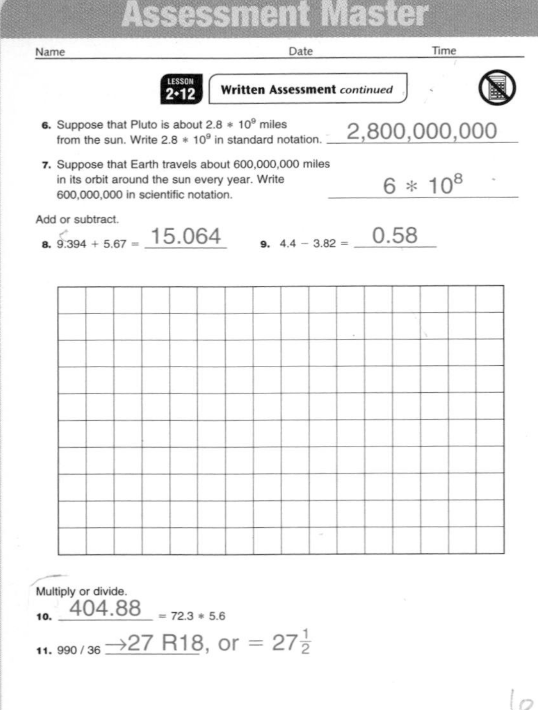

Assessment Master

Name Date Time

LESSON 2•12 Written Assessment *continued*

6. Suppose that Pluto is about $2.8 * 10^9$ miles from the sun. Write $2.8 * 10^9$ in standard notation. 2,800,000,000
7. Suppose that Earth travels about 600,000,000 miles in its orbit around the sun every year. Write 600,000,000 in scientific notation. $6 * 10^8$

Add or subtract.

8. 9.394 + 5.67 = 15.064
9. 4.4 − 3.82 = 0.58

Multiply or divide.

10. 404.88 = 72.3 ∗ 5.6
11. 990 / 36 → 27 R18, or = $27\frac{1}{2}$

Assessment Handbook, p. 146

Assessment Master

Name Date Time

LESSON 2•12 Written Assessment *continued*

Part B

12. Write each of the following numbers in expanded notation.
Example: 23.89 = (2 ∗ 10) + (3 ∗ 1) + (8 ∗ 0.1) + (9 ∗ 0.01)
   a. 67,051 (6 ∗ 10,000) + (7 ∗ 1,000) + (5 ∗ 10) + (1 ∗ 1)
   b. 2.904 (2 ∗ 1) + (9 ∗ 0.1) + (4 ∗ 0.001)

13. Use a calculator to help you convert the numbers written in exponential notation to standard notation.
   a. 13^5 = 371,293
   b. 8^{-6} = 0.0000038

Metric Measurements		
Length	Capacity	Mass
1 meter (m) = 100 centimeters (cm)	1 liter (L) = 1,000 milliliters (mL)	1 kilogram (kg) = 1,000 grams (g)
1 centimeter (cm) = 10 millimeters (mm)	1 kiloliter (kL) = 1,000 liters (L)	1 gram (g) = 1,000 milligrams (mg)

14. Use the table of metric measurements above to complete the following.
   a. 245 cm = 2.45 m
   b. 3.6 L = 3,600 mL
   c. 19,200 g = 19.2 kg
   d. 591 mL = 0.591 L

N M K L
0.9 0.95 1.0

Name the point on the number line above that represents each of the following numbers.

15. 0.958 M
16. 0.925 N
17. 0.995 L

18. Use the number line above to help you round 0.908 to the nearest hundredth. 0.91

Assessment Handbook, p. 147

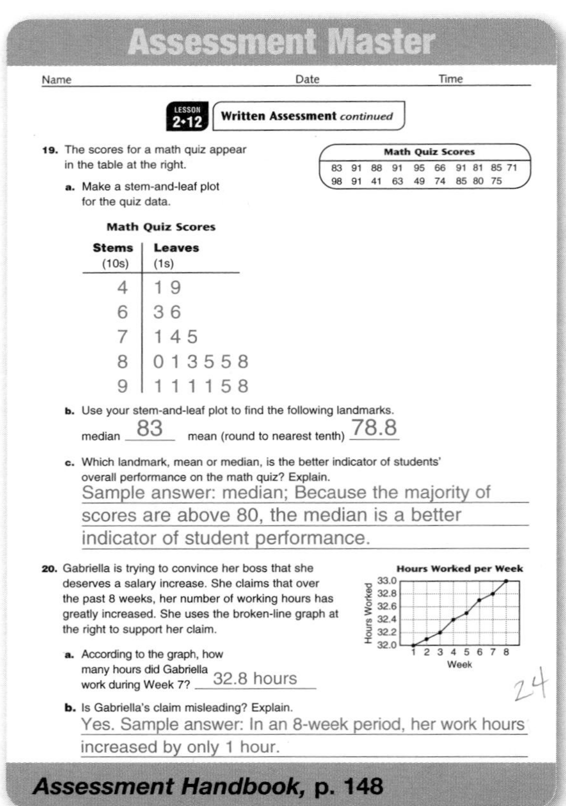

Assessment Master

Name Date Time

LESSON 2•12 Written Assessment *continued*

19. The scores for a math quiz appear in the table at the right.

Math Quiz Scores									
83	91	88	91	95	66	91	81	85	71
98	91	41	63	49	74	85	80	75	

   a. Make a stem-and-leaf plot for the quiz data.

Math Quiz Scores

Stems (10s)	Leaves (1s)
4	1 9
6	3 6
7	1 4 5
8	0 1 3 5 5 8
9	1 1 1 1 5 8

   b. Use your stem-and-leaf plot to find the following landmarks.
   median 83 mean (round to nearest tenth) 78.8
   c. Which landmark, mean or median, is the better indicator of students' overall performance on the math quiz? Explain.
   Sample answer: median; Because the majority of scores are above 80, the median is a better indicator of student performance.

20. Gabriella is trying to convince her boss that she deserves a salary increase. She claims that over the past 8 weeks, her number of working hours has greatly increased. She uses the broken-line graph at the right to support her claim.

   a. According to the graph, how many hours did Gabriella work during Week 7? 32.8 hours
   b. Is Gabriella's claim misleading? Explain.
   Yes. Sample answer: In an 8-week period, her work hours increased by only 1 hour.

Assessment Handbook, p. 148

▶ Open Response

INDEPENDENT ACTIVITY

(*Assessment Handbook,* p. 149)

Planning a Pizza Party

The open-response item requires students to apply skills and concepts from Unit 2 to solve a multistep problem. See the *Assessment Handbook,* pages 63–67 for rubrics and student work samples for this problem.

Assessment Master

Name Date Time

LESSON 2•12 **Open Response** Progress Check 2

Planning a Pizza Party

Your class is planning the menu for the end-of-year party for 36 people. Each person will get 2 slices of pizza. You have been assigned to find the least expensive restaurant from which to order the pizza. Several local restaurants and their prices are shown in the table below.

Restaurant	Pizza Price	Slices Per Pizza
Not-So-Crusty Pizza	$10.80	8
Supreme Pizza	$12.25	10
Perfection Pizza	$8.25	6

From which restaurant should you buy the pizza?

Write an explanation of how you made your decision. Your explanation should be clear and easy to follow. You can use pictures or tables to help you organize your work.

See the *Assessment Handbook* for rubrics and sample answers.

Assessment Handbook, p. 149

2 Building Background for Unit 3

▶ Math Boxes 2•12

INDEPENDENT ACTIVITY

(*Math Journal 1,* p. 81)

Mixed Practice This Math Boxes page previews Unit 3 content.

▶ Study Link 2•12: Unit 3 Family Letter

INDEPENDENT ACTIVITY

(*Math Masters,* pp. 67–70)

Home Connection The Unit 3 Family Letter provides parents and guardians with information and activities related to Unit 3 topics.

Study Link Masters

Name Date Time

STUDY LINK 2•12 **Unit 3: Family Letter**

Variables, Formulas, and Graphs

In Unit 3, students will be introduced to variables—symbols such as *x, y,* and *m*—that stand for a specific number or any number in a range of values. The authors of *Everyday Mathematics* believe that work with variables is too important to be delayed until high-school algebra courses. The problem "Solve $3x + 40 = 52$" might be difficult for some high-school students because they see it as merely symbol manipulation. Problems such as these are posed to *Everyday Mathematics* students as puzzles that can be unraveled by asking, "What number makes the equation true?" *I need to add 12 to 40 to get 52. Three times what number yields 12? The answer is* $x = 4$.

In addition to being used in algebraic equations, variables are also used to describe general patterns, to form expressions that show relationships, and to write rules and formulas. Unit 3 will focus on these three uses of variables.

In this unit, your child will work with "What's My Rule?" tables like the one below (introduced in early grades of *Everyday Mathematics*). He or she will learn to complete such tables following rules described in words or by algebraic expressions. Your child will also determine rules or formulas from information given in tables and graphs.

Rule: $y = (4 * x) + -3$

x	y
5	17
2	
0	
	37

In addition, your child will learn how to name cells in a spreadsheet and write formulas to express the relationships among spreadsheet cells. If you use computer spreadsheets at work or at home, you may want to share your experiences with your child. The class will play *Spreadsheet Scramble,* in which students practice computation and mental addition of positive and negative numbers. Encourage your child to play a game at home. See the *Practice through Games* section of this letter for some suggestions.

	A	B	C	D	E	F
1						Total
2						
3						
4						
5	Total					

Please keep this Family Letter for reference as your child works through Unit 3.

Math Masters, pp. 67–70

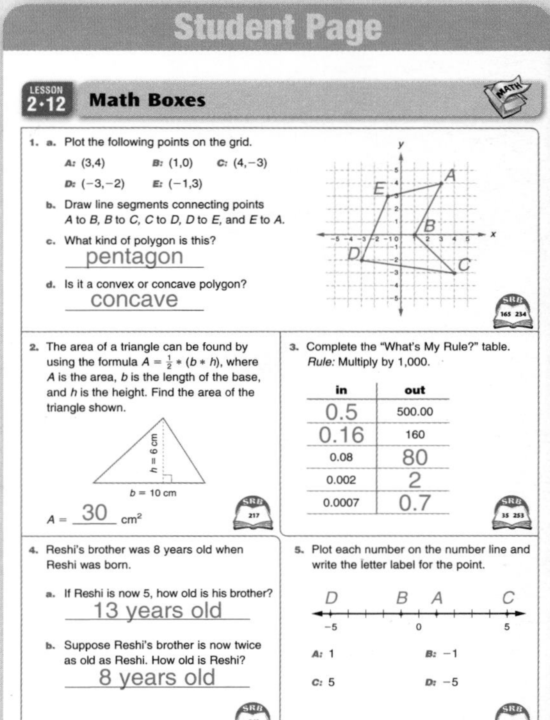

Student Page

LESSON 2•12 **Math Boxes**

1. a. Plot the following points on the grid.
   A: (3,4) B: (1,0) C: (4,−3)
   D: (−3,−2) E: (−1,3)
   b. Draw line segments connecting points A to B, B to C, C to D, D to E, and E to A.
   c. What kind of polygon is this? pentagon
   d. Is it a convex or concave polygon? concave

2. The area of a triangle can be found by using the formula $A = \frac{1}{2} * (b * h)$, where A is the area, b is the length of the base, and h is the height. Find the area of the triangle shown.
   $h = 6$ cm, $b = 10$ cm
   $A =$ 30 cm²

3. Complete the "What's My Rule?" table. *Rule:* Multiply by 1,000.

in	out
0.5	500.00
0.16	160
0.08	80
0.002	2
0.0007	0.7

4. Reshi's brother was 8 years old when Reshi was born.
   a. If Reshi is now 5, how old is his brother? 13 years old
   b. Suppose Reshi's brother is now twice as old as Reshi. How old is Reshi? 8 years old

5. Plot each number on the number line and write the letter label for the point.
   A: 1 B: −1
   C: 5 D: −5

Math Journal 1, p. 81

Unit 3 Organizer

Variables, Formulas, and Graphs

Overview

The lessons in this unit provide instruction and practice representing functions using words, algebraic notation, tables, and graphs, and using these representations to solve problems. One objective is to continue to prepare students for middle and secondary school science and algebra courses. Another objective is to continue linking the ideas and skills of mathematics to everyday situations and applications. Unit 3 has five main areas of focus:

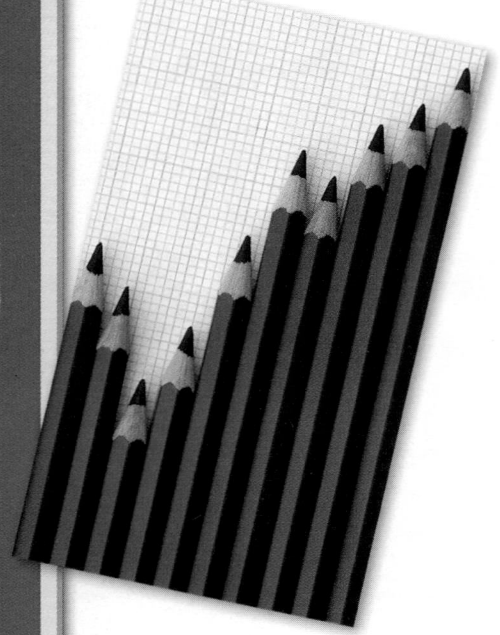

- To use variables to describe number patterns,
- To write and evaluate algebraic equations,
- To use tables, formulas, and graphs for making predictions, drawing conclusions, and analyzing real-world situations,
- To estimate products and quotients of decimal numbers, and
- To develop strategies for multiplying and dividing decimals.

Contents

Unit 3 Organizer

Learning In Perspective

	Lesson Objectives	Links to the Past	Links to the Future
3•1	To describe general number patterns in words; and to write special cases for general number patterns.	In Grade 5, students write algebraic expressions to represent situations described in words and express rules for "What's My Rule?" tables.	In Unit 9, students recognize and describe the general patterns used to write the distributive properties.
3•2	To write special cases having two variables; and to describe general patterns using two variables.	In Grade 5, students extend the "What's My Rule?" routine to rules with algebraic expressions. They develop and apply formulas for rates, area, and volume.	In Unit 9, students write different statements of the distributive properties for numerical and algebraic expressions.
3•3	To write and evaluate algebraic expressions.	In Grade 5, students write algebraic expressions to represent situations described in words and to express rules for "What's My Rule?" tables.	In Unit 9, students use the distributive property to simplify algebraic expressions. After Grade 6, students use symbolic algebra to represent and explain mathematical relationships.
3•4	To examine how formulas are derived; and to evaluate formulas.	In Grade 5, students develop and apply formulas for area, perimeter, and volume.	In Unit 9, students review, use, and evaluate formulas for perimeter, area, and volume.
3•5	To represent rates with data tables, rules expressed in words, formulas, and line graphs.	In Grade 5, students use tables, formulas, and graphs to represent, solve, and interpret rate problems based on real-world situations.	In Lessons 3-9 and 3-10, students use graphs to represent and analyze situations over a given period of time. After Grade 6, students extend graphs to predict changes in data (extrapolation).
3•6	To use diagrams, formulas, and graphs for making predictions and drawing conclusions.	In Grade 5, students complete and interpret various problem-solving diagrams. They use a formula and draw a graph to predict eruption times for a geyser.	After Grade 6, students explore relationships between symbolic expressions and graphs of lines, paying particular attention to the meaning of intercept and slope.
3•7	To introduce spreadsheets; and to use variables, formulas, and operations in spreadsheets.	In Grade 5, students express rates as formulas and use them to generate tables and graphs.	In Unit 9, students learn how labels, numbers, and formulas are entered and displayed in a spreadsheet.
3•8	To practice spreadsheet computation; and to practice finding sums of signed numbers.	In Grade 5, students develop rules for adding positive and negative numbers.	In Unit 6, students use a number line model to add and subtract positive and negative numbers. They also use the rule for subtraction of positive and negative numbers.
3•9	To interpret and draw graphs that correspond to given situations.	In Unit 1, students match mystery line plots with descriptions. In Grade 5, students match data descriptions with line plots and stem-and-leaf plots.	After Grade 6, students use graphs to analyze the nature of changes in quantities in linear relationships.
3•10	To analyze a real-world situation by making and using a data table and a graph.	In Grade 5, students use tables and a variety of graphs to represent real-world data. They analyze the graphs and draw conclusions.	In Unit 8, students represent and interpret rates in words, rules, formulas, tables, and graphs.

Key Concepts and Skills

	Key Concepts and Skills	Grade 6 Goals*
3•1	Apply a general pattern to find 10% of a number.	Number and Numeration Goal 2
	Extend numeric patterns.	Patterns, Functions, and Algebra Goal 2
	Write a number sentence containing a variable to describe a general pattern.	Patterns, Functions, and Algebra Goal 1
	Apply general patterns to explore multiplicative and additive inverses.	Patterns, Functions, and Algebra Goal 4
3•2	Use numeric expressions involving all four operations, parentheses, and exponents to write equivalent names for whole numbers and fractions.	Number and Numeration Goal 4
	Describe a general number pattern in words and with a number sentence (2 variables).	Patterns, Functions, and Algebra Goal 1
	Write special cases for the basic arithmetic operations.	Patterns, Functions, and Algebra Goal 1
3•3	Apply multiplication and division facts to evaluate algebraic expressions.	Operations and Computation Goal 2
	Write and evaluate an algebraic expression for a situation.	Patterns, Functions, and Algebra Goal 1
	Use a variable to represent unknown quantities.	Patterns, Functions, and Algebra Goal 1
3•4	Apply multiplication facts and strategies to find the area of a geometric shape.	Operations and Computation Goal 2
	Use formulas to solve area and perimeter problems.	Measurement and Reference Frames Goal 2
	Find the value of one variable in a formula when the values of other variables are given.	Patterns, Functions, and Algebra Goal 2
3•5	Apply basic multiplication and division facts to find an equivalent rate.	Operations and Computation Goal 2
	Construct and interpret a line graph.	Data and Chance Goals 1 and 2
	Plot data values from a table.	Measurement and Reference Frames Goal 3
	Use a formula to complete a table and analyze a function.	Patterns, Functions, and Algebra Goal 1
3•6	Apply multiplication and division facts to calculate rates.	Operations and Computation Goal 2
	Construct a graph and interpret its shape.	Data and Chance Goals 1 and 2
	Plot data values from a table.	Measurement and Reference Frames Goal 3
	Use a formula to complete a table and analyze a function.	Patterns, Functions, and Algebra Goal 1
3•7	Mentally add signed numbers.	Operations and Computation Goal 1
	Write formulas using spreadsheet cell names.	Patterns, Functions, and Algebra Goal 1
	Evaluate algebraic expressions and formulas.	Patterns, Functions, and Algebra Goal 3
3•8	Mentally add signed numbers.	Operations and Computation Goal 1
	Calculate the mean using a spreadsheet formula.	Data and Chance Goal 2
	Evaluate algebraic expressions and formulas.	Patterns, Functions, and Algebra Goal 3
3•9	Construct a graph that corresponds to a given situation.	Data and Chance Goal 1
	Write a "time story" based on the shape of a graph.	Data and Chance Goal 2
	Use a graph to represent and interpret a function.	Patterns, Functions, and Algebra Goal 1
3•10	Apply multiplication and division facts to calculate rates.	Operations and Computation Goal 2
	Construct, extend, and interpret a line graph.	Data and Chance Goals 1 and 2
	Plot data values from a table.	Measurement and Reference Frames Goal 3
	Express rates as formulas.	Patterns, Functions, and Algebra Goal 1

* See the Appendix for a complete list of Grade 6 Goals.

Ongoing Learning and Practice

Math Boxes

Math Boxes are paired across lessons as shown in the brackets below. This makes them useful as assessment tools. Math Boxes also preview content of the next unit.

Mixed practice	[3•1, 3•3], [3•2, 3•4], [3•5, 3•7], [3•6, 3•9], [3•8, 3•10]
Mixed practice with multiple choice	3•3, 3•4, 3•7, 3•8, 3•9, 3•10
Mixed practice with writing/reasoning opportunity	3•1, 3•2, 3•5, 3•6, 3•8

Practice through Games

Games are an essential component of practice in the *Everyday Mathematics* program. Games offer skills practice and promote strategic thinking.

Lesson	Game	Skill Practiced
3•2	*Factor Captor*	**Reviewing multiplication and division facts and finding factors of numbers** Number and Numeration Goal 3
3•5	*Division Top-It*	**Practicing whole-number division** Operations and Computation Goal 2
3•5	*Over and Up Squares*	**Naming and plotting ordered pairs** Measurement and Reference Frames Goal 3
3•7, 3•8	*Spreadsheet Scramble*	**Practicing mental addition of positive and negative numbers** Operations and Computation Goal 1
3•7	*Credits/Debits Game*	**Reviewing addition of signed numbers** Operations and Computation Goal 1
3•9	*Scientific Notation Toss*	**Practicing translation between scientific and standard notations** Number and Numeration Goal 1
3•10	*Getting to One*	**Reviewing place-value concepts of decimal numbers** Number and Numeration Goal 1

See the *Differentiation Handbook* for ways to adapt games to meet students' needs.

Home Communication

Study Links provide homework and home communication.

◀ ***Home Connection Handbook*** provides more ideas to communicate effectively with parents.

Unit 3 Family Letter provides families with an overview, Do-Anytime Activities, Building Skills Through Games, and a list of vocabulary.

Problem Solving

Encourage students to use a variety of strategies to solve problems and to explain those strategies. Strategies that students might use in this unit:

- Identifying and using patterns
- Using a table
- Writing number sentences and algebraic expressions
- Using formulas
- Drawing, analyzing, and interpreting a graph
- Trying and checking
- Using estimation

Lessons that teach *through* problem solving, not just *about* problem solving

Lesson	Activity
3•1, 3•2	Describe general number patterns with variables.
3•3	Represent situations with algebraic expressions.
3•4, 3•6	Solve number stories by substituting values, evaluating formulas, and analyzing graphs.
3•5	Represent rates in a variety of ways.
3•9	Construct a graph from a "time story."
3•10	Compare graphs to draw conclusions.

See Chapter 18 in the *Teacher's Reference Manual* for more information about problem solving.

Planning Tips

Pacing

Pacing depends on a number of factors, such as students' individual needs and how long your school has been using *Everyday Mathematics.* At the beginning of Unit 3, review your *Content by Strand* Poster to help you set a monthly pace.

SEPTEMBER	OCTOBER	NOVEMBER

← MOST CLASSROOMS → (late October – early November)

NCTM Standards

Unit 3 Lessons	3•1	3•2	3•3	3•4	3•5	3•6	3•7	3•8	3•9	3•10
NCTM Standards	1, 2, 6–8	1, 2, 6–8	2, 6–9	2, 5–10	2, 4–5, 8–10	2, 4–10	1, 2, 6, 8–10	1, 2, 6, 8–10	4–5, 8–10	2, 4–5, 6–10

Content Standards: 1 Number and Operations, **2** Algebra, **3** Geometry, **4** Measurement, **5** Data Analysis and Probability
Process Standards: 6 Problem Solving, **7** Reasoning and Proof, **8** Communication, **9** Connections, **10** Representation

Balanced Assessment

Ongoing Assessment

Recognizing Student Achievement

Opportunities to assess students' progress toward Grade 6 Goals:

Lesson	Content Assessed
3◆1	Write special cases for a general pattern. [Patterns, Functions, and Algebra Goal 1]
3◆2	Write a general pattern with two variables to represent a special case. [Patterns, Functions, and Algebra Goal 1]
3◆3	Find decimal solutions to whole-number division problems. [Operations and Computation Goal 2]
3◆4	Use algebraic notation to describe general patterns. [Patterns, Functions, and Algebra Goal 1]
3◆5	Complete a table from a formula and then graph the data. [Patterns, Functions, and Algebra Goal 1]
3◆6	Complete a table from a formula and then graph the data. [Patterns, Functions, and Algebra Goal 1]
3◆7	Add positive and negative numbers. [Operations and Computation Goal 1]
3◆8	Solve open number sentences involving signed numbers. [Operations and Computation Goal 1]
3◆9	Analyze the shape of a graph and draw conclusions about data trends. [Data and Chance Goal 2]
3◆10	Name a spreadsheet cell and identify a spreadsheet formula for calculating a total. [Patterns, Functions, and Algebra Goal 1]

Use the **Assessment Management System** to collect and analyze data about students' progress thoughout the year.

Informing Instruction

To anticipate common student errors and to highlight problem-solving strategies:

Lesson 3◆1 Recognize what special cases have in common

Lesson 3◆2 Develop a strategy for writing special cases

Lesson 3◆5 Recognize a fraction as a division problem

Lesson 3◆10 Develop rules from values in a table

Lesson 3◆10 Recognize the increments along the vertical axis of a graph

Periodic Assessment

3•11 Progress Check 3

CONTENT ASSESSED	ASSESSMENT ITEMS			
	Self	Oral/Slate	Written	Open Response
Find factors and multiples of numbers. [Number and Numeration Goal 3]			✔	
Find equivalent names for numbers. [Number and Numeration Goal 4]	✔	✔	✔	
Add positive and negative numbers. [Operations and Computation Goal 1]	✔	✔	✔	
Multiply and divide whole numbers and decimals. [Operations and Computation Goal 2]	✔		✔	
Estimate products and quotients of decimals. [Operations and Computation Goal 5]	✔	✔	✔	
Use and interpret data landmarks and data representations. [Data and Chance Goal 2]			✔	
Use formulas. [Measurement and Reference Frames Goal 2]	✔		✔	
Represent rates with formulas, tables, and graphs. Translate from one representation to another and use representations to solve problems involving functions. [Patterns, Functions, and Algebra Goal 1]	✔		✔	✔
Describe general patterns with words and number sentences. Extend and describe rules for patterns and use them to solve problems [Patterns, Functions, and Algebra Goal 1]	✔		✔	✔
Evaluate expressions. [Patterns, Functions, and Algebra Goal 3]		✔	✔	

Portfolio Opportunities

Opportunities to gather samples of students' mathematical writings, drawings, and creations to add balance to the assessment process:

- Connecting number patterns and special cases, **Lesson 3•1**
- Explaining general patterns, **Lesson 3•2**
- Deriving a formula, **Lesson 3•4**
- Converting between notations, **Lesson 3•5**
- Evaluating a distance formula, **Lesson 3•8**
- Constructing mystery graphs, **Lesson 3•9**
- Reviewing representations of function, **Lesson 3•10**

Assessment Handbook

Unit 3 Assessment Support

- Grade 6 Goals, pp. 37–50
- Unit 3 Assessment Overview, pp. 68–75
- Unit 3 Open Response
  - Detailed rubric, p. 72
  - Sample student responses, pp. 73–75

Unit 3 Assessment Masters

- Unit 3 Self Assessment, p. 150
- Unit 3 Written Assessment, pp. 151–154
- Unit 3 Open Response, p. 155
- Unit 3 Class Checklist, pp. 236, 237, and 275
- Quarterly Checklist: Quarter 1, pp. 266 and 267
- Unit 3 Individual Profile of Progress, pp. 234, 235, and 274
- Exit Slip, p. 283
- Math Logs, pp. 278–280
- Other Student Assessment Forms, pp. 276, 277, and 281

Differentiated Instruction

Daily Lesson Support

ENGLISH LANGUAGE LEARNERS

- **3•3** Building a Math Word Bank
- **3•5** Building a Math Word Bank
- **3•7** Building a Math Word Bank
- **3•8** Modeling squares and square roots

EXTRA PRACTICE

- **3•3** Writing algebraic expressions
- **3•4** Solving custom-made Math Boxes
- **3•5** Solving rate problems

5-Minute Math

- **3•1** Extending numeric patterns
- **3•8** Finding sums of signed numbers
- **3•9** Finding landmarks of a data set
- **3•10** Using graphs to represent actions

READINESS

- **3•1** Applying the "What's My Rule?" routine
- **3•2** Describing general patterns
- **3•4** Evaluating area formulas
- **3•5** Naming and plotting ordered pairs
- **3•6** Evaluating expressions
- **3•7** Reviewing addition of signed numbers
- **3•8** Solving a *Spreadsheet Scramble* problem
- **3•9** Matching mystery graphs
- **3•10** Reviewing representations of a function

ENRICHMENT

- **3•1** Exploring figurate numbers
- **3•2** Examining number sentences
- **3•2** Reading about variables in poetry
- **3•3** Extending the "What's My Rule?" routine
- **3•4** Deriving a formula
- **3•6** Using graphs to make predictions
- **3•7** Working with computer spreadsheets
- **3•8** Using spreadsheet software
- **3•9** Constructing mystery graphs
- **3•10** Exploring graph shapes

Adjusting the Activity

- **3•1** Reviewing the concept of opposites **ELL**
- **3•2** Finding general patterns in special cases **ELL**
- **3•4** Using a systematic approach to evaluate formulas **ELL**
- **3•5** Comparing the meanings of *rate* **ELL**
- **3•6** Calculating and estimating distance **ELL**
- **3•7** Generating spreadsheets
- **3•7** Computing sums of signed numbers
- **3•8** Demonstrating good strategies for *Spreadsheet Scramble*
- **3•9** Making statements about graph shapes

AUDITORY • KINESTHETIC • TACTILE • VISUAL

Cross-Curricular Links

Literature

Lesson 3•2 Students learn about mathematical topics through poetic dialogue.

Science

Lesson 3•6 Students throw balls straightup and calculate their speeds and heights.
Lesson 3•10 Students explore how graph shapes correspond to situations.

Social Studies

Lesson 3•4 Students derive a brick-wall formula.

Consumer Education

Lesson 3•7and 3•8 Students use spreadsheet software to evaluate formulas.
Lesson 3•10 Students analyze potential profits from summer jobs.

Using the Projects

Use Project 6, Anthropometry Project: Formulas for Body Height and Neck Circumference, during or after Unit 3. Students investigate formulas that relate body measurements. See the *Differentiation Handbook* for modifications to Project 6.

Differentiation Handbook

See the *Differentiation Handbook* for materials on Unit 3.

Language Support

Everyday Mathematics provides lesson-specific suggestions to help all students, including non-native English speakers, to acquire, process, and express mathematical ideas.

Unit 3 Vocabulary

algebraic expression
cell
column
Commutative Property of Addition
Commutative Property of Multiplication
evaluate (a formula)
evaluate an expression
formula
general pattern
horizon
line graph
rate
row
special case
speed
spreadsheet
square root
substitute
time graph
unit rate
update (revise) a spreadsheet
variable

Connecting Math and Literacy

Anno's Magic Seeds, by Mitsumasa Anno, Philomel Books, 1992
The King's Chessboard, by David Birch, Puffin Books, 1988
Lesson 3•2 *Math Talk: Mathematical Ideas in Poems for Two Voices,* by Theoni Pappas, Wide World Publishing, 1991

Student Reference Book

pp. 104–106, 142, 240, 245–247, 285, 286, 312, 321, 331, 334 and 336

Multiage Classroom ◆ Companion Lessons

Companion Lessons from Grade 5 can help you meet instructional needs of a multiage classroom. The full Scope and Sequence can be found in the Appendix.

Grade 5			10•3	9•6	10•4 10•6				5•10 5•11 10•7	10•4 10•6	
Grade 6	**3•1**	**3•2**	**3•3**	**3•4**	**3•5**	**3•6**	**3•7**	**3•8**	**3•9**	**3•10**	**3•11**

Professional Development

Teacher's Reference Manual Links

Lesson	Topic	Section
All Lessons	Functions	17.1.3
3•1–3•5	Algebra and Uses of Variables	17.2
3•5, 3•9, 3•10	Organizing and Displaying Data: Data Tables and Line Graphs	12.2.3
3•6	Formulas with Linear Measures	14.3.1
3•7, 3•8	Variables and Formulas in Spreadsheets	3.1.3

Unit 3 Organizer

Materials

Lesson	Masters	Manipulative Kit Items	Other Items
3◆1	Study Link Master, p. 74 Teaching Masters, pp. 71–73	calculator	
3◆2	Study Link 3◆1 Study Link Master, p. 75 Game Masters, pp. 437 and 438 Teaching Master, p. 76	calculator	coin-size counters; *Math Talk: Mathematical Ideas in Poems for Two Voices*
3◆3	Study Link 3◆2 Study Link Master, p. 77 Teaching Masters, pp. 78 and 79	calculator*	
3◆4	Study Link 3◆3 Study Link Master, p. 80 Teaching Masters, pp. 81 and 82 Teaching Aid Master, p. 405	calculator	ruler or tape measure
3◆5	Study Link 3◆4 Study Link Master, p. 83 Game Masters, pp. 465, 466, and 478 Teaching Master, p. 84	per group: 4 each of number cards 1–9; calculator; 2 six-sided dice	straightedge; per group: 2 different-color pencils
3◆6	Study Link 3◆5 transparency of *Math Masters,* p. 85* Study Link Masters, pp. 86 and 87 Teaching Master, p. 88	calculator	straightedge
3◆7	Study Link 3◆6 Game Masters, pp. 429, 430, and 474 transparency of *Math Masters,* p. 475* Study Link Master, p. 89	slate per group: 1 deck of number cards	large-screen display*; per group: computer/spreadsheet software
3◆8	Study Link 3◆7 Game Master, p. 474 transparency of *Math Masters,* p. 475* Study Link Master, p. 90 Teaching Master, p. 91 Teaching Aid Master, p. 408	calculator	*The World Almanac*/reference books; computer/spreadsheet software
3◆9	Study Link 3◆8 transparency of *Math Masters,* p. 92* Study Link Master, p. 93 Game Master, p. 472 Teaching Masters, pp. 94 and 95	per group: 2 six-sided dice	straightedge; per group: scissors, tape or glue; 1 or 2 sheets of paper
3◆10	Study Link 3◆9 Study Link Master, p. 96 Game Master, p. 448 Teaching Masters, pp. 97–99	calculator Geometry Template or ruler	straightedge; overhead calculator*; per group: 3 or 4 containers of various shapes and sizes; measuring cups (mL) and water
3◆11	Study Link 3◆10 Assessment Masters, pp. 150–155 Study Link Masters, pp. 100–104		

Technology
Assessment Management System, Unit 3
iTLG, Unit 3

* Denotes optional materials

Mathematical Background

The discussion below highlights the major content ideas presented in Unit 3 and helps establish instructional priorities.

Uses of Variables (All Lessons)

Variables in mathematics are symbols that stand for numbers. In general, a variable is a placeholder that can be replaced by a particular number or any number from a range of numbers. Variables are analogous to pronouns—just as the meaning of a pronoun comes from knowing its antecedent, the value of an algebraic expression comes from replacing the variables with numbers.

Most uses of variables fall into one of the following categories, the first four of which are considered in his unit:

Formulas

Examples include area, perimeter, and volume formulas. Thousands of relationships are expressed in similar ways.

Properties of number systems

For example, the "turn-around rule," or Commutative Property of Addition, can be expressed as $a + b = b + a$, where a and b can be replaced by any numbers.

Expressions

For example, if Galen is 6 years older than DeShawn and g is Galen's age, then DeShawn's age can be expressed as $g - 6$.

Input-output rules

In mathematics, these rules are often called "functions" or "relations." Generally speaking, they can be used to generate tables or concisely express the relationships in a table.

in	out
x	$x + 5$
4	9
7	12
53	58
−6	−1

Open sentences

The number sentence $2x + 3 = 9$ is true if x is replaced by 3 (or its equivalent) and false for any other value. For many people, solving open sentences, particularly equations, is the hallmark of algebra. However, it is actually less important in everyday life than other uses of variables.

In *Fourth Grade Everyday Mathematics,* the term *variable* was introduced, and variables were used in place of numbers in open sentences. Later, variables were used in formulas to find the areas and perimeters of polygons.

In earlier grades, students used words to express the relationship between inputs and outputs in "What's My Rule?" tables. In *Fifth Grade Everyday Mathematics,* they used variables and algebraic expressions to represent the rules. These input-output rules, known formally as "functions," will continue to receive attention. Several lessons in Unit 3 deal with rules and formulas, the tables derived from rules and formulas, and graphs that represent the data in such tables.

Unit 6 provides instruction in algorithm procedures for finding solutions to even more complicated equations. Informal work with open sentences continues throughout *Sixth Grade Everyday Mathematics*.

Section 17.2 of the *Teacher's Reference Manual* gives additional information about variables and their uses.

Rule: $y = (7 * x) + -8$

x	y
5	27
2	
0	−8
	20

Algebraic Expressions (Lessons 3◆1–3◆5)

Lessons 3-1 and 3-2 concentrate on the use of variables to generalize patterns. Lesson 3-3 focuses on variables in algebraic expressions. In Lessons 3-4 and 3-5, variables are used in formulas and rules.

For further information about variables and formulas, consult Section 3.1.3 of the *Teacher's Reference Manual.*

Formulas, Tables, and Graphs

(Lessons 3◆5, 3◆9, and 3◆10)

Lesson 3-5 reminds students that a rate describes a relationship between two quantities with different units. For example, speed is a rate that describes the relationship between distance traveled and time spent traveling that distance. Students represent rates with data tables, while rules are expressed in words, formulas, and graphs.

In Lesson 3-9, students are asked to match "mystery graphs" with situations that the graphs might represent.

The following situations could be matched with the three graphs shown on this page:

- The number of people in a school
- The number of people who are in their own homes
- The number of people who are driving a car

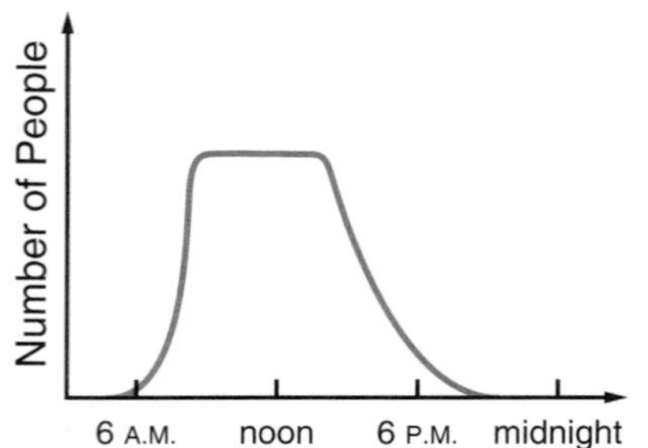

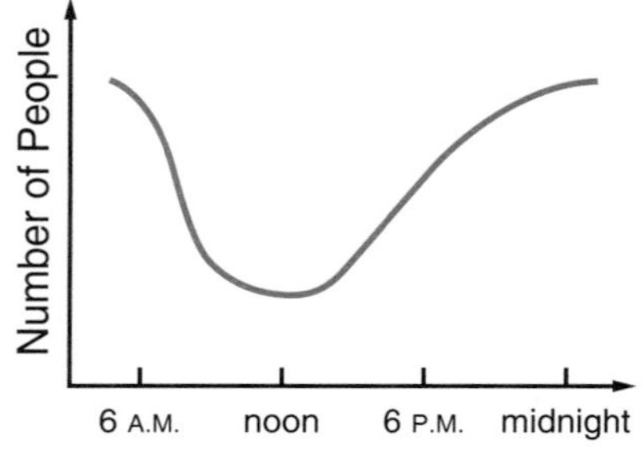

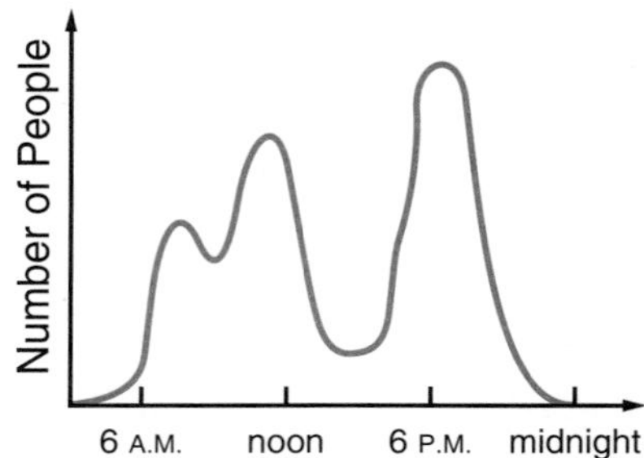

In Lesson 3-10, students explore a real-world situation involving summer job profits. They use the information in the problem to make a table of data and to develop rules that describe the relationship between the pairs of data. Finally, the data are displayed in a graph. Students learn that the data table, rule, and graph are simply different ways of representing the same relationship.

For further information about Functions, consult Section 17.1.3 of the *Teacher's Reference Manual.*

A Science Experiment (Lesson 3◆6)

The behavior of a falling object and the origins of the formulas are discussed on pages 104 and 105 of the *Student Math Journal 1.*

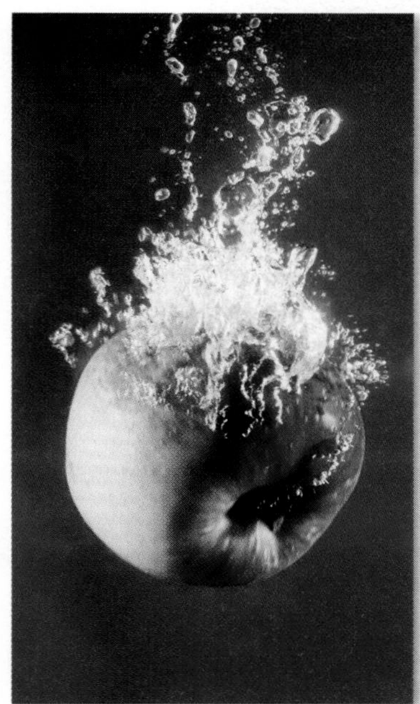

Variables and Formulas in Spreadsheets (Lessons 3◆7–3◆8)

Spreadsheets of numerical information have been a business tool for a long time, but creating spreadsheets by hand on ledger paper limited their utility. In the early days of the personal computer, a program called VisiCalc made it possible to use spreadsheets quickly by linking entries together so that a change in one entry was instantly reflected in all related entries. Since then, spreadsheet programs have become increasingly sophisticated and can now solve complex financial problems and create three-dimensional graphs.

	A	B	C
1	**Student**	**Books**	**Money**
2	Carlos	5	$12.50
3	Robin	16	$40.00
4	Akira	30	$75.00
5	Tyronne	13	$32.50
6	**Total**	64	$160.00

This lesson provides students with paper-and-pencil experience with spreadsheet formulas. It can be greatly enriched if students have access to computer spreadsheet programs in school or at home.

	A	B	C	D
1	**Student**	**Test 1**	**Test 2**	**Average**
2	Miriam	85	90	87.5
3	David	70	86	78
4	Amir	78	64	71
5	Elizabeth	65	81	73

For further information about spreadsheets, refer to Section 3.1.3 of the *Teacher's Reference Manual.*

3•1 Using Variables to Describe Number Patterns

Objectives To describe general number patterns in words; and to write special cases for general number patterns.

1 Teaching the Lesson

Key Activities

Students describe a general number pattern in words and write examples or special cases of it. They are given special cases for a general pattern and describe it with a number sentence having one variable.

Key Concepts and Skills

- Apply a general pattern to find 10% of a number. [Number and Numeration Goal 2]
- Extend numeric patterns. [Patterns, Functions, and Algebra Goal 2]
- Write a number sentence containing a variable to describe a general pattern. [Patterns, Functions, and Algebra Goal 1]
- Apply general patterns to explore multiplicative and additive inverses. [Patterns, Functions, and Algebra Goal 4]

Key Vocabulary

general pattern • variable • special case

Ongoing Assessment: Informing Instruction See page 182.

materials

- ☐ *Math Journal 1,* pp. 82–84
- ☐ *Student Reference Book,* p. 105
- ☐ calculator

2 Ongoing Learning & Practice

Students practice and maintain skills through Math Boxes and Study Link activities.

Ongoing Assessment: Recognizing Student Achievement Use journal page 85. [Patterns, Functions, and Algebra Goal 1]

materials

- ☐ *Math Journal 1,* p. 85
- ☐ Study Link Master (*Math Masters,* p. 74)
- ☐ calculator

3 Differentiation Options

READINESS

Students use the "What's My Rule?" routine to relate general number patterns and special cases.

ENRICHMENT

Students describe patterns and relationships among triangular numbers, square numbers, and rectangular numbers.

EXTRA PRACTICE

Students write rules to describe numeric patterns.

materials

- ☐ Teaching Masters (*Math Masters,* pp. 71–73)
- ☐ *5-Minute Math,* pp.158, 240, and 242

Technology

Assessment Management System
Math Boxes, Problem 2
See the **iTLG.**

Getting Started

Mental Math and Reflexes

Students rename mixed numbers and whole numbers as fractions. *Suggestions:*

●○○ $1\frac{1}{4}$ $\frac{5}{4}$
$2\frac{2}{3}$ $\frac{8}{3}$

●●○ $8\frac{1}{4}$ $\frac{33}{4}$
5 $\frac{5}{1}$

●●● $3\frac{1}{7}$ $\frac{22}{7}$
64 $\frac{64}{1}$

Math Message

1. Write the number that is the opposite of

a. 15 −15 **b.** −8 8 **c.** π −π **d.** 0 0 **e.** $-(-x)$ $-x$

2. Add.

a. $5 + -5$ 0 **b.** $-2.6 + 2.6$ 0

c. $-(-11) + (-11)$ 0 **d.** $y + (-y)$ 0

1 Teaching the Lesson

▶ Math Message Follow-Up

WHOLE-CLASS DISCUSSION

Have students share their answers. Pose additional problems, if necessary. *Suggestions:*

- What is the opposite of $-\frac{7}{8}$? $\frac{7}{8}$
- What is the sum of any number and its opposite? 0

Adjusting the Activity

ELL

To review the concept of opposites, have students refer to page 105 in the *Student Reference Book.* Most students are familiar with *opposite* in relation to position; as in *opposite sides of a rectangle are congruent.* Draw a number line on the board and show the positional relationship between a number and its opposite to zero. Model the sum of any number and its opposite on the number line.

A U D I T O R Y ◆ K I N E S T H E T I C ◆ T A C T I L E ◆ V I S U A L

▶ Describing General Number Patterns with Variables

PARTNER ACTIVITY

(*Math Journal 1,* pp. 82 and 83)

Read and discuss the text at the top of journal page 82. Have students complete Problem 1 and discuss their solutions. Be sure to cover the following points:

▷ Rules that describe patterns are sometimes called **general patterns.**

▷ A general pattern may be described in words.

▷ A general numeric pattern may be described with symbols, at least one of which represents a number. Symbols that represent numbers are called **variables.**

▷ A variable can have *any one of many possible numeric values.* A common misunderstanding of variables is that a variable always stands for one particular number.

Student Page

Date Time

LESSON 3•1 **Patterns and Variables** SRB 103

Study the number sentences at the right. All three sentences show the same **general pattern.**

$10\% \text{ of } 50 = \frac{10}{100} * 50$

$10\% \text{ of } 200 = \frac{10}{100} * 200$

$10\% \text{ of } 8 = \frac{10}{100} * 8$

◆ This general pattern may be described in words: To find 10% of a number, multiply the number by $\frac{10}{100}$ (or 0.10, or $\frac{1}{10}$).

◆ The pattern may also be described by a number sentence that contains a variable: 10% of $n = \frac{10}{100} * n$.

A **variable** is a symbol, such as *n, x, A,* or □. A variable can stand for any one of many possible numeric values in a number sentence.

◆ Number sentences like 10% of $50 = \frac{10}{100} * 50$ and 10% of $200 = \frac{10}{100} * 200$ are examples, or **special cases,** for the general pattern described by 10% of $n = \frac{10}{100} * n$.

To write a special case for a general pattern, replace the variable with a number.

Example:

General pattern 10% of $n = \frac{10}{100} * n$

Special case 10% of **35** $= \frac{10}{100} *$ **35**

1. Here are 3 special cases for a general pattern. $\frac{10}{10} = 1$ $\frac{725}{725} = 1$ $\frac{\frac{1}{2}}{\frac{1}{2}} = 1$

Sample answers:

a. Describe the pattern in words.
Any number divided by itself equals 1.

b. Give 2 other special cases for the pattern.
$\frac{9}{9} = 1$ $\frac{500}{500} = 1$

2. Here are 3 special cases for another general pattern. $15 + (-15) = 0$ $3 + (-3) = 0$ $\frac{1}{4} + (-\frac{1}{4}) = 0$

Sample answers:

a. Describe the pattern in words.
Any number added to its opposite equals zero.

b. Give 2 other special cases for the pattern.
$0.75 + (-0.75) = 0$ $100 + (-100) = 0$

Math Journal 1, p. 82

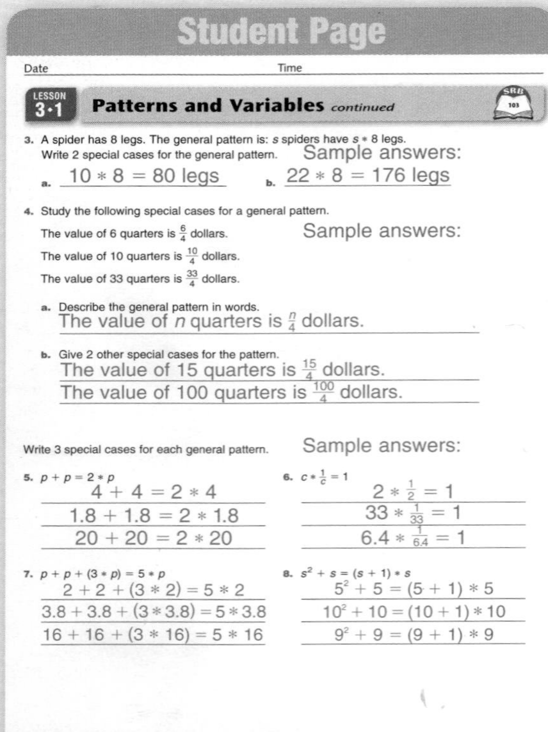

Student Page

Date ______ Time ______

LESSON 3·1 **Patterns and Variables** *continued*

3. A spider has 8 legs. The general pattern is: s spiders have $s * 8$ legs.
Write 2 special cases for the general pattern. Sample answers:
a. $10 * 8 = 80$ legs b. $22 * 8 = 176$ legs

4. Study the following special cases for a general pattern. Sample answers:
The value of 6 quarters is $\frac{6}{4}$ dollars.
The value of 10 quarters is $\frac{10}{4}$ dollars.
The value of 33 quarters is $\frac{33}{4}$ dollars.
a. Describe the general pattern in words.
The value of n quarters is $\frac{n}{4}$ dollars.
b. Give 2 other special cases for the pattern.
The value of 15 quarters is $\frac{15}{4}$ dollars.
The value of 100 quarters is $\frac{100}{4}$ dollars.

Write 3 special cases for each general pattern. Sample answers:

5. $p + p = 2 * p$
$4 + 4 = 2 * 4$
$1.8 + 1.8 = 2 * 1.8$
$20 + 20 = 2 * 20$

6. $c * \frac{1}{c} = 1$
$2 * \frac{1}{2} = 1$
$33 * \frac{1}{33} = 1$
$6.4 * \frac{1}{64} = 1$

7. $p + p + (3 * p) = 5 * p$
$2 + 2 + (3 * 2) = 5 * 2$
$3.8 + 3.8 + (3 * 3.8) = 5 * 3.8$
$16 + 16 + (3 * 16) = 5 * 16$

8. $s^2 + s = (s + 1) * s$
$5^2 + 5 = (5 + 1) * 5$
$10^2 + 10 = (10 + 1) * 10$
$9^2 + 9 = (9 + 1) * 9$

Math Journal 1, p. 83

NOTE General patterns may be described in words or by an open number sentence. Whenever *Everyday Mathematics* asks students to write a general pattern, they should write a number sentence that describes the pattern, unless the directions specifically state that they are to describe it in words.

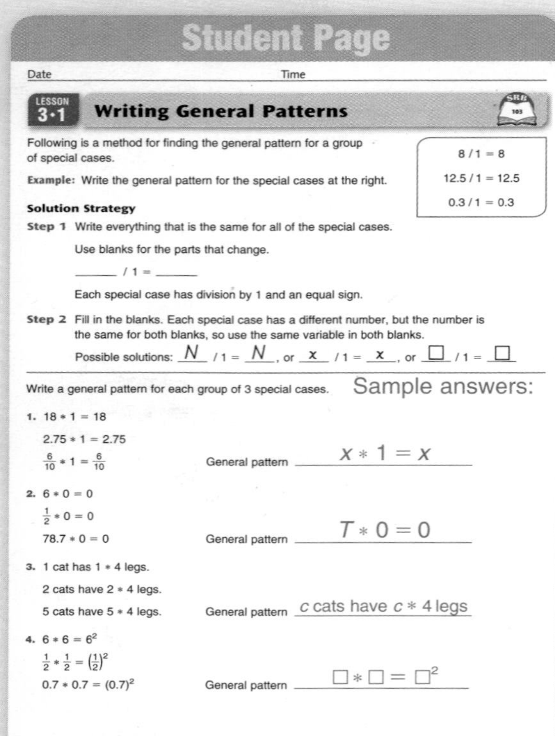

Student Page

Date ______ Time ______

LESSON 3·1 **Writing General Patterns**

Following is a method for finding the general pattern for a group of special cases.

Example: Write the general pattern for the special cases at the right.

$8 / 1 = 8$
$12.5 / 1 = 12.5$
$0.3 / 1 = 0.3$

Solution Strategy

Step 1 Write everything that is the same for all of the special cases.
Use blanks for the parts that change.
_____ / 1 = _____
Each special case has division by 1 and an equal sign.

Step 2 Fill in the blanks. Each special case has a different number, but the number is the same for both blanks, so use the same variable in both blanks.
Possible solutions: $N / 1 = N$, or $x / 1 = x$, or $\square / 1 = \square$

Write a general pattern for each group of 3 special cases. Sample answers:

1. $18 * 1 = 18$
$2.75 * 1 = 2.75$
$\frac{6}{10} * 1 = \frac{6}{10}$
General pattern $x * 1 = x$

2. $6 * 0 = 0$
$\frac{1}{2} * 0 = 0$
$78.7 * 0 = 0$
General pattern $T * 0 = 0$

3. 1 cat has $1 * 4$ legs.
2 cats have $2 * 4$ legs.
5 cats have $5 * 4$ legs.
General pattern c cats have $c * 4$ legs

4. $6 * 6 = 6^2$
$\frac{1}{2} * \frac{1}{2} = (\frac{1}{2})^2$
$0.7 * 0.7 = (0.7)^2$
General pattern $\square * \square = \square^2$

Math Journal 1, p. 84

▷ When a particular number is substituted for the variable in a general pattern, the result is called an example, or a **special case,** of the general pattern.

▷ There are many ways to describe the same pattern using variables. For example, $\frac{n}{n} = 1$, $\frac{b}{b} = 1$, and $\frac{\square}{\square} = 1$ all describe the pattern in Problem 1 on journal page 82.

To support English language learners, discuss the everyday meaning of *variable* and of *special case,* as well as their meanings in this context.

Have partners complete journal pages 82 and 83. They may use calculators.

NOTE There are no actual calculations required on these pages, but some students may want to verify that a particular number sentence is true. This may involve the use of parentheses keys (( ) ( )).

When most students have completed the journal pages, ask volunteers to share their solutions.

Have students describe each general pattern in their own words before giving special cases for the pattern. There is often more than one way to describe a pattern in words. Two ways of describing the general pattern $\frac{n}{n} = 1$ follow.

1. If the numerator and denominator of a fraction are the same number (except 0), the fraction is equivalent to 1.
2. If a nonzero number is divided by itself, the result is equal to 1.

A general pattern that is written with a variable looks the same as any of the special cases for that pattern. The only difference is that the variable has been replaced by a specific value. (*See margin.*)

▶ Describing General Patterns with Number Sentences

PARTNER ACTIVITY

(*Math Journal 1*, p. 84)

As a class, read and discuss the problem and solution strategy at the top of journal page 84. Ask students to decide which parts stay the same in all of the special cases and which parts change from case to case.

Circulate and assist as needed. When most students have completed the page, ask volunteers to share their solutions.

Ongoing Assessment: Informing Instruction

Watch for students who do not recognize what the special cases have in common. Some students may benefit from circling all the numbers and symbols that stay the same from one special case to the next.

2 Ongoing Learning & Practice

▶ Math Boxes 3•1

 INDEPENDENT ACTIVITY

(*Math Journal 1,* p. 85)

Mixed Practice Math Boxes in this lesson are paired with Math Boxes in Lesson 3-3. The skills in Problems 5 and 6 preview Unit 4 content.

Writing/Reasoning Have students write a response to the following: *Explain how you know where to place the decimal point in the quotient of Problem 4.* Sample answer: I estimated. 90 divided by 6 is 15, so 93.6 divided by 6 is about 15.

Ongoing Assessment: Recognizing Student Achievement

Math Boxes Problem 2 ★

Use **Math Boxes, Problem 2** to assess students' ability to write special cases for a general pattern. Students are making adequate progress if they are able to write three special cases. Some students may recognize the general pattern as illustrative of the Distributive Property of Multiplication over Addition.

[Patterns, Functions, and Algebra Goal 1]

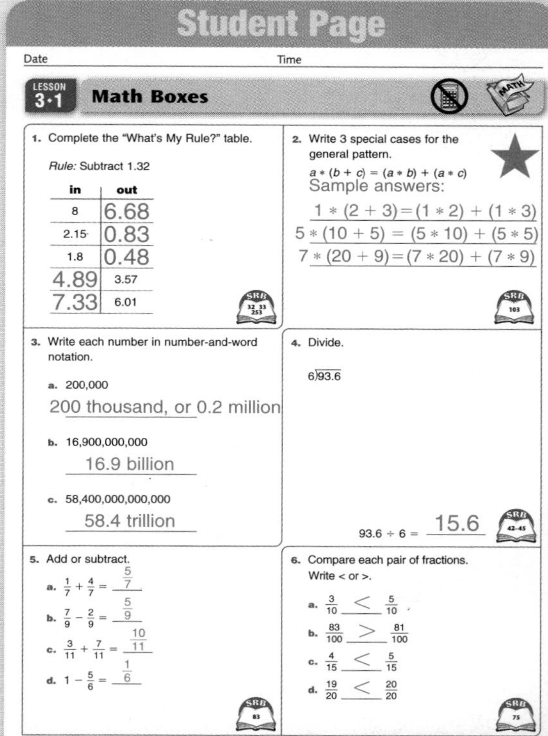

Student Page

Date Time

LESSON 3•1 **Math Boxes**

1. Complete the "What's My Rule?" table.

Rule: Subtract 1.32

in	out
8	6.68
2.15	0.83
1.8	0.48
4.89	3.57
7.33	6.01

2. Write 3 special cases for the general pattern.

$a * (b + c) = (a * b) + (a * c)$

Sample answers:

$1 * (2 + 3) = (1 * 2) + (1 * 3)$

$5 * (10 + 5) = (5 * 10) + (5 * 5)$

$7 * (20 + 9) = (7 * 20) + (7 * 9)$

3. Write each number in number-and-word notation.

a. 200,000 — 200 thousand, or 0.2 million

b. 16,900,000,000 — 16.9 billion

c. 58,400,000,000,000 — 58.4 trillion

4. Divide.

$6\overline{)93.6}$

$93.6 \div 6 =$ 15.6

5. Add or subtract.

a. $\frac{1}{7} + \frac{4}{7} = \frac{5}{7}$

b. $\frac{7}{9} - \frac{2}{9} = \frac{5}{9}$

c. $\frac{3}{11} + \frac{7}{11} = \frac{10}{11}$

d. $1 - \frac{5}{6} = \frac{1}{6}$

6. Compare each pair of fractions. Write < or >.

a. $\frac{3}{10} < \frac{5}{10}$

b. $\frac{83}{100} > \frac{81}{100}$

c. $\frac{4}{15} < \frac{5}{15}$

d. $\frac{19}{20} < \frac{20}{20}$

Math Journal 1, p. 85

▶ Study Link 3•1

INDEPENDENT ACTIVITY

(*Math Masters,* p. 74)

Home Connection Students practice describing general patterns with words and number sentences having one variable. They write special cases for general patterns.

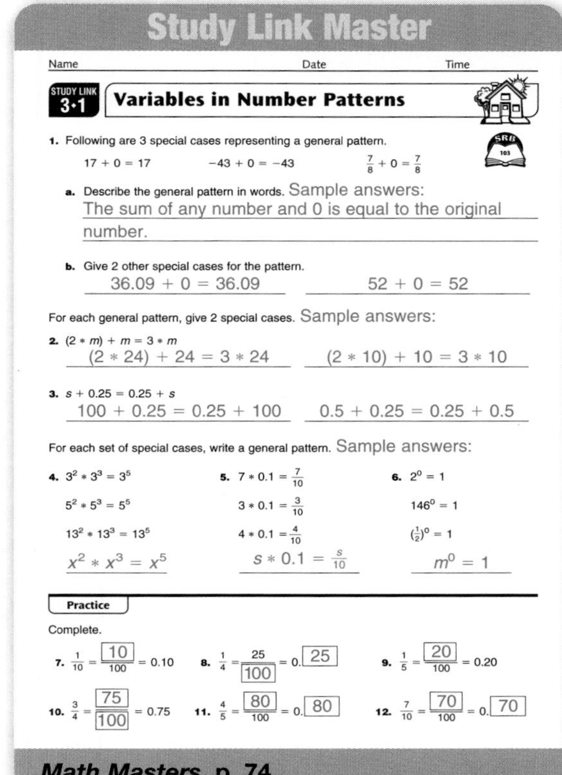

Study Link Master

Name Date Time

STUDY LINK 3•1 **Variables in Number Patterns**

1. Following are 3 special cases representing a general pattern.

$17 + 0 = 17$ $-43 + 0 = -43$ $\frac{7}{8} + 0 = \frac{7}{8}$

a. Describe the general pattern in words. Sample answers: The sum of any number and 0 is equal to the original number.

b. Give 2 other special cases for the pattern. $36.09 + 0 = 36.09$ $52 + 0 = 52$

For each general pattern, give 2 special cases. Sample answers:

2. $(2 * m) + m = 3 * m$ — $(2 * 24) + 24 = 3 * 24$ — $(2 * 10) + 10 = 3 * 10$

3. $s + 0.25 = 0.25 + s$ — $100 + 0.25 = 0.25 + 100$ — $0.5 + 0.25 = 0.25 + 0.5$

For each set of special cases, write a general pattern. Sample answers:

4. $3^2 * 3^3 = 3^5$; $5^2 * 5^3 = 5^5$; $13^2 * 13^3 = 13^5$; $x^2 * x^3 = x^5$

5. $7 * 0.1 = \frac{7}{10}$; $3 * 0.1 = \frac{3}{10}$; $4 * 0.1 = \frac{4}{10}$; $s * 0.1 = \frac{s}{10}$

6. $2^0 = 1$; $146^0 = 1$; $(\frac{1}{2})^0 = 1$; $m^0 = 1$

Practice

Complete.

7. $\frac{1}{10} = \frac{10}{100} = 0.10$

8. $\frac{1}{4} = \frac{25}{100} = 0.25$

9. $\frac{1}{5} = \frac{20}{100} = 0.20$

10. $\frac{3}{4} = \frac{75}{100} = 0.75$

11. $\frac{4}{5} = \frac{80}{100} = 0.80$

12. $\frac{7}{10} = \frac{70}{100} = 0.70$

Math Masters, p. 74

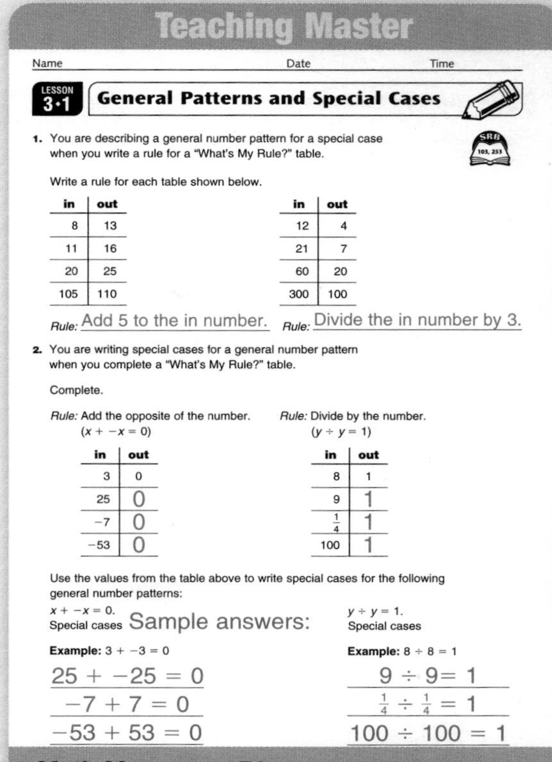

Teaching Master

Name Date Time

LESSON 3•1 **General Patterns and Special Cases**

1. You are describing a general number pattern for a special case when you write a rule for a "What's My Rule?" table.

Write a rule for each table shown below.

in	out
8	13
11	16
20	25
105	110

Rule: Add 5 to the in number.

in	out
12	4
21	7
60	20
300	100

Rule: Divide the in number by 3.

2. You are writing special cases for a general number pattern when you complete a "What's My Rule?" table.

Complete.

Rule: Add the opposite of the number. $(x + -x = 0)$

in	out
3	0
25	0
−7	0
−53	0

Rule: Divide by the number. $(y \div y = 1)$

in	out
8	1
9	1
$\frac{1}{4}$	1
100	1

Use the values from the table above to write special cases for the following general number patterns:

$x + -x = 0$. Special cases Sample answers:

Example: $3 + -3 = 0$

$25 + -25 = 0$

$-7 + 7 = 0$

$-53 + 53 = 0$

$y \div y = 1$. Special cases

Example: $8 \div 8 = 1$

$9 \div 9 = 1$

$\frac{1}{4} \div \frac{1}{4} = 1$

$100 \div 100 = 1$

Math Masters, p. 71

Teaching Master

Name ____ Date ____ Time ____

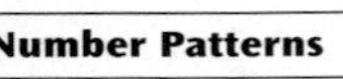

LESSON 3·1 Number Patterns

Triangular, square, and rectangular numbers are examples of number patterns that can be shown by geometric arrangements of dots. Study the number patterns shown below.

Triangular Numbers

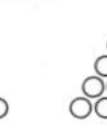
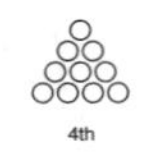
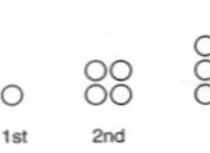
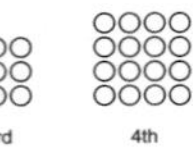

1st 2nd 3rd 4th

Square Numbers

1st 2nd 3rd 4th

Rectangular Numbers

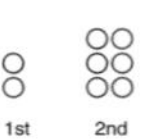
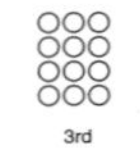

1st 2nd 3rd 4th

1. Use the number patterns to complete the table.

Number of Dots in Arrangement										
	1st	2nd	3rd	4th	5th	6th	7th	8th	9th	10th
Triangular Number	1	3	6	10	15	21	28	36	45	55
Square Number	1	4	9	16	25	36	49	64	81	100
Rectangular Number	2	6	12	20	30	42	56	72	90	110

2. What is the 11th triangular number? 66

How does the 11th triangular number compare to the 10th triangular number?
It is 11 more than the 10th triangular number.

Math Masters, **p. 72**

3 Differentiation Options

READINESS

INDEPENDENT ACTIVITY

5–15 Min

▶ Connecting General Number Patterns and Special Cases

(*Math Masters,* p. 71)

Portfolio Ideas

To provide experience with algebraic notation, have students use the "What's My Rule?" routine. By completing "What's My Rule?" tables, some students may more easily make the connection between general number patterns and special cases in Part 1 of this lesson.

ENRICHMENT

PARTNER ACTIVITY

5–15 Min

▶ Exploring Number Patterns

(*Math Masters,* pp. 72 and 73)

To apply students' understanding of general patterns, have them work with a partner to discover some relationships among figurate numbers—special numbers associated with geometric figures. For example, the sum of two successive triangular numbers is a square number; and the sum of a rectangular number and its corresponding square number is a triangular number.

EXTRA PRACTICE

SMALL-GROUP ACTIVITY

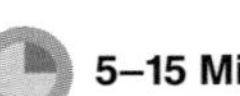

5–15 Min

▶ *5-Minute Math*

To offer more practice extending and describing numeric patterns, see *5-Minute Math*, pages 157, 240, and 242.

Teaching Master

Name ____ Date ____ Time ____

LESSON 3·1 Number Patterns *continued*

3. Describe what you notice about the sum of 2 triangular numbers that are next to each other in the table.
Sample answer: The sum is a square number.

4. Add the second square number and the second rectangular number; the third square number and the third rectangular number. What do you notice about the sum of a square number and its corresponding rectangular number?
The sum is a triangular number.

5. Describe any other patterns you notice.
Sample answer: Rectangular numbers are twice the corresponding triangular numbers.

6. You can write triangular numbers as the sum of 4 triangular numbers when repetitions are allowed. For example: 6 = 1 + 1 + 1 + 3

Find 3 other triangular numbers that can be written as sums of *exactly* 4 triangular numbers.
Sample answers:
10 = 1 + 3 + 3 + 3
15 = 3 + 3 + 3 + 6
21 = 3 + 6 + 6 + 6

Math Masters, **p. 73**

3•2 General Patterns (Two Variables)

Objectives To write special cases having two variables; and to describe general patterns using two variables.

1 Teaching the Lesson

Key Activities

Students examine, describe, and write general patterns having two variables. They identify special cases of such general patterns.

Key Concepts and Skills

- Use numeric expressions involving all four operations, parentheses, and exponents to write equivalent names for whole numbers and fractions. [Number and Numeration Goal 4]
- Describe a general number pattern in words and with a number sentence (2 variables). [Patterns, Functions, and Algebra Goal 1]
- Write special cases for the basic arithmetic operations. [Patterns, Functions, and Algebra Goal 1]

Key Vocabulary

Commutative Property of Addition • Commutative Property of Multiplication

Ongoing Assessment: Informing Instruction See page 187.

Ongoing Assessment: Recognizing Student Achievement Use journal page 87. [Patterns, Functions, and Algebra Goal 1]

materials

- ☐ *Math Journal 1,* pp. 86 and 87
- ☐ *Student Reference Book,* pp. 104–106
- ☐ Study Link 3•1
- ☐ calculator (optional)

2 Ongoing Learning & Practice

Students review multiplication and division facts and practice finding factors of numbers by playing *Factor Captor.*

Students practice and maintain skills through Math Boxes and Study Link activities.

materials

- ☐ *Math Journal 1,* p. 88
- ☐ *Student Reference Book,* p. 312
- ☐ Study Link Master (*Math Masters,* p. 75)
- ☐ Game Masters (*Math Masters,* pp. 437 and 438)
- ☐ calculator; coin-size counters

See **Advance Preparation**

3 Differentiation Options

READINESS

Students develop a strategy for writing general patterns with variables.

ENRICHMENT

Students solve challenging problems involving general patterns and special cases.

ENRICHMENT

Students read the poem "Variables."

materials

- ☐ Teaching Master (*Math Masters,* p. 76)
- ☐ *Math Talk: Mathematical Ideas in Poems for Two Voices*

Additional Information

Advance Preparation For Part 2, make copies of Grid 1 or Grid 2 (*Math Masters,* pp. 437 and 438) for each pair of students.

Technology

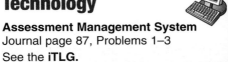

Assessment Management System
Journal page 87, Problems 1–3
See the **iTLG.**

Getting Started

Mental Math and Reflexes

Students find 10% of a number mentally.

Suggestions:

●○○	10% of 300 30	10% of 140 14
●●○	10% of 70 7	10% of 30 3
●●●	10% of 145 14.5	10% of 75 7.5

Math Message

Study the example at the top of journal page 86. Write two more special cases for the general pattern.

Study Link 3·1 Follow-Up

Review answers. Check that students understand that while there may be only one general pattern, there are an infinite number of special cases.

1 Teaching the Lesson

▶ Math Message Follow-Up

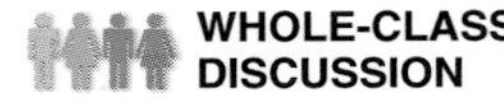

(*Math Journal 1,* p. 86)

Write the general pattern on the board, as well as the special cases from the journal page:

General Pattern: $a * (b - 1) = a * b - a$

Special Cases: $5 * (4 - 1) = 5 * 4 - 5$

$72 * (13 - 1) = 72 * 13 - 72$

$6 * (6 - 1) = 6 * 6 - 6$

Ask students to suggest other special cases. Mention the following as you record and discuss their suggestions:

▷ The number sentence that describes the general pattern contains two variables. Each variable can stand for *any one of many possible* numeric values.

▷ When numbers are substituted for the variables, the result is a special case of the general pattern.

▷ The general pattern looks the same as any of the special cases for that pattern. The only difference is that in the special cases, specific values have been substituted for the variables.

Some students may think that because the variables have different letter names, they must represent different numbers. Point out that in the third special case, the value 6 has been substituted for both variables. Ask students to give other special cases in which the same number is substituted for both variables.

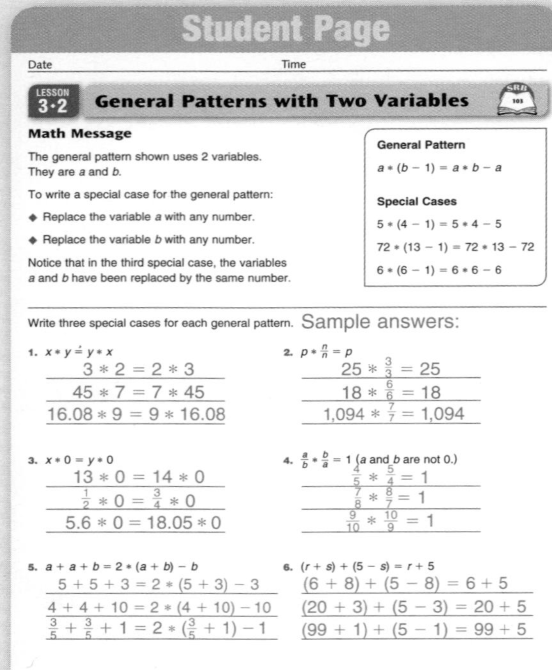

Student Page

Date Time

LESSON 3·2 **General Patterns with Two Variables** SRB 103

Math Message

The general pattern shown uses 2 variables. They are *a* and *b*.

To write a special case for the general pattern:

- Replace the variable *a* with any number.
- Replace the variable *b* with any number.

Notice that in the third special case, the variables *a* and *b* have been replaced by the same number.

General Pattern

$a * (b - 1) = a * b - a$

Special Cases

$5 * (4 - 1) = 5 * 4 - 5$

$72 * (13 - 1) = 72 * 13 - 72$

$6 * (6 - 1) = 6 * 6 - 6$

Write three special cases for each general pattern. Sample answers:

1. $x * y = y * x$
   - $3 * 2 = 2 * 3$
   - $45 * 7 = 7 * 45$
   - $16.08 * 9 = 9 * 16.08$

2. $p * \frac{n}{n} = p$
   - $25 * \frac{3}{3} = 25$
   - $18 * \frac{6}{6} = 18$
   - $1{,}094 * \frac{7}{7} = 1{,}094$

3. $x * 0 = y * 0$
   - $13 * 0 = 14 * 0$
   - $\frac{1}{2} * 0 = \frac{3}{4} * 0$
   - $5.6 * 0 = 18.05 * 0$

4. $\frac{a}{b} * \frac{b}{a} = 1$ (*a* and *b* are not 0.)
   - $\frac{4}{5} * \frac{5}{4} = 1$
   - $\frac{7}{8} * \frac{8}{7} = 1$
   - $\frac{9}{10} * \frac{10}{9} = 1$

5. $a + a + b = 2 * (a + b) - b$
   - $5 + 5 + 3 = 2 * (5 + 3) - 3$
   - $4 + 4 + 10 = 2 * (4 + 10) - 10$
   - $\frac{3}{5} + \frac{3}{5} + 1 = 2 * (\frac{3}{5} + 1) - 1$

6. $(r + s) + (5 - s) = r + 5$
   - $(6 + 8) + (5 - 8) = 6 + 5$
   - $(20 + 3) + (5 - 3) = 20 + 5$
   - $(99 + 1) + (5 - 1) = 99 + 5$

Math Journal 1, p. 86

▶ Writing Special Cases for General Patterns

PARTNER ACTIVITY

(*Math Journal 1,* p. 86)

Partners work on journal page 86. They may use calculators. There are no actual calculations required on this page, but some students may want to verify that a particular special case is true. When most students have completed the journal page, have them share their solutions.

Ongoing Assessment: Informing Instruction

Watch for students who find it difficult to write special cases when the general pattern contains two variables. Suggest that they substitute one variable at a time. For example, for the general pattern $x * y = y * x$, first substitute a value for x, such as 15, and write $15 * y = y * 15$. Then substitute a value for y, such as 3, and write $15 * 3 = 3 * 15$.

▶ Describing General Patterns Using Two Variables

PARTNER ACTIVITY

(*Math Journal 1,* p. 87)

As a class, review the example and solution strategy at the top of journal page 87. Ask students to decide which parts of the special cases stay the same and which parts change from case to case.

Have students work with partners to solve the remaining problems. When most students have completed the page, have students share their solutions.

Adjusting the Activity

ELL

Suggest the following change in Step 2 on journal page 87. Suppose you want to find the general pattern for the following special cases:

$$7 * (5 - 2) = (7 * 5) - (7 * 2)$$
$$7 * (4 - 3) = (7 * 4) - (7 * 3)$$
$$7 * (6 - 1) = (7 * 6) - (7 * 1)$$

1. First write everything that is common to the special cases.
   7 ∗ (_____ − _____) = (7 ∗ _____) − (7 ∗ _____)
2. Now use only the first special case, replacing each different number with its own unique letter or symbol. For example, you might replace each 5 with a circle and each 2 with a triangle. This results in the following general pattern:
   7 ∗ (○ − △) = (7 ∗ ○) − (7 ∗ △)
3. Finally, check the general pattern by comparing it to the other special cases.

AUDITORY ◆ KINESTHETIC ◆ TACTILE ◆ VISUAL

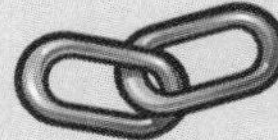

Links to the Future

Some general patterns in Lessons 3-1 and 3-2 describe mathematical properties, such as the **Commutative Properties of Addition** and **Multiplication** (turnaround facts in previous grades). Expect students to recognize and name these properties. Naming these properties is not a Grade 6 Goal, but will provide students with practice for identifying and naming some of the basic properties they will encounter in seventh and eighth grades. Refer students to pages 104–106 in the *Student Reference Book* if necessary.

Student Page

Date Time

LESSON 3·2 General Patterns with Two Variables *continued*

Example: Write a general pattern with 2 variables for the special cases at the right.

$7 + 3 = 3 + 7$

$\frac{1}{2} + \frac{3}{2} = \frac{3}{2} + \frac{1}{2}$

$4 + (-2) = -2 + 4$

Solution Strategy

Step 1 Write everything that is the same for all of the special cases. Use blanks for the parts that change.

_____ + _____ = _____ + _____

Each special case has two additions and an equal sign.

Step 2 Each special case has 2 different numbers. Use different variables (letters or other symbols) for the numbers that vary. Write them on the blanks.

$a + b = b + a$

Step 3 Check that the special cases given fit the general pattern.

Write a number sentence with 2 variables for each general pattern.

1. $4 * \frac{2}{7} = 2 * \frac{4}{7}$
   $10 * \frac{2}{3} = 2 * \frac{10}{3}$
   $29 * \frac{2}{8} = 2 * \frac{29}{8}$
   General pattern $c * \frac{2}{d} = 2 * \frac{c}{d}$

2. $(5 * 2) + (5 * 6) = 5 * (2 + 6)$
   $(5 * 4) + (5 * 1) = 5 * (4 + 1)$
   $(5 * 2) + (5 * 100) = 5 * (2 + 100)$
   General pattern $(5 * g) + (5 * h) = 5 * (g + h)$

3. Write a general pattern using variables.
   Let d = number of dogs.
   Let b = number of birds.
   3 dogs and 5 birds have $(3 * 4) + (5 * 2)$ legs.
   5 dogs and 9 birds have $(5 * 4) + (9 * 2)$ legs.
   17 dogs and 6 birds have $(17 * 4) + (6 * 2)$ legs.
   d dogs and b birds have $(d * 4) + (b * 2)$ legs.

4. For the general pattern $x^2 * y^2 = (x * y)^2$, write the special case.
   a. $x = 4$ and $y = 5$
      $4^2 * 5^2 = (4 * 5)^2$
   b. $x = 10$ and $y = 10$
      $10^2 * 10^2 = (10 * 10)^2$
   c. Is the general pattern true, no matter which numbers you use? Yes

Math Journal 1, p. 87

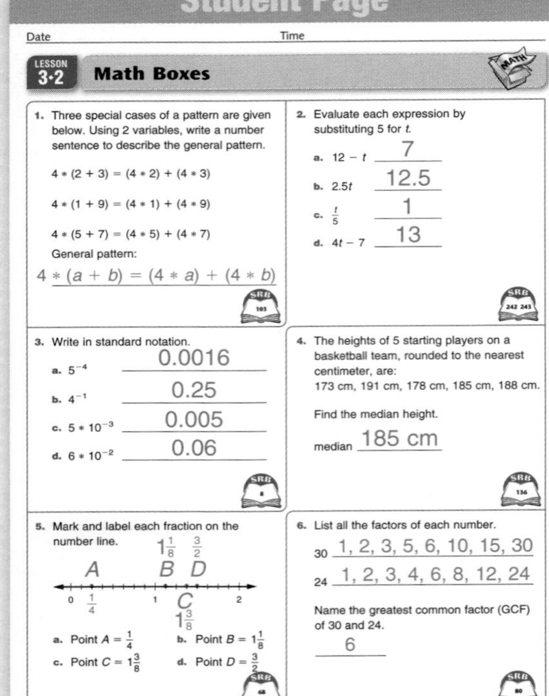

Date Time

LESSON 3·2 **Math Boxes**

1. Three special cases of a pattern are given below. Using 2 variables, write a number sentence to describe the general pattern.

$4 * (2 + 3) = (4 * 2) + (4 * 3)$

$4 * (1 + 9) = (4 * 1) + (4 * 9)$

$4 * (5 + 7) = (4 * 5) + (4 * 7)$

General pattern:

$4 * (a + b) = (4 * a) + (4 * b)$

2. Evaluate each expression by substituting 5 for t.

a. $12 - t$ 7

b. $2.5t$ 12.5

c. $\frac{t}{5}$ 1

d. $4t - 7$ 13

3. Write in standard notation.

a. 5^{-4} 0.0016

b. 4^{-1} 0.25

c. $5 * 10^{-3}$ 0.005

d. $6 * 10^{-2}$ 0.06

4. The heights of 5 starting players on a basketball team, rounded to the nearest centimeter, are:
173 cm, 191 cm, 178 cm, 185 cm, 188 cm.

Find the median height.

median 185 cm

5. Mark and label each fraction on the number line.

a. Point $A = \frac{1}{4}$

b. Point $B = 1\frac{1}{8}$

c. Point $C = 1\frac{3}{8}$

d. Point $D = \frac{3}{2}$

6. List all the factors of each number.

30 1, 2, 3, 5, 6, 10, 15, 30

24 1, 2, 3, 4, 6, 8, 12, 24

Name the greatest common factor (GCF) of 30 and 24.

6

Math Journal 1, p. 88

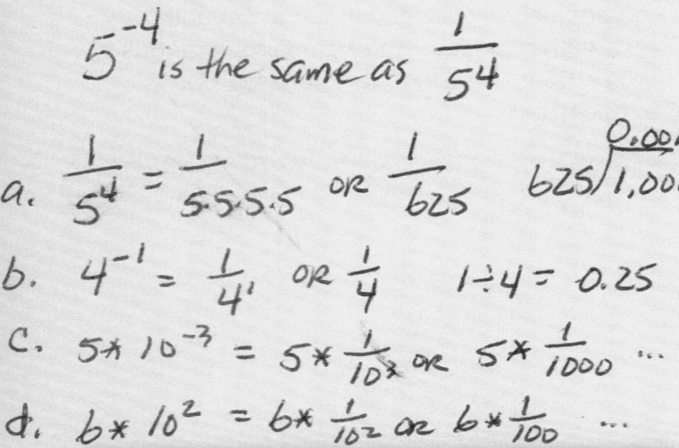

5^{-4} is the same as $\frac{1}{5^4}$
a. $\frac{1}{5^4} = \frac{1}{5 \cdot 5 \cdot 5 \cdot 5}$ or $\frac{1}{625}$ 625)1,000 0.0016
b. $4^{-1} = \frac{1}{4^1}$ or $\frac{1}{4}$ 1÷4 = 0.25
c. $5 * 10^{-3} = 5 * \frac{1}{10^3}$ or $5 * \frac{1}{1000}$ ...
d. $6 * 10^{2} = 6 * \frac{1}{10^2}$ or $6 * \frac{1}{100}$ ...

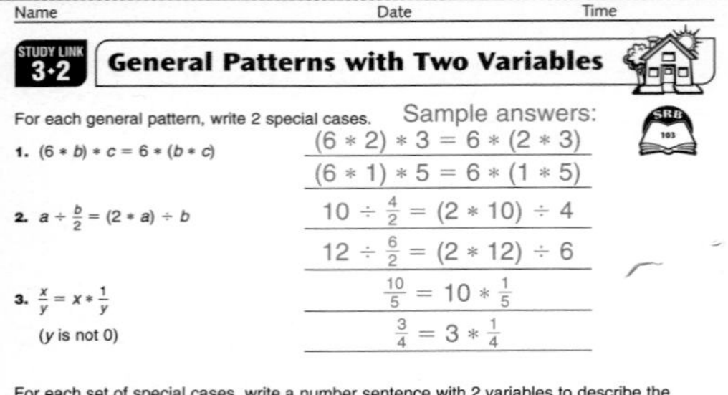

Study Link Master

Name Date Time

STUDY LINK 3·2 **General Patterns with Two Variables**

For each general pattern, write 2 special cases. Sample answers:

1. $(6 * b) * c = 6 * (b * c)$ $(6 * 2) * 3 = 6 * (2 * 3)$; $(6 * 1) * 5 = 6 * (1 * 5)$

2. $a \div \frac{b}{2} = (2 * a) \div b$ $10 \div \frac{4}{2} = (2 * 10) \div 4$; $12 \div \frac{6}{2} = (2 * 12) \div 6$

3. $\frac{x}{y} = x * \frac{1}{y}$ (y is not 0) $\frac{10}{5} = 10 * \frac{1}{5}$; $\frac{3}{4} = 3 * \frac{1}{4}$

For each set of special cases, write a number sentence with 2 variables to describe the general pattern.

4. $7 - 5 = 7 + (-5)$

$12 - 8 = 12 + (-8)$

$9 - 1 = 9 + (-1)$

General pattern: $a - b = a + (-b)$

5. $\frac{4}{6} = \frac{4 * 3}{6 * 3}$

$\frac{1}{2} = \frac{1 * 3}{2 * 3}$

$\frac{2}{5} = \frac{2 * 3}{5 * 3}$

General pattern: $\frac{m}{n} = \frac{m * 3}{n * 3}$

6. $\frac{6}{10} = \frac{6 \div 2}{10 \div 2}$

$\frac{4}{12} = \frac{4 \div 2}{12 \div 2}$

$\frac{2}{4} = \frac{2 \div 2}{4 \div 2}$

General pattern: $\frac{s}{t} = \frac{s \div 2}{t \div 2}$

7. $\frac{1}{5} * \frac{1}{2} = \frac{1 * 1}{5 * 2}$

$\frac{2}{3} * \frac{1}{2} = \frac{2 * 1}{3 * 2}$

$\frac{3}{4} * \frac{1}{2} = \frac{3 * 1}{4 * 2}$

General pattern: $\frac{c}{d} * \frac{1}{2} = \frac{c * 1}{d * 2}$

Practice

Write each fraction as a decimal.

8. $\frac{250}{100}$ = 2.5

9. $\frac{106}{100}$ = 1.06

10. $\frac{100}{100}$ = 1.00

Math Masters, p. 75

Ongoing Assessment: Recognizing Student Achievement

Journal page 87 Problems 1–3

Use **journal page 87, Problems 1–3** to assess students' ability to write a general pattern with two variables to represent a special case. Students are making adequate progress if they are able to write general patterns for Problems 1–3. Some students may be able to apply their understanding of special cases to complete Problem 4.

[Patterns, Functions, and Algebra Goal 1]

2 Ongoing Learning & Practice

▶ Playing *Factor Captor*

(*Student Reference Book,* p. 312; *Math Masters,* pp. 437 and 438)

Distribute calculators, grids, and counters to each pair of students. Read and discuss the rules on page 312 of the *Student Reference Book* with the class and play a few practice rounds.

▶ Math Boxes 3·2

(*Math Journal 1,* p. 88)

Mixed Practice Math Boxes in this lesson are paired with Math Boxes in Lesson 3-4. The skills in Problems 5 and 6 preview Unit 4 content.

Writing/Reasoning Have students write a response to the following: *Explain the general pattern you wrote for Problem 1 in your own words.* Sample answer: The product of a number and a sum is equal to the sum of the products of the number and each addend.

▶ Study Link 3·2

(*Math Masters,* p. 75)

Home Connection Students make up special cases for general patterns and write general patterns for sets of special cases.

3 Differentiation Options

READINESS

SMALL-GROUP ACTIVITY

5–15 Min

▶ Describing General Patterns with Variables

To provide more experience with special cases for general patterns, have students develop a strategy for writing general patterns with one variable that they can extend to their work with two variables.

Provide students with the following special cases:

▷ $5 * 10^{-2} = 5 \div 100$
▷ $9 * 10^{-2} = 9 \div 100$
▷ $3.5 * 10^{-2} = 3.5 \div 100$

Have students highlight the symbols and numbers that are common to the special cases and then record them.

$\_\_\_\_ * 10^{-2} = \_\_\_\_ \div 100$

Using only the first special case, have students replace each different non-highlighted number with its own unique symbol or letter.

$\bigcirc * 10^{-2} = \bigcirc \div 100$

Ask students to check this general pattern by comparing it to the other two special cases. Have them continue to work with this strategy by writing general patterns with one variable.
Suggestions:

$12 * \frac{2}{3} = (12 * 2) \div 3$

$15 * \frac{2}{3} = (15 * 2) \div 3$

$18 * \frac{2}{3} = (18 * 2) \div 3$

$y * \frac{2}{3} = (y * 2) \div 3$

$5^{-2} = \frac{1}{5^2}$

$10^{-2} = \frac{1}{10^2}$

$25^{-2} = \frac{1}{25^2}$

$x^{-2} = \frac{1}{x^2}$

ENRICHMENT

INDEPENDENT ACTIVITY

15–30 Min

▶ Finding True and Not True Special Cases

(*Math Masters,* p. 76)

To further explore special cases, students solve problems involving number sentences that are not necessarily true for all variable replacements. Problems 1 and 2 involve number sentences that do not describe a general pattern. The sentence in Problem 1 is true if $m = n = 0$ or if $m = 6$ and $n = 1.2$ and in general if $n = m / (m - 1)$; it is not true for values such as $m = n = 1$. The sentence in Problem 2 is true only if $a = 0$.

ENRICHMENT

PARTNER ACTIVITY

5–15 Min

▶ Reading about Variables in Poetry

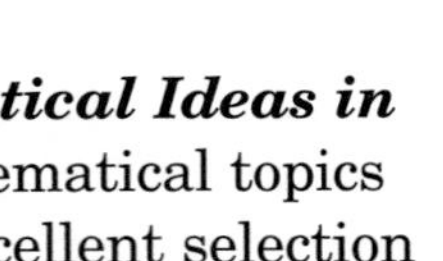

Literature Link ***Math Talk: Mathematical Ideas in Poems for Two Voices*** presents mathematical topics through poetic dialogues. "Variables" is an excellent selection to share with students.

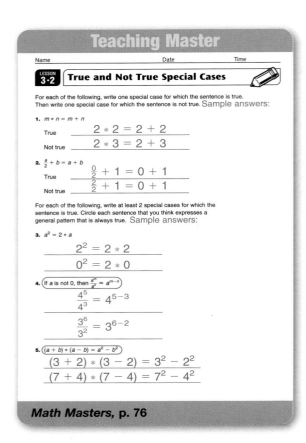

Teaching Master

Name Date Time

LESSON 3•2 **True and Not True Special Cases**

For each of the following, write one special case for which the sentence is true. Then write one special case for which the sentence is not true. Sample answers:

1. $m * n = m + n$

   True $2 * 2 = 2 + 2$

   Not true $2 * 3 = 2 + 3$

2. $\frac{a}{2} + b = a + b$

   True $\frac{0}{2} + 1 = 0 + 1$

   Not true $\frac{2}{2} + 1 = 0 + 1$

For each of the following, write at least 2 special cases for which the sentence is true. Circle each sentence that you think expresses a general pattern that is always true. Sample answers:

3. $a^2 = 2 * a$

   $2^2 = 2 * 2$

   $0^2 = 2 * 0$

4. (If a is not 0, then $\frac{a^m}{a^n} = a^{m-n}$)

   $\frac{4^5}{4^3} = 4^{5-3}$

   $\frac{3^6}{3^2} = 3^{6-2}$

5. ($(a + b) * (a - b) = a^2 - b^2$)

   $(3 + 2) * (3 - 2) = 3^2 - 2^2$

   $(7 + 4) * (7 - 4) = 7^2 - 4^2$

Math Masters, p. 76

Algebraic Expressions

Objective To write and evaluate algebraic expressions.

1 Teaching the Lesson

Key Activities

Students write and evaluate algebraic expressions for situations described in words.

Key Concepts and Skills

- Apply multiplication and division facts to evaluate algebraic expressions. [Operations and Computation Goal 2]
- Write and evaluate an algebraic expression for a situation. [Patterns, Functions, and Algebra Goal 1]
- Use a variable to represent unknown quantities. [Patterns, Functions, and Algebra Goal 1]

Key Vocabulary

algebraic expression • evaluate an expression

materials

- ☐ *Math Journal 1,* pp. 89 and 90
- ☐ *Student Reference Book,* p. 240
- ☐ Study Link 3•2
- ☐ calculator (optional)

2 Ongoing Learning & Practice

Students practice solving division problems with decimal quotients.

Students practice and maintain skills through Math Boxes and Study Link activities.

Ongoing Assessment: Recognizing Student Achievement Use journal page 91. [Operations and Computation Goal 2]

materials

- ☐ *Math Journal 1,* pp. 91 and 92
- ☐ Study Link Master (*Math Masters,* p. 77)

3 Differentiation Options

ENRICHMENT

Students extend the "What's My Rule?" routine by using algebraic expressions to describe geometric patterns.

EXTRA PRACTICE

Students practice writing and evaluating algebraic expressions.

ELL SUPPORT

Students add verbal and algebraic expressions to their Math Word Banks.

materials

- ☐ Teaching Masters (*Math Masters,* pp. 78 and 79)
- ☐ *Differentiation Handbook*

Technology

Assessment Management System
Math Boxes, Problem 4
See the **iTLG.**

Getting Started

Mental Math and Reflexes

Students complete the following on their slates:

●○○ $\frac{11}{12} * 1 = \frac{11}{12}$ $\qquad$ $\frac{1}{2} * \underline{\ 1\ } = \frac{1}{2}$

●●○ $25 * \frac{4}{4} = \underline{\ 25\ }$ $\qquad$ $\frac{1}{5} * 5 = \underline{\ 1\ }$

●●● $\frac{2}{3} * \underline{\ \frac{3}{2}\ } = 1$ $\qquad$ $\underline{\ \frac{3}{7}\ } * \frac{7}{3} = 1$

Math Message

John is 4 years older than Mike. How old is John?

Study Link 3·2 Follow-Up

Briefly go over the answers.

1 Teaching the Lesson

▶ Math Message Follow-Up

Use the Math Message to introduce algebraic expressions. Write key ideas and examples on the board to support English language learners. One answer to the question, "How old is John?" is simply, "I can't tell. Knowing John's age depends on knowing Mike's age, and I don't know Mike's age."

Another answer is to assign an age to Mike: "If Mike is 5 years old, then John is 9 years old. If Mike is 10 years old, then John is 14 years old," and so on.

One way to represent John's age is to write an algebraic expression in which a variable stands for Mike's age. For example, if m represents Mike's age in years, then $m + 4$ represents John's age.

An **algebraic expression** is a group of symbols that states a relationship between quantities and contains at least one variable. It may also contain numbers, operation symbols ($+$, $-$, $*$, $/$), and grouping symbols (such as parentheses). All algebraic expressions in this lesson contain a single variable.

Ask students to propose algebraic expressions to represent verbal expressions.

Examples:

▷ Chan weighs 15 pounds less than Henry. If h = Henry's weight, then $h - 15$ represents Chan's weight.

▷ Janine has twice as many stamps in her collection as Santiago. If s = the number of stamps in Santiago's collection, then $2 * s$, or $2s$, represents the number of stamps in Janine's collection.

▷ There were one-third as many tests in history class as in Spanish class. If t = the number of tests in Spanish class, then there were $\frac{1}{3} * t$, or $\frac{1}{3}t$, or $\frac{t}{3}$ tests in history class.

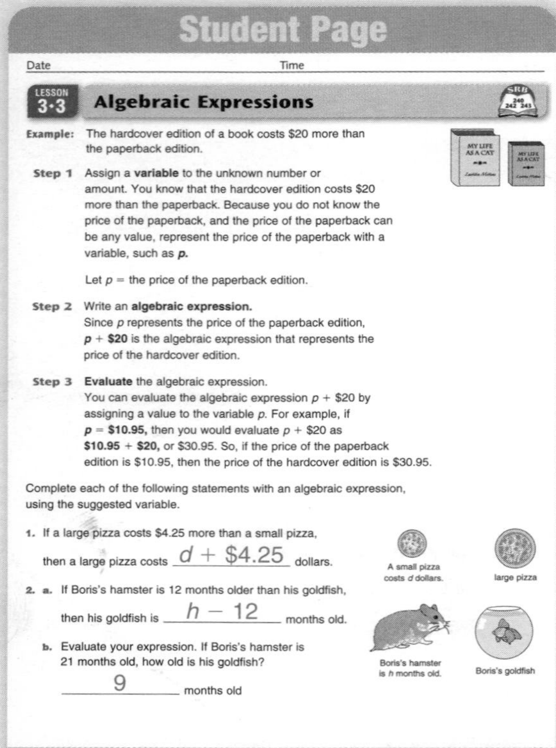

Student Page

Date $\qquad$ Time

LESSON 3·3 **Algebraic Expressions**

SRB 240 242 243

Example: The hardcover edition of a book costs $20 more than the paperback edition.

Step 1 Assign a **variable** to the unknown number or amount. You know that the hardcover edition costs $20 more than the paperback. Because you do not know the price of the paperback, and the price of the paperback can be any value, represent the price of the paperback with a variable, such as ***p***.

Let p = the price of the paperback edition.

Step 2 Write an **algebraic expression.**
Since p represents the price of the paperback edition, **p + $20** is the algebraic expression that represents the price of the hardcover edition.

Step 3 **Evaluate** the algebraic expression.
You can evaluate the algebraic expression p + $20 by assigning a value to the variable p. For example, if **p = $10.95,** then you would evaluate p + $20 as **$10.95 + $20,** or $30.95. So, if the price of the paperback edition is $10.95, then the price of the hardcover edition is $30.95.

Complete each of the following statements with an algebraic expression, using the suggested variable.

1. If a large pizza costs $4.25 more than a small pizza, then a large pizza costs <u>d + $4.25</u> dollars.

2. a. If Boris's hamster is 12 months older than his goldfish, then his goldfish is <u>h − 12</u> months old.

   b. Evaluate your expression. If Boris's hamster is 21 months old, how old is his goldfish?
   <u>9</u> months old

A small pizza costs *d* dollars.

large pizza

Boris's hamster is *h* months old.

Boris's goldfish

Math Journal 1, p. 89

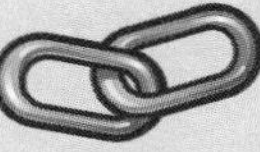

Links to the Future

Expect that some students may be confused by the omission of the multiplication symbol in algebraic expressions such as $2n$, $\frac{1}{3}y$, and $5(x + 5)$. For the most part, the multiplication symbol appears in this unit, but you should omit the symbol occasionally to expose students to the notation they will see and use in Units 6 and 9.

▶ Representing Situations with Algebraic Expressions

PARTNER ACTIVITY

(*Math Journal 1,* pp. 89 and 90)

Before students start working in their journals, consider having them read about algebraic expressions on page 240 of the *Student Reference Book.*

Discuss the example and steps on journal page 89. Have students work in pairs to complete the remaining statements on journal pages 89 and 90.

When discussing students' answers, point out that there are often several ways to write a given algebraic expression. See alternative answers for Problems 3a, 5a, 6, and 7a.

Some problems give a numeric value for the variable and ask students to evaluate the algebraic expression. Explain that **evaluating an expression** is similar to writing a special case for a general pattern—students will replace the variable with a specific value.

2 Ongoing Learning & Practice

▶ Practicing Division with Decimal Quotients

INDEPENDENT ACTIVITY

(*Math Journal 1,* p. 92)

Students estimate quotients and then divide numbers using partial-quotients division or another method of their choice. They use their estimates to determine decimal solutions.

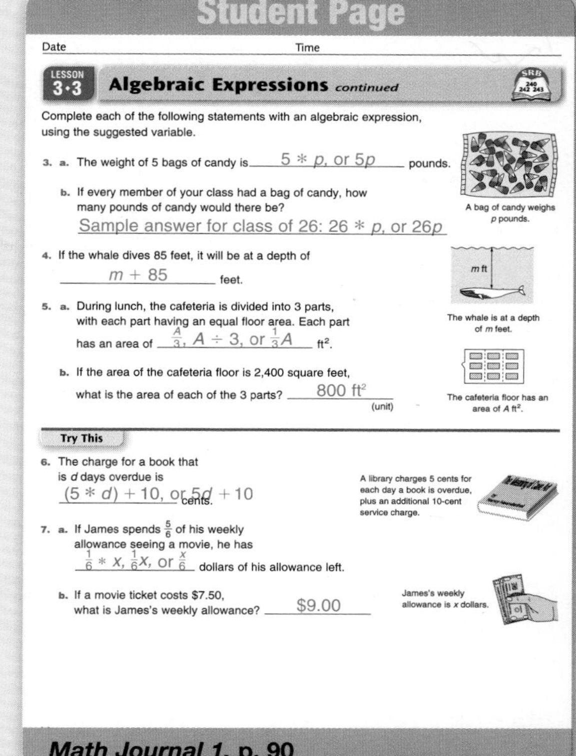

Student Page

Date Time

LESSON 3•3 **Algebraic Expressions** *continued*

Complete each of the following statements with an algebraic expression, using the suggested variable.

3. a. The weight of 5 bags of candy is $5 * p$, or $5p$ pounds.

b. If every member of your class had a bag of candy, how many pounds of candy would there be? Sample answer for class of 26: $26 * p$, or $26p$

A bag of candy weighs p pounds.

4. If the whale dives 85 feet, it will be at a depth of $m + 85$ feet.

The whale is at a depth of m feet.

5. a. During lunch, the cafeteria is divided into 3 parts, with each part having an equal floor area. Each part has an area of $\frac{A}{3}$, $A \div 3$, or $\frac{1}{3}A$ ft².

b. If the area of the cafeteria floor is 2,400 square feet, what is the area of each of the 3 parts? 800 ft² (unit)

The cafeteria floor has an area of A ft².

Try This

6. The charge for a book that is d days overdue is $(5 * d) + 10$, or $5d + 10$ cents.

A library charges 5 cents for each day a book is overdue, plus an additional 10-cent service charge.

7. a. If James spends $\frac{5}{6}$ of his weekly allowance seeing a movie, he has $\frac{1}{6} * x$, $\frac{1}{6}x$, or $\frac{x}{6}$ dollars of his allowance left.

b. If a movie ticket costs $7.50, what is James's weekly allowance? $9.00

James's weekly allowance is x dollars.

Math Journal 1, p. 90

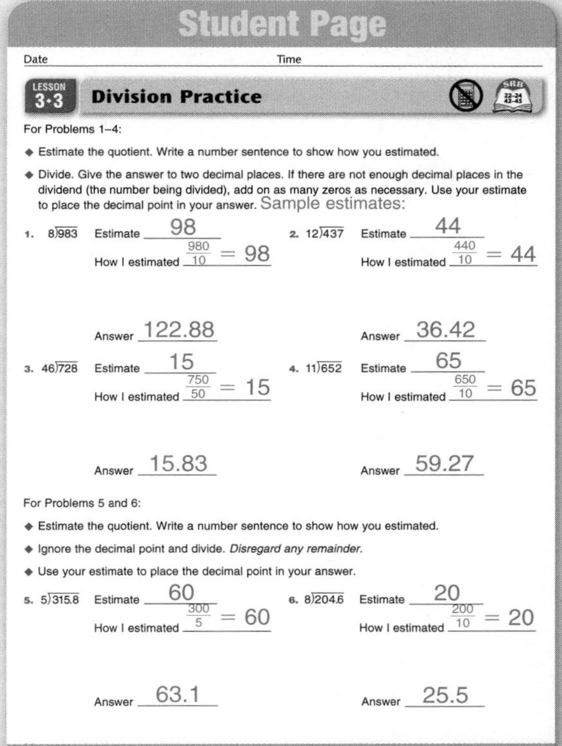

Student Page

Date Time

LESSON 3•3 **Division Practice**

For Problems 1–4:

◆ Estimate the quotient. Write a number sentence to show how you estimated.

◆ Divide. Give the answer to two decimal places. If there are not enough decimal places in the dividend (the number being divided), add on as many zeros as necessary. Use your estimate to place the decimal point in your answer. Sample estimates:

1. 8)983 Estimate 98 How I estimated $\frac{980}{10} = 98$ Answer 122.88

2. 12)437 Estimate 44 How I estimated $\frac{440}{10} = 44$ Answer 36.42

3. 46)728 Estimate 15 How I estimated $\frac{750}{50} = 15$ Answer 15.83

4. 11)652 Estimate 65 How I estimated $\frac{650}{10} = 65$ Answer 59.27

For Problems 5 and 6:

◆ Estimate the quotient. Write a number sentence to show how you estimated.

◆ Ignore the decimal point and divide. *Disregard any remainder.*

◆ Use your estimate to place the decimal point in your answer.

5. 5)315.8 Estimate 60 How I estimated $\frac{300}{5} = 60$ Answer 63.1

6. 8)204.6 Estimate 20 How I estimated $\frac{200}{10} = 20$ Answer 25.5

Math Journal 1, p. 92

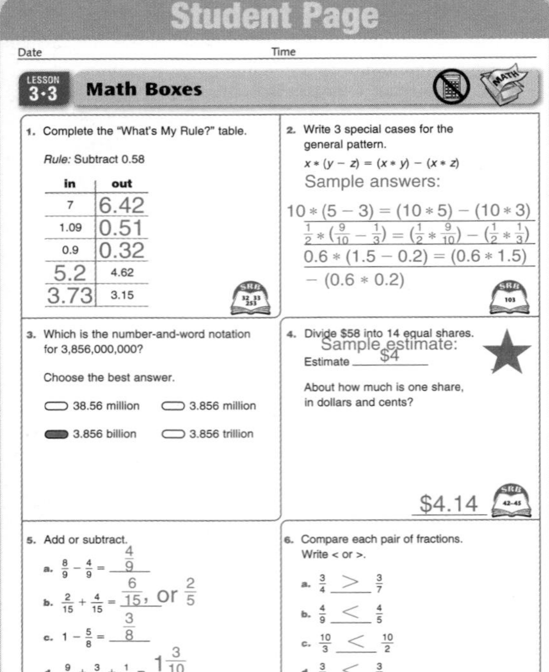

Student Page

Date Time

LESSON 3·3 **Math Boxes**

1. Complete the "What's My Rule?" table.

Rule: Subtract 0.58

in	out
7	6.42
1.09	0.51
0.9	0.32
5.2	4.62
3.73	3.15

2. Write 3 special cases for the general pattern.

$x * (y - z) = (x * y) - (x * z)$

Sample answers:

$10 * (5 - 3) = (10 * 5) - (10 * 3)$

$\frac{1}{2} * (\frac{9}{10} - \frac{1}{3}) = (\frac{1}{2} * \frac{9}{10}) - (\frac{1}{2} * \frac{1}{3})$

$0.6 * (1.5 - 0.2) = (0.6 * 1.5) - (0.6 * 0.2)$

3. Which is the number-and-word notation for 3,856,000,000?

Choose the best answer.

- 38.56 million
- 3.856 million
- 3.856 billion (filled)
- 3.856 trillion

4. Divide $58 into 14 equal shares.

Estimate Sample estimate: $4

About how much is one share, in dollars and cents? $4.14

5. Add or subtract.

a. $\frac{8}{9} - \frac{4}{9} = \frac{4}{9}$

b. $\frac{2}{15} + \frac{4}{15} = \frac{6}{15}$, or $\frac{2}{5}$

c. $1 - \frac{5}{8} = \frac{3}{8}$

d. $\frac{9}{10} + \frac{3}{10} + \frac{1}{10} = 1\frac{3}{10}$

6. Compare each pair of fractions. Write < or >.

a. $\frac{3}{4} > \frac{3}{7}$

b. $\frac{4}{9} < \frac{4}{5}$

c. $\frac{10}{3} < \frac{10}{2}$

d. $\frac{3}{5} < \frac{3}{3}$

Math Journal 1, p. 91

▶ Math Boxes 3·3

INDEPENDENT ACTIVITY

(*Math Journal 1*, p. 91)

Mixed Practice Math Boxes in this lesson are paired with Math Boxes in Lesson 3-1. The skills in Problems 5 and 6 preview Unit 4 content.

Ongoing Assessment: Recognizing Student Achievement

Math Boxes Problem 4 

Use **Math Boxes, Problem 4** to assess students' ability to find decimal solutions to whole-number division problems. Students are making adequate progress if they are able to make a reasonable estimate and choose a reliable algorithm to solve Problem 4. Some students may be able to interpret the remainder and adjust the quotient accordingly.

[Operations and Computation Goal 2]

▶ Study Link 3·3

INDEPENDENT ACTIVITY

(*Math Masters*, p. 77)

Home Connection Students practice writing algebraic expressions to represent situations described in words. Students evaluate algebraic expressions.

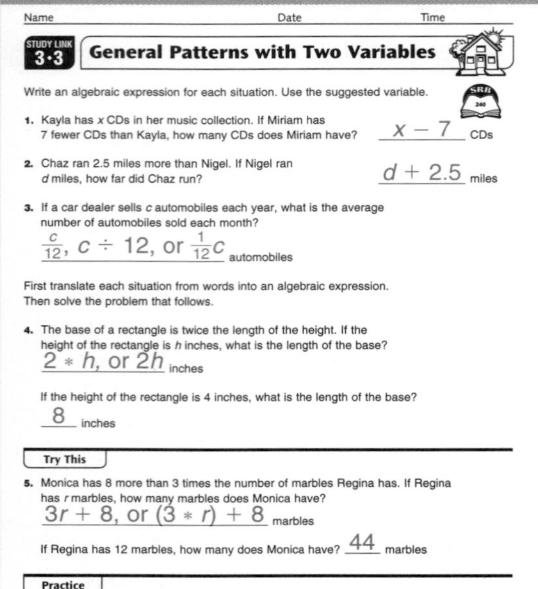

Study Link Master

Name Date Time

STUDY LINK 3·3 **General Patterns with Two Variables**

Write an algebraic expression for each situation. Use the suggested variable.

1. Kayla has *x* CDs in her music collection. If Miriam has 7 fewer CDs than Kayla, how many CDs does Miriam have? $x - 7$ CDs

2. Chaz ran 2.5 miles more than Nigel. If Nigel ran *d* miles, how far did Chaz run? $d + 2.5$ miles

3. If a car dealer sells *c* automobiles each year, what is the average number of automobiles sold each month? $\frac{c}{12}$, $c \div 12$, or $\frac{1}{12}c$ automobiles

First translate each situation from words into an algebraic expression. Then solve the problem that follows.

4. The base of a rectangle is twice the length of the height. If the height of the rectangle is *h* inches, what is the length of the base? $2 * h$, or $2h$ inches

If the height of the rectangle is 4 inches, what is the length of the base? 8 inches

Try This

5. Monica has 8 more than 3 times the number of marbles Regina has. If Regina has *r* marbles, how many marbles does Monica have? $3r + 8$, or $(3 * r) + 8$ marbles

If Regina has 12 marbles, how many does Monica have? 44 marbles

Practice

6. 2.75 m = 275 cm
7. 3.5 cm = 35 mm
8. 500 m = 0.5 km

Math Masters, p. 77

3 Differentiation Options

ENRICHMENT

▶ Continuing Geometric Patterns

INDEPENDENT ACTIVITY

15–30 Min

(*Math Masters*, p. 78)

Students extend the "What's My Rule?" routine to include algebraic expressions. They use a variable to represent the relationship between two sets of values.

EXTRA PRACTICE

▶ Writing and Evaluating Algebraic Expressions

INDEPENDENT ACTIVITY

15–30 Min

(*Math Masters*, p. 79)

Students practice writing and evaluating algebraic expressions that involve sums, differences, products, and quotients.

ELL SUPPORT

INDEPENDENT ACTIVITY

5–15 Min

▶ Building a Math Word Bank

(*Differentiation Handbook*)

To provide language support for algebra, have students use the Word Bank template in the *Differentiation Handbook.* Ask students to write verbal expressions and related algebraic expressions using contexts that are familiar to them. See the *Differentiation Handbook* for more information.

Teaching Master

Name　　　　Date　　　　Time

LESSON 3•3 **"What's My Rule?" for Geometric Patterns**

1. When you cut a circular pizza, each cut goes through the center.

Cuts	Pieces
1	2
2	4
3	6
4	8
6	12
8	16

1 cut　2 cuts　3 cuts

Fill in the missing numbers in the table. Then write an algebraic expression that describes how many pieces you have when you make *c* cuts.

$c * 2$ pieces

2. Fold a sheet of paper in half. Now fold it in half again. And again. And again, until you can't make another fold.

After each fold, count the number of rectangles into which the paper has been divided. Fill in the missing numbers in the table. Write an algebraic expression to name the number of rectangles you have after you have folded the paper *k* times.

2^k rectangles

Folds	Rectangles
0	1
1	2
2	4
3	8
4	16
5	32
6	64

3. Below are the first 4 designs in a pattern made with square blocks. Draw Design 5 in this pattern.

Design 1　Design 2　Design 3　Design 4　Design 5

4. How many square blocks will there be in

a. Design 10? 19 blocks

b. Design *n*? $n + (n - 1)$, or $2 * n - 1$, or $2(n - 1)$

Math Masters, p. 78

Teaching Master

Name　　　　Date　　　　Time

LESSON 3•3 **More Algebraic Expressions**

Write each word phrase as an algebraic expression.

1. *t* increased by 5 $t + 5$
2. the product of *w* and 3 $w * 3$, or $3w$
3. 7 less than *g* $g - 7$
4. *m* halved $\frac{m}{2}$, or $\frac{1}{2}m$
5. *k* shared equally by 8 people $k \div 8$, or $\frac{k}{8}$
6. 24 less than *x* tripled $(3 * x) - 24$, or $3x - 24$
7. *b* decreased by 12 $b - 12$

Evaluate each expression when $y = 9.05$.

8. $y + 4.98$ 14.03　9. $y - 8.9$ 0.15　10. $y * 10^2$ 905

Write an algebraic expression for each situation. Then solve the problem that follows.

11. Talia earns *d* dollars per week.

How much does Talia earn in 10 weeks? $10d$ dollars

If Talia earns $625.75 per week, how much does she earn in 10 weeks? $6,257.50 dollars

12. Michelle is 5 years younger than Ruby, who is *r* years old. Kyle is twice as old as Michelle.

a. Using Ruby's age, *r*, write an expression for:

Michelle's age $r - 5$ years old

Kyle's age $2(r - 5)$ years old

b. Suppose Ruby is 12 years old. Find:

Michelle's age 7 years old

Kyle's age 14 years old

Math Masters, p. 79

Formulas

Objectives To examine how formulas are derived; and to evaluate formulas.

1 Teaching the Lesson

Key Activities

Students examine geometric formulas to see how they can be derived. They use substitution to evaluate formulas and use formulas as rules to complete "What's My Rule?" tables.

Key Concepts and Skills

- Apply multiplication facts and strategies to find the area of a geometric shape. [Operations and Computation Goal 2]
- Use formulas to solve area and perimeter problems. [Measurement and Reference Frames Goal 2]
- Find the value of one variable in a formula when the values of other variables are given. [Patterns, Functions, and Algebra Goal 2]

Key Vocabulary

formula • evaluate (a formula) • substitute

Ongoing Assessment: Recognizing Student Achievement Use the Math Message. [Patterns, Functions, and Algebra Goal 1]

materials

- ☐ *Math Journal 1,* pp. 93–95
- ☐ *Student Reference Book,* pp. 245–247
- ☐ Study Link 3•3
- ☐ calculator

2 Ongoing Learning & Practice

Students practice and maintain skills through Math Boxes and Study Link activities.

materials

- ☐ *Math Journal 1,* p. 96
- ☐ Study Link Master (*Math Masters,* p. 80)

3 Differentiation Options

READINESS

Students make the connection between writing special cases and evaluating formulas.

ENRICHMENT

Students apply their understanding of general patterns to derive a formula for estimating the number of bricks needed to build a wall of any size.

EXTRA PRACTICE

Students complete teacher-generated Math Boxes.

materials

- ☐ Teaching Masters (*Math Masters,* pp. 81 and 82)
- ☐ Teaching Aid Master (*Math Masters,* p. 405)
- ☐ calculator
- ☐ ruler or tape measure

See **Advance Preparation**

Additional Information

Advance Preparation Locate a section of brick wall on your school grounds that students could use for the optional Enrichment activity in Part 3.

Technology

Assessment Management System
Math Message
See the **iTLG.**

Getting Started

Mental Math and Reflexes

Students make ballpark estimates for products and quotients. As time permits, have volunteers share strategies. *Suggestions:*

●○○ 1.3 * 15 13 = (1.3 * 10), or 15 = (1 * 15)
150 / 60 3 = (150 / 50), or 2 = (120 / 60)

●●○ 0.6 * 21.8 11 = (0.5 * 22), or 22 = (1 * 22)
27 / 12 2.7 = (27 / 10), or 3 = (36 / 12)

●●● 0.325 * 154 50 = ($\frac{1}{3}$ * 150), or 75 = (0.5 * 150)
11.3 ÷ 0.5 20 = (10 ÷ 0.5), or 22 = (11 ÷ 0.5)

Math Message 

Write an algebraic expression for the following. Use the suggested variable(s).

The perimeter of a square is 4 times the length of one side. If the length of one side is s, *what is the perimeter?*

Study Link 3·3 Follow-Up

Discuss students' answers. For Problems 1–3, have students evaluate the algebraic expression. For example, if Kayla has 23 CDs, how many CDs does Miriam have? 16 CDs

1 Teaching the Lesson

▶ Math Message Follow-Up

WHOLE-CLASS DISCUSSION

In previous lessons, students wrote and evaluated algebraic expressions for given situations. In this lesson, students apply these skills to use and evaluate formulas.

Ongoing Assessment: Recognizing Student Achievement

Math Message

Use the **Math Message** to assess students' ability to use algebraic notation to describe general patterns. Students are making adequate progress if they write an expression like 4 * *s*, 4*s*, or *s* + *s* + *s* + *s*. Some students may be able to evaluate the expression for several values of *s*—for example, *s* = 15 cm 60 cm and *s* = 25.5 ft. 102 ft

[Patterns, Functions, and Algebra Goal 1]

Ask students whether the general pattern $P = 4 * s$ (where the variable P stands for perimeter) can be used to find the perimeter of any square. Yes Explain that $P = 4 * s$ (or $P = 4s$) is a **formula.** Students can think of a formula as a general pattern or rule for finding the value of something. The variables in a formula are usually the first letters of the quantities they stand for, for example, P for perimeter. To **evaluate a formula** means to find the value of one variable in the formula when values of the other variables are given. For example, if $s = 15$ cm, then $P = 60$ cm.

NOTE The *Student Reference Book* summarizes many of the concepts in this lesson. If time permits, have students read pages 245 and 246.

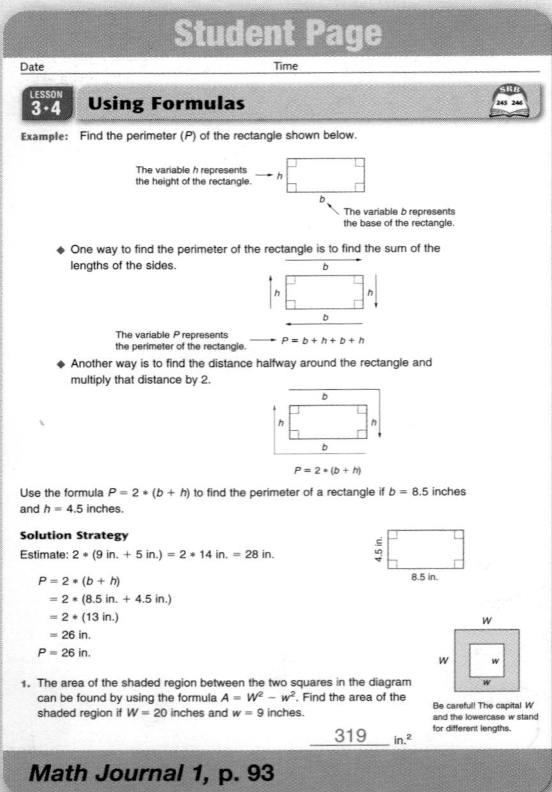

Math Journal 1, p. 93

NOTE The order of operations is discussed on page 247 of the *Student Reference Book.*

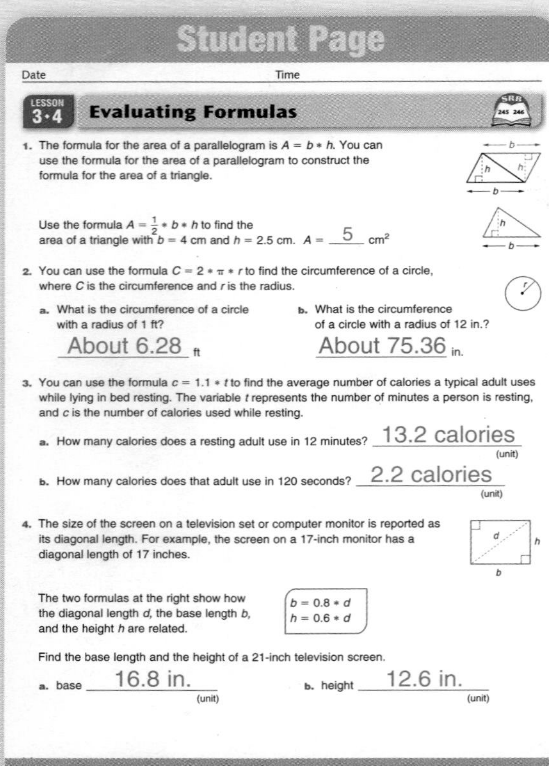

Math Journal 1, p. 94

▶ Using Formulas

WHOLE-CLASS ACTIVITY

(*Math Journal 1,* p. 93)

Work through the example and problems on journal page 93 as a class. Address the following points:

▷ For the perimeter of a rectangle, the sum of b and h is half the distance around the rectangle. Therefore, the perimeter is twice as much: $P = 2 * (b + h)$.

▷ In Problem 1, the larger square has an area of $W * W$, or W^2. The smaller square has an area of $w * w$, or w^2. To find the area of the shaded region, find the area of the larger square and subtract the area of the smaller square: $A = W^2 - w^2$.

Adjusting the Activity

ELL

Have students use a systematic approach to evaluate formulas.

Step 1 Write the formula on the first line, using a different color for each unique variable.
$P = 2 * (b + h)$.

Step 2 On the second line, **substitute** numeric values for all variables that are known or given.
Since $b = 8.5$ inches and $h = 4.5$ inches, then
$P = 2 * (8.5 \text{ in.} + 4.5 \text{ in.})$.

Step 3 Perform the necessary computation to find the value of the one remaining variable. Use the order of operations.
$P = 2 * (13 \text{ in.})$
$P = 26 \text{ in.}$

AUDITORY ◆ KINESTHETIC ◆ TACTILE ◆ VISUAL

▶ Evaluating Formulas

PARTNER ACTIVITY

(*Math Journal 1,* p. 94)

Have students complete journal page 94. When most students have completed the page, discuss their answers. Cover the following points:

▷ A rectangle is a parallelogram, so these figures have the same area formula ($A = b * h$). A parallelogram is formed by two identical triangles, so the area of a triangle is half the area of a parallelogram ($A = \frac{1}{2} b * h$).

▷ For Problem 1, ask students how to evaluate the formula if the values for b and h are in different units. For example, if $b = 4$ centimeters and $h = 1$ inch, both b and h must be expressed in the same unit, so area could be calculated in either square inches or square centimeters.

▷ Problems 2 and 3 offer more opportunities to discuss consistency of units. The radius is the same in Parts a and b in Problem 2, but the measurements are given in different units. The circumference formula does not specify particular units. The unit used for r will be the unit for C. Similarly, in Problem 3, the time in Part a is given in minutes; in Part b, it is given in seconds. Since t is the time in minutes, students must convert the time in Part b (120 seconds) to minutes (2 minutes).

▶ Using Formulas as Rules for "What's My Rule?" Tables

INDEPENDENT ACTIVITY

(Math Journal 1, p. 95)

Students complete "What's My Rule?" tables. Each rule is given as an algebraic expression or a formula. Students also write a general pattern in words to describe a rule.

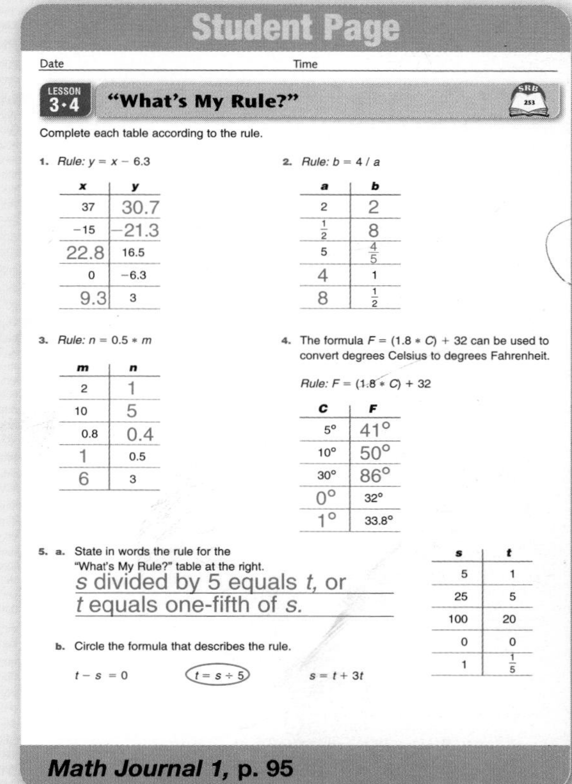

Student Page

Date Time

LESSON 3•4 **"What's My Rule?"**

Complete each table according to the rule.

1. *Rule:* $y = x - 6.3$

x	y
37	30.7
−15	−21.3
22.8	16.5
0	−6.3
9.3	3

2. *Rule:* $b = 4 / a$

a	b
2	2
$\frac{1}{2}$	8
5	$\frac{4}{5}$
4	1
8	$\frac{1}{2}$

3. *Rule:* $n = 0.5 * m$

m	n
2	1
10	5
0.8	0.4
1	0.5
6	3

4. The formula $F = (1.8 * C) + 32$ can be used to convert degrees Celsius to degrees Fahrenheit.

Rule: $F = (1.8 * C) + 32$

C	F
5°	41°
10°	50°
30°	86°
0°	32°
1°	33.8°

5. a. State in words the rule for the "What's My Rule?" table at the right.
s divided by 5 equals t, or t equals one-fifth of s.

s	t
5	1
25	5
100	20
0	0
1	$\frac{1}{5}$

b. Circle the formula that describes the rule.

$t - s = 0$ ($t = s \div 5$) $s = t + 3t$

Math Journal 1, p. 95

2 Ongoing Learning & Practice

▶ Math Boxes 3•4

INDEPENDENT ACTIVITY

(Math Journal 1, p. 96)

Mixed Practice Math Boxes in this lesson are paired with Math Boxes in Lesson 3-2. The skills in Problems 5 and 6 preview Unit 4 content.

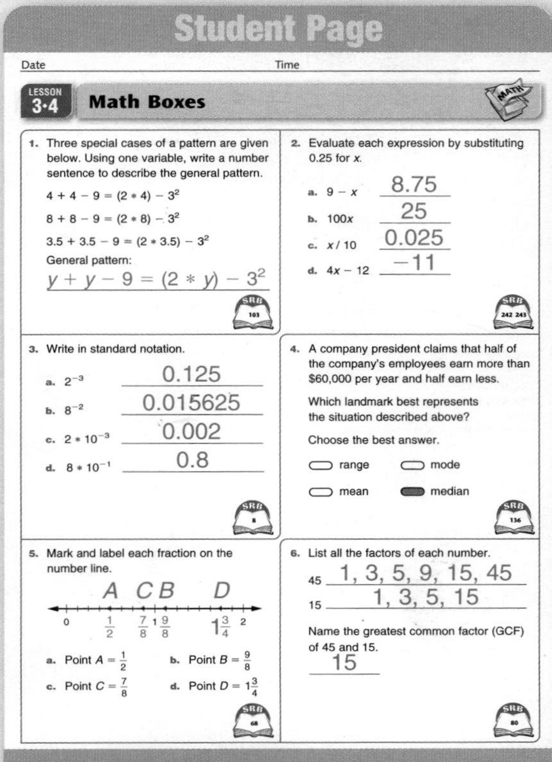

Student Page

Date Time

LESSON 3•4 **Math Boxes**

1. Three special cases of a pattern are given below. Using one variable, write a number sentence to describe the general pattern.
$4 + 4 - 9 = (2 * 4) - 3^2$
$8 + 8 - 9 = (2 * 8) - 3^2$
$3.5 + 3.5 - 9 = (2 * 3.5) - 3^2$
General pattern:
$y + y - 9 = (2 * y) - 3^2$

2. Evaluate each expression by substituting 0.25 for x.
a. $9 - x$ 8.75
b. $100x$ 25
c. $x / 10$ 0.025
d. $4x - 12$ −11

3. Write in standard notation.
a. 2^{-3} 0.125
b. 8^{-2} 0.015625
c. $2 * 10^{-3}$ 0.002
d. $8 * 10^{-1}$ 0.8

4. A company president claims that half of the company's employees earn more than $60,000 per year and half earn less.
Which landmark best represents the situation described above?
Choose the best answer.
○ range ○ mode
○ mean ● median

5. Mark and label each fraction on the number line.
A C B D (number line 0 to 2, marks at $\frac{1}{2}$, $\frac{7}{8}$, 1, $\frac{9}{8}$, $1\frac{3}{4}$, 2)
a. Point $A = \frac{1}{2}$ b. Point $B = \frac{9}{8}$
c. Point $C = \frac{7}{8}$ d. Point $D = 1\frac{3}{4}$

6. List all the factors of each number.
45 1, 3, 5, 9, 15, 45
15 1, 3, 5, 15
Name the greatest common factor (GCF) of 45 and 15.
15

Math Journal 1, p. 96

▶ Study Link 3•4

INDEPENDENT ACTIVITY

(Math Masters, p. 80)

Home Connection Students write rules for "What's My Rule?" tables and identify formulas that correspond to those rules.

Study Link Master

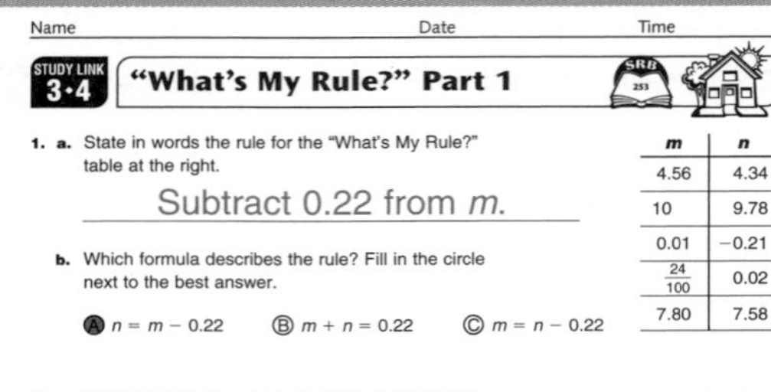

Name Date Time

STUDY LINK 3·4 **"What's My Rule?" Part 1**

1. a. State in words the rule for the "What's My Rule?" table at the right.

   Subtract 0.22 from *m*.

   b. Which formula describes the rule? Fill in the circle next to the best answer.

   (A) $n = m - 0.22$ (B) $m + n = 0.22$ (C) $m = n - 0.22$

m	*n*
4.56	4.34
10	9.78
0.01	−0.21
$\frac{24}{100}$	0.02
7.80	7.58

2. a. State in words the rule for the "What's My Rule?" table at the right.

   Multiply *r* by $\frac{1}{2}$, or divide *r* by 2.

   b. Which formula describes the rule? Fill in the circle next to the best answer.

   (A) $r - 0.25 = t$ (B) $t + 0.12 = r$ (C) $r * 0.5 = t$

r	*t*
20	10
15	7.5
1	0.5
1.5	0.75
3.4	1.7

3. Which formula describes the rule for the "What's My Rule?" table at the right? Fill in the circle next to the best answer.

   (A) $q - 13 = p$ (B) $q = (2 * p) - 2$ (C) $q = 2 * (p - 2)$

p	*q*
7	12
10	18
1	0
15	28
30	58

Practice

4. 180 in. = 15 feet
5. $3\frac{1}{2}$ minutes = 210 seconds
6. 5,280 ft = 1,760 yards
7. $5\frac{1}{2}$ miles = 29,040 feet

***Math Masters,* p. 80**

Teaching Master

Name Date Time

LESSON 3·4 **Special Cases for Formulas**

A formula is an example of a general pattern. When you substitute values for the variables in a formula, you are writing a special case for the formula.

Area Formulas

Example:

To find the area of a rectangle, use the formula $A = b * h$.

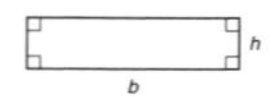

Write a special case for the formula using $b = 12$ cm and $h = 3$ cm.

First substitute only the value of *b*. $A =$ **12 cm** $* h$

Next substitute the value of *h*. $A = 12$ cm $*$ **3 cm**

Now find the value of *A* and write the special case.

36 cm² = 12 cm * 3 cm

1. To find the area of a triangle, use the formula $A = \frac{1}{2} * (b * h)$.

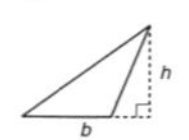

   Find the value of *A* and write a special case for the formula using $b = 4.5$ cm and $h = 4.8$ cm.

   10.8 cm² = $\frac{1}{2}$ * (4.5 cm * 4.8 cm)

2. To find the area of a square, use the formula $A = s^2$.

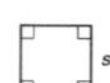

   Find the value of *A* and write a special case for the formula using $b = 2.5$ ft and $h = 2.5$ ft.

   6.25 ft² = 2.5^2 ft²

***Math Masters,* p. 81**

3 Differentiation Options

READINESS

INDEPENDENT ACTIVITY

▶ Special Cases for Formulas

5–15 Min

(*Math Masters,* p. 81)

To provide experience with special cases, have students evaluate area formulas by substituting one variable at a time. The focus of the activity is on the connection between writing special cases and evaluating formulas—not practicing computation—so encourage the use of calculators.

ENRICHMENT

INDEPENDENT ACTIVITY

▶ Deriving a Brick-Wall Formula

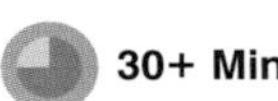

30+ Min

(*Math Masters,* p. 82)

Social Studies Link The activity should not take much time, but allow several days to complete it.

Students usually practice using formulas that are given to them and rarely derive a formula themselves. This problem provides students with the opportunity to explore the process of deriving a formula. Several approaches follow.

▷ *Rough square foot:* Do not measure any mortar joints. Just note that a stack of 5 bricks is about 8 inches long and $11\frac{1}{4}$ inches high. With mortar between them, 5 bricks would provide a surface of about 8 inches by 12 inches, or an area of about $\frac{2}{3}$ square foot. So there are about $2\frac{1}{2}$ bricks for $\frac{1}{3}$ square foot of wall area, or $7\frac{1}{2}$ bricks for each square foot. $N = 7.5 * l * h$

▷ *Careful square foot:* Measure the mortar joints. (Most mortar joints are about $\frac{1}{4}$ inch.) Suppose the mortar joint is $\frac{1}{4}$ inch wide. Each brick, with mortar, is about $2\frac{1}{4}$ inches + $\frac{1}{4}$ inch high and 8 inches + $\frac{1}{4}$ inch long. Thus, the surface area would be 2.5 inches ∗ 8.25 inches = 20.625 square inches. Since 1 square foot = 144 square inches, there are about 144 ÷ 20.625 = $6.9\overline{81}$, or about 7, bricks for each square foot of wall surface area.

$N = 7 * l * h$

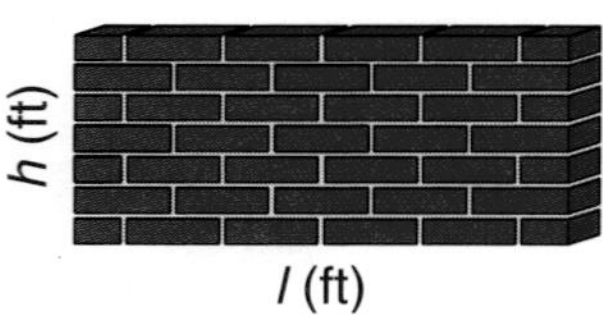

Surface area of the wall = $l * h$ square feet

▷ *Careful drawings:* Some students may make drawings, either actual size or to scale. Some students may take a rubbing of a section of an actual brick wall and use this rubbing to measure and estimate.

▷ *Data-based estimate:* Students may use their actual count of bricks in a section of wall to make an estimate. For example, if they count 144 bricks in a 5-foot-by-4-foot section of wall, students should conclude that there are about $\frac{144}{20}$, or 7.2, bricks for each square foot.
$N = 7.2 * l * h$

In practice, bricklayers are most likely to use the formula $N = 7 * l * h$.

EXTRA PRACTICE

INDEPENDENT ACTIVITY

5–15 Min

▶ Writing Custom-Made Math Boxes

(*Math Masters,* p. 405)

To provide extra practice, have students use *Math Masters,* page 405 to generate Math Boxes questions that focus on a particular concept or skill with which they need extra practice.

Teaching Aid Master

Name ____ Date ____ Time ____

Math Boxes

***Math Masters,* p. 405**

Teaching Master

Name ____ Date ____ Time ____

LESSON 3·4 **Formula for a Brick Wall**

Suppose you were going to build a brick wall. It would be useful to estimate the number of bricks you would need. You could do this if you had a formula for estimating the number of bricks for any size wall.

mortar joint width

mortar

Study the following information. Then follow the instructions for measuring an actual brick wall. Try to devise a formula for estimating the number of bricks needed to build any size wall.

- A brick wall is built by putting layers of bricks on top of one another. The space between the bricks is filled with a material called *mortar,* which hardens and holds the bricks in place. The mortar between the bricks forms the *mortar joint.*
- A standard building brick is $2\frac{1}{4}$ inches by 8 inches by $3\frac{3}{4}$ inches. The face that is $2\frac{1}{4}$ inches by 8 inches is the part of the brick that is visible in a wall.

$2\frac{1}{4}$ in. 8 in. $3\frac{3}{4}$ in.

Equivalents: 1 ft = 12 in. $1\ ft^2 = 12\ in. * 12\ in. = 144\ in.^2$

1. Find a brick wall in your school, home, or neighborhood. Using a ruler or tape measure, measure the length and height of the wall or part of the wall. Count the bricks in the area you measured. Answers vary.

   a. Length ____ (unit) b. Height ____ (unit) c. Number of bricks ____

   d. Measure the width of the mortar joint in several places. Decide on a typical value for this measurement.

   The mortar joints are each about ____ inch(es) wide.

h (ft) l (ft)

2. Devise a formula for calculating the number of bricks needed to build a wall. Let l stand for the length of the wall in feet. Let h stand for the height of the wall in feet. Let N stand for the estimated number of bricks needed to build the wall.

   a. The area of this wall (the side you see) is $l * h$ square feet.

   b. My formula for the estimated number of bricks: $N = (l * h) * 7.5$

3. Test your formula. Use the length and width you measured in Problem 1. Does the formula predict the number of bricks you counted?
   Answers vary.

***Math Masters,* p. 82**

Formulas, Tables, and Graphs: Part 1

Objective To represent rates with data tables, rules expressed in words, formulas, and line graphs.

1 Teaching the Lesson

Key Activities

Students review the concept of rate. They represent rates in different ways and discuss the advantages and disadvantages of these various representations.

Key Concepts and Skills

- Apply basic multiplication and division facts to find an equivalent rate. [Operations and Computation Goal 2]
- Construct and interpret a line graph. [Data and Chance Goals 1 and 2]
- Plot data values from a table. [Measurement and Reference Frames Goal 3]
- Use a formula to complete a table and analyze a function. [Patterns, Functions, and Algebra Goal 1]

Key Vocabulary

rate • speed • unit rate • line graph

Ongoing Assessment: Informing Instruction See page 203.

Ongoing Assessment: Recognizing Student Achievement Use journal page 100. [Patterns, Functions, and Algebra Goal 1]

materials

- ☐ *Math Journal 1,* pp. 98–101
- ☐ Study Link 3•4
- ☐ calculator
- ☐ straightedge

2 Ongoing Learning & Practice

Students practice whole-number division by playing the advanced version of *Division Top-It.*

Students practice and maintain skills through Math Boxes and Study Link activities.

materials

- ☐ *Math Journal 1,* p. 97
- ☐ *Student Reference Book,* p. 336
- ☐ Study Link Master (*Math Masters,* p. 83)
- ☐ Game Master (*Math Masters,* p. 478)
- ☐ 4 each of number cards 1–9 (from the Everything Math Deck, if available)

3 Differentiation Options

READINESS

Students play *Over and Up Squares* to review and practice plotting ordered pairs in Quadrant I.

EXTRA PRACTICE

Students solve rate problems.

ELL SUPPORT

Students add *rate* to their Math Word Banks.

materials

- ☐ Teaching Master (*Math Masters,* p. 84)
- ☐ Game Masters (*Math Masters,* pp. 465 and 466)
- ☐ *Differentiation Handbook*
- ☐ Per partnership:
- ☐ 2 different-color pencils
- ☐ 2 six-sided dice
- ☐ calculator

Additional Information

Advance Preparation Review the rules for *Over and Up Squares* (*Math Masters,* p. 465) for the optional Readiness activity in Part 3. Make a copy of the gameboard (*Math Masters,* p. 466) for each pair of students.

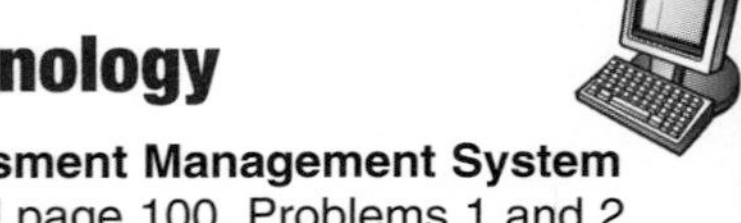

Technology

Assessment Management System
Journal page 100, Problems 1 and 2
See the **iTLG.**

Getting Started

Mental Math Reflexes

Students compare the mean and median for each data set using <, >, or =.

●○○ 10, 4, 11, 33, 7, 13, 6 mean (12) > median (10)

●●○ 4.2, 3.5, 3.1, 2.7, 4.0 mean (3.5) = median (3.5)

●●● 5.76, 2.31, 3.04, 7.49 mean (4.65) > median (4.4)

Math Message

Complete Problems 1 and 2 on journal page 98.

Study Link 3·4 Follow-Up

Briefly go over the answers.

1 Teaching the Lesson

▶ Math Message Follow-Up

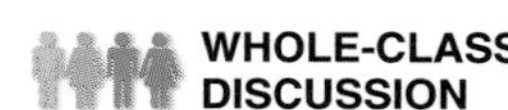

WHOLE-CLASS DISCUSSION

(*Math Journal 1,* p. 98)

Remind students that a **rate** is a comparison of two quantities with different units. **Speed** is a rate that compares a *distance* traveled to the *time* required to travel that distance.

Rates are often expressed by phrases that include the word *per,* as in 480 miles per hour, \$2 per pound, and 10 rainy days per month. Ask students to give other examples of rates. Be sure that the quantities in their suggested rates have different units: $\frac{\text{miles}}{\text{second}}$, $\frac{\text{price}}{\text{ounce}}$, and $\frac{\text{dollars}}{\text{hour}}$. Leave these rates posted on the board throughout the discussion.

Have students share strategies for the Math Message problem. For example, since there are 60 minutes in 1 hour, a rate of 12 miles per hour is the same as 12 miles per 60 minutes. At that rate, Lord Montague would travel $\frac{12\text{ mi}}{60\text{ min}}$, or $\frac{1\text{ mi}}{5\text{ min}}$, or 0.2 mile in 1 minute. 12 miles per hour and 1 mile per 5 minutes are equivalent rates.

Ongoing Assessment: Informing Instruction

Watch for students who do not recognize a fraction as a division problem. The rate $\frac{12\text{ mi}}{60\text{ min}}$ is another way of writing 12 mi ÷ 60 min. The quotient represents the number of miles per 1 minute, or the **unit rate.** List additional examples of unit rates on the board to support English language learners. Ask students to express rates such as $\frac{\$6.99}{3\text{ boxes}}$ and $\frac{250\text{ calories}}{10\text{ crackers}}$ as division problems. Then have them find the unit rates. \$2.33/box, 25 calories/cracker

Adjusting the Activity

ELL

Write the word *rate* on the board and discuss its everyday usage, for example, *How would you rate the movie?* Compare the everyday and mathematical meanings of *rate*.

AUDITORY ◆ KINESTHETIC ◆ TACTILE ◆ VISUAL

Student Page

Date Time

LESSON 3·5 **Representing Speed**

SRB 253 254

Math Message

Ever since the early years of the automobile, police have been trying to catch speeding motorists. At first, officers were equipped with bicycles and stopwatches. They hid behind trees or rocks and came out to pursue speeders. An Englishman, Lord Montague of Beaulieu, received a ticket for driving 12 miles per hour.

Source: Beyond Belief!

"Eagle Eye" Gus Schalkman holds the record for ticket writing. He got his 135th car on his post near the Queensboro bridge on Aug. 14, 1929.

UPI - Bettman

1. At a speed of 12 miles per hour, about how many miles could Lord Montague travel in 1 minute? 0.2 mi
2. Tell how you solved this problem. Sample answer: I divided 12 miles by the 60 minutes in 1 hour.

3. Complete the table. Use the formula $d = 0.2 * t$.

A car traveling at a speed of 12 miles per hour is traveling 0.2 mile per minute. You can use the following rule to calculate the distance traveled for any number of minutes.

Distance traveled (d) = 0.2 mile per minute * number of minutes (t)

You can also use the formula $d = 0.2 * t$ where d stands for the distance traveled in miles and t for the time traveled in minutes.

For example, in 1 minute, the car will travel 0.2 mile (0.2 * 1). In 2 minutes, it will travel 0.4 mile (0.2 * 2).

Time (min) t	Distance (mi) $0.2 * t$
1	0.2
2	0.4
3	0.6
4	0.8
5	1.0
6	1.2
7	1.4
8	1.6
9	1.8
10	2.0

Math Journal 1, p. 98

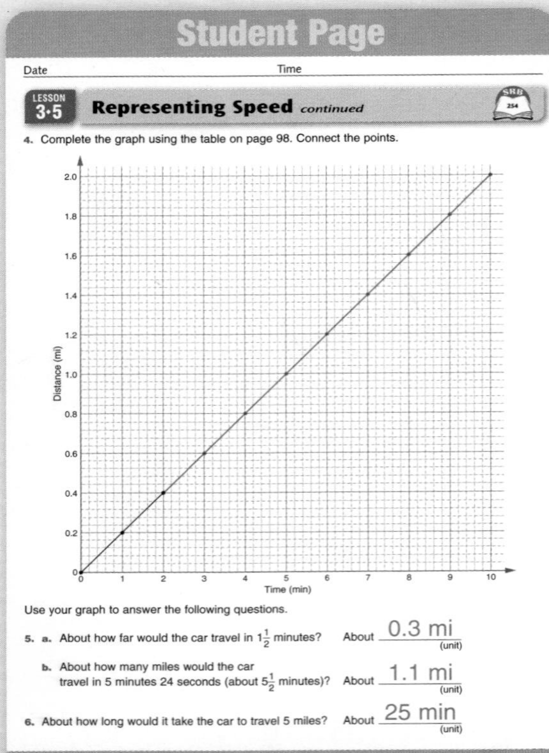

Student Page

Date Time

LESSON 3·5 **Representing Speed** *continued* SRB 254

4. Complete the graph using the table on page 98. Connect the points.

Use your graph to answer the following questions.

5. a. About how far would the car travel in $1\frac{1}{2}$ minutes? About 0.3 mi (unit)

b. About how many miles would the car travel in 5 minutes 24 seconds (about $5\frac{1}{2}$ minutes)? About 1.1 mi (unit)

6. About how long would it take the car to travel 5 miles? About 25 min (unit)

Math Journal 1, p. 99

Representing Speed with a Table and Line Graph

(*Math Journal 1,* pp. 98 and 99)

Pose problems based on the unit rate 0.2 mile per minute.

Example:

- At this rate, how far will a car travel in 11 minutes? 2.2 miles In $2\frac{1}{2}$ minutes? 0.5 mile

Students will see that to calculate the distance traveled, they must multiply the number of minutes of travel by the speed, 0.2 mile per minute. This idea can be expressed by the following rule:

$$\text{Distance traveled} = \text{0.2 mile per minute} * \text{Number of minutes}$$

or, in an abbreviated form, by the following formula:

$d = 0.2 * t,$ where d is the distance traveled and t is the time in minutes it takes to travel that distance.

Remind students that the letters d and t are variables—their values vary, depending on the particular situation.

In the problems on journal pages 98 and 99, students use the formula $d = 0.2 * t$ to build a table of values and display these values on a **line graph.** Students may complete the problems independently, in pairs, or as a whole class. Discuss students' responses. Students may recognize that the table on page 98 could be a "What's My Rule?" table. They should also notice that when the points marked on the graph are connected, they all lie on the same straight line.

Be sure that students understand how to obtain values from the graph. To determine how far the car will travel in $1\frac{1}{2}$ minutes (Problem 5a), locate 1.5 on the horizontal axis and mark the point on the graph directly above 1.5. Move left from there to the vertical axis, arriving at 0.3. (*See Figure 1.*) Thus, the car travels 0.3 mile in $1\frac{1}{2}$minutes. Repeat this routine with other examples until students understand the technique.

Then reverse the procedure. Pose several problems in which the distance is given and students use the graph to obtain the time; for example, it takes 1.5 minutes to travel 0.3 mile. (*See Figure 2.*)

Have students explain how they used the graph to solve Problem 6. On the graph, find the time it takes to travel 1 mile (5 minutes) and multiply this time by 5. It takes the car 25 minutes to travel 5 miles.

Figure 1

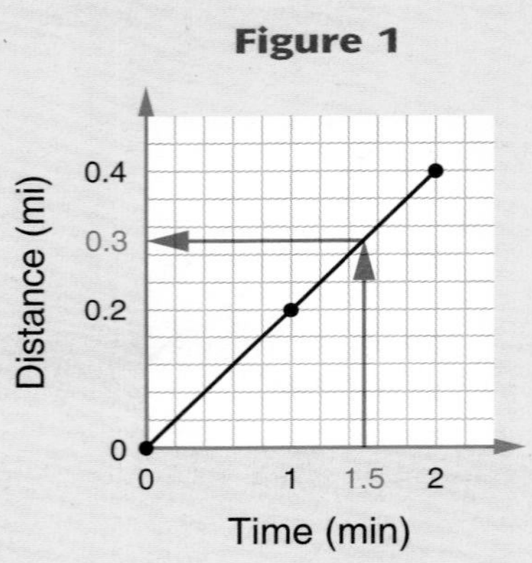

Figure 2

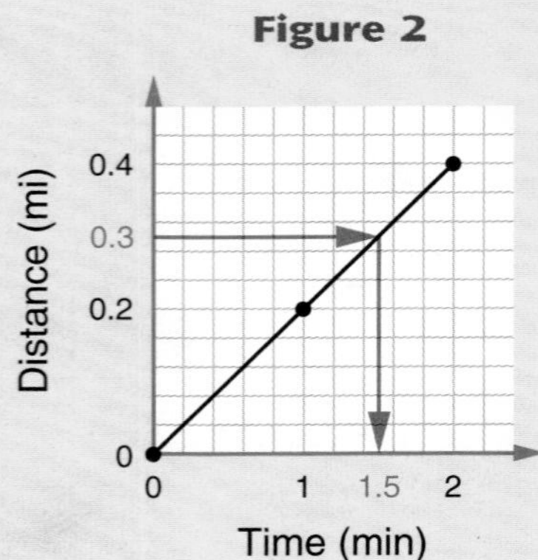

▶ Generating Tables and Making Line Graphs

(*Math Journal 1,* pp. 100 and 101)

Students work on rate problems. Circulate and assist.

Ongoing Assessment: Recognizing Student Achievement

Journal page 100 Problems 1 and 2 ★

Use **journal page 100, Problems 1 and 2** to assess students' abilities to complete a table from a formula and then graph the data. Students are making adequate progress if they can correctly complete the two tables and graphs in Problems 1 and 2. Some students may be able to use the line graphs to find values for Problems 1b and 2b.

[Patterns, Functions, and Algebra Goal 1]

▶ Comparing Ways to Represent Rates

(*Math Journal 1,* pp. 100 and 101)

Rules, formulas, tables, and graphs are different ways of representing the same relationships. Each way has advantages and disadvantages. An example of each representation appears on journal pages 100 and 101.

▷ A rule in words expresses a relationship, but in a lengthy way.

▷ A formula summarizes a relationship with symbols and can be used to find values easily, but you need to know what the variables represent. (Formulas and rules in words are similar. Formulas are more compact and easier to use.)

▷ A table is easy to understand and gives specific values, but you need to know the rule or formula to find additional values.

▷ Graphs give a quick picture of the relationship, but depending on the graph, are not always as useful as a formula for accurately finding specific values.

2 Ongoing Learning & Practice

▶ Playing *Division Top-It* (Advanced Version)

(*Student Reference Book,* p. 336; *Math Masters,* p. 478)

Divide the class into pairs and distribute four each of number cards 1–9 (from the Everything Math Deck, if available) to each partnership, as well as a game record sheet (*Math Masters,* p. 478). Encourage students to play a practice game.

Student Page

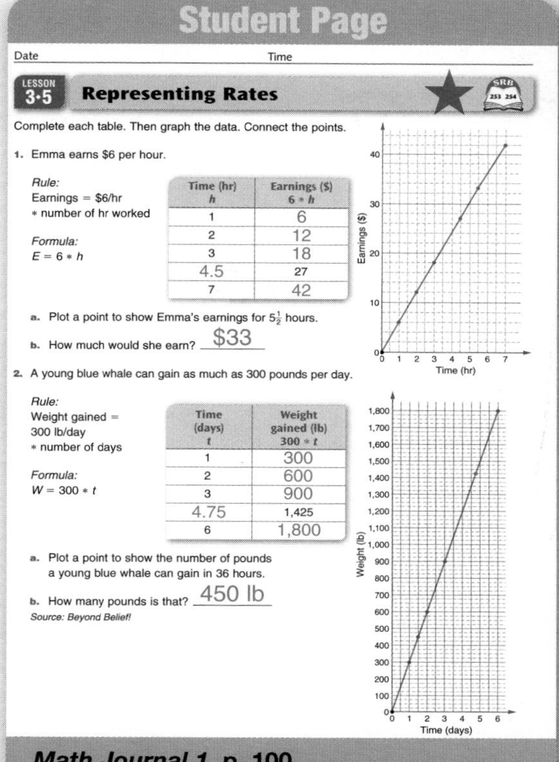

Date Time

LESSON 3·5 **Representing Rates**

Complete each table. Then graph the data. Connect the points.

1. Emma earns $6 per hour.

Rule: Earnings = $6/hr ∗ number of hr worked

Formula: $E = 6 * h$

Time (hr) h	Earnings ($) $6 * h$
1	6
2	12
3	18
4.5	27
7	42

a. Plot a point to show Emma's earnings for $5\frac{1}{2}$ hours.

b. How much would she earn? $33

2. A young blue whale can gain as much as 300 pounds per day.

Rule: Weight gained = 300 lb/day ∗ number of days

Formula: $W = 300 * t$

Time (days) t	Weight gained (lb) $300 * t$
1	300
2	600
3	900
4.75	1,425
6	1,800

a. Plot a point to show the number of pounds a young blue whale can gain in 36 hours.

b. How many pounds is that? 450 lb

Source: Beyond Belief!

Math Journal 1, **p. 100**

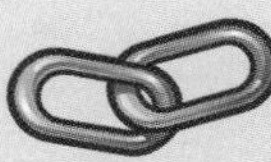

Links to the Future

Lesson 3-5 is one of several lessons dealing with various representations of simple functions, such as rates. Students will use tables, formulas, and graphs to analyze and compare rates in Lessons 3-6 and 3-10.

Student Page

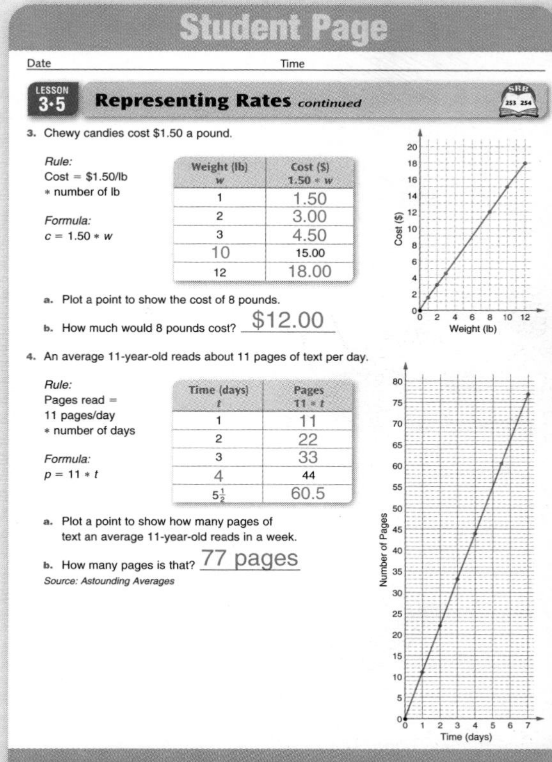

Date Time

LESSON 3·5 **Representing Rates** *continued*

3. Chewy candies cost $1.50 a pound.

Rule: Cost = $1.50/lb ∗ number of lb

Formula: $c = 1.50 * w$

Weight (lb) w	Cost ($) $1.50 * w$
1	1.50
2	3.00
3	4.50
10	15.00
12	18.00

a. Plot a point to show the cost of 8 pounds.

b. How much would 8 pounds cost? $12.00

4. An average 11-year-old reads about 11 pages of text per day.

Rule: Pages read = 11 pages/day ∗ number of days

Formula: $p = 11 * t$

Time (days) t	Pages $11 * t$
1	11
2	22
3	33
4	44
$5\frac{1}{2}$	60.5

a. Plot a point to show how many pages of text an average 11-year-old reads in a week.

b. How many pages is that? 77 pages

Source: Astounding Averages

Math Journal 1, **p. 101**

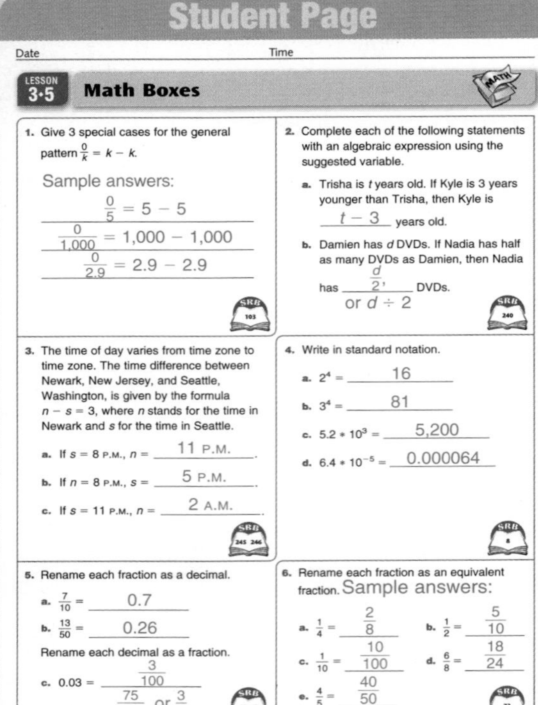

Student Page

Date Time

LESSON 3·5 **Math Boxes**

1. Give 3 special cases for the general pattern $\frac{0}{k} = k - k$.
   Sample answers:
   $\frac{0}{5} = 5 - 5$
   $\frac{0}{1,000} = 1,000 - 1,000$
   $\frac{0}{2.9} = 2.9 - 2.9$

2. Complete each of the following statements with an algebraic expression using the suggested variable.
   a. Trisha is *t* years old. If Kyle is 3 years younger than Trisha, then Kyle is $t - 3$ years old.
   b. Damien has *d* DVDs. If Nadia has half as many DVDs as Damien, then Nadia has $\frac{d}{2}$, or $d \div 2$ DVDs.

3. The time of day varies from time zone to time zone. The time difference between Newark, New Jersey, and Seattle, Washington, is given by the formula $n - s = 3$, where *n* stands for the time in Newark and *s* for the time in Seattle.
   a. If s = 8 P.M., n = 11 P.M.
   b. If n = 8 P.M., s = 5 P.M.
   c. If s = 11 P.M., n = 2 A.M.

4. Write in standard notation.
   a. $2^4 =$ 16
   b. $3^4 =$ 81
   c. $5.2 * 10^3 =$ 5,200
   d. $6.4 * 10^{-5} =$ 0.000064

5. Rename each fraction as a decimal.
   a. $\frac{7}{10} =$ 0.7
   b. $\frac{13}{50} =$ 0.26
   Rename each decimal as a fraction.
   c. $0.03 = \frac{3}{100}$
   d. $0.75 = \frac{75}{100}$, or $\frac{3}{4}$

6. Rename each fraction as an equivalent fraction. Sample answers:
   a. $\frac{1}{4} = \frac{2}{8}$
   b. $\frac{1}{2} = \frac{5}{10}$
   c. $\frac{1}{10} = \frac{10}{100}$
   d. $\frac{6}{8} = \frac{18}{24}$
   e. $\frac{4}{5} = \frac{40}{50}$

Math Journal 1, p. 97

▶ Math Boxes 3·5

INDEPENDENT ACTIVITY

(*Math Journal 1,* p. 97)

Mixed Practice Math Boxes in this lesson are paired with Math Boxes in Lesson 3-7. The skills in Problems 5 and 6 preview Unit 4 content.

Writing/Reasoning Have students write a response for the following: *For Problem 4, explain how you can use 2^4 to write 2^8 in standard notation.* Sample answer: I know that 2^8 equals $2 * 2 * 2 * 2 * 2 * 2 * 2 * 2$, or $2^4 * 2^4$. From my answer to Problem 4a, I know that $2^4 = 16$, so $2^8 = 16 * 16 = 256$.

▶ Study Link 3·5

INDEPENDENT ACTIVITY

(*Math Masters,* p. 83)

Home Connection Students solve "What's My Rule?" problems in which some rules are expressed as formulas.

Study Link Master

Name Date Time

STUDY LINK 3·5 **"What's My Rule?" Part 2**

1. *Rule:* Subtract the *in* number from $11\frac{1}{2}$.

in	out
n	$11\frac{1}{2} - n$
1	$10\frac{1}{2}$
2	$9\frac{1}{2}$
$8\frac{1}{2}$	3
$6\frac{1}{2}$	5
12	$-\frac{1}{2}$

2. *Formula:* $r = 4 * s$

in	out
s	*r*
12	48
6	24
0.3	1.2
$\frac{1}{4}$	1
$\frac{1}{2}$	2

3. *Rule:* Triple the *in* number and add −6.

in	out
x	$(3x) + (-6)$
1	−3
2	0
7	15
8	18
0	−6

4. For the table below, write the rule in words and as a formula.
   Rule: Divide the *in* number by 3.
   Formula: $d = b \div 3$

in	out
b	*d*
1.5	0.5
$6\frac{3}{4}$	$2\frac{1}{4}$
24	8
81	27
9.75	3.25

5. Make up your own.
   Rule: Answers vary.
   Formula:

in	out
x	*y*

Practice

6. $3 + -6 =$ −3
7. $-17 + 5 =$ −12
8. $8 + (-2) + (-9) =$ −3
9. $5 + 3 + (-5) + 7 =$ 10

Math Masters, p. 83

3 Differentiation Options

READINESS

PARTNER ACTIVITY

▶ Playing *Over and Up Squares*

15–30 Min

(*Math Masters,* pp. 465 and 466)

To provide experience with naming and plotting ordered pairs in Quadrant I of a coordinate grid, have students play *Over and Up Squares.* After reviewing the game directions on *Math Masters,* page 465, distribute two 6-sided dice, two different-color pencils, and a copy of the gameboard (*Math Masters,* p. 466) to each pair of students.

EXTRA PRACTICE

INDEPENDENT ACTIVITY

▶ Solving Rate Problems

5–15 Min

(*Math Masters*, p. 84)

Students use a "What's My Rule?" routine to solve rate problems.

ELL SUPPORT

INDEPENDENT ACTIVITY

▶ Building the Math Word Bank

5–15 Min

(*Differentiation Handbook*)

To provide language support for rate problems, have students use the Word Bank template in the *Differentiation Handbook.* Have students write *rate* and describe the term with words, pictures, and real-life examples. See the *Differentiation Handbook* for more information.

Teaching Master

Name Date Time

LESSON 3·5 **Rates**

Solve the rate problems. You can use tables similar to "What's My Rule?" tables to help you find the answers, if needed.

1. Renee reads 30 pages per hour.
   a. At this rate, how many pages can she read in 3 hours? 90 pages (unit)
   b. Would she be able to read a 220-page book in 7 hours? No

Hours	Pages
1	30
2	60
3	90

2. Wilson was paid $105 to cut 7 lawns. At this rate, how much was he paid per lawn? $15

Lawns	Dollars
7	105
6	90
5	75

3. Gabriel blinks 80 times in 5 minutes.
   a. At this rate, how many times does he blink in 2 minutes? 32 times (unit)
   b. In 4 minutes? 64 times (unit)

Minutes	Blinks
5	80
4	64
3	48

4. Michael can bake 9 batches of cookies in 3 hours.
   At this rate, how many batches can he bake in 2 hours? 6 batches (unit)

Hours	Batches
3	9
2	6
1	3

5. Elizabeth can run 5 miles in $\frac{2}{3}$ of an hour.
   At this rate, how long does it take her to run 1 mile?
   $\frac{2}{15}$ hour, or 8 minutes (unit)

Hours	Miles
$\frac{2}{3}$	5
$\frac{1}{3}$	$2\frac{1}{2}$
1	$7\frac{1}{2}$

Math Masters, p. 84

Game Master

Name Date Time

Over and Up Squares

Materials ☐ 1 *Over and Up Squares* gameboard and record sheet
☐ 1 color pencil per player (different color for each player)
☐ 2 six-sided dice

Players 2

Object of the game

To score the most points by connecting ordered pairs on a grid.

Directions

1. Player 1 rolls two dice and uses the numbers to make an ordered pair. Either number can be used to name the *x*-coordinate (over) of the ordered pair. The other number is used to name the *y*-coordinate (up) of the ordered pair. After deciding which ordered pair to use, the player uses a color pencil to plot the point.
2. Player 1 records the ordered pair and the score in the record sheet. A player earns 10 points each time an ordered pair is plotted correctly.
3. Player 2 rolls the dice and decides how to make an ordered pair. If both possible ordered pairs are already plotted, the player rolls the dice again. (Variation: If both possible ordered pairs are already plotted, the player can change one or both of the numbers to 0.)
4. Player 2 uses the other color pencil to plot the ordered pair and records his or her score on the record sheet.
5. Players continue to take turns rolling dice, plotting ordered pairs, and recording the results. If, on any player's turn, two plotted points are next to each other on the same side of one of the small grid squares, the player connects the points with a line segment. A player scores an additional 10 points for each line segment. Sometimes a player may draw more than one line segment in a single turn.
6. If a player draws a line segment that completes a grid square (so that all 4 sides of the square are drawn), that player shades in the square. A player earns an additional 50 points each time a square is completed.
7. The player with the most points after 10 rounds wins the game.

Math Masters, p. 465

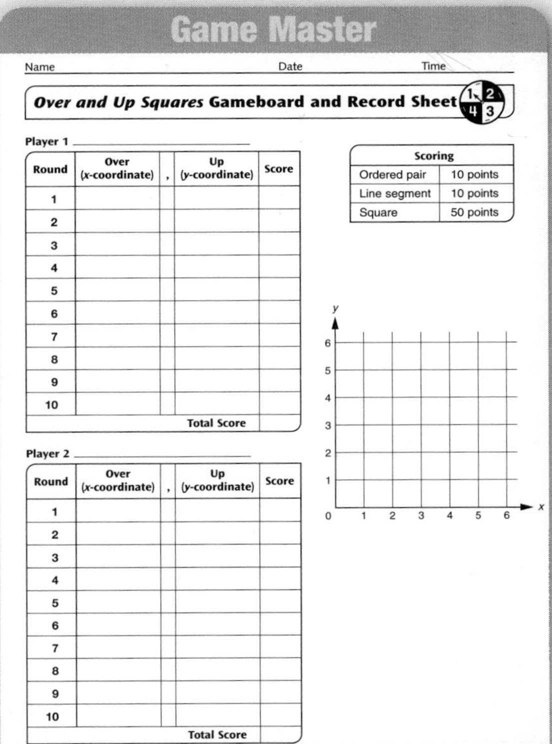

Game Master

Name Date Time

***Over and Up Squares* Gameboard and Record Sheet**

Player 1 ____

Round	Over (*x*-coordinate)	,	Up (*y*-coordinate)	Score
1				
2				
3				
4				
5				
6				
7				
8				
9				
10				
			Total Score	

Scoring	
Ordered pair	10 points
Line segment	10 points
Square	50 points

Player 2 ____

Round	Over (*x*-coordinate)	,	Up (*y*-coordinate)	Score
1				
2				
3				
4				
5				
6				
7				
8				
9				
10				
			Total Score	

Math Masters, p. 466

3•6 A Science Experiment

Objective **To use diagrams, formulas, and graphs for making predictions and drawing conclusions.**

1 Teaching the Lesson

Key Activities

Students use formulas to complete tables and draw graphs. They use the tables and graphs to answer questions.

Key Concepts and Skills

- Apply multiplication and division facts to calculate rates.
  [Operations and Computation Goal 2]
- Construct a graph and interpret its shape.
  [Data and Chance Goals 1 and 2]
- Plot data values from a table.
  [Measurement and Reference Frames Goal 3]
- Use a formula to complete a table and analyze a function.
  [Patterns, Functions, and Algebra Goal 1]

materials

- ☐ *Math Journal 1,* pp. 102, 104–106
- ☐ Study Link 3•5
- ☐ Transparency (*Math Masters,* p. 85; optional)
- ☐ calculator
- ☐ straightedge

2 Ongoing Learning & Practice

Students use unit rates to make comparisons.

Students practice and maintain skills through Math Boxes and Study Link activities.

Ongoing Assessment: Recognizing Student Achievement Use journal page 107.
[Patterns, Functions, and Algebra Goal 1]

materials

- ☐ *Math Journal 1,* pp. 103 and 107
- ☐ Study Link Masters (*Math Masters,* pp. 86 and 87)

3 Differentiation Options

READINESS

Students evaluate expressions.

ENRICHMENT

Students use multiple representations of a continuing pattern to solve problems and predict values.

materials

- ☐ Teaching Master (*Math Masters,* p. 88)

Additional Information

Background Information The formulas introduced in Part 1 ignore the effects of air resistance. For free falls through short distances, air resistance has a negligible effect on a compact, dense object, such as a baseball. But for free falls through long distances, air resistance may have a considerable effect, and the formulas may no longer apply.

Technology

Assessment Management System
Math Boxes, Problem 3
See the **iTLG.**

Getting Started

Mental Math and Reflexes

Students write an equivalent fraction for a given fraction.

Suggestions:

●○○ $\frac{1}{2} = \frac{x}{10}$ $x = 5$
$\frac{2}{5} = \frac{x}{10}$ $x = 4$

●●○ $\frac{1}{4} = \frac{x}{20}$ $x = 5$
$\frac{4}{25} = \frac{x}{50}$ $x = 8$

●●● $\frac{13}{25} = \frac{x}{100}$ $x = 52$
$\frac{39}{50} = \frac{x}{100}$ $x = 78$

Math Message

Complete the problems on journal page 102.

Study Link 3•5 Follow-Up

Discuss students' solution strategies. If time permits, have volunteers share their rules and formulas for Problem 5.

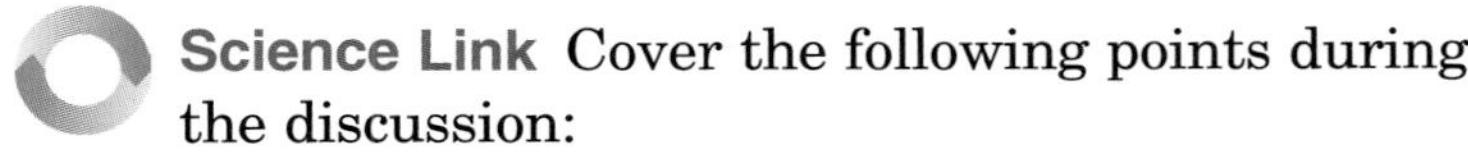

1 Teaching the Lesson

▶ Math Message Follow-Up

WHOLE-CLASS DISCUSSION

(*Math Journal 1,* p. 102)

Science Link Cover the following points during the discussion:

▷ The flash photographs of a falling ball track the ball at time intervals of $\frac{1}{20}$-second.

▷ The table shows the total distance the ball travels from the time it starts falling to the end of each $\frac{1}{20}$-second interval. Thus, during the first $\frac{3}{20}$ second, the ball falls a total distance of about 0.36 foot. During the first $\frac{1}{4}$ second ($\frac{5}{20}$ second), the ball falls about 1 foot. During the first $\frac{1}{2}$ second ($\frac{10}{20}$ second), the ball falls about 4 feet.

▷ During any $\frac{1}{20}$-second interval, the ball falls a greater distance than it fell during the previous $\frac{1}{20}$-second interval. This means that the ball travels increasingly faster the farther it falls.

To give a practical example of the idea that falling objects pick up speed, ask students what would happen if a baseball were dropped from a distance of 1 inch above their toes. Sample answer: They would feel the ball, but it wouldn't hurt. Then ask what would happen if the same ball were dropped from a distance of 20 feet above their toes. The impact could injure their toes because the ball would have picked up considerable speed.

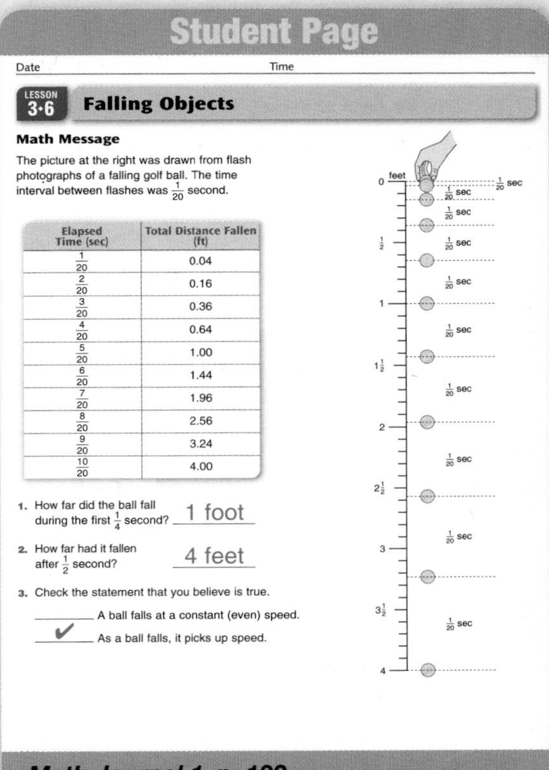

Student Page

Date Time

LESSON 3•6 **Falling Objects**

Math Message

The picture at the right was drawn from flash photographs of a falling golf ball. The time interval between flashes was $\frac{1}{20}$ second.

Elapsed Time (sec)	Total Distance Fallen (ft)
$\frac{1}{20}$	0.04
$\frac{2}{20}$	0.16
$\frac{3}{20}$	0.36
$\frac{4}{20}$	0.64
$\frac{5}{20}$	1.00
$\frac{6}{20}$	1.44
$\frac{7}{20}$	1.96
$\frac{8}{20}$	2.56
$\frac{9}{20}$	3.24
$\frac{10}{20}$	4.00

1. How far did the ball fall during the first $\frac{1}{4}$ second? 1 foot

2. How far had it fallen after $\frac{1}{2}$ second? 4 feet

3. Check the statement that you believe is true.

   ______ A ball falls at a constant (even) speed.

   ✔ As a ball falls, it picks up speed.

Math Journal 1, p. 102

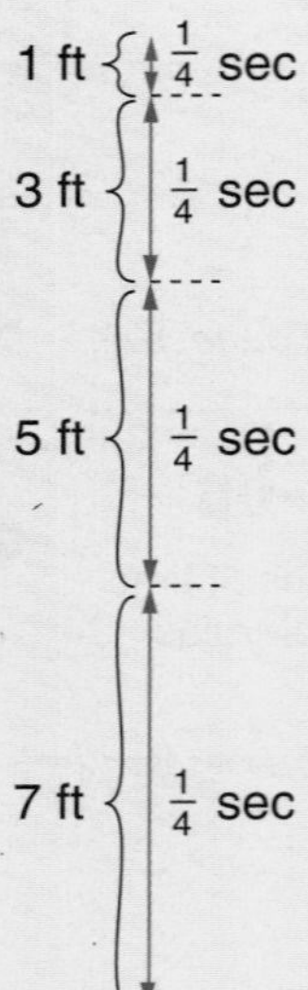

The distance the ball travels in 1 second

Adjusting the Activity

ELL

Extend the discussion.

- Have students calculate the distance the ball falls in each of the first five $\frac{1}{20}$-second intervals. About 0.04 ft, 0.12 ft, 0.20 ft, 0.28 ft, and 0.36 ft. For example, the ball falls 0.16 − 0.4, or 0.12, ft during the second $\frac{1}{20}$-second interval. Students may notice that the distance the ball falls increases by 0.08 foot in each successive $\frac{1}{20}$-second interval.
- Ask students to estimate the distance the ball will travel during the third $\frac{1}{4}$-second interval About 5 ft and during the fourth $\frac{1}{4}$-second interval. About 7 ft Ask: *What distance do you think the ball will fall in 1 second?* 1 ft + 3 ft + 5 ft + 7 ft = 16 ft Illustrate this distance with a diagram. (*See margin.*) These estimates can be checked by increasing the distance the ball falls by 0.08 foot in each successive $\frac{1}{20}$-second interval.

AUDITORY ◆ KINESTHETIC ◆ TACTILE ◆ VISUAL

Student Page

Date Time

LESSON 3·6 **What Happens When an Object Is Dropped?**

Galileo was an Italian physicist who lived from 1564 to 1642. His work led to the following rule for the distance traveled by a freely falling object.

Distance traveled in feet = 16 ∗ square of the elapsed time in seconds

Written as a formula, the rule is $d = 16 * t * t$; or $d = 16 * t^2$, where d is the distance traveled by the object in feet and t is the time in seconds that has elapsed since the object started falling. For example, after 1 second, an object will have traveled 16 feet (16 ∗ 1 ∗ 1); after 2 seconds, it will have traveled 64 feet (16 ∗ 2 ∗ 2).

Galileo's formula really applies only in a vacuum, where there is no air resistance to slow an object's fall. However, it is a good approximation for the fall of a dense object, such as a bowling ball, over a fairly short distance.

1. The following table shows the approximate distance traveled by a freely falling object at 1-second intervals. Use Galileo's formula to complete the table.

Elapsed time (sec) t	0	1	2	3	4	5	6	7	8	9
Distance (ft) $16 * t^2$	0	16	64	144	256	400	576	784	1,024	1,296

2. Graph the data from the table above onto the grid on page 105.

3. Use the graph to estimate the number of seconds it takes an object to fall 500 feet, ignoring air resistance. About 5.6 seconds

Try This

4. a. About how many seconds would it take an object to fall 1 mile, ignoring air resistance? Use your calculator. (*Hint:* 1 mile = 5,280 feet) About 18 seconds

   b. In the table at the right, evaluate Galileo's distance formula for at least two other values of t (time). Sample answers:

t	12 sec	20 sec
$16 * t^2$	2,304 ft	6,400 ft

***Math Journal 1*, p. 104**

▶ Introducing the Distance Formula for Free-Falling Objects

WHOLE-CLASS ACTIVITY

(*Math Journal 1,* pp. 104 and 105; *Math Masters,* p. 85)

During this whole-class activity, cover the following points.

▷ The formulas students will use are for objects falling in a vacuum. However, these formulas provide good approximations for compact, dense objects falling a short distance through air. To support English language learners, explain the meaning of *objects falling in a vacuum.*

▷ The formula $d = 16 * t * t$ (or $d = 16 * t^2$) can be used to calculate the distance an object falls in any given time interval. Discuss how the distances shown in the table in Problem 1 were obtained:

For 1 second, distance = 16 ∗ 1 ∗ 1 = 16 feet

For 2 seconds, distance = 16 ∗ 2 ∗ 2 = 64 feet

For 3 seconds, distance = 16 ∗ 3 ∗ 3 = 144 feet

▷ To provide practice using the formula, ask students to calculate about how far an object will fall in 10 seconds. 16 ∗ 10 ∗ 10 = 1,600 ft In $5\frac{1}{2}$ seconds. 16 ∗ 5.5 ∗ 5.5 = 484 ft Students can use the formula to complete the table on journal page 104.

▷ Have students graph the data from the table on the grid on journal page 105. You may do the same on a transparency of *Math Masters,* page 85. Students should not connect the plotted points at this time.

▷ If you are using the transparency, model how to draw a curve through the points on the graph.

▷ Discuss the shape of the graph. Ask: *How is the shape of this graph different from the shape of the graph you made on journal page 99?* The graph on journal page 99 is a straight line; it shows a constant increase in distance as time passes. The graph for falling objects is curved and shows a larger and larger increase in the distance covered per second the longer the object falls.

▶ Introducing Formulas for Speed of Free-Falling Objects

WHOLE-CLASS ACTIVITY

(*Math Journal 1,* p. 106)

By now it should be clear to most students that an object in free fall goes faster and faster the longer the object falls. In other words, the object's speed increases during each successive time interval. The formula $s = 32 * t$ can be used to calculate the speed of a falling object at any instant.

Introduce journal page 106, making sure that students understand the formula for the speed of a falling object before they start working.

Verify that students can answer questions both by reading the graph and by using the formula. Compare the graphs on journal pages 105 and 106. The graph on journal page 105 is a curve that shows a *greater and greater increase in distance per unit of time* as time goes by; that is, the distance the object falls during one second becomes greater and greater the longer the object travels. The graph on journal page 106 is a straight line that shows a *constant increase in speed per unit of time* as time goes by; that is, the increase in speed during each second is constant as time goes by.

Student Page

Date Time

LESSON 3•6 **When an Object Is Dropped** *continued*

Math Journal 1, p. 105

Student Page

Date Time

LESSON 3•6 **When an Object Is Dropped** *continued*

The speed of a freely falling object increases the longer it continues to fall. You can calculate the speed of a falling object at any given instant by using the rule

speed in feet per second = 32 ∗ elapsed time in seconds, or by

using the formula $s = 32 * t$.

In the formula, s is the speed of the object in feet per second and t is the elapsed time in seconds since the object started falling.

For example, after 1 second, the object is traveling at a speed of about 32 feet per second (32 ∗ 1); and after 2 seconds, at a speed of about 64 feet per second (32 ∗ 2).

5. Use this formula to complete the table. Then graph the data in the table.

Elapsed time (sec) t	Speed (ft per sec) $32 * t$
1	32
2	64
3	96
4	128
5	160
6	192

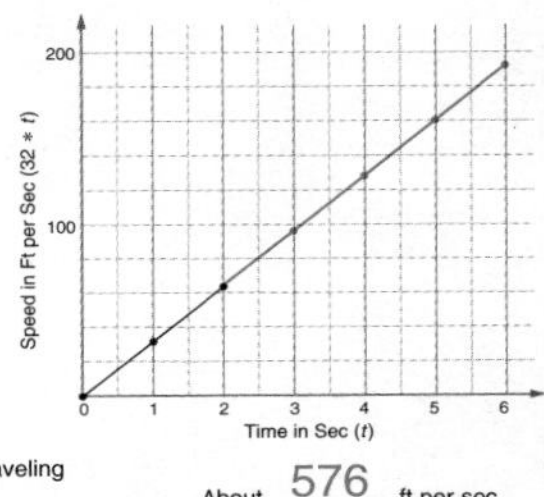

6. At about what speed would an object be traveling 18 seconds after it started falling? About 576 ft per sec

7. If a freely falling object is traveling at a speed of 290 feet per second, about how long has it been falling? About 9 sec

Math Journal 1, p. 106

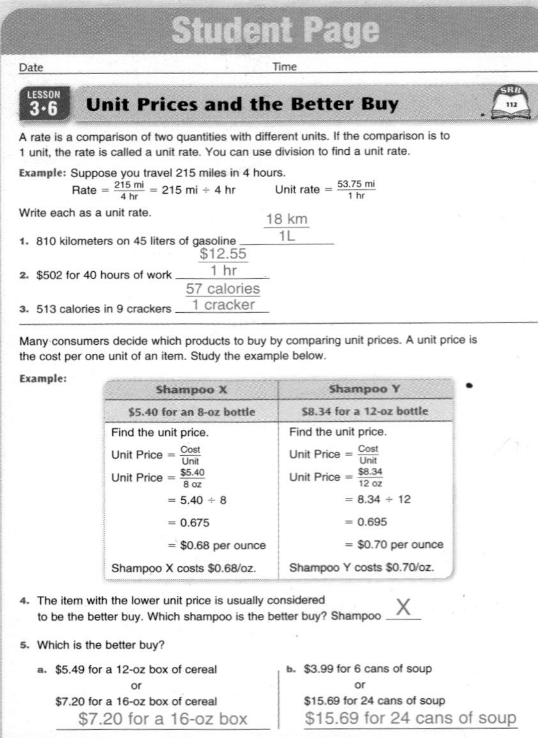
Student Page

Date ______ Time ______

LESSON 3•6 **Unit Prices and the Better Buy** SRB 112

A rate is a comparison of two quantities with different units. If the comparison is to 1 unit, the rate is called a unit rate. You can use division to find a unit rate.

Example: Suppose you travel 215 miles in 4 hours.
Rate = $\frac{215 \text{ mi}}{4 \text{ hr}}$ = 215 mi ÷ 4 hr   Unit rate = $\frac{53.75 \text{ mi}}{1 \text{ hr}}$

Write each as a unit rate.

1. 810 kilometers on 45 liters of gasoline $\frac{18 \text{ km}}{1 \text{L}}$
2. $502 for 40 hours of work $\frac{\$12.55}{1 \text{ hr}}$
3. 513 calories in 9 crackers $\frac{57 \text{ calories}}{1 \text{ cracker}}$

Many consumers decide which products to buy by comparing unit prices. A unit price is the cost per one unit of an item. Study the example below.

Example:

Shampoo X	Shampoo Y
$5.40 for an 8-oz bottle	$8.34 for a 12-oz bottle
Find the unit price.	Find the unit price.
Unit Price = $\frac{\text{Cost}}{\text{Unit}}$	Unit Price = $\frac{\text{Cost}}{\text{Unit}}$
Unit Price = $\frac{\$5.40}{8 \text{ oz}}$	Unit Price = $\frac{\$8.34}{12 \text{ oz}}$
= 5.40 ÷ 8	= 8.34 ÷ 12
= 0.675	= 0.695
= $0.68 per ounce	= $0.70 per ounce
Shampoo X costs $0.68/oz.	Shampoo Y costs $0.70/oz.

4. The item with the lower unit price is usually considered to be the better buy. Which shampoo is the better buy? Shampoo X

5. Which is the better buy?

a. $5.49 for a 12-oz box of cereal or $7.20 for a 16-oz box of cereal — $7.20 for a 16-oz box

b. $3.99 for 6 cans of soup or $15.69 for 24 cans of soup — $15.69 for 24 cans of soup

Math Journal 1, p. 103

2 Ongoing Learning & Practice

Using Unit Rates to Make Comparisons

PARTNER ACTIVITY

(*Math Journal 1*, p. 103)

Students calculate and compare unit prices to determine the better buy. They apply place-value concepts to round money amounts to the nearest cent.

Math Boxes 3•6

INDEPENDENT ACTIVITY

(*Math Journal 1*, p. 107)

Mixed Practice Math Boxes in this lesson are paired with Math Boxes in Lesson 3-9. The skills in Problems 4 and 5 preview Unit 4 content.

Writing/Reasoning Have students write a response to the following: *Describe the strategy you used to rename 0.3 as a percent in Problem 4.* Sample answer: Since $0.3 = \frac{3}{10}$ and percent means *per hundred,* I multiplied the numerator and denominator by 10. $\frac{3}{10} * \frac{10}{10} = \frac{30}{100} = 30\%$

Ongoing Assessment: Recognizing Student Achievement

Math Boxes Problem 3

Use **Math Boxes, Problem 3** to assess students' abilities to complete a table from a formula and graph the data. Students are making adequate progress if they can complete the table and accurately plot and connect the points on a grid.

[Patterns, Functions, and Algebra Goal 1]

Study Link 3•6

INDEPENDENT ACTIVITY

(*Math Masters,* pp. 86 and 87)

Home Connection Students use formulas to find the perimeters and areas of various squares, given the lengths of the sides. Students graph the data and use their graphs to draw conclusions and answer questions.

Student Page

Date ______ Time ______

LESSON 3•6 **Math Boxes**

1. The area *A* of a circle can be found by using the formula $A = \pi * r * r$. Use π = 3.14.
   a. Find the area if r = 3 centimeters. 28.26 cm²
   b. Find the area if d = 10 inches. 78.5 in.²
   SRB 218

2. Give 3 special cases for the general pattern below.
   $(b * h) + 4 = 4 + (h * b)$
   Sample answers:
   $(5 * 6) + 4 = 4 + (6 * 5)$
   $(0 * 9) + 4 = 4 + (9 * 0)$
   $(\frac{1}{2} * \frac{1}{4}) + 4 = 4 + (\frac{1}{4} * \frac{1}{2})$
   SRB 103

3. Complete the table. Then graph the data and connect the plotted points.
   Samantha earns $9 for each yard she mows.
   Rule: Earnings = $9 * number of yards mowed

Number of yards (y)	Earnings ($) (9 * y)
0	0
1	9
2	18
3	27
5	45
6	54

SRB 254

4. Rename each decimal as a percent.
   a. 0.49 = 49%
   b. 0.03 = 3%
   c. 0.3 = 30%
   d. 0.045 = 4.5%
   SRB 59 60

5. List the first 6 multiples of each number.
   18 — 18, 36, 54, 72, 90, 108
   72 — 72, 144, 216, 288, 360, 432
   Name the least common multiple (LCM) of 18 and 72. 72
   SRB 78

Math Journal 1, p. 107

3 Differentiation Options

READINESS

SMALL-GROUP ACTIVITY

▶ Evaluating Expressions

5–15 Min

To provide experience with formulas, have students evaluate expressions. Include expressions involving square numbers. Discuss students' mental math strategies.

Suggestions: Evaluate when

- ▷ $x = 3$ $32x$ 96 x^2 9 $16x^2$ 144
- ▷ $y = 10$ $15y + 5y$ 200 $y^3 - y^2$ 900 $(y + 5)^2$ 225
- ▷ $w = 5$ $2.5w$ 12.5 $w^1 + w^2 + w^3$ 155 $w^2 + 6w + 9$ 64

ENRICHMENT

INDEPENDENT ACTIVITY

▶ Using Graphs and Formulas to Make Predictions

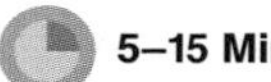

5–15 Min

(*Math Masters,* p. 88)

Students explore a real-world situation to identify a continuing pattern and represent this pattern using a table, graph, and formula. They use these representations to extend the pattern and predict values.

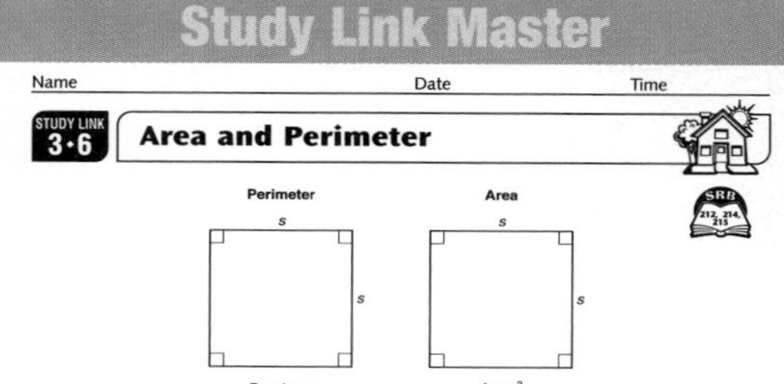

Study Link Master

Name Date Time

STUDY LINK 3•6 **Area and Perimeter**

Perimeter: $P = 4 * s$ Area: $A = s^2$

1. Use the perimeter and area formulas for squares to complete the table.

Length of side (in.)	Perimeter (in.)	Area (in.^{2})
1	4	1
2	8	4
3	12	9
4	16	16
5	20	25

Use the table above to complete the graphs on *Math Masters,* page 87.

Math Masters, p. 86

Teaching Master

Name Date Time

LESSON 3•6 **Using Graphs to Make Predictions**

Radio station WSUM has a contest in which listeners call in to win money. The contest begins with a \$200 jackpot. One caller each hour can win the jackpot by correctly answering a math question. If the caller does not give a correct answer, \$25 is added to the jackpot for the next hour.

1. Some available jackpot amounts for callers appear in the table below. Complete the table. Then graph the data values from the table.

Caller Number (n)	Jackpot Amount (\$)
1	200
2	225
3	250
4	275
5	300

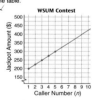

WSUM Contest (graph: Jackpot Amount (\$) 150–500 vs. Caller Number (n) 1–10)

2. Suppose you were the eighth caller to WSUM and you answered correctly. Extend your graph to predict the amount of money you would win. \$375

3. The formula $(n - 1) * \$25 + \$200$ can be used to express the jackpot amount for any caller. Use this formula to complete the table below. Refer to page 247 of the *Student Reference Book* if you need to review the order of operations.

Rule: $(n - 1) * \$25 + \$200$

in	out
n	$(n - 1) * \$25 + \$200$
2	\$225
4	\$275
15	\$550
26	\$825
101	\$2,700

Try This

Predict the number of the caller who would win a jackpot of \$1,000,000. Use the formula $(n - 1) * \$25 + \$200$ to check your prediction.

The 39,993rd caller would win \$1,000,000.

Math Masters, p. 88

Study Link Master

Name Date Time

STUDY LINK 3•6 **Area and Perimeter** *continued*

2. Graph the perimeter data from the table on page 86. Use the grid at the right.

Use the graph you made in Problem 2 to answer the following questions.

3. If the length of the side of a square is $2\frac{1}{2}$ inches, what is the perimeter of the square? 10 in. (unit)

4. If the length of the side of a square is $4\frac{1}{4}$ inches, what is the perimeter of the square? 17 in. (unit)

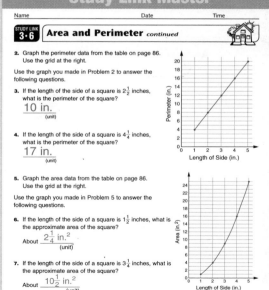

(graph: Perimeter (in.) 0–20 vs. Length of Side (in.) 0–5)

5. Graph the area data from the table on page 86. Use the grid at the right.

Use the graph you made in Problem 5 to answer the following questions.

6. If the length of the side of a square is $1\frac{1}{2}$ inches, what is the approximate area of the square? About $2\frac{1}{4}$ in.^{2} (unit)

7. If the length of the side of a square is $3\frac{1}{4}$ inches, what is the approximate area of the square? About $10\frac{1}{2}$ in.^{2} (unit)

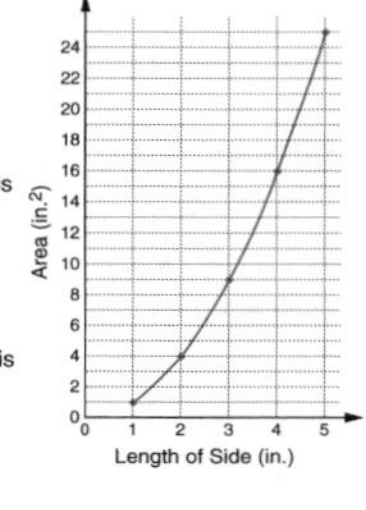

Practice

Find the missing dimension for each rectangle.

8. $b = 5.5$ cm; $h = 9.9$ cm; $A =$ 54.45 cm^2
9. $b = 36$ in.; $h =$ 4.2 in.; $A = 151.2$ in.^{2}

Math Masters, p. 87

3•7 Variables and Formulas in Spreadsheets: Part 1

Objectives To introduce spreadsheets; and to use variables, formulas, and operations in spreadsheets.

1 Teaching the Lesson

Key Activities

Students discuss the history and uses of spreadsheets. They write formulas using spreadsheet cell names as variables. Students play *Spreadsheet Scramble,* in which they practice mental addition of positive and negative numbers.

Key Concepts and Skills

- Mentally add signed numbers. [Operations and Computation Goal 1]
- Write formulas using spreadsheet cell names. [Patterns, Functions, and Algebra Goal 1]
- Evaluate algebraic expressions and formulas. [Patterns, Functions, and Algebra Goal 3]

Key Vocabulary

spreadsheet • update (revise) a spreadsheet • cell • column • row

Ongoing Assessment: Recognizing Student Achievement Use journal page 109. [Operations and Computation Goal 1]

materials

- ☐ *Math Journal 1,* pp. 108 and 109
- ☐ *Student Reference Book,* pp. 142 and 334
- ☐ Study Link 3•6
- ☐ Game Master (*Math Masters,* p. 474)
- ☐ Transparency (*Math Masters,* p. 475; optional)
- ☐ slates
- ☐ computer software (optional)
- ☐ large-screen display (optional)

See **Advance Preparation**

2 Ongoing Learning & Practice

Students practice fraction computation skills.

Students practice and maintain skills through Math Boxes and Study Link activities.

materials

- ☐ *Math Journal 1,* pp. 110 and 111
- ☐ Study Link Master (*Math Masters,* p. 89)

3 Differentiation Options

READINESS

Students play the basic *Credits/Debits Game* to review addition of signed numbers.

ENRICHMENT

Students use spreadsheet software to name cells and write formulas.

ELL SUPPORT

Students add *spreadsheet, cell,* and *formula* to their Math Word Banks.

materials

- ☐ Game Masters (*Math Masters,* pp. 429 and 430)
- ☐ *Differentiation Handbook*

Per partnership:

- ☐ 1 deck of number cards
- ☐ computer/spreadsheet software

Additional Information

Advance Preparation Consider using spreadsheet software to demonstrate the concepts in Parts 1 and 3 of this lesson.

Technology

Assessment Management System
Journal page 109
See the **iTLG.**

Getting Started

Mental Math and Reflexes

Students answer on their slates.

Suggestions:

●○○ 4 + (−6) −2
−12 + 16 4

●●○ −5 + (−31) −36
−7 + (−11) + 7 + 11 0

●●● 19 + (−5) + (−19) + 6 1
−42 + (−73) + 2 + 100 −13

Math Message

Read Student Reference Book, *page 142 with a partner. What is the balance due to the electric company? Which parts of the spreadsheet will change when Everyday Rentals pays the balance due on the water bill?*

Study Link 3·6 Follow-Up

Go over the answers. Students may notice the following patterns in the tables and graphs:

▷ As the length of the side increases by 1, the perimeter increases by 4. The perimeter graph is a straight line that shows a constant increase.

▷ As the length of the side increases by 1, the area increases by the pattern 3, 5, 7, 9, and so on. The area graph is a curve that shows a greater and greater increase.

1 Teaching the Lesson

▶ Math Message Follow-Up

WHOLE-CLASS DISCUSSION

(*Student Reference Book,* p. 142)

Go over the answers to the Math Message questions as you discuss page 142 in the *Student Reference Book*. Cover the following points. Support English language learners by writing and discussing unfamiliar words.

▷ **Spreadsheets** got their name from ledger sheets used to keep financial records, similar to the one shown on page 142 in the *Student Reference Book*. These sheets were often large pages, folded or taped, that were spread out for examination.

▷ When one or more numbers on a spreadsheet are changed, related numbers on the sheet may need to be recalculated and changed. This is called **updating** or **revising the spreadsheet.** For example, the balance due on the water bill is $13.12. When this balance is paid, the amount in the Amount Paid column will be changed to reflect this payment. As a result, the balance due will be $0.00. The totals in both the Amount Paid and the Balance Due columns will also change as a result of the payment.

▷ Computer (electronic) spreadsheets have been available for more than 30 years. Updating a computer spreadsheet is simple and does not require erasing, recalculating, or rewriting numbers by hand. When changes are entered, the computer automatically recalculates all related numbers and inserts the new, correct values.

NOTE Students are not expected to understand accounting or how the calculations were arrived at in the sample spreadsheet on *Student Reference Book,* page 142. The example is intended to give them a sense of spreadsheets and how changing one entry may affect related numbers on the spreadsheet.

Student Page

Data and Probability

History and Uses of Spreadsheets

Everyday Rentals–Debit Statement for May, 1964

Company	Type	Invoice #	Invoice Amount	Amount Paid	Balance Due
Electric	Utility	2704-3364	342.12	100.00	242.12
Gas	Utility	44506-309	129.43	50.00	79.43
Phone	Utility	989-2209	78.56	78.56	0.00
Water	Utility	554-2-1018	13.12		13.12
NW Bank	Mortgage	May 1964	1,264.00	1,264.00	0.00
Waste Removal	Garbage	387-219	23.00		23.00
NW Lumber	Supplies	e-318	239.47	50.00	189.47
Total			2,089.70	1,542.56	547.14

Above is a copy of a financial record for Everyday Rentals Corporation for May, 1964. A financial record often had more columns of figures than would fit on one sheet of paper, so accountants taped several sheets together. They folded the sheets for storage and spread them out to read or make entries. Such sheets came to be called **spreadsheets.**

Note that the "Balance Due" **column** and the "Total" **row** are calculated from other numbers in the spreadsheet. Before they had computers, accountants wrote spreadsheets by hand. If an accountant changed a number in one row or column, several other numbers would have to be erased, recalculated, and reentered.

For example, when Everyday Rentals Corporation pays the $23 owed to Waste Removal, the accountant must enter that amount in the "Amount Paid" column. That means the total of the "Amount Paid" column must be changed as well. That's not all–making a payment changes the amount in the "Balance Due" column and the total of the "Balance Due" column. One entry requires three other changes to **update** (revise) the spreadsheet.

When personal computers were developed, spreadsheet programs were among the first applications. Spreadsheet programs save time by making changes automatically. Suppose the record at the top of this page is on a computer spreadsheet. When the accountant enters the payment of $23, the computer automatically recalculates all of the numbers that are affected by that payment.

Did You Know?

In mathematics and science, computer spreadsheets are used to store large amounts of data and to perform complicated calculations. People use spreadsheets at home to keep track of budgets, payments, and taxes.

Student Reference Book, p. 142

▶ Examining Variables and Formulas in Spreadsheets

PARTNER ACTIVITY

(*Math Journal 1,* p. 108)

Read the top half of journal page 108 as a class. Make sure students understand the following points:

- ▷ **Cells** of the spreadsheet are named by a **column** letter and a **row** number; for example, A1, A2, C2, and so on.
- ▷ A cell may contain text or a number, or it may be empty.
- ▷ Cell names may be used to write formulas.
- ▷ Updating (revising) the entry in one cell may require making changes in other cells. To support English language learners, discuss the scientific meaning of *cell* as well as its meaning in this context.

Have students work in pairs to complete the rest of the page. Discuss answers before moving on to the spreadsheet game. Point out that the cell of a spreadsheet contains both a hidden formula and the result of that formula. Only the result is visible.

Student Page

Date Time

LESSON 3·7 **Variables and Formulas in Spreadsheets** SRB 142-144

A typical computer spreadsheet has **columns,** identified by letters, and **rows,** identified by numbers. Columns and rows intersect to form boxes called **cells.**

Each cell in a spreadsheet is named by the letter of the column and the number of the row it is in. For example, cell A1 is in column A, row 1. There is no space in the name between the letter and the number. Cells can contain text, numbers, or nothing at all.

Example: The spreadsheet at the right shows the number of hits made and runs scored by players on a softball team. The statistics are for the first 5 games played. As more games are played, the numbers will be updated.

	A	B	C
1	Player	Hits	Runs
2	Carl	9	4
3	Amala	5	2
4	Doug	1	0
5	Noreen	11	5
6	David	3	3
7	Annina	2	1
8	Ted	7	3
9	Raoul	12	7
10	Cheryl	3	0
11			
12	**Total**	**53**	**25**

Carl made 9 hits and scored 4 runs. His name is in cell A2, the number 9 is in cell B2, and the number 4 is in cell C2.

Think of a cell name as a variable. As the team plays more games, Carl will probably make more hits and score more runs, and the numbers in cells B2 and C2 will change.

The total number of hits, 53, in cell B12 is the following sum:

$53 = 9 + 5 + 1 + 11 + 3 + 2 + 7 + 12 + 3$

This is a special case of a formula that can be written using the cell names.

$B12 = B2 + B3 + B4 + B5 + B6 + B7 + B8 + B9 + B10$

1. a. What is in cell A5? Noreen b. What is in cell B3? 5
2. a. Which cell contains the word Runs? C1
   b. Which cell contains the number 12? B9
   c. Which cell contains the total number of runs scored by all of the players? C12
3. Write a formula for calculating C12 that uses the cell names.
   $C12 = C2 + C3 + C4 + C5 + C6 + C7 + C8 + C9 + C10$
4. Suppose Raoul scored only 4 runs instead of 7. Which cell entries would change, and what would they change to?
   C9 would change to 4 and C12 would change to 22.

Math Journal 1, p. 108

Adjusting the Activity

Use computer software to generate the spreadsheet and illustrate the concepts on journal page 108. Demonstrate how revising the entry in one cell changes the total. Display any formulas you used.

AUDITORY ◆ KINESTHETIC ◆ TACTILE ◆ VISUAL

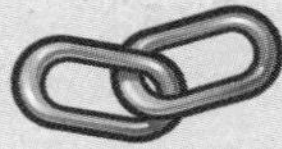

Links to the Future

In Unit 9, students learn how labels, numbers, and formulas are entered and displayed in a spreadsheet.

▶ Playing *Spreadsheet Scramble*

PARTNER ACTIVITY

(*Math Journal 1,* p. 109; *Student Reference Book,* p. 334; *Math Masters,* pp. 474 and 475)

Read the rules together and play several games against the class. You might want to use a transparency of *Math Masters,* page 475, which is an individual game mat. Expect students to quickly master the rules and scoring procedures. Have students play several games on their own.

Student Page

Date Time

LESSON 3·7 ***Spreadsheet Scramble* Game Mats** SRB 334

	A	B	C	D	E	F
1						Total
2						
3						
4						
5	Total					

	A	B	C	D	E	F
1						Total
2						
3						
4						
5	Total					

	A	B	C	D	E	F
1						Total
2						
3						
4						
5	Total					

	A	B	C	D	E	F
1						Total
2						
3						
4						
5	Total					

	A	B	C	D	E	F
1						Total
2						
3						
4						
5	Total					

	A	B	C	D	E	F
1						Total
2						
3						
4						
5	Total					

	A	B	C	D	E	F
1						Total
2						
3						
4						
5	Total					

	A	B	C	D	E	F
1						Total
2						
3						
4						
5	Total					

Math Journal 1, p. 109

Adjusting the Activity

Suggest and demonstrate one or both of the following strategies for computing sums of signed numbers (credits and debits in *Spreadsheet Scramble*):

- ▷ Think of the operation as a slide on a thermometer scale. For example, to solve the problem $6 + (-4)$, begin at 6 degrees above 0; add -4 degrees by sliding down the scale 4 degrees; you end at 2 degrees.
- ▷ Interpret the operation as a net balance procedure, such that credits (+) and debits (−) are aggregated. For example, to solve the problem $5 + (-2) + (-4) + 3$, think \$8 in credits and \$6 in debits, for a net balance of \$2 credits, or +2.

AUDITORY ◆ KINESTHETIC ◆ TACTILE ◆ VISUAL

Ongoing Assessment: Recognizing Student Achievement

Journal page 109

Use **journal page 109** to assess students' ability to add positive and negative numbers. Students are making adequate progress if they are able to calculate both row and column totals correctly. Some students may be able to apply their knowledge of signed addends to develop a strategy for placing numbers in cells.

[Operations and Computation Goal 1]

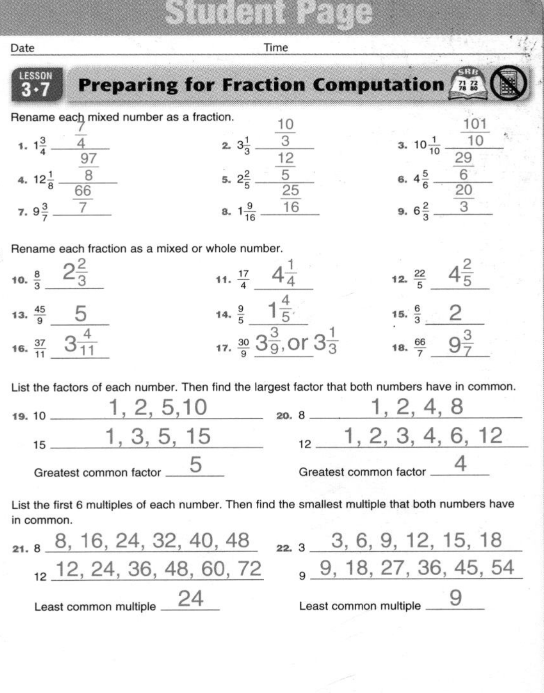

Student Page

Date Time

LESSON 3·7 **Preparing for Fraction Computation**

Rename each mixed number as a fraction.

1. $1\frac{3}{4}$ $\frac{7}{4}$
2. $3\frac{1}{3}$ $\frac{10}{3}$
3. $10\frac{1}{10}$ $\frac{101}{10}$
4. $12\frac{1}{8}$ $\frac{97}{8}$
5. $2\frac{2}{5}$ $\frac{12}{5}$
6. $4\frac{5}{6}$ $\frac{29}{6}$
7. $9\frac{3}{7}$ $\frac{66}{7}$
8. $1\frac{9}{16}$ $\frac{25}{16}$
9. $6\frac{2}{3}$ $\frac{20}{3}$

Rename each fraction as a mixed or whole number.

10. $\frac{8}{3}$ $2\frac{2}{3}$
11. $\frac{17}{4}$ $4\frac{1}{4}$
12. $\frac{22}{5}$ $4\frac{2}{5}$
13. $\frac{45}{9}$ 5
14. $\frac{9}{5}$ $1\frac{4}{5}$
15. $\frac{6}{3}$ 2
16. $\frac{37}{11}$ $3\frac{4}{11}$
17. $\frac{30}{9}$ $3\frac{3}{9}$, or $3\frac{1}{3}$
18. $\frac{66}{7}$ $9\frac{3}{7}$

List the factors of each number. Then find the largest factor that both numbers have in common.

19. 10 1, 2, 5,10
    15 1, 3, 5, 15
    Greatest common factor 5
20. 8 1, 2, 4, 8
    12 1, 2, 3, 4, 6, 12
    Greatest common factor 4

List the first 6 multiples of each number. Then find the smallest multiple that both numbers have in common.

21. 8 8, 16, 24, 32, 40, 48
    12 12, 24, 36, 48, 60, 72
    Least common multiple 24
22. 3 3, 6, 9, 12, 15, 18
    9 9, 18, 27, 36, 45, 54
    Least common multiple 9

Math Journal 1, p. 110

2 Ongoing Learning & Practice

▶ Converting Fractions and Mixed Numbers

INDEPENDENT ACTIVITY

(*Math Journal 1,* p. 110)

Students practice converting between fractions and mixed numbers, as well as finding greatest common factors and least common multiples. These skills are prerequisites for computation with fractions in Unit 4.

▶ Math Boxes 3·7

INDEPENDENT ACTIVITY

(*Math Journal 1,* p. 111)

Mixed Practice Math Boxes in this lesson are paired with Math Boxes in Lesson 3-5. The skills in Problems 5 and 6 preview Unit 4 content.

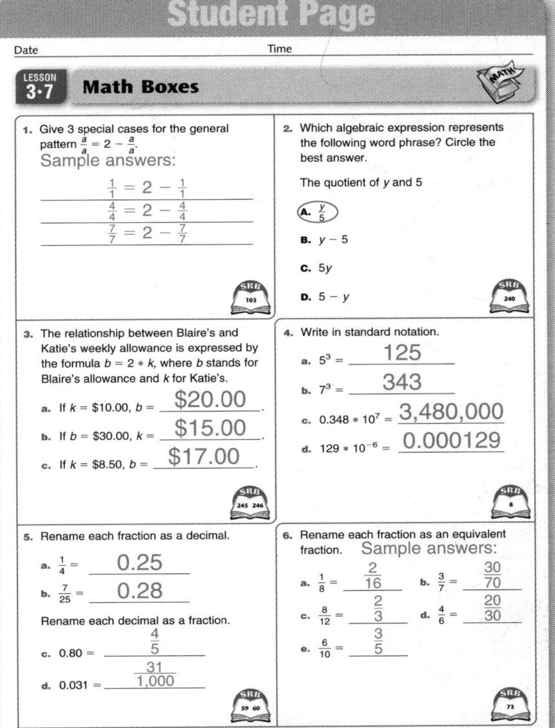

Student Page

Date Time

LESSON 3·7 **Math Boxes**

1. Give 3 special cases for the general pattern $\frac{a}{a} = 2 - \frac{a}{a}$.
   Sample answers:
   $\frac{1}{1} = 2 - \frac{1}{1}$
   $\frac{4}{4} = 2 - \frac{4}{4}$
   $\frac{7}{7} = 2 - \frac{7}{7}$
   SRB 103

2. Which algebraic expression represents the following word phrase? Circle the best answer.
   The quotient of y and 5
   A. $\frac{y}{5}$ (circled)
   B. $y - 5$
   C. $5y$
   D. $5 - y$
   SRB 240

3. The relationship between Blaire's and Katie's weekly allowance is expressed by the formula $b = 2 * k$, where b stands for Blaire's allowance and k for Katie's.
   a. If k = \$10.00, b = \$20.00.
   b. If b = \$30.00, k = \$15.00.
   c. If k = \$8.50, b = \$17.00.
   SRB 245 246

4. Write in standard notation.
   a. 5^3 = 125
   b. 7^3 = 343
   c. $0.348 * 10^7$ = 3,480,000
   d. $129 * 10^{-6}$ = 0.000129
   SRB 8

5. Rename each fraction as a decimal.
   a. $\frac{1}{4}$ = 0.25
   b. $\frac{7}{25}$ = 0.28
   Rename each decimal as a fraction.
   c. 0.80 = $\frac{4}{5}$
   d. 0.031 = $\frac{31}{1,000}$
   SRB 59 60

6. Rename each fraction as an equivalent fraction. Sample answers:
   a. $\frac{1}{8}$ = $\frac{2}{16}$
   b. $\frac{3}{7}$ = $\frac{30}{70}$
   c. $\frac{8}{12}$ = $\frac{2}{3}$
   d. $\frac{4}{6}$ = $\frac{20}{30}$
   e. $\frac{6}{10}$ = $\frac{3}{5}$
   SRB 73

Math Journal 1, p. 111

Study Link Master

Name ____________ Date ____________ Time ____________

STUDY LINK 3·7 Spreadsheet Practice

Ms. Villanova keeps a spreadsheet of her monthly expenses. Use her spreadsheet to answer the questions below.

	A	B	C	D	E
1		January	February	March	**Total**
2	Groceries	$125.25	$98.00	$138.80	$362.05
3	Phone Bill	$34.90	$58.50	$25.35	$118.75
4	Car Expenses	$25.00	$115.95	$12.00	$152.95
5	Rent	$875.00	$875.00	$875.00	$2,625.00

1. What is shown in cell B1? January
2. What is shown in cell C4? $115.95
3. Which cell contains the word *Rent*? A5
4. Which cell contains the amount $58.50? C3
5. Ms. Villanova used column E to show the total for each row. Find the missing totals and enter them on the spreadsheet.
6. Write a formula for calculating E3 that uses cell names. E3 = B3 + C3 + D3
7. Write a formula for calculating E5 that uses cell names. E5 = B5 + C5 + D5
8. Ms. Villanova found that she made a mistake in recording her March phone bill. Instead of $25.35, she should have entered $35.35. After she corrects her spreadsheet, what will the new total be in cell E3? $128.75

Practice

Find the missing dimension for each square.

9. s = 12 cm; A = 144 cm²
10. s = 9 in.; A = 81 in.²
11. s = 8.6 mm; A = 73.96 mm²
12. s = 17 ft; A = 289 ft²

Math Masters, p. 89

Game Master

Name ____________ Date ____________ Time ____________

Credits/Debits Game

Materials ☐ recording sheets (*Math Masters,* p. 430)
☐ 1 complete deck of number cards

Players 2

Object of the Game To have the most money at the end of 10 draws.

Directions

1. Shuffle the deck and lay it facedown between the players.
2. The black-numbered cards are the credits (+), and the blue- (or red-) numbered cards are the debits (−).
3. Each player begins with a bottom line of +$10. As credits and debits are recorded, players will adjust the bottom line.
4. Players take turns. On your turn, do the following.
   - Draw a card. The card tells you the dollar amount and whether it is a credit or debit to the bottom line. Record the credit or debit in the Change column.
   - Use the credit or debit to adjust the bottom line.
   - Record the result in the table.

Example 1: Cleo has a Start balance of +$10. He draws a blue (or red) 12. This is a debit of $12, so he records −$12 in the Change column. He adds −$12 to the bottom line: $10 + (−$12) = −$2. Cleo then records −$2 in the End, and next start column. He also records −$2 in the Start column on the next line.

Example 2: Aisha has a Start balance of +$20. She draws a black 9. This is a credit of $9, so she records +$9 in the Change column, and she adds $9 to the bottom line: $20 + $9 = $29. Aisha then records +$29 in the End, and next start column. She also records +$29 in the Start column of the next line.

Scoring
At the end of 10 draws each, the player with the most money is the winner of the round. If both players have negative dollar amounts, the player whose amount is closer to 0 wins.

Math Masters, p. 429

▶ Study Link 3·7

INDEPENDENT ACTIVITY

(*Math Masters,* p. 89)

Home Connection Students identify cells in a spreadsheet detailing monthly expenses. They also use cell names to write formulas.

3 Differentiation Options

READINESS

PARTNER ACTIVITY

5–15 Min

▶ Reviewing Addition of Signed Numbers

(*Math Masters,* pp. 429 and 430)

To provide students experience finding sums of signed numbers, have them play the basic *Credits/Debits Game.* Make one copy each of the game directions and the recording sheet (*Math Masters,* pp. 429 and 430) for each pair of students.

ENRICHMENT

WHOLE-CLASS ACTIVITY

15–30 Min

▶ Working with Computer Spreadsheets

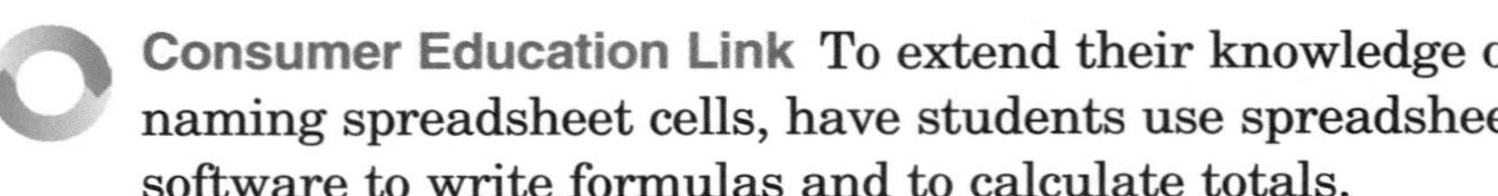

Consumer Education Link To extend their knowledge of naming spreadsheet cells, have students use spreadsheet software to write formulas and to calculate totals.

ELL SUPPORT

INDEPENDENT ACTIVITY

5–15 Min

▶ Building the Math Word Bank

(*Differentiation Handbook*)

To provide language support for spreadsheets, have students use the Word Bank template in the *Differentiation Handbook.* Ask students to write the terms *spreadsheet, cell,* and *formula.* Have them draw pictures relating to each term and write other related words. See the *Differentiation Handbook* for more information.

3•8 Variables and Formulas in Spreadsheets: Part 2

Objectives To practice spreadsheet computation; and to practice finding sums of signed numbers.

1 Teaching the Lesson

Key Activities

Students practice spreadsheet computation by filling in missing numbers on spreadsheets. They play *Spreadsheet Scramble* to practice mental addition of positive and negative numbers.

Key Concepts and Skills

- Mentally add signed numbers. [Operations and Computation Goal 1]
- Calculate the mean using a spreadsheet formula. [Data and Chance Goal 2]
- Evaluate algebraic expressions and formulas. [Patterns, Functions, and Algebra Goal 3]

Key Vocabulary

horizon • square root

Ongoing Assessment: Recognizing Student Achievement Use Mental Math and Reflexes. [Operations and Computation Goal 1]

materials

- ☐ *Math Journal 1,* pp. 109 and 112
- ☐ *Student Reference Book,* p. 334
- ☐ Study Link 3•7
- ☐ Game Master (*Math Masters,* p. 474)
- ☐ Transparency (*Math Masters,* p. 475; optional)

2 Ongoing Learning & Practice

Students use a formula to calculate the greatest distance they can see from various locations.

Students practice and maintain skills through Math Boxes and Study Link activities.

materials

- ☐ *Math Journal 1,* pp. 113 and 114
- ☐ *Student Reference Book,* pp. 285 and 286
- ☐ Study Link Master (*Math Masters,* p. 90)
- ☐ calculator
- ☐ *The World Almanac*/reference books

3 Differentiation Options

READINESS

Students examine completed *Spreadsheet Scramble* game mats and manipulate cell values.

ENRICHMENT

Students use spreadsheet software to calculate a formula.

EXTRA PRACTICE

Students apply properties of addition to find sums of signed numbers.

ELL SUPPORT

Students model the relationship between the square and square root of a number.

materials

- ☐ Teaching Master (*Math Masters,* p. 91)
- ☐ computer/spreadsheet software
- ☐ Teaching Aid Master (*Math Masters,* p. 408)
- ☐ *5-Minute Math,* pp. 189 and 190

See **Advance Preparation**

Additional Information

Advance Preparation Consider having students use spreadsheet software to evaluate formulas, order data values, and find data landmarks.

Technology

Assessment Management System
Mental Math and Reflexes
See the **iTLG.**

Getting Started

Mental Math and Reflexes 

Students find the missing sums or addends.

Suggestions:

●○○ $-6 + 5 = s$ $s = -1$

●●○ $5 + (-2) + 3 = s$ $s = 6$

●●● $-3 + (-5) + 4 + (-6) = s$ $s = -10$

$5 + a = -2$ $a = -7$

$-4 + 6 + a = -3$ $a = -5$

$6 + a + (-6) + (-3) = 1$ $a = 4$

Math Message

Complete the problems on journal page 112.

Study Link 3·7 Follow-Up

Briefly go over the answers.

Ongoing Assessment: Recognizing Student Achievement

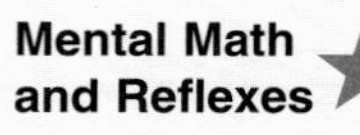

Use **Mental Math and Reflexes** to assess students' ability to solve open number sentences involving signed numbers. Students are making adequate progress if they can calculate the missing sums. Some students may be able to solve the problems involving missing addends.

[Operations and Computation Goal 1]

1 Teaching the Lesson

▶ Math Message Follow-Up

(*Math Journal 1,* p. 112)

Discuss students' responses to the Math Message.

Student Page

Date Time

LESSON 3·8 **Spreadsheet Practice**

Math Message

Students are selling coupon books to raise money for the school band. A coupon book sells for \$2.50. When the spreadsheet at the right is completed, it will show how many books these 4 students sold and how much money they collected.

	A	B	C
1	Student	Books	Money
2	Luigi	5	\$12.50
3	Robin	16	\$40.00
4	Akira	30	\$75.00
5	Gloria	13	\$32.50
6	Total	64	\$160.00

1. Fill in cell B6 to show the total number of books sold.
2. Fill in cells C3, C4, and C5 to show how much money Robin, Akira, and Gloria collected.
3. Fill in cell C6 to show the total amount of money collected.

The spreadsheet below shows students' test scores for 2 different tests.

	A	B	C	D
1	Student	Test 1	Test 2	Average
2	Amy	85	90	87.5
3	David	70	86	78
4	Amit	78	64	71
5	Beth	65	81	73

4. Calculate the remaining average test scores. Fill in the spreadsheet.
5. David's Test 1 score is in which cell? B3
6. The lowest test score shown is in cell C4.
7. Circle the correct formula for calculating Beth's average score.

D4 = (B4 + C4) / 2 D5 = B5 + C5 D5 = (B5 + C5) / 2

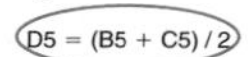

Math Journal 1, **p. 112**

▶ Playing *Spreadsheet Scramble*

(*Math Journal 1,* p. 109; *Student Reference Book,* p. 334; *Math Masters,* pp. 474 and 475)

Give students time to play *Spreadsheet Scramble*. Ask partners to take turns going first and to keep track of the winners by starting position. For example, "We played 6 games. The player going first won two games. The player going second won four games."

Bring the class together and combine students' results. Ask whether there is any advantage in playing first or second. You should have enough results from the class to show that there is no clear advantage and that *Spreadsheet Scramble* is a fair game. However, there are different strategies for making the best of a player's starting position.

Adjusting the Activity

Use the transparency of *Math Masters,* page 475 (*Spreadsheet Scramble* game mat) to demonstrate good strategies and situations to avoid.

AUDITORY ◆ KINESTHETIC ◆ TACTILE ◆ VISUAL

2 Ongoing Learning & Practice

▶ Evaluating a Distance Formula

PARTNER ACTIVITY

(*Math Journal 1,* p. 113; *Student Reference Book,* pp. 285 and 286)

Portfolio Ideas

Have students work in pairs to complete journal page 113. They can refer to *Student Reference Book,* pages 285 and 286 for information on how to use a calculator to find the **square root** of a number.

Make sure students understand that the distance formula on journal page 113 applies to the distance one can see along the surface of Earth. Mountain peaks 100 miles away can be seen because they rise above the surface. One can also see the Sun, because it is about 93 million miles from Earth and, therefore, also above Earth's surface. However, one's view along Earth's surface is limited by Earth's curvature.

To add more locations to the table in Problem 2, students will need to use reference books, such as *The World Almanac*. If such books are not available, you might assign this problem as a part of Study Link 3-8.

The formula $d = 1.25 * \sqrt{h}$ contains two variables, d and h. If students know the value of h, they should have little difficulty evaluating the formula to find the value of d. They substitute the specific value of h, take the square root of that value, and multiply by 1.25. All of the calculations required for Problem 2 are of this form.

Some students may have difficulty with Problem 3. The distance d (10 miles) is known, but the value of h is not known. Substituting 10 for d in the formula yields $10 = 1.25 * \sqrt{h}$. One approach is to use a trial-and-error strategy.

Example:

If $h = 25$, then $1.25 * \sqrt{25} = 6.25$ too small

If $h = 100$, then $1.25 * \sqrt{100} = 12.5$ too large

If $h = 81$, then $1.25 * \sqrt{81} = 11.25$ too large

If $h = 64$, then $1.25 * \sqrt{64} = 10$ correct

Another approach is to reason that $\sqrt{h} = 10 / 1.25$, or 8. If $\sqrt{h} = 8$, then h must be the square of 8, or $8 * 8 = 64$.

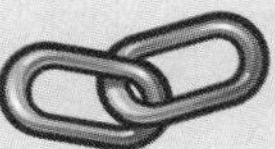

Links to the Future

Most students will be able to use the calculator to evaluate the formula $d = 1.25 * \sqrt{h}$, but not all students will be able to solve for the value under the radical. Solving equations involving square roots is not a Grade 6 Goal, but will provide students with exposure to equations and solutions they will encounter in future algebra classes.

Student Page

Date Time

LESSON 3·8 **How Far Can You See?**

Suppose you are outdoors in a flat place where your view is not blocked by buildings or trees. You can see objects at ground level for several miles. The higher you are above ground or water level, the farther you can see. The distance you can see along Earth's surface is limited because Earth is curved. The **horizon**—where Earth and sky appear to intersect—is the farthest you can see along Earth's surface.

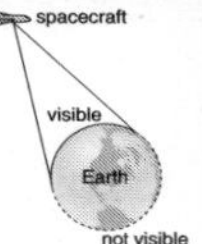

The formula $d = 1.25 * \sqrt{h}$ gives the approximate distance d in miles you can see on a clear day, when h is the height of your eyes above ground or water level, measured in feet.

Reminder: $\sqrt{\ }$ means ***square root*** *of.* For example, 2 is the square root of 4 ($\sqrt{4} = 2$), because $2 * 2 = 4$.

1. You are standing on a boat deck. Your eyes are 15 feet above water level. As you look across the water, about how far can you see? (Round to the nearest mile.)
   The distance is about 5 miles.

2. Use the formula to fill in the table. Calculate the distance to the nearest tenth mile. Then add two more locations and calculate the distances. Use a reference book to find the heights of interesting places.

Place	Height	Distance
Observation deck, Eiffel Tower, Paris, France	900 feet	About 37.5 miles
Top of Sears Tower, Chicago, Illinois, U.S.A.	1,454 feet	About 47.7 miles
Airplane in flight	30,000 feet	About 216.5 miles
Answers vary.		About ___ miles
		About ___ miles

Try This

3. If you see the horizon about 10 miles away, your eye is about 64 feet (unit) above ground level.

Math Journal 1, p. 113

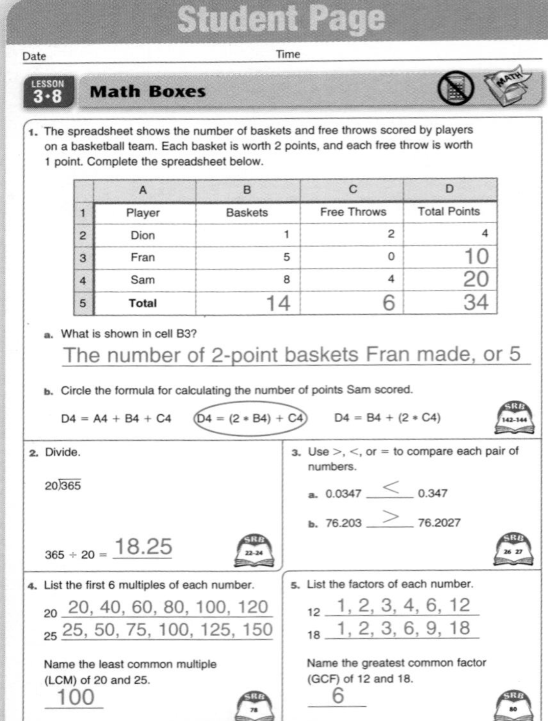
Student Page

Date Time

LESSON 3•8 **Math Boxes**

1. The spreadsheet shows the number of baskets and free throws scored by players on a basketball team. Each basket is worth 2 points, and each free throw is worth 1 point. Complete the spreadsheet below.

	A	B	C	D
1	Player	Baskets	Free Throws	Total Points
2	Dion	1	2	4
3	Fran	5	0	10
4	Sam	8	4	20
5	**Total**	14	6	34

a. What is shown in cell B3?
The number of 2-point baskets Fran made, or 5

b. Circle the formula for calculating the number of points Sam scored.
D4 = A4 + B4 + C4 (D4 = (2 ∗ B4) + C4) D4 = B4 + (2 ∗ C4)

2. Divide.
20)365
365 ÷ 20 = 18.25

3. Use >, <, or = to compare each pair of numbers.
a. 0.0347 < 0.347
b. 76.203 > 76.2027

4. List the first 6 multiples of each number.
20 20, 40, 60, 80, 100, 120
25 25, 50, 75, 100, 125, 150
Name the least common multiple (LCM) of 20 and 25.
100

5. List the factors of each number.
12 1, 2, 3, 4, 6, 12
18 1, 2, 3, 6, 9, 18
Name the greatest common factor (GCF) of 12 and 18.
6

Math Journal 1, p. 114

▶ Math Boxes 3•8

INDEPENDENT ACTIVITY

(*Math Journal 1,* p. 114)

Mixed Practice Math Boxes in this lesson are paired with Math Boxes in Lesson 3-10. The skills in Problems 4 and 5 preview Unit 4 content.

Writing/Reasoning Have students write a response to the following: *Explain the strategy you used to compare the numbers in Problem 3b.* Sample answer: I attached a zero to the end of 76.203, compared $\frac{2,030}{10,000}$ to $\frac{2,027}{10,000}$, and determined that 76.203 is greater.

▶ Study Link 3•8

INDEPENDENT ACTIVITY

(*Math Masters,* p. 90)

Home Connection Students practice adding positive and negative numbers.

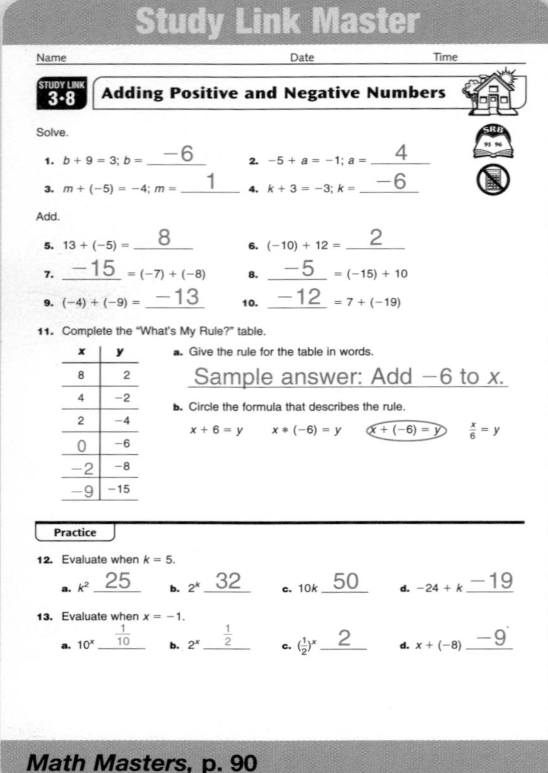
Study Link Master

Name Date Time

STUDY LINK 3•8 **Adding Positive and Negative Numbers**

Solve.

1. b + 9 = 3; b = −6
2. −5 + a = −1; a = 4
3. m + (−5) = −4; m = 1
4. k + 3 = −3; k = −6

Add.

5. 13 + (−5) = 8
6. (−10) + 12 = 2
7. −15 = (−7) + (−8)
8. −5 = (−15) + 10
9. (−4) + (−9) = −13
10. −12 = 7 + (−19)

11. Complete the "What's My Rule?" table.

x	y
8	2
4	−2
2	−4
0	−6
−2	−8
−9	−15

a. Give the rule for the table in words.
Sample answer: Add −6 to x.

b. Circle the formula that describes the rule.
x + 6 = y x ∗ (−6) = y (x + (−6) = y) $\frac{x}{6}$ = y

Practice

12. Evaluate when k = 5.
a. k^2 25 b. 2^k 32 c. 10k 50 d. −24 + k −19

13. Evaluate when x = −1.
a. 10^x $\frac{1}{10}$ b. 2^x $\frac{1}{2}$ c. $(\frac{1}{2})^x$ 2 d. x + (−8) −9

Math Masters, p. 90

3 Differentiation Options

READINESS

PARTNER ACTIVITY

▶ Solving a *Spreadsheet Scramble* Problem

5–15 Min

(*Math Masters,* p. 91)

To provide students with experience selecting addends that yield a positive or negative sum, have them simulate a round of *Spreadsheet Scramble.* Ask students to interchange signed numbers in cells and calculate new totals based on the revised placement of those numbers.

ENRICHMENT

INDEPENDENT ACTIVITY

▶ Using Spreadsheet Software to Evaluate Formulas

15–30 Min

Consumer Education Link To further explore the uses of spreadsheets, have students use software to make a spreadsheet like the one shown below. Ask them to input the appropriate spreadsheet formulas for calculating circumferences and areas of circles with radii of 10 cm, 25 cm, and 89 cm. Have students use formatting features to round areas to the nearest tenth. Challenge them to write a formula that will convert area measurements to meters.

	A	B	C
1	Radius (cm)	Circumference (cm)	Area (cm^2)
2			
3	1	6.3	3.1
4	10	62.8	314.0
5	25	157.0	1,962.5
6	89	558.9	24,871.9

EXTRA PRACTICE

SMALL-GROUP ACTIVITY

▶ *5-Minute Math*

5–15 Min

To offer more practice finding sums of signed numbers, see *5-Minute Math,* pages 189 and 190.

ELL SUPPORT

SMALL-GROUP ACTIVITY

▶ Modeling Squares and Square Roots

5–15 Min

(*Math Masters,* p. 408)

To provide language support for square roots, have students draw and label squares having the following areas on grid paper: $4u^2$, $9u^2$, $16u^2$, $25u^2$, and $36u^2$. For each square, ask students to share their strategies for determining the length of a side. Use the appropriate language and symbols to discuss the relationship between the square and the side length. For example, ask: *What is the length of the side of a square whose area is 9 square units?* Say: *The length of a square whose area is 9 square units is 3 units,* as you write $\sqrt{9u^2} = 3u$ on the board. Explain how the symbol $\sqrt{}$ means the square root of a number. Have students practice reading equations that include the square root symbol, such as $\sqrt{25} = 5$ and $\sqrt{36} = 6$.

Teaching Master

Name Date Time

LESSON 3•8 ***Spreadsheet Scramble* Problems**

Study the completed *Spreadsheet Scramble* game mat at the right.

Player 1 gets 1 point each for F3, F4, and C5.

Player 2 gets 1 point each for F2 and E5.

Player 1 wins the game, 3 points to 2 points.

Notice that if the numbers in cells C2 and B4 were interchanged and new totals were calculated, Player 2 would win the game, 4 points to 2 points.

	A	B	C	D	E	F
1						Total
2		−1	−6	3	−5	−9
3		4	2	−4	6	+8
4		−3	5	1	−2	+1
5	Total	0	+1	0	−1	

	A	B	C	D	E	F
1						Total
2		−1	−6	3	−5	−9
3		4	2	−4	6	+8
4		−3	5	1	−2	+1
5	Total	0	+1	0	−1	

→

	A	B	C	D	E	F
1						Total
2		−1	−3	3	−5	−6
3		4	2	−4	6	+8
4		−6	5	1	−2	−2
5	Total	−3	+4	0	−1	

Can you switch the values of two other cells so that Player 2 would win the game? Answers vary.

1. Which cells would you interchange? ________

2. What would be the new score of the game? Player 1 ______ Player 2 ______

3. Fill in the new game mat.

	A	B	C	D	E	F
1						Total
2						
3						
4						
5	Total					

Math Masters, p. 91

3•9 Reading and Drawing Graphs

Objective To interpret and draw graphs that correspond to given situations.

1 Teaching the Lesson

Key Activities

Students draw graphs to illustrate situations and write stories that explain graphs. Students match graphs with situations they might represent.

Key Concepts and Skills

- Construct a graph that corresponds to a given situation. [Data and Chance Goal 1]
- Write a "time story" based on the shape of a graph. [Data and Chance Goal 2]
- Use a graph to represent and interpret a function. [Patterns, Functions, and Algebra Goal 1]

Key Vocabulary

time graph

Ongoing Assessment: Recognizing Student Achievement Use journal page 115. [Data and Chance Goal 2]

materials

- ☐ *Math Journal 1,* pp. 115–117
- ☐ Study Link 3•8
- ☐ Transparency (*Math Masters,* p. 92; optional)
- ☐ straightedge

2 Ongoing Learning & Practice

Students practice translating between scientific and standard notations by playing *Scientific Notation Toss.*

Students practice and maintain skills through Math Boxes and Study Link activities.

materials

- ☐ *Math Journal 1,* p. 118
- ☐ *Student Reference Book,* p. 331
- ☐ Study Link Master (*Math Masters,* p. 93)
- ☐ Game Master (*Math Masters,* p. 472)

Per partnership:

- ☐ 2 six-sided dice

3 Differentiation Options

READINESS

Students match mystery graphs with situations and the data they represent.

ENRICHMENT

Students construct mystery graphs.

EXTRA PRACTICE

Students practice finding landmarks of a data set containing signed numbers.

materials

- ☐ Teaching Masters (*Math Masters,* pp. 94 and 95)
- ☐ Per partnership: scissors; tape or glue; 1 or 2 sheets of paper
- ☐ *5-Minute Math,* p. 198

Technology

Assessment Management System
Journal page 115
See the **iTLG.**

Getting Started

Mental Math and Reflexes

Students order sets of signed numbers from least to greatest.

●○○ −2, −9, 3, −1 *−9, −2, −1, 3*

●●○ 1, 0, −2, −4, 2 *−4, −2, 0, 1, 2*

●●● 8, −15, −21, −16, $-\frac{1}{2}$, $\frac{3}{4}$ *−21, −16, −15, $-\frac{1}{2}$, $\frac{3}{4}$, 8*

Math Message

Complete the problems on journal page 115.

Study Link 3·8 Follow-Up

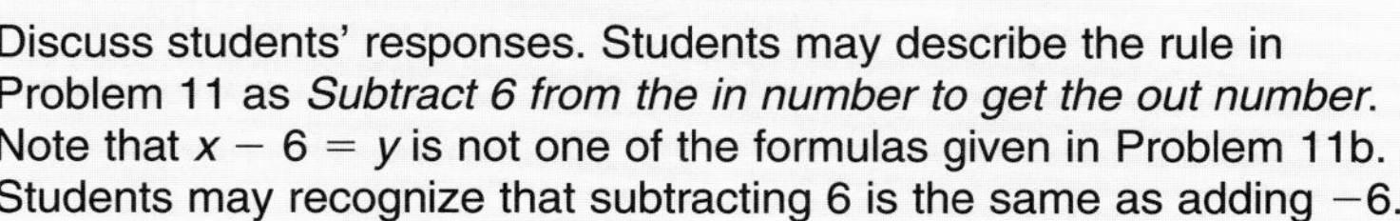

Discuss students' responses. Students may describe the rule in Problem 11 as *Subtract 6 from the in number to get the out number.* Note that $x - 6 = y$ is not one of the formulas given in Problem 11b. Students may recognize that subtracting 6 is the same as adding −6.

1 Teaching the Lesson

▶ Math Message Follow-Up

WHOLE-CLASS DISCUSSION

(*Math Journal 1,* p. 115)

In Lessons 3-5 and 3-6, students used formulas and tables to construct graphs depicting various relationships—in particular, between time and speed. In this lesson, students use the shape of a graph to draw conclusions about the data or relationship the graph represents.

Discuss the graphs in the Math Message on journal page 115 and go over students' answers. Have students complete the following statement about the relationship displayed by each of graphs A–D.

"As time passes, the speed of the car ________." *Graph A: decreases; Graph B: increases; Graph C: stays the same—it is zero; Graph D: stays the same.*

Ask students to reword Problem 5 using a statement similar to what they used for Graphs A–D. For example, "As time passes, the speed at which the woman moves ________." *stays the same, then increases, then stays the same.*

Ongoing Assessment: Recognizing Student Achievement

Journal page 115

Use **journal page 115** to assess students' abilities to analyze the shape of a graph and draw conclusions about data trends. Students are making adequate progress if they are able to match the situations and graphs. Some students may be able to draw the graph for Problem 5.

[Data and Chance Goal 2]

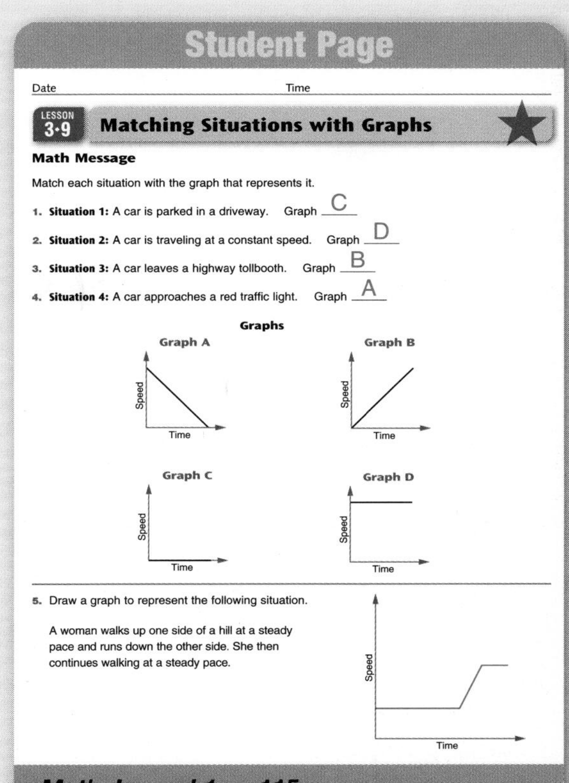

Student Page

Date Time

LESSON 3·9 **Matching Situations with Graphs**

Math Message

Match each situation with the graph that represents it.

1. **Situation 1:** A car is parked in a driveway. Graph C
2. **Situation 2:** A car is traveling at a constant speed. Graph D
3. **Situation 3:** A car leaves a highway tollbooth. Graph B
4. **Situation 4:** A car approaches a red traffic light. Graph A

Graphs

5. Draw a graph to represent the following situation.

A woman walks up one side of a hill at a steady pace and runs down the other side. She then continues walking at a steady pace.

Math Journal 1, p. 115

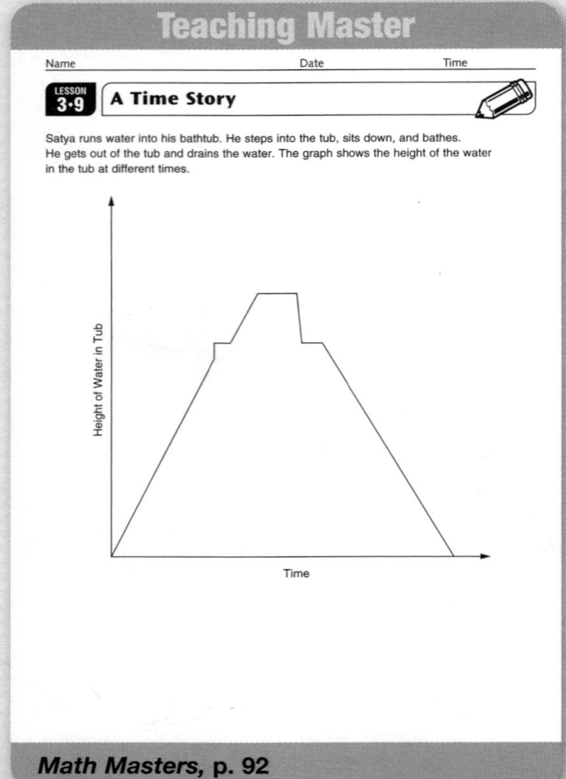
Teaching Master

Name Date Time

LESSON 3·9 A Time Story

Satya runs water into his bathtub. He steps into the tub, sits down, and bathes. He gets out of the tub and drains the water. The graph shows the height of the water in the tub at different times.

Math Masters, p. 92

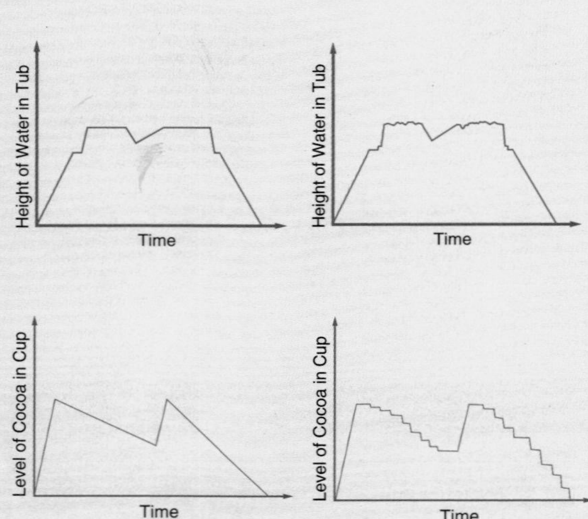

▶ Constructing a Graph from a "Time Story"

WHOLE-CLASS ACTIVITY

(*Math Masters,* p. 92)

Introduce this activity by telling a simple time story. Use the transparency of *Math Masters,* page 92 or draw the graph on the board. Read the story and explain that the graph shows the height of the water in the tub at different times. Students might recall this problem from their work with mystery graphs in *Fifth Grade Everyday Mathematics.*

Tell a new version of the story to the class: *Satya runs water into his bathtub. He steps into the tub, sits down, and begins to bathe. The water in the tub begins to cool, so he drains some water and adds more hot water. Satya finishes bathing, gets out of the tub, and drains the water.*

As a class, draw a **time graph** that illustrates the story you just told. Include as many details as possible.

A simple time-graph solution and a more complex version are shown in the margin. The graph on the left focuses on the main features of the story. The graph on the right adds details, such as changes in the height of water when Satya's feet enter it and when he moves during the bath.

▶ Exploring Time Graphs

PARTNER ACTIVITY

(*Math Journal 1,* p. 116)

Give students time to complete journal page 116.

Ask students to share the stories they wrote to explain the graph in Problem 1. Sample answer: Mr. Olds begins the trip in a 20-mph zone. He stops for a stop sign at 2 minutes. He resumes driving in a 30-mph zone. At $3\frac{1}{2}$ minutes, he begins to slow down for a curve in the road or a slower car. Six minutes into his trip, Mr. Olds stops at a traffic light. He resumes driving in a 30-mph zone. At 9 minutes, he speeds up to pass a car. He slows to 20 mph at $11\frac{1}{2}$ minutes, and at 13 minutes he reaches the school.

For Problem 2, answers vary, depending on the amount of detail students decide to include. A simple time graph and a more complex version that illustrates Monica's individual sips from the cup are shown in the margin.

▶ Interpreting Mystery Graphs

(*Math Journal 1,* p. 117)

Five graphs are shown on journal page 117. Ask students to match each situation described on the left side of the page with the appropriate graph on the right side of the page. In each graph, time is represented on the horizontal axis, and the number of people is represented on the vertical axis.

Adjusting the Activity

Ask students to complete the following statement about the relationship displayed by each graph: "As time passes, the number of people ______."

For Graph D, the completed statement might be, "As time passes, the number of people briefly increases, then decreases, increases, and finally decreases again."

After students have completed the relationship statement for each graph, they can look for the situation that would match that statement.

AUDITORY ◆ KINESTHETIC ◆ TACTILE ◆ VISUAL

When most students have completed the page, discuss answers.

- ▷ Graph A represents Situation 3. Typically, the greatest number of people will be at home during the night. Between 6 A.M. and 12 noon, people are leaving for work, school, or errands. Between 12 noon and 6 P.M., people are arriving home.
- ▷ Graph B represents Situation 1. A typical school day goes from about 9 A.M. to 3 P.M. There is a fairly constant number of people in a school between those hours. The early arrival and late departure of the staff account for the gradual increase of people before 9 A.M. and the gradual decrease of people after 3 P.M.
- ▷ Graph C represents Situation 2. The number of people in a restaurant is greatest around 8 A.M., 12 noon, and 6 P.M.—typical times for breakfast, lunch, and dinner.
- ▷ Graph D represents Situation 5. The greatest number of people driving corresponds to the times that most people commute to and from work. Morning rush hour is a concentrated amount of time, while the evening rush hour is more spread out to account for those who work overtime.
- ▷ Graph E represents Situation 4. The number of patients in a hospital stays about the same. However, the increase in the number of people in the early evening could be due to visitors arriving. The decrease in the late evening could be due to fewer hospital employees working the night shift.

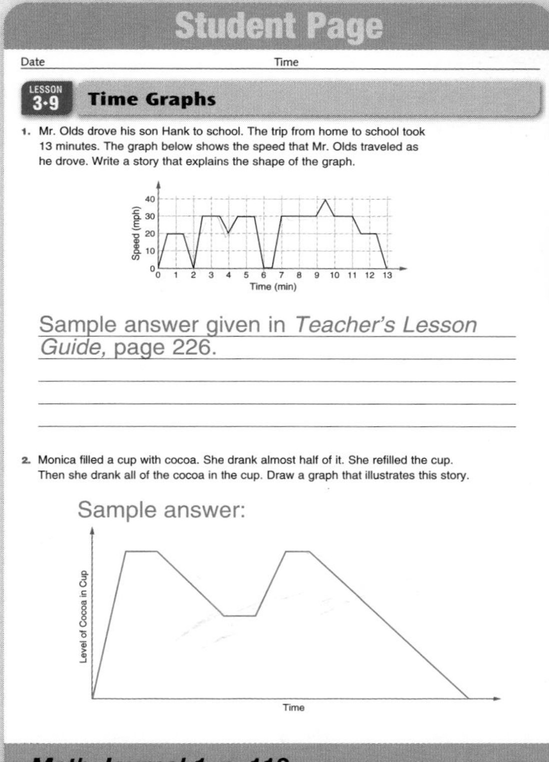

Student Page

Date Time

LESSON 3·9 **Time Graphs**

1. Mr. Olds drove his son Hank to school. The trip from home to school took 13 minutes. The graph below shows the speed that Mr. Olds traveled as he drove. Write a story that explains the shape of the graph.

Sample answer given in *Teacher's Lesson Guide,* page 226.

2. Monica filled a cup with cocoa. She drank almost half of it. She refilled the cup. Then she drank all of the cocoa in the cup. Draw a graph that illustrates this story.

Sample answer:

***Math Journal 1,* p. 116**

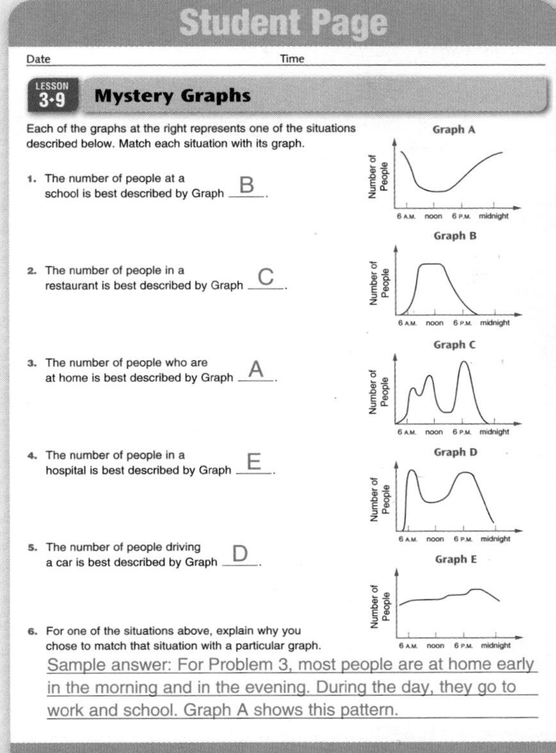

Student Page

Date Time

LESSON 3·9 **Mystery Graphs**

Each of the graphs at the right represents one of the situations described below. Match each situation with its graph.

1. The number of people at a school is best described by Graph B.
2. The number of people in a restaurant is best described by Graph C.
3. The number of people who are at home is best described by Graph A.
4. The number of people in a hospital is best described by Graph E.
5. The number of people driving a car is best described by Graph D.
6. For one of the situations above, explain why you chose to match that situation with a particular graph.

Sample answer: For Problem 3, most people are at home early in the morning and in the evening. During the day, they go to work and school. Graph A shows this pattern.

***Math Journal 1,* p. 117**

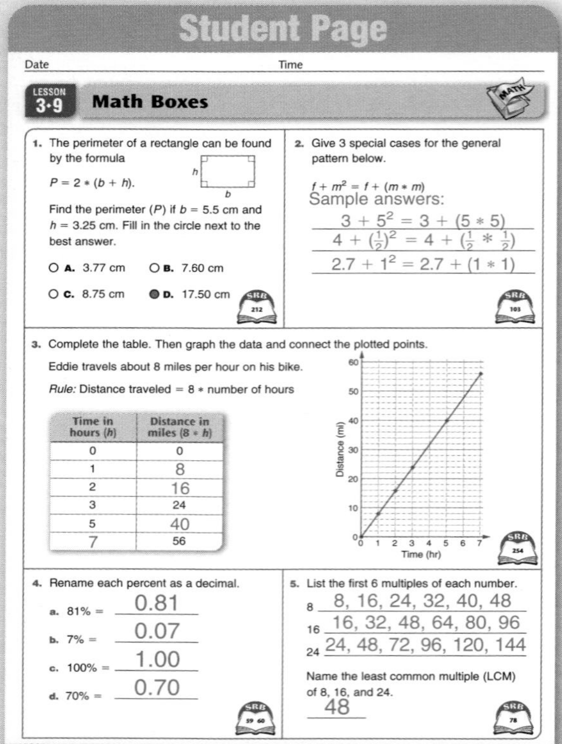

Student Page

Date Time

LESSON 3·9 **Math Boxes**

1. The perimeter of a rectangle can be found by the formula

$P = 2 * (b + h)$.

Find the perimeter (P) if $b = 5.5$ cm and $h = 3.25$ cm. Fill in the circle next to the best answer.

○ A. 3.77 cm ○ B. 7.60 cm
○ C. 8.75 cm ● D. 17.50 cm

SRB 212

2. Give 3 special cases for the general pattern below.

$f + m^2 = f + (m * m)$

Sample answers:

$3 + 5^2 = 3 + (5 * 5)$

$4 + (\frac{1}{2})^2 = 4 + (\frac{1}{2} * \frac{1}{2})$

$2.7 + 1^2 = 2.7 + (1 * 1)$

SRB 103

3. Complete the table. Then graph the data and connect the plotted points.

Eddie travels about 8 miles per hour on his bike.

Rule: Distance traveled = 8 * number of hours

Time in hours (h)	Distance in miles ($8 * h$)
0	0
1	8
2	16
3	24
5	40
7	56

SRB 254

4. Rename each percent as a decimal.

a. 81% = 0.81
b. 7% = 0.07
c. 100% = 1.00
d. 70% = 0.70

SRB 59 60

5. List the first 6 multiples of each number.

8 8, 16, 24, 32, 40, 48
16 16, 32, 48, 64, 80, 96
24 24, 48, 72, 96, 120, 144

Name the least common multiple (LCM) of 8, 16, and 24.
48

SRB 78

Math Journal 1, p. 118

2 Ongoing Learning & Practice

▶ Playing *Scientific Notation Toss*

(*Student Reference Book,* p. 331; *Math Masters,* p. 472)

Distribute two 6-sided dice to each pair of students, as well as a game record sheet (*Math Masters,* p. 472). Have students read the directions on page 331 in the *Student Reference Book*. Ask a volunteer to demonstrate how the game is played. Encourage students to play a practice game.

▶ Math Boxes 3·9

INDEPENDENT ACTIVITY

(*Math Journal 1,* p. 118)

Mixed Practice Math Boxes in this lesson are paired with Math Boxes in Lesson 3-6. The skills in Problems 4 and 5 preview Unit 4 content.

▶ Study Link 3·9

INDEPENDENT ACTIVITY

(*Math Masters,* p. 93)

Home Connection Students answer questions about a graph displaying the relationship between the distance of a Ferris wheel passenger from the ground and the time the passenger spends on the ride.

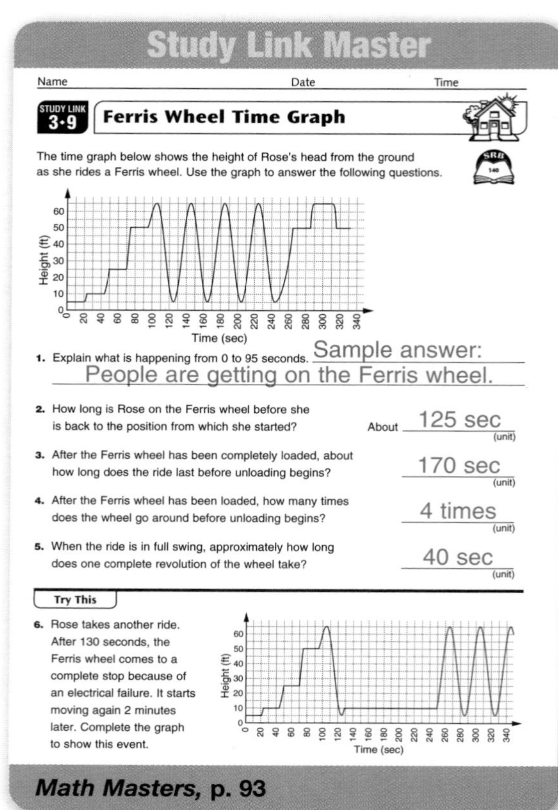

Study Link Master

Name Date Time

STUDY LINK 3·9 **Ferris Wheel Time Graph**

The time graph below shows the height of Rose's head from the ground as she rides a Ferris wheel. Use the graph to answer the following questions.

SRB 140

1. Explain what is happening from 0 to 95 seconds. Sample answer: People are getting on the Ferris wheel.

2. How long is Rose on the Ferris wheel before she is back to the position from which she started? About 125 sec (unit)

3. After the Ferris wheel has been completely loaded, about how long does the ride last before unloading begins? 170 sec (unit)

4. After the Ferris wheel has been loaded, how many times does the wheel go around before unloading begins? 4 times (unit)

5. When the ride is in full swing, approximately how long does one complete revolution of the wheel take? 40 sec (unit)

Try This

6. Rose takes another ride. After 130 seconds, the Ferris wheel comes to a complete stop because of an electrical failure. It starts moving again 2 minutes later. Complete the graph to show this event.

Math Masters, p. 93

3 Differentiation Options

READINESS

PARTNER ACTIVITY

▶ Mystery Graph Match

5–15 Min

(*Math Masters,* p. 94)

Students practice analyzing graph shapes by matching a graph with the situation and data table that represent it. Provide each pair of students with a copy of *Math Masters,* page 94, scissors, tape or glue, and one or two sheets of paper.

When all students have finished, review the following answers as a group.

▷ A fern was growing rapidly in its pot for a while until it didn't get enough water. The fern then stopped growing. Table 4; Graph B

▷ A fern was growing slowly in its pot due to a lack of sunlight. When the fern was moved to a nearby windowsill, it began to grow more rapidly. Table 3; Graph D

▷ A fern was growing rapidly in its pot for a while until it was knocked over and a dog bit off the top. It stopped growing for a while before it eventually began to grow again. Table 1; Graph A

▷ Table 2 and Graph C are left over when students are finished. Encourage students to write a situation that would match Table 2; Graph C. Sample answer: A fern received the correct amount of sunlight, water, and nutrients; it grew at a constant rate.

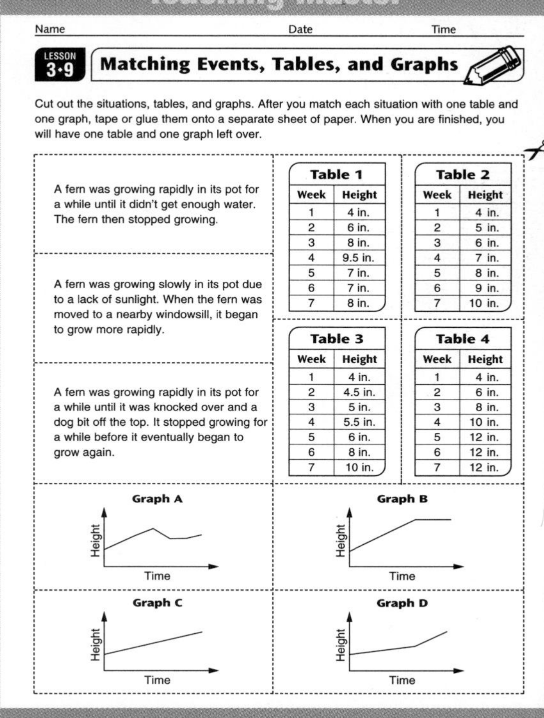

Teaching Master

Name Date Time

LESSON 3·9 Matching Events, Tables, and Graphs

Cut out the situations, tables, and graphs. After you match each situation with one table and one graph, tape or glue them onto a separate sheet of paper. When you are finished, you will have one table and one graph left over.

A fern was growing rapidly in its pot for a while until it didn't get enough water. The fern then stopped growing.

A fern was growing slowly in its pot due to a lack of sunlight. When the fern was moved to a nearby windowsill, it began to grow more rapidly.

A fern was growing rapidly in its pot for a while until it was knocked over and a dog bit off the top. It stopped growing for a while before it eventually began to grow again.

Table 1

Week	Height
1	4 in.
2	6 in.
3	8 in.
4	9.5 in.
5	7 in.
6	7 in.
7	8 in.

Table 2

Week	Height
1	4 in.
2	5 in.
3	6 in.
4	7 in.
5	8 in.
6	9 in.
7	10 in.

Table 3

Week	Height
1	4 in.
2	4.5 in.
3	5 in.
4	5.5 in.
5	6 in.
6	8 in.
7	10 in.

Table 4

Week	Height
1	4 in.
2	6 in.
3	8 in.
4	10 in.
5	12 in.
6	12 in.
7	12 in.

Math Masters, p. 94

ENRICHMENT

INDEPENDENT ACTIVITY

▶ Constructing Mystery Graphs

15–30 Min

(*Math Masters,* p. 95)

Portfolio Ideas

To further explore graphing, have students construct original mystery graphs and describe the situations the graphs represent on *Math Masters,* page 95. Ask students to analyze their peers' graphs and determine the situations.

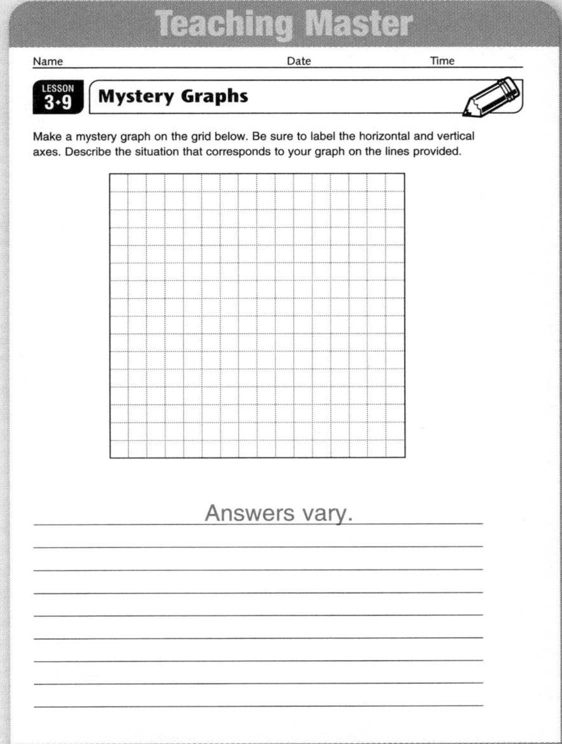

Teaching Master

Name Date Time

LESSON 3·9 Mystery Graphs

Make a mystery graph on the grid below. Be sure to label the horizontal and vertical axes. Describe the situation that corresponds to your graph on the lines provided.

Answers vary.

Math Masters, p. 95

EXTRA PRACTICE

SMALL-GROUP ACTIVITY

▶ *5-Minute Math*

5–15 Min

To offer more practice finding landmarks of a data set, see *5-Minute Math,* page 198.

3•10 Formulas, Tables, and Graphs: Part 2

Objective To analyze a real-world situation by making and using a data table and a graph.

1 Teaching the Lesson

Key Activities

Students compare two summer jobs by analyzing their potential profits. They construct a data table, develop earnings formulas, graph the data, and interpret the graph.

Key Concepts and Skills

- Apply multiplication and division facts to calculate rates. [Operations and Computation Goal 2]
- Construct, extend, and interpret a line graph. [Data and Chance Goals 1 and 2]
- Plot data values from a table. [Measurement and Reference Frames Goal 3]
- Express rates as formulas. [Patterns, Functions, and Algebra Goal 1]

Ongoing Assessment: Informing Instruction See pages 231 and 232.

materials

- ☐ *Math Journal 1,* pp. 120 and 121
- ☐ Study Link 3•9
- ☐ straightedge

2 Ongoing Learning & Practice

Students review place-value concepts of decimal numbers by playing *Getting to One.*

Students practice and maintain skills through Math Boxes and Study Link activities.

Ongoing Assessment: Recognizing Student Achievement Use journal page 119. [Patterns, Functions, and Algebra Goal 1]

materials

- ☐ *Math Journal 1,* p. 119
- ☐ *Student Reference Book,* p. 321
- ☐ Study Link Master (*Math Masters,* p. 96)
- ☐ Game Master (*Math Masters,* p. 448)
- ☐ calculator
- ☐ overhead calculator (optional)

3 Differentiation Options

READINESS

Students use a rule describing a situation to make a table and construct a graph.

ENRICHMENT

Students conduct an experiment, graph the results, and analyze their findings.

EXTRA PRACTICE

Students sketch graphs to represent actions over time.

materials

- ☐ Teaching Masters (*Math Masters,* pp. 97–99
- ☐ Per partnership: 3 or 4 containers of various shapes and sizes; measuring cups (mL) and water
- ☐ Geometry Template or ruler
- ☐ *5-Minute Math,* p. 203

***See* Advance Preparation**

Additional Information

Advance Preparation Refer to *Math Masters,* page 99 for ideas about container shapes.

Technology

Assessment Management System
Math Boxes, Problem 1
See the **iTLG.**

Getting Started

Mental Math and Reflexes

Students solve mental computation problems with positive and negative numbers. *Suggestions:*

●○○ 100 + (−40) 60
−50 + (−25) −75

●●○ 60 + (−200) −140
−49 + 74 25

●●● 62 + (−322) −260
−42.3 + 38.9 −3.4

Math Message

Suppose you get a summer job that pays $5.20 per hour and you work $3\frac{1}{2}$ hours each day, 5 days per week. Estimate the number of weeks it would take you to earn a total of $800.

Study Link 3·9 Follow-Up

Briefly go over the answers.

1 Teaching the Lesson

▶ Math Message Follow-Up

WHOLE-CLASS DISCUSSION

Have students share their estimation strategies. Estimates should be between 8 and 9 weeks. Working at this rate, a person would earn $819 at the end of 9 weeks.

Remind students that in Lesson 3-5, they learned how to represent a rate with a data table, a formula, and a line graph. In this lesson, students use these representations to analyze and compare two rates.

▶ Comparing the Profits for Summer Jobs

PARTNER ACTIVITY

(*Math Journal 1,* p. 120)

Consumer Education Link Partners complete journal page 120. Discuss students' answers. Chloe will have made more money by the end of 3 weeks, but Haylee will have made more money by the end of the 10-week period.

As part of a follow-up discussion, have students use the table to develop rules for the money earned by Haylee and Chloe in terms of the time it takes to earn the money.

Ongoing Assessment: Informing Instruction

Watch for students who are unable to develop these rules on their own. Write the rules on the board and have students verify that the rules are correct for several in (weeks) and out (dollars) values.

Date Time

LESSON 3·10 **Formulas, Tables, and Graphs** SRB 254

Haylee and Chloe want to earn money during summer vacation.

Haylee's Summer Job	Chloe's Summer Job
Haylee is going to mow lawns. Her father will lend her $190 to buy a lawn mower. She figures that she can mow 10 lawns per week and make $12 per lawn after paying for oil and gasoline.	Chloe is going to work in an ice cream shop. The owner will provide a uniform free of charge and pay her $5.20 per hour. She will work $3\frac{1}{2}$ hours per day, 5 days per week.

1. Complete the table at the right to show how much profit each girl will have made after 2 weeks, 3 weeks, and so on. (Assume they do not have to pay taxes.)

Time (weeks)	Profit (dollars)	
	Haylee	Chloe
Start	−190	0
1	−70	91
2	50	182
3	170	273
4	290	364
5	410	455
6	530	546
7	650	637
8	770	728
9	890	819
10	1,010	910

2. Use the table to answer the following questions.
   a. Who will have made more money by the end of 3 weeks? Chloe
   b. How much money will that girl have made? $273
   c. Who will make more money during the summer? Haylee

Math Journal 1, p. 120

Haylee

in (weeks)	out (dollars)
start	−190
1	−70
2	50
3	170
4	290
5	410
6	530
7	650
8	770
9	890
10	1,010

Chloe

in (weeks)	out (dollars)
start	0
1	91
2	182
3	273
4	364
5	455
6	546
7	637
8	728
9	819
10	910

It may help students to think in terms of "What's My Rule?" tables. In each table, the *in* values are amounts of time (weeks), and the *out* values are profits earned (dollars). (*See margin.*)

▷ Chloe's rule is easy to determine: $out = in * 5.20 * 3.5 * 5$

▷ Haylee's rule is less obvious, and students may not discover it on their own: $out = (in * 10 * 12) - 190$

Chloe's and Haylee's rules are general patterns.

Have students examine the general pattern they may have used to arrive at Haylee's data. Ask them to write each computation in the form of a special case:

0 weeks: $(0 * 10 * 12) - 190 = -190$ or $-\$190$

1 week: $(1 * 10 * 12) - 190 = -70$ or $-\$70$

4 weeks: $(4 * 10 * 12) - 190 = 290$ or $\$290$

▶ Graphing Profit Data and Interpreting the Graph

(*Math Journal 1,* pp. 120 and 121)

Have students graph the profit data from their tables onto the grid on journal page 121. They should plot two graphs on the same grid—one graph to represent Haylee's profits and one graph to represent Chloe's profits.

Ongoing Assessment: Informing Instruction

Watch for students who may not recognize the intervals along the vertical axis of the graph. Suggest that these students write the in-between amounts between the labeled increments before graphing the profit data.

Comments for follow-up discussion:

▷ Students need to plot only three time-and-profit results for each girl. For example, plot (0,−190), (1,−70), and (2,50) for Haylee; plot (0,0), (1,91), and (2,182) for Chloe. Students should then use a straightedge to connect these points and extend the line for each girl. They can use the graph to determine each girl's profit after 11, 12, and 13 weeks.

▷ The point at which the graphs intersect represents the time at which Haylee's profit equals Chloe's profit.

▷ How quickly a line graph rises or falls reveals a great deal about the data it represents. In the case of Haylee's and Chloe's profit data, the rising line graphs indicate that each girl continues to make a profit as time passes.

▷ Haylee's line graph crosses the horizontal axis just after Week 1. This point of intersection with the *x*-axis indicates that Haylee has earned enough money to pay her father back and can begin to make a profit.

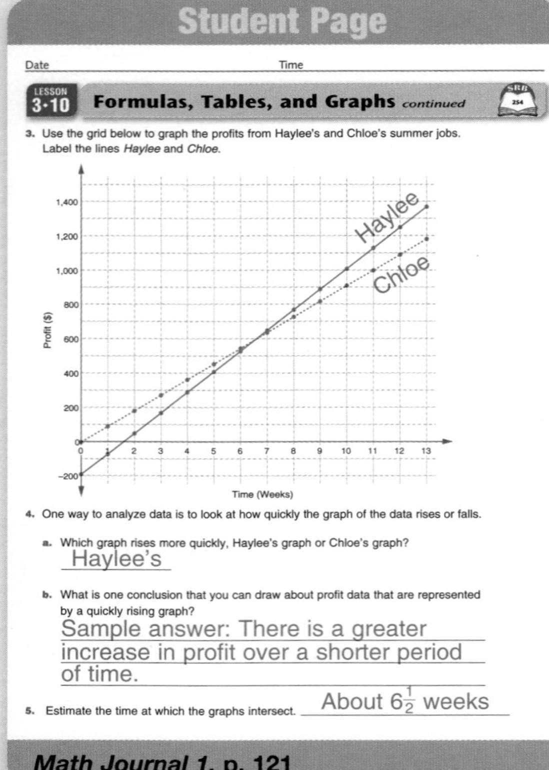
Student Page

Date Time

LESSON 3·10 **Formulas, Tables, and Graphs** *continued*

3. Use the grid below to graph the profits from Haylee's and Chloe's summer jobs. Label the lines *Haylee* and *Chloe.*

4. One way to analyze data is to look at how quickly the graph of the data rises or falls.

a. Which graph rises more quickly, Haylee's graph or Chloe's graph? Haylee's

b. What is one conclusion that you can draw about profit data that are represented by a quickly rising graph? Sample answer: There is a greater increase in profit over a shorter period of time.

5. Estimate the time at which the graphs intersect. About $6\frac{1}{2}$ weeks

Math Journal 1, p. 121

2 Ongoing Learning & Practice

▶ Playing *Getting to One*

PARTNER ACTIVITY

(*Student Reference Book,* p. 321; *Math Masters,* p. 448)

Distribute a calculator to each pair of students, as well as a game record sheet (*Math Masters,* p. 448). Students read the directions on *Student Reference Book,* page 321. Have a volunteer demonstrate the game on an overhead calculator, if available. Encourage students to play a practice game.

▶ Math Boxes 3•10

INDEPENDENT ACTIVITY

(*Math Journal 1,* p. 119)

Mixed Practice Math Boxes in this lesson are paired with Math Boxes in Lesson 3-8. The skills in Problems 4 and 5 preview Unit 4 content.

Ongoing Assessment: Recognizing Student Achievement

Math Boxes Problem 1 

Use **Math Boxes, Problem 1** to assess students' abilities to name a spreadsheet cell (Problem 1a) and to identify a spreadsheet formula for calculating a total (Problem 1b). Students are making adequate progress if they can correctly complete Problems 1a and 1b. Some students may be able to write a spreadsheet formula for calculating the total earnings for Monday (Problem 1c).

[Patterns, Functions, and Algebra Goal 1]

▶ Study Link 3•10

INDEPENDENT ACTIVITY

(*Math Masters,* p. 96)

Home Connection Students analyze pet-sitting profits by making and using a table of data and a related graph.

Student Page

Date Time

LESSON 3•10 **Math Boxes**

1. Darin charges $5 an hour to baby-sit on weekdays and $7 an hour on weekends. The spreadsheet is a record of the baby-sitting Darin did during one week. Complete the spreadsheet.

	A	B	C
1	Day of the Week	Number of Hours	Earnings ($)
2	Monday	4	20
3	Wednesday	2	10
4	Saturday	5	35
5	**Total**	11	65

a. Which cell contains the number of hours Darin worked on Saturday? B4

b. Circle the formula Darin should NOT use to calculate his total earnings.

C5 = C2 + C3 + C4 (C5 = 6 * B5) C5 = (5 * B2) + (5 * B3) + (7 * B4)

c. Write a formula that Darin can use to calculate his earnings for Monday.
C2 = 5 * B2

2. Divide.

18)435.6

435.6 ÷ 18 = 24.2

3. Order from least to greatest.

a. 0.23, 0.32, 0.023, 0.323
0.023, 0.23, 0.32, 0.323

b. 36.837, 36.783, 36.878, 36.8375
36.783, 36.837, 36.8375, 36.878

4. List the first 6 multiples of each number.

5 5, 10, 15, 20, 25, 30

6 6, 12, 18, 24, 30, 36

Name the least common multiple (LCM) of 5 and 6.
30

5. Name the greatest common factor (GCF) of each pair of numbers.

a. 9 and 36 9

b. 50 and 20 10

c. 18 and 7 1

Math Journal 1, p. 119

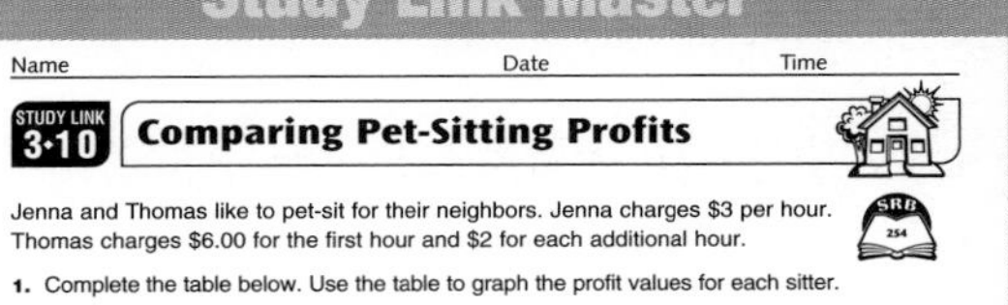

Study Link Master

Name Date Time

STUDY LINK 3•10 **Comparing Pet-Sitting Profits**

Jenna and Thomas like to pet-sit for their neighbors. Jenna charges $3 per hour. Thomas charges $6.00 for the first hour and $2 for each additional hour.

1. Complete the table below. Use the table to graph the profit values for each sitter.

Time (hours)	Jenna's Profit ($)	Thomas's Profit ($)
1	$3	$6
2	$6	$8
3	$9	$10
4	$12	$12
5	$15	$14

2. Extend both line graphs to find the profit each sitter will make for 6 hours.
Jenna (6 hours) $18 Thomas (6 hours) $16

3. Which sitter, Jenna or Thomas, earns more money for jobs of 5 hours or more? Jenna

4. Which line graph rises more quickly? Jenna's

5. Complete each statement. For every hour that passes, Jenna's profit increases by $3; Thomas's profit increases by $2.

6. At what point do the line graphs intersect?
(4,12)

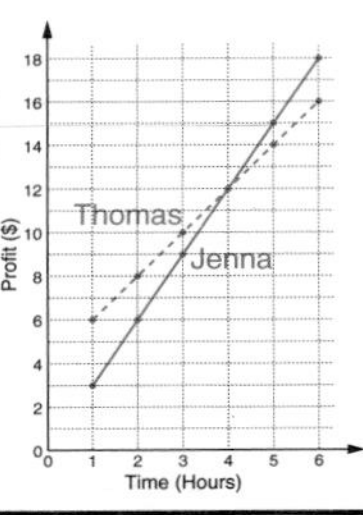

Practice

7. Evaluate when $m = 3$.

a. m^4 81 b. 20^m 8,000 c. $4^m + 4m$ 76 d. $10^m - 5^m$ 875 e. $\frac{m^3}{m^2}$ 3

Math Masters, p. 96

Teaching Master

Name Date Time

LESSON 3·10 **Reviewing Rules, Tables, and Graphs**

Rule:

in	out

(Label for y-axis)

(Label for x-axis)

***Math Masters*, p. 97**

NOTE You can quickly modify this activity by providing students with situations that involve more than one operation.

Example:

Dalia's hourly wage at her new job (x) is $1 more than twice the wage of her old job (w); ($x = 2w + 1$).

3 Differentiation Options

READINESS

PARTNER ACTIVITY

5–15 Min

▶ Custom-Made Representations

(*Math Masters*, p. 97)

Portfolio Ideas

This activity provides students with opportunities to review the particular representation(s) of function with which they may be struggling. Present students with a situation and ask them to write a rule, complete a table, or make a graph representing that situation. Some students might need help labeling axes and assigning value increments to each axis.

Examples:

▷ Every year Bart earns $150 more than he earned the previous year.

Rule:
Previous year's earnings (p) + $150 = Present year's earnings

in	out
(p)	(p + $150)
$0	$150
$75	$225
$150	$300
$200	$350
$300	$450

▷ Gloria earns $5.00 for every hour she baby-sits.

Rule:
Number of hours baby-sitting (n) * $5 = Gloria's total earnings

in	out
(n)	(n * $5)
0	$0
4	$20
9	$45
10	$50
12	$60

ENRICHMENT

▶ The Shape of Change

PARTNER ACTIVITY

30+ Min

(*Math Masters,* pp. 98 and 99)

Science Link To further explore how graph shapes correspond to situations, have students conduct an experiment. Provide students with three or four bottles or glasses of various shapes, metric measuring cups (for example, a medicine cup or beaker), the Geometry Template or metric ruler, and water. Students pour the same amount of water into each bottle. With a metric ruler, they measure the height of the water level after each addition of water until each bottle is full. Students record and graph results on *Math Masters,* page 98. Graphs should show that the height of the water in a particular bottle increases more slowly as the bottle becomes wider; the height increases more quickly as the bottle becomes narrower. For example, the height of the water level in Bottle 1 increases more quickly as water fills the base and neck of the bottle. Since Bottle 2 is a cylinder, Graph 2 reveals a steady change in water height as the volume of water increases. (*See margin.*)

After completing the experiment and analyzing their results, students match mystery graphs with various bottle shapes (*Math Masters,* p. 99).

▶ *5-Minute Math*

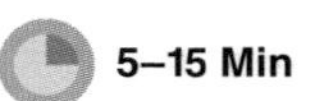

5–15 Min

To offer more practice using graphs to represent actions over time, see *5-Minute Math,* page 203.

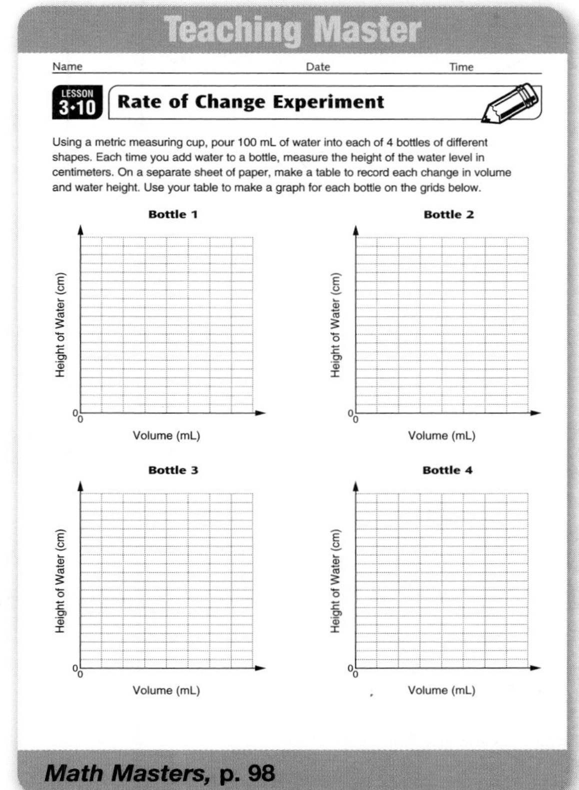

Teaching Master

Name Date Time

LESSON 3•10 **Rate of Change Experiment**

Using a metric measuring cup, pour 100 mL of water into each of 4 bottles of different shapes. Each time you add water to a bottle, measure the height of the water level in centimeters. On a separate sheet of paper, make a table to record each change in volume and water height. Use your table to make a graph for each bottle on the grids below.

Math Masters, p. 98

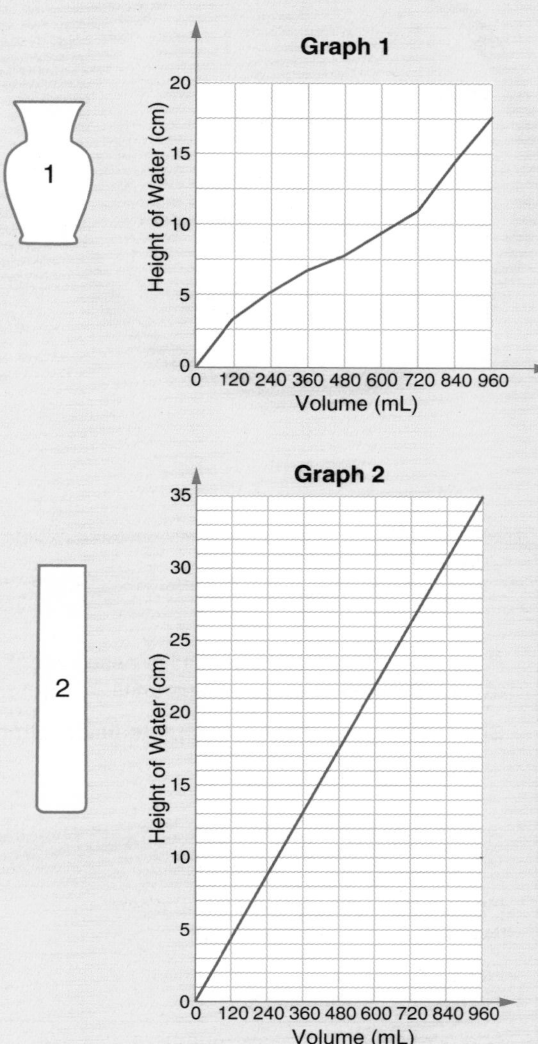

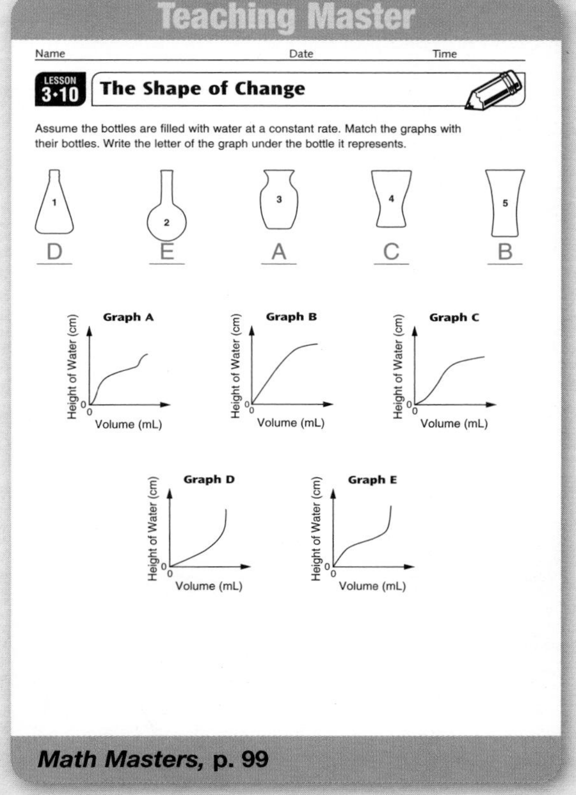

Teaching Master

Name Date Time

LESSON 3•10 **The Shape of Change**

Assume the bottles are filled with water at a constant rate. Match the graphs with their bottles. Write the letter of the graph under the bottle it represents.

Math Masters, p. 99

3•11 Progress Check 3

Objective To assess students' progress on mathematical content through the end of Unit 3.

1 Assessing Progress

Progress Check 3 is a cumulative assessment of concepts and skills taught in Unit 3 and in previous units.

See the Appendix for a complete list of Grade 6 Goals.

materials

- ☐ Study Link 3•10
- ☐ Assessment Masters (*Assessment Handbook,* pp. 150–155)
- ☐ slate

CONTENT ASSESSED	LESSON(S)	ASSESSMENT ITEMS			
		SELF	ORAL/SLATE	WRITTEN	
				PART A	PART B
Find factors and multiples of numbers. [Number and Numeration Goal 3]	3•2, 3•4, 3•6, 3•7, 3•9, 3•10				16, 17
Find equivalent names for numbers. [Number and Numeration Goal 4]	3•2	4	4		14, 15, 19
Add positive and negative numbers. [Operations and Computation Goal 1]	3•7, 3•8, 3•10	5	3	7d, 8b	
Multiply and divide whole numbers and decimals. [Operations and Computation Goal 2]	3•1, 3•4	4		3–7, 8b, 9	19
Estimate products and quotients of decimals. [Operations and Computation Goal 5]	3•3	4	2	5	18
Use and interpret data landmarks and data representations. [Data and Chance Goal 2]	3•6, 3•8–3•10			8b 10–13	20
Use formulas. [Measurement and Reference Frames Goal 2]	3•4	2		3–6, 8a, 8c	
Represent rates with formulas, tables, and graphs. [Patterns, Functions, and Algebra Goal 1]	3•3, 3•5–3•7, 3•9, 3•10	3		9	
Describe general patterns with words and number sentences. [Patterns, Functions, and Algebra Goal 1]	3•1–3•4, 3•7, 3•8	1, 6		1, 2	
Evaluate expressions. [Patterns, Functions, and Algebra Goal 3]	3•3		1	7, 9	

2 Building Background for Unit 4

Math Boxes 3•11 previews and practices skills for Unit 4.

The **Unit 4 Family Letter** introduces families to Unit 4 topics and terms.

materials

- ☐ *Math Journal 1,* p. 122
- ☐ Study Link Masters (*Math Masters,* pp. 100–104)

Additional Information

See *Assessment Handbook,* pages 68–75 for additional assessment information. For assessment checklists, see pages 234–237.

Technology

Assessment Management System
Progress Check 3
See the **iTLG.**

Getting Started

Math Message • Self Assessment

Complete the Self Assessment (Assessment Handbook, *p. 150*).

Study Link 3·10 Follow-Up

Briefly review students' answers.

1 Assessing Progress

▶ Math Message Follow-Up

(Self Assessment, *Assessment Handbook,* p. 150)

The Self Assessment offers students the opportunity to reflect upon their progress.

▶ Oral and Slate Assessments

Problems 1 and 3 provide summative information and can be used for grading purposes. Problems 2 and 4 provide formative information that can be useful in planning future instruction.

Oral Assessment

1. Give an algebraic expression to represent the situations. *Suggestions:* Suppose t stands for Tina's age now, and f stands for her father's age now.
   - How old will Tina be in 5 years? $t + 5$
   - If Tina's father is 30 years older than Tina, how old is her father? $t + 30$
   - If Tina's father is 4 times as old as Tina is now, how old is her father? $4 * t$
   - If Tina's father is 20 years older than Tina, how old is Tina? $f - 20$
2. Estimate using close numbers. *Suggestions:* Sample answers:
   - $41.6 * 5.2$ 200
   - $63.6 / 7.7$ 8
   - $0.92 * 15.04$ 15

Slate Assessment

3. Mentally add the following numbers. *Suggestions:*
   - $3 + (-3)$ 0
   - $70 + (-30)$ 40
   - $-140 + 60$ -80
   - $-80 + (-70)$ -150
   - $-120 + 120$ 0
   - $15 + (-265)$ -250
4. Rename fractions as decimals. *Suggestions:*
   - $\frac{9}{10}$ 0.9
   - $\frac{17}{20}$ 0.85
   - $\frac{7}{4}$ 1.75
   - $\frac{1}{250}$ 0.004

Assessment Master

Name Date Time

LESSON 3·11 **Self Assessment** Progress Check 3

Think about each skill listed below. Assess your own progress by checking the most appropriate box.

Skills	I can do this on my own and explain how to do it.	I can do this on my own.	I can do this if I get help or look at an example.
1. Describe a general number pattern in words and with a number sentence.			
2. Use a formula.			
3. Complete a table for a given rule. Then graph the data.			
4. Apply multiplication and division facts and strategies to solve problems.			
5. Mentally add positive and negative numbers.			
6. Write spreadsheet cell names and formulas.			

Assessment Handbook, **p. 150**

Assessment Master

Name Date Time

LESSON 3·11 **Written Assessment** Progress Check 3

Part A

1. Give two special cases for the general pattern $m + m + k = (2 * m) + k$.
   Sample answers:
   $4 + 4 + 3 = (2 * 4) + 3$ $\frac{1}{2} + \frac{1}{2} + 1 = (2 * \frac{1}{2}) + 1$
2. Circle each statement below (a–d) that describes the special cases at the right.
   (a.) Doubling a number is the same as adding it to itself.
   b. $2 * n = 2 + 2$ c. $2 * a = a - a$ (d.) $2 * a = a + a$

   $2 * 7 = 7 + 7$
   $2 * 1.5 = 1.5 + 1.5$
   $2 * 0 = 0 + 0$

You can use the formula $c = 2.54 * i$ to find length in centimeters (c) when length in inches (i) is known. Use this formula for Problems 3–5.

3. How many centimeters are in 2 inches? 5.08 cm (unit)
4. How many centimeters are in 100 inches? 254 cm (unit)
5. Circle the best estimate for the number of centimeters in 1 foot.
   24 (30) 40 50
6. Use the formulas at the right to find the perimeter and area of the rectangle.

   3.2 m
   1.5 m

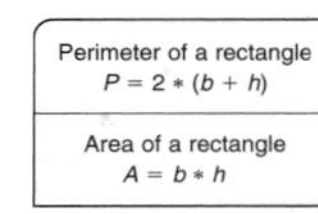

   a. Perimeter = 9.4 m (unit)
   b. Area = $4.8\ m^2$ (unit)

Assessment Handbook, **p. 151**

Name Date Time

7. Evaluate each expression when $x = 3$.

a. $2.7 * 10^x$ 2,700 b. $x^4 + 3^x$ 108

c. $x * 10^{-5}$ 0.00003 d. $x^0 + -3$ −2

8. Mr. Ricco used the spreadsheet at the right to record his students' scores on 3 math quizzes. The mean score for the 3 quizzes appears in Column E.

	A	B	C	D	E
1	Student	Quiz 1	Quiz 2	Quiz 3	Mean
2	Cheri	100	100	100	100
3	Briana	50	80	74	68
4	Lamar	100	95	95	97
5	Sam	80	100	90	90

a. Name the cell that contains Lamar's score on Quiz 2. C4

b. Calculate Sam's mean score and record it in cell E5.

c. Using cell names, write a formula for calculating the value in E5.
E5 = (B5 + C5 + D5) ÷ 3

9. Complete the table for the given rule. Then plot and connect the points to make a line graph.

Rule: $y = (\frac{1}{2} * x) + 1$

in	out
x	*y*
0	1
1	$1\frac{1}{2}$
2	2
4	3
5	$3\frac{1}{2}$

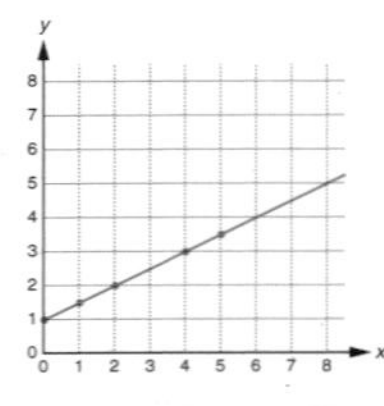

***Assessment Handbook,* p. 152**

Assessment Master

Name Date Time

LESSON 3•11 Written Assessment *continued*

Each of the graphs represents one of the situations described below. Match each situation with its graph.

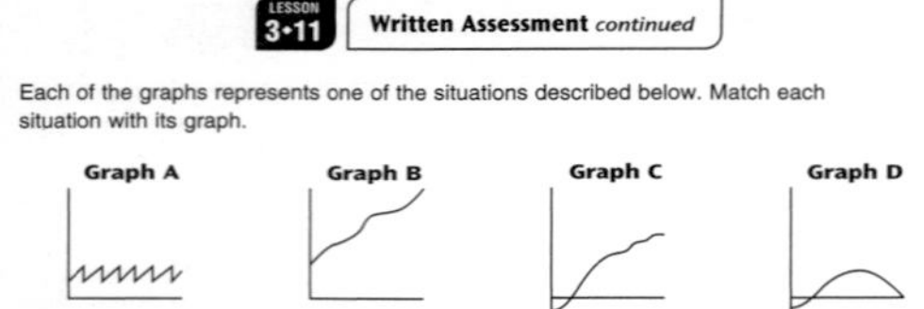

10. The height of a plant, starting as a seed. Graph C

11. The height of a human male between the ages of 5 and 12. Graph B

12. The height of the red liquid in a thermometer during a January day in Chicago, Illinois. Graph D

13. The height of the grass in a soccer field during a playing season. Graph A

Part B

14. Rename each fraction as a mixed number or whole number.

a. $\frac{29}{4}$ $7\frac{1}{4}$ b. $\frac{32}{8}$ 4 c. $\frac{15}{2}$ $7\frac{1}{2}$ d. $\frac{80}{16}$ 5

15. Rename each mixed number as a fraction.

a. $5\frac{3}{8}$ $\frac{43}{8}$ b. $4\frac{1}{2}$ $\frac{9}{2}$ c. $7\frac{9}{16}$ $\frac{121}{16}$ d. $4\frac{3}{4}$ $\frac{19}{4}$

16. Name the greatest common factor of each pair of numbers.

a. 8 and 24 8 b. 49 and 50 1

***Assessment Handbook,* p. 153**

▶ Written Assessment

INDEPENDENT ACTIVITY

(*Assessment Handbook,* pp. 151–154)

Part A Recognizing Student Achievement

Problems 1–13 provide summative information and may be used for grading purposes.

Problem(s)	Description
1, 2	Relate general patterns and special cases.
3–6	Use a formula to convert between inches and centimeters; find the perimeter and area of a rectangle; apply multiplication and division facts and strategies to solve problems.
7, 9	Evaluate expressions.
8	Use spreadsheet formulas.
9	Construct a graph from a table, rule, or formula.
10–13	Match a situation with the graph that represents it.

Part B Informing Instruction

Problems 14–20 provide formative information that can be useful in planning future instruction.

Problem(s)	Description
14, 15	Convert between fractions and mixed/whole numbers.
16, 17	Find the GCF and LCM of a set of numbers.
18	Use estimation to insert the decimal point in a quotient.
19	Multiply decimals by powers of 10.
20	Write a time story based on a graph.

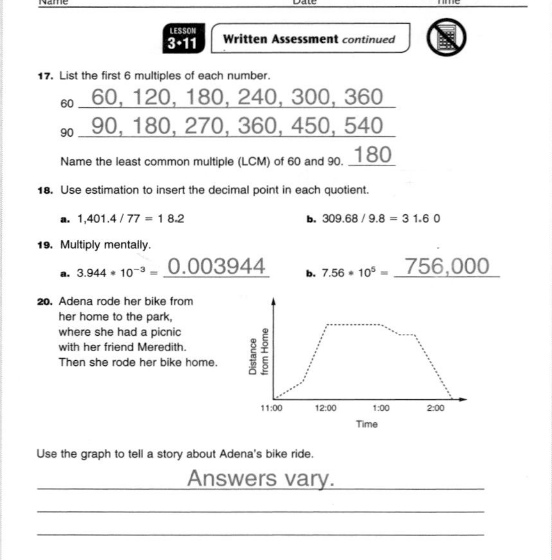
Assessment Master

Name Date Time

LESSON 3•11 Written Assessment *continued*

17. List the first 6 multiples of each number.

60 60, 120, 180, 240, 300, 360

90 90, 180, 270, 360, 450, 540

Name the least common multiple (LCM) of 60 and 90. 180

18. Use estimation to insert the decimal point in each quotient.

a. 1,401.4 / 77 = 18.2 b. 309.68 / 9.8 = 31.60

19. Multiply mentally.

a. $3.944 * 10^{-3}$ = 0.003944 b. $7.56 * 10^5$ = 756,000

20. Adena rode her bike from her home to the park, where she had a picnic with her friend Meredith. Then she rode her bike home.

Use the graph to tell a story about Adena's bike ride.

Answers vary.

***Assessment Handbook,* p. 154**

▶ Open Response

INDEPENDENT ACTIVITY

(*Assessment Handbook,* p. 155)

Representing Rates

The open-response item requires students to apply skills and concepts from Unit 3 to solve a multistep problem. See the *Assessment Handbook,* pages 71–75 for rubrics and student work samples for this problem.

2 Building Background for Unit 4

▶ Math Boxes 3•11

INDEPENDENT ACTIVITY

(*Math Journal 1,* p. 122)

Mixed Practice This Math Boxes page previews Unit 4 content.

▶ Study Link 3•11: Unit 4 Family Letter

INDEPENDENT ACTIVITY

(*Math Masters,* pp. 100–104)

Home Connection The Unit 4 Family Letter provides parents and guardians with information and activities related to Unit 4 topics.

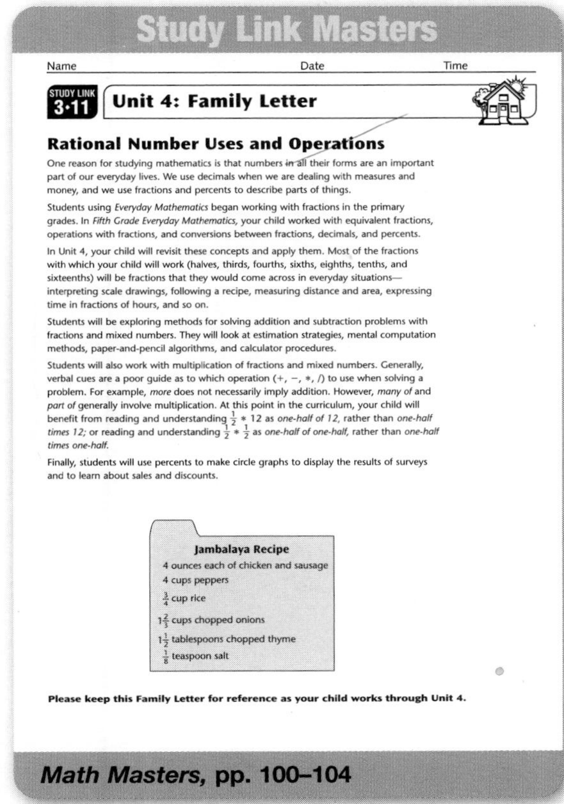

Study Link Masters

Name Date Time

STUDY LINK 3•11 **Unit 4: Family Letter**

Rational Number Uses and Operations

One reason for studying mathematics is that numbers in all their forms are an important part of our everyday lives. We use decimals when we are dealing with measures and money, and we use fractions and percents to describe parts of things.

Students using *Everyday Mathematics* began working with fractions in the primary grades. In *Fifth Grade Everyday Mathematics,* your child worked with equivalent fractions, operations with fractions, and conversions between fractions, decimals, and percents.

In Unit 4, your child will revisit these concepts and apply them. Most of the fractions with which your child will work (halves, thirds, fourths, sixths, eighths, tenths, and sixteenths) will be fractions that they would come across in everyday situations—interpreting scale drawings, following a recipe, measuring distance and area, expressing time in fractions of hours, and so on.

Students will be exploring methods for solving addition and subtraction problems with fractions and mixed numbers. They will look at estimation strategies, mental computation methods, paper-and-pencil algorithms, and calculator procedures.

Students will also work with multiplication of fractions and mixed numbers. Generally, verbal cues are a poor guide as to which operation (+, −, ∗, /) to use when solving a problem. For example, *more* does not necessarily imply addition. However, *many of* and *part of* generally involve multiplication. At this point in the curriculum, your child will benefit from reading and understanding $\frac{1}{2} * 12$ as *one-half of 12,* rather than *one-half times 12;* or reading and understanding $\frac{1}{2} * \frac{1}{2}$ as *one-half of one-half,* rather than *one-half times one-half.*

Finally, students will use percents to make circle graphs to display the results of surveys and to learn about sales and discounts.

Jambalaya Recipe
4 ounces each of chicken and sausage
4 cups peppers
$\frac{3}{4}$ cup rice
$1\frac{2}{3}$ cups chopped onions
$1\frac{1}{2}$ tablespoons chopped thyme
$\frac{1}{8}$ teaspoon salt

Please keep this Family Letter for reference as your child works through Unit 4.

Math Masters, pp. 100–104

Assessment Master

Name Date Time

LESSON 3•11 **Open Response** Progress Check 3

Representing Rates

Since January 1, you have kept track of the number of members belonging to two school clubs. The Math Club currently has 200 members, and it adds 50 new members per month. The Science Club currently has 400 members, and it adds 25 new members per month. Use the representations below to figure out how many months it will take for the two clubs to have the same number of members if no one quits.

Math Club
Rule: Total Members = 200 + (50 ∗ Number of Months)
Formula: $m = 50x + 200$

Number of Months	Total Members
x	$50x + 200$
0	200
1	250

Science Club
Rule: Total Members = 400 + (25 ∗ Number of Months)
Formula: $m = 25x + 400$

Number of Months	Total Members
x	$25x + 400$
0	400
1	425

Club Memberships
Total Members: 0, 200, 400, 600, 800
Number of Months: 0, 4, 8, 12

The clubs will have the same number of members after _____ months.

On a separate sheet of paper, explain how you used the representations (graph, table, formulas) to solve the problem. See the *Assessment Handbook* for rubrics and sample answers.

***Assessment Handbook,* p. 155**

Student Page

Date Time

LESSON 3•11 **Math Boxes**

1. Compare each pair of fractions. Write < or >.
   a. $\frac{23}{25}$ > $\frac{21}{25}$
   b. $\frac{3}{10}$ < $\frac{7}{20}$
   c. $\frac{1}{7}$ > $\frac{1}{8}$
   d. $\frac{5}{6}$ > $\frac{5}{9}$
   SRB 75

2. List all the factors of each number.
   24 1, 2, 3, 4, 6, 8, 12, 24
   36 1, 2, 3, 4, 6, 9, 12, 18, 36
   Name the greatest common factor (GCF) of 24 and 36. 12
   SRB 80

3. Rename each fraction as a decimal.
   a. $\frac{1}{5}$ = 0.2
   b. $\frac{4}{25}$ = 0.16
   Rename each decimal as a fraction.
   c. 0.02 = $\frac{2}{100}$, or $\frac{1}{50}$
   d. 0.20 = $\frac{20}{100}$, $\frac{2}{10}$, or $\frac{1}{5}$
   SRB 59 60

4. List the first 6 multiples of each number.
   12 12, 24, 36, 48, 60, 72
   15 15, 30, 45, 60, 75, 90
   Name the least common multiple (LCM) of 12 and 15. 60
   SRB 78

5. Rename each mixed number as a fraction.
   a. $3\frac{2}{3}$ $\frac{11}{3}$
   b. $7\frac{3}{4}$ $\frac{31}{4}$
   Rename each fraction as a mixed or whole number.
   c. $\frac{9}{2}$ $4\frac{1}{2}$ d. $\frac{23}{8}$ $2\frac{7}{8}$
   SRB 71 72

6. Complete.
   a. $\frac{2}{5} = \frac{20}{50}$
   b. $\frac{7}{9} = \frac{21}{27}$
   c. $\frac{5}{8} = \frac{35}{56}$
   d. $\frac{11}{16} = \frac{33}{48}$
   SRB 71

***Math Journal 1,* p. 122**

Unit 4 Organizer

Rational Number Uses and Operations

Overview

One goal of *Sixth Grade Everyday Mathematics* is to apply and extend many of the concepts that students were introduced to in *Grade 5 Everyday Mathematics.* Unit 4 has five main areas of focus:

- To review the notations for rational numbers—fractions, mixed numbers, decimals, and percents,
- To review the ordering of fractions,
- To review operations (addition, subtraction, and multiplication) with fractions and to extend the operations to mixed numbers,
- To build connections between how the value of whole- and decimal-number quotients are maintained and how a division algorithm for fractions works, and
- To review the meaning and uses of percents, and to solve problems involving percents and discounts.

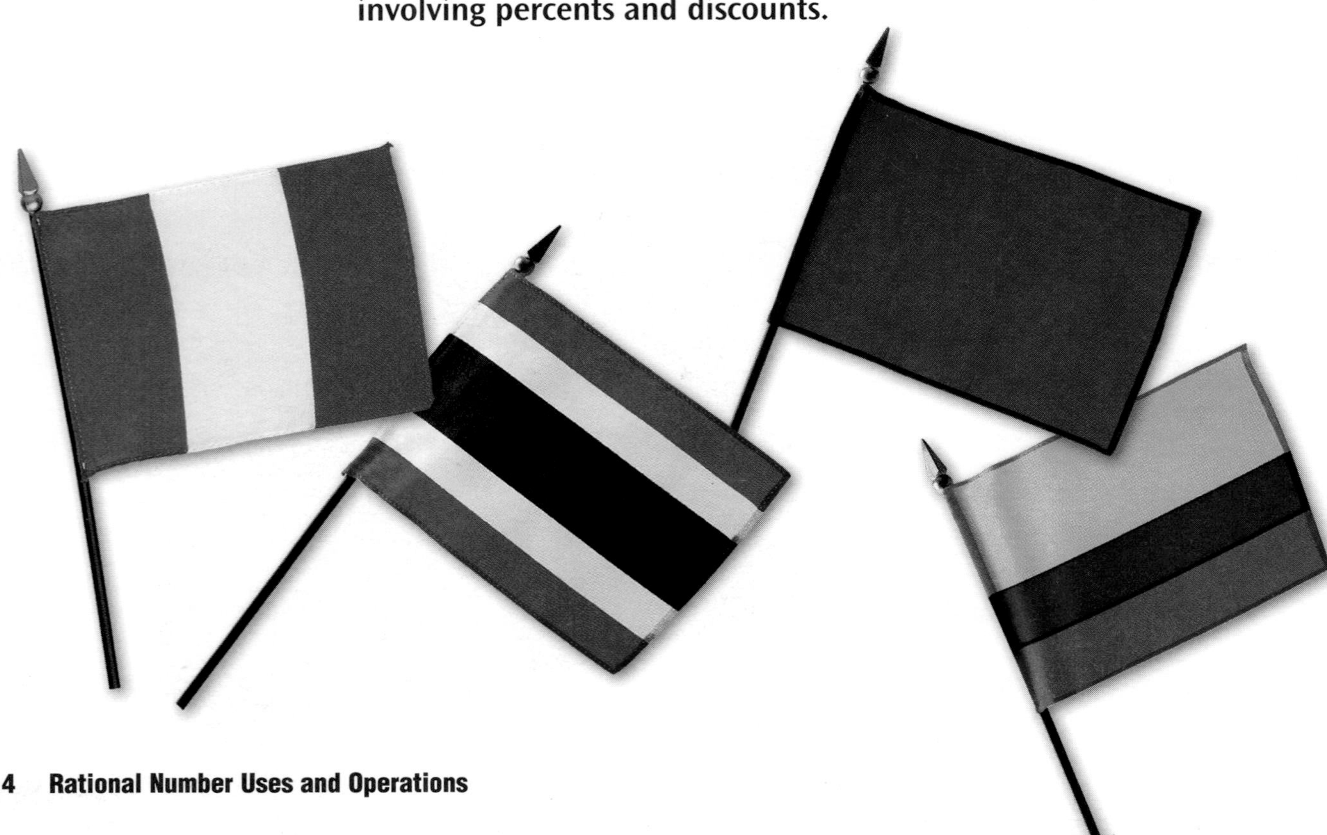

Contents

Unit 4 Organizer

Learning In Perspective

	Lesson Objectives	Links to the Past	Links to the Future
4•1	To review finding equivalent fractions and renaming fractions in simplest form.	In Grade 5, students rename fractions and mixed numbers in simplest form and find equivalent fractions.	Grade 6 and after: Applications and maintenance.
4•2	To compare fractions with unlike denominators.	In Grade 5, students compare and order fractions by renaming them with common denominators.	In Unit 8, students compare ratios by renaming them as *n*-to-1 ratios.
4•3	To review adding and subtracting fractions with like and unlike denominators.	In Grade 5, students use fraction-stick pieces to add fractions with like and unlike denominators.	In Units 6 and 9, students combine terms consisting of fractions and mixed numbers to simplify and solve equations. After Grade 6: Applications and maintenance.
4•4	To add and subtract mixed numbers with like denominators.	In Grade 5, students add and subtract mixed numbers having fractions with like denominators.	In Units 6 and 9, students combine terms consisting of fractions and mixed numbers to simplify and solve equations. After Grade 6: Applications and maintenance.
4•5	To add and subtract mixed numbers with unlike denominators.	In Grade 5, students add mixed numbers with unlike denominators. They estimate sums and differences of mixed numbers.	In Units 6 and 9, students combine terms consisting of fractions and mixed numbers to simplify and solve equations. After Grade 6: Applications and maintenance.
4•6	To represent the fraction multiplication algorithm as a general pattern; and to use the algorithm to find products of fractions.	In Grade 5, students solve "fraction-of" problems and number stories. They derive and use algorithms for multiplying fractions.	In Unit 7, students apply fraction multiplication to calculate expected outcomes and probabilities.
4•7	To multiply mixed numbers.	In Grade 5, students derive and use algorithms for multiplying mixed numbers.	In Unit 9, students apply distributive properties to calculate products of whole and mixed numbers.
4•8	To review converting between fractions, decimals, and percents.	In Grade 5, students use the Probability Meter to find equivalent fractions, decimals, and percents. They convert between fractions, decimals, and percents.	In Grade 6 and after, students work flexibly with fractions, decimals, and percents to solve problems.
4•9	To develop a rule for converting between decimals and percents; and to convert fractions to decimals and percents.	In Grade 5, students rename fractions as percents. They find decimal equivalents by using a Fraction-Stick Chart and by dividing with a calculator.	In Units 6 and 8, students find quotients to a given number of decimal places.
4•10	To represent data with circle graphs.	In Unit 1, students use the Percent Circle to interpret circle graphs. In Grade 5, students use the Percent Circle to draw and interpret circle graphs.	In Units 5 and 8, students calculate degree measures of sectors on circle graphs.
4•11	To review finding a percent of a number.	In Grade 5, students find the whole given a fraction or percent of the whole. They find a percent of a number.	In Unit 8, students solve percent problems using proportions.

Key Concepts and Skills

	Key Concepts and Skills	Grade 6 Goals*
4•1	Simplify a fraction by dividing the numerator and denominator by the greatest common factor.	Number and Numeration Goal 3
	Use an area model to find equivalent fractions.	Number and Numeration Goal 5
	Use multiplication and division facts to find equivalent fractions and simplify fractions.	Operations and Computation Goal 2
	Apply the Multiplication Property of One to find equivalent fractions and simplify fractions.	Patterns, Functions, and Algebra Goal 4
4•2	Apply the concept of a multiple to rename fractions with a common denominator and compare fractions.	Number and Numeration Goal 3
	Order fractions using benchmark comparisons.	Number and Numeration Goal 6
	Use multiplication and division facts to find equivalent fractions and simplify fractions.	Operations and Computation Goal 2
	Use signs of inequality to compare fractions.	Patterns, Functions, and Algebra Goal 2
4•3	Apply the concept of a multiple to rename fractions with a common denominator and to order fractions.	Number and Numeration Goal 3
	Convert between fractions and mixed numbers.	Number and Numeration Goal 5
	Use multiplication and division facts to simplify fractions.	Operations and Computation Goal 2
	Add and subtract fractions with like and unlike denominators.	Operations and Computation Goal 3
4•4	Convert between fractions and mixed numbers.	Number and Numeration Goal 5
	Use multiplication and division facts to find equivalent fractions and to simplify fractions.	Operations and Computation Goal 2
	Add and subtract mixed numbers with like denominators.	Operations and Computation Goal 3
4•5	Convert between fractions and mixed numbers.	Number and Numeration Goal 5
	Add and subtract mixed numbers with like and unlike denominators.	Operations and Computation Goal 3
	Measure a line segment to the nearest $\frac{1}{8}$ inch.	Measurement and Reference Frames Goal 1
	Apply the Associative Property of Addition to calculate sums of mixed numbers.	Patterns, Functions, and Algebra Goal 4
4•6	Apply the concept of GCF to rename a fraction in simplest form.	Number and Numeration Goal 3
	Convert between whole numbers and improper fractions.	Number and Numeration Goal 5
	Use an algorithm to multiply a fraction by a fraction.	Operations and Computation Goal 4
	Represent an algorithm as a general pattern with variables.	Patterns, Functions, and Algebra Goal 1
4•7	Convert between fractions and mixed numbers.	Number and Numeration Goal 5
	Multiply fractions.	Operations and Computation Goal 4
	Use area formulas to solve problems.	Measurement and Reference Frames Goal 2
	Apply the concept of congruence to calculate the surface area of a cube.	Geometry Goal 2
	Use the partial-products method (Distributive Property of Multiplication over Addition) to multiply mixed numbers.	Patterns, Functions, and Algebra Goal 4
4•8	Apply place-value concepts to per-hundred representations.	Number and Numeration Goal 1
	Convert between fractions, decimals, and percents.	Number and Numeration Goal 5
	Use multiplication and division facts to find equivalent fractions and simplify fractions.	Operations and Computation Goal 2
	Identify the missing value in an open number sentence.	Patterns, Functions, and Algebra Goal 2
4•9	Apply place-value concepts to round decimal quotients to the nearest hundredth.	Number and Numeration Goal 1
	Use a calculator to rename fractions as percents by dividing.	Operations and Computation Goal 2
	Interpret the remainder and adjust/truncate/round the quotient accordingly.	Operations and Computation Goal 5
	Apply the Identity Property of Multiplication to convert between decimals and percents.	Patterns, Functions, and Algebra Goal 4
4•10	Use multiplication and division facts to find equivalent fractions.	Operations and Computation Goal 2
	Use a magnitude estimate to place the decimal point in a quotient.	Operations and Computation Goal 5
	Use the Percent Circle to construct a circle graph.	Data and Chance Goal 1
	Interpret data displayed as percents and draw conclusions about changes reflected in the data.	Data and Chance Goal 2
4•11	Use a unit percent to calculate the percent of a number.	Number and Numeration Goal 2
	Apply the concept of GCF and divisibility rules to rename percents as fractions.	Number and Numeration Goal 3
	Add and subtract multidigit numbers.	Operations and Computation Goal 1
	Multiply a whole number by a fraction or a decimal.	Operations and Computation Goal 4

* See the Appendix for a complete list of Grade 6 Goals.

Ongoing Learning and Practice

Math Boxes

Math Boxes are paired across lessons as shown in the brackets below. This makes them useful as assessment tools. Math Boxes also preview content of the next unit.

Mixed practice	[4•1, 4•3], [4•2, 4•4], [4•5, 4•7], [4•6, 4•8, 4•10], [4•9, 4•11]
Mixed practice with multiple choice	4•3, 4•4, 4•7, 4•10, 4•11
Mixed practice with writing/reasoning opportunity	4•1, 4•2, 4•5, 4•6, 4•9

Practice through Games

Games are an essential component of practice in the *Everyday Mathematics* program. Games offer skills practice and promote strategic thinking.

Lesson	Game	Skill Practiced
4•1	*Fraction Capture*	**Naming equivalent fractions** Number and Numeration Goal 5
4•2	*Build It*	**Comparing and ordering fractions** Number and Numeration Goal 6
4•3	*Divisibility Dash*	**Reviewing divisibility rules** Number and Numeration Goal 3
4•4	*Fraction Action, Fraction Friction*	**Estimating sums of fractions** Operations and Computation Goal 5
4•7	*Mixed-Number Spin*	**Estimating sums and differences of fractions and/or mixed numbers** Operations and Computation Goal 5
4•8	*2-4-8 Frac-Tac-Toe* and *3-6-9 Frac-Tac-Toe* (Decimal Versions)	**Converting fractions to decimals** Number and Numeration Goal 5
4•9	*2-4-8 Frac-Tac-Toe and 3-6-9 Frac-Tac-Toe* (Percent Versions)	**Converting fractions to percents** Number and Numeration Goal 5

See the *Differentiation Handbook* for ways to adapt games to meet students' needs.

Home Communication

Study Links provide homework and home communication.

◀ ***Home Connection Handbook*** provides more ideas to communicate effectively with parents.

Unit 4 Family Letter provides families with an overview, Do-Anytime Activities, Building Skills Through Games, and a list of vocabulary.

Problem Solving

Encourage students to use a variety of strategies to solve problems and to explain those strategies. Strategies that students might use in this unit:

- Acting out the problem
- Writing algebraic expressions
- Identifying and using patterns
- Using data in tables
- Drawing and using pictures and graphs
- Using estimation
- Using computation

Lessons that teach *through* problem solving, not just *about* problem solving

Lesson	Activity
4•1, 4•6	Use pictures and paper folding to find equivalent fractions and products of fractions.
4•2	Encourage students to use number sense when comparing fractions.
4•3	Use parts of a square to model the addition of fractions.
4•5	Write algebraic expressions and solve addition and subtraction number stories to calculate the areas of oceans and lakes.
4•4, 4•5	Estimate sums and differences of fractions and mixed numbers.
4•6	Use special cases to develop a fraction multiplication algorithm.
4•10	Use data to calculate sector sizes on a circle graph.
4•11	Solve percent problems involving discounts and sale prices.

See Chapter 18 in the *Teacher's Reference Manual* for more information about problem solving.

Planning Tips

Pacing

Pacing depends on a number of factors, such as students' individual needs and how long your school has been using *Everyday Mathematics.* At the beginning of Unit 4, review your *Content by Strand* Poster to help you set a monthly pace.

← MOST CLASSROOMS →

OCTOBER	NOVEMBER	DECEMBER

NCTM Standards

Unit 4 Lessons	4•1	4•2	4•3	4•4	4•5	4•6	4•7	4•8	4•9	4•10	4•11
NCTM Standards	1, 6–8, 10	1, 6–8, 10	1, 6–8	1, 6–10	1, 6–10	1, 6–8	1, 6–8	1, 6–10	1, 6–9	4–10	1, 5–10

Content Standards: **1** Number and Operations, **2** Algebra, **3** Geometry, **4** Measurement, **5** Data Analysis and Probability
Process Standards: **6** Problem Solving, **7** Reasoning and Proof, **8** Communication, **9** Connections, **10** Representation

Balanced Assessment

Ongoing Assessment

Recognizing Student Achievement

Opportunities to assess students' progress toward Grade 6 Goals:

Lesson	Content Assessed
4•1	Rename fractions in simplest form. [Number and Numeration Goal 5]
4•2	Name the least common multiple (LCM) for a given number pair. [Number and Numeration Goal 3]
4•3	Add and subtract fractions with unlike denominators. [Operations and Computation Goal 3]
4•4	Add mixed numbers with like denominators. [Operations and Computation Goal 3]
4•5	Subtract mixed numbers. [Operations and Computation Goal 3]
4•6	Add and subtract fractions with unlike denominators. [Operations and Computation Goal 3]
4•7	Multiply and simplify fractions. [Operations and Computation Goal 4]
4•8	Convert between fractions, decimals, and percents. [Number and Numeration Goal 5]
4•9	Multiply a whole number by a fraction to find a fractional part of a number. [Operations and Computation Goal 4]
4•10	Rename fractions as decimals and percents. [Number and Numeration Goal 5]
4•11	Convert between fractions, decimals, and percents. [Number and Numeration Goal 5]

Use the **Assessment Management System** to collect and analyze data about students' progress throughout the year.

Informing Instruction

To anticipate common student errors and to highlight problem-solving strategies:

Lesson 4•1 Understand how equivalent fractions are generated

Lesson 4•6 Multiply with fractions

Lesson 4•9 Know how to translate fractions to percents

Periodic Assessment

4•12 Progress Check 4

CONTENT ASSESSED	ASSESSMENT ITEMS			
	Self	Oral/Slate	Written	Open Response
Find fractional parts of a region. Calculate the percent of a number. [Number and Numeration Goal 2]	✔	✔	✔	
Convert between fractions, mixed numbers, decimals, and percents. Express equivalent fractions in simplest form. [Number and Numeration Goal 5]	✔		✔	
Use signs of inequality to compare fractions; order fractions. [Number and Numeration Goal 6]	✔	✔	✔	
Divide a decimal by a whole number. [Operations and Computational Goal 2]			✔	
Add and subtract fractions and mixed numbers with unlike denominators. [Operations and Computational Goal 3]	✔		✔	✔
Estimate and find products of fractions and mixed numbers. [Operations and Computational Goal 4]	✔	✔	✔	
Construct a circle graph from percents. [Data and Chance Goal 1]	✔		✔	
Estimate length with and without tools. [Measurement and Reference Frames Goal 1]				✔
Find the perimeter and area of a rectangle. [Measurement and Reference Frames Goal 2]			✔	
Evaluate expression involving exponents and integers. [Patterns, Functions, and Algebra Goal 3]			✔	

Portfolio Opportunities

Opportunities to gather samples of students' mathematical writings, drawings, and creations to add balance to the assessment process:

- Exploring patterns related to the least common multiple, **Lesson 4•3**
- Explaining strategies to compare fractions, **Lesson 4•6**
- Modeling fraction multiplication, **Lesson 4•6**
- Comparing and ordering fractions, **Lesson 4•9**
- Conducting a survey and representing the results, **Lesson 4•10**
- Exploring ways to collect, represent, and interpret survey data, **Lesson 4•11**

Assessment Handbook

Unit 4 Assessment Support

- Grade 6 Goals, pp. 37–50
- Unit 4 Assessment Overview, pp. 76–83
- Unit 4 Open Response
  - Detailed rubric, p. 80
  - Sample student responses, pp. 81–83

Unit 4 Assessment Masters

- Unit 4 Self Assessment, p. 156
- Unit 4 Written Assessment, pp. 157–159
- Unit 4 Open Response, p. 160
- Unit 4 Class Checklist, pp. 240, 241, and 275
- Unit 4 Individual Profile of Progress, pp. 238, 239, and 274
- Exit Slip, p. 283
- Math Logs, pp. 278–280
- Other Student Assessment Forms, pp. 276, 277, and 281

Differentiated Instruction

Daily Lesson Support

ENGLISH LANGUAGE LEARNERS

4•9 Supporting language with patterns
4•11 Explaining to support language

EXTRA PRACTICE

4•4 Modeling and renaming mixed numbers
4•5 Writing custom-made Math Boxes
4•7 Multiplying mixed numbers
4•9 Renaming percents

5-Minute Math **4•3** Comparing and ordering fractions; **4•6** Adding, subtracting, and multiplying fractions; **4•10** Estimating products and percents of given numbers

READINESS

4•1 Using factor rainbows to list factors
4•2 Using benchmark fractions
4•3 Using fraction strips
4•4 Using a calculator to count by fractions
4•5 Representing mixed numbers
4•6 Modeling fraction multiplication
4•7 Modeling mixed-number multiplication
4•8 Representing fractions, decimals, and percents equivalencies
4•10 Estimating and measuring sector size
4•11 Modeling fractional parts of a number

ENRICHMENT

4•1 Solving real-world GCF problems
4•2 Comparing fractions
4•3 Exploring patterns related to LCM
4•4 Reading about fractions in poetry
4•5 Creating subtraction problems
4•6 Solving a multistep problem
4•8 Using spreadsheet software
4•8 Reading and writing percentage stories
4•9 Examining prime factors
4•10 Using computer graphing software
4•11 Taking a survey and interpreting results

Adjusting the Activity

4•1 Showing equivalent names
4•1 Simplifying and renaming fractions
4•2 Comparing fractions
4•3 Using shapes to compare fractions **ELL**
4•3 Using calculators with fractions
4•4 Modeling mixed numbers **ELL**
4•5 Adding and subtracting mixed numbers
4•6 Recording general patterns
4•7 Calculating areas **ELL**
4•9 Connecting the % and ¢ symbols
4•10 Constructing circle graphs
4•11 Discussing vocabulary terms **ELL**
4•11 Solving percent problems mentally

AUDITORY • KINESTHETIC • TACTILE • VISUAL

Cross-Curricular Links

Literature

Lesson 4•4 Students read the poem "Proper Fractions."
Lesson 4•8 Students read *Twizzlers™ Percentages Book.*

Consumer Education

Lesson 4•8 Students use spreadsheet software to convert between fractions, decimals, and percents.
Lesson 4•11 Students discuss terms related to prices and interest.

Geography

Lesson 4•5 Students write algebraic expressions and solve number stories involving areas of oceans and lakes.

Science

Lesson 4•10 Students calculate sector sizes and construct a circle graph.
Lesson 4•11 Students further explore ways to collect, represent, and interpret data.

Using the Projects 

Use Project 6, Anthropometry Project during or after Unit 4, to measure body parts, plot measurements as data pairs, and investigate formulas that relate body measurements. See the *Differentiation Handbook* for modifications to Project 6.

Differentiation Handbook

See the *Differentiation Handbook* for materials on Unit 4.

Language Support

Everyday Mathematics provides lesson-specific suggestions to help all students, including non-native English speakers, to acquire, process, and express mathematical ideas.

Connecting Math and Literacy

Lesson 4•4 *Math Talk: Mathematical Ideas in Poems for Two Voices,* by Theoni Pappas, Wide World Publishing/Tetra, 1991
Lesson 4•8 *Twizzlers™ Percentages Book,* by Jerry Pallotta, Scholastic, Inc., 2001

Student Reference Book

pp. 11, 49, 50, 59, 60, 74–77, 83–86, 146, 214–217, 273, 274, 307, 309, 314–318, 327

Unit 4 Vocabulary

common denominator
common factor
discount
equivalent fractions
greatest common factor (GCF)
improper fraction
interest
least common denominator (LCD)
least common multiple (LCM)
mixed number
percent
proper fraction
quick common denominator (QCD)
regular price
sale price
simplest form

Multiage Classroom ◆ Companion Lessons

Companion Lessons from Grade 5 can help you meet instructional needs of a multiage classroom. The full Scope and Sequence can be found in the Appendix.

Grade 5	5•1–5•4	5•1–5•4, 8•1–8•3	6•8, 8•7, 8•8	6•8	6•8	8•7, 8•8	8•7, 8•8	5•1–5•11	5•8		
Grade 6	**4•1**	**4•2**	**4•3**	**4•4**	**4•5**	**4•6**	**4•7**	**4•8**	**4•9**	**4•10**	**4•11**

Professional Development

Teacher's Reference Manual Links

Lesson	Topic	Section
4•1, 4•2	Fractions, Decimals, Percents, and Rational Numbers	9.3.1, 9.3.2, and 9.3.4
4•3–4•7	Algorithms for Fractions	11.3
4•3–4•8	Algorithms on Calculators	11.4
4•8–4•11	Fraction/Decimal/Percent Conversions	11.4.3
4•10	Interpreting and Displaying Data	12.2.3

Materials

Lesson	Masters	Manipulative Kit Items	Other Items
4•1	Study Link Master, p. 105 Game Master, p. 447 Teaching Masters, pp. 106–108	per group: 2 six-sided dice	per student: 2 sheets notebook paper
4•2	Study Link 4•1 Study Link Master, p. 109 Game Masters, pp. 427 and 428 Teaching Master, p. 110	slate Geometry Template	scissors
4•3	Study Link 4•2 Teaching Masters, pp. 112*, 113*, 115, and 116 transparency of *Math Masters,* p. 111* Study Link Master, p. 114 Game Master, p. 432 Teaching Aid Master, p. 416	per group: 4 each of number cards 0–9; 2 each of number cards 2, 3, 5, 6, 9, and 10	scissors
4•4	Study Link 4•3 Teaching Masters, pp. 117 and 119 Study Link Master, p. 118 Game Master, p. 446	Geometry Template calculator	scissors; *Math Talk: Mathematical Ideas in Poems for Two Voices;* coins and bills of various denominations
4•5	Study Link 4•4 Teaching Masters, pp. 120 and 122 Study Link Master, p. 121 Teaching Aid Master, p. 405	slate Geometry Template or protractor	
4•6	Study Link 4•5 Study Link Master, p. 123 Teaching Masters, pp. 124 and 125	Geometry Template or protractor	2 different-colored pencils or markers
4•7	Study Link 4•6 Teaching Masters, pp. 126, 127*, and 128* Study Link Master, p. 129 Game Masters, pp. 458 and 459	Geometry Template or protractor	per group: 1 large paper clip
4•8	Study Link 4•7 Study Link Master, p. 132 Game Masters, pp. 439–441 and 444* Teaching Master, p. 133	Geometry Template or protractor per group: 4 each of number cards 0–10	Probability Meter Poster; 2-color counters or pennies; *Twizzlers™ Percentages Book;* computer/spreadsheet software
4•9	Study Link 4•8 Study Link Master, p. 134 Game Master, pp. 439, 442, 443, and 445* Teaching Master, p. 135	calculator slate per group: 4 each of number cards 0–10	per group: 2-color counters or pennies
4•10	Study Link 4•9 Teaching Master, pp. 136 and 138 Study Link Master, p. 137	calculator compass Geometry Template or protractor	straightedge; color pencils or markers; computer/graphing software
4•11	Study Link 4•10 Study Link Master, p. 139 Teaching Master, p. 140	calculator	computer/graphing software
4•12	Study Link 4•11 Assessment Masters, pp. 156–160 Study Link Masters, pp. 141–144	slate Geometry Template	

Technology

Assessment Management System, Unit 4
iTLG, Unit 4

* Denotes optional materials

Mathematical Background

The discussion below highlights the major content ideas presented in Unit 4 and helps establish instructional priorities.

Historical Roots of Fractions and Decimal Notation for Rational Numbers

Every human society throughout history has invented counting words and counting systems. Many cultures went beyond counting words to invent symbol systems for writing and calculating with whole numbers. As commerce and trade developed, people found they needed numbers between whole numbers to express parts of measures, such as length, capacity, weight, and money. Hence, they first invented words and eventually written notations for the in-between numbers. Some of these notations used symbols that we now see as precursors to decimal notation. Only in relatively recent times have notations for percents been used. Even more recently, mathematics has come to terms with the endless repeating decimals that often result from changing fractions to decimals. Finally, fractions, decimals (including repeating decimals), and percents (usually as rounded decimals) have all been recognized as equivalent forms of what in modern mathematics are called rational numbers.

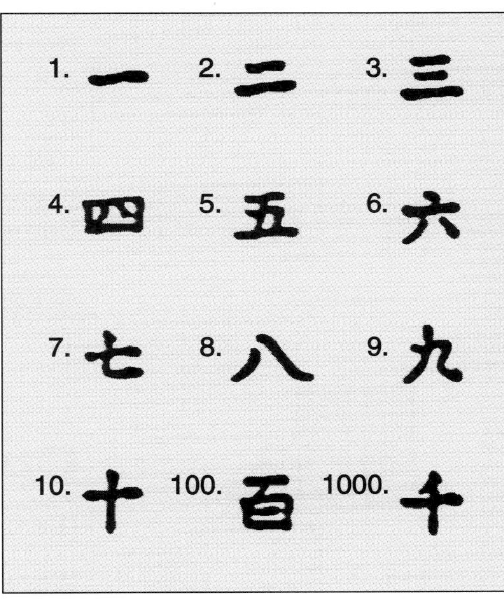

Chinese numerals

6,579 written with Chinese numerals

For more information about fraction and decimal notation, refer to the *Teacher's Reference Manual,* Section 9.3.1.

Note: Consider setting up a Fractions, Decimals, Percents Museum in your classroom. Ask students to look in magazines and newspapers for examples of how fractions, decimals, and percents are used in everyday life.

Using Common Denominators in Operations with Fractions

(Lessons 4◆1–4◆5)

The fact that every fraction has an unlimited number of names is an enormous convenience in arithmetic. For any two (or more) fractions, there is an unlimited supply of common denominators, which makes it easy to order, add, and subtract fractions, and also to divide fractions (a concept and skill to be explored in Unit 6.)

Traditional school arithmetic provides extensive teaching and practice using common denominators, and especially in finding a "least common denominator" (LCD) for two or more fractions. While some of this work is useful, the authors of *Everyday Mathematics* believe that the emphasis on finding LCDs is usually overdone, too formal, and without much meaning for many people. In particular, the authors believe that the pervasive search in schools for least common denominators wastes time, and that excessive attention to LCDs as the only permissible denominators may interfere with the acquisition of some algebraic concepts.

For adding, subtracting, or ordering easy fractions, it is simple to find common denominators once one understands what is needed. Students might do this first by simply scanning lists of equivalent names (including prime factors), perhaps finding several possibilities.

One way to find a common denominator of two fractions is to multiply the two denominators. *Everyday Mathematics* calls this product a "quick common denominator" (QCD). Finding a QCD always works. QCDs are frequently used for fraction problems in the algebra courses your students will soon be taking. This is because algebra models for solving problems usually involve variables, and since actual numbers are not known, finding an LCD is impossible.

whole

More information about adding and subtracting with common denominators can be found in the *Teacher's Reference Manual,* Section 11.3.

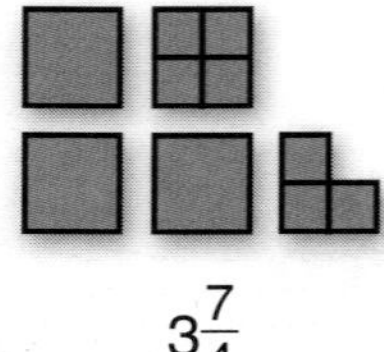

$3\frac{7}{4}$

Operations with Mixed Numbers

(Lessons 4◆4, 4◆5, and 4◆7)

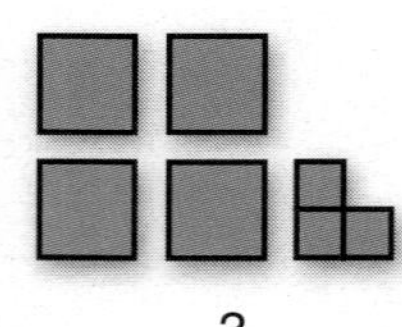

$4\frac{3}{4}$

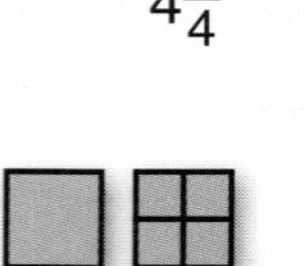

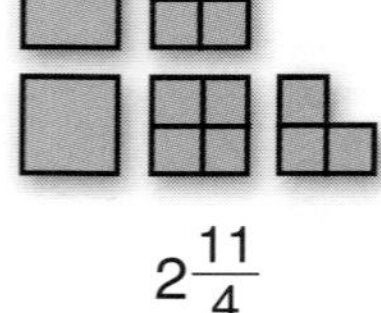

$2\frac{11}{4}$

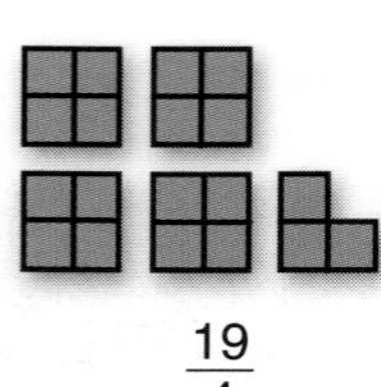

$\frac{19}{4}$

When working with mixed numbers, it is important to keep in mind that a mixed number is the sum of a whole number and a fraction (for example, $4\frac{2}{3} = 4 + \frac{2}{3}$). Mixed numbers are usually more meaningful if the fraction part is a "proper" fraction; that is, a fraction in which the numerator is less than the denominator, as in $4\frac{2}{3}$. However, when doing operations with mixed numbers, it is often useful to convert between mixed numbers and fractions. Thus, much of what is new in adding, subtracting, multiplying, and dividing mixed numbers involves the renaming of mixed numbers and fractions. For example:

- The sum of mixed numbers may be a mixed number in which the fraction part is not a proper fraction, such as $5\frac{4}{3}$ or $8\frac{4}{4}$. Students need to know how to rename such sums as whole numbers or as mixed numbers in which the fraction part is a proper fraction.
- In some subtraction problems, the fraction part of the first number (the minuend) may be less than the fraction part of the second number (the subtrahend). In such problems, the minuend must be renamed so that its fraction part is equal to or greater than the fraction part of the subtrahend. (For example, in $5\frac{1}{4} - 2\frac{3}{4}$, $5\frac{1}{4}$ is renamed as $4\frac{5}{4}$.)
- One way to multiply mixed numbers is to first rename the mixed-number factors as fractions, then to multiply the fractions, and finally to rename the resulting fraction as a mixed number. For example:

$$4\frac{1}{3} * 2\frac{3}{4} =$$

$$\frac{13}{3} * \frac{11}{4} = \frac{143}{12} = 11\frac{11}{12}$$

Refer to the *Teacher's Reference Manual,* Section 18.4.2, for ideas about sharing students' strategies and solutions.

Before students can master the operations with mixed numbers, they must have a good understanding of fraction and mixed-number notation and be skilled at performing the corresponding operations with fractions. Complete mastery of operations with mixed numbers is not expected of all students in this unit. There will be plenty of opportunities for practice in later units.

Refer to the *Teacher's Reference Manual,* Section 11.3.3, to learn more about operations with mixed numbers.

Conversions between Fraction, Decimal, and Percent Notations

(Lessons 4◆8 and 4◆9)

Everyday Mathematics treats fractions, decimals, and percents as interchangeable notations for the same set of numbers. In previous grades, students have practiced fraction-decimal-percent equivalencies. After some reminders, student should be able to name decimal (and percent) forms of "easy" fractions, such as halves, fourths, fifths, tenths, and hundredths, fairly automatically. The Probability Meter Poster can also be used to find equivalent fractions, as well as to convert between fractions, decimals, and percents.

Note: When you use the ready-made *Everyday Mathematics* posters with English language learners, you should display either the English version only or both the English and Spanish versions simultaneously; do not display the Spanish version only.

Many fractions, when converted to decimals, go on forever in a repeating pattern (for example, $\frac{1}{3} = 0.333\ldots$). This poses no difficulty when converting from fractions to decimals. Students generally use a calculator for the division and then round the resulting decimal to the desired number of significant digits. It is, however, more difficult to go from a repeating decimal such as 0.090909 . . . to its fraction equivalent ($\frac{1}{11}$). Also, nonrepeating decimals (or irrational numbers), such as π (3.14159 . . .) and 0.090090009 . . . cannot be converted to fractions.

Refer to the *Teacher's Reference Manual,* Section 11.4.3, for more about conversions between fractions, decimals, and percents.

Applications of Percents

(Lessons 4◆10 and 4◆11)

The two most common applications of percents involve:

- finding what percent of a total a quantity is.
- finding the value of a given percent of a total.

In Lesson 4-10, students address the first application by converting the results of surveys to percents and then using this information to construct circle graphs. In Lesson 4-11, the second application is presented, and students calculate the discount and sale price of items.

Section 9.3.5 in the *Teacher's Reference Manual* contains further information on the applications of percents.

Equivalent Fractions

Objective To review finding equivalent fractions and renaming fractions in simplest form.

1 Teaching the Lesson

Key Activities
Students model the multiplication and division rules for finding equivalent fractions. They also review how to rename fractions in simplest form.

Key Concepts and Skills
- Simplify a fraction by dividing the numerator and denominator by the greatest common factor. [Number and Numeration Goal 3]
- Use an area model to find equivalent fractions. [Number and Numeration Goal 5]
- Use multiplication and division facts to find equivalent fractions and simplify fractions. [Operations and Computation Goal 2]
- Apply the Multiplication Property of One to find equivalent fractions and simplify fractions. [Patterns, Functions, and Algebra Goal 4]

Key Vocabulary
equivalent fractions • simplest form • greatest common factor (GCF) • common factor

Ongoing Assessment: Recognizing Student Achievement Use journal page 125. [Number and Numeration Goal 5]

Ongoing Assessment: Informing Instruction See page 258.

materials
- ☐ *Math Journal 1,* pp. 123–125
- ☐ *Student Reference Book,* pp. 74, 76, 77, 273, and 274
- ☐ notebook paper (2 sheets per student)

2 Ongoing Learning & Practice

Students practice naming equivalent fractions by playing *Fraction Capture.*

Students practice and maintain skills through Math Boxes and Study Link activities.

materials
- ☐ *Math Journal 1,* p. 126
- ☐ *Student Reference Book,* p. 318
- ☐ Study Link Master (*Math Masters,* p. 105)
- ☐ Game Master (*Math Masters,* p. 447)
- ☐ Per partnership: 2 six-sided dice

3 Differentiation Options

READINESS
Students develop a strategy for systematically listing all factors of a number.

ENRICHMENT
Students apply their understanding of the greatest common factor to solve real-world problems.

materials
- ☐ Teaching Masters (*Math Masters,* pp. 106–108)

Additional Information

Background Information Students are expected to know how to find common factors, as well as the greatest common factor, of pairs of numbers. These skills were first introduced in *Fifth Grade Everyday Mathematics* and were practiced in Unit 3 Math Boxes.

Technology

Assessment Management System
Journal page 125, Problems 5 and 6
See the **iTLG.**

Getting Started

Mental Math and Reflexes

Students name the greatest common factor for each pair of numbers. *Suggestions:*

●○○ 4 and 12 4
8 and 10 2

●●○ 6 and 27 3
35 and 36 1

●●● 18 and 90 18
23 and 138 23

Math Message

Complete Problem 1 on journal page 123.

1 Teaching the Lesson

▶ Math Message Follow-Up

WHOLE-CLASS ACTIVITY

(*Math Journal 1,* p. 123)

Students show that $\frac{2}{3}$ of their paper is shaded. Have them follow the directions for Problem 2 as you model the procedure. Emphasize that $\frac{2}{3}$ and $\frac{8}{12}$ are called **equivalent fractions.** The same amount of space on the paper is shaded, but the space can be named in different ways.

Students fold another piece of paper to complete Problem 3 and record their results on journal page 123. If necessary, model each step for the class.

Adjusting the Activity

Remind students of their work in previous grades with name-collection boxes, which provide another way to show equivalent names for the same number. (*See margin.*)

AUDITORY ◆ KINESTHETIC ◆ TACTILE ◆ VISUAL

The Fraction-Stick Chart on pages 76 and 77 in the *Student Reference Book* and reference pages at the back of *Math Journal 1* provide a visual representation of equivalent fractions.

▶ Reviewing Equivalent Fractions

WHOLE-CLASS ACTIVITY

(*Math Journal 1,* p. 123)

Demonstrate how paper folding is related to the multiplication rule for generating equivalent fractions. In Problem 2, for example, the vertical folding corresponds to multiplying the numerator and denominator by 4.

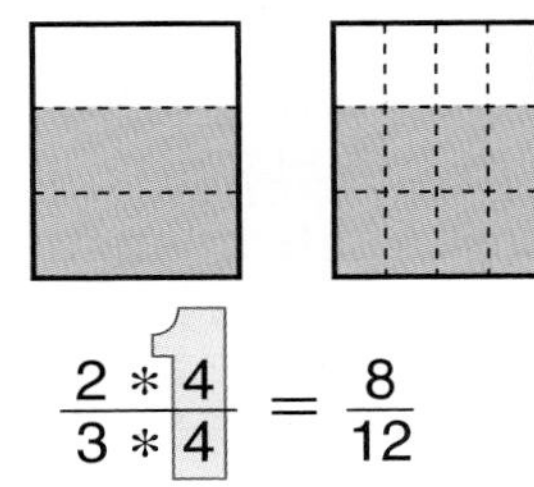

$$\frac{2 * 4}{3 * 4} = \frac{8}{12}$$

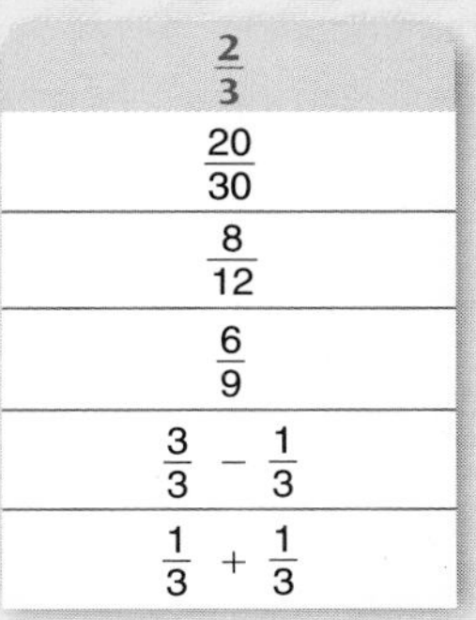

$\frac{2}{3}$
$\frac{20}{30}$
$\frac{8}{12}$
$\frac{6}{9}$
$\frac{3}{3} - \frac{1}{3}$
$\frac{1}{3} + \frac{1}{3}$

Name-collection box for $\frac{2}{3}$

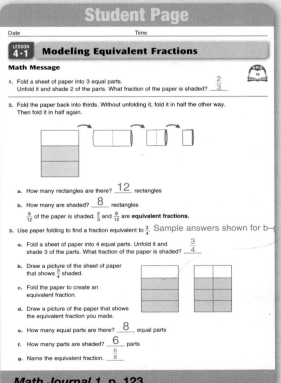

Student Page

Date Time

LESSON 4•1 **Modeling Equivalent Fractions**

Math Message

1. Fold a sheet of paper into 3 equal parts. Unfold it and shade 2 of the parts. What fraction of the paper is shaded? $\frac{2}{3}$

2. Fold the paper back into thirds. Without unfolding it, fold it in half the other way. Then fold it in half again.

   a. How many rectangles are there? 12 rectangles

   b. How many are shaded? 8 rectangles

   $\frac{8}{12}$ of the paper is shaded. $\frac{2}{3}$ and $\frac{8}{12}$ are **equivalent fractions.**

3. Use paper folding to find a fraction equivalent to $\frac{3}{4}$. Sample answers shown for b–g.

   a. Fold a sheet of paper into 4 equal parts. Unfold it and shade 3 of the parts. What fraction of the paper is shaded? $\frac{3}{4}$

   b. Draw a picture of the sheet of paper that shows $\frac{3}{4}$ shaded.

   c. Fold the paper to create an equivalent fraction.

   d. Draw a picture of the paper that shows the equivalent fraction you made.

   e. How many equal parts are there? 8 equal parts

   f. How many parts are shaded? 6 parts

   g. Name the equivalent fraction. $\frac{6}{8}$

Math Journal 1, p. 123

Ask students to demonstrate their answers to Problem 3, again making the connection between paper folding and the multiplication rule for generating equivalent fractions.

Draw diagrams to illustrate finding equivalent fractions.

The same kind of diagram can explain the division rule for equivalent fractions. Dividing corresponds to erasing the vertical lines, just as multiplying corresponds to drawing them. This is another example of the reversibility of operations. (*See margin.*)

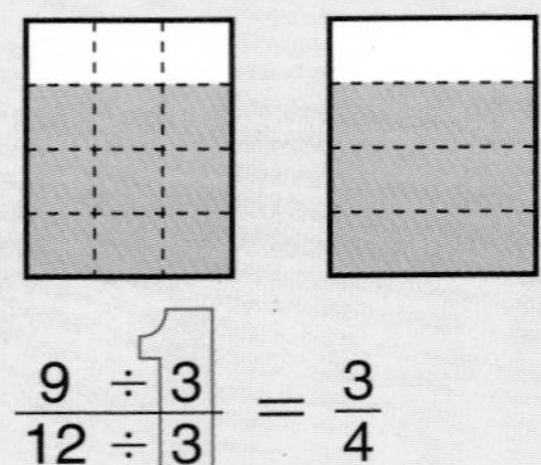

$$\frac{9 \div 3}{12 \div 3} = \frac{3}{4}$$

▶ Renaming Fractions in Simplest Form

Write the fraction $\frac{24}{60}$ on the board and ask whether it is in **simplest form.** Discuss why it is not in simplest form and ask a volunteer to show how to rename it. To support English language learners, write the important ideas on the board. The discussion should include the following points:

- ▷ A fraction is in simplest form if its numerator and denominator have only one factor in common—the number 1. The numbers 24 and 60 have five other factors in common: 2, 3, 4, 6, and 12.
- ▷ To rename a fraction as an equivalent fraction in simplest form, you can divide the numerator and denominator of the fraction by the **greatest common factor (GCF)** of the two numbers. The greatest common factor of 24 and 60 is 12, so divide the numerator and denominator by 12. In simplest form:

$$\frac{24 \div 12}{60 \div 12} = \frac{2}{5}$$

One way to find the GCF is to use prime factorization. (*See margin.*)

NOTE In *Fifth Grade Everyday Mathematics,* students used prime factorization to find the greatest common factor.

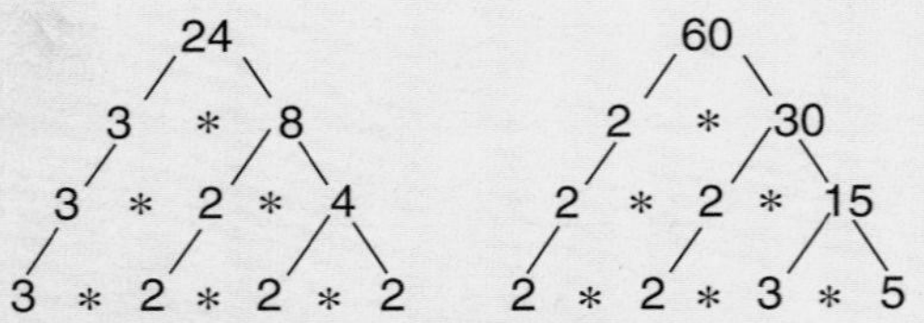

From the factor trees:
24 = 2 * 2 * 2 * 3
60 = 2 * 2 * 3 * 5

Circle pairs of **common factors.**

24 = (2) * (2) * 2 * (3)
60 = (2) * (2) * (3) * 5

Multiply *one* factor *in each pair* of circled factors.

The greatest common factor of 24 and 60 is 2 * 2 * 3, or 12.

Adjusting the Activity

Some students may benefit from working in smaller steps. For example, to rename the fraction $\frac{12}{18}$, first divide by 2 or 3 and divide again by the remaining common factor.

If students have fraction calculators, have them work with a partner to learn how to enter fractions, rename improper fractions as mixed numbers, and simplify fractions. Students can share their findings with the class. (See *Student Reference Book,* pp. 273 and 274.)

AUDITORY ◆ KINESTHETIC ◆ TACTILE ◆ VISUAL

The phrases *simplest form* and *lowest terms* are synonymous. *Everyday Mathematics* uses *simplest form,* but you should mention the phrase *lowest terms* because students are likely to see it on standardized tests. For extra practice renaming fractions, use the Check Your Understanding problems on page 74 of the *Student Reference Book.* To support English language learners, discuss the various ways the words *common* and *simplest* are used.

Finding Missing Numerators and Denominators

WHOLE-CLASS DISCUSSION

Write this problem on the board and ask a volunteer to find the missing number: $\frac{2}{3} = \frac{x}{12}$.

One way to solve the problem is to draw a rectangle to represent the whole, divide it horizontally into 3 equal parts, and shade 2 of the parts to represent $\frac{2}{3}$. Then draw vertical lines to divide the whole into 4 equal vertical strips. As a result, the whole is divided into 12 equal parts. Eight of the parts, or $\frac{8}{12}$ of the whole, is shaded. Thus, $x = 8$.

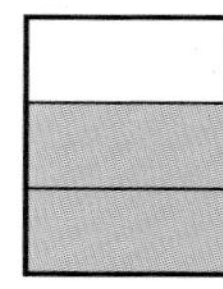

$\frac{2}{3} = \frac{x}{12}$

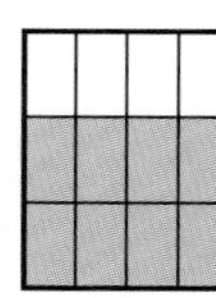

$x = 8$

Another way is to calculate. The denominator of the second fraction (12) is 4 times as great as the denominator of the first fraction (3). Therefore, the numerator of the second fraction must be 4 times as great as the numerator of the first fraction. $2 * 4 = 8$, so $x = 8$.

Pose a few more problems for the class to solve.

Suggestions: $\frac{1}{4} = \frac{y}{8}$; $y = 2$

$\frac{3}{5} = \frac{9}{z}$; $z = 15$

$\frac{6}{24} = \frac{1}{w}$; $w = 4$

$\frac{f}{12} = \frac{5}{6}$; $f = 10$

Finding Equivalent Fractions

INDEPENDENT ACTIVITY

(*Math Journal 1,* pp. 124 and 125)

Students complete the journal pages. Emphasize that multiplying or dividing the numerator and the denominator by the same (nonzero) number is the same as multiplying or dividing the original fraction by 1.

Ongoing Assessment: Recognizing Student Achievement

Journal page 125 Problems 5 and 6

Use **journal page 125, Problems 5 and 6** to assess students' ability to rename fractions in simplest form. Students are making adequate progress if they are able to apply multiplication and division rules to complete Problems 5 and 6. Some students may be able to find the missing numerators and denominators in Problem 7.

[Number and Numeration Goal 5]

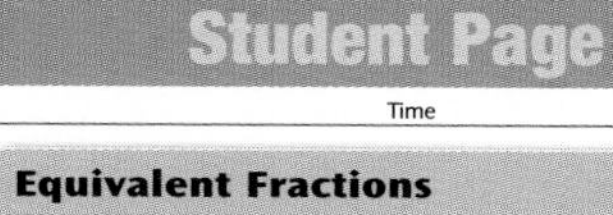

Date Time

LESSON 4·1 **Equivalent Fractions**

You can find equivalent fractions in the following ways:

Multiplication Rule	**Division Rule**
To find an equivalent fraction, *multiply* the numerator and the denominator of the original fraction by the same (nonzero) number. **Example:** $\frac{2}{3}$ $\frac{2 * 2}{3 * 2} = \frac{4}{6}$	To find an equivalent fraction, *divide* the numerator and the denominator of the original fraction by the same (nonzero) number. **Example:** $\frac{20}{12}$ $\frac{20 \div 4}{12 \div 4} = \frac{5}{3}$

Sample answers:

1. Find an equivalent fraction by multiplying.
   a. $\frac{3}{5}$ $\frac{6}{10}$
   b. $\frac{5}{3}$ $\frac{10}{6}$
   c. $\frac{3}{10}$ $\frac{6}{20}$
   d. $\frac{3}{4}$ $\frac{6}{8}$
   e. $\frac{2}{5}$ $\frac{4}{10}$

2. Find an equivalent fraction by dividing.
   a. $\frac{6}{8}$ $\frac{3}{4}$
   b. $\frac{8}{12}$ $\frac{2}{3}$
   c. $\frac{50}{75}$ $\frac{2}{3}$
   d. $\frac{30}{100}$ $\frac{3}{10}$
   e. $\frac{36}{24}$ $\frac{3}{2}$

3. Write three equivalent fractions for each given fraction.
   a. $\frac{2}{3}$ $\frac{4}{6}, \frac{6}{9}, \frac{8}{12}$
   b. $\frac{5}{10}$ $\frac{1}{2}, \frac{3}{6}, \frac{4}{8}$
   c. $\frac{5}{8}$ $\frac{10}{16}, \frac{15}{24}, \frac{20}{32}$
   d. $\frac{50}{45}$ $\frac{10}{9}, \frac{20}{18}, \frac{100}{90}$
   e. $\frac{45}{50}$ $\frac{9}{10}, \frac{18}{20}, \frac{27}{30}$
   f. $\frac{16}{28}$ $\frac{4}{7}, \frac{8}{14}, \frac{12}{21}$

4. Any whole number can be written as a fraction. For example: $2 = \frac{4}{2} = \frac{6}{3} = \frac{8}{4}$. Write at least two equivalent fractions for each whole number.
   a. 3 $\frac{6}{2}, \frac{9}{3}$
   b. 4 $\frac{8}{2}, \frac{12}{3}$
   c. 0 $\frac{0}{2}, \frac{0}{3}$
   d. 1 $\frac{2}{2}, \frac{3}{3}$

Math Journal 1, p. 124

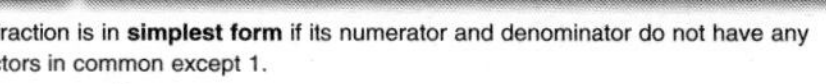

Date Time

LESSON 4·1 **Equivalent Fractions** *continued*

A fraction is in **simplest form** if its numerator and denominator do not have any factors in common except 1.

For example, $\frac{2}{3}$ is in simplest form because the only **common factor** of 2 and 3 is 1. $\frac{4}{8}$ is not in simplest form, because 4 is a common factor of 4 and 8.

5. Circle the fractions that are in simplest form.

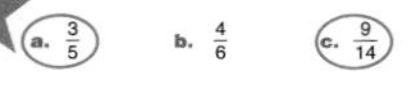
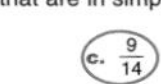

   a. $\frac{3}{5}$ b. $\frac{4}{6}$ c. $\frac{9}{14}$ d. $\frac{12}{13}$ e. $\frac{12}{15}$ f. $\frac{8}{18}$

6. One way to find the simplest form of a fraction is to divide its numerator and denominator by the **greatest common factor** of the 2 numbers.

   Example 1:
   Rename $\frac{8}{12}$ as a fraction in simplest form.
   The greatest common factor of 8 and 12 is 4. $\frac{8}{12} = \frac{8 \div 4}{12 \div 4} = \frac{2}{3}$

   Write each fraction in simplest form.
   a. $\frac{12}{16} = \frac{3}{4}$ b. $\frac{3}{9} = \frac{1}{3}$ c. $\frac{8}{14} = \frac{4}{7}$ d. $\frac{9}{15} = \frac{3}{5}$
   e. $\frac{18}{45} = \frac{2}{5}$ f. $\frac{24}{32} = \frac{3}{4}$ g. $\frac{9}{24} = \frac{3}{8}$ h. $\frac{20}{25} = \frac{4}{5}$

7. Find the missing numbers.

   Example 2: $\frac{3}{4} = \frac{x}{8}$

   The denominator of the second fraction is twice as much as the denominator of the first fraction. Therefore, the numerator of the second fraction must also be twice as much as the numerator of the first fraction.

   $\frac{3}{4} = \frac{3 * 2}{4 * 2} = \frac{6}{8}$; $x = 6$

   Example 3: $\frac{9}{15} = \frac{3}{y}$

   The numerator of the second fraction is one-third as much as the numerator of the first fraction. Therefore, the denominator of the second fraction must also be one-third as much as the denominator of the first fraction.

   $\frac{9}{15} = \frac{9 \div 3}{15 \div 3} = \frac{3}{5}$; $y = 5$

   a. $\frac{1}{4} = \frac{3}{y}$ $y =$ 12 b. $\frac{3}{z} = \frac{30}{50}$ $z =$ 5 c. $\frac{w}{8} = \frac{24}{32}$ $w =$ 6
   d. $\frac{2}{3} = \frac{10}{x}$ $x =$ 15 e. $\frac{d}{4} = \frac{18}{24}$ $d =$ 3 f. $\frac{15}{25} = \frac{r}{5}$ $r =$ 3

Math Journal 1, p. 125

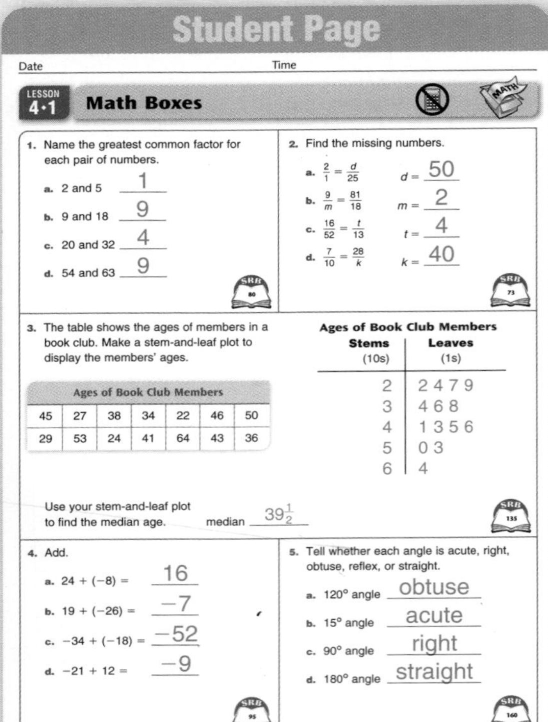

Student Page

Date Time

LESSON 4•1 **Math Boxes**

1. Name the greatest common factor for each pair of numbers.
   a. 2 and 5 1
   b. 9 and 18 9
   c. 20 and 32 4
   d. 54 and 63 9

2. Find the missing numbers.
   a. $\frac{2}{1} = \frac{d}{25}$ $d =$ 50
   b. $\frac{9}{m} = \frac{81}{18}$ $m =$ 2
   c. $\frac{16}{52} = \frac{t}{13}$ $t =$ 4
   d. $\frac{7}{10} = \frac{28}{k}$ $k =$ 40

3. The table shows the ages of members in a book club. Make a stem-and-leaf plot to display the members' ages.

Ages of Book Club Members						
45	27	38	34	22	46	50
29	53	24	41	64	43	36

Ages of Book Club Members

Stems (10s)	Leaves (1s)
2	2 4 7 9
3	4 6 8
4	1 3 5 6
5	0 3
6	4

Use your stem-and-leaf plot to find the median age. median $39\frac{1}{2}$

4. Add.
   a. $24 + (-8) =$ 16
   b. $19 + (-26) =$ −7
   c. $-34 + (-18) =$ −52
   d. $-21 + 12 =$ −9

5. Tell whether each angle is acute, right, obtuse, reflex, or straight.
   a. 120° angle obtuse
   b. 15° angle acute
   c. 90° angle right
   d. 180° angle straight

Math Journal 1, p. 126

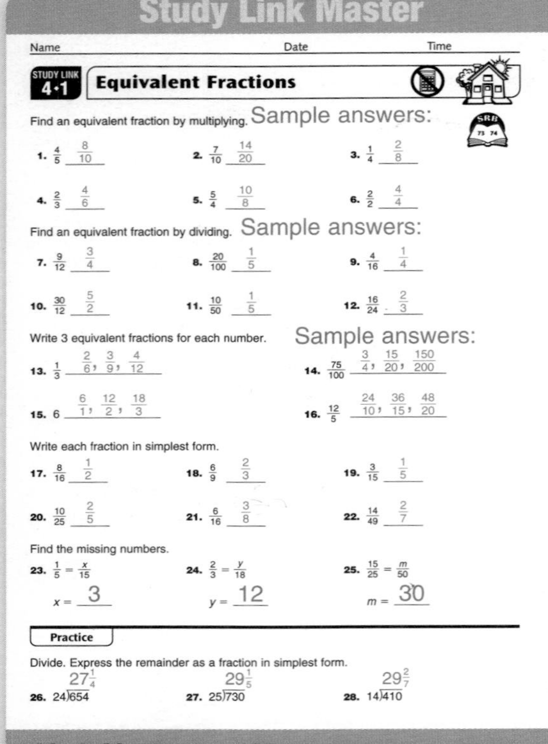

Study Link Master

Name Date Time

STUDY LINK 4•1 **Equivalent Fractions**

Find an equivalent fraction by multiplying. Sample answers:

1. $\frac{4}{5}$ $\frac{8}{10}$ 2. $\frac{7}{10}$ $\frac{14}{20}$ 3. $\frac{1}{4}$ $\frac{2}{8}$
4. $\frac{2}{3}$ $\frac{4}{6}$ 5. $\frac{5}{4}$ $\frac{10}{8}$ 6. $\frac{2}{2}$ $\frac{4}{4}$

Find an equivalent fraction by dividing. Sample answers:

7. $\frac{9}{12}$ $\frac{3}{4}$ 8. $\frac{20}{100}$ $\frac{1}{5}$ 9. $\frac{4}{16}$ $\frac{1}{4}$
10. $\frac{30}{12}$ $\frac{5}{2}$ 11. $\frac{10}{50}$ $\frac{1}{5}$ 12. $\frac{16}{24}$ $\frac{2}{3}$

Write 3 equivalent fractions for each number. Sample answers:

13. $\frac{1}{3}$ $\frac{2}{6}, \frac{3}{9}, \frac{4}{12}$ 14. $\frac{75}{100}$ $\frac{3}{4}, \frac{15}{20}, \frac{150}{200}$
15. 6 $\frac{6}{1}, \frac{12}{2}, \frac{18}{3}$ 16. $\frac{12}{5}$ $\frac{24}{10}, \frac{36}{15}, \frac{48}{20}$

Write each fraction in simplest form.

17. $\frac{8}{16}$ $\frac{1}{2}$ 18. $\frac{6}{9}$ $\frac{2}{3}$ 19. $\frac{3}{15}$ $\frac{1}{5}$
20. $\frac{10}{25}$ $\frac{2}{5}$ 21. $\frac{6}{16}$ $\frac{3}{8}$ 22. $\frac{14}{49}$ $\frac{2}{7}$

Find the missing numbers.

23. $\frac{1}{5} = \frac{x}{15}$ $x =$ 3 24. $\frac{2}{3} = \frac{y}{18}$ $y =$ 12 25. $\frac{15}{25} = \frac{m}{50}$ $m =$ 30

Practice

Divide. Express the remainder as a fraction in simplest form.

26. $24\overline{)654}$ $27\frac{1}{4}$ 27. $25\overline{)730}$ $29\frac{1}{5}$ 28. $14\overline{)410}$ $29\frac{2}{7}$

Math Masters, p. 105

Ongoing Assessment: Informing Instruction

Watch for students who assume that adding or subtracting the same nonzero number to the numerator and the denominator will yield an equivalent fraction. Give them examples, such as $\frac{1}{2} + \frac{2}{2} = \frac{3}{2}$ and $\frac{1}{2} * \frac{2}{2} = \frac{2}{4}$. Compare each answer to $\frac{1}{2}$.

2 Ongoing Learning & Practice

▶ Playing *Fraction Capture*

(*Student Reference Book,* p. 318; *Math Masters,* p. 447)

Distribute two 6-sided dice and a gameboard (*Math Masters,* p. 447) to each pair of students. Students read the directions on page 318 in the *Student Reference Book.* Ask a volunteer to summarize the object of the game and to demonstrate how the game is played. Encourage students to play a practice game.

▶ Math Boxes 4•1

(*Math Journal 1,* p. 126)

Mixed Practice Math Boxes in this lesson are paired with Math Boxes in Lesson 4-3. The skill in Problem 5 previews Unit 5 content.

Writing/Reasoning Have students write a response to the following: *Explain how you found the value of* m *in Problem 2b.* Sample answer: I compared the numerators. 81 is 9 times as great as 9, so 18 must be 9 times as great as m, or $9m = 18$. I know that $9 * 2$ equals 18, so $m = 2$.

▶ Study Link 4•1

(*Math Masters,* p. 105)

Home Connection Students find equivalent fractions, write fractions in simplest form, and find missing numerators in pairs of equivalent fractions.

3 Differentiation Options

READINESS

PARTNER ACTIVITY

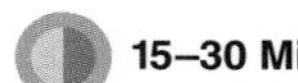

15–30 Min

▶ Using Factor Rainbows to List Factors

(*Math Masters,* pp. 106 and 107)

To provide experience with identifying factors, have students study the examples and discuss the steps on *Math Masters*, page 106 for making a factor rainbow. Then have them complete and create factor rainbows for given numbers.

ENRICHMENT

INDEPENDENT ACTIVITY

5–15 Min

▶ Solving GCF Problems

(*Math Masters,* p. 108)

To explore applications of the GCF, students solve real-world problems that involve finding the greatest common factor of a set of numbers.

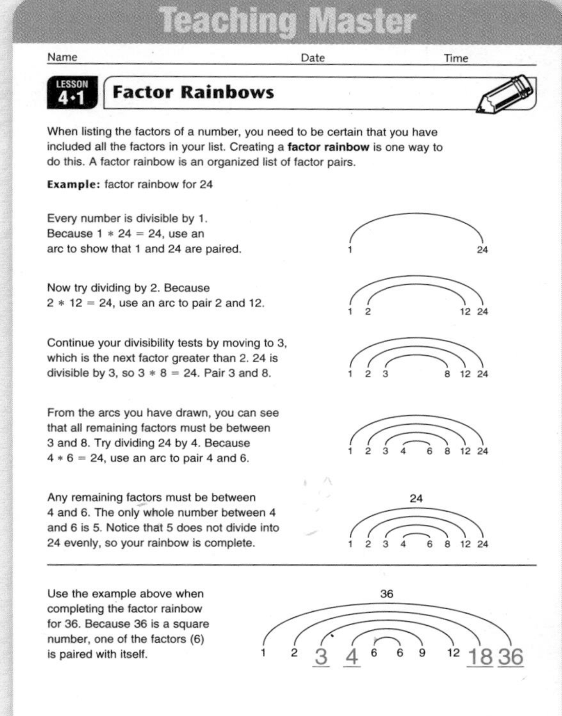

Teaching Master

Name Date Time

LESSON 4•1 **Factor Rainbows**

When listing the factors of a number, you need to be certain that you have included all the factors in your list. Creating a **factor rainbow** is one way to do this. A factor rainbow is an organized list of factor pairs.

Example: factor rainbow for 24

Every number is divisible by 1. Because 1 ∗ 24 = 24, use an arc to show that 1 and 24 are paired.

1 24

Now try dividing by 2. Because 2 ∗ 12 = 24, use an arc to pair 2 and 12.

1 2 12 24

Continue your divisibility tests by moving to 3, which is the next factor greater than 2. 24 is divisible by 3, so 3 ∗ 8 = 24. Pair 3 and 8.

1 2 3 8 12 24

From the arcs you have drawn, you can see that all remaining factors must be between 3 and 8. Try dividing 24 by 4. Because 4 ∗ 6 = 24, use an arc to pair 4 and 6.

1 2 3 4 6 8 12 24

Any remaining factors must be between 4 and 6. The only whole number between 4 and 6 is 5. Notice that 5 does not divide into 24 evenly, so your rainbow is complete.

24

1 2 3 4 6 8 12 24

Use the example above when completing the factor rainbow for 36. Because 36 is a square number, one of the factors (6) is paired with itself.

36

1 2 3 4 6 6 9 12 18 36

Math Masters, p. 106

Teaching Master

Name Date Time

LESSON 4•1 **Applications of the GCF**

Some real-world problems involve finding the greatest common factor (GCF) of a set of numbers.

Solve.

1. Tyrone is preparing snack packs for the class field trip. He has 60 bags of chips and 90 bottles of fruit juice. Each pack should have the same number of bags of chips and the same number of bottles of fruit juice. What is the greatest number of snack packs that Tyrone can make with no bags or bottles left over?

   The greatest number of snack packs that he can make is 30.

   Each snack pack will have 2 bags of chips and 3 bottles of fruit juice.

2. Carla has 30 blue beads, 60 red beads, and 72 white beads. What is the maximum number of friends to whom Carla can give the same number of beads and have no beads left over?

   The maximum number of friends to get beads is 6.

   Each friend will get 5 blue beads, 10 red beads, and 12 white beads.

3. Ms. Mendis wants to split her class into groups for a bridge-building contest. There are 32 students in her class. She has 16 bottles of wood glue, 1,200 craft sticks, and 24 jars of paint. What is the greatest number of groups that Ms. Mendis can make so each group gets the same number of supplies and no supplies are left over?

   The greatest number of groups that she can make is 8.

   Each group will get 2 bottles of wood glue, 150 craft sticks, and 3 jars of paint.

Math Masters, p. 108

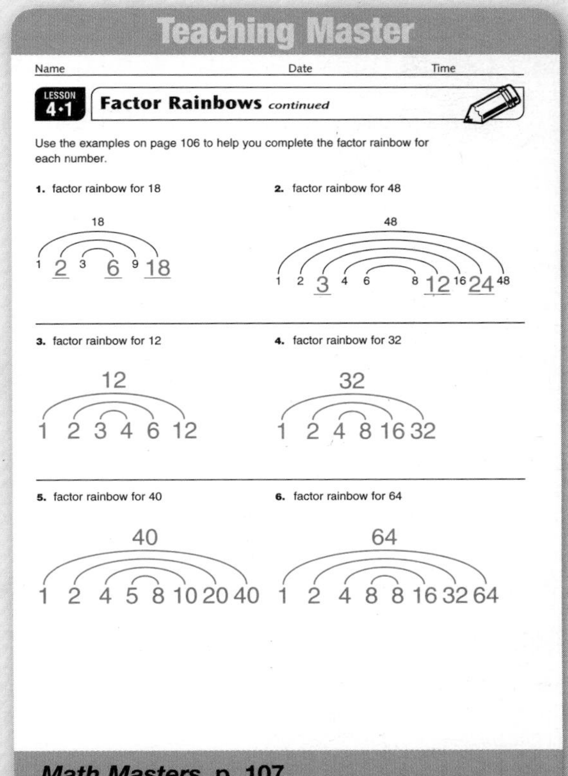

Teaching Master

Name Date Time

LESSON 4•1 **Factor Rainbows** *continued*

Use the examples on page 106 to help you complete the factor rainbow for each number.

1. factor rainbow for 18

   18

   1 2 3 6 9 18

2. factor rainbow for 48

   48

   1 2 3 4 6 8 12 16 24 48

3. factor rainbow for 12

   12

   1 2 3 4 6 12

4. factor rainbow for 32

   32

   1 2 4 8 16 32

5. factor rainbow for 40

   40

   1 2 4 5 8 10 20 40

6. factor rainbow for 64

   64

   1 2 4 8 8 16 32 64

Math Masters, p. 107

4•2 Comparing Fractions

Objective To compare fractions with unlike denominators.

1 Teaching the Lesson

materials

- ☐ *Math Journal 1,* p. 127
- ☐ *Student Reference Book,* p. 75
- ☐ Study Link 4•1
- ☐ slate

Key Activities

Students use and discuss various strategies for comparing fractions.

Key Concepts and Skills

- Apply the concept of a multiple to rename fractions with a common denominator and compare fractions. [Number and Numeration Goal 3]
- Order fractions using benchmark comparisons. [Number and Numeration Goal 6]
- Use multiplication and division facts to find equivalent fractions and simplify fractions. [Operations and Computation Goal 2]
- Use signs of inequality to compare fractions. [Patterns, Functions, and Algebra Goal 2]

Key Vocabulary

common denominator • quick common denominator (QCD) • least common denominator (LCD) • least common multiple (LCM)

Ongoing Assessment: Recognizing Student Achievement Use Mental Math and Reflexes. [Number and Numeration Goal 3]

2 Ongoing Learning & Practice

materials

- ☐ *Math Journal 1,* p. 128
- ☐ *Student Reference Book,* p. 307
- ☐ Study Link Master (*Math Masters,* p. 109)
- ☐ Game Masters (*Math Masters,* pp. 427 and 428)
- ☐ Geometry Template; scissors

Students practice comparing and ordering fractions by playing *Build It.*

Students practice and maintain skills through Math Boxes and Study Link activities.

3 Differentiation Options

materials

- ☐ Teaching Master (*Math Masters,* p. 110)
- ☐ scissors

READINESS

Students use the benchmarks 0, $\frac{1}{2}$, and 1 to order a set of fractions from smallest to largest.

ENRICHMENT

Students use cross products to compare fractions.

Additional Information

Background Information Finding common multiples and finding least common multiples were first introduced in *Fifth Grade Everyday Mathematics.*

Technology

Assessment Management System
Mental Math and Reflexes
See the **iTLG.**

Getting Started

Mental Math and Reflexes 

Students name the least common multiple (LCM) of each number pair.

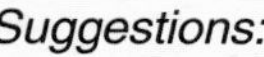

Suggestions:

●○○	4 and 8 8	8 and 12 24
●●○	3 and 7 21	10 and 25 50
●●●	15 and 60 60	36 and 48 144

Math Message

Complete Problems 1–4 on journal page 127.

Study Link 4·1 Follow-Up

Go over the answers. Spend extra time with Problems 23–25 if necessary. To be successful with the content of this lesson, it is important that students be able to solve problems such as these.

Ongoing Assessment: Recognizing Student Achievement

Mental Math and Reflexes ★

Use **Mental Math and Reflexes** to assess students' ability to find the least common multiple (LCM). Students are making adequate progress if they are able to correctly name the LCM for five of the suggested problems. Some students may be able to name the LCM of 36 and 48.

[Number and Numeration Goal 3]

1 Teaching the Lesson

▶ Math Message Follow-Up

WHOLE-CLASS DISCUSSION

(*Math Journal 1,* p. 127)

The answers to these problems should promote discussion. Encourage students to use number sense instead of formal comparison procedures, such as renaming fractions with a common denominator. The objective is to motivate and prepare students for formal procedures later in the lesson.

For example, if one student claims that $\frac{1}{8}$ is the smallest fraction that can be made that is greater than 0 (Problem 1) and another student claims that $\frac{1}{9}$ is smaller, help them see that the more equal parts there are, the smaller the parts will be. Ninths are smaller than eighths, so $\frac{1}{9}$ is less than $\frac{1}{8}$.

For Problem 2, some students may think that the answer is $\frac{8}{9}$. Remind them that because the numerator of a fraction may be equal to or greater than its denominator, $\frac{9}{1}$ is the largest possible fraction, and $\frac{8}{9}$ is the largest possible fraction less than 1.

NOTE Some students may identify $\frac{0}{9}$ as the smallest fraction that can be made using two digits. This is technically correct, so praise the insight and discuss it briefly, keeping the focus on ordering positive fractions.

Student Page

Date Time

LESSON 4·2 **Comparing Fractions**

Math Message

SRB 75 78 79

You can make any fraction using the digits 0, 1, 2, 3, 4, 5, 6, 7, 8, and 9. The fraction $\frac{3}{4}$ is made up of 2 digits; the fraction $\frac{23}{6}$ is made up of 3 digits. A fraction never has a denominator of 0.

Use only 2 digits to make the following fractions.

1. The least possible fraction that is greater than 0 $\frac{1}{9}$
2. The greatest possible fraction $\frac{9}{1}$
3. The greatest possible fraction that is less than 1 $\frac{8}{9}$
4. The least possible fraction that is greater than $\frac{1}{2}$ $\frac{5}{9}$

Compare each pair of fractions by first renaming them with a common denominator.

Write <, >, or =. Show how you got each answer.

Example: $\frac{3}{4}$ ______ $\frac{5}{6}$

One way: The QCD is 4 * 6 = 24. Rename each fraction so the denominator is 24.	Another way: The LCD of 4 and 6 is 12. Rename each fraction so the denominator is 12.
$\frac{3}{4} = \frac{x}{24}$; $x = 18$ $\frac{5}{6} = \frac{y}{24}$; $y = 20$	$\frac{3}{4} = \frac{x}{12}$; $x = 9$ $\frac{5}{6} = \frac{x}{12}$; $x = 10$
$\frac{3}{4} = \frac{18}{24}$ $\frac{5}{6} = \frac{20}{24}$	$\frac{3}{4} = \frac{9}{12}$ $\frac{5}{6} = \frac{10}{12}$
$\frac{18}{24} < \frac{20}{24}$, so $\frac{3}{4} < \frac{5}{6}$	$\frac{9}{12} < \frac{10}{12}$, so $\frac{3}{4} < \frac{5}{6}$

5. $\frac{2}{3} < \frac{4}{5}$
6. $\frac{2}{5} > \frac{3}{10}$
7. $\frac{1}{3} < \frac{5}{8}$
8. $\frac{2}{6} > \frac{1}{5}$
9. $\frac{3}{4} = \frac{18}{24}$
10. $\frac{7}{6} < \frac{11}{9}$

Math Journal 1, p. 127

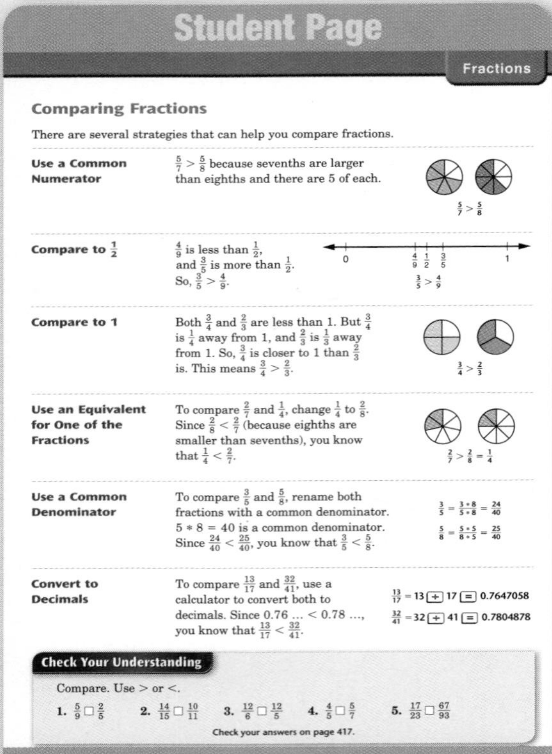

Student Page

Fractions

Comparing Fractions

There are several strategies that can help you compare fractions.

Use a Common Numerator	$\frac{5}{7} > \frac{5}{8}$ because sevenths are larger than eighths and there are 5 of each.	$\frac{5}{7} > \frac{5}{8}$
Compare to $\frac{1}{2}$	$\frac{4}{9}$ is less than $\frac{1}{2}$, and $\frac{3}{5}$ is more than $\frac{1}{2}$. So, $\frac{3}{5} > \frac{4}{9}$.	0, $\frac{4}{9}$, $\frac{1}{2}$, $\frac{3}{5}$, 1; $\frac{3}{5} > \frac{4}{9}$
Compare to 1	Both $\frac{3}{4}$ and $\frac{2}{3}$ are less than 1. But $\frac{3}{4}$ is $\frac{1}{4}$ away from 1, and $\frac{2}{3}$ is $\frac{1}{3}$ away from 1. So, $\frac{3}{4}$ is closer to 1 than $\frac{2}{3}$ is. This means $\frac{3}{4} > \frac{2}{3}$.	$\frac{3}{4} > \frac{2}{3}$
Use an Equivalent for One of the Fractions	To compare $\frac{2}{7}$ and $\frac{1}{4}$, change $\frac{1}{4}$ to $\frac{2}{8}$. Since $\frac{2}{8} < \frac{2}{7}$ (because eighths are smaller than sevenths), you know that $\frac{1}{4} < \frac{2}{7}$.	$\frac{2}{7} > \frac{2}{8} = \frac{1}{4}$
Use a Common Denominator	To compare $\frac{3}{5}$ and $\frac{5}{8}$, rename both fractions with a common denominator. $5 * 8 = 40$ is a common denominator. Since $\frac{24}{40} < \frac{25}{40}$, you know that $\frac{3}{5} < \frac{5}{8}$.	$\frac{3}{5} = \frac{3*8}{5*8} = \frac{24}{40}$; $\frac{5}{8} = \frac{5*5}{8*5} = \frac{25}{40}$
Convert to Decimals	To compare $\frac{13}{17}$ and $\frac{32}{41}$, use a calculator to convert both to decimals. Since 0.76 … < 0.78 …, you know that $\frac{13}{17} < \frac{32}{41}$.	$\frac{13}{17}$ = 13 [÷] 17 [=] 0.7647058; $\frac{32}{41}$ = 32 [÷] 41 [=] 0.7804878

Check Your Understanding

Compare. Use > or <.

1. $\frac{5}{9} \square \frac{2}{5}$ 2. $\frac{14}{15} \square \frac{10}{11}$ 3. $\frac{12}{6} \square \frac{12}{5}$ 4. $\frac{4}{5} \square \frac{5}{7}$ 5. $\frac{17}{23} \square \frac{67}{93}$

Check your answers on page 417.

Student Reference Book, p. 75

Problem 4 can be approached using a variety of strategies.

▷ One approach is to focus on the denominators and try various numerators for each denominator. For the denominator 3, $\frac{1}{3}$ is less than $\frac{1}{2}$ and $\frac{2}{3}$ is greater than $\frac{1}{2}$, so $\frac{2}{3}$ is the smallest fraction with 3 in the denominator that is greater than $\frac{1}{2}$. Using the same approach for the other denominators, $\frac{3}{4}$, $\frac{3}{5}$, $\frac{4}{6}$, $\frac{4}{7}$, $\frac{5}{8}$, and $\frac{5}{9}$ are the smallest fractions greater than $\frac{1}{2}$.

Next, compare fractions having the same numerator. The greater the number of equal parts (the denominator), the smaller the parts, so $\frac{3}{5}$ is less than $\frac{3}{4}$. Similarly, $\frac{4}{7}$ is less than $\frac{4}{6}$, and $\frac{5}{9}$ is less than $\frac{5}{8}$. Only the fractions $\frac{3}{5}$, $\frac{4}{7}$, and $\frac{5}{9}$ remain as possible candidates. Some students may have noticed that often (but not always) the closer the numerator is to the denominator, the larger the fraction. If you apply this reasoning, $\frac{5}{9}$ is the smallest of the fractions that is greater than $\frac{1}{2}$.

▷ Another approach is to compare two fractions at a time. For example, $\frac{4}{7}$ $(\frac{8}{14})$ and $\frac{5}{9}$ $(\frac{10}{18})$ are $\frac{1}{14}$ and $\frac{1}{18}$ greater than $\frac{1}{2}$, respectively. Because $\frac{1}{18}$ is less than $\frac{1}{14}$, we can conclude that $\frac{5}{9}$ is closer to $\frac{1}{2}$ than $\frac{4}{7}$ is.

▶ Using Number Sense to Compare Fractions

WHOLE-CLASS ACTIVITY

(*Student Reference Book,* p. 75)

Write pairs of fractions on the board. Ask students to compare the fractions and write <, >, or = on their slates. Discuss the answers to selected problems. Focus on the following kinds of fractions:

▷ Both fractions have the same denominator. $(\frac{6}{8} \underline{\ \ >\ \ } \frac{4}{8})$

▷ Both fractions have the same numerator. $(\frac{1}{4} \underline{\ \ >\ \ } \frac{1}{7}$, or $\frac{3}{8} \underline{\ \ <\ \ } \frac{3}{5})$

▷ One fraction is less than (or greater than) $\frac{1}{2}$ and the other fraction is $\frac{1}{2}$. $(\frac{1}{3} \underline{\ \ <\ \ } \frac{1}{2}$, or $\frac{3}{4} \underline{\ \ >\ \ } \frac{1}{2})$

▷ One fraction is less than $\frac{1}{2}$ and the other fraction is greater than $\frac{1}{2}$. $(\frac{2}{5} \underline{\ \ <\ \ } \frac{4}{6})$

▷ The fractions are equivalent. $(\frac{2}{3} \underline{\ \ =\ \ } \frac{6}{9})$

Several strategies for comparing fractions are summarized on page 75 of the *Student Reference Book.* Review this page as a class. Have students complete the Check Your Understanding problems. For each problem, ask students to identify the comparing strategy they used.

▶ Using Common Denominators to Compare Fractions

(*Math Journal 1,* p. 127)

Fractions with like denominators are easy to compare (for example, $\frac{2}{5}$ and $\frac{4}{5}$). One way to compare two fractions with unlike denominators is to rename one or both fractions as fractions with a **common denominator.** In *Fifth Grade Everyday Mathematics,* students learned to find the **quick common denominator (QCD)** by multiplying the denominators together.

The QCD for $\frac{1}{3}$ and $\frac{5}{6}$, for example, is $3 * 6$, or 18. The QCD method has two significant advantages: It is easy to do, and it is used in algebra and beyond to solve problems that involve variables rather than numbers.

The **least common denominator (LCD)** is the **least common multiple (LCM)** of two denominators. So, to find the LCD of $\frac{1}{4}$ and $\frac{5}{6}$, list a few multiples of 4 and 6:

4: 4, 8, **12,** 16, 20, 24, ...
6: 6, **12,** 18, 24, ...
The LCD is 12.

The LCD can also be found by dividing the product of the denominators by their greatest common factor. For example, the LCD of $\frac{1}{4}$ and $\frac{5}{6}$ is $(4 * 6) \div 2 = 24 \div 2 = 12$, where 2 is the GCF of 4 and 6.

Give pairs of fractions and ask students to find the common denominators. *Suggestions:*

$\frac{3}{8}$ and $\frac{2}{3}$ 24 $\qquad$ $\frac{2}{5}$ and $\frac{3}{10}$ 10 $\qquad$ $\frac{1}{6}$ and $\frac{3}{9}$ 18

After this brief review of common denominators, have students look at the example on journal page 127. Write it on the board and demonstrate how to rename both fractions using a common denominator.

Pose problems in which students compare two unlike fractions by renaming them using a common denominator. *Suggestions:*

$\frac{3}{8} < \frac{2}{3}$	$\frac{1}{2} < \frac{5}{8}$	$\frac{3}{5} > \frac{1}{3}$
$\frac{2}{5} > \frac{3}{10}$	$\frac{2}{5} > \frac{4}{15}$	$\frac{5}{6} > \frac{3}{4}$

Allow students to work alone or with a partner to complete the journal page. They may rename fractions using any method they choose. Circulate and assist.

Listing multiples to find the LCD seems to work well for most of the problems in this lesson. However, listing multiples is not always the most efficient way to determine the LCD. Prime factorization can also be used to find the least common multiple of a set of numbers.

Example:

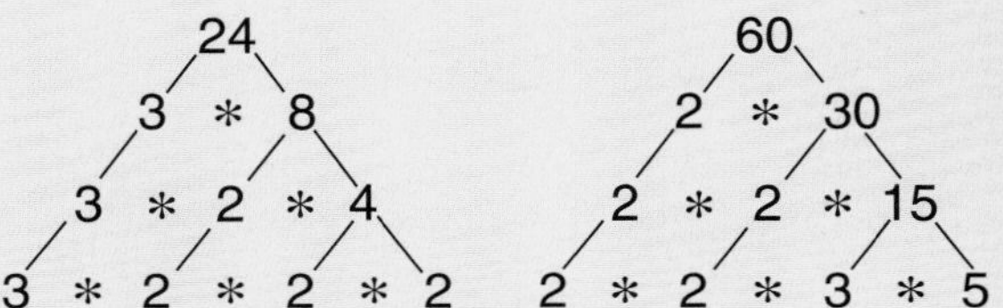

From the factor trees:
$24 = 2 * 2 * 2 * 3$
$60 = 2 * 2 * 3 * 5$

Circle pairs of common factors.

$24 = (2) * (2) * 2 * (3)$
$60 = (2) * (2) * (3) * 5$

Cross out one factor in each circled pair.

$24 = (\not{2}) * (\not{2}) * 2 * (\not{3})$
$60 = (2) * (2) * (3) * 5$

Multiply the factors that have not been crossed out.

LCM of 24 and 60 = $2 * 2 * 2 * 3 * 5 = 120$

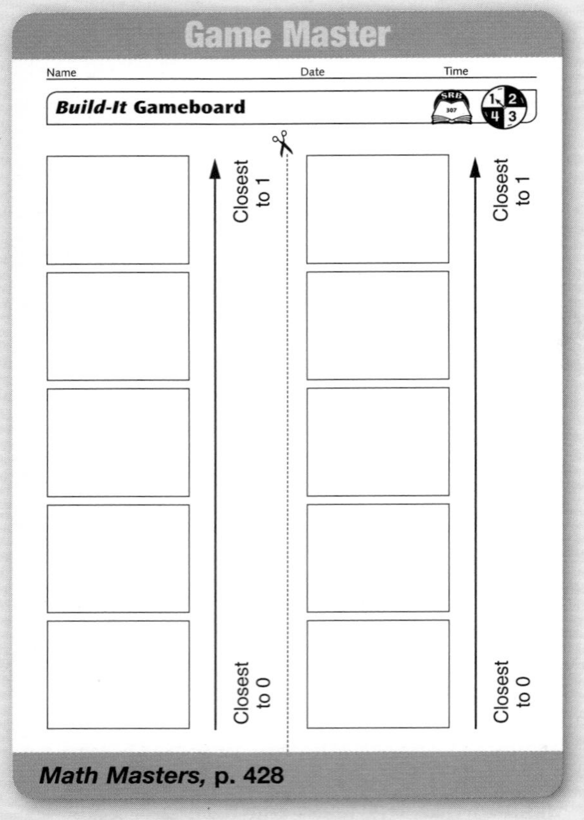

2 Ongoing Learning & Practice

▶ Playing *Build It*

PARTNER ACTIVITY

(*Student Reference Book,* p. 307; *Math Masters,* pp. 427 and 428)

Have pairs of students cut out one set of 16 fraction cards from *Math Masters,* page 427. They should also cut *Math Masters,* page 428 in half to create two gameboards.

Go over the directions on page 307 of the *Student Reference Book.* Remind students to apply number-sense strategies for comparing fractions. Make sure that students understand they cannot change the order of their five cards. They need to replace cards until the fractions are in order from smallest to largest.

Adjusting the Activity

Play the game using only cards showing fractions that have 3, 4, 8, and 12 as denominators. Add other denominators as students become more skillful. As students progress, consider having them make their own set of more difficult fraction cards.

AUDITORY ◆ KINESTHETIC ◆ TACTILE ◆ VISUAL

Game Master

Name ______ Date ______ Time ______

***Build-It* Gameboard**

Closest to 1 ↑ … Closest to 0 (two gameboards, five card boxes each)

Math Masters, p. 428

▶ Math Boxes 4·2

INDEPENDENT ACTIVITY

(*Math Journal 1,* p. 128)

Mixed Practice Math Boxes in this lesson are paired with Math Boxes in Lesson 4-4. The skill in Problem 5 previews Unit 5 content. Students will need the Percent Circle on the Geometry Template to complete Problem 5.

Writing/Reasoning Have students write a response to the following: *Explain how you solved Problems 2b and 2d.* Sample answer: In Problem 2b, the numerator of the first fraction (3) is half its denominator (6) so I know that $\frac{3}{6} = \frac{1}{2}$, and $\frac{1}{2} + \frac{1}{2} = 1$. For Problem 2d, I recognized that $\frac{6}{8}$ in simplest form is $\frac{3}{4}$, and $\frac{3}{4} - \frac{3}{4} = 0$.

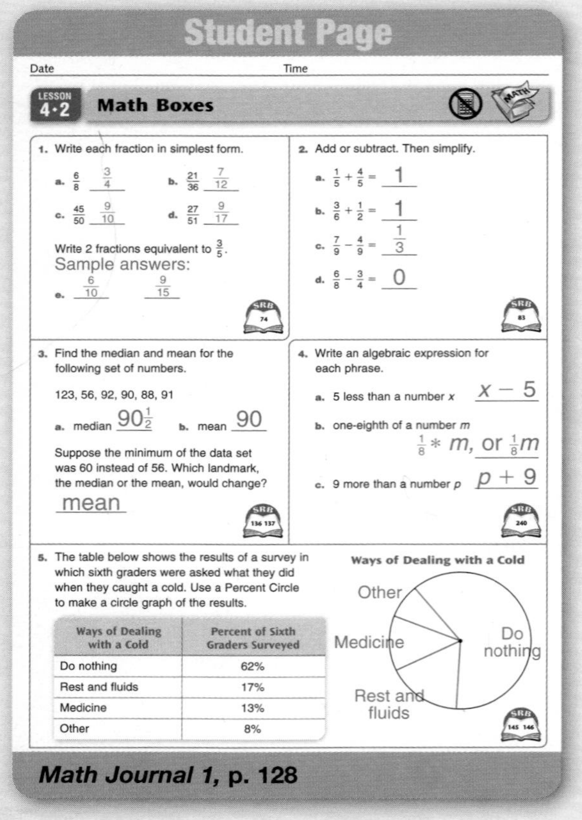

Student Page

Date ______ Time ______

LESSON 4·2 **Math Boxes**

1. Write each fraction in simplest form.
   a. $\frac{6}{8}$ $\frac{3}{4}$ b. $\frac{21}{36}$ $\frac{7}{12}$
   c. $\frac{45}{50}$ $\frac{9}{10}$ d. $\frac{27}{51}$ $\frac{9}{17}$
   Write 2 fractions equivalent to $\frac{3}{5}$.
   Sample answers:
   e. $\frac{6}{10}$ $\frac{9}{15}$
   SRB 74

2. Add or subtract. Then simplify.
   a. $\frac{1}{5} + \frac{4}{5} =$ 1
   b. $\frac{3}{6} + \frac{1}{2} =$ 1
   c. $\frac{7}{9} - \frac{4}{9} =$ $\frac{1}{3}$
   d. $\frac{6}{8} - \frac{3}{4} =$ 0
   SRB 83

3. Find the median and mean for the following set of numbers.
   123, 56, 92, 90, 88, 91
   a. median $90\frac{1}{2}$ b. mean 90
   Suppose the minimum of the data set was 60 instead of 56. Which landmark, the median or the mean, would change?
   mean
   SRB 136 137

4. Write an algebraic expression for each phrase.
   a. 5 less than a number x $x - 5$
   b. one-eighth of a number m $\frac{1}{8} * m$, or $\frac{1}{8}m$
   c. 9 more than a number p $p + 9$
   SRB 240

5. The table below shows the results of a survey in which sixth graders were asked what they did when they caught a cold. Use a Percent Circle to make a circle graph of the results.

Ways of Dealing with a Cold	Percent of Sixth Graders Surveyed
Do nothing	62%
Rest and fluids	17%
Medicine	13%
Other	8%

Ways of Dealing with a Cold
Other
Medicine
Do nothing
Rest and fluids

SRB 145 146

Math Journal 1, p. 128

▶ Study Link 4·2

INDEPENDENT ACTIVITY

(*Math Masters,* p. 109)

Home Connection Students compare and order fractions.

3 Differentiation Options

READINESS

PARTNER ACTIVITY

▶ Using Benchmark Fractions

5–15 Min

(*Math Masters,* p. 110)

To provide experience with ordering and comparing fractions, have students cut out the fraction cards on *Math Masters,* page 110 and lay the cards 0, $\frac{1}{2}$, and 1 on the floor in order from left to right. Then have them sort the remaining cards into three piles—fractions closest to 0, fractions closest to $\frac{1}{2}$, and fractions closest to 1. Working together, students decide where to place the fractions in relation to the benchmark cards. For example, students would position $\frac{1}{20}$ closest to the right of 0; $\frac{6}{10}$ closest to the right of $\frac{1}{2}$; and $\frac{9}{10}$ closest to the left of 1. Ask students to record their ordered set of fractions on the number line provided.

ENRICHMENT

SMALL-GROUP ACTIVITY

▶ Crossing to Compare

5–15 Min

To further explore comparing fractions, demonstrate a cross-product method such as the following:

$$7 * 2 = 14 \qquad 5 * 3 = 15$$

$$\frac{2}{5} \times \frac{3}{7}$$

$$14 < 15, \text{ so } \frac{2}{5} < \frac{3}{7}$$

Work through several examples, including one in which the cross products are equal. Emphasize to students that the larger cross product is always next to the larger fraction.

Have students use the method to compare fractions.
Suggestions:

$\frac{2}{9}$ _$>$_ $\frac{1}{5}$	$\frac{3}{4}$ _$<$_ $\frac{4}{5}$	$\frac{2}{5}$ _$<$_ $\frac{5}{11}$
$\frac{7}{20}$ _$>$_ $\frac{1}{3}$	$\frac{3}{8}$ _$<$_ $\frac{4}{10}$	$\frac{2}{6}$ _=_ $\frac{4}{12}$

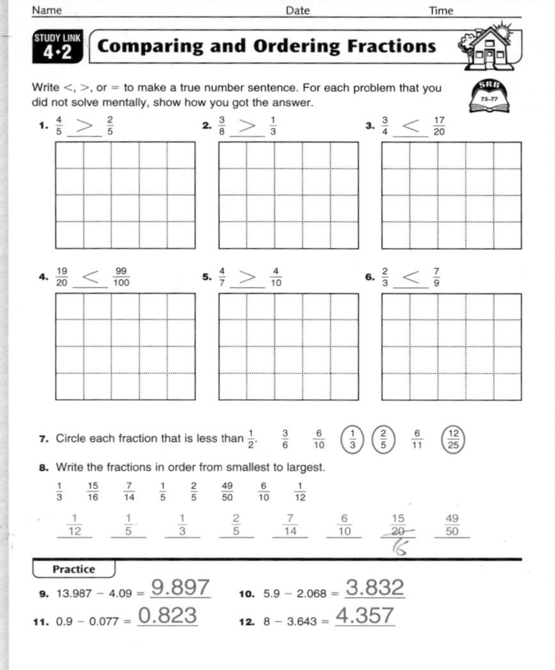

Study Link Master

Name Date Time

STUDY LINK 4•2 **Comparing and Ordering Fractions**

Write $<$, $>$, or = to make a true number sentence. For each problem that you did not solve mentally, show how you got the answer.

1. $\frac{4}{5} > \frac{2}{5}$
2. $\frac{3}{8} > \frac{1}{3}$
3. $\frac{3}{4} < \frac{17}{20}$
4. $\frac{19}{20} < \frac{99}{100}$
5. $\frac{4}{7} > \frac{4}{10}$
6. $\frac{2}{3} < \frac{7}{9}$
7. Circle each fraction that is less than $\frac{1}{2}$. $\frac{3}{6}$ $\frac{6}{10}$ ($\frac{1}{3}$) ($\frac{2}{5}$) $\frac{6}{11}$ ($\frac{12}{25}$)
8. Write the fractions in order from smallest to largest.
$\frac{1}{3}$ $\frac{15}{16}$ $\frac{7}{14}$ $\frac{1}{5}$ $\frac{2}{5}$ $\frac{49}{50}$ $\frac{6}{10}$ $\frac{1}{12}$
$\frac{1}{12}$, $\frac{1}{5}$, $\frac{1}{3}$, $\frac{2}{5}$, $\frac{7}{14}$, $\frac{6}{10}$, $\frac{15}{16}$, $\frac{49}{50}$

Practice

9. 13.987 − 4.09 = 9.897
10. 5.9 − 2.068 = 3.832
11. 0.9 − 0.077 = 0.823
12. 8 − 3.643 = 4.357

Math Masters, p. 109

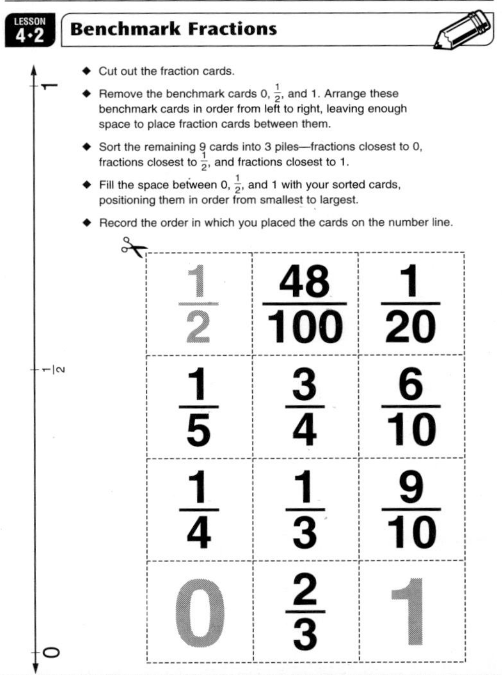

Teaching Master

Name Date Time

LESSON 4•2 **Benchmark Fractions**

- Cut out the fraction cards.
- Remove the benchmark cards 0, $\frac{1}{2}$, and 1. Arrange these benchmark cards in order from left to right, leaving enough space to place fraction cards between them.
- Sort the remaining 9 cards into 3 piles—fractions closest to 0, fractions closest to $\frac{1}{2}$, and fractions closest to 1.
- Fill the space between 0, $\frac{1}{2}$, and 1 with your sorted cards, positioning them in order from smallest to largest.
- Record the order in which you placed the cards on the number line.

$\frac{1}{2}$	$\frac{48}{100}$	$\frac{1}{20}$
$\frac{1}{5}$	$\frac{3}{4}$	$\frac{6}{10}$
$\frac{1}{4}$	$\frac{1}{3}$	$\frac{9}{10}$
0	$\frac{2}{3}$	1

Math Masters, p. 110

Adding and Subtracting Fractions

Objective To review adding and subtracting fractions with like and unlike denominators.

1 Teaching the Lesson

Key Activities

Students review methods of finding a common denominator and then apply these methods to add and subtract fractions with like and unlike denominators.

Key Concepts and Skills

- Apply the concept of a multiple to rename fractions with a common denominator and to order fractions. [Number and Numeration Goal 3]
- Convert between fractions and mixed numbers. [Number and Numeration Goal 5]
- Use multiplication and division facts to simplify fractions. [Operations and Computation Goal 2]
- Add and subtract fractions with like and unlike denominators. [Operations and Computation Goal 3]

Ongoing Assessment: Recognizing Student Achievement Use journal page 130. [Operations and Computation Goal 3]

materials

- ☐ *Math Journal 1,* pp. 129 and 130
- ☐ *Student Reference Book,* p. 83
- ☐ Study Link 4•2
- ☐ Teaching Masters (*Math Masters,* pp. 112 and 113; optional)
- ☐ Transparency (*Math Masters,* p. 111; optional)

2 Ongoing Learning & Practice

Students practice and apply rules of divisibility by playing *Divisibility Dash.*

Students practice and maintain skills through Math Boxes and Study Link activities.

materials

- ☐ *Math Journal 1,* p. 131
- ☐ *Student Reference Book,* pp. 11 and 309
- ☐ Study Link Master (*Math Masters,* p. 114)
- ☐ Game Master (*Math Masters,* p. 432)

Per group:

- ☐ 4 each of number cards 0–9
- ☐ 2 each of number cards 2, 3, 5, 6, 9, and 10

3 Differentiation Options

READINESS

Students use fraction strips to model sums and differences of fractions with unlike denominators.

ENRICHMENT

Students apply their knowledge of the least common multiple to identify a pattern.

EXTRA PRACTICE

Students compare and order fractions.

materials

- ☐ Teaching Masters (*Math Masters,* pp. 115 and 116)
- ☐ Teaching Aid Master (*Math Masters,* p. 416)
- ☐ *5-Minute Math,* pp. 173, 174, and 180
- ☐ scissors

Technology

Assessment Management System
Journal page 130, Problems 1–13
See the **iTLG.**

Getting Started

Mental Math and Reflexes

Students find sums of proper fractions. They record their answers in simplest form.

Suggestions:

●○○ $\frac{1}{5} + \frac{3}{5}$ $\frac{4}{5}$

$\frac{2}{7} + \frac{4}{7}$ $\frac{6}{7}$

●●○ $\frac{1}{2} + \frac{8}{16}$ 1

$\frac{2}{5} + \frac{3}{10}$ $\frac{7}{10}$

●●● $\frac{1}{4} + \frac{5}{12}$ $\frac{2}{3}$

$\frac{7}{12} + \frac{8}{9}$ $1\frac{17}{36}$

Math Message

Complete journal page 129.

Study Link 4•2 Follow-Up

Go over the answers. Expect that students were able to solve Problems 1, 4, 5, 7, and 8 using number sense. Ask students to explain their strategies.

1 Teaching the Lesson

▶ Math Message Follow-Up

WHOLE-CLASS DISCUSSION

(*Math Journal 1,* p. 129; *Math Masters,* pp. 111–113)

Have students share answers. Pose the following questions:

- How many A squares would cover the large square? 4
- How many B triangles would cover the large square? 8
- How many E triangles would cover the large square? 16
- How would you show that Parallelogram G covers the same area as Square A? Cut Parallelogram G vertically into two triangles and rearrange them into a square.

Students should be able to answer Problems 2a and 2b by looking at the picture. For the remaining problems, they can rename one of the fractions so both fractions have the same denominator.

Adjusting the Activity

ELL

Make an overhead transparency of *Math Masters,* page 111, which is identical to the journal page. Cut out each shape from *Math Masters,* pages 112 and 113. Invite students to demonstrate the relationships in Problems 1 and 2 on the overhead projector.

AUDITORY ♦ KINESTHETIC ♦ TACTILE ♦ VISUAL

NOTE This lesson assumes that students know how to add and subtract fractions with like denominators and to rename improper fractions as mixed numbers.

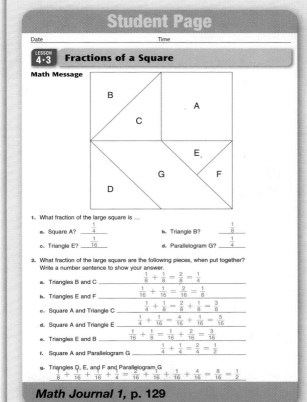

Student Page

Date Time

LESSON 4•3 **Fractions of a Square**

Math Message

1. What fraction of the large square is …
   a. Square A? $\frac{1}{4}$
   b. Triangle B? $\frac{1}{8}$
   c. Triangle E? $\frac{1}{16}$
   d. Parallelogram G? $\frac{1}{4}$
2. What fraction of the large square are the following pieces, when put together? Write a number sentence to show your answer.
   a. Triangles B and C $\frac{1}{8} + \frac{1}{8} = \frac{2}{8} = \frac{1}{4}$
   b. Triangles E and F $\frac{1}{16} + \frac{1}{16} = \frac{2}{16} = \frac{1}{8}$
   c. Square A and Triangle C $\frac{1}{4} + \frac{1}{8} = \frac{2}{8} + \frac{1}{8} = \frac{3}{8}$
   d. Square A and Triangle E $\frac{1}{4} + \frac{1}{16} = \frac{4}{16} + \frac{1}{16} = \frac{5}{16}$
   e. Triangles E and B $\frac{1}{16} + \frac{1}{8} = \frac{1}{16} + \frac{2}{16} = \frac{3}{16}$
   f. Square A and Parallelogram G $\frac{1}{4} + \frac{1}{4} = \frac{2}{4} = \frac{1}{2}$
   g. Triangles D, E, and F and Parallelogram G $\frac{1}{8} + \frac{1}{16} + \frac{1}{16} + \frac{1}{4} = \frac{2}{16} + \frac{1}{16} + \frac{1}{16} + \frac{4}{16} = \frac{8}{16} = \frac{1}{2}$

***Math Journal 1,* p. 129**

▶ Adding and Subtracting Fractions with Unlike Denominators

WHOLE-CLASS ACTIVITY

(*Student Reference Book,* p. 83)

Ask students to explain how to find the sum $\frac{1}{4} + \frac{5}{6}$. If necessary, review the following methods:

▷ Find the quick common denominator (QCD).

Multiply the denominators: $4 * 6 = 24$.

If 24 is the QCD, then

$$\frac{1}{4} + \frac{5}{6} = \frac{6}{24} + \frac{20}{24} = \frac{26}{24} = 1\frac{2}{24} = 1\frac{1}{12}.$$

▷ Find the least common denominator (LCD).

One way:

List some multiples of each denominator.

Multiples of 4: 4, 8, **12,** 16, 20, 24, ...

Multiples of 6: 6, **12,** 18, 24, 30, 36, ...

Least common multiple: **12**

12 is the LCD.

Another way:

Write the prime factorization of each number.

$4 = 2 * 2$

$6 = 2 * 3$

Circle pairs of common factors.

$4 = (2) * 2$

$6 = (2) * 3$

Cross out one factor in each circled pair.

$4 = (\not{2}) * 2$

$6 = (2) * 3$

Multiply the factors that have not been crossed out.

$2 * 2 * 3 = 12$

If 12 is the LCD, then

$$\frac{1}{4} + \frac{5}{6} = \frac{3}{12} + \frac{10}{12} = \frac{13}{12} = 1\frac{1}{12}.$$

Next, pose a subtraction problem, such as $\frac{5}{6} - \frac{2}{9}$. Have students find the QCD $6 * 9$, or 54 and the LCD or other common denominators. 18, 36 Record the solution on the board.

$$\frac{5}{6} - \frac{2}{9} = \frac{15}{18} - \frac{4}{18} = \frac{11}{18}$$

NOTE Students can arrive at the same answer by finding and using a common multiple of the denominators. For example, a common multiple of 4 and 6 is 36.

$$\frac{1}{4} + \frac{5}{6} = \frac{9}{36} + \frac{30}{36} = \frac{39}{36} = 1\frac{3}{36} = 1\frac{1}{12}$$

Student Page

Fractions

Addition and Subtraction of Fractions

To find the sum of fractions that have the same denominator, you add just the numerators. The denominator does not change. Subtraction of fractions with like denominators is done the same way.

Find $\frac{1}{4} + \frac{2}{4}$.

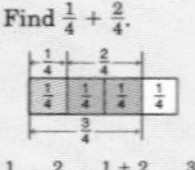

$\frac{1}{4} + \frac{2}{4} = \frac{1+2}{4} = \frac{3}{4}$

Find $\frac{4}{5} - \frac{3}{5}$.

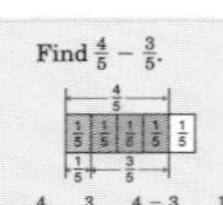

$\frac{4}{5} - \frac{3}{5} = \frac{4-3}{5} = \frac{1}{5}$

To find the sum of fractions that do not have the same denominator, first rename the fractions as fractions with a common denominator. Then proceed as above. Subtraction of fractions with unlike denominators is done the same way.

Examples Find $\frac{3}{4} + \frac{1}{8}$.

$\frac{3}{4} + \frac{1}{8} = \frac{6}{8} + \frac{1}{8} = \frac{7}{8}$ $(\frac{3}{4} = \frac{6}{8})$

So, $\frac{3}{4} + \frac{1}{8} = \frac{7}{8}$.

Find $\frac{5}{6} - \frac{1}{4}$.

$\frac{5}{6} - \frac{1}{4} = \frac{10}{12} - \frac{3}{12} = \frac{7}{12}$ $(\frac{5}{6} = \frac{10}{12}; \frac{1}{4} = \frac{2}{8} = \frac{3}{12})$

So, $\frac{5}{6} - \frac{1}{4} = \frac{7}{12}$.

It is possible to add and subtract fractions on some calculators. See if you can do this on your calculator.

Examples Find $\frac{3}{8} + \frac{1}{3}$.

On Calculator A:

Key in 3 [n] 8 [d] [+] 1 [n] 3 [d] [Enter]

Answer: $\frac{17}{24}$

Find $\frac{7}{8} - \frac{3}{5}$.

On Calculator B:

Key in 7 [b/c] 8 [−] 3 [b/c] 5 [=]

Answer: $\frac{11}{40}$.

Check Your Understanding

Solve each problem. Check the answers on a calculator.

1. $\frac{5}{9} + \frac{3}{9}$ 2. $\frac{7}{8} - \frac{1}{4}$ 3. $\frac{2}{3} + \frac{1}{4}$ 4. $\frac{13}{6} - \frac{7}{4}$ 5. $\frac{3}{8} + \frac{5}{6}$

Check your answers on page 417.

Student Reference Book, p. 83

Adjusting the Activity

If students have fraction calculators, have them enter each of the following problems, interpret the display, and generate an answer in simplest form.

$\frac{4}{5} - \frac{3}{10}$ $\frac{5}{10} = \frac{1}{2}$; $\frac{11}{12} - \frac{2}{3}$ $\frac{3}{12} = \frac{1}{4}$; $\frac{4}{15} - \frac{1}{10}$ $\frac{5}{30} = \frac{1}{6}$

AUDITORY ◆ KINESTHETIC ◆ TACTILE ◆ VISUAL

▶ Practicing Addition and Subtraction of Fractions

PARTNER ACTIVITY

(*Math Journal 1,* p. 130)

Have students complete journal page 130. Circulate and assist. Bring the class together and invite volunteers to model their solutions.

Ongoing Assessment: Recognizing Student Achievement

Journal Page 130 Problems 1–13 ★

Use **journal page 130, Problems 1–13** to assess students' ability to add and subtract fractions with unlike denominators. Students are making adequate progress if they are able to solve Problems 1–13. Some students may be able to make reasonable estimates for the sums and differences in Problems 14 and 15.

[Operations and Computation Goal 3]

2 Ongoing Learning & Practice

▶ Playing *Divisibility Dash*

PARTNER ACTIVITY

(*Student Reference Book,* pp. 11 and 309; *Math Masters,* p. 432)

Distribute four each of the number cards 0–9, two each of the number cards 2, 3, 5, 6, 9, and 10 (from two different Everything Math Decks, if available), and a game record sheet to each group. If students need to review divisibility rules, have them read page 11 of the *Student Reference Book.*

Remind students that a multiple of a number is always divisible by that number. For example, because 36 is a multiple of 6, it is divisible by 6.

Student Page

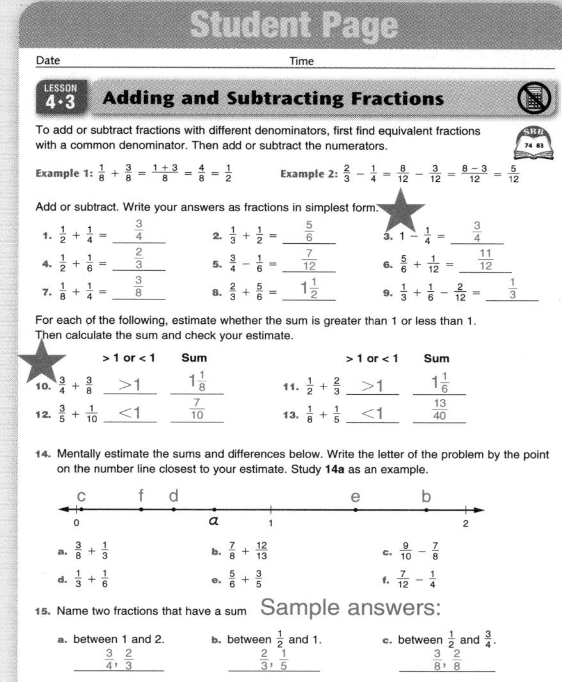

Date Time

LESSON 4·3 **Adding and Subtracting Fractions**

To add or subtract fractions with different denominators, first find equivalent fractions with a common denominator. Then add or subtract the numerators.

Example 1: $\frac{1}{8} + \frac{3}{8} = \frac{1+3}{8} = \frac{4}{8} = \frac{1}{2}$ Example 2: $\frac{2}{3} - \frac{1}{4} = \frac{8}{12} - \frac{3}{12} = \frac{8-3}{12} = \frac{5}{12}$

Add or subtract. Write your answers as fractions in simplest form.

1. $\frac{1}{2} + \frac{1}{4} =$ $\frac{3}{4}$
2. $\frac{1}{3} + \frac{1}{2} =$ $\frac{5}{6}$
3. $1 - \frac{1}{4} =$ $\frac{3}{4}$
4. $\frac{1}{2} + \frac{1}{6} =$ $\frac{2}{3}$
5. $\frac{3}{4} - \frac{1}{6} =$ $\frac{7}{12}$
6. $\frac{5}{6} + \frac{1}{12} =$ $\frac{11}{12}$
7. $\frac{1}{8} + \frac{1}{4} =$ $\frac{3}{8}$
8. $\frac{2}{3} + \frac{5}{6} =$ $1\frac{1}{2}$
9. $\frac{1}{3} + \frac{1}{6} - \frac{2}{12} =$ $\frac{1}{3}$

For each of the following, estimate whether the sum is greater than 1 or less than 1. Then calculate the sum and check your estimate.

	> 1 or < 1	Sum		> 1 or < 1	Sum
10. $\frac{3}{4} + \frac{3}{8}$	>1	$1\frac{1}{8}$	11. $\frac{1}{2} + \frac{2}{3}$	>1	$1\frac{1}{6}$
12. $\frac{3}{5} + \frac{1}{10}$	<1	$\frac{7}{10}$	13. $\frac{1}{8} + \frac{1}{5}$	<1	$\frac{13}{40}$

14. Mentally estimate the sums and differences below. Write the letter of the problem by the point on the number line closest to your estimate. Study **14a** as an example.

c f d a e b (number line: 0, 1, 2)

a. $\frac{3}{8} + \frac{1}{3}$ b. $\frac{7}{8} + \frac{12}{13}$ c. $\frac{9}{10} - \frac{7}{8}$

d. $\frac{1}{3} + \frac{1}{6}$ e. $\frac{5}{6} + \frac{3}{5}$ f. $\frac{7}{12} - \frac{1}{4}$

15. Name two fractions that have a sum Sample answers:

a. between 1 and 2. $\frac{3}{4}, \frac{2}{3}$ b. between $\frac{1}{2}$ and 1. $\frac{2}{3}, \frac{1}{5}$ c. between $\frac{1}{2}$ and $\frac{3}{4}$. $\frac{3}{8}, \frac{2}{8}$

Math Journal 1, **p. 130**

Student Page

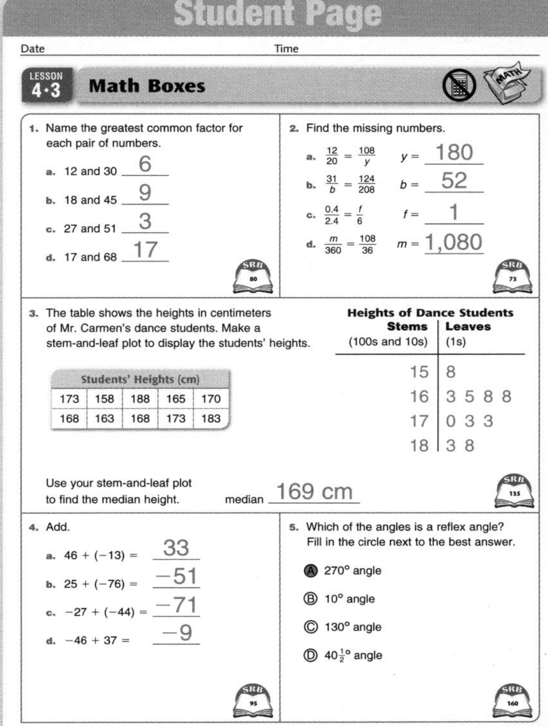

Date Time

LESSON 4·3 **Math Boxes**

1. Name the greatest common factor for each pair of numbers.
   a. 12 and 30 6
   b. 18 and 45 9
   c. 27 and 51 3
   d. 17 and 68 17

2. Find the missing numbers.
   a. $\frac{12}{20} = \frac{108}{y}$ $y =$ 180
   b. $\frac{31}{b} = \frac{124}{208}$ $b =$ 52
   c. $\frac{0.4}{2.4} = \frac{f}{6}$ $f =$ 1
   d. $\frac{m}{360} = \frac{108}{36}$ $m =$ 1,080

3. The table shows the heights in centimeters of Mr. Carmen's dance students. Make a stem-and-leaf plot to display the students' heights.

Students' Heights (cm)				
173	158	188	165	170
168	163	168	173	183

Heights of Dance Students

Stems (100s and 10s)	Leaves (1s)
15	8
16	3 5 8 8
17	0 3 3
18	3 8

Use your stem-and-leaf plot to find the median height. median 169 cm

4. Add.
   a. 46 + (−13) = 33
   b. 25 + (−76) = −51
   c. −27 + (−44) = −71
   d. −46 + 37 = −9

5. Which of the angles is a reflex angle? Fill in the circle next to the best answer.
   Ⓐ 270° angle (filled)
   Ⓑ 10° angle
   Ⓒ 130° angle
   Ⓓ $40\frac{1}{2}$° angle

Math Journal 1, **p. 131**

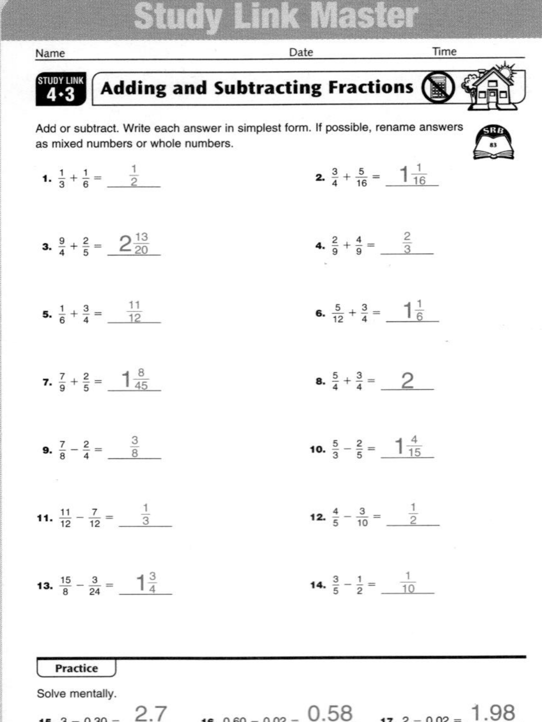
Study Link Master

Name Date Time

STUDY LINK 4•3 **Adding and Subtracting Fractions**

Add or subtract. Write each answer in simplest form. If possible, rename answers as mixed numbers or whole numbers.

1. $\frac{1}{3} + \frac{1}{6} = \frac{1}{2}$
2. $\frac{3}{4} + \frac{5}{16} = 1\frac{1}{16}$
3. $\frac{9}{4} + \frac{2}{5} = 2\frac{13}{20}$
4. $\frac{2}{9} + \frac{4}{9} = \frac{2}{3}$
5. $\frac{1}{6} + \frac{3}{4} = \frac{11}{12}$
6. $\frac{5}{12} + \frac{3}{4} = 1\frac{1}{6}$
7. $\frac{7}{9} + \frac{2}{5} = 1\frac{8}{45}$
8. $\frac{5}{4} + \frac{3}{4} = 2$
9. $\frac{7}{8} - \frac{2}{4} = \frac{3}{8}$
10. $\frac{5}{3} - \frac{2}{5} = 1\frac{4}{15}$
11. $\frac{11}{12} - \frac{7}{12} = \frac{1}{3}$
12. $\frac{4}{5} - \frac{3}{10} = \frac{1}{2}$
13. $\frac{15}{8} - \frac{3}{24} = 1\frac{3}{4}$
14. $\frac{3}{5} - \frac{1}{2} = \frac{1}{10}$

Practice

Solve mentally.

15. $3 - 0.30 = 2.7$ 16. $0.60 - 0.02 = 0.58$ 17. $2 - 0.02 = 1.98$

Math Masters, p. 114

▶ Math Boxes 4•3

INDEPENDENT ACTIVITY

(*Math Journal 1*, p. 131)

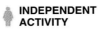

Mixed Practice Math Boxes in this lesson are paired with Math Boxes in Lesson 4-1. The skill in Problem 5 previews Unit 5 content.

▶ Study Link 4•3

INDEPENDENT ACTIVITY

(*Math Masters*, p. 114)

Home Connection Students add and subtract fractions with like and unlike denominators.

3 Differentiation Options

READINESS

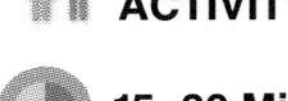

PARTNER ACTIVITY

15–30 Min

▶ Finding Sums and Differences with Fraction Strips

(*Math Masters*, pp. 115 and 416)

To provide experience adding and subtracting fractions with unlike denominators, have students model problems with fraction strips.

Provide students with a copy of *Math Masters,* page 416 and scissors. After students have labeled and cut out the strips, have them work through the examples and problems on page 115. Have students state addition and subtraction problems with fractions in their own words. *For example:* "I added one-third and one-half. My sum was five-sixths."

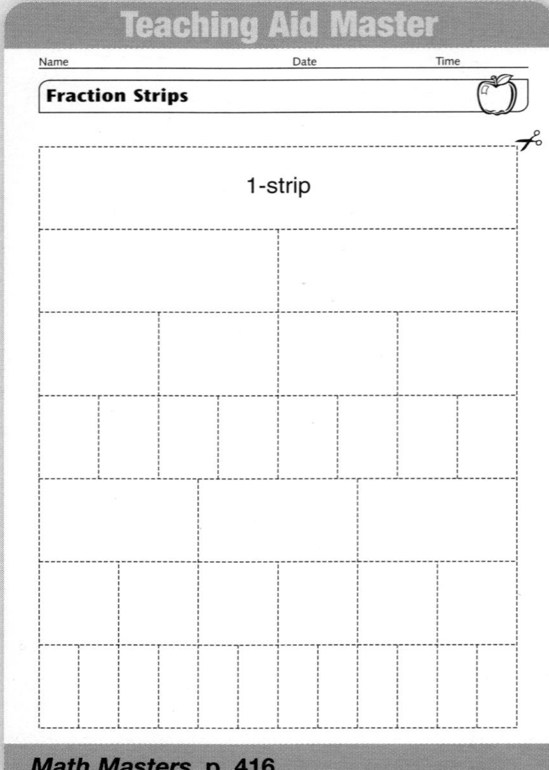
Teaching Aid Master

Name Date Time

Fraction Strips

1-strip

Math Masters, p. 416

SMALL-GROUP ACTIVITY

▶ Playing Paper Pool

5–15 Min

(*Math Masters,* p. 116)

To further explore patterns related to the least common multiple, students play Paper Pool.

Paper Pool is played with an imaginary ball and pool cue on a rectangular grid that represents a pool table. Play begins when the ball is hit from the lower left-hand pocket at a 45° angle. The ball continues to travel at a 45° angle along the diagonals of the squares of the pool table. When the ball hits a side of the table, it bounces off at a 45° angle and continues along a diagonal that has not already been crossed. Play ends when the ball lands in any of the four corner pockets. The length of the ball's path is found by counting the number of diagonals that the ball crosses before landing in a pocket.

After studying the example on *Math Masters,* page 116, students draw the ball's path on each of four different rectangular grids. They record each path's length and investigate the relationship between the length of the ball's path and the dimensions of the rectangular grid. Some students may recognize that the length of the path traveled by the ball is the least common multiple of the dimensions of the table.

NOTE Adapted from *Comparing and Scaling: Ratio, Proportion, and Percent, Connected Mathematics Project,* G. Lappan, J. Fey, W. Fitzgerald, S. Friel, and E. Phillips.

EXTRA PRACTICE

SMALL-GROUP ACTIVITY

▶ 5-Minute Math

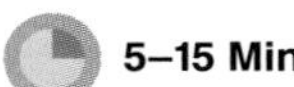
5–15 Min

To offer more practice comparing and ordering fractions, see *5-Minute Math,* pages 173, 174, and 180.

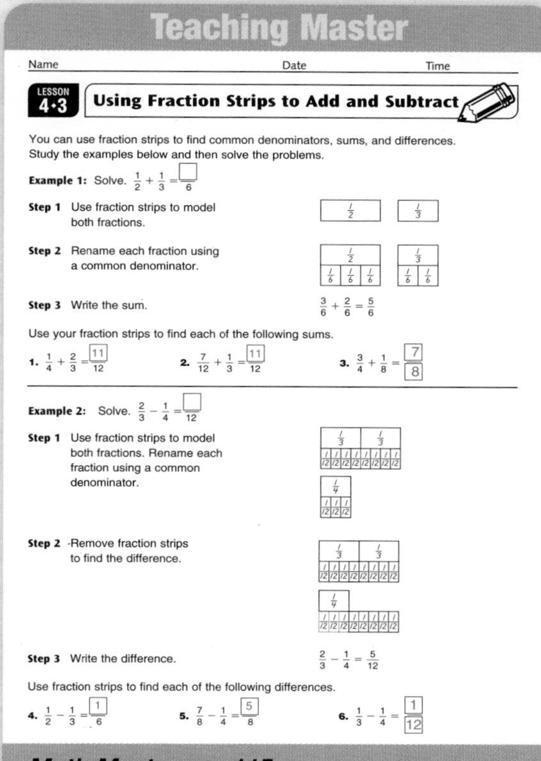

Teaching Master

Name Date Time

LESSON 4·3 **Using Fraction Strips to Add and Subtract**

You can use fraction strips to find common denominators, sums, and differences. Study the examples below and then solve the problems.

Example 1: Solve. $\frac{1}{2} + \frac{1}{3} = \frac{\square}{6}$

Step 1 Use fraction strips to model both fractions.

Step 2 Rename each fraction using a common denominator.

Step 3 Write the sum. $\frac{3}{6} + \frac{2}{6} = \frac{5}{6}$

Use your fraction strips to find each of the following sums.

1. $\frac{1}{4} + \frac{2}{3} = \frac{11}{12}$ **2.** $\frac{7}{12} + \frac{1}{3} = \frac{11}{12}$ **3.** $\frac{3}{4} + \frac{1}{8} = \frac{7}{8}$

Example 2: Solve. $\frac{2}{3} - \frac{1}{4} = \frac{\square}{12}$

Step 1 Use fraction strips to model both fractions. Rename each fraction using a common denominator.

Step 2 Remove fraction strips to find the difference.

Step 3 Write the difference. $\frac{2}{3} - \frac{1}{4} = \frac{5}{12}$

Use fraction strips to find each of the following differences.

4. $\frac{1}{2} - \frac{1}{3} = \frac{1}{6}$ **5.** $\frac{7}{8} - \frac{1}{4} = \frac{5}{8}$ **6.** $\frac{1}{3} - \frac{1}{4} = \frac{1}{12}$

Math Masters, **p. 115**

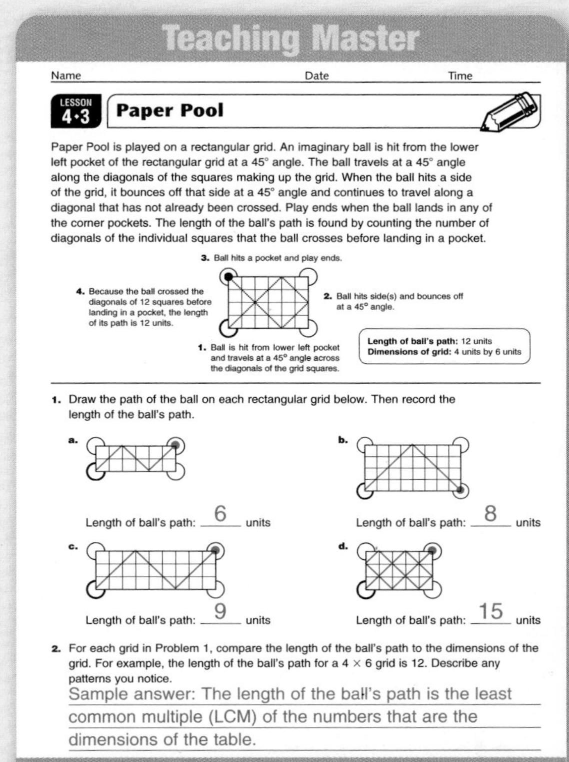

Teaching Master

Name Date Time

LESSON 4·3 **Paper Pool**

Paper Pool is played on a rectangular grid. An imaginary ball is hit from the lower left pocket of the rectangular grid at a 45° angle. The ball travels at a 45° angle along the diagonals of the squares making up the grid. When the ball hits a side of the grid, it bounces off that side at a 45° angle and continues to travel along a diagonal that has not already been crossed. Play ends when the ball lands in any of the corner pockets. The length of the ball's path is found by counting the number of diagonals of the individual squares that the ball crosses before landing in a pocket.

1. Draw the path of the ball on each rectangular grid below. Then record the length of the ball's path.

a. Length of ball's path: 6 units

b. Length of ball's path: 8 units

c. Length of ball's path: 9 units

d. Length of ball's path: 15 units

2. For each grid in Problem 1, compare the length of the ball's path to the dimensions of the grid. For example, the length of the ball's path for a 4 × 6 grid is 12. Describe any patterns you notice.

Sample answer: The length of the ball's path is the least common multiple (LCM) of the numbers that are the dimensions of the table.

Math Masters, **p. 116**

Adding and Subtracting Mixed Numbers with Like Denominators

Objective To add and subtract mixed numbers with like denominators.

1 Teaching the Lesson

Key Activities

Students practice adding and subtracting mixed numbers that have fractions with like denominators.

Key Concepts and Skills

- Convert between fractions and mixed numbers. [Number and Numeration Goal 5]
- Use multiplication and division facts to find equivalent fractions and to simplify fractions. [Operations and Computation Goal 2]
- Add and subtract mixed numbers with like denominators. [Operations and Computation Goal 3]

Key Vocabulary

mixed number • proper fraction • improper fraction • simplest form

Ongoing Assessment: Recognizing Student Achievement Use journal page 133. [Operations and Computation Goal 3]

materials

- ☐ *Math Journal 1,* pp. 132 and 133
- ☐ *Student Reference Book,* pp. 84–86
- ☐ Study Link 4•3
- ☐ Teaching Master (*Math Masters,* p. 117)
- ☐ scissors

See **Advance Preparation**

2 Ongoing Learning & Practice

Students practice estimating sums of fractions by playing *Fraction Action, Fraction Friction.*

Students practice and maintain skills through Math Boxes and Study Link activities.

materials

- ☐ *Math Journal 1,* p. 134
- ☐ *Student Reference Book,* p. 317
- ☐ Study Link Master (*Math Masters,* p. 118)
- ☐ Game Master (*Math Masters,* p. 446)
- ☐ Geometry Template; calculator

3 Differentiation Options

READINESS

Students use a calculator to practice counting by fractions and converting between improper fractions and mixed numbers.

ENRICHMENT

Students read a poem about fractions.

EXTRA PRACTICE

Students use bills and coins to model and simplify mixed numbers.

materials

- ☐ Teaching Master (*Math Masters,* p. 119)
- ☐ *Math Talk: Mathematical Ideas in Poems for Two Voices*
- ☐ calculator; coins and bills of various denominations

Additional Information

Advance Preparation For the Math Message in Part 1, make one copy of *Math Masters,* page 117 for every two students.

Technology

Assessment Management System
Journal page 133, Problems 9, 12, 14, and 15
See the **iTLG.**

Getting Started

Mental Math and Reflexes

Students rename improper fractions as mixed numbers. *Suggestions:*

●○○ $\frac{3}{2}$ $1\frac{1}{2}$ ●●○ $\frac{5}{3}$ $1\frac{2}{3}$ ●●● $\frac{75}{4}$ $18\frac{3}{4}$

$\frac{5}{4}$ $1\frac{1}{4}$ $\frac{13}{6}$ $2\frac{1}{6}$ $\frac{108}{5}$ $21\frac{3}{5}$

Math Message

Complete a copy of the Math Message problem.

Study Link 4·3 Follow-Up

Go over the answers.

1 Teaching the Lesson

▶ Math Message Follow-Up

WHOLE-CLASS DISCUSSION

(*Math Masters,* p. 117)

Ask a volunteer to demonstrate and explain how to use the paper ruler to measure the line segment. Sample answer: Line up the right end of $\overline{AB}$ with the mark for 4 in. on the ruler. The left end of $\overline{AB}$ is aligned with the mark for $\frac{5}{16}$ in. The total length of $\overline{AB}$ is 4 in. + $\frac{5}{16}$ in., or $4\frac{5}{16}$ in. This ruler shows the two parts of a mixed number: the whole number and the fraction. A **mixed number** can be viewed as the sum of a whole number and a fraction.

Discuss why fractions greater than 1 are easier to interpret when written as mixed numbers. For example, $2\frac{3}{4}$ clearly represents a number greater than 2 but less than 3. This is not as obvious when $2\frac{3}{4}$ is written as the improper fraction $\frac{11}{4}$.

NOTE If students are fairly skilled at finding sums and differences of fractions, this lesson may take less than one day.

▶ Writing Mixed Numbers in Simplest Form

WHOLE-CLASS DISCUSSION

Review the meanings of *proper fraction, improper fraction,* and *simplest form* with the class.

▷ A fraction in which the numerator is less than the denominator is called a **proper fraction.** A proper fraction names a number that is less than 1.

Examples: $\frac{3}{8}$, $\frac{9}{10}$, $\frac{0}{4}$

▷ A fraction in which the numerator is equal to or greater than the denominator is called an **improper fraction.** An improper fraction names a number that is greater than or equal to 1.

Examples: $\frac{5}{5}$, $\frac{7}{2}$, $\frac{9}{3}$

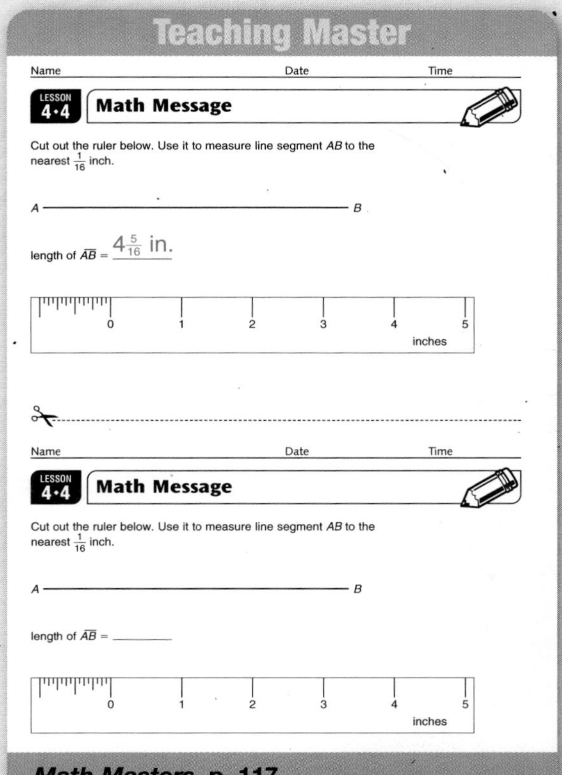

Teaching Master

Name Date Time

LESSON 4·4 **Math Message**

Cut out the ruler below. Use it to measure line segment *AB* to the nearest $\frac{1}{16}$ inch.

A ———— *B*

length of $\overline{AB}$ = $4\frac{5}{16}$ in.

0 1 2 3 4 5 inches

Name Date Time

LESSON 4·4 **Math Message**

Cut out the ruler below. Use it to measure line segment *AB* to the nearest $\frac{1}{16}$ inch.

A ———— *B*

length of $\overline{AB}$ = ______

0 1 2 3 4 5 inches

Math Masters, p. 117

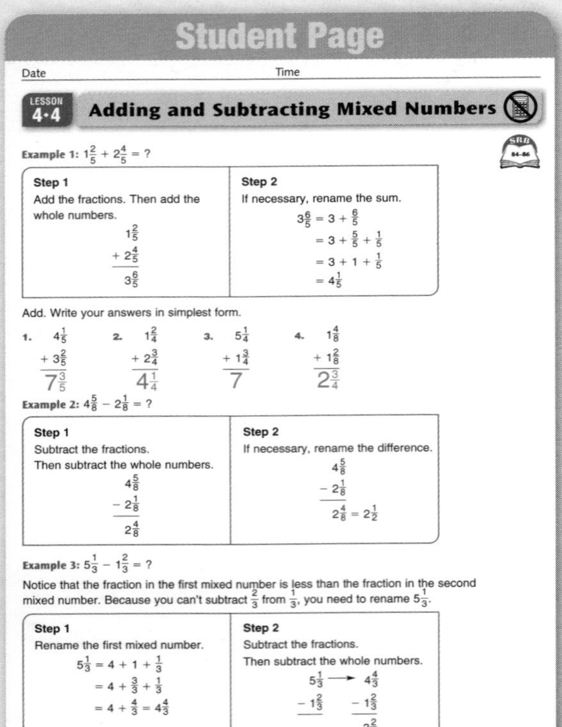

Math Journal 1, p. 132

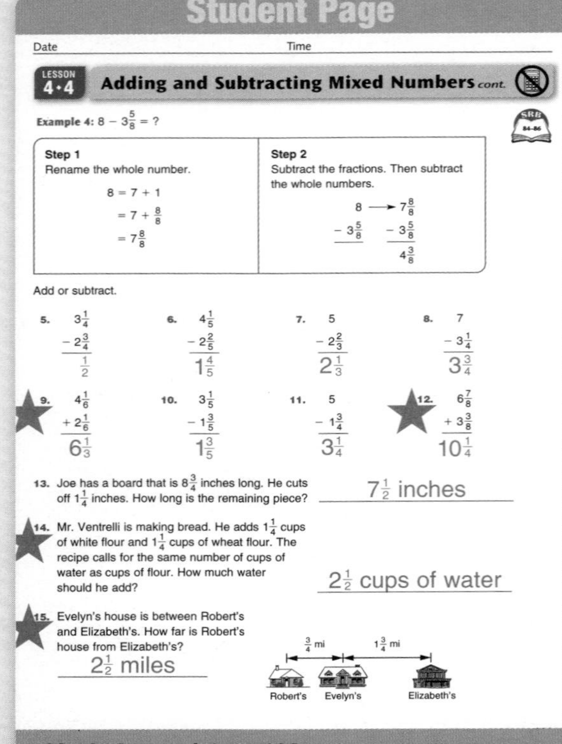

Math Journal 1, p. 133

▷ A mixed number is in **simplest form** if the fraction part is a proper fraction in simplest form.

Examples: $2\frac{4}{7}$ is in simplest form. $4\frac{8}{5}$ and $3\frac{9}{9}$ are not in simplest form because they contain an improper fraction. $3\frac{4}{8}$ is not in simplest form because $\frac{4}{8}$ is not in simplest form.

NOTE While *Everyday Mathematics* requests that mixed-number answers be written using proper fractions, the fraction part is not required to be in simplest form. Students should know how to name fractions in simplest form for standardized tests. However, they may often find it helpful to work with fractions or mixed numbers that are not in simplest form when they are computing with fractions.

Write $3\frac{5}{4}$ on the board and ask a volunteer to rename it in simplest form. Use pictures similar to those below to show the procedure.

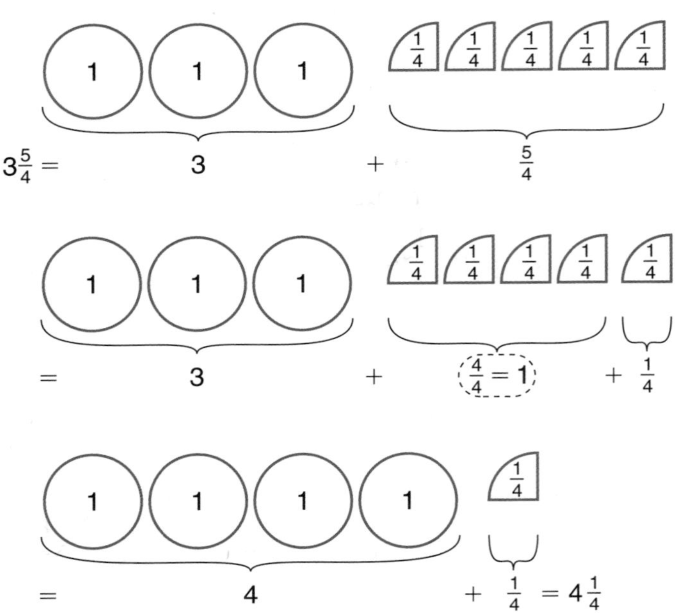

$3\frac{5}{4}$ can be renamed as $4\frac{1}{4}$.

Write several such mixed numbers on the board. Have students rename them in simplest form. *Suggestions:*

$7\frac{5}{5}$ 8 $\quad$ $4\frac{3}{2}$ $5\frac{1}{2}$ $\quad$ $2\frac{5}{3}$ $3\frac{2}{3}$ $\quad$ $1\frac{9}{6}$ $2\frac{1}{2}$

Adjusting the Activity

ELL

Have students model mixed numbers using bills and quarters. To model $3\frac{5}{4}$, use \$3 and 5 quarters. Five quarters is equal to \$1 and 1 quarter. Therefore, \$3 and 5 quarters = \$4 and 1 quarter.

AUDITORY ◆ KINESTHETIC ◆ TACTILE ◆ VISUAL

▶ Adding Mixed Numbers with Like Denominators

(*Math Journal 1,* p. 132; *Student Reference Book,* p. 84)

Write the following problem on the board: $1\frac{2}{5} + 2\frac{4}{5} = ?$ Ask students to solve and then share their strategies. Go over the steps on journal page 132 before having students complete Problems 1–4 on their own. Bring the class together to share solutions. If necessary, provide more practice, particularly with problems that require renaming. Refer students to page 84 in the *Student Reference Book.*

▶ Subtracting Mixed Numbers with Like Denominators

(*Math Journal 1,* pp. 132 and 133; *Student Reference Book,* p. 85)

Go over the three subtraction examples on journal pages 132 and 133 (Examples 2–4). Ask students to solve Problem 5. If successful, they should continue and complete the page. You may need to provide additional practice before continuing or refer students to page 85 in the *Student Reference Book.*

Ongoing Assessment: Recognizing Student Achievement

Journal Page 133 Problems 9, 12, 14, and 15 ★

Use **journal page 133, Problems 9, 12, 14, and 15** to assess students' ability to add mixed numbers with like denominators. Students are making adequate progress if they can calculate the sums in Problems 9, 12, 14, and 15. Some students may be able to calculate the differences in Problems 5–8, 10, 11, and 13.

[Operations and Computation Goal 3]

Student Page

Fractions

Addition of Mixed Numbers

One way to add mixed numbers is to add the fractions and the whole numbers separately. This may require renaming the sum.

Example Find $4\frac{5}{8} + 2\frac{7}{8}$.

Step 1: Add the fractions.	**Step 2:** Add the whole numbers.	**Step 3:** Rename the sum.
$4\frac{5}{8} + 2\frac{7}{8}$ → $\frac{12}{8}$	$4\frac{5}{8} + 2\frac{7}{8} = 6\frac{12}{8}$	$6\frac{12}{8} = 6 + \frac{8}{8} + \frac{4}{8}$ $= 6 + 1 + \frac{4}{8}$ $= 7\frac{4}{8}$ $= 7\frac{1}{2}$

$4\frac{5}{8} + 2\frac{7}{8} = 7\frac{1}{2}$

If the fractions do not have the same denominator, first rename the fractions so they have a common denominator.

Example Find $3\frac{3}{4} + 5\frac{2}{3}$.

Step 1: Rename and add the fractions.	**Step 2:** Add the whole numbers.	**Step 3:** Rename the sum.
$3\frac{3}{4} = 3\frac{9}{12}$ $+5\frac{2}{3} = +5\frac{8}{12}$ $\frac{17}{12}$	$3\frac{9}{12} + 5\frac{8}{12} = 8\frac{17}{12}$	$8\frac{17}{12} = 8 + \frac{12}{12} + \frac{5}{12}$ $= 8 + 1 + \frac{5}{12}$ $= 9\frac{5}{12}$

$3\frac{3}{4} + 5\frac{2}{3} = 9\frac{5}{12}$

Some calculators have special keys for entering mixed numbers.

Example Solve $3\frac{3}{4} + 5\frac{2}{3}$ on a calculator.

On Calculator A: Key in 3 [Unit] 3 [n] 4 [d] [+] 5 [Unit] 2 [n] 3 [d] [Enter]

On Calculator B: Key in 3 [a] 3 [b/c] 4 [+] 5 [a] 2 [b/c] 3 [=]

Check Your Understanding

Solve Problems 1–3 without a calculator. Solve Problem 4 with a calculator.

1. $2\frac{1}{8} + 7\frac{7}{8}$ **2.** $3\frac{4}{5} + 2\frac{1}{2}$ **3.** $6\frac{2}{3} + 3\frac{3}{4}$ **4.** $14\frac{4}{9} + 8\frac{6}{7}$

Student Reference Book, **p. 84**

Student Page

Fractions

Subtraction of Mixed Numbers

If the fractions do not have the same denominator, first rename them as fractions with a common denominator.

Example Find $3\frac{7}{8} - 1\frac{3}{4}$.

Step 1: Rename the fractions.	**Step 2:** Subtract the fractions.	**Step 3:** Subtract the whole numbers.
$3\frac{7}{8} = 3\frac{7}{8}$ $-1\frac{3}{4} = -1\frac{6}{8}$	$3\frac{7}{8} - 1\frac{6}{8}$ → $\frac{1}{8}$	$3\frac{7}{8} - 1\frac{6}{8} = 2\frac{1}{8}$

$3\frac{7}{8} - 1\frac{3}{4} = 2\frac{1}{8}$

To subtract a mixed number from a whole number, first rename the whole number as the sum of a whole number and a fraction that is equivalent to 1.

Example Find $5 - 2\frac{2}{3}$.

Step 1: Rename the whole number.	**Step 2:** Subtract the fractions.	**Step 3:** Subtract the whole numbers.
$5 = 4\frac{3}{3}$ $-2\frac{2}{3} = -2\frac{2}{3}$	$4\frac{3}{3} - 2\frac{2}{3}$ → $\frac{1}{3}$	$4\frac{3}{3} - 2\frac{2}{3} = 2\frac{1}{3}$

$5 - 2\frac{2}{3} = 2\frac{1}{3}$

When subtracting mixed numbers, rename the larger mixed number if it contains a fraction that is less than the fraction in the smaller mixed number.

Example Find $7\frac{1}{5} - 3\frac{3}{5}$.

Step 1: Rename the larger mixed number.	**Step 2:** Subtract the fractions.	**Step 3:** Subtract the whole numbers.
$7\frac{1}{5} = 6\frac{6}{5}$ $-3\frac{3}{5} = -3\frac{3}{5}$	$6\frac{6}{5} - 3\frac{3}{5}$ → $\frac{3}{5}$	$6\frac{6}{5} - 3\frac{3}{5} = 3\frac{3}{5}$

$7\frac{1}{5} - 3\frac{3}{5} = 3\frac{3}{5}$

Student Reference Book, **p. 85**

Game Master

Name Date Time

Fraction Action, Fraction Friction Card Deck

$\frac{1}{2}$	$\frac{1}{3}$	$\frac{2}{3}$	$\frac{1}{4}$
$\frac{3}{4}$	$\frac{1}{6}$	$\frac{1}{6}$	$\frac{5}{6}$
$\frac{1}{12}$	$\frac{1}{12}$	$\frac{5}{12}$	$\frac{5}{12}$
$\frac{7}{12}$	$\frac{7}{12}$	$\frac{11}{12}$	$\frac{11}{12}$

***Math Masters*, p. 446**

2 Ongoing Learning & Practice

▶ Playing *Fraction Action, Fraction Friction*

(*Student Reference Book*, p. 317; *Math Masters*, p. 446)

Distribute one set of 16 *Fraction Action, Fraction Friction* cards and one or more calculators to each group of two or three players. Review game directions on page 317 of the *Student Reference Book*. Play a few practice rounds with the class.

▶ Math Boxes 4•4

(*Math Journal 1*, p. 134)

Mixed Practice Math Boxes in this lesson are paired with Math Boxes in Lesson 4-2. The skill in Problem 5 previews Unit 5 content. Students will need the Percent Circle on the Geometry Template to complete Problem 5.

▶ Study Link 4•4

(*Math Masters*, p. 118)

Home Connection Students practice addition and subtraction of mixed numbers.

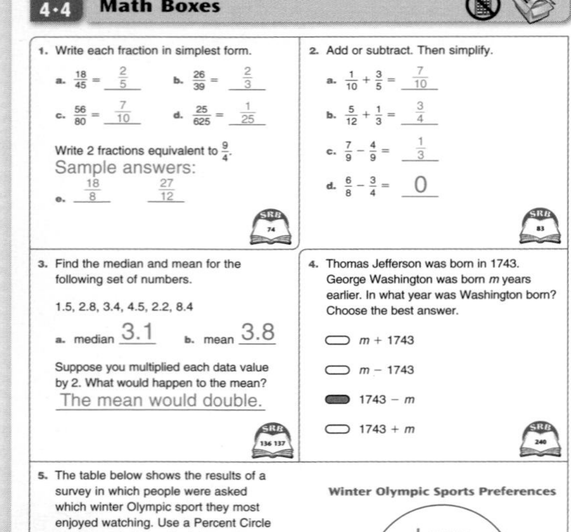

Student Page

Date Time

LESSON 4•4 **Math Boxes**

1. Write each fraction in simplest form.
   a. $\frac{18}{45} = \frac{2}{5}$ b. $\frac{26}{39} = \frac{2}{3}$
   c. $\frac{56}{80} = \frac{7}{10}$ d. $\frac{25}{625} = \frac{1}{25}$
   Write 2 fractions equivalent to $\frac{9}{4}$.
   Sample answers:
   e. $\frac{18}{8}$ $\frac{27}{12}$
   SRB 74
2. Add or subtract. Then simplify.
   a. $\frac{1}{10} + \frac{3}{5} = \frac{7}{10}$
   b. $\frac{5}{12} + \frac{1}{3} = \frac{3}{4}$
   c. $\frac{7}{9} - \frac{4}{9} = \frac{1}{3}$
   d. $\frac{6}{8} - \frac{3}{4} = 0$
   SRB 83
3. Find the median and mean for the following set of numbers.
   1.5, 2.8, 3.4, 4.5, 2.2, 8.4
   a. median 3.1 b. mean 3.8
   Suppose you multiplied each data value by 2. What would happen to the mean?
   The mean would double.
   SRB 136 137
4. Thomas Jefferson was born in 1743. George Washington was born *m* years earlier. In what year was Washington born? Choose the best answer.
   ○ $m + 1743$
   ○ $m - 1743$
   ● $1743 - m$
   ○ $1743 + m$
   SRB 240
5. The table below shows the results of a survey in which people were asked which winter Olympic sport they most enjoyed watching. Use a Percent Circle to make a circle graph of the results.

Favorite Sport	Percent of People Surveyed
Luge	35%
Ice hockey	15%
Figure skating	40%
Other	10%

***Math Journal 1*, p. 134**

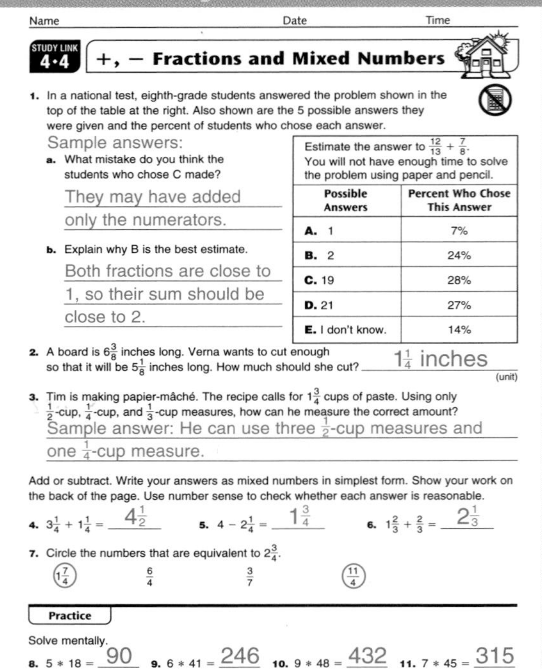

Study Link Master

Name Date Time

STUDY LINK 4•4 **+, − Fractions and Mixed Numbers**

1. In a national test, eighth-grade students answered the problem shown in the top of the table at the right. Also shown are the 5 possible answers they were given and the percent of students who chose each answer.

Estimate the answer to $\frac{12}{13} + \frac{7}{8}$. You will not have enough time to solve the problem using paper and pencil.

Possible Answers	Percent Who Chose This Answer
A. 1	7%
B. 2	24%
C. 19	28%
D. 21	27%
E. I don't know.	14%

Sample answers:
   a. What mistake do you think the students who chose C made?
   They may have added only the numerators.
   b. Explain why B is the best estimate.
   Both fractions are close to 1, so their sum should be close to 2.
2. A board is $6\frac{3}{8}$ inches long. Verna wants to cut enough so that it will be $5\frac{1}{8}$ inches long. How much should she cut? $1\frac{1}{4}$ inches (unit)
3. Tim is making papier-mâché. The recipe calls for $1\frac{3}{4}$ cups of paste. Using only $\frac{1}{2}$-cup, $\frac{1}{4}$-cup, and $\frac{1}{3}$-cup measures, how can he measure the correct amount?
   Sample answer: He can use three $\frac{1}{2}$-cup measures and one $\frac{1}{4}$-cup measure.

Add or subtract. Write your answers as mixed numbers in simplest form. Show your work on the back of the page. Use number sense to check whether each answer is reasonable.

4. $3\frac{1}{4} + 1\frac{1}{4} = 4\frac{1}{2}$
5. $4 - 2\frac{1}{4} = 1\frac{3}{4}$
6. $1\frac{2}{3} + \frac{2}{3} = 2\frac{1}{3}$
7. Circle the numbers that are equivalent to $2\frac{3}{4}$.
   ($1\frac{7}{4}$) $\frac{6}{4}$ $\frac{3}{7}$ ($\frac{11}{4}$)

Practice

Solve mentally.

8. $5 * 18 = 90$
9. $6 * 41 = 246$
10. $9 * 48 = 432$
11. $7 * 45 = 315$

***Math Masters*, p. 118**

3 Differentiation Options

READINESS

PARTNER ACTIVITY

▶ Using a Calculator for Fraction Counts

5–15 Min

(*Math Masters,* p. 119)

To provide experience with fractions and mixed numbers, have students use the constant function on a calculator to define and generate fraction counts. They also study and apply patterns involving unit fractions, improper fractions, and mixed numbers.

ENRICHMENT

PARTNER ACTIVITY

▶ Reading about Fractions in Poetry

5–15 Min

Literature Link To further explore fractions, have students read the poem "Proper Fractions" in *Math Talk: Mathematical Ideas in Poems for Two Voices.* Suggest that students recite the poem in their spare time and present it to the class.

EXTRA PRACTICE

PARTNER ACTIVITY

▶ Modeling Mixed Numbers with Bills and Coins

5–15 Min

To provide extra practice simplifying mixed numbers, have students use bills and coins to model renaming procedures. *Suggestions:*

$2\frac{4}{4}$ \$2 and 4 quarters; 3	$2\frac{13}{10}$ \$2 and 13 dimes; $3\frac{3}{10}$
$1\frac{9}{4}$ \$1 and 9 quarters; $3\frac{1}{4}$	$3\frac{31}{20}$ \$3 and 31 nickels; $4\frac{11}{20}$

Teaching Master

Name Date Time

LESSON 4•4 **Fraction Counts and Conversions**

Most calculators have a function that lets you repeat an operation, such as adding $\frac{1}{4}$ to a number. This is called the constant function. To use the constant function of your calculator to count by $\frac{1}{4}$s, follow one of the key sequences below, depending on the calculator you are using.

Calculator A	Calculator B
Press: (Op1) (+) (1) (n) (4) (d) (Op1) (Op1) (Op1) (Op1) (Op1) (Op1)	Press: (1) (b/c) (4) (+) (+) (0) (=) (=) (=) (=) (=)
Display: 5 $1\frac{1}{4}$	Display: K $\frac{5}{4}$
Press: (U n/d ↔ n/d)	Press: (a b/c ↔ d/c)
Display: $\frac{5}{4}$	Display: $1\frac{1}{4}$

1. Using a calculator, start at 0 and count by $\frac{1}{4}$s to answer the following questions.
   a. How many counts of $\frac{1}{4}$ are needed to display $\frac{6}{4}$? 6
   b. How many counts of $\frac{1}{4}$ are needed to display $1\frac{1}{2}$? 6

2. Use a calculator to convert mixed numbers to improper fractions or whole numbers.
   a. $2\frac{3}{4}$ = $\frac{11}{4}$
   b. $1\frac{7}{4}$ = $\frac{11}{4}$
   c. $2\frac{4}{4}$ = 3
   d. $3\frac{12}{4}$ = 6

3. How many $\frac{1}{4}$s are between the following numbers?
   a. $\frac{3}{4}$ and 2 5
   b. $\frac{6}{4}$ and $2\frac{3}{4}$ 5
   c. $1\frac{3}{4}$ and 4 9
   d. 3 and $4\frac{1}{2}$ 6

Math Masters, p. 119

4•5 Adding and Subtracting Mixed Numbers with Unlike Denominators

Objective To add and subtract mixed numbers with unlike denominators.

1 Teaching the Lesson

Key Activities

Students review methods for finding sums and differences of mixed numbers with like denominators and extend these methods to find sums and differences of mixed numbers with unlike denominators.

Key Concepts and Skills

- Convert between fractions and mixed numbers.
  [Number and Numeration Goal 5]
- Add and subtract mixed numbers with like and unlike denominators.
  [Operations and Computation Goal 3]
- Measure a line segment to the nearest $\frac{1}{8}$ inch.
  [Measurement and Reference Frames Goal 1]
- Apply the Associative Property of Addition to calculate sums of mixed numbers.
  [Patterns, Functions, and Algebra Goal 4]

materials

- ☐ *Math Journal 1,* pp. 136 and 137
- ☐ Study Link 4•4
- ☐ Teaching Master (*Math Masters,* p. 120)
- ☐ slate

See Advance Preparation

2 Ongoing Learning & Practice

Students practice writing algebraic expressions.

Students practice and maintain skills through Math Boxes and Study Link activities.

Ongoing Assessment: Recognizing Student Achievement Use journal page 135.
[Operations and Computation Goal 3]

materials

- ☐ *Math Journal 1,* pp. 135 and 138
- ☐ Study Link Master (*Math Masters,* p. 121)
- ☐ Geometry Template or protractor

3 Differentiation Options

READINESS

Students represent mixed numbers using pictures, sums, improper fractions, and quotients.

ENRICHMENT

Students create subtraction problems for given results.

EXTRA PRACTICE

Students complete teacher-generated Math Boxes.

materials

- ☐ Teaching Master (*Math Masters,* p. 122)
- ☐ Teaching Aid Master (*Math Masters,* p. 405)

Additional Information

Advance Preparation For Part 1, make one copy of *Math Masters,* page 120 for every two students. Cut it into half-sheets and distribute as the Math Message.

Technology

Assessment Management System
Math Boxes, Problem 2
See the **iTLG.**

Getting Started

Mental Math and Reflexes

Students estimate sums and differences, writing "> 1," "< 1," or "= 1" on their slates. Have students explain their strategies. *Suggestions:*

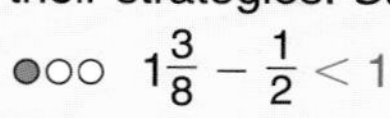

●○○ $1\frac{3}{8} - \frac{1}{2} < 1$ $\quad \frac{1}{3} + \frac{4}{6} = 1$

●●○ $\frac{4}{5} + \frac{7}{10} > 1$ $\quad 2\frac{4}{7} - 1\frac{5}{6} < 1$

●●● $\frac{9}{10} + \frac{9}{100} < 1$ $\quad \frac{1}{2} + \frac{1}{4} + \frac{1}{3} > 1$

Math Message

Complete a copy of the Math Message problems.

Study Link 4·4 Follow-Up

Briefly go over the problems.

1 Teaching the Lesson

▶ Math Message Follow-Up

WHOLE-CLASS DISCUSSION

(*Math Masters,* p. 120)

Use Problems 1–5 to check students' progress with calculating sums and differences of mixed numbers having like denominators. If necessary, pose additional problems before discussing Problems 6–8.

Point out paired Problems 5 and 6; 7 and 8. Guide students to find the equivalent fractions ($\frac{2}{8}$ and $\frac{1}{4}$; $\frac{6}{12}$ and $\frac{1}{2}$). Students can solve these problems using the methods they learned in Lesson 4-4.

▶ Adding and Subtracting Mixed Numbers with Unlike Fractions

WHOLE-CLASS ACTIVITY

(*Math Journal 1,* pp. 136 and 137)

Work through one or more examples as a class.

Example: $2\frac{5}{6} + 1\frac{2}{3} = ?$ Estimate: $3 + 2 = 5$

$$\begin{array}{r} 2\frac{5}{6} \\ +\ 1\frac{2}{3} \\ \hline \end{array} \rightarrow \begin{array}{r} 2\frac{5}{6} \\ +\ 1\frac{4}{6} \\ \hline 3\frac{9}{6} \end{array} = 4\frac{3}{6} = 4\frac{1}{2}$$

Example: $8\frac{7}{10} - 2\frac{4}{5} = ?$ Estimate: $9 - 3 = 6$

$$\begin{array}{r} 8\frac{7}{10} \\ -\ 2\frac{4}{5} \\ \hline \end{array} \rightarrow \begin{array}{r} 8\frac{7}{10} \\ -\ 2\frac{8}{10} \\ \hline \end{array} \rightarrow \begin{array}{r} 7\frac{17}{10} \\ -\ 2\frac{8}{10} \\ \hline 5\frac{9}{10} \end{array}$$

Teaching Master

Name Date Time

LESSON 4·5 **Math Message**

Add or subtract. Be ready to explain your solution strategies for Problems 6 and 8.

1. $2\frac{1}{5} + 3\frac{3}{5} = 5\frac{4}{5}$
2. $6\frac{3}{8} + 5\frac{7}{8} = 12\frac{1}{4}$
3. $10\frac{7}{9} - 4\frac{1}{9} = 6\frac{2}{3}$
4. $5\frac{1}{4} - 3\frac{3}{4} = 1\frac{1}{2}$
5. $2\frac{2}{8} + 3\frac{1}{8} = 5\frac{3}{8}$
6. $2\frac{1}{4} + 3\frac{1}{8} = 5\frac{3}{8}$
7. $2\frac{7}{12} - 1\frac{6}{12} = 1\frac{1}{12}$
8. $2\frac{7}{12} - 1\frac{1}{2} = 1\frac{1}{12}$

Name Date Time

LESSON 4·5 **Math Message**

Add or subtract. Be ready to explain your solution strategies for Problems 6 and 8.

1. $2\frac{1}{5} + 3\frac{3}{5}$
2. $6\frac{3}{8} + 5\frac{7}{8}$
3. $10\frac{7}{9} - 4\frac{1}{9}$
4. $5\frac{1}{4} - 3\frac{3}{4}$
5. $2\frac{2}{8} + 3\frac{1}{8}$
6. $2\frac{1}{4} + 3\frac{1}{8}$
7. $2\frac{7}{12} - 1\frac{6}{12}$
8. $2\frac{7}{12} - 1\frac{1}{2}$

Math Masters, p. 120

Student Page

Date Time

LESSON 4·5 **More Adding and Subtracting Mixed Numbers**

Fill in the missing number to rename the mixed number.

1. $\frac{5}{3} = 1\frac{2}{3}$
2. $3\frac{7}{4} = 4\frac{3}{4}$
3. $6\frac{12}{8} = 7\frac{4}{8}$
4. $5\frac{2}{5} = 4\frac{7}{5}$
5. $8\frac{2}{3} = 7\frac{5}{3}$
6. $2\frac{3}{8} = 1\frac{11}{8}$

Use what you know about adding and subtracting fractions to help you add and subtract mixed numbers with different denominators.

Example 1: $1\frac{1}{3} + 3\frac{5}{6} = ?$

Estimate: 1 + 4 = 5

Rename $\frac{1}{3}$ as $\frac{2}{6}$. Add and then simplify.

$1\frac{1}{3} + 3\frac{5}{6} \rightarrow 1\frac{2}{6} + 3\frac{5}{6} = 4\frac{7}{6} \rightarrow 5\frac{1}{6}$

Example 2: $8\frac{2}{5} - 2\frac{1}{2} = ?$

Estimate: $8\frac{1}{2} - 2\frac{1}{2} = 6$

Rename $\frac{2}{5}$ as $\frac{4}{10}$ and $\frac{1}{2}$ as $\frac{5}{10}$. Rename $8\frac{4}{10}$ as $7\frac{14}{10}$. Then subtract.

$8\frac{2}{5} - 2\frac{1}{2} \rightarrow 8\frac{4}{10} - 2\frac{5}{10} \rightarrow 7\frac{14}{10} - 2\frac{5}{10} = 5\frac{9}{10}$

First estimate. Then add or subtract. Show your work. Sample estimates given.

7. $1\frac{3}{4} + 3\frac{2}{8}$ = 5 Estimate: 5
8. $3\frac{1}{2} - 1\frac{1}{4}$ = $2\frac{1}{4}$ Estimate: 2
9. $6 - 2\frac{1}{5}$ = $3\frac{4}{5}$ Estimate: 4
10. $2\frac{7}{8} + 1\frac{3}{4}$ = $4\frac{5}{8}$ Estimate: 5
11. $6\frac{1}{8} - 5\frac{1}{4} = ?$ Estimate: 1; $6\frac{1}{8} - 5\frac{1}{4} = \frac{7}{8}$
12. $5\frac{1}{3} - 4\frac{3}{4} = ?$ Estimate: 1; $5\frac{1}{3} - 4\frac{3}{4} = \frac{7}{12}$

Math Journal 1, p. 136

Student Page

Date Time

LESSON 4·5 **More Adding and Subtracting Mixed Numbers** *cont.*

13. To check your answer to Problem 10, draw a line segment that is $2\frac{7}{8}$ inches long. Then make it $1\frac{3}{4}$ inches longer.

$2\frac{7}{8}$ in. $1\frac{3}{4}$ in.

Measure the whole line segment. How long is it? $4\frac{5}{8}$ inches

14. Tim walked $\frac{1}{2}$ mile from school to the park. Then he walked $\frac{1}{4}$ mile to the store to get milk and orange juice. These items cost $2\frac{1}{2}$ dollars. Then he walked another $\frac{3}{4}$ mile to go home.

How far did Tim walk in all? $1\frac{1}{2}$ miles

Find a way to solve these problems without finding common denominators. Write number sentences to show the order in which you added and subtracted.

15. $1\frac{1}{2} + 3\frac{7}{8} + 4\frac{1}{2} + 1\frac{1}{8} =$ 11
$(3\frac{7}{8} + 1\frac{1}{8}) + (1\frac{1}{2} + 4\frac{1}{2}) = 5 + 6 = 11$

16. $3\frac{1}{2} + 4\frac{2}{3} - 1\frac{1}{2} =$ $6\frac{2}{3}$
$(3\frac{1}{2} - 1\frac{1}{2}) + 4\frac{2}{3} = 2 + 4\frac{2}{3} = 6\frac{2}{3}$

17. If you drive $5\frac{4}{5}$ miles from Alphatown along Highway 1, you reach Betaville. Driving farther, you reach Gamma, which is $8\frac{1}{10}$ miles from Alphatown.

a. Plot the locations of Betaville and Gamma on the number line below.

Alphatown — Betaville — Gamma; 0 1 2 3 4 5 6 7 8 9 10 Miles

b. How far is it from Betaville to Gamma? $2\frac{3}{10}$ miles

Math Journal 1, p. 137

Additional practice suggestions:

Addition		**Subtraction**	
$5\frac{1}{3} + 3\frac{1}{4}$	$8\frac{7}{12}$	$2\frac{3}{4} - 1\frac{5}{8}$	$1\frac{1}{8}$
$4\frac{1}{6} + 3\frac{3}{4}$	$7\frac{11}{12}$	$3\frac{1}{3} - 2\frac{5}{8}$	$\frac{17}{24}$
$2\frac{7}{9} + 8\frac{2}{3}$	$11\frac{4}{9}$	$4\frac{2}{5} - 3\frac{5}{6}$	$\frac{17}{30}$

Adjusting the Activity

Demonstrate an alternative method of addition and subtraction, in which the mixed numbers are renamed as fractions. The resulting fractions are added or subtracted, and the sums or differences are renamed as mixed numbers.

Example:

$$5\frac{1}{3} + 3\frac{1}{4} \rightarrow \frac{16}{3} + \frac{13}{4} \rightarrow \frac{64}{12} + \frac{39}{12} \rightarrow \frac{64+39}{12} = \frac{103}{12} = 8\frac{7}{12}$$

AUDITORY ◆ KINESTHETIC ◆ TACTILE ◆ VISUAL

The best method of computation may depend on the numbers involved. Sometimes using mental math is faster than using a paper-and-pencil method. For example, a quick way to find the sum $7\frac{3}{8} + 2\frac{1}{4} + 1\frac{5}{8} + 4\frac{1}{2}$ is to group mixed numbers according to the denominators of the fractions and add mentally:

$$(7\frac{3}{8} + 1\frac{5}{8}) + (2\frac{1}{4} + 4\frac{1}{2})$$
$$= (7 + 1 + 1) + (2 + 4 + \frac{3}{4})$$
$$= (9 + 6\frac{3}{4}) = 15\frac{3}{4}$$

Using a paper-and-pencil algorithm is not always the most efficient way to calculate a sum. Finding a common denominator to solve $4\frac{5}{7} + 7\frac{9}{10} + 3\frac{7}{15}$, for example, may be time-consuming. The best computation method in this case is to use a calculator. The calculator is a good tool for less commonly used fractions, such as $\frac{5}{7}$ and $\frac{7}{15}$. Have students use calculators to find the sum $4\frac{5}{7} + 7\frac{9}{10} + 3\frac{7}{15}$. $16\frac{17}{210}$

Regardless of the computation method that students choose, they should always begin by making a ballpark estimate. When they obtain an answer, they should check their answer against their estimate for reasonableness.

Have students work on journal pages 136 and 137. Circulate and assist.

2 Ongoing Learning & Practice

▶ Writing Algebraic Expressions

INDEPENDENT ACTIVITY

(*Math Journal 1,* p. 138)

Geography Students write algebraic expressions and solve addition and subtraction number stories involving the areas of oceans and lakes.

▶ Math Boxes 4•5

INDEPENDENT ACTIVITY

(*Math Journal 1,* p. 135)

Mixed Practice Math Boxes in this lesson are paired with Math Boxes in Lesson 4-7. The skill in Problem 6 previews Unit 5 content. Students will need a Geometry Template or a protractor to complete Problem 6.

Writing/Reasoning Have students write a response to the following: *Is* $302.7 * 10^{-3}$ *equal to* $302.7 \div 1{,}000$*? Explain.* Sample answer: Yes. $302.7 * 10^{-3}$ equals $302.7 * \frac{1}{1{,}000}$, which is the same as $\frac{302.7}{1{,}000}$, or $302.7 \div 1{,}000$.

Ongoing Assessment: Recognizing Student Achievement

Math Boxes Problem 2

Use **Math Boxes, Problem 2** to assess students' ability to subtract mixed numbers. Students are making adequate progress if they can calculate differences involving like denominators (Problems 2a and 2b). Some students may be able to calculate differences involving unlike denominators (Problems 2c and 2d).

[Operations and Computation Goal 3]

▶ Study Link 4•5

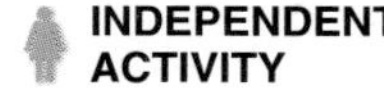

INDEPENDENT ACTIVITY

(*Math Masters,* p. 121)

Home Connection Students practice adding and subtracting mixed numbers having like and unlike denominators.

Student Page

Date Time

LESSON 4•5 **Water Problems**

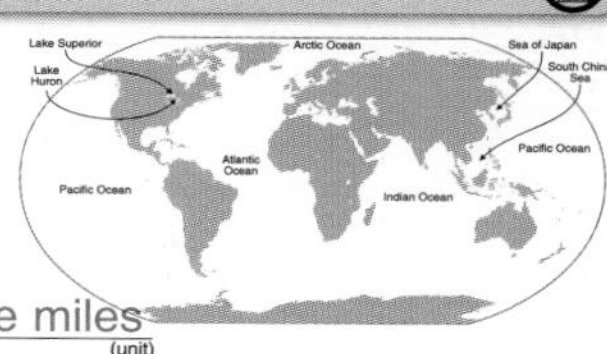

1. The largest ocean is the Pacific Ocean. Its area is about 64 million square miles. The second largest ocean is the Atlantic Ocean. Let *P* stand for the area of the Pacific Ocean. If $P - 30.6$ stands for the area of the Atlantic, then what is the approximate area of the Atlantic?
   33.4 million square miles (unit)
2. The third largest ocean is the Indian Ocean. Its area is about 28.3 million square miles. Write an algebraic expression using *P* that represents the approximate area of the Indian Ocean.
   $P - 35.7$
3. The fourth largest ocean is the Arctic Ocean. If $\frac{P}{12}$ stands for the approximate area of the Arctic Ocean, then what is the approximate area of the Arctic Ocean?
   5.3 million square miles (unit)
4. Let *A* stand for the area of the Arctic Ocean. The area of the South China Sea, the largest sea in the world, is about $\frac{1}{5}$ the area of the Arctic Ocean.
   a. Use the variable *A* to write an algebraic expression that represents the area of the South China Sea. $\frac{A}{5}$, or $\frac{1}{5} * A$
   b. What is the approximate area of the South China Sea?
   1.06 million square miles (unit)
5. The deepest point in the Sea of Japan is about 5,468 feet below sea level. The deepest point in the Indian Ocean is 7,534 feet deeper. About how many feet below sea level is the deepest point in the Indian Ocean?
   13,002 feet (unit)
6. The area of Lake Superior, the largest of the Great Lakes, is about 31,699 square miles. The area of Lake Huron, the second largest, is approximately 23,004 square miles. About how much larger is Lake Superior than Lake Huron?
   8,695 square miles (unit)

***Math Journal 1,* p. 138**

Student Page

Date Time

LESSON 4•6 **A Fraction Multiplication Algorithm**

Math Message

1. Use the number line to help you solve the problems in Columns 1 and 2 below.
   Reminder: The word *of* often means *times.*

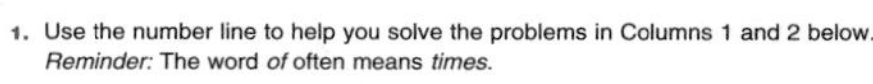

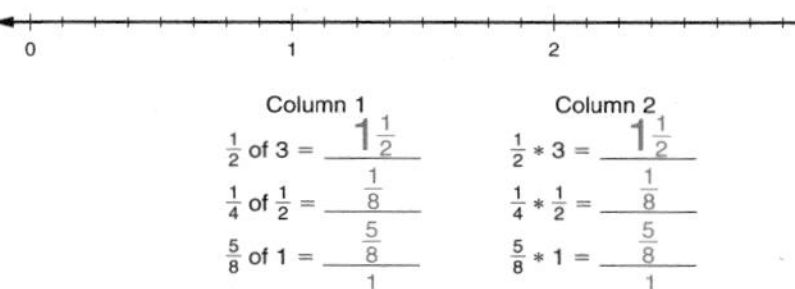

Column 1	Column 2
$\frac{1}{2}$ of 3 = $1\frac{1}{2}$	$\frac{1}{2} * 3 = 1\frac{1}{2}$
$\frac{1}{4}$ of $\frac{1}{2}$ = $\frac{1}{8}$	$\frac{1}{4} * \frac{1}{2} = \frac{1}{8}$
$\frac{5}{8}$ of 1 = $\frac{5}{8}$	$\frac{5}{8} * 1 = \frac{5}{8}$
$\frac{1}{3}$ of $\frac{3}{4}$ = $\frac{1}{4}$	$\frac{1}{3} * \frac{3}{4} = \frac{1}{4}$

2. How are the problems in Column 1 like their partner problems in Column 2?
   They have the same factors and answers.
3. Circle the general pattern(s) below for the partner problems in Columns 1 and 2.
   $a + b = b + a$ $a * b = b * c$ (a of $b = a * b$) $a \div b = b \div a$

Six special cases of a general pattern are given below. Write the answer in simplest form for each special case. Study the first one.

4. $\frac{1}{5} * \frac{2}{3} = \frac{1 * 2}{5 * 3} = \frac{2}{15}$
5. $\frac{3}{4} * \frac{1}{2} = \frac{3 * 1}{4 * 2} = \frac{3}{8}$
6. $\frac{2}{1} * \frac{2}{4} = \frac{2 * 2}{1 * 4} = 1$
7. $\frac{2}{4} * \frac{3}{5} = \frac{2 * 3}{4 * 5} = \frac{3}{10}$
8. $\frac{4}{6} * \frac{1}{2} = \frac{4 * 1}{6 * 2} = \frac{1}{3}$
9. $\frac{3}{7} * \frac{1}{3} = \frac{3 * 1}{7 * 3} = \frac{1}{7}$
10. Describe the general pattern in words. (*Hint:* Look at the numerators and denominators of the factors and products.)
    Sample answer: The product of two fractions is a fraction whose numerator is the product of the numerators, and whose denominator is the product of the denominators.

***Math Journal 1,* p. 135**

Study Link Master

STUDY LINK 4·5 **Mixed-Number Practice**

1. Answer the following questions about the rectangle shown at the right. Include units in your answers.

   (Rectangle: $2\frac{3}{4}$ in. by $1\frac{1}{2}$ in.)

   a. What is the perimeter? $8\frac{1}{2}$ in.

   b. If you were to trim this rectangle so that it was a square measuring $1\frac{1}{4}$ inches on a side, how much would you cut from the base? $1\frac{1}{2}$ in. from the height? $\frac{1}{4}$ in.

2. Michael bought 1 peck of Empire apples, 1 peck of Golden Delicious apples, a $\frac{1}{2}$-bushel of Red Delicious apples, and $1\frac{1}{2}$ bushels of McIntosh apples.

   1 peck = $\frac{1}{4}$ bushel

   a. How many bushels of apples did he buy in all? $2\frac{1}{2}$ bushels

   b. Michael estimates that he can make about 12 quarts of applesauce per bushel of apples. About how many quarts of applesauce can he make from the apples he bought? 30 quarts

Add or subtract. Show your work and estimates on the back of the page.

3. $2\frac{1}{3} + 1\frac{2}{3} = 4$
4. $6\frac{1}{3} - 5\frac{2}{3} = \frac{2}{3}$
5. $4\frac{1}{2} + \frac{2}{3} = 5\frac{1}{6}$
6. $6 - 5\frac{4}{9} = \frac{5}{9}$
7. $4\frac{3}{8} - 2\frac{3}{4} = 1\frac{5}{8}$
8. $3\frac{1}{4} + 2\frac{3}{4} = 6$
9. $9 - 2\frac{2}{5} = 6\frac{3}{5}$
10. $4\frac{1}{4} - 2\frac{5}{6} = 1\frac{5}{12}$
11. $5\frac{1}{4} - 2\frac{7}{10} = 2\frac{11}{20}$

Practice

Solve mentally.

12. $1\frac{1}{2} + 4\frac{2}{3} + 2\frac{1}{2} + 5\frac{1}{3} = 14$
13. $4.5 + 3.4 + 7.5 + 2.5 = 17.9$
14. $2.35 + $9.60 + $8.05 + $1.99 = $21.99
15. $5\frac{5}{8} + 3\frac{3}{4} + 2\frac{1}{4} + 8\frac{3}{8} = 20$

Math Masters, p. 121

Teaching Master

Name Date Time

LESSON 4·5 **Representing Mixed Numbers**

Study the example row. Then complete the table. Use Row 5 to represent a mixed number of your choice.

Picture	As Mixed Number	As Sum	Whole Number as Fraction	As Improper Fraction	As Quotient
Example:	$1\frac{1}{3}$	$1 + \frac{1}{3}$	$\frac{3}{3} + \frac{1}{3}$	$\frac{4}{3}$	$4 \div 3$
1.	$1\frac{5}{6}$	$1 + \frac{5}{6}$	$\frac{6}{6} + \frac{5}{6}$	$\frac{11}{6}$	$11 \div 6$
2.	$2\frac{1}{2}$	$2 + \frac{1}{2}$	$\frac{4}{2} + \frac{1}{2}$	$\frac{5}{2}$	$5 \div 2$
3.	$2\frac{1}{5}$	$2 + \frac{1}{5}$	$\frac{10}{5} + \frac{1}{5}$	$\frac{11}{5}$	$11 \div 5$
4. Sample answer:	$3\frac{3}{4}$	$3 + \frac{3}{4}$	$\frac{12}{4} + \frac{3}{4}$	$\frac{15}{4}$	$15 \div 4$
5. Answers will vary.					

Math Masters, p. 122

3 Differentiation Options

READINESS

▶ Representing Mixed Numbers

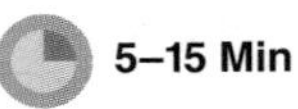

(*Math Masters,* p. 122)

Provide students with a copy of *Math Masters,* page 122. After reviewing the example, students use pictures, sums, improper fractions, and quotients to represent mixed numbers. Working with these representations provides students with experience in renaming the minuend of a mixed-number subtraction problem.

ENRICHMENT

▶ Creating Problems with Mixed Numbers

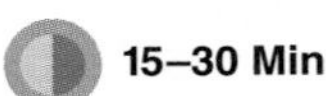

Students create subtraction problems involving mixed numbers with unlike denominators that result in the differences given below. This provides students an opportunity to further explore regrouping.

$8\frac{4}{9}$ $3\frac{5}{12}$ $2\frac{5}{7}$ $11\frac{1}{3}$

Each problem should require regrouping.

Examples:

$14 - 5\frac{5}{9} = 8\frac{4}{9}$ $5\frac{1}{4} - 1\frac{5}{6} = 3\frac{5}{12}$

$3\frac{9}{14} - \frac{13}{14} = 2\frac{5}{7}$ $14\frac{2}{15} - 2\frac{4}{5} = 11\frac{1}{3}$

EXTRA PRACTICE

▶ Writing Custom-Made Math Boxes

5–15 Min

(*Math Masters,* p. 405)

Use *Math Masters,* page 405 to generate Math Box questions that focus on a particular concept or skill for which students need extra practice.

Fraction Multiplication

Objectives **To represent the fraction multiplication algorithm as a general pattern; and to use the algorithm to find products of fractions.**

1 Teaching the Lesson

Key Activities

Students use a number-line model to review multiplication of fractions. They represent the standard fraction multiplication algorithm as a general pattern and use the algorithm to solve fraction-of multiplication problems.

Key Concepts and Skills

- Apply the concept of GCF to rename a fraction in simplest form. [Number and Numeration Goal 3]
- Convert between whole numbers and improper fractions. [Number and Numeration Goal 5]
- Use an algorithm to multiply a fraction by a fraction. [Operations and Computation Goal 4]
- Represent an algorithm as a general pattern with variables. [Patterns, Functions, and Algebra Goal 1]

Ongoing Assessment: Informing Instruction See page 285.

materials

- ☐ *Math Journal 1,* pp. 140 and 141
- ☐ Study Link 4•5

2 Ongoing Learning & Practice

Students practice renaming and computing with mixed numbers.

Students practice and maintain skills through Math Boxes and Study Link activities.

Ongoing Assessment: Recognizing Student Achievement Use journal page 139. [Operations and Computation Goal 3]

materials

- ☐ *Math Journal 1,* pp. 139, 142, and 143
- ☐ Study Link Master (*Math Masters,* p. 123)
- ☐ Geometry Template or protractor

3 Differentiation Options

READINESS

Students use an area model to visualize fraction multiplication.

ENRICHMENT

Students solve a multistep problem that involves finding products of fractions.

EXTRA PRACTICE

Students add, subtract, and multiply fractions.

materials

- ☐ Teaching Masters (*Math Masters,* pp. 124 and 125)
- ☐ two different-colored pencils or markers
- ☐ *5-Minute Math*, pp. 98, 99, 101, 113, 184, and 185

Technology

Assessment Management System
Math Boxes, Problem 4
See the **iTLG.**

Getting Started

Mental Math and Reflexes

Students write fractions and mixed numbers in simplest form.

Suggestions:

●○○ $\frac{6}{10}$ $\frac{3}{5}$

$\frac{9}{12}$ $\frac{3}{4}$

●●○ $\frac{15}{3}$ 5

$\frac{30}{24}$ $1\frac{1}{4}$

●●● $1\frac{8}{4}$ 3

$2\frac{6}{4}$ $3\frac{1}{2}$

Math Message

Complete Problems 1–3 on journal page 140.

Study Link 4·5 Follow-Up

Briefly go over the answers. If you assigned the Practice problems, ask students to express the decimal addends and sums as fractions.

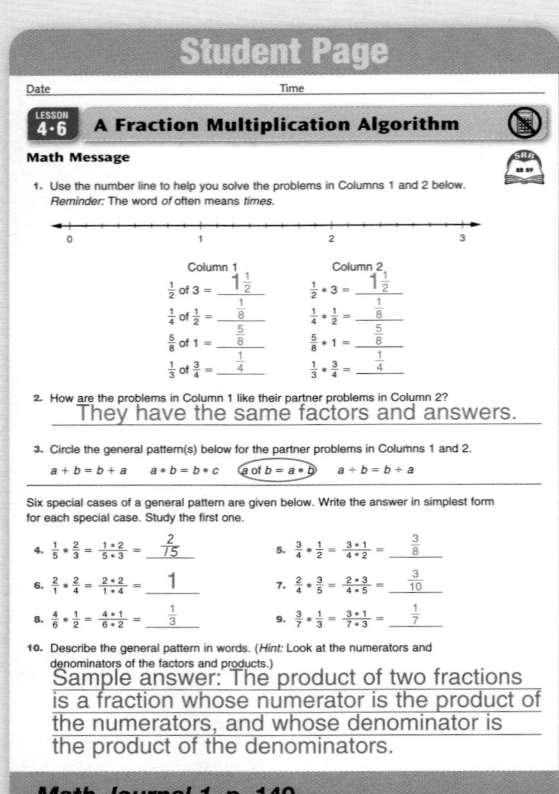

Student Page

Date ______ Time ______

LESSON 4·6 **A Fraction Multiplication Algorithm**

Math Message

SRB 88 89

1. Use the number line to help you solve the problems in Columns 1 and 2 below. *Reminder:* The word *of* often means *times.*

0 1 2 3

Column 1	Column 2
$\frac{1}{2}$ of 3 = $1\frac{1}{2}$	$\frac{1}{2} * 3 = 1\frac{1}{2}$
$\frac{1}{4}$ of $\frac{1}{2}$ = $\frac{1}{8}$	$\frac{1}{4} * \frac{1}{2} = \frac{1}{8}$
$\frac{5}{8}$ of 1 = $\frac{5}{8}$	$\frac{5}{8} * 1 = \frac{5}{8}$
$\frac{1}{3}$ of $\frac{3}{4}$ = $\frac{1}{4}$	$\frac{1}{3} * \frac{3}{4} = \frac{1}{4}$

2. How are the problems in Column 1 like their partner problems in Column 2?
They have the same factors and answers.

3. Circle the general pattern(s) below for the partner problems in Columns 1 and 2.
$a + b = b + a$ $a * b = b * c$ (a of $b = a * b$) $a \div b = b \div a$

Six special cases of a general pattern are given below. Write the answer in simplest form for each special case. Study the first one.

4. $\frac{1}{5} * \frac{2}{3} = \frac{1 * 2}{5 * 3} = \frac{2}{15}$
5. $\frac{3}{4} * \frac{1}{2} = \frac{3 * 1}{4 * 2} = \frac{3}{8}$
6. $\frac{2}{1} * \frac{2}{4} = \frac{2 * 2}{1 * 4} = 1$
7. $\frac{2}{4} * \frac{3}{5} = \frac{2 * 3}{4 * 5} = \frac{3}{10}$
8. $\frac{4}{6} * \frac{1}{2} = \frac{4 * 1}{6 * 2} = \frac{1}{3}$
9. $\frac{3}{7} * \frac{1}{3} = \frac{3 * 1}{7 * 3} = \frac{1}{7}$
10. Describe the general pattern in words. (*Hint:* Look at the numerators and denominators of the factors and products.)
Sample answer: The product of two fractions is a fraction whose numerator is the product of the numerators, and whose denominator is the product of the denominators.

***Math Journal 1,* p. 140**

1 Teaching the Lesson

▶ Math Message Follow-Up

WHOLE-CLASS DISCUSSION

(*Math Journal 1,* p. 140)

Review the idea that *of* indicates multiplication. Go over the answers to Problem 1. Have volunteers explain how they could use the number line to help solve the problems. One way is to visualize jumps on the number line, starting at 0. The fraction tells the size of the jump; the whole number tells the number of jumps. Thus, $3 * \frac{1}{2}$ is 3 jumps, each $\frac{1}{2}$ unit long, for a total of $1\frac{1}{2}$ units.

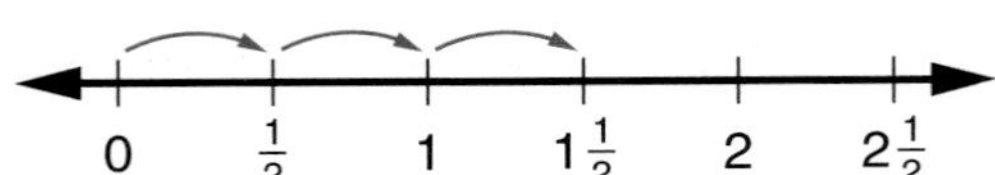

Another way is to fold the number line. To solve $\frac{1}{2} * 3$, imagine taking the number line from 0 to 3 and folding it in half. The result shows that $\frac{1}{2}$ of 3 is $1\frac{1}{2}$. This method has the advantage of working when both factors are fractions.

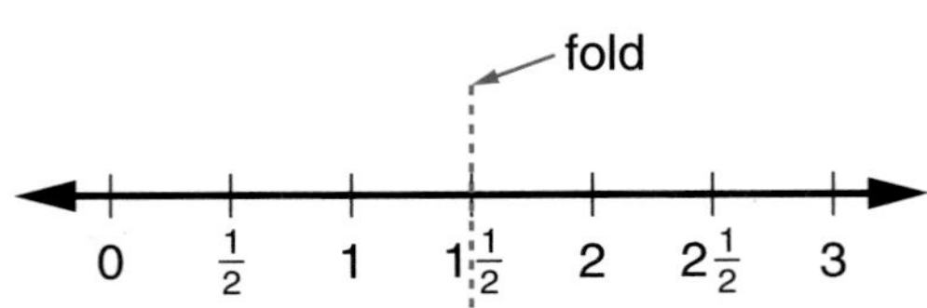

Have students share answers to Problem 2. Expect observations such as the following:

- ▷ For each problem in Column 1, there is a partner problem in Column 2 that has the same answer.
- ▷ Problems in each column involve multiplication.
- ▷ Problems have the same factors and products.

Go over the general patterns in Problem 3.

Adjusting the Activity

Review how variables are used to record general patterns. Offer examples of special cases, such as $1 + 2 = 2 + 1$, $3 + 6 = 6 + 3$, and so on. Ask students to use variables to write a general pattern. $a + b = b + a$ Then return to Problem 3, writing each general pattern on the board and checking it against the special cases in Problem 1.

AUDITORY ◆ KINESTHETIC ◆ TACTILE ◆ VISUAL

▶ Using the Fraction Multiplication Algorithm

PARTNER ACTIVITY

(*Math Journal 1,* pp. 140 and 141)

Have partners work to complete journal pages 140 and 141. Circulate and assist.

Bring the class together to discuss the multiplication algorithm and go over answers.

Draw attention to the relationship between the whole-number factors and products in Problems 24a–d. Students often think of multiplication as *making bigger.* These problems clearly show multiplication *making smaller.*

Ongoing Assessment: Informing Instruction

Watch for students who multiply both the numerator and the denominator by the whole number in Problems 24a–d. For example, when solving $3 * \frac{3}{4}$, some students may multiply $\frac{(3 * 3)}{(3 * 4)}$ to get $\frac{9}{12}$, or $\frac{3}{4}$.

Discuss Problem 26. Highlight the idea of finding a fraction of a fraction to reinforce the concept that *of* indicates multiplication.

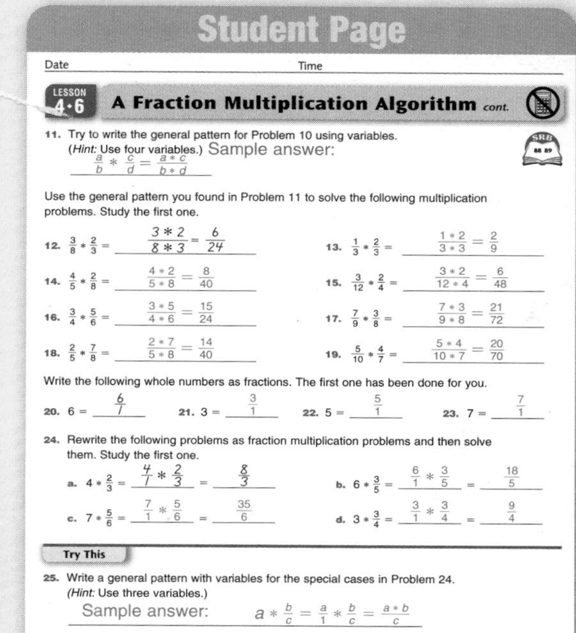

Student Page

Date Time

LESSON 4·6 **A Fraction Multiplication Algorithm** *cont.*

11. Try to write the general pattern for Problem 10 using variables. (*Hint:* Use four variables.) Sample answer: $\frac{a}{b} * \frac{c}{d} = \frac{a * c}{b * d}$

Use the general pattern you found in Problem 11 to solve the following multiplication problems. Study the first one.

12. $\frac{3}{8} * \frac{2}{3} = \frac{3 * 2}{8 * 3} = \frac{6}{24}$
13. $\frac{1}{3} * \frac{2}{3} = \frac{1 * 2}{3 * 3} = \frac{2}{9}$
14. $\frac{4}{5} * \frac{2}{8} = \frac{4 * 2}{5 * 8} = \frac{8}{40}$
15. $\frac{3}{12} * \frac{2}{4} = \frac{3 * 2}{12 * 4} = \frac{6}{48}$
16. $\frac{3}{4} * \frac{5}{6} = \frac{3 * 5}{4 * 6} = \frac{15}{24}$
17. $\frac{7}{9} * \frac{3}{8} = \frac{7 * 3}{9 * 8} = \frac{21}{72}$
18. $\frac{2}{5} * \frac{7}{8} = \frac{2 * 7}{5 * 8} = \frac{14}{40}$
19. $\frac{5}{10} * \frac{4}{7} = \frac{5 * 4}{10 * 7} = \frac{20}{70}$

Write the following whole numbers as fractions. The first one has been done for you.

20. $6 = \frac{6}{1}$
21. $3 = \frac{3}{1}$
22. $5 = \frac{5}{1}$
23. $7 = \frac{7}{1}$

24. Rewrite the following problems as fraction multiplication problems and then solve them. Study the first one.

a. $4 * \frac{2}{3} = \frac{4}{1} * \frac{2}{3} = \frac{8}{3}$

b. $6 * \frac{3}{5} = \frac{6}{1} * \frac{3}{5} = \frac{18}{5}$

c. $7 * \frac{5}{6} = \frac{7}{1} * \frac{5}{6} = \frac{35}{6}$

d. $3 * \frac{3}{4} = \frac{3}{1} * \frac{3}{4} = \frac{9}{4}$

Try This

25. Write a general pattern with variables for the special cases in Problem 24. (*Hint:* Use three variables.)
Sample answer: $a * \frac{b}{c} = \frac{a}{1} * \frac{b}{c} = \frac{a * b}{c}$

26. Mark took a timed multiplication test and finished $\frac{3}{4}$ of the problems. He correctly answered $\frac{1}{2}$ of the problems he finished. What fraction of the problems on the test did Mark answer correctly?
$\frac{3}{8}$ of the problems

Math Journal 1, p. 141

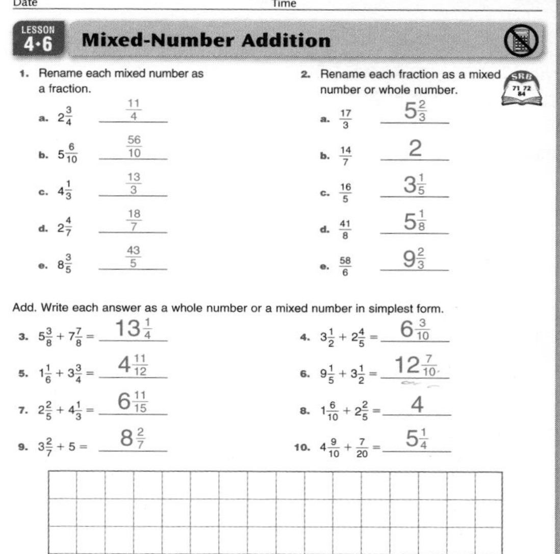

Student Page

Date Time

LESSON 4·6 **Mixed-Number Addition**

1. Rename each mixed number as a fraction.

a. $2\frac{3}{4}$ $\frac{11}{4}$

b. $5\frac{6}{10}$ $\frac{56}{10}$

c. $4\frac{1}{3}$ $\frac{13}{3}$

d. $2\frac{4}{7}$ $\frac{18}{7}$

e. $8\frac{3}{5}$ $\frac{43}{5}$

2. Rename each fraction as a mixed number or whole number.

a. $\frac{17}{3}$ $5\frac{2}{3}$

b. $\frac{14}{7}$ 2

c. $\frac{16}{5}$ $3\frac{1}{5}$

d. $\frac{41}{8}$ $5\frac{1}{8}$

e. $\frac{58}{6}$ $9\frac{2}{3}$

Add. Write each answer as a whole number or a mixed number in simplest form.

3. $5\frac{3}{8} + 7\frac{7}{8} = 13\frac{1}{4}$
4. $3\frac{1}{2} + 2\frac{4}{5} = 6\frac{3}{10}$
5. $1\frac{1}{6} + 3\frac{3}{4} = 4\frac{11}{12}$
6. $9\frac{1}{5} + 3\frac{1}{2} = 12\frac{7}{10}$
7. $2\frac{2}{5} + 4\frac{1}{3} = 6\frac{11}{15}$
8. $1\frac{6}{10} + 2\frac{2}{5} = 4$
9. $3\frac{2}{7} + 5 = 8\frac{2}{7}$
10. $4\frac{9}{10} + \frac{7}{20} = 5\frac{1}{4}$

Math Journal 1, p. 142

Student Page

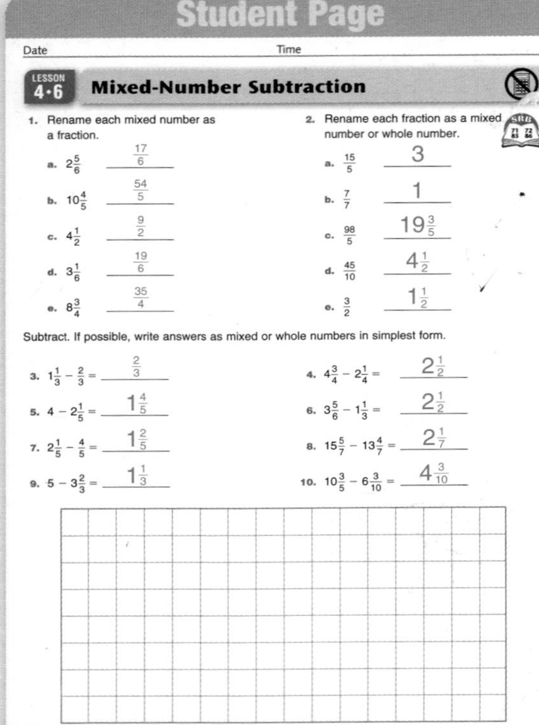
Date Time

LESSON 4·6 **Mixed-Number Subtraction**

1. Rename each mixed number as a fraction.
   a. $2\frac{5}{6}$ $\frac{17}{6}$
   b. $10\frac{4}{5}$ $\frac{54}{5}$
   c. $4\frac{1}{2}$ $\frac{9}{2}$
   d. $3\frac{1}{6}$ $\frac{19}{6}$
   e. $8\frac{3}{4}$ $\frac{35}{4}$

2. Rename each fraction as a mixed number or whole number.
   a. $\frac{15}{5}$ 3
   b. $\frac{7}{7}$ 1
   c. $\frac{98}{5}$ $19\frac{3}{5}$
   d. $\frac{45}{10}$ $4\frac{1}{2}$
   e. $\frac{3}{2}$ $1\frac{1}{2}$

Subtract. If possible, write answers as mixed or whole numbers in simplest form.

3. $1\frac{1}{3} - \frac{2}{3} =$ $\frac{2}{3}$
4. $4\frac{3}{4} - 2\frac{1}{4} =$ $2\frac{1}{2}$
5. $4 - 2\frac{1}{5} =$ $1\frac{4}{5}$
6. $3\frac{5}{6} - 1\frac{1}{3} =$ $2\frac{1}{2}$
7. $2\frac{1}{5} - \frac{4}{5} =$ $1\frac{2}{5}$
8. $15\frac{5}{7} - 13\frac{4}{7} =$ $2\frac{1}{7}$
9. $5 - 3\frac{2}{3} =$ $1\frac{1}{3}$
10. $10\frac{3}{5} - 6\frac{3}{10} =$ $4\frac{3}{10}$

Math Journal 1, p. 143

Student Page

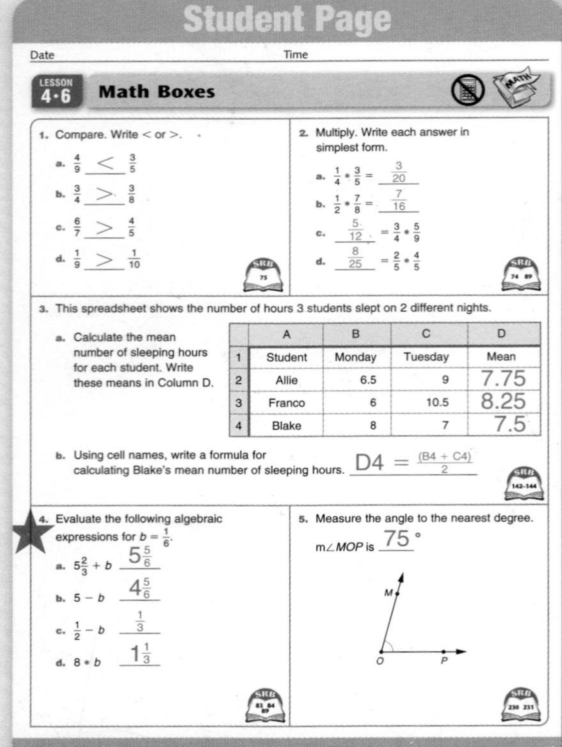
Date Time

LESSON 4·6 **Math Boxes**

1. Compare. Write < or >.
   a. $\frac{4}{9} < \frac{3}{5}$
   b. $\frac{3}{4} > \frac{3}{8}$
   c. $\frac{6}{7} > \frac{4}{5}$
   d. $\frac{1}{9} > \frac{1}{10}$

2. Multiply. Write each answer in simplest form.
   a. $\frac{1}{4} * \frac{3}{5} = \frac{3}{20}$
   b. $\frac{1}{2} * \frac{7}{8} = \frac{7}{16}$
   c. $\frac{5}{12} = \frac{3}{4} * \frac{5}{9}$
   d. $\frac{8}{25} = \frac{2}{5} * \frac{4}{5}$

3. This spreadsheet shows the number of hours 3 students slept on 2 different nights.
   a. Calculate the mean number of sleeping hours for each student. Write these means in Column D.

	A	B	C	D
1	Student	Monday	Tuesday	Mean
2	Allie	6.5	9	7.75
3	Franco	6	10.5	8.25
4	Blake	8	7	7.5

   b. Using cell names, write a formula for calculating Blake's mean number of sleeping hours. D4 $= \frac{(B4 + C4)}{2}$

4. Evaluate the following algebraic expressions for $b = \frac{1}{6}$.
   a. $5\frac{2}{3} + b$ $5\frac{5}{6}$
   b. $5 - b$ $4\frac{5}{6}$
   c. $\frac{1}{2} - b$ $\frac{1}{3}$
   d. $8 * b$ $1\frac{1}{3}$

5. Measure the angle to the nearest degree.
   m∠MOP is 75°

Math Journal 1, p. 139

2 Ongoing Learning & Practice

▶ Adding and Subtracting Mixed Numbers

INDEPENDENT ACTIVITY

(*Math Journal 1*, pp. 142 and 143)

Students convert between fractions and mixed numbers. They find sums and differences of mixed numbers with like and unlike denominators.

▶ Math Boxes 4·6

INDEPENDENT ACTIVITY

(*Math Journal 1*, p. 139)

Mixed Practice Math Boxes in this lesson are paired with Math Boxes in Lessons 4-8 and 4-10. The skill in Problem 5 previews Unit 5 content. Students will need a Geometry Template or a protractor to complete Problem 5.

Writing/Reasoning Have students write a response to the following: *Explain the strategy you used to compare the fractions in Problems 1a and 1b.* Sample answer: For Problem 1a, I multiplied the denominators (9 and 5) to find a quick common denominator (45). I then multiplied the numerators and denominators by the appropriate numbers to get the equivalent fractions $\frac{20}{45}$ and $\frac{27}{45}$. Because $\frac{20}{45} < \frac{27}{45}$, $\frac{4}{9} < \frac{3}{5}$. The fractions in Problem 1b have the same numerator. Greater denominators mean smaller parts, so $\frac{3}{8} < \frac{3}{4}$.

Ongoing Assessment: Recognizing Student Achievement

Math Boxes Problem 4

Use **Math Boxes, Problem 4** to assess students' ability to add and subtract fractions with unlike denominators. Students are making adequate progress if they can calculate the sum and differences in Problems 4a–c. Some students may be able to calculate the product in Problem 4d.

[Operations and Computation Goal 3]

▶ Study Link 4·6

INDEPENDENT ACTIVITY

(*Math Masters*, p.123)

Home Connection Students practice solving fraction multiplication problems.

3 Differentiation Options

READINESS

▶ Modeling Fraction Multiplication

(*Math Masters,* p. 124)

INDEPENDENT ACTIVITY

15–30 Min

To provide experience with fraction multiplication, distribute a copy of *Math Masters,* page 124 and two different-colored pencils or markers to each student. After reviewing the example, students shade the areas representing factors and find the intersection of those shaded areas. Have students compare the sizes of factor and product areas to better understand how multiplication can "make smaller." To support English language learners, have students describe their shaded models.

Example:

"In Problem 3, I shaded 4 of the 7 columns of the grid blue to show $\frac{4}{7}$. I shaded 2 of the 3 rows red to show $\frac{2}{3}$. I know that the product is the part of the grid that is shaded both blue and red, which is 8 out of 21 squares, or $\frac{8}{21}$."

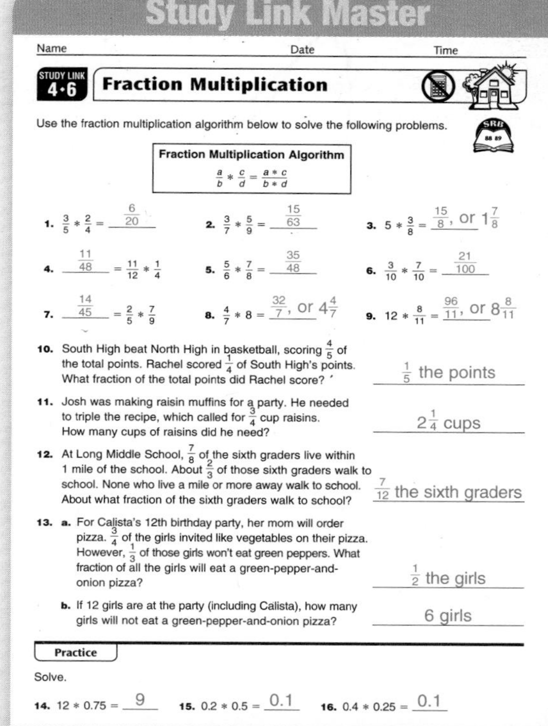

Study Link Master

Name ______ Date ______ Time ______

STUDY LINK 4·6 **Fraction Multiplication**

Use the fraction multiplication algorithm below to solve the following problems.

SRB 88 89

Fraction Multiplication Algorithm

$\frac{a}{b} * \frac{c}{d} = \frac{a * c}{b * d}$

1. $\frac{3}{5} * \frac{2}{4} = \frac{6}{20}$
2. $\frac{3}{7} * \frac{5}{9} = \frac{15}{63}$
3. $5 * \frac{3}{8} = \frac{15}{8}$, or $1\frac{7}{8}$
4. $\frac{11}{48} = \frac{11}{12} * \frac{1}{4}$
5. $\frac{5}{6} * \frac{7}{8} = \frac{35}{48}$
6. $\frac{3}{10} * \frac{7}{10} = \frac{21}{100}$
7. $\frac{14}{45} = \frac{2}{5} * \frac{7}{9}$
8. $\frac{4}{7} * 8 = \frac{32}{7}$, or $4\frac{4}{7}$
9. $12 * \frac{8}{11} = \frac{96}{11}$, or $8\frac{8}{11}$
10. South High beat North High in basketball, scoring $\frac{4}{5}$ of the total points. Rachel scored $\frac{1}{4}$ of South High's points. What fraction of the total points did Rachel score? $\frac{1}{5}$ the points
11. Josh was making raisin muffins for a party. He needed to triple the recipe, which called for $\frac{3}{4}$ cup raisins. How many cups of raisins did he need? $2\frac{1}{4}$ cups
12. At Long Middle School, $\frac{7}{8}$ of the sixth graders live within 1 mile of the school. About $\frac{2}{3}$ of those sixth graders walk to school. None who live a mile or more away walk to school. About what fraction of the sixth graders walk to school? $\frac{7}{12}$ the sixth graders
13. a. For Calista's 12th birthday party, her mom will order pizza. $\frac{3}{4}$ of the girls invited like vegetables on their pizza. However, $\frac{1}{3}$ of those girls won't eat green peppers. What fraction of all the girls will eat a green-pepper-and-onion pizza? $\frac{1}{2}$ the girls
    b. If 12 girls are at the party (including Calista), how many girls will not eat a green-pepper-and-onion pizza? 6 girls

Practice

Solve.

14. $12 * 0.75 = 9$
15. $0.2 * 0.5 = 0.1$
16. $0.4 * 0.25 = 0.1$

Math Masters, p. 123

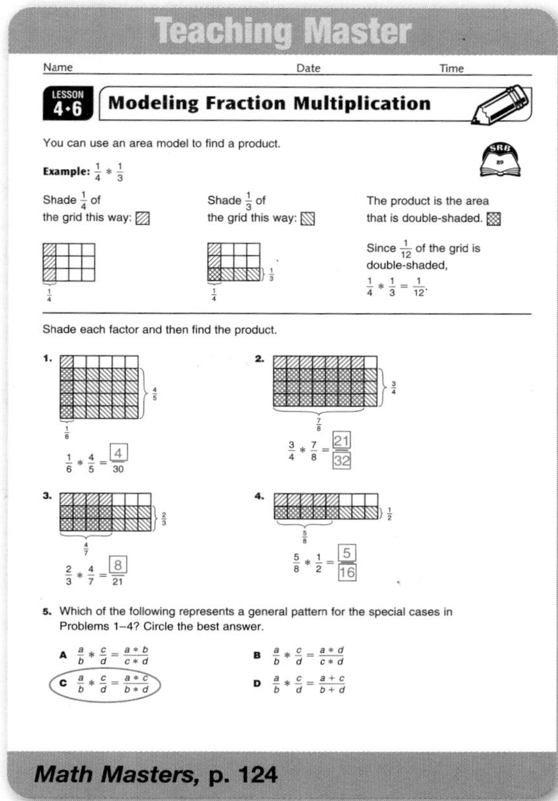

Teaching Master

Name ______ Date ______ Time ______

LESSON 4·6 **Modeling Fraction Multiplication**

You can use an area model to find a product.

SRB 89

Example: $\frac{1}{4} * \frac{1}{3}$

Shade $\frac{1}{4}$ of the grid this way:

Shade $\frac{1}{3}$ of the grid this way:

The product is the area that is double-shaded.

Since $\frac{1}{12}$ of the grid is double-shaded, $\frac{1}{4} * \frac{1}{3} = \frac{1}{12}$.

Shade each factor and then find the product.

1. $\frac{1}{6} * \frac{4}{5} = \frac{4}{30}$
2. $\frac{3}{4} * \frac{7}{8} = \frac{21}{32}$
3. $\frac{2}{3} * \frac{4}{7} = \frac{8}{21}$
4. $\frac{5}{8} * \frac{1}{2} = \frac{5}{16}$
5. Which of the following represents a general pattern for the special cases in Problems 1–4? Circle the best answer.

A $\frac{a}{b} * \frac{c}{d} = \frac{a * b}{c * d}$

B $\frac{a}{b} * \frac{c}{d} = \frac{a * d}{c * d}$

C $\frac{a}{b} * \frac{c}{d} = \frac{a * c}{b * d}$ (circled)

D $\frac{a}{b} * \frac{c}{d} = \frac{a + c}{b + d}$

Math Masters, p. 124

Teaching Master

Name Date Time

LESSON 4·6 **A Nature Hike Problem**

Pavan, Jonathan, Nisha, and Gloria walked on the sixth-grade nature hike. They finished $\frac{1}{2}$ the length of the trail in the first hour. Then they slowed down. In the second hour, they walked $\frac{1}{2}$ the distance that was left. In the third hour, they moved even more slowly and walked only $\frac{1}{2}$ the remaining distance.

If they continue slowing down at this rate, what fraction of the trail will they walk in their fourth hour of hiking? $\frac{1}{16}$ the trail

Explain or show how you solved the problem. Sample answer: Since the hikers walk half the length of the trail they walked the previous hour, by the fourth hour of walking, they will cover $[(((\frac{1}{2})\ \frac{1}{2})\ \frac{1}{2})\ \frac{1}{2}]$, or $\frac{1}{16}$, of the trail.

Name Date Time

LESSON 4·6 **A Nature Hike Problem**

Pavan, Jonathan, Nisha, and Gloria walked on the sixth-grade nature hike. They finished $\frac{1}{2}$ the length of the trail in the first hour. Then they slowed down. In the second hour, they walked $\frac{1}{2}$ the distance that was left. In the third hour, they moved even more slowly and walked only $\frac{1}{2}$ the remaining distance.

If they continue slowing down at this rate, what fraction of the trail will they walk in their fourth hour of hiking?

Explain or show how you solved the problem.

Math Masters, p. 125

ENRICHMENT

PARTNER ACTIVITY

5–15 Min

▶ Solving a Fraction Multiplication Number Story

(*Math Masters,* p. 125)

To further explore fraction multiplication, students read and solve "A Nature Hike Problem" and discuss their solution strategies with a partner. The illustration below represents one possible strategy.

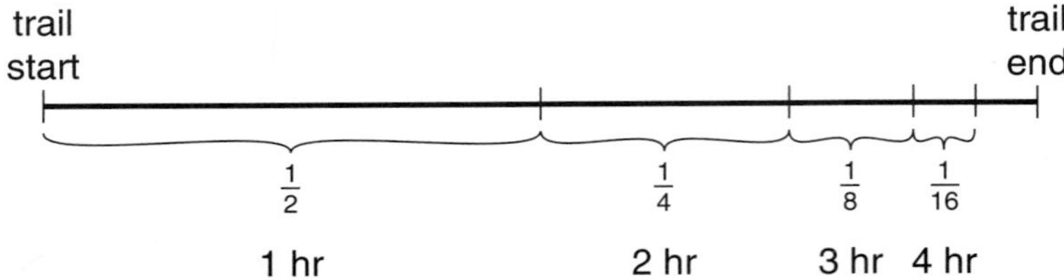

Ask students how long it will take the hikers to reach the end of the trail if their speed keeps decreasing by half. For any given number of hours, it can be shown that the hikers have not yet reached the end of the trail. For example, after 8 hours the hikers will have traveled $(\frac{1}{2^1} + \frac{1}{2^2} + \frac{1}{2^3} + \frac{1}{2^4} + \frac{1}{2^5} + \frac{1}{2^6} + \frac{1}{2^7} + \frac{1}{2^8})$ of the trail, which is only 99.6% of the total length. The same argument can be used to show that for any finite number of hours, the hikers are still short of 100%.

EXTRA PRACTICE

SMALL-GROUP ACTIVITY

5–15 Min

▶ *5-Minute Math*

To offer more practice adding, subtracting, and multiplying fractions and mixed numbers, see *5-Minute Math,* pages 98, 99, 101, 113, 184, and 185.

Multiplication of Mixed Numbers

Objective To multiply mixed numbers.

1 Teaching the Lesson

Key Activities

Students convert between mixed numbers and fractions. They examine two methods for finding the product of mixed numbers and practice multiplying mixed numbers using the method of their choice.

Key Concepts and Skills

- Convert between fractions and mixed numbers. [Number and Numeration Goal 5]
- Multiply fractions. [Operations and Computation Goal 4]
- Use area formulas to solve problems. [Measurement and Reference Frames Goal 2]
- Apply the concept of congruence to calculate the surface area of a cube. [Geometry Goal 2]
- Use the partial-products method (Distributive Property of Multiplication over Addition) to multiply mixed numbers. [Patterns, Functions, and Algebra Goal 4]

Ongoing Assessment: Recognizing Student Achievement Use Mental Math and Reflexes. [Operations and Computation Goal 4]

materials

- ☐ *Math Journal 1,* pp. 144 and 145
- ☐ *Student Reference Book,* pp. 214–217
- ☐ Study Link 4•6
- ☐ Teaching Masters (*Math Masters,* p. 126; pp. 127 and 128; optional)

***See* Advance Preparation**

2 Ongoing Learning & Practice

Students practice estimating sums and differences of fractions and/or mixed numbers by playing *Mixed-Number Spin.*

Students practice and maintain skills through Math Boxes and Study Link activities.

materials

- ☐ *Math Journal 1,* p. 146
- ☐ *Student Reference Book,* p. 327
- ☐ Study Link Master (*Math Masters,* p. 129)
- ☐ Game Masters (*Math Masters,* pp. 458 and 459)
- ☐ 1 large paper clip
- ☐ Geometry Template or protractor

3 Differentiation Options

READINESS

Students use an area model to visualize and keep track of partial products.

EXTRA PRACTICE

Students practice mixed-number multiplication by calculating areas.

materials

- ☐ Teaching Masters (*Math Masters,* pp. 130 and 131)

Additional Information

Advance Preparation For Part 1, make one copy of *Math Masters,* page 126 for every two students. Cut the copies apart and distribute.

Technology

Assessment Management System
Mental Math and Reflexes
See the **iTLG.**

Getting Started

Mental Math and Reflexes ★

Students solve the following problems mentally and give the answers in simplest form.

Suggestions:

●○○ $\frac{1}{4} * \frac{3}{5}$ $\frac{3}{20}$

$\frac{3}{3} * \frac{5}{5}$ 1

●●○ $36 * \frac{1}{6}$ 6

$\frac{3}{5} * \frac{5}{10}$ $\frac{3}{10}$

●●● $21 * \frac{3}{7}$ 9

$18 * \frac{5}{6}$ 15

Math Message

Complete a copy of the Math Message problems.

Study Link 4·6 Follow-Up

Briefly go over the answers. Ask students to convert the decimal factors and products to fractions.

Ongoing Assessment: Recognizing Student Achievement

Mental Math and Reflexes 

Use **Mental Math and Reflexes** to assess students' abilities to multiply and simplify fractions. Some students may be able to solve $21 * \frac{3}{7}$ and $18 * \frac{5}{6}$ mentally.

[Operations and Computation Goal 4]

1 Teaching the Lesson

▶ Math Message Follow-Up

WHOLE-CLASS DISCUSSION

(*Math Masters,* p. 126)

Have volunteers demonstrate their strategies for solving $3\frac{3}{8} * 1\frac{2}{5}$ (Problem 13).

▶ Multiplying with Mixed Numbers

WHOLE-CLASS ACTIVITY

(*Math Journal 1,* pp. 144 and 145; *Student Reference Book,* pp. 214 and 217; *Math Masters,* pp. 127 and 128)

Go over the two methods for multiplying mixed numbers on journal page 144.

Ask students to use both methods to solve each of the following problems:

$8 * 3\frac{7}{8}$ 31 $\quad 6\frac{1}{2} * 6\frac{1}{2}$ $42\frac{1}{4}$ $\quad 2\frac{3}{4} * 1\frac{8}{9}$ $5\frac{7}{36}$ $\quad 4\frac{3}{5} * 5\frac{5}{6}$ $26\frac{5}{6}$

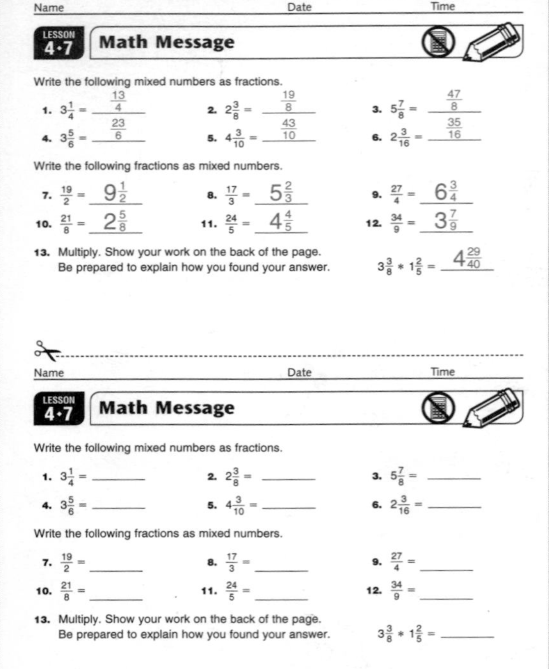

Teaching Master

Name Date Time

LESSON 4·7 **Math Message**

Write the following mixed numbers as fractions.

1. $3\frac{1}{4}$ = $\frac{13}{4}$
2. $2\frac{3}{8}$ = $\frac{19}{8}$
3. $5\frac{7}{8}$ = $\frac{47}{8}$
4. $3\frac{5}{6}$ = $\frac{23}{6}$
5. $4\frac{3}{10}$ = $\frac{43}{10}$
6. $2\frac{3}{16}$ = $\frac{35}{16}$

Write the following fractions as mixed numbers.

7. $\frac{19}{2}$ = $9\frac{1}{2}$
8. $\frac{17}{3}$ = $5\frac{2}{3}$
9. $\frac{27}{4}$ = $6\frac{3}{4}$
10. $\frac{21}{8}$ = $2\frac{5}{8}$
11. $\frac{24}{5}$ = $4\frac{4}{5}$
12. $\frac{34}{9}$ = $3\frac{7}{9}$
13. Multiply. Show your work on the back of the page. Be prepared to explain how you found your answer. $3\frac{3}{8} * 1\frac{2}{5}$ = $4\frac{29}{40}$

Name Date Time

LESSON 4·7 **Math Message**

Write the following mixed numbers as fractions.

1. $3\frac{1}{4}$ = ______
2. $2\frac{3}{8}$ = ______
3. $5\frac{7}{8}$ = ______
4. $3\frac{5}{6}$ = ______
5. $4\frac{3}{10}$ = ______
6. $2\frac{3}{16}$ = ______

Write the following fractions as mixed numbers.

7. $\frac{19}{2}$ = ______
8. $\frac{17}{3}$ = ______
9. $\frac{27}{4}$ = ______
10. $\frac{21}{8}$ = ______
11. $\frac{24}{5}$ = ______
12. $\frac{34}{9}$ = ______
13. Multiply. Show your work on the back of the page. Be prepared to explain how you found your answer. $3\frac{3}{8} * 1\frac{2}{5}$ = ______

Math Masters, p. 126

Go over each answer and ask students which method they prefer. Expect a variety of responses. For the first two problems, students may prefer the partial-products method because the parts of the mixed numbers are easy to work with. The partial-products method is more difficult to use with the last two problems because they involve addition of unlike fractions.

Have students solve the problems on journal pages 144 and 145. If students are unsure about how to find the areas of the figures in Problems 9–12 on page 145, refer them to pages 214–217 in the *Student Reference Book*.

Adjusting the Activity

ELL

Encourage students to discuss the Try This problem with a partner. Consider distributing copies of *Math Masters,* pages 127 and 128 to each pair. Students can use the photos and photo album page to model the problem. They can draw rectangles to calculate the area or count the squares in the uncovered spaces.

AUDITORY ◆ KINESTHETIC ◆ TACTILE ◆ VISUAL

Links to the Future

The partial-products algorithm is a direct application of the Distributive Property of Multiplication over Addition. Students will use this property to solve equations in Unit 9 and to multiply polynomials such as $(x + 2) * (x + 3)$ in future algebra courses.

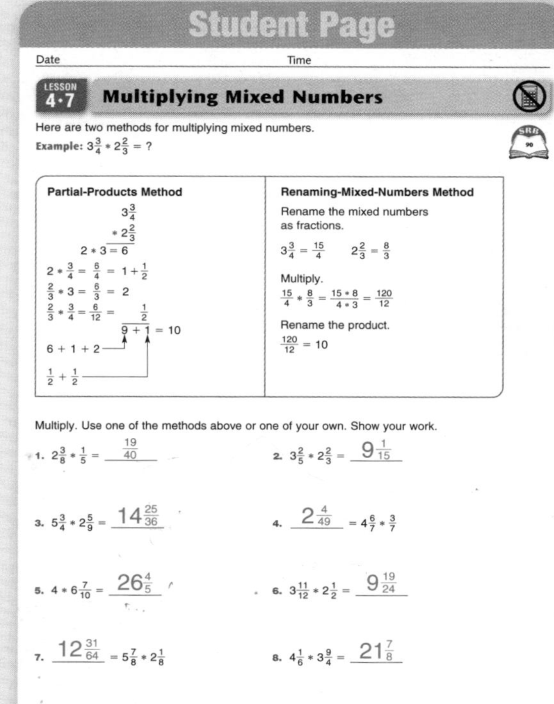

Student Page

Date Time

LESSON 4·7 **Multiplying Mixed Numbers**

Here are two methods for multiplying mixed numbers.

Example: $3\frac{3}{4} * 2\frac{2}{3} = ?$

Partial-Products Method	Renaming-Mixed-Numbers Method
$3\frac{3}{4}$ $* 2\frac{2}{3}$ $2 * 3 = 6$ $2 * \frac{3}{4} = \frac{6}{4} = 1 + \frac{1}{2}$ $\frac{2}{3} * 3 = \frac{6}{3} = 2$ $\frac{2}{3} * \frac{3}{4} = \frac{6}{12} = \frac{1}{2}$ $9 + 1 = 10$ $6 + 1 + 2$ $\frac{1}{2} + \frac{1}{2}$	Rename the mixed numbers as fractions. $3\frac{3}{4} = \frac{15}{4}$ $2\frac{2}{3} = \frac{8}{3}$ Multiply. $\frac{15}{4} * \frac{8}{3} = \frac{15 * 8}{4 * 3} = \frac{120}{12}$ Rename the product. $\frac{120}{12} = 10$

Multiply. Use one of the methods above or one of your own. Show your work.

1. $2\frac{3}{8} * \frac{1}{5} =$ $\frac{19}{40}$
2. $3\frac{2}{5} * 2\frac{2}{3} =$ $9\frac{1}{15}$
3. $5\frac{3}{4} * 2\frac{5}{9} =$ $14\frac{25}{36}$
4. $2\frac{4}{49}$ $= 4\frac{6}{7} * \frac{3}{7}$
5. $4 * 6\frac{7}{10} =$ $26\frac{4}{5}$
6. $3\frac{11}{12} * 2\frac{1}{2} =$ $9\frac{19}{24}$
7. $12\frac{31}{64}$ $= 5\frac{7}{8} * 2\frac{1}{8}$
8. $4\frac{1}{6} * 3\frac{9}{4} =$ $21\frac{7}{8}$

Math Journal 1, p. 144

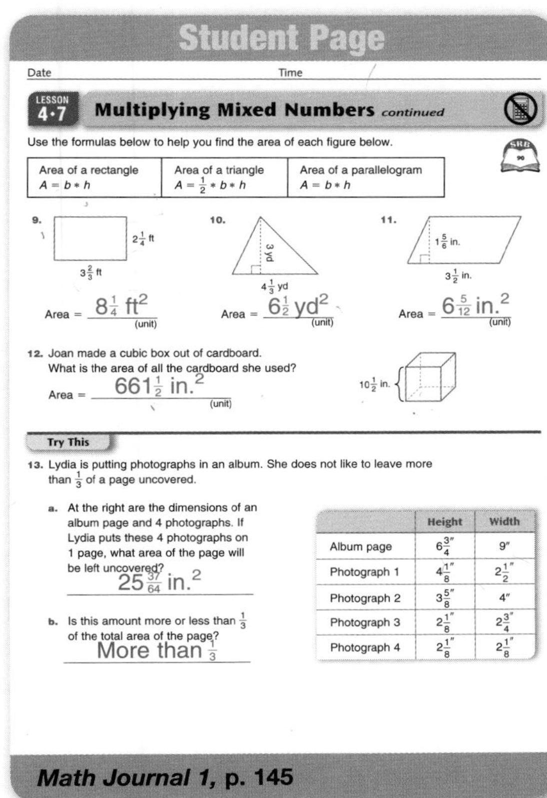

Student Page

Date Time

LESSON 4·7 **Multiplying Mixed Numbers** *continued*

Use the formulas below to help you find the area of each figure below.

Area of a rectangle $A = b * h$	Area of a triangle $A = \frac{1}{2} * b * h$	Area of a parallelogram $A = b * h$

9. $2\frac{1}{4}$ ft; $3\frac{2}{3}$ ft
Area = $8\frac{1}{4}$ ft^2 (unit)

10. 3 yd; $4\frac{1}{3}$ yd
Area = $6\frac{1}{2}$ yd^2 (unit)

11. $1\frac{5}{6}$ in.; $3\frac{1}{2}$ in.
Area = $6\frac{5}{12}$ in.^{2} (unit)

12. Joan made a cubic box out of cardboard.
What is the area of all the cardboard she used?
Area = $661\frac{1}{2}$ in.^{2} (unit)
$10\frac{1}{2}$ in.

Try This

13. Lydia is putting photographs in an album. She does not like to leave more than $\frac{1}{3}$ of a page uncovered.

a. At the right are the dimensions of an album page and 4 photographs. If Lydia puts these 4 photographs on 1 page, what area of the page will be left uncovered?
$25\frac{37}{64}$ in.^{2}

b. Is this amount more or less than $\frac{1}{3}$ of the total area of the page?
More than $\frac{1}{3}$

	Height	Width
Album page	$6\frac{3}{4}''$	$9''$
Photograph 1	$4\frac{1}{8}''$	$2\frac{1}{2}''$
Photograph 2	$3\frac{5}{8}''$	$4''$
Photograph 3	$2\frac{1}{8}''$	$2\frac{3}{4}''$
Photograph 4	$2\frac{1}{8}''$	$2\frac{1}{8}''$

Math Journal 1, p. 145

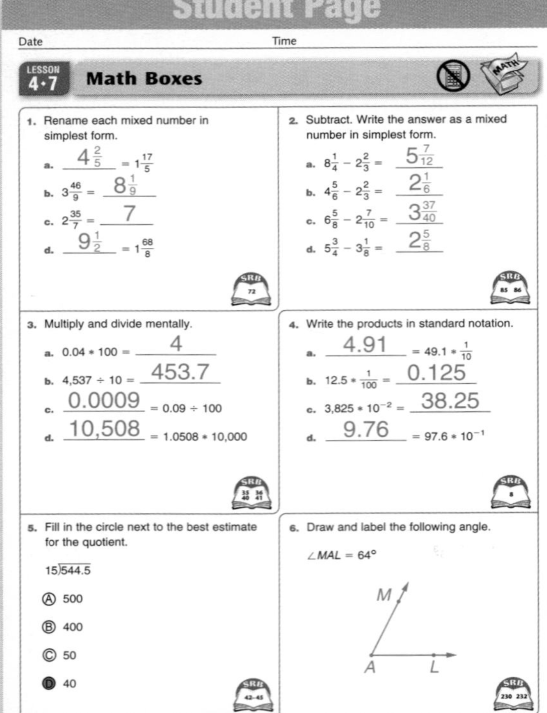
Student Page

Date Time

LESSON 4·7 **Math Boxes**

1. Rename each mixed number in simplest form.
   a. $4\frac{2}{5} = 1\frac{17}{5}$
   b. $3\frac{46}{9} = 8\frac{1}{9}$
   c. $2\frac{35}{7} = 7$
   d. $9\frac{1}{2} = 1\frac{68}{8}$

2. Subtract. Write the answer as a mixed number in simplest form.
   a. $8\frac{1}{4} - 2\frac{2}{3} = 5\frac{7}{12}$
   b. $4\frac{5}{6} - 2\frac{2}{3} = 2\frac{1}{6}$
   c. $6\frac{5}{8} - 2\frac{7}{10} = 3\frac{37}{40}$
   d. $5\frac{3}{4} - 3\frac{1}{8} = 2\frac{5}{8}$

3. Multiply and divide mentally.
   a. $0.04 * 100 = 4$
   b. $4{,}537 \div 10 = 453.7$
   c. $0.0009 = 0.09 \div 100$
   d. $10{,}508 = 1.0508 * 10{,}000$

4. Write the products in standard notation.
   a. $4.91 = 49.1 * \frac{1}{10}$
   b. $12.5 * \frac{1}{100} = 0.125$
   c. $3{,}825 * 10^{-2} = 38.25$
   d. $9.76 = 97.6 * 10^{-1}$

5. Fill in the circle next to the best estimate for the quotient.
   $15\overline{)544.5}$
   Ⓐ 500
   Ⓑ 400
   Ⓒ 50
   ● 40

6. Draw and label the following angle.
   $\angle MAL = 64°$
   M A L

Math Journal 1, p. 146

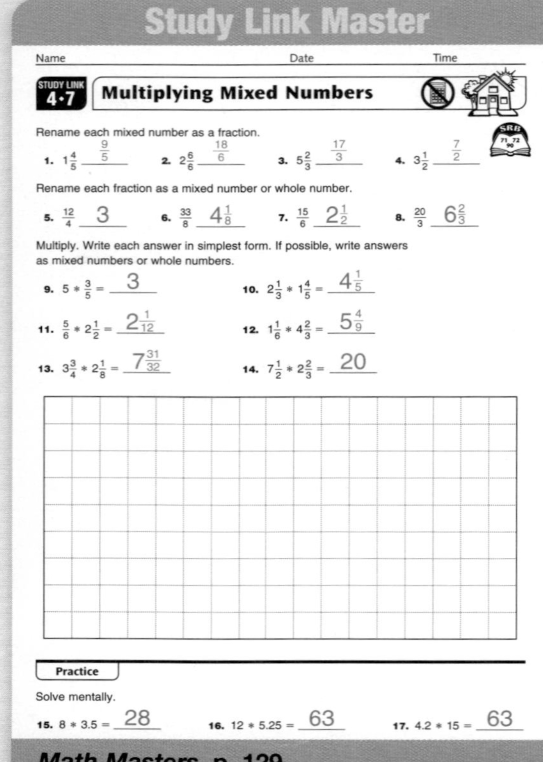
Study Link Master

Name Date Time

STUDY LINK 4·7 **Multiplying Mixed Numbers**

Rename each mixed number as a fraction.

1. $1\frac{4}{5} = \frac{9}{5}$ 2. $2\frac{6}{6} = \frac{18}{6}$ 3. $5\frac{2}{3} = \frac{17}{3}$ 4. $3\frac{1}{2} = \frac{7}{2}$

Rename each fraction as a mixed number or whole number.

5. $\frac{12}{4} = 3$ 6. $\frac{33}{8} = 4\frac{1}{8}$ 7. $\frac{15}{6} = 2\frac{1}{2}$ 8. $\frac{20}{3} = 6\frac{2}{3}$

Multiply. Write each answer in simplest form. If possible, write answers as mixed numbers or whole numbers.

9. $5 * \frac{3}{5} = 3$ 10. $2\frac{1}{3} * 1\frac{4}{5} = 4\frac{1}{5}$

11. $\frac{5}{6} * 2\frac{1}{2} = 2\frac{1}{12}$ 12. $1\frac{1}{6} * 4\frac{2}{3} = 5\frac{4}{9}$

13. $3\frac{3}{4} * 2\frac{1}{8} = 7\frac{31}{32}$ 14. $7\frac{1}{2} * 2\frac{2}{3} = 20$

Practice

Solve mentally.

15. $8 * 3.5 = 28$ 16. $12 * 5.25 = 63$ 17. $4.2 * 15 = 63$

Math Masters, p. 129

2 Ongoing Learning & Practice

▶ Playing *Mixed-Number Spin*

PARTNER ACTIVITY

(*Student Reference Book,* p. 327; *Math Masters,* pp. 458 and 459)

Distribute one copy of *Math Masters,* page 458 to each partnership. To make the spinner, students use a pencil to anchor a large paper clip at the center of the spinner circle. Each pair record their estimates on a game record sheet (*Math Masters,* p. 459).

The directions for this game are on page 327 of the *Student Reference Book.*

▶ Math Boxes 4·7

INDEPENDENT ACTIVITY

(*Math Journal 1,* p. 146)

Mixed Practice Math Boxes in this lesson are paired with Math Boxes in Lesson 4-5. The skill in Problem 6 previews Unit 5 content. Students will need a Geometry Template or a protractor to complete Problem 6.

▶ Study Link 4·7

INDEPENDENT ACTIVITY

(*Math Masters,* p. 129)

Home Connection Students rename mixed numbers as fractions, rename fractions as mixed or whole numbers, and multiply mixed numbers. They write each answer in simplest form.

3 Differentiation Options

READINESS

▶ Modeling Mixed-Number Multiplication

(*Math Masters,* p. 130)

To provide experience multiplying mixed numbers, have students use an area model to identify and calculate partial products of mixed-number factors.

EXTRA PRACTICE

▶ Buying an Aquarium

(*Math Masters,* p. 131)

Students practice mixed-number multiplication by calculating areas to design a floor plan.

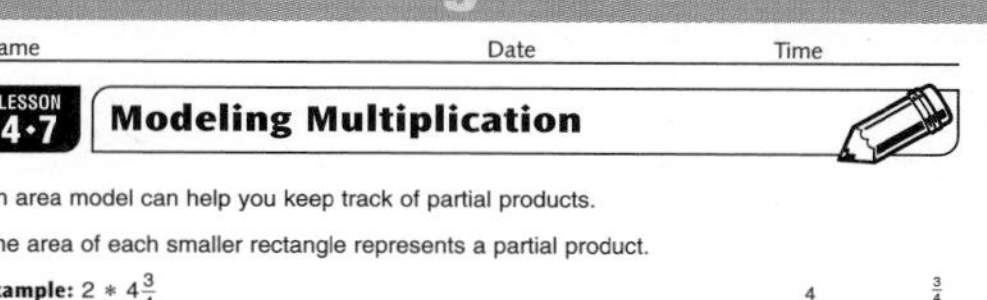

Teaching Master

Name ______ Date ______ Time ______

LESSON 4•7 **Modeling Multiplication**

An area model can help you keep track of partial products.

The area of each smaller rectangle represents a partial product.

Example: $2 * 4\frac{3}{4}$

Find the area of each smaller rectangle.

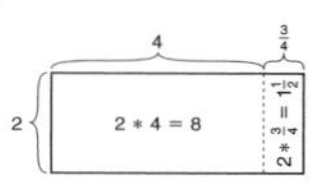

$2 * (4 + \frac{3}{4}) = (2 * 4) + (2 * \frac{3}{4})$

$2 * 4 = \mathbf{8}$ $\quad 2 * \frac{3}{4} = \mathbf{1\frac{1}{2}}$

Then add the two areas to find the area of the largest rectangle. $\mathbf{8 + 1\frac{1}{2} = 9\frac{1}{2}}$

So, $2 * 4\frac{3}{4} = 9\frac{1}{2}$

Find the area of each smaller rectangle. Then add the areas.

1. $2\frac{1}{4} * 5 = (2 + \frac{1}{4}) * 5$

   $2 * 5 =$ 10 $\quad \frac{1}{4} * 5 =$ $1\frac{1}{4}$

   So, $2\frac{1}{4} * 5 =$ $11\frac{1}{4}$

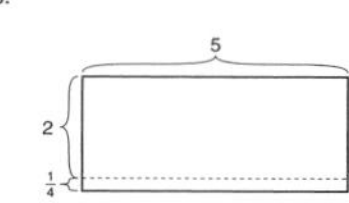

2. $2\frac{2}{3} * 3\frac{3}{4} = (2 + \frac{2}{3}) * (3 + \frac{3}{4})$

   $2 * 3 =$ 6 $\quad 2 * \frac{3}{4} =$ $1\frac{1}{2}$

   $\frac{2}{3} * 3 =$ 2 $\quad \frac{2}{3} * \frac{3}{4} =$ $\frac{6}{12}$, or $\frac{1}{2}$

   So, $2\frac{2}{3} * 3\frac{3}{4} =$ 10

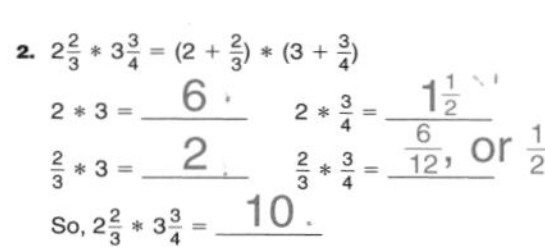

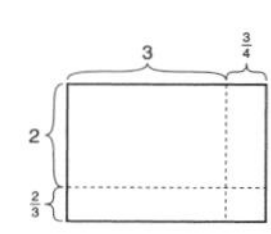

3. $1\frac{7}{8} * 3\frac{1}{2} = (1 + \frac{7}{8}) * (3 + \frac{1}{2})$

   $1 * 3 =$ 3 $\quad 1 * \frac{1}{2} =$ $\frac{1}{2}$

   $\frac{7}{8} * 3 =$ $\frac{21}{8}$, or $2\frac{5}{8}$ $\quad \frac{7}{8} * \frac{1}{2} =$ $\frac{7}{16}$

   So, $1\frac{7}{8} * 3\frac{1}{2} =$ $6\frac{9}{16}$

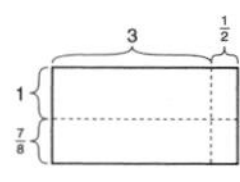

***Math Masters,* p. 130**

Game Master

Name ______ Date ______ Time ______

***Mixed-Number Spin* Record Sheet** SRB 327

Materials ☐ *Math Masters,* page 458
☐ large paper clip

Players 2

Object of the Game To be the first player to generate 10 true number sentences using fractions and mixed numbers.

Directions

1. Each player writes his or her name in one of the boxes below.
2. Take turns spinning. When it is your turn, write the fraction or mixed number you spin in one of the blanks below your name.
3. The first player to complete 10 true sentences is the winner.

Name	Name
______ + ______ < 3	______ + ______ < 3
______ + ______ > 3	______ + ______ > 3
______ – ______ < 1	______ – ______ < 1
______ – ______ > $\frac{1}{2}$	______ – ______ > $\frac{1}{2}$
______ + ______ > 1	______ + ______ > 1
______ + ______ < 1	______ + ______ < 1
______ + ______ < 2	______ + ______ < 2
______ – ______ = 3	______ – ______ = 3
______ – ______ > 1	______ – ______ > 1
______ + ______ > $\frac{1}{2}$	______ + ______ > $\frac{1}{2}$
______ + ______ < 3	______ + ______ < 3
______ + ______ > 2	______ + ______ > 2

***Math Masters,* p. 459**

Teaching Master

Name ______ Date ______ Time ______

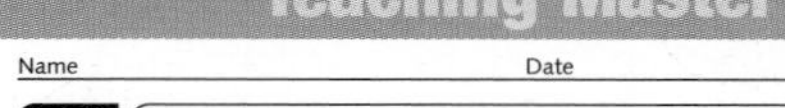

LESSON 4•7 **Buying an Aquarium**

Robert wants to buy an aquarium for his bedroom.

Use the dimensions below to figure out whether Robert has enough floor space for a free-standing aquarium after his furniture is in the room. Ignore doors and windows and work with only total floor space. Robert will need enough space to walk around his furniture. Drawing a floor plan might help.

How much floor space is available after Robert places the furniture but before he buys the aquarium?

$49\frac{3}{8}$ ft^2

Does Robert have enough space for the aquarium?

Yes

	Length (ft)	Width (ft)	Area (ft^2)
Room	$9\frac{1}{2}$	$9\frac{3}{4}$	$92\frac{5}{8}$
Desk	$3\frac{1}{4}$	$2\frac{1}{2}$	$8\frac{1}{8}$
Bed	$6\frac{1}{4}$	$3\frac{3}{4}$	$23\frac{7}{16}$
Dresser	$3\frac{1}{4}$	$2\frac{1}{4}$	$7\frac{5}{16}$
Bookcase	$1\frac{1}{4}$	$3\frac{1}{2}$	$4\frac{3}{8}$
Aquarium	2	1	2

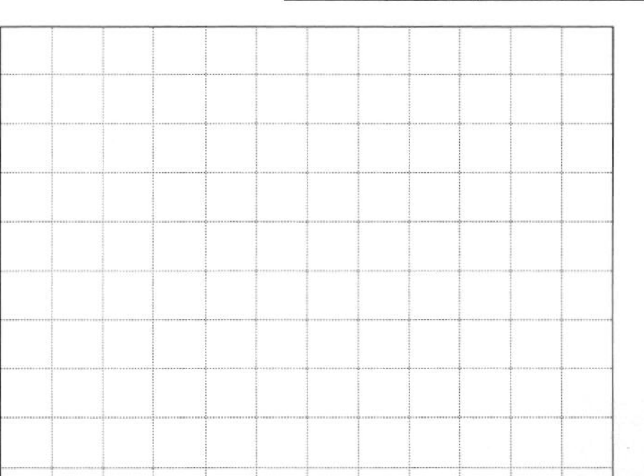

***Math Masters,* p. 131**

Fractions, Decimals, and Percents

Objective To review converting between fractions, decimals, and percents.

1 Teaching the Lesson

Key Activities

Students find equivalent fractions that have denominators of 100 and rename them as decimals and percents. They convert from percents to decimals and fractions.

Key Concepts and Skills

- Apply place-value concepts to per-hundred representations. [Number and Numeration Goal 1]
- Convert between fractions, decimals, and percents. [Number and Numeration Goal 5]
- Use multiplication and division facts to find equivalent fractions and simplify fractions. [Operations and Computation Goal 2]
- Identify the missing value in an open number sentence. [Patterns, Functions, and Algebra Goal 2]

Key Vocabulary percent

Ongoing Assessment: Recognizing Student Achievement Use journal page 149. [Number and Numeration Goal 5]

materials

- ☐ *Math Journal 1,* pp. 148 and 149
- ☐ *Student Reference Book,* pp. 59 and 60
- ☐ Study Link 4•7
- ☐ Probability Meter Poster

See **Advance Preparation**

2 Ongoing Learning & Practice

Students practice renaming fractions as decimals by playing the decimal version of *2-4-8 Frac-Tac-Toe* or *3-6-9 Frac-Tac-Toe.*

Students practice and maintain skills through Math Boxes and Study Link activities.

materials

- ☐ *Math Journal 1,* p. 147
- ☐ *Student Reference Book,* pp. 314–316
- ☐ Study Link Master (*Math Masters,* p. 132)
- ☐ Game Masters (*Math Masters,* pp. 439–441; 444 optional)
- ☐ Geometry Template or protractor
- ☐ Per partnership: 4 each of number cards 0–10; 2-color counters or pennies; calculator

3 Differentiation Options

READINESS

Students use a 10 × 10 grid to review fraction, decimal, and percent equivalencies.

ENRICHMENT

Students use spreadsheet formulas to convert between fractions, decimals, and percents.

ENRICHMENT

Students read percentage stories and then write and illustrate their own stories.

materials

- ☐ Teaching Master (*Math Masters,* p. 133)
- ☐ *Twizzlers™ Percentages Book*
- ☐ computer/spreadsheet software

Additional Information

Advance Preparation Cut the Probability Meter Poster into two pieces and tape the pieces together at the 50% mark. Display the poster in an accessible and visible area of the classroom. Display either the English version only or both the English and Spanish versions simultaneously; do not display the Spanish version only.

Technology

Assessment Management System
Journal page 149, Problems 12–35
See the **iTLG.**

Getting Started

Mental Math and Reflexes

Students find the value of x so the fractions are equivalent. *Suggestions:*

●○○ $\frac{2}{5} = \frac{x}{100}$ $x = 40$

●●○ $\frac{x}{25} = \frac{16}{100}$ $x = 4$

●●● $\frac{7}{4} = \frac{x}{100}$ $x = 175$

$\frac{7}{20} = \frac{35}{x}$ $x = 100$

$\frac{13}{x} = \frac{26}{100}$ $x = 50$

$\frac{(\frac{1}{2})}{10} = \frac{x}{100}$ $x = 5$

Math Message

Complete Problems 1–3 on journal page 148.

Study Link 4•7 Follow-Up

Briefly go over the answers. Ask students how to solve the problems using mixed numbers.

1 Teaching the Lesson

▶ Math Message Follow-Up

(*Math Journal 1,* p. 148)

Briefly go over the answers to the Math Message problems. In the context of the problems, $\frac{2}{5} = \frac{40}{100}$ means, "If Sari got 2 hits every 5 times at bat, then she would get 40 hits in 100 times at bat."

Ask students how to rename $\frac{2}{5}$ as a decimal. Two possibilities are given below.

$\frac{2}{5} = \frac{40}{100}$, and $\frac{40}{100}$ can be written as 0.40. So, $\frac{2}{5} = 0.40$.

$\frac{2}{5} = \frac{4}{10} = 0.4$

Discuss how the shaded grid and the decimal 0.40 represent the same quantity. Remind students that **percent** means *per hundred*, or *out of a hundred*. Ask questions such as the following:

- What percent of the times at bat would Sari get a hit? 40%, because she would get 40 hits in 100 times at bat
- How many hits would she get in 15 times at bat? 6 This can be shown by the number sentence $\frac{2}{5} = \frac{y}{15}$, $y = 6$.

NOTE Discuss how Sari's batting average would be printed in a newspaper. .400 A batting average is not an average (or mean). Instead, it is a rate—number of hits per number of times at bat—expressed as a decimal to three decimal places. If the batter walks, it is not counted as a time at bat. Discuss the advantages of recording batting averages to the thousandths place instead of the tenths or hundredths place.

Student Page

Date Time

LESSON 4•8 **Fractions, Decimals, and Percents**

Math Message

During the baseball season, Sari got a hit 2 out of every 5 times she was at bat.

1. Shade $\frac{2}{5}$ of the square at the right.
2. How many hundredths are shaded? 40
3. $\frac{2}{5} = \frac{x}{100}$ $x =$ 40

You can rename some fractions as decimals by first renaming them as equivalent fractions with 10 or 100 in the denominator.

Example 1:	**Example 2:**
$\frac{3}{5} = \frac{b}{10}$ $b = 6$	$\frac{3}{20} = \frac{d}{100}$ $d = 15$
If $\frac{6}{10} = 0.6$, then $\frac{3}{5} = 0.6$.	If $\frac{15}{100} = 0.15$, then $\frac{3}{20} = 0.15$.

Find the value of the variable. Use it to rename the fraction as a decimal.

4. $\frac{1}{4} = \frac{f}{100}$; $f =$ 25
   $\frac{1}{4} = 0.$25
5. $\frac{4}{5} = \frac{r}{100}$; $r =$ 80
   $\frac{4}{5} = 0.$80
6. $\frac{7}{20} = \frac{z}{100}$; $z =$ 35
   $\frac{7}{20} = 0.$35
7. $\frac{9}{2} = \frac{n}{100}$; $n =$ 450
   $\frac{9}{2} = 4.$50

Rename each fraction as a decimal.

8. $\frac{3}{4} = 0.$75
9. $\frac{12}{25} = 0.$48
10. $\frac{19}{50} = 0.$38
11. $\frac{3}{2} = 1.$5

Math Journal 1, p. 148

Student Page

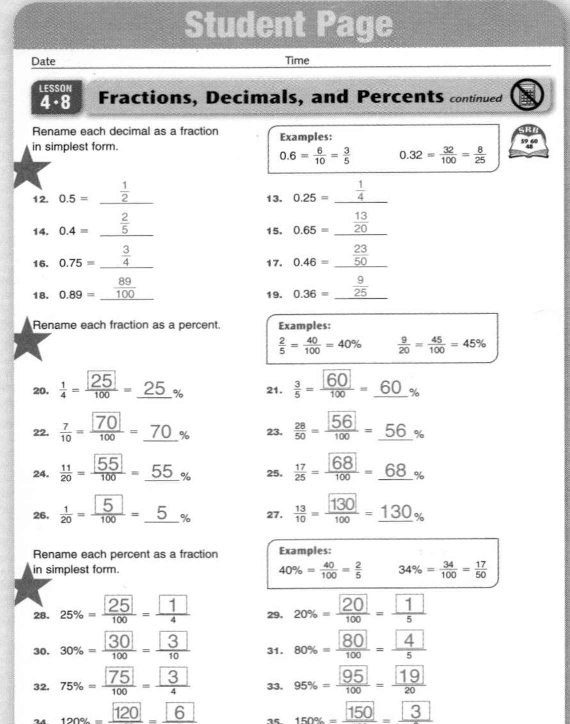
Date Time

LESSON 4·8 **Fractions, Decimals, and Percents** *continued*

Rename each decimal as a fraction in simplest form.

Examples: $0.6 = \frac{6}{10} = \frac{3}{5}$ $0.32 = \frac{32}{100} = \frac{8}{25}$

12. $0.5 = \frac{1}{2}$
13. $0.25 = \frac{1}{4}$
14. $0.4 = \frac{2}{5}$
15. $0.65 = \frac{13}{20}$
16. $0.75 = \frac{3}{4}$
17. $0.46 = \frac{23}{50}$
18. $0.89 = \frac{89}{100}$
19. $0.36 = \frac{9}{25}$

Rename each fraction as a percent.

Examples: $\frac{2}{5} = \frac{40}{100} = 40\%$ $\frac{9}{20} = \frac{45}{100} = 45\%$

20. $\frac{1}{4} = \frac{25}{100} = 25\%$
21. $\frac{3}{5} = \frac{60}{100} = 60\%$
22. $\frac{7}{10} = \frac{70}{100} = 70\%$
23. $\frac{28}{50} = \frac{56}{100} = 56\%$
24. $\frac{11}{20} = \frac{55}{100} = 55\%$
25. $\frac{17}{25} = \frac{68}{100} = 68\%$
26. $\frac{1}{20} = \frac{5}{100} = 5\%$
27. $\frac{13}{10} = \frac{130}{100} = 130\%$

Rename each percent as a fraction in simplest form.

Examples: $40\% = \frac{40}{100} = \frac{2}{5}$ $34\% = \frac{34}{100} = \frac{17}{50}$

28. $25\% = \frac{25}{100} = \frac{1}{4}$
29. $20\% = \frac{20}{100} = \frac{1}{5}$
30. $30\% = \frac{30}{100} = \frac{3}{10}$
31. $80\% = \frac{80}{100} = \frac{4}{5}$
32. $75\% = \frac{75}{100} = \frac{3}{4}$
33. $95\% = \frac{95}{100} = \frac{19}{20}$
34. $120\% = \frac{120}{100} = \frac{6}{5}$
35. $150\% = \frac{150}{100} = \frac{3}{2}$

Math Journal 1, p. 149

▶ Converting between Fractions, Decimals, and Percents

(*Math Journal 1*, pp. 148 and 149; *Student Reference Book*, pp. 59 and 60)

The material on journal pages 148 and 149 was covered in previous grades. Most students should be able to work the problems, using the *Student Reference Book* as necessary.

Students were introduced to the Probability Meter Poster in *Fifth Grade Everday Mathematics*. The Probability Meter Poster is a number line from 0 to 1 marked to show fraction, decimal, and percent divisions. It can be used to find equivalent fractions and to convert between fractions, decimals, and percents. A copy of the poster appears in the reference pages of *Math Journal 1*.

NOTE When you use the *Everyday Mathematics* posters with English language learners, you should display either the English version only or both the English and Spanish versions simultaneously.

Ongoing Assessment: Recognizing Student Achievement

Journal Page 149 Problems 12–35

Use **journal page 149, Problems 12–35** to assess students' ability to convert between fractions, decimals, and percents. Students are making adequate progress if they can rename decimals and percents as fractions in simplest form. Some students may be able to rename fractions and percents greater than 1.

[Number and Numeration Goal 5]

Links to the Future

In this unit, students use an open proportion when they solve for the missing value in a pair of equivalent fractions ($\frac{17}{25} = \frac{x}{100}$). In Unit 8, students will expand their use of proportions to solve rate, size-change, and percent problems. They will continue to use proportions to solve problems in future mathematics courses.

Game Master

Name Date Time

2-4-8 Frac-Tac-Toe (Decimals)

If you use a standard deck of playing cards:

- Use queens as zeros (0).
- Use aces as ones (1).
- Discard jacks and kings.

If you use an Everything Math Deck, discard cards greater than 10.

Use different color counters or coins as markers. If you use coins, one player is HEADS and the other player is TAILS.

Numerator Pile: All remaining cards

Denominator Pile: Two each of the 2, 4, and 8 cards

> 2.0	0 or 1	> 1.5	0 or 1	> 2.0
1.5	0.125	0.25	0.375	1.5
> 1.0	0.5	0.25 or 0.75	0.5	> 1.0
2.0	0.625	0.75	0.875	2.0
> 2.0	0 or 1	1.125	0 or 1	> 2.0

Math Masters, p. 440

Game Master

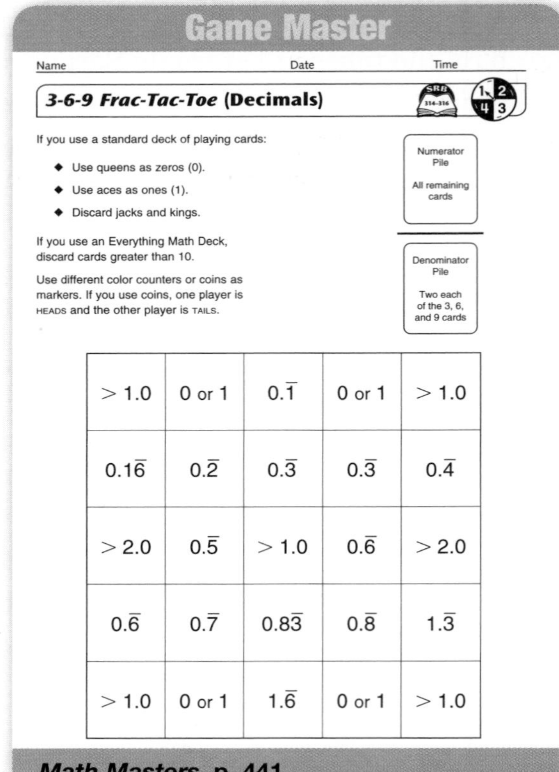
Name Date Time

3-6-9 Frac-Tac-Toe (Decimals)

If you use a standard deck of playing cards:

- Use queens as zeros (0).
- Use aces as ones (1).
- Discard jacks and kings.

If you use an Everything Math Deck, discard cards greater than 10.

Use different color counters or coins as markers. If you use coins, one player is HEADS and the other player is TAILS.

Numerator Pile: All remaining cards

Denominator Pile: Two each of the 3, 6, and 9 cards

> 1.0	0 or 1	$0.\overline{1}$	0 or 1	> 1.0
$0.1\overline{6}$	$0.\overline{2}$	$0.\overline{3}$	$0.\overline{3}$	$0.\overline{4}$
> 2.0	$0.\overline{5}$	> 1.0	$0.\overline{6}$	> 2.0
$0.\overline{6}$	$0.\overline{7}$	$0.8\overline{3}$	$0.\overline{8}$	$1.\overline{3}$
> 1.0	0 or 1	$1.\overline{6}$	0 or 1	> 1.0

Math Masters, p. 441

2 Ongoing Learning & Practice

▶ Playing *2-4-8 Frac-Tac-Toe* and *3-6-9 Frac-Tac-Toe* (Decimal Versions)

PARTNER ACTIVITY

(*Student Reference Book,* pp. 314–316; *Math Masters,* pp. 439–441; p. 444)

Organize the game cards using *Math Masters,* page 439. Depending on students' needs, use *Math Masters,* page 440 to work with denominators of 2, 4, and 8 or page 441 to work with denominators of 3, 6, and 9. Consider using *Math Masters,* page 444 for students who need additional practice converting fractions with denominators of 2, 4, 5, and 10 to decimals. Players may use a calculator or the Table of Decimal Equivalents for Fractions, which appears in the reference section of *Math Journal 1,* to convert fractions to decimals.

NOTE Store *Frac-Tac-Toe* materials for future use (Lesson 5-7).

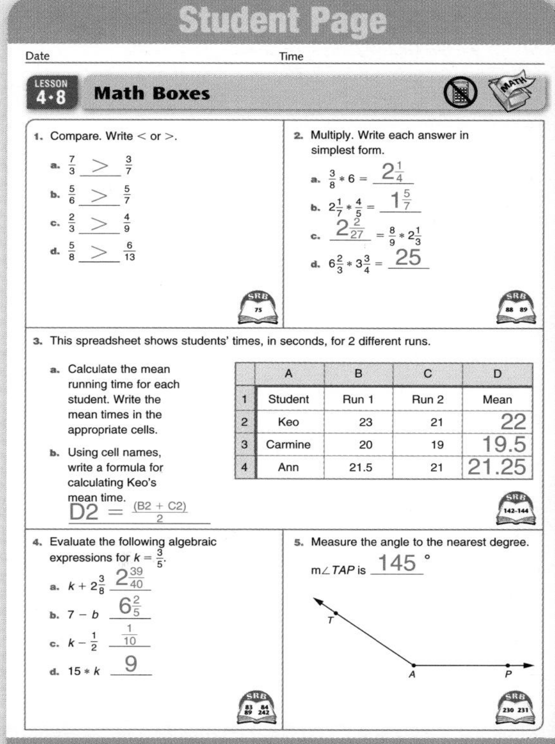

Student Page

Date Time

LESSON 4•8 Math Boxes

1. Compare. Write < or >.
   - a. $\frac{7}{3}$ > $\frac{3}{7}$
   - b. $\frac{5}{6}$ > $\frac{5}{7}$
   - c. $\frac{2}{3}$ > $\frac{4}{9}$
   - d. $\frac{5}{8}$ > $\frac{6}{13}$

SRB 75

2. Multiply. Write each answer in simplest form.
   - a. $\frac{3}{8} * 6 = 2\frac{1}{4}$
   - b. $2\frac{1}{7} * \frac{4}{5} = 1\frac{5}{7}$
   - c. $2\frac{2}{27} = \frac{8}{9} * 2\frac{1}{3}$
   - d. $6\frac{2}{3} * 3\frac{3}{4} = 25$

SRB 88 89

3. This spreadsheet shows students' times, in seconds, for 2 different runs.
   - a. Calculate the mean running time for each student. Write the mean times in the appropriate cells.
   - b. Using cell names, write a formula for calculating Keo's mean time. $D2 = \frac{(B2 + C2)}{2}$

	A	B	C	D
1	Student	Run 1	Run 2	Mean
2	Keo	23	21	22
3	Carmine	20	19	19.5
4	Ann	21.5	21	21.25

SRB 142-144

4. Evaluate the following algebraic expressions for $k = \frac{3}{5}$.
   - a. $k + 2\frac{3}{8}$ $2\frac{39}{40}$
   - b. $7 - b$ $6\frac{2}{5}$
   - c. $k - \frac{1}{2}$ $\frac{1}{10}$
   - d. $15 * k$ 9

SRB 83 84 89 242

5. Measure the angle to the nearest degree.

   m∠*TAP* is 145 °

SRB 230 231

***Math Journal 1,* p. 147**

▶ Math Boxes 4•8

INDEPENDENT ACTIVITY

(*Math Journal 1,* p. 147)

Mixed Practice Math Boxes in this lesson are paired with Math Boxes in Lessons 4-6 and 4-10. The skill in Problem 5 previews Unit 5 content. Students will need a Geometry Template or a protractor to complete Problem 5.

▶ Study Link 4•8

INDEPENDENT ACTIVITY

(*Math Masters,* p. 132)

Home Connection Students practice converting between fractions, decimals, and percents. They also conduct a brief survey about the types of numbers people are likely to name.

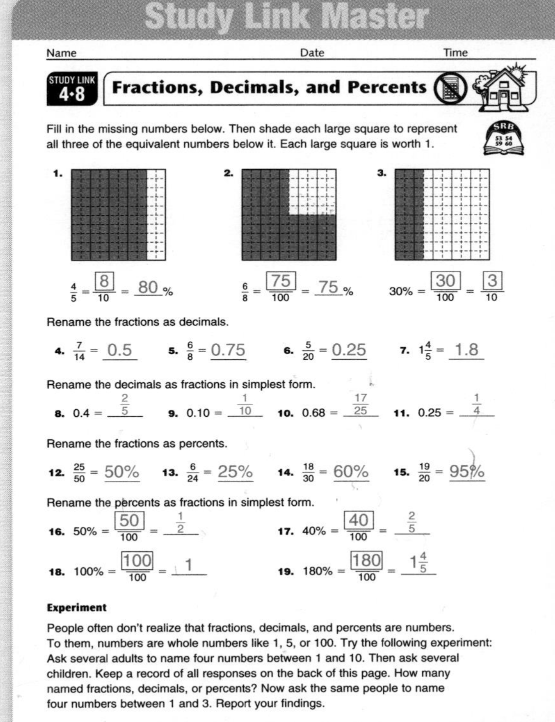

Study Link Master

Name Date Time

STUDY LINK 4•8 Fractions, Decimals, and Percents

Fill in the missing numbers below. Then shade each large square to represent all three of the equivalent numbers below it. Each large square is worth 1.

SRB 53 54 59 60

1. $\frac{4}{5} = \frac{8}{10} = 80\%$
2. $\frac{6}{8} = \frac{75}{100} = 75\%$
3. $30\% = \frac{30}{100} = \frac{3}{10}$

Rename the fractions as decimals.

4. $\frac{7}{14} = 0.5$ 5. $\frac{6}{8} = 0.75$ 6. $\frac{5}{20} = 0.25$ 7. $1\frac{4}{5} = 1.8$

Rename the decimals as fractions in simplest form.

8. $0.4 = \frac{2}{5}$ 9. $0.10 = \frac{1}{10}$ 10. $0.68 = \frac{17}{25}$ 11. $0.25 = \frac{1}{4}$

Rename the fractions as percents.

12. $\frac{25}{50} = 50\%$ 13. $\frac{6}{24} = 25\%$ 14. $\frac{18}{30} = 60\%$ 15. $\frac{19}{20} = 95\%$

Rename the percents as fractions in simplest form.

16. $50\% = \frac{50}{100} = \frac{1}{2}$ 17. $40\% = \frac{40}{100} = \frac{2}{5}$

18. $100\% = \frac{100}{100} = 1$ 19. $180\% = \frac{180}{100} = 1\frac{4}{5}$

Experiment

People often don't realize that fractions, decimals, and percents are numbers. To them, numbers are whole numbers like 1, 5, or 100. Try the following experiment: Ask several adults to name four numbers between 1 and 10. Then ask several children. Keep a record of all responses on the back of this page. How many named fractions, decimals, or percents? Now ask the same people to name four numbers between 1 and 3. Report your findings.

***Math Masters,* p. 132**

3 Differentiation Options

READINESS

SMALL-GROUP ACTIVITY

5–15 Min

▶ Representing Fractions, Decimals, and Percents

(*Math Masters,* p. 133)

Students review strategies for renaming fractions as decimals and percents. Use *Math Masters,* page 133 to create representation problems that address students' needs and abilities. Some students may need practice shading 10×10 grids to represent fractions that have denominators such as 10, 20, 25, and 50. Other students may need to review fraction-to-decimal and/or decimal-to-percent conversions.

ENRICHMENT

SMALL-GROUP ACTIVITY

15–30 Min

▶ Renaming with Computer Spreadsheets

Consumer Education Link To extend their knowledge of renaming, students use spreadsheet software to make a table like the one shown below. Have them input the appropriate formula for dividing numbers in the numerator column by numbers in the denominator column. Ask students to use formatting features that round decimals to thousandths and then rename them as percents.

	A	B	C	D
1	Numerator	Denominator	Decimal	Percent
2				
3	1	2	0.500	50.0%
4	2	3	0.667	66.7%
5	3	4	0.750	75.0%
6	4	5	0.800	80.0%
7	5	6	0.833	83.3%
8	6	7	0.857	85.7%
9	7	8	0.875	87.5%

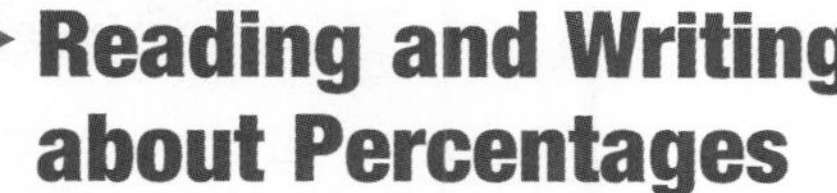

ENRICHMENT

PARTNER ACTIVITY

30+ Min

▶ Reading and Writing about Percentages

Literature Link To further explore the representations and uses of percentages, students read *Twizzlers™ Percentages Book*. The book focuses on renaming fractions as decimals and percents. After reading the supporting text for each illustration, students write and illustrate their own stories about percentages.

Teaching Master

Name ______ Date ______ Time ______

LESSON 4·8 **Renaming Fractions**

Fraction: $\frac{\square}{100}$
Decimal: ______
Percent: ______%

Fraction: $\frac{\square}{100}$
Decimal: ______
Percent: ______%

Fraction: $\frac{\square}{100}$
Decimal: ______
Percent: ______%

Fraction: $\frac{\square}{100}$
Decimal: ______
Percent: ______%

Math Masters, p. 133

4•9 More Difficult Conversions

Objectives To develop a rule for converting between decimals and percents; and to convert fractions to decimals and percents.

1 Teaching the Lesson

Key Activities

Students develop and apply rules and strategies for converting between decimals and percents.

Key Concepts and Skills

- Apply place-value concepts to round decimal quotients to the nearest hundredth. [Number and Numeration Goal 1]
- Use a calculator to rename fractions as percents by dividing. [Operations and Computation Goal 2]
- Interpret the remainder and adjust/truncate/round the quotient accordingly. [Operations and Computation Goal 5]
- Apply the Identity Property of Multiplication to convert between decimals and percents. [Patterns, Functions, and Algebra Goal 4]

Ongoing Assessment: Informing Instruction See page 304.

materials

- ☐ *Math Journal 1,* p. 150
- ☐ Study Link 4•8
- ☐ calculator
- ☐ slate

2 Ongoing Learning & Practice

Students practice renaming fractions as percents by playing the percent version of *2-4-8 Frac-Tac-Toe* or *3-6-9 Frac-Tac-Toe.*

Students practice and maintain skills through Math Boxes and Study Link activities.

Ongoing Assessment: Recognizing Student Achievement Use journal page 151. [Operations and Computation Goal 4]

materials

- ☐ *Math Journal 1,* p. 151
- ☐ *Student Reference Book,* pp. 314–316
- ☐ Study Link Master (*Math Masters,* p. 134)
- ☐ Game Masters (*Math Masters,* pp. 439, 442, and 443; 445 optional)
- ☐ Per partnership: 4 each of number cards 0–10; 2-color counters or pennies; calculator

3 Differentiation Options

ENRICHMENT

Students examine prime factors to develop a rule for predicting whether a decimal number will terminate or repeat.

EXTRA PRACTICE

Students rename percents greater than or less than 1% as equivalent decimals.

ELL SUPPORT

Students use tables and patterns to support language development.

materials

- ☐ Teaching Master (*Math Masters,* p. 135)
- ☐ calculator

Technology

Assessment Management System
Math Boxes, Problem 4
See the **iTLG.**

Getting Started

Mental Math and Reflexes

Students translate between fractions and the division problems that represent them. They express the quotients as decimals.

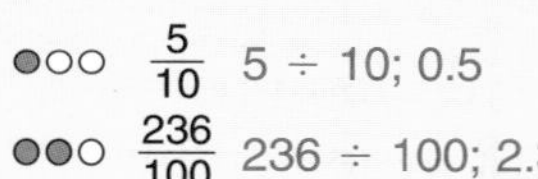

●○○ $\frac{5}{10}$ 5 ÷ 10; 0.5 $\frac{1}{4}$ 1 ÷ 4; 0.25

●●○ $\frac{236}{100}$ 236 ÷ 100; 2.36 $\frac{49}{50}$ 49 ÷ 50; 0.98

●●● $1\frac{4}{5}$ 9 ÷ 5; 1.8 $\frac{3}{25}$ 3 ÷ 25; 0.12

Math Message

Complete Problems 1–4 on journal page 150.

Study Link 4•8 Follow-Up

Go over the answers. Discuss the experiment. Ask: *Did people think of fractions, decimals, or percents when they were asked to name numbers between 1 and 10? Between 1 and 3?*

1 Teaching the Lesson

▶ Math Message Follow-Up

WHOLE-CLASS DISCUSSION

(*Math Journal 1,* p. 150)

Discuss the first problem with the class. Write the steps below on the board and ask students to justify each one.

$0.36 = 0.36 * 1$ Any number multiplied by 1 equals the number; $a * 1 = a$.

$= 0.36 * \frac{100}{100}$ A fraction whose numerator and denominator are the same is equal to 1; $\frac{a}{a} = 1$.

$= \frac{(0.36 * 100)}{100}$ Fraction multiplication algorithm; $a * \frac{b}{c} = \frac{a}{1} * \frac{b}{c} = \frac{a * b}{c}$

$= \frac{36}{100}$ $0.36 * 100 = 36$

$= 36\%$ *Percent* means *per hundred.*

Then go over the answers to the rest of the Math Message problems, recording the answers in a T-chart on the board as shown below.

Decimal	Percent
0.36	36%
0.7	70%
0.09	9%
4.602	460.2%

Summary: To rename a decimal as a percent, multiply the decimal by 100 and write a percent symbol after the answer.

Examples:

$0.394 = (0.394 * 100)\% = 39.4\%$

$2.8 = (2.8 * 100)\% = 280\%$

Student Page

Date Time

LESSON 4•9 **Converting Between Decimals and Percents**

Math Message

Fill in the blanks.

1. $0.36 = \frac{0.36 * 100}{100} = \frac{36}{100} = 36\%$

2. $0.7 = \frac{0.7 * 100}{100} = \frac{70}{100} = 70\%$

3. $0.09 = \frac{0.09 * 100}{100} = \frac{9}{100} = 9\%$

4. $4.602 = \frac{4.602 * 100}{100} = \frac{460.2}{100} = 460.2\%$

Rename each decimal as a percent.

5. 0.42 = 42% 6. 0.08 = 8% 7. 1.5 = 150% 8. 7.36 = 736%

Rename each percent as a decimal.

9. 23% = 0.23 10. 4% = 0.04 11. 314% = 3.14 12. 1,260% = 12.60

13. Divide using a calculator to fill in the table. Study the first problem.

Fraction	Decimal (Quotient)	Percent	Percent (to the nearest whole)
$\frac{1}{9}$	0.1111111111	11.11111111%	11%
$\frac{2}{3}$	0.6666666667	66.66666667%	67%
$\frac{3}{7}$	0.4285714286	42.85714286%	43%
$\frac{5}{9}$	0.5555555556	55.55555556%	56%
$\frac{7}{1}$	7	700%	700%
$\frac{7}{8}$	0.875	87.5%	88%

Math Journal 1, p. 150

▶ Converting between Decimals and Percents

Introduce the following shortcuts based on power-of-10 strategies.

Converting decimals to percents

To convert a decimal to a percent, move the decimal point two places to the right and write the percent symbol after the number.

Examples: 0.394 = 0.3 9.4%

2.8 = 2.8 0. %

When using the shortcut, students must attach a zero to numbers such as 2.8 before they can move the decimal point two places to the right.

Ask students to use the shortcut to verify each result in the T-chart you recorded on the board. Include a few more decimal entries in the chart and ask students to rename them as percents on their slates. (*See margin.*)

Suggestions: 0.87 87%; 0.6 60%; 0.572 57.2%; 2.59 259%; 0.031 3.1%; 0.001 0.1%

Decimal	Percent
0.36	36%
0.7	70%
0.09	9%
4.602	460.2%
0.87	87%
0.6	60%
0.572	57.2%
2.59	259%
0.031	3.1%
0.001	0.1%
0.68	68%
0.335	33.5%
3.84	384%
0.05	5%

Converting percents to decimals

To convert a percent to a decimal, move the decimal point two places to the left and omit the percent symbol.

Examples: 46% = 0.4 6.

7% = 0.0 7.

Students must insert a zero in front of the 7 in 7% before they can move the decimal point. Extend the chart on the board to include a few percents. Ask students to rename them as decimals on their slates. (*See margin.*)

Suggestions: 68% 0.68; 33.5% 0.335; 384% 3.84; 5% 0.05

▶ Using Division to Rename Fractions as Percents

WHOLE-CLASS ACTIVITY

Ask a volunteer to show how to use equivalent fractions to rename $\frac{3}{4}$ as a percent (as was done in Lesson 4-8).

$$\frac{3}{4} = \frac{x}{100};\ x = 75$$

$$\text{So, } \frac{3}{4} = \frac{75}{100} = 75\%$$

Have the class rename $\frac{2}{3}$ as a percent, using the same method.

$$\frac{2}{3} = \frac{x}{100};\ x = ?$$

Guide students to see that they can easily rename $\frac{3}{4}$ as an equivalent fraction $\frac{x}{100}$ because 100 is divisible by 4, but they cannot easily rename $\frac{2}{3}$ because 100 is not divisible by 3.

One way to rename any fraction as a decimal is to divide the numerator by the denominator. The resulting decimal can then be renamed as a percent. Demonstrate this method using the fraction $\frac{3}{4}$.

Step 1: Estimate the quotient. It must be less than 1 but greater than $\frac{1}{2}$.

Step 2: Rewrite the dividend, 3, as 3.00. Divide 3.00 by 4, using the partial-quotients division algorithm. Ignoring the decimal point in 3.00 means dividing 300 by 4. (*See margin.*)

Step 3: Use the estimate to place the decimal point in the quotient. 0.75

Step 4: Rename the decimal as a percent. 0.75 = 75%

```
4)300
 - 200 | 50
   100 |
 - 100 | 25
     0   75
```

Use this procedure to show how to rename $\frac{2}{3}$ as a percent. (*See margin.*) The remainder is not 0, so 0.66 is not the exact answer. $\frac{2}{3}$ must be greater than 0.66 but less than 0.67. Because the remainder, 2, is more than half the divisor, 3, round 0.66 up to 0.67. $\frac{2}{3}$ is renamed as 67%, to the nearest whole percent.

```
3)200
 - 150 | 50
    50 |
  - 30 | 10
    20 |
  - 18 |  6
     2   66
```

Do two more problems on the board: $\frac{1}{3}$ and $\frac{5}{7}$. Round the results to the nearest whole percent. Compare results for $\frac{1}{3}$ 0.33 with results for $\frac{2}{3}$ 0.67. Briefly discuss how rounding affects results.

Finally, ask students to divide using their calculators to rename fractions as percents.

Example: Depending on the calculator:

Press: 1 [÷] 3 [▶%] [Enter] or 1 [÷] 3 [%] [=]

Display: 33.33333333% or 33.333333

Record the results in a table on the board. (*See margin.*)

Suggestions: $\frac{1}{3}$, $\frac{5}{7}$, $\frac{5}{6}$, $\frac{1}{12}$, $\frac{3}{13}$

Fraction	Decimal Quotient	Percent	Percent (to the nearest whole)
$\frac{1}{3}$	0.3333333	33.33333%	33%
$\frac{5}{7}$	0.7142857	71.42857%	71%
$\frac{5}{6}$	0.8333333	83.33333%	83%
$\frac{1}{12}$	0.0833333	8.333333%	8%
$\frac{3}{13}$	0.2307692	23.07692%	23%

Adjusting the Activity

Have students think of the % symbol as the ¢ symbol when renaming percents as decimals. *For example:* 8% → 8¢ → 0.08

AUDITORY ◆ KINESTHETIC ◆ TACTILE ◆ VISUAL

▶ Converting between Fractions, Decimals, and Percents

INDEPENDENT ACTIVITY

(*Math Journal 1,* p. 150)

Students complete the rest of the journal page. They convert between decimals and percents and rename fractions as percents using division.

Ongoing Assessment: Informing Instruction

Watch for students who merely attach the percent symbol to the decimal form of the fraction when they rename decimals as percents. *Percent* implies hundredths.

Therefore, 0.42 is $\frac{42}{100}$, but 0.42% is $\frac{0.42}{100} = \frac{\left(\frac{42}{100}\right)}{100} = 0.0042$.

2 Ongoing Learning & Practice

▶ Playing *2-4-8 Frac-Tac-Toe* and *3-6-9 Frac-Tac-Toe* (Percent Versions)

PARTNER ACTIVITY

(*Student Reference Book,* pp. 314–316; *Math Masters,* pp. 439, 442, and 443; p. 445)

Organize the game cards using *Math Masters,* page 439. Depending on students' needs, use *Math Masters,* page 442 to work with denominators of 2, 4, and 8 or page 443 to work with denominators of 3, 6, and 9. Consider using *Math Masters,* page 445 for students who need additional practice converting fractions with denominators of 2, 4, 5, and 10 to percents. Players may use a calculator or the Equivalent Fractions, Decimals, and Percents table in the reference section of *Math Journal 1* to convert their fractions to percents.

NOTE Store Frac-Tac-Toe materials for future use (Lesson 5-7).

▶ Math Boxes 4•9

INDEPENDENT ACTIVITY

(*Math Journal 1,* p. 151)

Mixed Practice Math Boxes in this lesson are paired with Math Boxes in Lesson 4-11. The skill in Problem 6 previews Unit 5 content.

Writing/Reasoning Have students write a response to the following: *Explain the strategies you used to compare and order the fractions in Problem 1.* Sample answer: I compared the fractions in relation to 0, $\frac{1}{2}$, and 1. Because the numerator 7 is close to the denominator 8, I know $\frac{7}{8}$ is close to 1. In $\frac{5}{12}$, the numerator is about half the denominator, so $\frac{5}{12}$ is close to $\frac{1}{2}$. I used the common denominator 100 to rename $\frac{1}{5}$ and $\frac{6}{10}$ as $\frac{20}{100}$ and $\frac{60}{100}$ and then compared them to $\frac{99}{100}$. To decide which fraction, $\frac{7}{8}$ or $\frac{99}{100}$, is closer to 1, I rewrote 7 as 7.00, divided it by 8, and got the quotient 0.875, which is less than 0.99, or $\frac{99}{100}$.

Ongoing Assessment: Recognizing Student Achievement

Math Boxes Problem 4

Use **Math Boxes, Problem 4** to assess students' ability to multiply a whole number by a fraction to find a fractional part of the number. Students are making adequate progress if they can calculate the products. Some students may be able to find the products mentally.

[Operations and Computation Goal 4]

▶ Study Link 4•9

INDEPENDENT ACTIVITY

(*Math Masters,* p. 134)

Home Connection Students divide to rename fractions as decimals. They also convert between decimals and percents.

3 Differentiation Options

ENRICHMENT

PARTNER ACTIVITY

▶ Predicting Terminating or Repeating Decimal Forms

5–15 Min

To further explore the relationship between fractions and decimals, students examine patterns and predict whether decimal forms of fractions will terminate or repeat. In their work with renaming fractions as decimals, students have seen that the decimal forms of some fractions terminate, while the decimal forms of other fractions repeat. For example, the decimal form of $\frac{1}{2}$ is 0.5 and the decimal form of $\frac{7}{200}$ is 0.035; the decimal form of $\frac{1}{9}$ is 0.111111... and the decimal form of $\frac{4}{11}$ is 0.363636... .

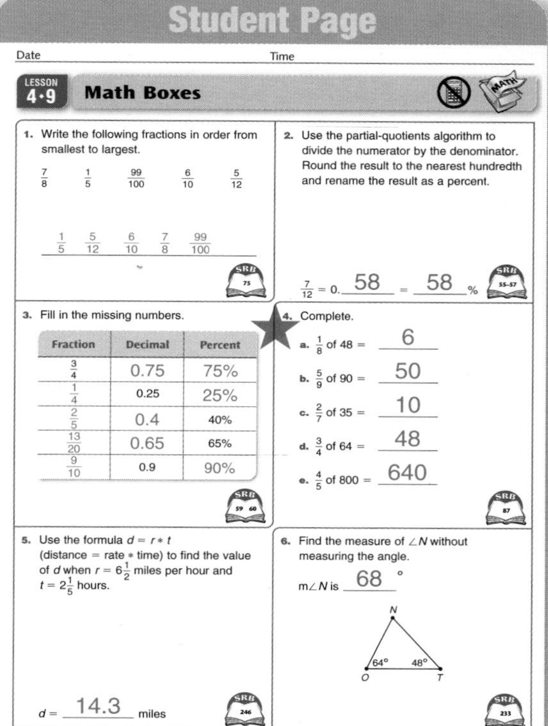

Student Page

Date Time

LESSON 4•9 **Math Boxes**

1. Write the following fractions in order from smallest to largest.
$\frac{7}{8}$ $\frac{1}{5}$ $\frac{99}{100}$ $\frac{6}{10}$ $\frac{5}{12}$
$\frac{1}{5}$ $\frac{5}{12}$ $\frac{6}{10}$ $\frac{7}{8}$ $\frac{99}{100}$

2. Use the partial-quotients algorithm to divide the numerator by the denominator. Round the result to the nearest hundredth and rename the result as a percent.
$\frac{7}{12}$ = 0.58 = 58 %

3. Fill in the missing numbers.

Fraction	Decimal	Percent
$\frac{3}{4}$	0.75	75%
$\frac{1}{4}$	0.25	25%
$\frac{2}{5}$	0.4	40%
$\frac{13}{20}$	0.65	65%
$\frac{9}{10}$	0.9	90%

4. Complete.
a. $\frac{1}{8}$ of 48 = 6
b. $\frac{5}{9}$ of 90 = 50
c. $\frac{2}{7}$ of 35 = 10
d. $\frac{3}{4}$ of 64 = 48
e. $\frac{4}{5}$ of 800 = 640

5. Use the formula $d = r * t$ (distance = rate * time) to find the value of d when $r = 6\frac{1}{2}$ miles per hour and $t = 2\frac{1}{5}$ hours.
d = 14.3 miles

6. Find the measure of ∠N without measuring the angle.
m∠N is 68 °

Math Journal 1, **p. 151**

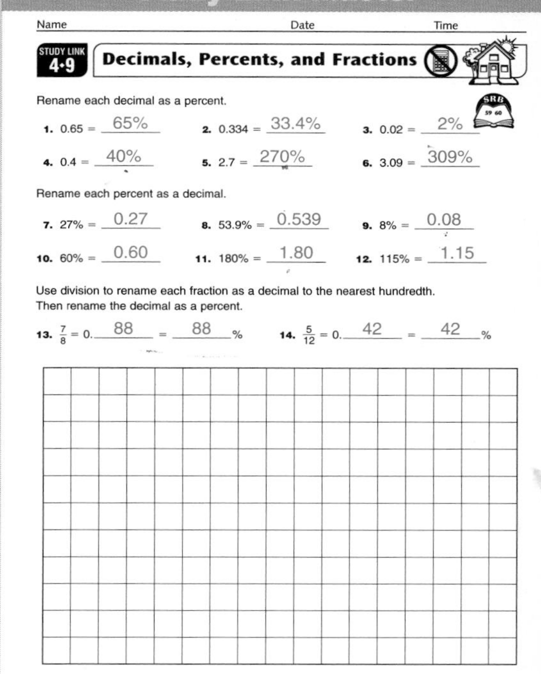

Study Link Master

Name Date Time

STUDY LINK 4•9 **Decimals, Percents, and Fractions**

Rename each decimal as a percent.

1. 0.65 = 65%
2. 0.334 = 33.4%
3. 0.02 = 2%
4. 0.4 = 40%
5. 2.7 = 270%
6. 3.09 = 309%

Rename each percent as a decimal.

7. 27% = 0.27
8. 53.9% = 0.539
9. 8% = 0.08
10. 60% = 0.60
11. 180% = 1.80
12. 115% = 1.15

Use division to rename each fraction as a decimal to the nearest hundredth. Then rename the decimal as a percent.

13. $\frac{7}{8}$ = 0.88 = 88 %
14. $\frac{5}{12}$ = 0.42 = 42 %

Math Masters, **p. 134**

Teaching Master

Name Date Time

LESSON 4·9 **Fractions, Decimals, and Percents**

Write each fraction or decimal as a percent.

1. $\frac{11}{50}$ = 22%
2. $\frac{3}{5}$ = 60%
3. $\frac{7}{8}$ = 87.5%
4. 0.45 = 45%
5. 0.745 = 74.5%
6. 0.0925 = 9.25%

Write each percent as a decimal.

7. 65% = 0.65
8. 4% = 0.04
9. 9.2% = 0.092
10. $15\frac{1}{2}$% = 0.155
11. 20% = 0.20
12. 2% = 0.02
13. Enter your results from Problems 11 and 12 on the appropriate lines below. Then complete the pattern.

200%	20%	2%	0.2%	0.02%	0.002%
2.00	0.20	0.02	0.002	0.0002	0.00002

Percents Greater Than and Less Than 1%

You can apply the meaning of *percent* and a power-of-10 strategy to rename percents greater than or less than 1 percent as equivalent decimals.

Example:	**Example:**
Write 125% as a decimal.	Write 0.15% as a decimal.
125% means 125 *per hundred.*	0.15% means 0.15 *per hundred.*
or $\frac{125}{100}$	or $\frac{0.15}{100}$
= 125 ÷ 100	= 0.15 ÷ 100
= 1.25.	= 0.0015

Write each percent as a decimal.

14. 375% = 3.75
15. 278% = 2.78
16. $400\frac{1}{2}$% = 4.005
17. 0.165% = 0.00165
18. 0.03% = 0.0003
19. 0.005% = 0.00005

Math Masters, p. 135

Have students use their calculators to find the decimal form of each of the following fractions:

$\frac{3}{8}$ 0.375 $\frac{5}{16}$ 0.3125 $\frac{7}{25}$ 0.28 $\frac{1}{3}$ $0.\overline{3}$ $\frac{5}{6}$ $0.8\overline{3}$ $\frac{11}{15}$ $0.7\overline{3}$

Then have students write the prime factorization of the denominators of each fraction mentioned in the previous examples and in the fractions above.

2 2; 200 $2^3 * 5^2$; 9 3^2; 11 11; 8 2^3; 16 2^4; 25 5^2; 3 3; 6 $2 * 3$; 15 $3 * 5$

Have partners examine the prime factorizations of the denominators and develop a rule that they can use to predict whether the decimal form of a fraction terminates or repeats. Encourage students to use several fractions to test their rule.

Suggestions:

$\frac{7}{18}$ repeats $\frac{4}{21}$ repeats $\frac{13}{40}$ terminates

$\frac{19}{30}$ repeats $\frac{97}{150}$ repeats $\frac{79}{250}$ terminates

If the prime factorization of the denominator consists only of 2s and/or 5s, the decimal will terminate. Otherwise, it will repeat. Thus, $\frac{19}{30}$ repeats because $30 = 2 * 3 * 5$; $\frac{13}{40}$ terminates because $40 = 2^3 * 5$.

EXTRA PRACTICE

INDEPENDENT ACTIVITY

15–30 Min

▶ Renaming Percents Greater Than and Less Than 1%

(*Math Masters,* p. 135)

Students convert between fractions, decimals, and percents. They apply the meaning of percent and a power-of-ten strategy to rename percents greater than or less than 1 percent.

ELL SUPPORT

SMALL-GROUP ACTIVITY

5–15 Min

▶ Supporting Language with Patterns

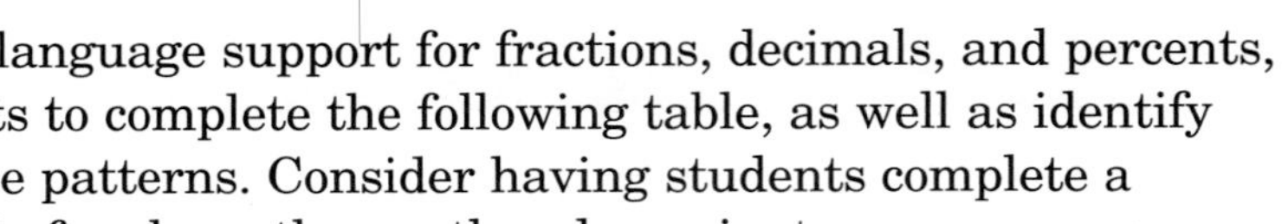

To provide language support for fractions, decimals, and percents, ask students to complete the following table, as well as identify and describe patterns. Consider having students complete a similar table for elevenths or other denominators.

Fraction	Decimal Quotient	Percent	Percent (to the nearest whole)
$\frac{1}{9}$	0.1111111111	11.11111111	11%
$\frac{2}{9}$	0.2222222222	22.22222222	22%
$\frac{3}{9}$	0.3333333333	33.33333333	33%
$\frac{4}{9}$	0.4444444444	44.44444444	44%

Graphing Garbage

Objective To represent data with circle graphs.

1 Teaching the Lesson

Key Activities

Students convert data, given as counts and measures, to percents. They represent these percents with circle graphs. They analyze changes in data.

Key Concepts and Skills

- Use multiplication and division facts to find equivalent fractions. [Operations and Computation Goal 2]
- Use a magnitude estimate to place the decimal point in a quotient. [Operations and Computation Goal 5]
- Use the Percent Circle to construct a circle graph. [Data and Chance Goal 1]
- Interpret data displayed as percents and draw conclusions about changes reflected in the data. [Data and Chance Goal 2]

Ongoing Assessment: Recognizing Student Achievement Use the Math Message. [Number and Numeration Goal 5]

materials

- ☐ *Math Journal 1,* pp. 152, 154, and 155
- ☐ *Student Reference Book,* p. 146
- ☐ Study Link 4•9
- ☐ Teaching Master (*Math Masters,* p. 136)
- ☐ calculator
- ☐ compass
- ☐ Geometry Template
- ☐ straightedge

***See* Advance Preparation**

2 Ongoing Learning & Practice

Students practice multiplying fractions and mixed numbers.

Students practice and maintain skills through Math Boxes and Study Link activities.

materials

- ☐ *Math Journal 1,* pp. 153 and 156
- ☐ Study Link Master (*Math Masters,* p. 137)
- ☐ Geometry Template or protractor

3 Differentiation Options

READINESS

Students estimate sector sizes and use the Percent Circle to check estimates.

ENRICHMENT

Students take a survey and use computer software to generate a circle graph of the results.

EXTRA PRACTICE

Students estimate products and percents of given numbers.

materials

- ☐ Teaching Master (*Math Masters,* p. 138)
- ☐ color pencils or markers
- ☐ Geometry Template
- ☐ computer/graphing software
- ☐ *5-Minute Math*, pp. 103 and 179

Additional Information

Advance Preparation For Part 1, make one copy of *Math Masters,* page 136 for every two students, cut apart, and distribute for the Math Message.

Technology

Assessment Management System
Math Message, Problem 1
See the **iTLG.**

Getting Started

Mental Math and Reflexes

Students solve problems mentally, using the partial-products algorithm as a possible strategy.

Suggestions:

●○○ 10.7 * 10 (10 * 10) + (0.7 * 10) = 107
●●○ 12.5 * 4 (12 * 4) + (0.5 * 4) = 50
●●● 3.25 * 20 (3 * 20) + (0.25 * 20) = 65

4.5 * 2 (4 * 2) + (0.5 * 2) = 9
5.1 * 50 (5 * 50) + (0.1 * 50) = 255
40 * 1.75 (40 * 1) + (40 * 0.75) = 70

Math Message 

Solve the Math Message problems.

Study Link 4·9 Follow-Up

Go over the answers.

1 Teaching the Lesson

▶ Math Message Follow-Up

WHOLE-CLASS ACTIVITY

(*Math Masters,* p. 136)

Ongoing Assessment: Recognizing Student Achievement

Math Message Problem 1 

Use **Math Message, Problem 1** to assess students' ability to rename fractions as decimals and percents. Students are making adequate progress if they correctly express the decimal and percent forms of each fraction. Some students might recognize that they can simplify $\frac{51}{75}$ by dividing the numerator and denominator by 3 to get $\frac{17}{25}$.

[Number and Numeration Goal 5]

Most students should have no trouble mentally solving the first two problems in the table. Here are some possible strategies for the rest of the problems.

Problem 1

$$\frac{13}{25} = \frac{13}{25} * \frac{4}{4} = \frac{52}{100} = 0.52 = 52\%$$

$$\frac{6}{30} = \frac{1}{5} = \frac{20}{100} = 0.20 = 20\%$$

$$\frac{51}{75} = \frac{17}{25} = \frac{68}{100} = 0.68 = 68\%$$

Problem 2

$$\frac{72}{90} = 72.0 \div 90 = 0.8 = 80\%$$

Teaching Master

Name Date Time

LESSON 4·10 **Math Message**

1. Find the equivalent decimal and percent for each of the fractions in the table below. Use a mental math and/or paper-and-pencil strategy to complete the table.

Fraction	Decimal	Percent
$\frac{1}{10}$	0.1	10%
$\frac{1}{4}$	0.25	25%
$\frac{13}{25}$	0.52	52%
$\frac{6}{30}$	0.2	20%
$\frac{51}{75}$	0.68	68%

2. There were 90 questions on the math final exam. Max correctly answered 72 questions. What percent of the questions did he answer correctly? 80%

Name Date Time

LESSON 4·10 **Math Message**

1. Find the equivalent decimal and percent for each of the fractions in the table below. Use a mental math and/or paper-and-pencil strategy to complete the table.

Fraction	Decimal	Percent
$\frac{1}{10}$		
$\frac{1}{4}$		
$\frac{13}{25}$		
$\frac{6}{30}$		
$\frac{51}{75}$		

2. There were 90 questions on the math final exam. Max correctly answered 72 questions. What percent of the questions did he answer correctly? ______

Math Masters, **p. 136**

▶ Constructing Circle Graphs

PARTNER ACTIVITY

(*Math Journal 1,* p. 152)

Explain that to make the most accurate graph, students should graph the smallest category first and the largest one last. A small error in a large percentage is relatively less important than a small error in a small percentage. For example, if a category is only 2% of the total and the sector is off by 1%, that is a fairly large error (50%). However, if a category is 34% of the total and the sector is off by 1%, the error is much less significant (only 3%).

Go over Steps 1 and 2 at the top of journal page 152.

Partners complete the percent columns in the two tables. Encourage them to work mentally or with paper and pencil, but without their calculators.

After a few minutes, bring the class together to share strategies. Write the correct percents on the board. One strategy is to use equivalent fractions as shown below.

Problem 1

Art $\frac{8}{40} = \frac{1}{5} = 20\%$

Barb $\frac{10}{40} = \frac{1}{4} = 25\%$

Cyrus $\frac{22}{40} = \frac{11}{20} = \frac{55}{100} = 55\%$

Another strategy to find the percent for Cyrus:

20% + 25% = 45%; 100% – 45% will give the remaining amount for the graph, so the remaining sector must represent 55%.

Problem 2

Doug $\frac{5}{12.5} = \frac{10}{25} = \frac{40}{100} = 40\%$

Bree $\frac{4.5}{12.5} = \frac{9}{25} = \frac{36}{100} = 36\%$

Fred $\frac{3}{12.5} = \frac{6}{25} = \frac{24}{100} = 24\%$

Some students may choose to divide. For example, to find the percent of driving time for Doug, divide 5 by 12.5, using the following method:

1. Estimate the quotient: $6 \div 12 = \frac{1}{2}$, so $5 \div 12.5$ is less than $\frac{1}{2}$, or less than 0.5.
2. Rename the dividend, 5, as 5.00. Ignore the decimal points and divide 500 by 125. The answer is 4.
3. Use the estimated quotient to locate the decimal point in the answer. Because the estimated quotient is less than 0.5, $5 \div 12.5 = 0.4$.
4. Rename 0.4 as a percent: 0.4 = 0.40 = 40%.

Have students use the Percent Circle to make circle graphs for the completed data tables. Emphasize the importance of estimating the size of the sectors to check for reasonableness. Circulate and assist as needed.

Student Page

Date Time

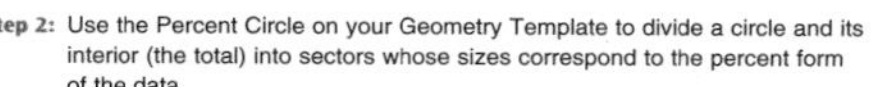

LESSON 4·10 **How to Draw a Circle Graph**

To draw a circle graph:

Step 1: Express each part of the data as a percent of the total.

Step 2: Use the Percent Circle on your Geometry Template to divide a circle and its interior (the total) into sectors whose sizes correspond to the percent form of the data.

1. Art, Barb, and Cyrus ran for sixth-grade class president. The election results are shown in the table below. Fill in the percent column. Then use your Percent Circle to draw a circle graph of the data.

Election Results

Name	Number of Votes	Percent of Total Vote
Art	8	20%
Barb	10	25%
Cyrus	22	55%
Total	**40**	**100%**

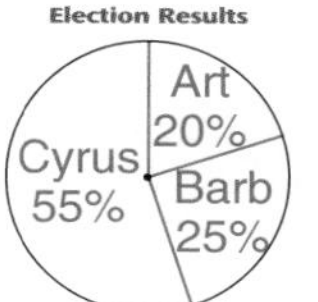

2. Doug, Bree, and Fred drove from Denver, Colorado, to Kansas City, Missouri. The number of hours each one drove is shown in the table below. Fill in the percent column. Then use your Percent Circle to draw a circle graph of the data.

Driving Times

Name	Number of Hours	Percent of Total Time
Doug	5	40%
Bree	4.5	36%
Fred	3	24%
Total	**12.5**	**100%**

Math Journal 1, **p. 152**

Adjusting the Activity

Review the steps for constructing a circle graph provided on page 146 of the *Student Reference Book.*

AUDITORY ◆ KINESTHETIC ◆ TACTILE ◆ VISUAL

Student Page

Data and Probability

How to Draw a Circle Graph Using a Percent Circle

Example Draw a circle graph to show the following information. The students in Mr. Zajac's class were asked to name their favorite colors: 9 students chose blue, 7 students chose green, 4 students chose yellow, and 5 chose red.

Step 1: Find what percent of the total each part represents. The total number of students who voted was 9 + 7 + 4 + 5 = 25.

- 9 out of 25 chose blue. $\frac{9}{25} = \frac{36}{100}$ = 36%, so 36% chose blue.
- 7 out of 25 chose green. $\frac{7}{25} = \frac{28}{100}$ = 28%, so 28% chose green.
- 4 out of 25 chose yellow. $\frac{4}{25} = \frac{16}{100}$ = 16%, so 16% chose yellow.
- 5 out of 25 chose red. $\frac{5}{25} = \frac{20}{100}$ = 20%, so 20% chose red.

Step 2: Check that the sum of the percents is 100%. 36% + 28% + 16% + 20% = 100%

Step 3: Draw a circle. Then use the Percent Circle on the Geometry Template to mark off the sectors.

- To mark off 36%, place the center of the Percent Circle over the center of the circle graph. Make a mark at 0% and 36%.
- To mark off 28%, make a mark at 64% (36% + 28% = 64%), without moving the Percent Circle.
- To mark off 16%, make a mark at 80% (64% + 16% = 80%).
- Check that the final sector represents 20%.

Step 4: Draw the sector lines (radii). Label each sector. Color the sectors.

0% 80% 64% 36% Step 3

red blue yellow green Step 4

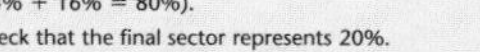

Check Your Understanding

Draw a circle graph to display the following information:

- The basketball team scored 30 points in one game.
- Frank scored 3 points.
- Jill scored 6 points.
- Leah scored 6 points.
- Dave scored 15 points.

Check your answer on page 419.

Student Reference Book, **p. 146**

▶ Weighing Garbage

PARTNER ACTIVITY

(*Math Journal 1*, pp. 154 and 155)

Science Link Introduce the activity. Discuss the footnotes to the table on journal page 154. Mention that while the data include all garbage generated, not all of that garbage is dumped in landfills or burned. At the turn of the millennium (2000), about 30% of the total was recycled.

Students may use calculators to complete the table. Work through several similar percent calculations, using the 1960 data, if necessary. (The percents for 1960 have been calculated and appear in the table.) Notice that all percents have been rounded to the nearest whole percent.

Compare and discuss students' graphs and answers. Point out that in 2000, 4.44 pounds is 100% of the garbage generated per person per day, but the total of the percent column is less than 100% due to rounding. Look for the following information in student responses to Problem 6 on journal page 155:

▷ Paper has always made up the greatest part of our garbage by weight. The percent of paper has increased slightly—from 34% in 1960 to 40% in 2000. The actual weight of paper garbage has nearly doubled since 1960.

▷ The increase in the amount of plastics has been remarkable. By actual weight, we generated 47 times as much plastics waste in 2000 as in 1960. Plastics accounted for less than 1% of garbage in 1960 but accounted for about 11% in 2000.

▷ The amount of wasted food found in our garbage has been reduced. It accounted for 14% of garbage in 1960 but accounted for only 10% in 2000. The amount may have been reduced through the use of garbage disposals or by renewed interest in composting.

▷ The weight of yard trimmings has been greatly reduced since 1960. In 1960, yard trimmings accounted for 23% of all garbage. By 2000, they accounted for only about 10%.

Ask students to share their conclusions from the garbage data about the technological and cultural changes that have occurred over the last 50 years.

Student Page

Date Time

LESSON 4·10 **How Much Does Your Garbage Weigh?**

Composition of Garbage Generated, per Person per Day

Material[1]	1960	1980	2000	2005[2]
	Weight (lb)			
Paper and paperboard	0.91	1.32	1.77	1.64
Glass	0.20	0.36	0.24	0.24
Metals	0.32	0.35	0.36	0.35
Plastics	0.01	0.19	0.47	0.49
Other (rubber, textiles, wood)	0.24	0.44	0.68	0.71
Food wastes	0.37	0.32	0.46	0.52
Yard trimmings	0.61	0.66	0.46	0.57
Total garbage generated	**2.66**	**3.64**	**4.44**	**4.52**

Source: United States Environmental Protection Agency

[1]Included in table: household garbage and appliances; garbage from offices, businesses, restaurants, schools, hospitals, and libraries. Not included in table: car bodies, sludge, industrial and agricultural wastes.
[2]Estimated

1. The percent column for 1960 has been completed in the table below. Complete the percent column for 2000. Round each answer to the nearest percent.

Material	1960		2000	
	Weight (lb)	Percent of Total Weight	Weight (lb)	Percent of Total Weight
Paper and paperboard	0.91	34%	1.77	40%
Glass	0.20	8%	0.24	5%
Metals	0.32	12%	0.36	8%
Plastics	0.01	0% (< 0.004%)	0.47	11%
Other (rubber, textiles, wood)	0.24	9%	0.68	15%
Food wastes	0.37	14%	0.46	10%
Yard trimmings	0.61	23%	0.46	10%
Total garbage generated	**2.66**	**100%**	**4.44**	100%*

*Column total is actually less than 100% due to rounding.

***Math Journal 1*, p. 154**

Student Page

Date Time

LESSON 4·10 **How Much Does Your Garbage Weigh?** *cont.*

2. Study the circle graph for the 1960 data. Then draw a circle graph for the 2000 data. Remember to graph the smallest sector first.

Garbage by Weight—1960

Yard trimmings 23%
Paper 34%
Food wastes 14%
Other 9%
Metals 12%
Glass 8%
Plastics 0%

Garbage by Weight—2000

Yard trimmings 10%
Food wastes 10%
Paper 40%
Other 15%
Plastics 11%
8%
Metals
5% Glass

3. What material makes up the largest part of Americans' garbage, by weight? paper

4. According to information for the year 2005, about how many pounds of garbage did a person generate, on average, in

1 day? 5 pounds 1 week? 35 pounds 1 month (30 days)? 150 pounds

5. About how many months did it take a person to generate 1 ton of garbage in 2005? 13 months

6. Describe the changes that took place in the composition of garbage from 1960 to 2000.
Sample answer: People produced more garbage overall, with plastics and other garbage (rubber, textiles, and wood) increasing the most.

***Math Journal 1*, p. 155**

2 Ongoing Learning & Practice

▶ Multiplying Fractions and Mixed Numbers

INDEPENDENT ACTIVITY

(*Math Journal 1,* p. 156)

Students practice multiplying fractions and mixed numbers.

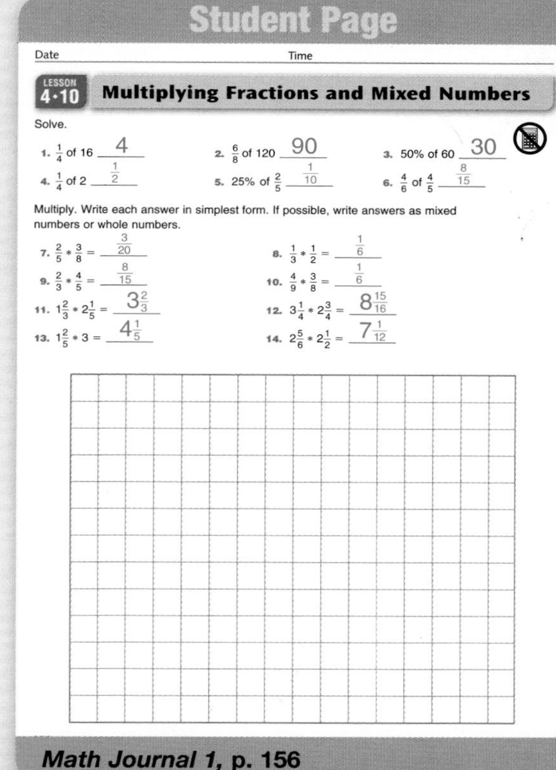

Student Page

Date Time

LESSON 4•10 **Multiplying Fractions and Mixed Numbers**

Solve.

1. $\frac{1}{4}$ of 16 4
2. $\frac{6}{8}$ of 120 90
3. 50% of 60 30
4. $\frac{1}{4}$ of 2 $\frac{1}{2}$
5. 25% of $\frac{2}{5}$ $\frac{1}{10}$
6. $\frac{4}{6}$ of $\frac{4}{5}$ $\frac{8}{15}$

Multiply. Write each answer in simplest form. If possible, write answers as mixed numbers or whole numbers.

7. $\frac{2}{5} * \frac{3}{8} = \frac{3}{20}$
8. $\frac{1}{3} * \frac{1}{2} = \frac{1}{6}$
9. $\frac{2}{3} * \frac{4}{5} = \frac{8}{15}$
10. $\frac{4}{9} * \frac{3}{8} = \frac{1}{6}$
11. $1\frac{2}{3} * 2\frac{1}{5} = 3\frac{2}{3}$
12. $3\frac{1}{4} * 2\frac{3}{4} = 8\frac{15}{16}$
13. $1\frac{2}{5} * 3 = 4\frac{1}{5}$
14. $2\frac{5}{6} * 2\frac{1}{2} = 7\frac{1}{12}$

Math Journal 1, p. 156

▶ Math Boxes 4•10

INDEPENDENT ACTIVITY

(*Math Journal 1,* p. 153)

Mixed Practice Math Boxes in this lesson are paired with Math Boxes in Lessons 4-6 and 4-8. The skill in Problem 5 previews Unit 5 content. Students will need a Geometry Template or a protractor to complete Problem 5.

▶ Study Link 4•10

INDEPENDENT ACTIVITY

(*Math Masters,* p. 137)

Home Connection Students estimate sector sizes of circle graphs.

3 Differentiation Options

READINESS

▶ Estimating and Measuring Sector Size

INDEPENDENT ACTIVITY

5–15 Min

(*Math Masters,* p. 138)

To provide prerequisite knowledge for creating circle graphs, have students estimate percents and fractions of a circle. Then have them use the Percent Circle of the Geometry Template to check their estimates.

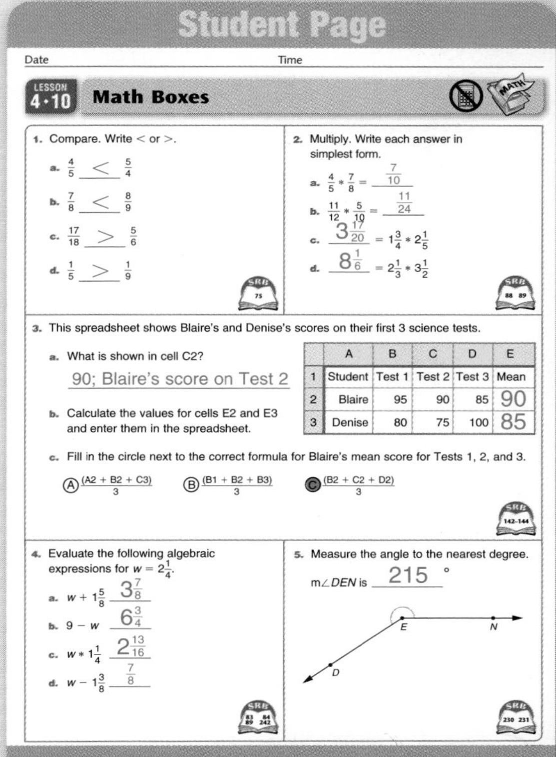

Student Page

Date Time

LESSON 4•10 **Math Boxes**

1. Compare. Write < or >.
   a. $\frac{4}{5} < \frac{5}{4}$
   b. $\frac{7}{8} < \frac{8}{9}$
   c. $\frac{17}{18} > \frac{5}{6}$
   d. $\frac{1}{5} > \frac{1}{9}$

SRB 75

2. Multiply. Write each answer in simplest form.
   a. $\frac{4}{5} * \frac{7}{8} = \frac{7}{10}$
   b. $\frac{11}{12} * \frac{5}{10} = \frac{11}{24}$
   c. $3\frac{17}{20} = 1\frac{3}{4} * 2\frac{1}{5}$
   d. $8\frac{1}{6} = 2\frac{1}{3} * 3\frac{1}{2}$

SRB 88 89

3. This spreadsheet shows Blaire's and Denise's scores on their first 3 science tests.
   a. What is shown in cell C2? 90; Blaire's score on Test 2
   b. Calculate the values for cells E2 and E3 and enter them in the spreadsheet.

	A	B	C	D	E
1	Student	Test 1	Test 2	Test 3	Mean
2	Blaire	95	90	85	90
3	Denise	80	75	100	85

   c. Fill in the circle next to the correct formula for Blaire's mean score for Tests 1, 2, and 3.

   (A) $\frac{(A2 + B2 + C3)}{3}$ (B) $\frac{(B1 + B2 + B3)}{3}$ (C) $\frac{(B2 + C2 + D2)}{3}$

SRB 142-144

4. Evaluate the following algebraic expressions for $w = 2\frac{1}{4}$.
   a. $w + 1\frac{5}{8}$ $3\frac{7}{8}$
   b. $9 - w$ $6\frac{3}{4}$
   c. $w * 1\frac{1}{4}$ $2\frac{13}{16}$
   d. $w - 1\frac{3}{8}$ $\frac{7}{8}$

SRB 83 89 84 242

5. Measure the angle to the nearest degree.

   m∠*DEN* is 215 °

SRB 230 231

Math Journal 1, p. 153

Study Link Master

Name Date Time

STUDY LINK 4•10 **Circle Graphs**

Use estimation to make a circle graph displaying the data in each problem. (*Hint:* For each percent, think of a simple fraction that is close to the value of the percent. Then estimate the size of the sector for each percent.) Remember to graph the smallest sector first.

1. According to the 2000 Census, 21.2% of the U.S. population was under the age of 15, 12.6% was age 65 or older, and 66.2% was between the ages of 15 and 64.

Age of U.S. Population

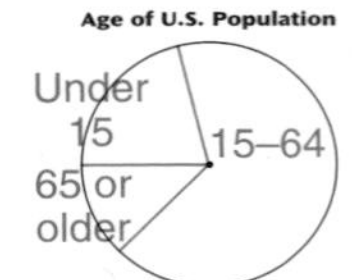

2. In 2004, NASA's total budget was $15.4 billion. 51% was spent on Science, Aeronautics, and Exploration. 48.8% was spent on Space Flight Capabilities, and 0.2% was spent on the Inspector General.

NASA Budget

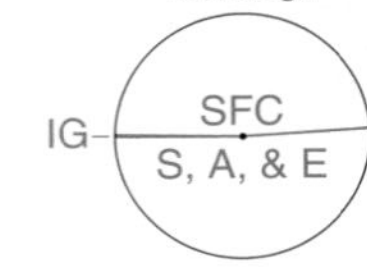

3. 98.3% of households in the United States have at least one television.

Households with TV

no TV

at least 1 TV

4. The projected school enrollment for the United States in 2009 is 72 million students. 23.2% will be in college, 22.9% will be in high school, and 53.9% will be in Grades Pre-K–8.

U.S. School Enrollment

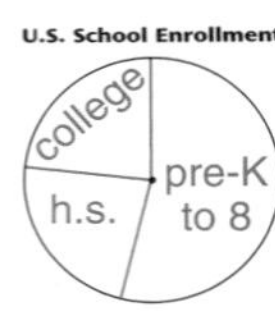

Math Masters, p. 137

ENRICHMENT

▶ Collecting and Comparing Survey Data

To further explore the uses of circle graphs, students conduct a survey. They think of a survey question to ask their classmates, collect the data, and use a spreadsheet or graphing program to generate a circle graph of the results. Students may consider surveying two different groups and creating separate circle graphs to compare and contrast. *Suggestions for survey questions:*

▷ How many siblings do you have?

▷ What is your main source for news about current events? (TV, radio, newspaper, Internet)

▷ What is your favorite sport? Favorite school subject?

EXTRA PRACTICE

SMALL-GROUP ACTIVITY

▶ *5-Minute Math*

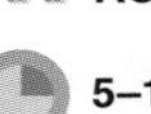

To offer more practice estimating products and percents of given numbers, see *5-Minute Math,* pages 103 and 179.

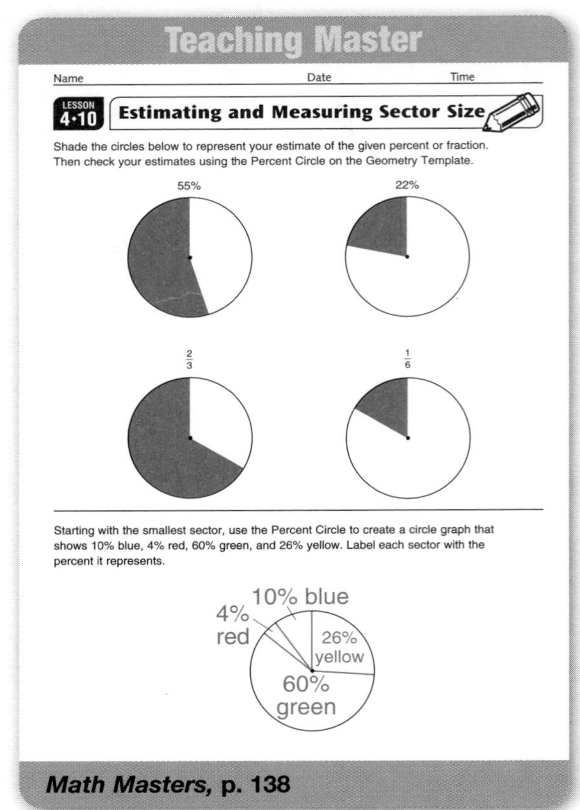

Teaching Master

Name Date Time

LESSON 4•10 **Estimating and Measuring Sector Size**

Shade the circles below to represent your estimate of the given percent or fraction. Then check your estimates using the Percent Circle on the Geometry Template.

55%

22%

$\frac{2}{3}$

$\frac{1}{6}$

Starting with the smallest sector, use the Percent Circle to create a circle graph that shows 10% blue, 4% red, 60% green, and 26% yellow. Label each sector with the percent it represents.

Math Masters, p. 138

4•11 Percent of a Number

Objective To review finding a percent of a number.

1 Teaching the Lesson

Key Activities

Students review finding a percent of a number and then solve number stories that involve finding percents of numbers.

Key Concepts and Skills

- Use a unit percent to calculate the percent of a number. [Number and Numeration Goal 2]
- Apply concept of GCF and divisibility rules to rename percents as fractions. [Number and Numeration Goal 3]
- Add and subtract multidigit numbers. [Operations and Computation Goal 1]
- Multiply a whole number by a fraction or a decimal. [Operations and Computation Goal 4]

Key Vocabulary

regular price • discount • sale price • interest

materials

- ☐ *Math Journal 1,* pp. 158 and 159
- ☐ *Student Reference Book,* pp. 49 and 50
- ☐ Study Link 4•10
- ☐ calculator

2 Ongoing Learning & Practice

Students practice using a division algorithm to rename fractions as percents.

Students practice and maintain skills through Math Boxes and Study Link activities.

Ongoing Assessment: Recognizing Student Achievement Use journal page 157. [Number and Numeration Goal 5]

materials

- ☐ *Math Journal 1,* pp. 157 and 160
- ☐ Study Link Master (*Math Masters,* p. 139)

3 Differentiation Options

READINESS

Students use a diagram to model and calculate fractional parts of a number.

ENRICHMENT

Students use a computer software program to generate a graph to display survey results.

ELL SUPPORT

Students use language development techniques.

materials

- ☐ *Math Journal 1,* p. 159
- ☐ Teaching Master (*Math Masters,* p. 140)
- ☐ computer/graphing software

Additional Information

If you have set up a Graphs Museum in your classroom, ask students to look in magazines and newspapers for graphs that display percents. Students who participate in the optional Enrichment activity may want to add the graphs they generate to the Graphs Museum.

Technology

Assessment Management System
Math Boxes, Problem 3
See the **iTLG.**

Getting Started

Mental Math and Reflexes

Students rename percents as fractions in simplest form. *Suggestions:*

●○○ 10%	$\frac{1}{10}$	●●○ 5%	$\frac{1}{20}$	●●● 45%	$\frac{9}{20}$
50%	$\frac{1}{2}$	20%	$\frac{1}{5}$	12.5%	$\frac{1}{8}$
25%	$\frac{1}{4}$	80%	$\frac{4}{5}$	66.7%	$\frac{2}{3}$

Math Message

Working with a partner, review the methods for finding a percent of a number on Student Reference Book, *pages 49 and 50. Use one of the methods to solve Problems 1 and 2 on journal page 158. Be prepared to explain why you prefer one method over another.*

Study Link 4·10 Follow-Up

Draw circles on the board for students to show their answers.

NOTE Consider using diagrams to support the presentation of vocabulary and concepts. Draw attention to how the size of the dollar sign ($) changes in each diagram.

Suggestions:

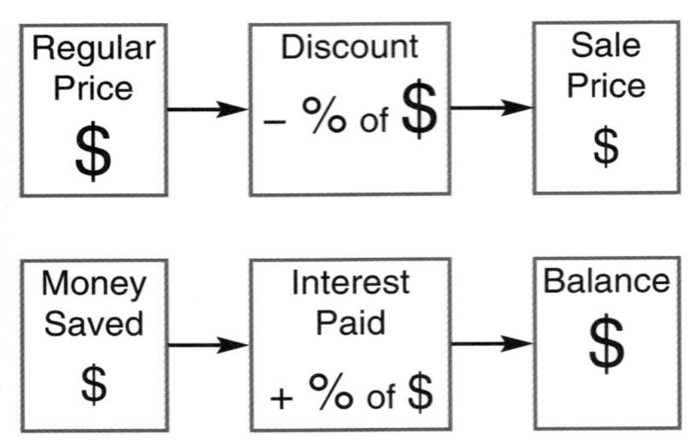

Student Page

Date Time

LESSON 4·11 **Percent Problems**

Math Message

A DVD that regularly costs $25 is on sale for 20% off.

1. What is the discount in dollars? $5.00
2. What is the sale price? $20.00

Solve Problems 3–5 using paper and pencil.

3. An electronic handheld game player that costs $120 is on sale for 25% off.
   a. What is the discount in dollars? $30.00
   b. What is the sale price? $90.00
4. A bank offers a simple interest rate of 6% per year.
   a. What is the interest on $100 at the end of 1 year? $6.00
   b. What is the interest on $500 at the end of 1 year? $30.00
   c. What is the interest on $1,000 at the end of 1 year? $60.00
5. The $2.50 price of a hot dog at a neighborhood baseball park is shared as follows:
   20% pays for the hot dog, bun, and fixings.
   20% pays the concession stand workers.
   10% is profit for the concession stand owner.
   10% pays for the electricity/fuel costs to cook and heat the hot dogs.
   40% pays for rental fees on the stand and cooking equipment.
   a. How much do the hot dog, bun, and fixings cost? $0.50
   b. How much goes to rental fees? $1.00
   c. How much does the concession stand owner get? $0.25

You may use a calculator to help you solve Problems 6–9.

6. A CD that regularly costs $14.95 is on sale for 20% off.
   a. What is the discount in dollars? $2.99
   b. What is the sale price? $11.96

***Math Journal 1*, p. 158**

1 Teaching the Lesson

▶ Math Message Follow-Up

WHOLE-CLASS ACTIVITY

(*Math Journal 1,* p. 158; *Student Reference Book,* pp. 49 and 50)

Consumer Education Link Briefly discuss the meaning of the following terms. To support English language learners, write the terms on the board along with examples. (*See margin.*)

▷ The **regular price** (sometimes called the list price) of an item is the price without a discount.

▷ The **discount** is the amount you save in dollars and cents.

▷ The **sale price** (or discounted price) is the amount you pay after subtracting the discount from the regular price.

▷ **Interest** is an amount paid for the use of someone's money.

Adjusting the Activity

ELL

Sketch diagrams on the board to show the relationship among the vocabulary terms. Present examples of how newspaper and magazine ads use these terms. Include these examples in your Fractions, Decimals, Percents Museum.

AUDITORY ◆ KINESTHETIC ◆ TACTILE ◆ VISUAL

Review students' solutions to the Math Message problems on journal page 158. Have volunteers summarize how to use the methods on pages 49 and 50 of the *Student Reference Book* to calculate sale price. Ask students which method they prefer for the situation described.

Use a Fraction

$20\% = \frac{1}{5}$, so 20% of \$15 is the same as $\frac{1}{5}$ of \$15.

$\frac{1}{5} * \$15 = \$3$, so 20% of \$15 is \$3.

Use Decimal Multiplication

$20\% = 0.20$, so 20% of \$15 is the same as $0.20 * \$15$.

$0.20 * \$15 = \$3$

Use a Unit Percent

$1\% = \frac{1}{100}$, so 1% of \$15 is the same as $\frac{1}{100}$ of \$15.

$\frac{1}{100} * \$15 = \$0.15$, so 20% of \$15 is $20 * \$0.15$, or \$3.

The discount is \$3. The sale price is $\$15 - \$3 = \$12$.

Emphasize that the preceding methods involve two steps—first finding the discount, or amount of money that is saved, and then subtracting the discount from the regular price to find the sale price. The following method can be used to calculate the sale price in one step.

Use a Part of the Whole

Because the discount is 20%, the sale price is 100% – 20%, or 80% of the regular price. Find 80% of \$15.

$80\% = \frac{4}{5}$, so 80% of \$15 is the same as $\frac{4}{5}$ of \$15.

$\frac{4}{5}$ of $\$15 = 4 * (\frac{1}{5} * \$15) = 4 * \$3 = \$12$

Links to the Future

Expect that students will be able to use a method to find the given percent of a number, but do not expect them to use the same method to solve problems in which the whole is unknown. (*For example:* 6% of *x* is 30.) Students will set up and use proportions to solve a variety of percent problems in Unit 8.

▶ Solving Percent Problems

PARTNER ACTIVITY

(*Math Journal 1,* pp. 158 and 159)

Students solve Problems 3–9. They should use a mental or paper-and-pencil strategy for Problems 3–5; they may use calculators to solve Problems 6–9.

Adjusting the Activity

Demonstrate a strategy that involves first calculating 10% of the number and then multiplying, dividing, adding, or subtracting accordingly.

Examples:

35% of 90 = (10% + 10% + 10% + 5%) of 90

= 9 + 9 + 9 + 4.5 = 31.5

40% of 2.50 = (50% – 10%) of 2.50

= 1.25 – 0.25 = 1.00

AUDITORY ♦ KINESTHETIC ♦ TACTILE ♦ VISUAL

Student Page

Date ______ Time ______

LESSON 4·11 **Percent Problems** *continued*

7. The table below shows the results of a science literacy test given to 1,574 adults in 2001. Round to the nearest whole number to find the number of people who correctly answered each question.

Question	Percent Correct	Number of People
How long does it take Earth to go around the Sun: One day, one month, or one year? *Answer:* One year	54%	850
True or false: Lasers work by focusing sound waves. *Answer:* false	45%	708
Which travels faster, light or sound? *Answer:* light	76%	1,196
True or false: The earliest humans lived at the same time as the dinosaurs. *Answer:* false	48%	756

Source: Science and Engineering Indicators—2002

8. In 1998, there were about 14.5 million high school students in the United States. The number of high school students is expected to increase about 7% between 1998 and 2010.

   a. About how many more high school students will there be in 2010? About 1 million

   b. About how many high school students will there be in all in 2010? About 15.5 million

Source: National Center for Education Statistics (NCES)

9. Suppose elementary school students make up about 15% of the U.S. population. About how many elementary school students would you expect to live in a town that has a population of 50,000? About 7,500 elementary school students

Math Journal 1, p. 159

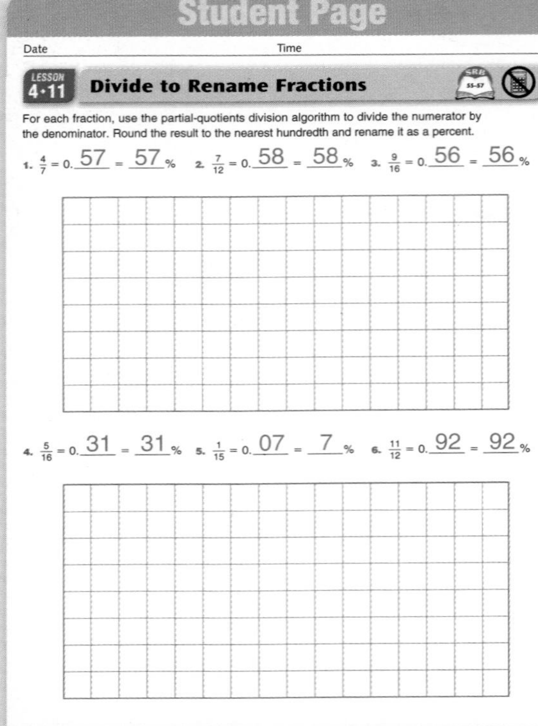
Student Page

Date Time

LESSON 4·11 **Divide to Rename Fractions**

For each fraction, use the partial-quotients division algorithm to divide the numerator by the denominator. Round the result to the nearest hundredth and rename it as a percent.

1. $\frac{4}{7}$ = 0.57 = 57%
2. $\frac{7}{12}$ = 0.58 = 58%
3. $\frac{9}{16}$ = 0.56 = 56%
4. $\frac{5}{16}$ = 0.31 = 31%
5. $\frac{1}{15}$ = 0.07 = 7%
6. $\frac{11}{12}$ = 0.92 = 92%

Math Journal 1, p. 160

2 Ongoing Learning & Practice

▶ Renaming Fractions as Decimals and Percents

INDEPENDENT ACTIVITY

(*Math Journal 1,* p. 160)

Students practice using the partial-quotients division algorithm to rename fractions as decimals and percents.

▶ Math Boxes 4·11

INDEPENDENT ACTIVITY

(*Math Journal 1,* p. 157)

Mixed Practice Math Boxes in this lesson are paired with Math Boxes in Lesson 4-9. The skill in Problem 6 previews Unit 5 content.

Ongoing Assessment: Recognizing Student Achievement

Math Boxes Problem 3 

Use **Math Boxes, Problem 3** to assess students' ability to convert between fractions, decimals, and percents. Students are making adequate progress if they can complete the table. Some students may be able to give the fraction equivalencies in simplest form.

[Number and Numeration Goal 5]

▶ Study Link 4·11

INDEPENDENT ACTIVITY

(*Math Masters,* p. 139)

Home Connection Students solve number stories similar to those in the lesson. They use survey results to complete tables involving percent number stories.

Student Page

Date Time

LESSON 4·11 **Math Boxes**

1. Write the following fractions in order from smallest to largest.

$\frac{1}{20}$ $\frac{6}{7}$ $\frac{9}{10}$ $\frac{1}{3}$ $\frac{5}{8}$

$\frac{1}{20}$ $\frac{1}{3}$ $\frac{5}{8}$ $\frac{6}{7}$ $\frac{9}{10}$

2. Which of the following percents is equivalent to $\frac{5}{6}$? Choose the best answer.

- ○ 5.6%
- ○ 57%
- ○ 8.3%
- ● 83%

3. Fill in the missing numbers.

Fraction	Decimal	Percent
$\frac{1}{5}$	0.2	20%
$\frac{5}{8}$	0.625	62.5%
$\frac{3}{5}$	0.6	60%
$\frac{9}{10}$	0.9	90%
$\frac{1}{20}$	0.05	5%

4. Complete.

a. $\frac{2}{5}$ of 75 = 30

b. $\frac{3}{8}$ of 24 = 9

c. $\frac{5}{6}$ of 48 = 40

d. $\frac{1}{2}$ of $2\frac{1}{2}$ = $1\frac{1}{4}$

e. $\frac{3}{12}$ of 32 = 8

5. Use the formula $i = \frac{c}{2.54}$ to convert centimeters to inches.

Evaluate the formula when c = 76.2.

$i = \frac{76.2}{2.54}$

76.2 cm = 30 in.

6. Find the measure of ∠R without measuring the angle.

m∠R is 60°

E A P R 125° 97° 78°

Math Journal 1, p. 157

3 Differentiation Options

READINESS

INDEPENDENT ACTIVITY

5–15 Min

▶ Modeling Fractional Parts of a Number

(*Math Masters,* p. 140)

To provide experience finding fractional parts of a number, give students a copy of *Math Masters,* page 140. After working through the example, have students use a diagram to solve "fraction of" number problems.

ENRICHMENT

INDEPENDENT ACTIVITY

30+ Min

▶ Taking a Survey and Interpreting Results

(*Math Journal 1,* p. 159)

Portfolio Ideas

Science Link Students further explore ways to collect, represent, and interpret data. Students ask a sample of adults the science questions in Problem 7 on journal page 159. They compare the results of their sample with the results in the original study. A side-by-side bar graph, generated with graphing software, would be an effective way to present such a comparison. Add the graphs that students generate to the Graphs Museum.

ELL SUPPORT

SMALL-GROUP ACTIVITY

5–15 Min

▶ Using Explanations to Support Language

To provide language support for finding the percent of a number, have students explain the following:

- two ways to find 25% of a number
- three ways to find 20% of a number

Require students to use examples in their explanations.

Study Link Master

Name Date Time

STUDY LINK 4•11 Percent Problems

SRB 49 50

The results of a survey about children's weekly allowances are shown at the right.

Amount of Allowance	Percent of Children
$0	30%
$1–$4	20%
$5	25%
$6 or more	25%

1. Lincoln School has about 500 students. Use the survey results to complete this table.

Amount of Allowance	Predicted Number of Students at Lincoln
$0	150 students
$1–$4	100 students
$5	125 students
$6 or more	125 students

2. The sixth grade at Lincoln has about 60 students. Use the survey results to complete this table.

Amount of Allowance	Predicted Number of Sixth-Grade Students at Lincoln
$0	18 students
$1–$4	12 students
$5	15 students
$6 or more	15 students

A rule of thumb for changing a number of meters to yards is to add the number of meters to 10% of the number of meters.

Examples: 5 m is about 5 + (10% of 5), or 5.5, yd.
10 m is about 10 + (10% of 10), or 11, yd.

3. Use this rule of thumb to estimate how many yards are in the following numbers of meters.
   a. 3 m is about 3 + (10% of 3), or 3.3, yd.
   b. 8 m is about 8 + (10% of 8), or 8.8, yd.
   c. 20 m is about 20 + (10% of 20), or 22, yd.

Math Masters, p. 139

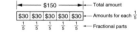

Teaching Master

Name Date Time

LESSON 4•11 Modeling Fractional Parts of a Number

SRB 87

You can use a diagram to model fractional parts of a number.

Example: Find $\frac{4}{5}$ of $150.

First, think about $150 being divided equally among 5 people.

$150 ← Total amount
| $30 | $30 | $30 | $30 | $30 | ← Amounts for each $\frac{1}{5}$
$\frac{1}{5}$ $\frac{1}{5}$ $\frac{1}{5}$ $\frac{1}{5}$ $\frac{1}{5}$ ← Fractional parts

One Way

$\frac{1}{5}$ of $150 = $30
$\frac{4}{5}$ of $150
= 4 ∗ ($\frac{1}{5}$ of $150)
= 4 ∗ $30 = $120
$\frac{4}{5}$ of $150 = $120

Another Way

$\frac{5}{5}$ of $150 = $150
$\frac{1}{5}$ of $150 = $30
$\frac{5}{5} - \frac{1}{5} = \frac{4}{5}$
$150 − $30 = $120

1. Use the diagram to find the amounts.

$30
| $2.50 | $2.50 | $2.50 | $2.50 | $2.50 | $2.50 | $2.50 | $2.50 | $2.50 | $2.50 | $2.50 | $2.50 |
$\frac{1}{12}$ (each)

$\frac{3}{12}$ of $30 = $7.50 $\frac{9}{12}$ of $30 = $22.50 $\frac{1}{3}$ of $30 = $10.00
$\frac{2}{3}$ of $30 = $20.00 $\frac{1}{6}$ of $30 = $5.00 $\frac{5}{12}$ of $30 = $12.50
$\frac{7}{12}$ of $30 = $17.50 $\frac{1}{4}$ of $30 = $7.50 $\frac{5}{6}$ of $30 = $25.00

2. Complete the diagram below. Then find the amounts.

$48
| $6 | $6 | $6 | $6 | $6 | $6 | $6 | $6 |
$\frac{1}{8}$ (each)

$\frac{1}{8}$ of $48 = $6.00 $\frac{7}{8}$ of $48 = $42.00 $\frac{3}{8}$ of $48 = $18.00
$\frac{1}{4}$ of $48 = $12.00 $\frac{1}{2}$ of $48 = $24.00 $\frac{3}{4}$ of $48 = $36.00

Math Masters, p. 140

Progress Check 4

Objective **To assess students' progress on mathematical content through the end of Unit 4.**

1 Assessing Progress

Progress Check 4 is a cumulative assessment of concepts and skills taught in Unit 4 and in previous units.

See the Appendix for a complete list of Grade 6 Goals.

materials

- ☐ Assessment Masters (*Assessment Handbook,* pp. 156–160)
- ☐ Study Link 4•11
- ☐ slate

CONTENT ASSESSED	LESSON(S)	ASSESSMENT ITEMS			
		SELF	ORAL/SLATE	WRITTEN	
				PART A	PART B
Find fractional parts of a region. Calculate the percent of a number. [Number and Numeration Goal 2]	4•6, 4•7, 4•10, 4•11	7	4	7a–c	8a–f
Convert between fractions, mixed numbers, decimals, and percents. Express equivalent fractions in simplest form. [Number and Numeration Goal 5]	4•1, 4•4, 4•8, 4•9	1–3		1a–d, 2a–h, 5, 6a–d	
Use signs of inequality to compare fractions; order fractions. [Number and Numeration Goal 6]	4•2	4	1, 3	3a–d	
Divide a decimal by a whole number. [Operations and Computation Goal 2]	4•5, 4•7				12
Add and subtract fractions and mixed numbers with unlike denominators. [Operations and Computation Goal 3]	4•3–4•5	5		4, 6a–d	10
Estimate and find products of fractions and mixed numbers. [Operations and Computation Goal 4]	4•6, 4•7	6	2	7a–c	10
Construct a circle graph from percents. [Data and Chance Goal 1]	4•10	8			9
Find the perimeter and area of a rectangle. [Measurement and Reference Frames Goal 2]	4•5, 4•7				10
Evaluate expressions involving exponents and integers. [Patterns, Functions, and Algebra Goal 3]	4•5, 4•9				11

2 Building Background for Unit 5

Math Boxes 4•12 previews and practices skills for Unit 5.

The **Unit 5 Family Letter** introduces families to Unit 5 topics and terms.

materials

- ☐ *Math Journal 1,* p. 161
- ☐ Geometry Template
- ☐ Study Link Masters (*Math Masters,* pp. 141–144)

Additional Information

See *Assessment Handbook,* pages 76–83 for additional assessment information. For assessment checklists, see pages 238–241.

Technology

Assessment Management System
Progress Check 4
See the **iTLG.**

Getting Started

Math Message • Self Assessment

Complete the Self Assessment (Assessment Handbook, *p. 156).*

Study Link 4·11 Follow-Up

Briefly review students' answers.

1 Assessing Progress

▶ Math Message Follow-Up

INDEPENDENT ACTIVITY

(Self Assessment, *Assessment Handbook,* p. 156)

The Self Assessment offers students the opportunity to reflect upon their progress.

▶ Oral and Slate Assessments

WHOLE-CLASS ACTIVITY

Problems 1–3 provide summative information and can be used for grading purposes. Problem 4 provides formative information that can be useful in planning future instruction.

Oral Assessment

1. Pose fraction addition problems. Students estimate the sum and say whether it is greater than or less than 1. Students describe the strategy they used to decide. *Suggestions:*
   - $\frac{1}{2} + \frac{3}{4} > 1$
   - $\frac{2}{3} + \frac{1}{4} < 1$
   - $\frac{7}{8} + \frac{1}{3} > 1$
   - $\frac{1}{10} + \frac{4}{5} < 1$
2. Students decide which product is larger and then explain how they know without actually solving the problems. *Suggestions:*
   - $\frac{4}{5} * \frac{1}{2}$ or $\frac{4}{5} * \frac{1}{4}$ $\frac{4}{5} * \frac{1}{2}$
   - $3 * \frac{9}{8}$ or $\frac{7}{8} * \frac{9}{8}$ $3 * \frac{9}{8}$
   - $10 * \frac{3}{5}$ or $10 * \frac{4}{5}$ $10 * \frac{4}{5}$
   - $\frac{1}{4} * \frac{1}{2}$ or $\frac{1}{4} * \frac{3}{4}$ $\frac{1}{4} * \frac{3}{4}$

Slate Assessment

3. Write groups of fractions on the board. Students list the fractions from smallest to largest on their slates. *Suggestions:*
   - $\frac{3}{6}, \frac{1}{8}, \frac{7}{13}, \frac{4}{16}, \frac{24}{25}$ — $\frac{1}{8}, \frac{4}{16}, \frac{3}{6}, \frac{7}{13}, \frac{24}{25}$
   - $\frac{1}{3}, \frac{1}{5}, \frac{3}{4}, \frac{10}{12}, \frac{1}{20}$ — $\frac{1}{20}, \frac{1}{5}, \frac{1}{3}, \frac{3}{4}, \frac{10}{12}$
4. Students calculate percents of numbers. *Suggestions:*
   - 10% of 50 5
   - 75% of 24 18
   - 1% of 200 2
   - 15% of 200 30
   - 5 % of 50 2.5
   - 25% of 24 6

Assessment Master

Name Date Time

LESSON 4·12 **Self Assessment** Progress Check 4

Think about each skill listed below. Assess your own progress by checking the most appropriate box.

Skills	I can do this on my own and explain how to do it.	I can do this on my own.	I can do this if I get help or look at an example.
1. Write fractions in simplest form.			
2. Convert between fractions and mixed numbers.			
3. Find equivalent fractions, mixed numbers, decimals, and percents.			
4. Compare fractions.			
5. Add or subtract fractions and mixed numbers with unlike denominators.			
6. Multiply fractions and mixed numbers.			
7. Find the percent of a number.			
8. Use the Percent Circle to make a circle graph.			

Assessment Handbook, **p. 156**

Assessment Master

Name Date Time

LESSON 4·12 **Written Assessment**

Part A

1. Write each of the following fractions in simplest form.

   a. $\frac{6}{8}$ $\frac{3}{4}$ b. $\frac{9}{12}$ $\frac{3}{4}$ c. $\frac{45}{100}$ $\frac{9}{20}$ d. $\frac{63}{108}$ $\frac{7}{12}$

2. Complete the table below. Simplify all fractions.

	Fraction	Decimal	Percent		Fraction	Decimal	Percent
a.	$\frac{9}{25}$	0.36	36%	e.	$\frac{97}{100}$	0.97	97%
b.	$\frac{22}{25}$	0.88	88%	f.	$\frac{3}{20}$	0.15	15%
c.	$\frac{1}{50}$	0.02	2%	g.	$\frac{13}{40}$	0.325	32.5%
d.	$\frac{3}{5}$	0.60	60%	h.	$1\frac{3}{5}$	1.60	160%

3. Compare using < or >.

   a. $\frac{1}{2} > \frac{4}{9}$ b. $2\frac{3}{8} < 2\frac{5}{12}$ c. $1\frac{1}{3} > \frac{7}{6}$ d. $3.57 < 3\frac{3}{5}$

4. When Monica began first grade, she was $45\frac{3}{4}$ in. tall. At the end of the year, she was $47\frac{3}{8}$ in. tall. How much had Monica grown? $1\frac{5}{8}$ in. (unit)

5. Evan uses a pencil to do his math work. He started the week with a new pencil, which measured 18.5 cm in length. At the end of 2 weeks, the pencil measured 10.8 cm in length. Find the difference between the 2 pencil lengths. Express your answer as a mixed number. $7\frac{7}{10}$ cm

6. Add. Write all answers greater than 1 as mixed numbers. Write all fractions in simplest form.

   a. $3\frac{5}{6} + 2\frac{1}{4} = 6\frac{1}{12}$ b. $2\frac{4}{5} + 1\frac{1}{3} = 4\frac{2}{15}$

   c. $2\frac{1}{8} + 1\frac{1}{6} + 1\frac{7}{8} = 5\frac{1}{6}$ d. $\frac{4}{9} + \frac{2}{3} = 1\frac{1}{9}$

30

Assessment Handbook, **p. 157**

Name ______ Date ______ Time ______

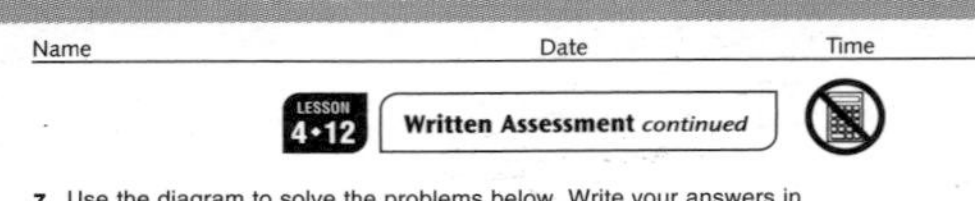

7. Use the diagram to solve the problems below. Write your answers in simplest form.

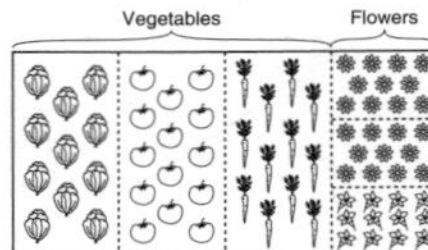

Mr. Dahli plants $\frac{3}{4}$ of his garden with vegetables and $\frac{1}{4}$ of it with flowers. He plants $\frac{2}{3}$ of the flower section with daisies and the rest of the flower section with lilies.

a. What fraction of the entire garden is lilies? $\frac{1}{12}$

b. Write a number model for the fraction of the entire garden that is daisies. $\frac{1}{4} * \frac{2}{3} = \frac{1}{6}$

c. Suppose Mr. Dahli's garden has an area of 1,408 ft². How many square feet are planted in vegetables? 1,056 ft²

Part B

8. Sixth graders were asked the following question: *If you could use only one of the following forms of entertainment, which would you choose?*

Complete the table below.

	Form of Entertainment	Number of Students	Percent of Students
a.	Computer with Internet access	120	25%
b.	TV or DVDs	168	35%
c.	Video games	96	20%
d.	Books or magazines	24	5%
e.	Music CDs	72	15%
f.	Total	480	100%

Assessment Handbook, p. 158

Assessment Master

Name ______ Date ______ Time ______

Written Assessment *continued*

9. Use the Percent Circle on the Geometry Template to make a circle graph of the data in Problem 8.

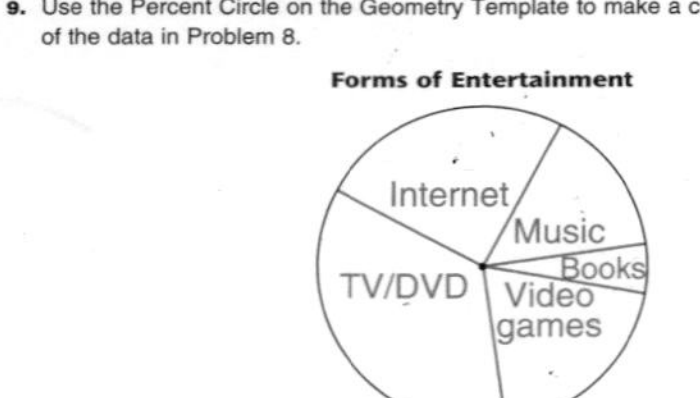

10. Find the perimeter and area of the rectangle shown below.

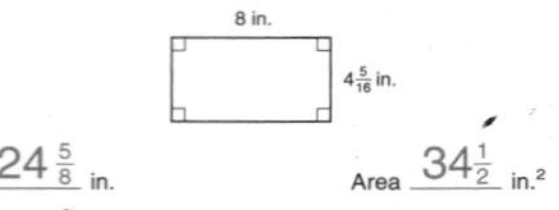

Perimeter $24\frac{5}{8}$ in. Area $34\frac{1}{2}$ in.²

11. Evaluate each expression when $x = 5$.

a. $0.0035 * 10^x$ 350 **b.** $2^x + 3^3$ 59

c. $-(x) + -18$ −23 **d.** $x^0 + -8$ −7

12. Estimate the quotient 928.8 ÷ 36. Then divide. Estimate Sample estimate: 30

36)928.8

928.8 ÷ 36 = 25.8

Assessment Handbook, p. 159

▶ Written Assessment

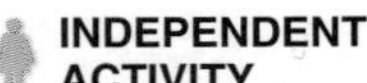

(*Assessment Handbook,* pp. 157–159)

Part A Recognizing Student Achievement

Problems 1–7 provide summative information and may be used for grading purposes.

Problem(s)	Description
1	Apply GCF to write fractions in simplest form.
2, 5	Convert between fractions, decimals, and percents.
3	Compare fractions with unlike denominators.
4, 6	Add and subtract fractions and mixed numbers with unlike denominators.
7	Use a diagram to find fractional parts of a region. Find products of fractions and mixed numbers.

Part B Informing Instruction

Problems 8–12 provide formative information that can be useful in planning future instruction.

Problem(s)	Description
8	Calculate the percent of a number.
9	Use the Percent Circle to construct a circle graph.
10	Find the perimeter and area of a rectangle.
11	Evaluate expressions involving exponents and integers.
12	Divide a decimal number by a whole number.

▶ Open Response

INDEPENDENT ACTIVITY

(*Assessment Handbook,* p. 160)

Making a Wooden Rack

The open-response item requires students to apply skills and concepts from Unit 4 to solve a multistep problem. See *Assessment Handbook,* pages 79–83 for rubrics and student work samples for this problem.

Assessment Master

Name Date Time

LESSON 4·12 **Open Response** Progress Check 4

Making a Wooden Rack

Patina is designing a wall-mounted wooden rack for hanging necklaces and belts. She has a strip of wood that is $17\frac{1}{2}$ inches long by $2\frac{3}{4}$ inches high.

She plans to drill 6 peg holes into this strip, each hole having a diameter of $\frac{7}{8}$ inch. She wants to position the holes so the distance between any two pegs (b) is the same. The space between each end of the rack and the first hole will also be the same (b).

What is the maximum distance between any two pegs?

Write an explanation of how you arrived at your answer. Describe each step in your solution clearly. Use the diagram below to help you.

See *Assessment Handbook* for sample answers and rubrics.

Assessment Handbook, p. 160

2 Building Background for Unit 5

▶ Math Boxes 4·12

INDEPENDENT ACTIVITY

(*Math Journal 1,* p. 161)

Mixed Practice This Math Boxes page previews Unit 5 content.

▶ Study Link 4·12: Unit 5 Family Letter

(*Math Masters,* pp. 141–144)

Home Connection The Unit 5 Family Letter provides parents and guardians with information and activities related to Unit 5 topics.

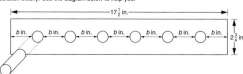

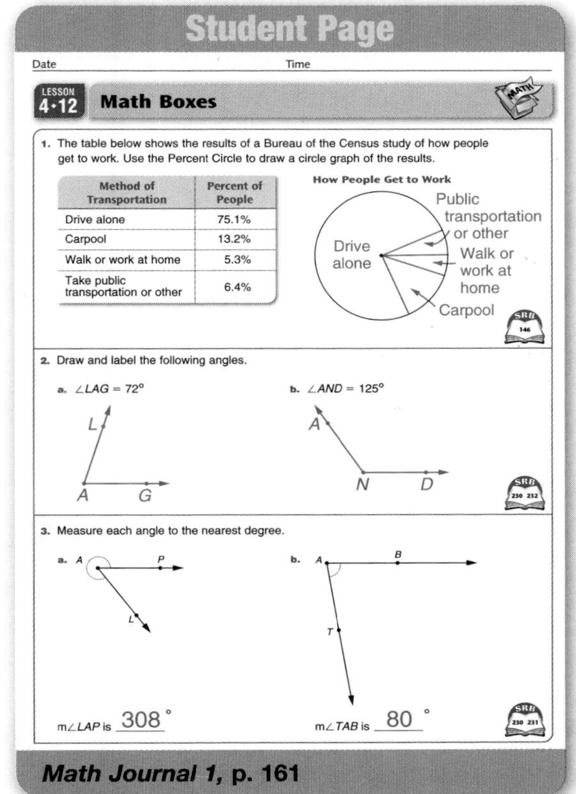

Student Page

Date Time

LESSON 4·12 **Math Boxes**

1. The table below shows the results of a Bureau of the Census study of how people get to work. Use the Percent Circle to draw a circle graph of the results.

Method of Transportation	Percent of People
Drive alone	75.1%
Carpool	13.2%
Walk or work at home	5.3%
Take public transportation or other	6.4%

2. Draw and label the following angles.

a. $\angle LAG = 72°$

b. $\angle AND = 125°$

3. Measure each angle to the nearest degree.

a. m$\angle LAP$ is 308 °

b. m$\angle TAB$ is 80 °

Math Journal 1, p. 161

Study Link Masters

Name Date Time

STUDY LINK 4·12 **Unit 5: Family Letter**

Geometry: Congruence, Constructions, and Parallel Lines

In *Fourth* and *Fifth Grade Everyday Mathematics,* students used a compass and straightedge to construct basic shapes and create geometric designs. In Unit 5 of *Sixth Grade Everyday Mathematics,* students will review some basic construction techniques and then devise their own methods for copying triangles and quadrilaterals and for constructing parallelograms. The term *congruent* will be applied to their copies of line segments, angles, and 2-dimensional figures. Two figures are congruent if they have the *same size* and the *same shape.*

Another approach to congruent figures in Unit 5 is through isometry transformations. These are rigid motions that take a figure from one place to another while preserving its size and shape. Reflections (flips), translations (slides), and rotations (turns) are basic isometry transformations (also known as rigid motions). A figure produced by an isometry transformation (the image) is congruent to the original figure (the preimage).

Students will continue to work with the Geometry Template, a tool that was introduced in *Fifth Grade Everyday Mathematics.* The Geometry Template contains protractors and rulers for measuring and cutouts for drawing geometric figures. Students will review how to measure and draw angles using the full-circle and half-circle protractors.

If the measure of any one angle is given, the measures of all the others can be found without measuring.

Students will also use a protractor to construct circle graphs that represent data collections. This involves converting the data to percents of a total, finding the corresponding degree measures around a circle, and drawing sectors of the appropriate size.

Measures often can be determined without use of a measuring tool. Students will apply properties of angles and sums of angles to find unknown measures in figures similar to those at the right.

The sum of the angles in a triangle is 180°. Angles *a* and *b* have the same measure, 70°.

One lesson in Unit 5 is a review and extension of work with the coordinate grid. Students will plot and name points on a 4-quadrant coordinate grid and use the grid for further study of geometric shapes.

Please keep this Family Letter for reference as your child works through Unit 5.

Math Masters, pp. 141–144

Unit 5 Organizer

Geometry: Congruence, Constructions, and Parallel Lines

Overview

Unit 5 serves as a transition to the geometry taught in seventh and eighth grades. More attention is given to notation conventions, the application of geometric properties, and the natural connections between geometry and algebra. Unit 5 has five main areas of focus:

- To classify and draw angles,
- To estimate the measure of angles with and without tools,
- To find angle measures and write equations by applying properties of orientations of angles and sums of angle measures in triangles and quadrangles,
- To identify and describe congruent figures; and to construct congruent figures using compass and straightedge, and
- To identify, describe, and sketch instances of reflections, translations, and rotations on a coordinate plane.

Contents

Unit 5 Organizer

Learning In Perspective

	Lesson Objectives	Links to the Past	Links to the Future
5•1	To provide practice in classifying angles by size; and to measure and draw angles with a protractor.	In Grade 4, students define acute, obtuse, straight, and reflex angles. In Grade 5, students identify types of angles. They use protractors to draw and measure angles.	In Unit 8, students explore relationships among the angle measures of similar figures. After Grade 6: Applications and maintenance.
5•2	To find angle measures by reasoning with angle definitions and with sums of angle measures in triangles and quadrangles.	In Grade 5, students measure and find the sums of angles in a polygon. They prove the sum of the interior angle measures of any triangle is 180°.	In Unit 10, students use interior angle measures of polygons to determine whether a figure will tessellate. After Grade 6, students use trigonometric relationships to determine angle measures.
5•3	To introduce how to calculate degree measures of sectors; and to use a protractor to draw circle graphs.	In Grade 5, students use a percent circle to draw and interpret circle graphs.	In Unit 8, students convert percents to degrees on circle graphs.
5•4	To plot ordered number pairs; to apply properties of polygons; and to explore the relationship between endpoints and midpoints.	In Grade 5, students locate, plot, and read ordered pairs on a coordinate grid. They classify and sort polygons.	Grade 6: Applications and maintenance. After Grade 6, students use Cartesian coordinates and polar systems to analyze geometric situations.
5•5	To review transformations that produce another figure while maintaining the same size and shape of the original figure.	In Grade 5, students transform ordered number pairs and explore the resulting transformations of geometric figures. They explore regular tessellations.	In Unit 10, students create tessellations. After Grade 6, students represent isometry transformations in the plane by using coordinates, vectors, function rotation, and matrices.
5•6	To explore the meaning of congruence; and to use drawing tools to construct congruent figures.	In Grade 5, students define congruent figures and construct congruent triangles using a compass and a straightedge.	In Unit 8, students explore the properties of similar figures. After Grade 6, students apply axioms and theorems about congruent and similar figures to solve problems.
5•7	To construct figures with a compass and a straightedge.	In Grades 4 and 5, students construct line segments, angles, and various polygons using a compass and straightedge.	In Unit 8, students construct a Golden Rectangle. After Grade 6, students construct representations of 2- and 3-dimensional geometric objects using a variety of tools.
5•8	To copy angles and construct perpendicular bisectors; and to solve construction problems.	In Grade 5, students copy angles and triangles using various tools.	In Unit 8, students construct a Golden Rectangle. After Grade 6, students construct representations of 2- and 3-dimensional geometric objects using a variety of tools.
5•9	To explore and apply angle relationships.	In Grade 5, students define vertical (opposite) and adjacent angles. They measure angles formed by intersecting lines and explore the relationships between their measures.	Grade 6 and after: Applications and maintenance.
5•10	To introduce the relationships between angles of parallelograms; and to construct a parallelogram using a compass and a straightedge.	In Grade 4, students review properties of parallelograms. In Grade 5, students apply properties of sums of angle measures in triangles and quadrangles.	Grade 6: Applications and maintenance. After Grade 6, students apply axioms and theorems about parallel lines to solve problems.

Key Concepts and Skills

	Key Concepts and Skills	Grade 6 Goals*
5•1	Subtract multidigit whole numbers.	Operations and Computation Goal 1
	Use appropriate strategies to draw and measure angles to the nearest degree.	Measurement and Reference Frames Goal 1
	Identify and classify angles according to size.	Geometry Goal 1
5•2	Add and subtract multidigit whole numbers.	Operations and Computation Goal 1
	Measure angles to the nearest degree.	Measurement and Reference Frames Goal 1
	Use appropriate notation to name angles.	Geometry Goal 1
	Determine angle measures by applying definitions and properties of angles, triangles, and quadrangles.	Geometry Goal 1
5•3	Apply place-value concepts to round decimals to the nearest whole number.	Number and Numeration Goal 1
	Recognize and use equivalent names for fractions, decimals, and percents.	Number and Numeration Goal 5
	Use appropriate strategies to construct circle graphs.	Data and Chance Goal 1
	Draw and measure angles to the nearest degree.	Measurement and Reference Frames Goal 1
5•4	Add integers.	Operations and Computation Goal 1
	Find the mean of two signed numbers.	Data and Chance Goal 2
	Plot, name, and label points in any four quadrants of a coordinate grid.	Measurement and Reference Frames Goal 3
	Extend a pattern to create a rule.	Patterns, Functions, and Algebra Goal 1
5•5	Plot, name, and label points in any of the four quadrants of a coordinate grid.	Measurement and Reference Frames Goal 3
	Identify congruent figures.	Geometry Goal 2
	Practice and perform isometry transformations with geometric figures.	Geometry Goal 3
	Classify a rotation by the number of degrees needed to produce a given image.	Geometry Goal 3
5•6	Identify congruent figures.	Geometry Goal 2
	Use a straightedge and compass to construct a figure that is congruent to the original.	Geometry Goal 2
	Apply the knowledge that a preimage and its image are congruent.	Geometry Goal 3
5•7	Use appropriate strategies to measure angles to the nearest degree.	Measurement and Reference Frames Goal 1
	Label the points and vertices of a preimage and its image.	Measurement and Reference Frames Goal 3
	Use a straightedge and compass to construct a figure that is congruent to the original.	Geometry Goal 2
5•8	Label the points and vertices of a preimage and its image.	Measurement and Reference Frames Goal 3
	Apply the properties of perpendicular lines to draw, identify, and classify right angles.	Geometry Goal 1
	Use appropriate tools to construct congruent figures.	Geometry Goal 2
	Apply the knowledge that a preimage and its image are congruent.	Geometry Goal 3
5•9	Add and subtract multidigit whole numbers.	Operations and Computation Goal 1
	Determine angle measures by applying definitions and properties of angles, triangles, and quadrangles.	Geometry Goal 1
	Identify congruent figures.	Geometry Goal 2
4•10	Add and subtract multidigit whole numbers.	Operations and Computation Goal 1
	Determine angle measures by applying definitions and properties of angles, triangles, and quadrangles.	Geometry Goal 1
	Use appropriate tools to construct congruent figures.	Geometry Goal 2
	Apply the knowledge that a preimage and its image are congruent.	Geometry Goal 3
	Write and evaluate algebraic expressions.	Patterns, Functions, and Algebra Goal 1

* See the Appendix for a complete list of Grade 6 Goals.

Ongoing Learning and Practice

Math Boxes

Math Boxes are paired across lessons as shown in the brackets below. This makes them useful as assessment tools. Math Boxes also preview content of the next unit.

Mixed practice	[5•1, 5•3], [5•2, 5•4], [5•5, 5•7], [5•6, 5•9], [5•8, 5•10]
Mixed practice with multiple choice	5•3, 5•4, 5•7, 5•9, 5•10
Mixed practice with writing/reasoning opportunity	5•1, 5•2, 5•5, 5•6, 5•8

Practice through Games

Games are an essential component of practice in the *Everyday Mathematics* program. Games offer skills practice and promote strategic thinking.

Lesson	Game	Skill Practiced
5•1, 5•2	*Angle Tangle*	**Estimating and measuring the size of angles** Measurement and Reference Frames Goal 1
5•4	*Spoon Scramble*	**Identifying equivalent expressions involving fractions** Number and Numeration Goal 5
5•4	*X and O—Tic-Tac-Toe*	**Reviewing ordered number pairs and finding their location on a four-quadrant coordinate grid** Measurement and Reference Frames Goal 3
5•7	*2-4-8* or *3-6-9 Frac-Tac-Toe* (Decimal Versions)	**Renaming fractions to decimals** Number and Numeration Goal 5
5•8	*Polygon Capture*	**Identifying properties of polygons** Geometry Goal 2
5•10	*3-D Shape Sort*	**Identifying properties of 3-D shapes** Geometry Goal 2

See the *Differentiation Handbook* for ways to adapt games to meet students' needs.

Home Communication

Study Links provide homework and home communication.

◀ ***Home Connection Handbook*** provides more ideas to communicate effectively with parents.

Unit 5 Family Letter provides families with an overview, Do-Anytime Activities, Building Skills Through Games, and a list of vocabulary.

Problem Solving

Encourage students to use a variety of strategies to solve problems and to explain those strategies. Strategies students might use in this unit:

- Using estimation
- Using a coordinate grid
- Using logical reasoning
- Drawing and using pictures and graphs

Lessons that teach *through* problem solving, not just *about* problem solving

Lesson	Activity
5•1	Play *Angle Tangle* to estimate and measure angle size.
5•2, 5•9 5•10	Find the measures of angles by applying angle orientations, relationships, and logical reasoning.
5•3	Use a circle graph to display given data.
5•4	Plot ordered number pairs to explore properties of polygons and midpoints of line segments.
5•5	Translate, reflect, and rotate geometric figures in all four quadrants of a coordinate grid.
5•6	Use appropriate tools to make an accurate drawing from a rough sketch.
5•7, 5•8 5•10	Use appropriate tools to construct line segments, bisectors, parallel lines, and polygons.

See Chapter 18 in the *Teacher's Reference Manual* for more information about problem solving.

Planning Tips

Pacing

Pacing depends on a number of factors, such as students' individual needs and how long your school has been using *Everyday Mathematics*. At the beginning of Unit 5, review your *Content by Strand* Poster to help you set a monthly pace.

DECEMBER	JANUARY (← MOST CLASSROOMS →)	FEBRUARY

NCTM Standards

Unit 5 Lessons	5•1	5•2	5•3	5•4	5•5	5•6	5•7	5•8	5•9	5•10	5•11
NCTM Standards	1, 3, 4, 8–10	3, 4, 6–10	7, 8, 10	3, 4, 6–10	3, 4, 6–8, 10	3, 7, 8, 10	3, 8–10	3, 8–10	1, 3, 6–10	3, 6–10	6–10

Content Standards: 1 Number and Operations, **2** Algebra, **3** Geometry, **4** Measurement, **5** Data Analysis and Probability
Process Standards: 6 Problem Solving, **7** Reasoning and Proof, **8** Communication, **9** Connections, **10** Representation

Balanced Assessment

Ongoing Assessment

Recognizing Student Achievement

Opportunities to assess students' progress toward Grade 6 Goals:

Lesson	Content Assessed
5◆1	Use a half-circle protractor to measure an angle. [Measurement and Reference Frames Goal 1]
5◆2	Name, label and measure angles. [Measurement and Reference Frames Goal 1; Geometry Goal 1]
5◆3	Apply the definitions of supplementary and vertical angles to find angle measures. [Geometry Goal 1]
5◆4	Use a strategy for solving problems involving percents and discounts. [Number and Numeration Goal 2]
5◆5	Name ordered number pairs in the third quadrant of a coordinate grid. [Measurement and Reference Frames Goal 3]
5◆6	Rotate a figure and name points on a coordinate grid. [Geometry Goal 3]
5◆7	Convert between fractions and decimals. [Number and Numeration Goal 5]
5◆8	Add, subtract, and multiply fractions and mixed numbers. [Operations and Computation Goals 3 and 4]
5◆9	Determine angle measures by applying properties of orientation of angles and sums of angle measures in triangles and quadrangles. [Geometry Goal 1]
5◆10	Calculate the degree measures of the sectors of a circle graph. Use a protractor to draw the sectors. [Number and Numeration Goal 2; Measurement and Reference Frames Goal 1]

Use the **Assessment Management System** to collect and analyze data about students' progress throughout the year.

Informing Instruction

To anticipate common student errors and to highlight problem-solving strategies:

Lesson 5◆2 Use mnemonic devices to recall definitions and properties of angles

Lesson 5◆4 Understand the order in which coordinates are given

Lesson 5◆7 Use appropriate tools to construct figures and to check constructions

Lesson 5◆9 Extend parallel lines to about the same length

Periodic Assessment

5•11 Progress Check 5

CONTENT ASSESSED	ASSESSMENT ITEMS Self	Oral/Slate	Written	Open Response
Rename fractions as decimals and percents. Calculate the percent of a number. [Number and Numeration Goal 2]	✔	✔	✔	
Find sums of whole and signed numbers. [Operations and Computation Goal 1]		✔	✔	✔
Estimate and find sums, differences, and products of fractions and mixed numbers. [Operations and Computation Goals 3–5]	✔		✔	
Use a protractor to construct a circle graph. [Data and Chance Goal 1]	✔		✔	
Measure/draw angles to the nearest degree using a protractor. [Measurement, Reference Frames Goal 1]			✔	
Plot ordered number pairs in four quadrants. Use ordered pairs to name points. [Measurement and Reference Frames Goal 3]			✔	
Classify angles. Apply properties of supplementary and vertical angles; of angles formed by two parallel lines and a transversal; of sums and angle measures of triangles and quadrangles. [Geometry Goal 1]	✔	✔	✔	✔
Use a compass and straightedge to construct geometric and congruent figures. [Geometry Goal 2]	✔		✔	
Perform isometry transformations on a coordinate grid. [Geometry Goal 3]	✔		✔	

Portfolio Opportunities

Opportunities to gather samples of students' mathematical writings, drawings, and creations to add balance to the assessment process:

- Converting fractions to decimals, **Lesson 5•1**
- Constructing a hexagon according to a set of specifications, **Lesson 5•1**
- Determining the sum of interior angle measures without using a protractor, **Lesson 5•2**
- Applying the inverse relationship between multiplication and division, **Lesson 5•5**
- Identifying rotations that produce the same image, **Lesson 5•6**
- Using pentominoes to explore isometry transformations and congruence, **Lesson 5•6**
- Using angle relationships to determine missing angle measures in a figure, **Lesson 5•8**

Assessment Handbook

Unit 5 Assessment Support

- Grade 6 Goals, pp. 37–50
- Unit 5 Assessment Overview, pp. 84–91
- Unit 5 Open Response
  - Detailed rubric, p. 88
  - Sample student responses pp. 89–91

Unit 5 Assessment Masters

- Unit 5 Self Assessment, p. 161
- Unit 5 Written Assessment, pp. 162–164
- Unit 5 Open Response, p. 165
- Unit 5 Class Checklist, pp. 244, 245, and 275
- Quarterly Checklist: Quarter 2, pp. 268 and 269
- Mid-Year Assessment, pp. 203–210
- Unit 5 Individual Profile of Progress, pp. 242, 243, and 274
- Exit Slip, p. 283
- Math Logs, pp. 278–280
- Other Student Assessment Forms, pp. 276, 277, and 281

Unit 5 Organizer

Differentiated Instruction

Daily Lesson Support

ENGLISH LANGUAGE LEARNERS

- **5•5** Building a Math Word Bank
- **5•9** Supporting language with drawings
- **5•10** Creating graphic organizers to support language

EXTRA PRACTICE

- **5•2** Writing custom-made Math Boxes
- **5•7** Making congruent shapes
- **5•8** Constructing perpendicular bisectors

5-Minute Math

- **5•1** Classifying and estimating angles
- **5•6** Describing polygons and other shapes

READINESS

- **5•1** Modeling and classifying angles
- **5•2** Finding sums of angle measures in triangles and quadrangles
- **5•3** Finding fractions of 360°
- **5•4** Plotting ordered number pairs
- **5•5** Reviewing degrees and directions of rotation
- **5•6** Sorting quadrangles
- **5•7** Anchoring and rotating a compass
- **5•8** Bisecting an angle
- **5•10** Reviewing quadrangle relationships

ENRICHMENT

- **5•1** Constructing a hexagon
- **5•2** Constructing a five-pointed star
- **5•3** Finding sums of angles in polygons
- **5•4** Plotting vertices in four quadrants
- **5•5** Performing a scaling transformation
- **5•6** Exploring isometry transformations
- **5•7** Constructing an octagon
- **5•8** Inscribing a circle in a triangle
- **5•9** Determining missing angle measures
- **5•9** Finding examples of linear perspective
- **5•10** Using quadrangles to classify quadrangles

Adjusting the Activity

- **5•1** Reviewing the definitions of *right* **ELL**
- **5•1** Providing tips for using protractors
- **5•2** Naming and sketching angles **ELL**
- **5•4** Using a ladder metaphor
- **5•5** Identifying locations on a grid
- **5•5** Using a mirror to see the reversal of points on a reflected image
- **5•5** Manually rotating a figure
- **5•6** Identifying pairs of corresponding sides and angles
- **5•7** Using alternative ways to construct line segments and triangles
- **5•9** Recalling the definition of *parallel*
- **5•10** Discussing *consecutive* **ELL**
- **5•10** Extending the sides and diagonals of a parallelogram

AUDITORY • KINESTHETIC • TACTILE • VISUAL

Cross-Curricular Links

Language Arts
Lesson 5•5 Students learn the etymology of *isometry.*

Art
Lesson 5•9 Students find examples of linear perspective in comics and sketches.

Using the Projects

Use Project 7, Paper-Throwing Experiments, during or after Unit 5 to give students an opportunity to apply data analysis and geometry skills. See the *Differentiation Handbook* for modifications to Project 7.

Differentiation Handbook

See the *Differentiation Handbook* for materials on Unit 5.

Language Support

Everyday Mathematics provides lesson-specific suggestions to help all students, including non-native English speakers, to acquire, process, and express mathematical ideas.

Connecting Math and Literacy

Pigs on the Ball, by Amy Axelrod, Simon & Schuster Books, 1998
The Greedy Triangle, by Marilyn Burns, Scholastic, Inc., 1994
Sir Cumference and the Great Knight of Angleland, by Cindy Neuschwander, Charlesbridge, 2001

Student Reference Book

pp. 59, 60, 147, 160, 163, 166, 169, 178, 180, 181, 188–190, 193–200, 233, 234, 306, 314–316, 330, 333, 335, and 372

Multiage Classroom ◆ Companion Lessons

Companion Lessons from Grade 5 can help you meet instructional needs of a multiage classroom. The full Scope and Sequence can be found in the Appendix.

Unit 5 Vocabulary

accurate drawing
acute angle
adjacent angles
anchor (of a compass)
axis
bisect
compass-and-straightedge construction
concentric circles
congruent
consecutive angles
coordinate
corresponding (sides, angles)
image
inscribed
isometry transformation
line of reflection
midpoint
obtuse angle
ordered number pair
origin
parallel line segments
parallel lines
perpendicular
perpendicular bisector
preimage
rectangular coordinate grid
reflection (flip)
reflex angle
right angle
rotation (turn)
rough sketch
sector
skew
straight angle
supplementary angles
transformation
translation (slide)
transversal
vertex (of an angle)
vertical (opposite) angles

Grade 5	3◆3	3◆3–3◆5	3◆4	9◆1–9◆3		3◆6	3◆5	3◆5		9◆5–9◆6	
Grade 6	**5◆1**	**5◆2**	**5◆3**	**5◆4**	**5◆5**	**5◆6**	**5◆7**	**5◆8**	**5◆9**	**5◆10**	**5◆11**

Professional Development

Teacher's Reference Manual Links

Lesson	Topic	Section
5◆1, 5◆3	Angles: Drawing and Measuring	3.2.5, 13.4.1, 14.7
	Degree Measures of Sectors of Circle Graphs	14.11.2
5◆1, 5◆2, 5◆9, 5◆10	Reasoning with Angle Measures	13.4.2
	Parallel Lines and Angle Relationships	13.6.1 13.6.3
5◆4	Coordinate Geometry	13.9
5◆5	Isometry Transformations	13.7
	Congruence	13.6.2
5◆7	Congruent Figures	13.6.2
5◆7, 5◆8	Constructions: Tools and Techniques	3.2.4 13.13.1

Unit 5 Organizer

Materials

Lesson	Masters	Manipulative Kit Items	Other Items
5◆1	Game Master, p. 426 Study Link Master, p. 145 Teaching Masters, pp. 146 and 147	Geometry Template straws connectors	protractor
5◆2	Study Link 5◆1 Study Link Master, p. 148 Game Master, p. 426 Teaching Masters, pp. 149–151 Teaching Aid Master, p. 405	Geometry Template	scissors; tape or glue; protractor
5◆3	Study Link 5◆2 transparencies of *Math Masters,* pp. 152 and 153* Study Link Master, p. 154 Teaching Masters, pp. 155 and 156	compass Geometry Template calculator	scissors; tape; board compass and protractor (for demonstration purposes); colored pencils or markers; protractor
5◆4	Study Link 5◆3 transparency of *Math Masters,* p. 417* Study Link Master, p. 157 Teaching Masters, pp. 158 and 159 Teaching Aid Master, p. 417	per group: 4 each of number cards 0–10	per group: 3 spoons; 3" x 5" index cards*; per group: straightedge
5◆5	Study Link 5◆4 Teaching Aid Master, p. 404 Study Link Master, p. 160 Teaching Masters, pp. 161 and 162	transparent mirror Geometry Template per student: 1 trapezoid pattern block compass	tracing paper*; protractor; inch ruler
5◆6	Study Link 5◆5 transparency of Study Link 5◆5* Study Link Master, p. 163 Teaching Masters, pp. 164 and 165 Teaching Aid Master, p. 418	compass Geometry Template	ruler; board compass and protractor (for demonstration purposes); tracing paper*; metric ruler; scissors; tape/glue; 5 square tiles; protractor; large sheets of paper
5◆7	Study Link 5◆6 Study Link Master, p. 166 Teaching Aid Masters, p. 404 and 419 Game Masters, pp. 439–441 Teaching Masters, pp. 167 and 168	compass Geometry Template per group: 4 each of number cards 0–10	straightedge; ruler; tape; 2-color counters or pennies; scissors; per group: 2 geoboards with rubber bands, or dot paper; protractor; board compass and meterstick (for demonstration purposes)
5◆8	Study Link 5◆7 Study Link Master, p. 169 Game Masters, pp. 470 and 471 Teaching Masters, pp. 170 and 171	Geometry Template compass	straightedge; ruler; scissors; tape; protractor; board compass and meterstick (for demonstration purposes)
5◆9	Study Link 5◆8 transparency of Study Link 5◆8* Study Link Master, p. 172 Teaching Master, p. 173	compass	straightedge; ruler
5◆10	Study Link 5◆9 Study Link Master, p. 174 Game Masters, p. 476 and 477 Teaching Masters, pp. 164 and 175	compass calculator	protractor; straightedge; ruler; board compass and meter stick (for demonstration purposes); 11" × 17" paper; scissors
5◆11	Study Link 5◆10 Assessment Masters, pp. 161–165 Study Link Masters, pp. 176–179	slate compass	straightedge; protractor

* Denotes optional materials

Technology

Assessment Management System, Unit 5
iTLG, Unit 5

Mathematical Background

The discussion below highlights the major content ideas presented in Unit 5 and helps establish instructional priorities.

Tools for Measuring and Drawing

(Lessons 5◆1 and 5◆6–5◆10)

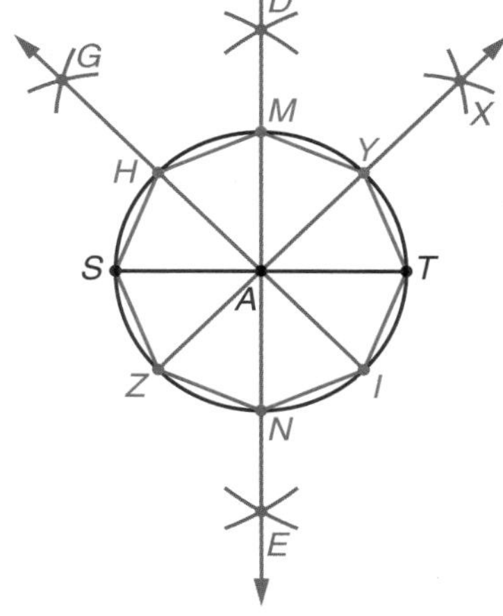

Euclidean geometry and all of the classical Greek geometries were developed without measuring tools—rulers and protractors were never used. Present-day school geometry, on the other hand, is based on assumptions that make crucial use of both drawing and measuring tools.

In *Everyday Mathematics,* students use a variety of tools, such as the shapes on the Geometry Template for tracing figures, a straightedge for drawing straight lines, a ruler for measuring line segments, and a protractor for measuring and drawing angles. In Lesson 5-1, students measure angles between 0° and 360° with a full-circle protractor, and measure and draw angles whose measures are between 0° and 180° with a half-circle protractor.

In Lessons 5-6 through 5-8, drawing and measuring tools are used to explore properties of congruent polygons. In Lesson 5-6, students use any tools they wish to make congruent copies of triangles and quadrilaterals. In Lessons 5-7 and 5-8, students are limited to a compass and a straightedge; measuring tools are not permitted. (If a rule is used to serve as a straightedge, it may *not* be used for measuring.) First, students review two basic compass-and-straightedge constructions—copying a line segment and copying an angle. Then they devise their own methods for copying triangles and quadrilaterals. In Lessons 5-9 and 5-10, compass-and-straightedge constructions are used to explore the properties of parallel lines and parallelograms.

You may need to demonstrate some of these constructions at the board, using a board compass and straightedge, or you may want to use an overhead projector. Remind students that they are to use the straightedge only for drawing straight lines, *not for measuring.*

See Section 3.2.4 and 3.2.5 of the *Teacher's Reference Manual* for more information about geometry and measuring tools.

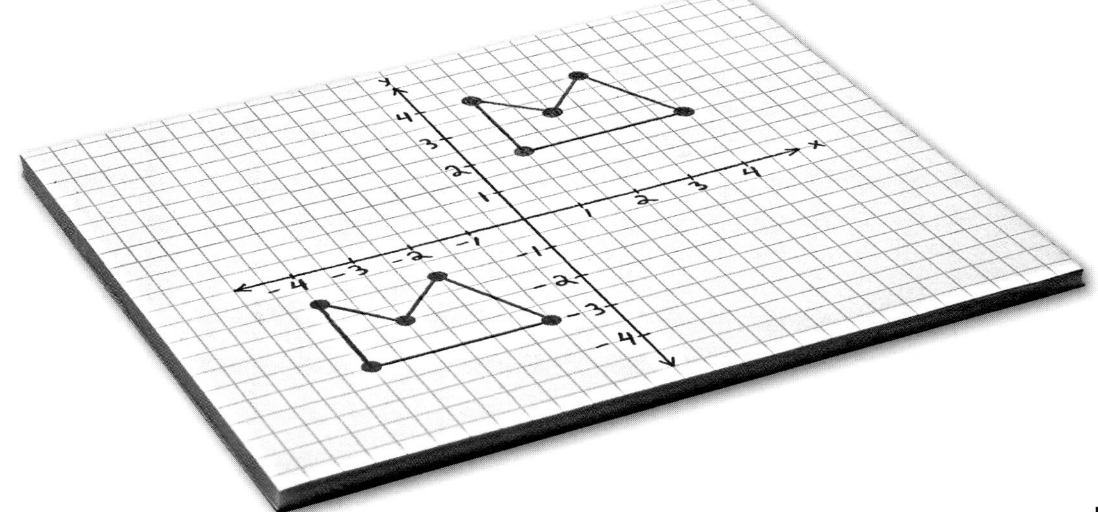

Making Circle Graphs with a Protractor (Lesson 5◆3)

Since drawing a circle graph with a protractor is a fairly complicated task, students have used the Percent Circle on the Geometry Template to construct circle graphs. In this lesson, students rename fractions and multiply fractions or decimals by 360 to calculate the degree measures of sectors. They then use a protractor to construct circle graphs.

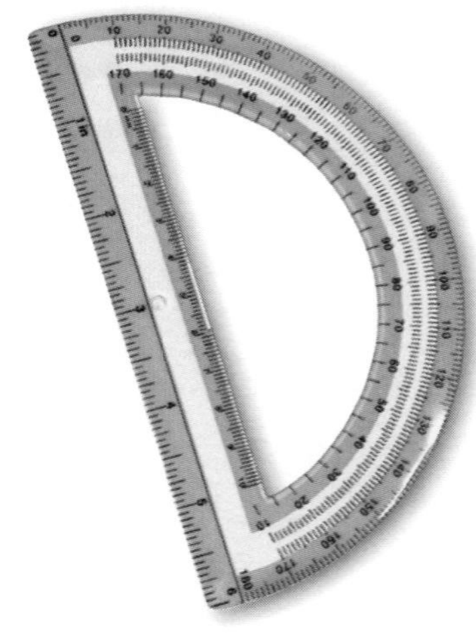

Section 14.11.2 of the *Teacher's Reference Manual* gives more information about protractors and the Percent Circle.

Coordinate Geometry (Lesson 5◆4)

In *Fourth Grade Everyday Mathematics,* students used coordinates and grid lines to locate places and regions on a map. They were also introduced to the coordinate grid system of latitude and longitude.

In *Fifth Grade Everyday Mathematics,* students practiced plotting and reading ordered number pairs in the first quadrant of a rectangular coordinate system. Negative and fractional coordinates, as well as whole-number coordinates, were explored.

In Lesson 5-4, students review coordinate geometry skills and investigate the relationship between the coordinates of the endpoints and midpoint of line segments. In Lesson 5-5, they graph geometric figures in all four quadrants.

To learn more about coordinate geometry, see Section 13.9 of the *Teacher's Reference Manual.*

Isometry Transformations and Congruence (Lessons 5◆5–5◆8)

Lesson 5-5 is a review of isometry transformations—motions that take a figure from one place to another while preserving the size and shape of the figure. Translations (slides), reflections (flips), and rotations (turns) are basic isometry transformations. Isometry transformations are also known as rigid transformations.

In *Sixth Grade Everyday Mathematics,* students explore rigid transformations within the four quadrants of a rectangular coordinate system.

Lessons 5-5 through 5-8 focus on congruent figures. Two figures that are exactly the same size and shape are congruent. A translation image is always congruent to its preimage.

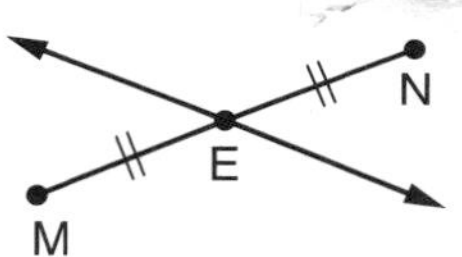

On an intuitive level, congruent figures can be thought of as copies made by tracing, constructing, or measuring. On a formal level, two polygons are said to be congruent if all pairs of corresponding sides are the same length and all pairs of corresponding angles have equal degree measures. Hence, to say that two triangles are congruent implies six independent congruencies—three for paired sides and three for paired angles. For congruent quadrangles (quadrilaterals), there are eight congruencies—four paired sides and four paired angles.

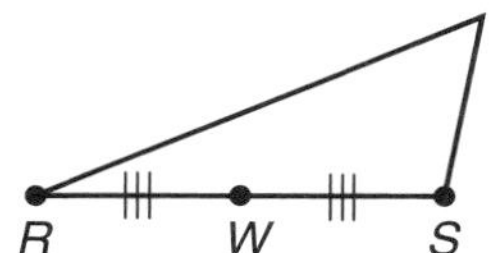

The classic congruence theorems of plane geometry for triangles state that congruence can be determined by examining three of the six congruencies. For example, the side-side-side theorem (also known as SSS) states that two triangles are congruent if pairs of corresponding sides are congruent. If all three pairs of corresponding sides of a triangle are known to be congruent, there is no need to examine the congruencies of their corresponding angles. While these congruence theorems are not presented explicitly in these lessons, they are implicit in one construction activity in which students copy a triangle by copying its sides.

For more about isometry transformations and congruence, see the *Teacher's Reference Manual,* Sections 13.6 and 13.7.

Properties of Parallel Lines and Parallelograms (Lesson 5◆9 and 5◆10)

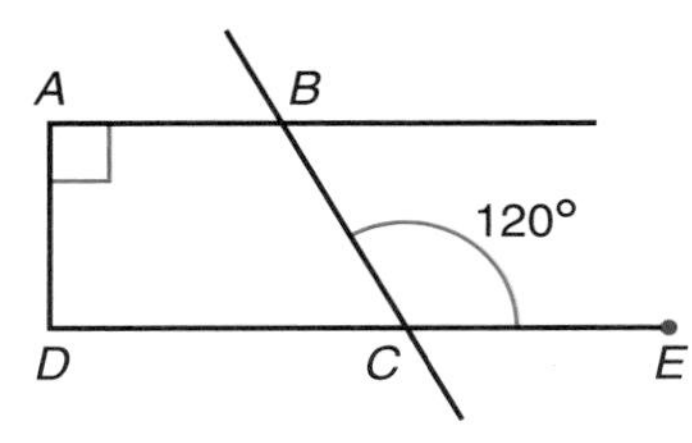

In Lesson 5-9, students explore the relationships between angles formed by two parallel lines and a transversal. In Lesson 5-10, they apply these relationships by exploring the properties of the angles of parallelograms.

More information about parallel lines and parallelograms can be found in the *Teacher's Reference Manual,* Section 13.6.1.

5·1 Measuring and Drawing Angles

Objectives To provide practice in classifying angles by size; and to measure and draw angles with a protractor.

1 Teaching the Lesson

Key Activities

Students use full-circle and half-circle protractors to measure angles, and a half-circle protractor to draw angles. They also practice estimating and finding the measures of angles by playing *Angle Tangle.*

Key Concepts and Skills

- Subtract multidigit whole numbers.
  [Operations and Computation Goal 1]
- Use appropriate strategies to draw and measure angles to the nearest degree.
  [Measurement and Reference Frames Goal 1]
- Identify and classify angles according to size.
  [Geometry Goal 1]

Key Vocabulary

right angle • straight angle • acute angle • obtuse angle • reflex angle • vertex (of an angle)

materials

- ☐ *Math Journal 1,* pp. 162 and 163
- ☐ *Student Reference Book,* pp. 160 and 306
- ☐ Game Master (*Math Masters,* p. 426)
- ☐ Geometry Template/protractor

2 Ongoing Learning & Practice

Students solve *percent of* problems.

Students practice and maintain skills through Math Boxes and Study Link activities.

Ongoing Assessment: Recognizing Student Achievement Use journal page 165.
[Measurement and Reference Frames Goal 1]

materials

- ☐ *Math Journal 1,* pp. 164 and 165
- ☐ Study Link Master (*Math Masters,* p. 145)
- ☐ Geometry Template/protractor

3 Differentiation Options

READINESS

Students make a circular protractor and use it to classify angles and to form angles of given measures.

ENRICHMENT

Students construct a hexagon according to a set of specifications.

EXTRA PRACTICE

Students practice classifying angles and estimating angle measures.

materials

- ☐ *Student Reference Book,* p. 160
- ☐ Teaching Masters (*Math Masters,* pp. 146 and 147)
- ☐ *5-Minute Math,* pp. 59, 142, 143, and 222–225
- ☐ Geometry Template
- ☐ straws; connectors

See **Advance Preparation**

Additional Information

Advance Preparation For the optional Readiness activity in Part 3, students will need full-length, $\frac{3}{4}$-length, and $\frac{1}{2}$-length straws. Make one copy of *Math Masters,* page 146 for every two students.

Technology

Assessment Management System
Math Boxes, Problem 1
See the **iTLG.**

Getting Started

Mental Math and Reflexes

Students mentally solve problems such as the following. If time permits, have a volunteer share her or his strategy.

Suggestions:

●○○ 90 − 47 43
180 − 119 61

●●○ 360 − 109 251
360 − 89 271

●●● 180 − (62 + 75) 43

Math Message

Do Problems 1–5 on journal page 162. Use page 160 of the Student Reference Book *to check your answers.*

1 Teaching the Lesson

▶ Math Message Follow-Up

WHOLE-CLASS DISCUSSION

(*Math Journal 1,* p. 162; *Student Reference Book,* p. 160)

Briefly go over the answers. Remind students of the angle symbol (∠) and that angles are usually measured in degrees (°). Have students find different types of angles in the classroom.

Also remind students that a 90° angle is a **right angle.** A small square marked in the corner of an angle indicates a right angle. Mention that a 180° angle is a **straight angle** because the two sides (rays) of the angle form a straight line.

Adjusting the Activity

ELL

To support English language learners, review the everyday meaning of *right* and then contrast that meaning to the one used here to classify angles. For example, students should not interpret right angles as correct angles. Left angles do not exist.

AUDITORY ◆ KINESTHETIC ◆ TACTILE ◆ VISUAL

▶ Measuring and Drawing Angles

PARTNER ACTIVITY

(*Math Journal 1,* pp. 162 and 163)

Ask students to identify the full-circle and half-circle protractors on the Geometry Template. Remind them of the following facts. To support English language learners, write the important ideas on the board.

▷ Before measuring an angle, classify the angle as **acute,** right, **obtuse,** straight, or **reflex.** Then use the classification to check the reasonableness of the measurement.

Student Page

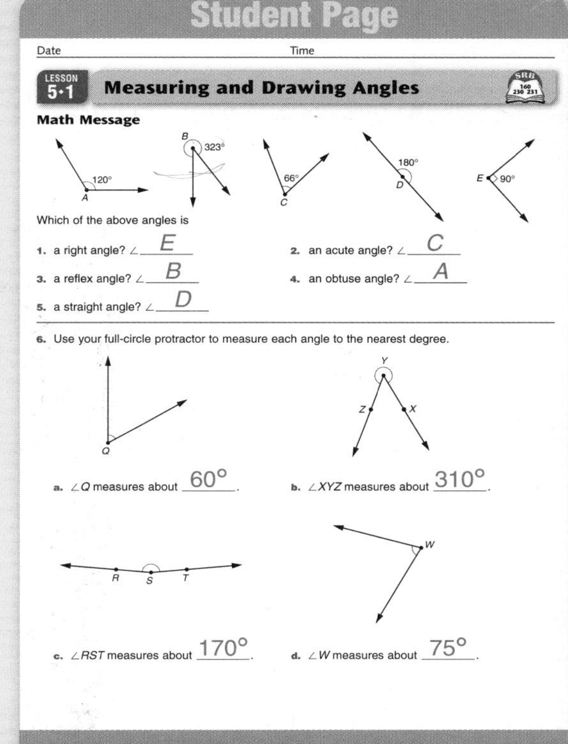

Math Journal 1, p. 162

360
323
37

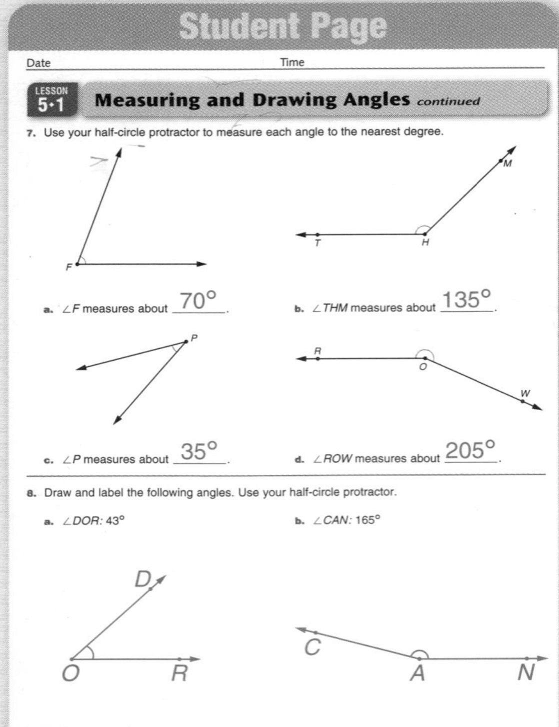

Student Page

Date Time

LESSON 5·1 **Measuring and Drawing Angles** *continued*

7. Use your half-circle protractor to measure each angle to the nearest degree.

a. ∠F measures about 70°.

b. ∠THM measures about 135°.

c. ∠P measures about 35°.

d. ∠ROW measures about 205°.

8. Draw and label the following angles. Use your half-circle protractor.

a. ∠DOR: 43°

b. ∠CAN: 165°

Math Journal 1, p. 163

NOTE Students are asked to use the full-circle protractor to complete Problem 6 and the half-circle protractor to complete Problem 7. It is important that they practice with each type of protractor. Because the sides of angle *P* in Problem 7c do not reach the edge of the half-circle protractor, students will have to extend the sides to measure the angle.

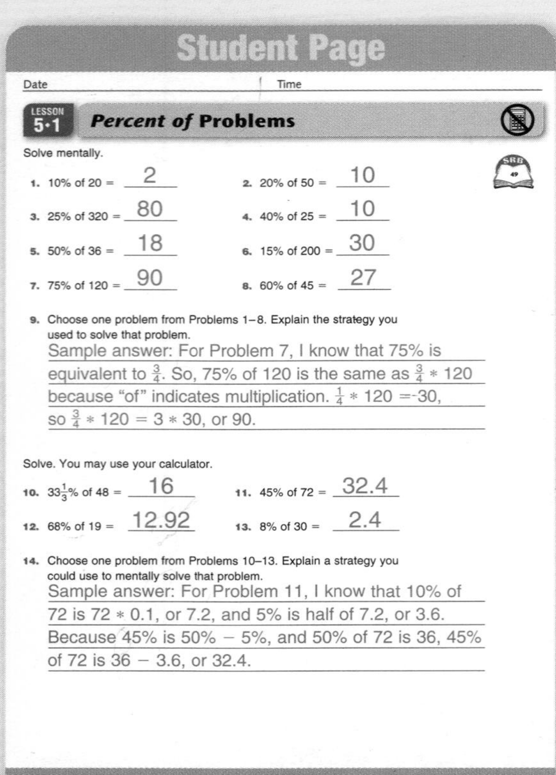

Student Page

Date Time

LESSON 5·1 ***Percent of* Problems**

Solve mentally.

1. 10% of 20 = 2
2. 20% of 50 = 10
3. 25% of 320 = 80
4. 40% of 25 = 10
5. 50% of 36 = 18
6. 15% of 200 = 30
7. 75% of 120 = 90
8. 60% of 45 = 27

9. Choose one problem from Problems 1–8. Explain the strategy you used to solve that problem.
Sample answer: For Problem 7, I know that 75% is equivalent to $\frac{3}{4}$. So, 75% of 120 is the same as $\frac{3}{4} * 120$ because "of" indicates multiplication. $\frac{1}{4} * 120 = 30$, so $\frac{3}{4} * 120 = 3 * 30$, or 90.

Solve. You may use your calculator.

10. $33\frac{1}{3}$% of 48 = 16
11. 45% of 72 = 32.4
12. 68% of 19 = 12.92
13. 8% of 30 = 2.4

14. Choose one problem from Problems 10–13. Explain a strategy you could use to mentally solve that problem.
Sample answer: For Problem 11, I know that 10% of 72 is 72 ∗ 0.1, or 7.2, and 5% is half of 7.2, or 3.6. Because 45% is 50% − 5%, and 50% of 72 is 36, 45% of 72 is 36 − 3.6, or 32.4.

Math Journal 1, p. 164

▷ Measurements are approximations. Always measure carefully, but understand that a measurement obtained with a protractor, ruler, or other measuring device does not give the exact size of the object being measured.

▷ The half-circle protractor on the Geometry Template can be used to measure and draw angles. The full-circle protractor can be used to measure angles but not to draw them, because there are no openings on the template to mark the angle.

▷ To draw a reflex angle, draw an angle whose measure is 360° minus the intended measure of the reflex angle.

▷ An angle can be named by a single capital letter, which also names the **vertex** of the angle, or with three capital letters—the first letter names a point (not the vertex) on one side of the angle, the middle letter names the vertex of the angle, and the third letter names a point (not the vertex) on the other side. Students will see in later lessons that angles may also be named by a single letter (usually lowercase) that does not name the vertex of the angle.

Adjusting the Activity

Provide tips for using each type of protractor. *Suggestions:*

1. To use the full-circle protractor, imagine that the angle is on a clock face. The 0° line should line up with the side of the angle that would point to the smaller clock-face number.
2. To use the half-circle protractor, first estimate whether the angle is more or less than 90°. Then imagine the angle as a fan that is opening up from the 0° line. Read the scale (inside or outside) that matches the direction in which the angle opens.

AUDITORY ◆ KINESTHETIC ◆ TACTILE ◆ VISUAL

Assign the problems on journal pages 162 and 163.

When reviewing the answers, select at least one measuring problem and one drawing problem and ask students to demonstrate their methods for solving both types.

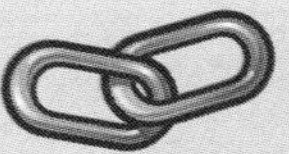

Links to the Future

The activities in this lesson will prepare students for drawing circle graphs using protractors in Lesson 5-3.

▶ Playing *Angle Tangle*

PARTNER ACTIVITY

(*Student Reference Book,* p. 306; *Math Masters,* p. 426)

Angle Tangle provides practice in estimating and finding the measures of angles. Provide each partnership with a game record sheet (*Math Masters,* p. 426). Review the directions on page 306 of the *Student Reference Book* as a class.

2 Ongoing Learning & Practice

▶ Solving *Percent of* Problems

INDEPENDENT ACTIVITY

(*Math Journal 1,* p. 164)

The problems on journal page 164 provide practice with finding a percent of a number. Students will use this skill in Lesson 5-3 to make circle graphs using protractors.

▶ Math Boxes 5•1

INDEPENDENT ACTIVITY

(*Math Journal 1,* p. 165)

Mixed Practice Math Boxes in this lesson are paired with Math Boxes in Lesson 5-3. The skills in Problems 5 and 6 preview Unit 6 content.

Portfolio Ideas

Writing/Reasoning Have students write a response to the following: *Explain how to convert each fraction in Problem 4c to a decimal.* Sample answer: Find equivalent fractions with denominators of 100 and then use a power-of-10 strategy to place the decimal point.

Ongoing Assessment: Recognizing Student Achievement

Math Boxes Problem 1

Use **Math Boxes, Problem 1** to assess students' ability to use a half-circle protractor to measure an angle. Students are making adequate progress if they are able to measure the angle within ± 2°. Some students may be able to make an estimate that is very close to the actual measurement.

[Measurement and Reference Frames Goal 1]

▶ Study Link 5•1

INDEPENDENT ACTIVITY

(*Math Masters,* p. 145)

Home Connection Students measure and classify angles. They find the sum of the measures of the angles of a triangle and of a quadrangle. Remind students that they will need their Geometry Template or a protractor to complete the assignment.

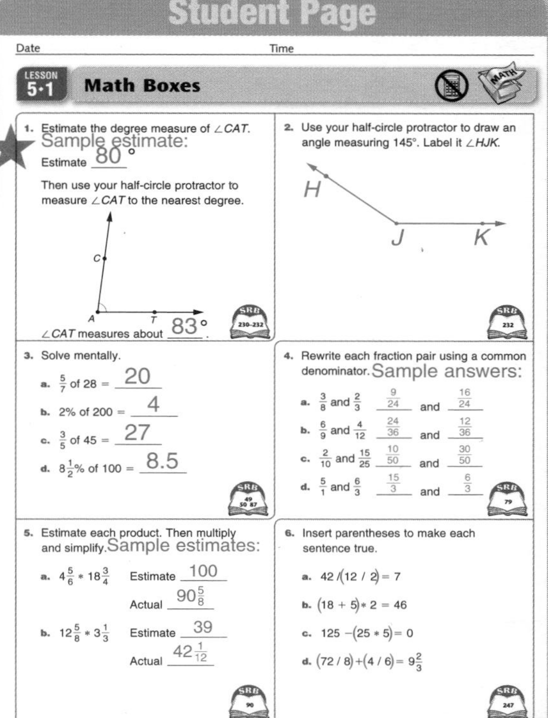

Student Page

Date Time

LESSON 5•1 **Math Boxes**

1. Estimate the degree measure of ∠*CAT*. Sample estimate: Estimate 80 °
Then use your half-circle protractor to measure ∠*CAT* to the nearest degree.
∠*CAT* measures about 83 °

2. Use your half-circle protractor to draw an angle measuring 145°. Label it ∠*HJK*.

3. Solve mentally.
a. $\frac{5}{7}$ of 28 = 20
b. 2% of 200 = 4
c. $\frac{3}{5}$ of 45 = 27
d. $8\frac{1}{2}$% of 100 = 8.5

4. Rewrite each fraction pair using a common denominator. Sample answers:
a. $\frac{3}{8}$ and $\frac{2}{3}$ — $\frac{9}{24}$ and $\frac{16}{24}$
b. $\frac{6}{9}$ and $\frac{4}{12}$ — $\frac{24}{36}$ and $\frac{12}{36}$
c. $\frac{2}{10}$ and $\frac{15}{25}$ — $\frac{10}{50}$ and $\frac{30}{50}$
d. $\frac{5}{1}$ and $\frac{6}{3}$ — $\frac{15}{3}$ and $\frac{6}{3}$

5. Estimate each product. Then multiply and simplify. Sample estimates:
a. $4\frac{5}{6} * 18\frac{3}{4}$ Estimate 100 Actual $90\frac{5}{8}$
b. $12\frac{5}{8} * 3\frac{1}{3}$ Estimate 39 Actual $42\frac{1}{12}$

6. Insert parentheses to make each sentence true.
a. 42 /(12 / 2) = 7
b. (18 + 5) * 2 = 46
c. 125 −(25 * 5) = 0
d. (72 / 8) + (4 / 6) = $9\frac{2}{3}$

Math Journal 1, p. 165

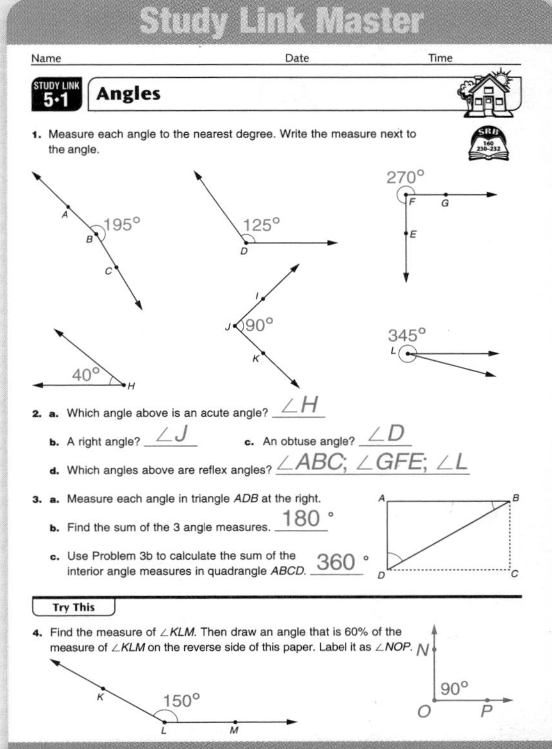

Study Link Master

Name Date Time

STUDY LINK 5•1 **Angles**

1. Measure each angle to the nearest degree. Write the measure next to the angle.
195° 125° 270° 90° 345° 40°

2. a. Which angle above is an acute angle? ∠H
b. A right angle? ∠J c. An obtuse angle? ∠D
d. Which angles above are reflex angles? ∠ABC; ∠GFE; ∠L

3. a. Measure each angle in triangle *ADB* at the right.
b. Find the sum of the 3 angle measures. 180 °
c. Use Problem 3b to calculate the sum of the interior angle measures in quadrangle *ABCD*. 360 °

Try This

4. Find the measure of ∠*KLM*. Then draw an angle that is 60% of the measure of ∠*KLM* on the reverse side of this paper. Label it as ∠*NOP*.
150° 90°

Math Masters, p. 145

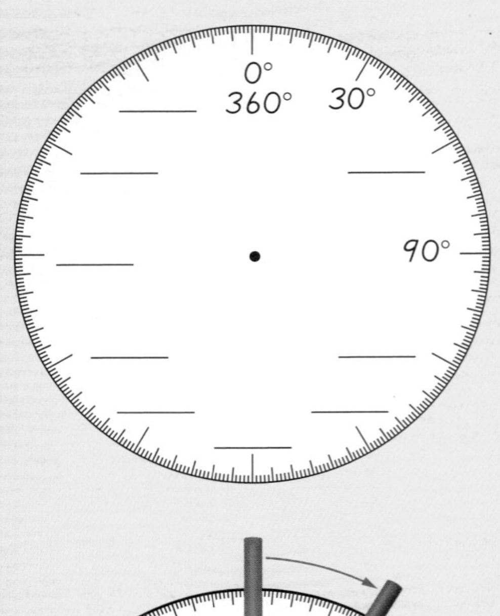

Teaching Master

Name ______ Date ______ Time ______

LESSON 5·1 **Constructing a Hexagon**

Follow the directions below to draw hexagon *ABCDEF*. Line segment *AF* at the bottom of the page is one of the sides of the hexagon. The completed drawing should be a convex hexagon. Use your Geometry Template and a pencil with a sharp point.

1. Draw a 130° angle with its vertex at point *A*. One side of the angle is $\overline{AF}$. Draw a point on the other side that is 5 centimeters from point *A*. Label this point *B*.

   B 5 cm 130° A F

2. Draw a 115° angle with its vertex at point *B*. One side of the angle is $\overline{AB}$. Draw a point on the other side that is $1\frac{1}{2}$ inches from point *B*. Label it point *C*.
3. Draw a 145° angle with its vertex at point *C*. One side of the angle is $\overline{BC}$. Draw a point on the other side that is 6.5 centimeters from point *C*. Label it point *D*.
4. Draw a 90° angle with its vertex at point *D*. One side of the angle is $\overline{CD}$. Draw a point on the other side that is $2\frac{3}{4}$ inches from point *D*. Label it point *E*. Then draw $\overline{EF}$ to complete the hexagon.
5. What is the measure of ∠*E*? 120°
   of ∠*F*? 120°
6. What is the length of $\overline{EF}$ to the nearest $\frac{1}{8}$ inch? 2 in.
7. What is the sum of the measures of the angles of your hexagon? 720°

The closer this sum is to 720°, the more accurate your drawing is.

D C E B A F

Math Masters, p. 147

3 Differentiation Options

READINESS

5–15 Min

▶ Modeling and Classifying Angles

(*Student Reference Book,* p. 160; *Math Masters,* p. 146)

To provide practice modeling and classifying angles, have students record degree measures on an angle measurer (*Math Masters,* p. 146), beginning at the 12-o'clock position with 0°/360° and listing multiples of 30° until they have filled all write-on lines. Then have them position straw-and-connector angles on the labeled measurer and model acute, right, obtuse, straight, and reflex angles. (*See margin.*)

ENRICHMENT

15–30 Min

▶ Constructing a Hexagon

(*Math Masters,* p. 147)

Portfolio Ideas

To further explore complex geometric constructions, students complete *Math Masters,* page 147, constructing a hexagon according to a set of specifications. The activity also provides practice measuring angles with a protractor, as well as measuring line segments to the nearest $\frac{1}{2}$ centimeter and the nearest $\frac{1}{8}$ inch.

EXTRA PRACTICE

SMALL-GROUP ACTIVITY

5–15 Min

▶ *5-Minute Math*

To offer more practice classifying angles as well as estimating and finding angle measures, see *5-Minute Math,* pages 59, 142, 143, and 222–225.

Reasoning with Angle Measures

Objective To find angle measures by reasoning with angle definitions and with sums of angle measures in triangles and quadrangles.

1 Teaching the Lesson

Key Activities

Students solve problems involving supplementary and vertical angles. They also determine angle measures and angle sums in triangles and quadrangles.

Key Concepts and Skills

- Add and subtract multidigit whole numbers. [Operations and Computation Goal 1]
- Measure angles to the nearest degree. [Measurement and Reference Frames Goal 1]
- Use appropriate notation to name angles. [Geometry Goal 1]
- Determine angle measures by applying definitions and properties of angles, triangles, and quadrangles. [Geometry Goal 1]

Key Vocabulary

supplementary angles • vertical (opposite) angles • adjacent angles

Ongoing Assessment: Informing Instruction See page 342.

materials

- ☐ *Math Journal 1,* pp. 166 and 167
- ☐ *Student Reference Book,* pp. 163 and 233
- ☐ Study Link 5•1
- ☐ Geometry Template/protractor

2 Ongoing Learning & Practice

Students practice estimating and measuring the size of angles by playing *Angle Tangle.*

Students practice and maintain skills through Math Boxes and Study Link activities.

Ongoing Assessment: Recognizing Student Achievement Use *Math Masters,* page 426. [Measurement and Reference Frames Goal 1; Geometry Goal 1]

materials

- ☐ *Math Journal 1,* p. 168
- ☐ *Student Reference Book,* p. 306
- ☐ Study Link Master (*Math Masters,* p. 148)
- ☐ Game Master (*Math Masters,* p. 426)
- ☐ Geometry Template/protractor

3 Differentiation Options

READINESS

Students cut out and align angles to determine the sum of angle measures in triangles and quadrangles.

ENRICHMENT

Students apply angle relationships to find angle measures of a regular pentagon and a five-pointed star.

EXTRA PRACTICE

Students complete teacher-generated Math Boxes.

materials

- ☐ Teaching Masters (*Math Masters,* pp. 149–151)
- ☐ Teaching Aid Master (*Math Masters,* p. 405)
- ☐ Geometry Template
- ☐ scissors; tape or glue

See **Advance Preparation**

Additional Information

Advance Preparation Cut out the triangles and quadrangles on *Math Masters,* page 149 for the optional Readiness activity.

Technology

Assessment Management System
Math Masters, page 426
See the **iTLG.**

Getting Started

Mental Math and Reflexes

Students solve multidigit addition problems on their slates. *Suggestions*:

●○○ 90 + ? + 90 + 90 = 360 90
115 + 65 + 115 + ? = 360 65
●●○ 80 + 120 + ? + 66 = 360 94
●●● 51 + ? + 140 + 120 = 360 49

Math Message

Measure the angles in Problems 1 and 2 on journal page 166. Then answer the question in Problem 3.

Study Link 5·1 Follow-Up

Briefly review the answers to Problems 1 and 2. Discuss Problem 3 in more detail. Ask students what they found for the sum of the angle measures in triangle *ADB* and quadrangle *ABCD*. Remind students that for any triangle, the sum of the interior angle measures is 180°; for any quadrangle, the sum of the interior angle measures is 360°.

Supplementary
8Opplementary
/8Opplementary

1 Teaching the Lesson

▶ Math Message Follow-Up

WHOLE-CLASS DISCUSSION

(*Math Journal 1*, p. 166)

To support English language learners, write the important terms and ideas from this discussion on the board. Some students should notice that the adjacent angles in the figure are **supplementary** (two angles whose measures add to 180°) and that the vertical angles are equal in measure. Take advantage of students' observations to introduce the terms **vertical angles** (angles **opposite** each other, with no sides in common, formed from two intersecting lines) and **adjacent angles** (two angles with a common side that do not otherwise overlap). Verify that students understand the abbreviation m∠*APC* is read as "the measure of angle *APC*."

Ongoing Assessment: Informing Instruction

Watch for students who confuse supplementary, vertical, and adjacent angles. Write each term on the board. Alter the *s* and the *u* in ***su**pplementary* to resemble *80.* Then insert a 1. (*See margin.*) Underline the *j* in *adjacent,* telling students that adjacent angles are joined at a side. Encourage students to brainstorm a mnemonic device for vertical angles.

Student Page

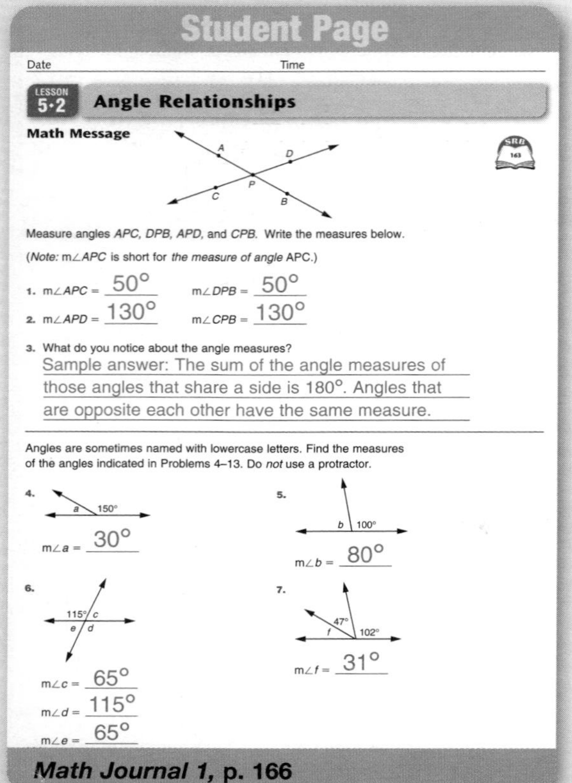

Date Time

LESSON 5·2 **Angle Relationships**

Math Message

Measure angles *APC, DPB, APD,* and *CPB.* Write the measures below.
(*Note:* m∠*APC* is short for *the measure of angle* APC.)

1. m∠*APC* = 50° m∠*DPB* = 50°
2. m∠*APD* = 130° m∠*CPB* = 130°
3. What do you notice about the angle measures?
Sample answer: The sum of the angle measures of those angles that share a side is 180°. Angles that are opposite each other have the same measure.

Angles are sometimes named with lowercase letters. Find the measures of the angles indicated in Problems 4–13. Do *not* use a protractor.

4. m∠*a* = 30°
5. m∠*b* = 80°
6. m∠*c* = 65° m∠*d* = 115° m∠*e* = 65°
7. m∠*f* = 31°

Math Journal 1, p. 166

▶ Solving Problems about Angle Relationships

PARTNER ACTIVITY

(*Math Journal 1,* pp. 166 and 167; *Student Reference Book,* pp. 163 and 233)

Pages 163 and 233 of the *Student Reference Book* explain the angle relationships students must understand and apply to complete journal pages 166 and 167. Have students read the pages independently, with a partner, or as a class.

Direct students' attention to how angles are named. Some angles are named using a single lowercase letter, such as $\angle a$. Other angles are named using a single-digit number, like $\angle 1$. Pose sample problems and assign the journal pages. Be sure to discuss students' solutions to several of the more complicated problems.

Adjusting the Activity

ELL

Summarize the various ways to name angles on the board. Sketch an angle to illustrate each of the following:

- an uppercase letter that names the vertex
- three uppercase letters naming the vertex and points on the angle
- a single lowercase letter
- a single-digit number

Consider using a graphic organizer, such as the folowing:

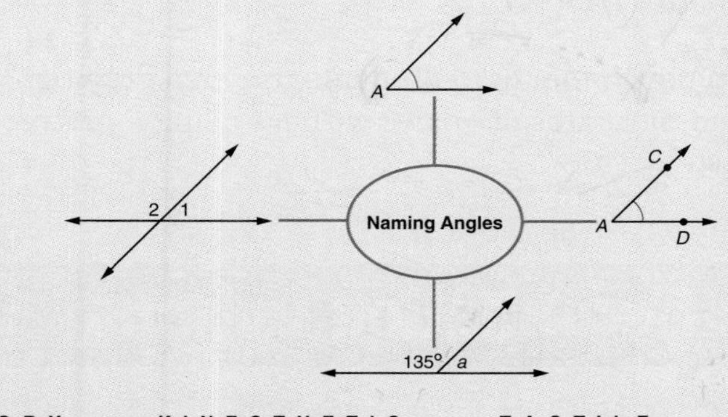

AUDITORY ◆ KINESTHETIC ◆ TACTILE ◆ VISUAL

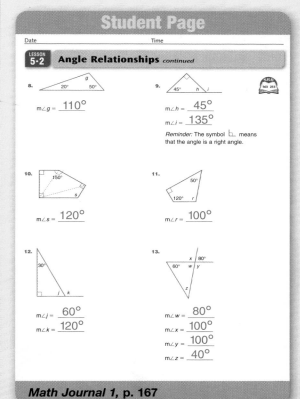

Student Page

Date Time

LESSON 5•2 **Angle Relationships** *continued*

8. $m\angle g =$ 110°

9. $m\angle h =$ 45°
$m\angle i =$ 135°

Reminder: The symbol ∟ means that the angle is a right angle.

10. $m\angle s =$ 120°

11. $m\angle r =$ 100°

12. $m\angle j =$ 60°
$m\angle k =$ 120°

13. $m\angle w =$ 80°
$m\angle x =$ 100°
$m\angle y =$ 100°
$m\angle z =$ 40°

***Math Journal 1,* p. 167**

2 Ongoing Learning & Practice

▶ Playing *Angle Tangle*

PARTNER ACTIVITY

(*Student Reference Book*, p. 306; *Math Masters,* p. 426)

Provide each student with an *Angle Tangle* Record Sheet (*Math Masters,* p. 426). List the various ways for labeling angles on the board. Have students label the angles they draw, using a different way each round. When students finish playing the game, have them submit the record sheets on which they drew and labeled their angles.

Ongoing Assessment: Recognizing Student Achievement

***Math Masters* Page 426**

Use ***Math Masters,* page 426** to assess students' abilities to label and measure angles. Students are making adequate progress if they correctly use one of the conventions to name angles. Students' recorded degree measures indicate their ability to accurately measure angles. Some students may be able to make estimates that are very close to the actual degree measures.

[Measurement and Reference Frames Goal 1; Geometry Goal 1]

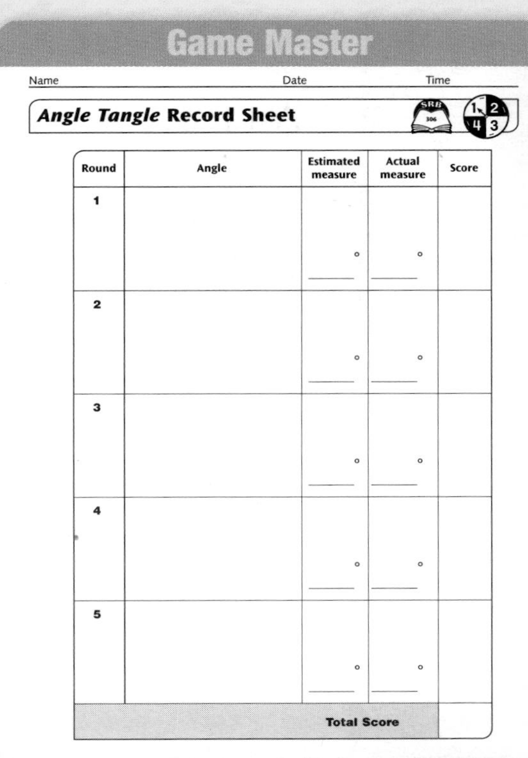

Game Master

Name Date Time

***Angle Tangle* Record Sheet**

Round	Angle	Estimated measure	Actual measure	Score
1		____°	____°	
2		____°	____°	
3		____°	____°	
4		____°	____°	
5		____°	____°	
		Total Score		

***Math Masters 1,* p. 426**

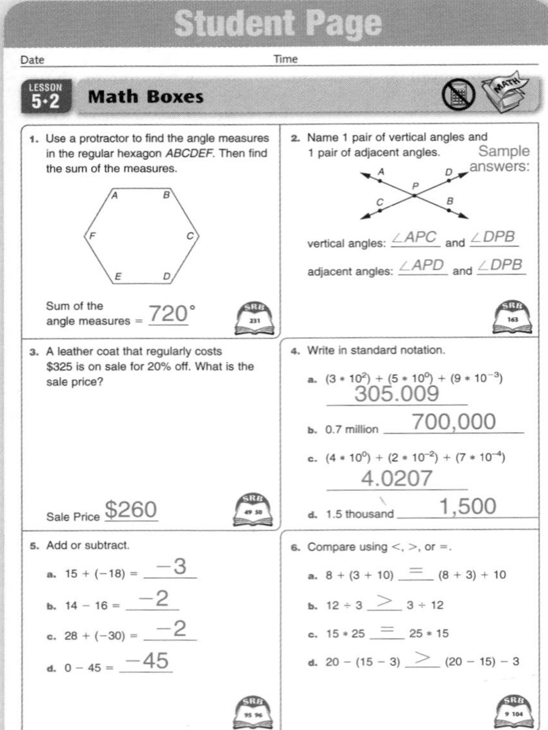
Student Page

Date Time

LESSON 5·2 **Math Boxes**

1. Use a protractor to find the angle measures in the regular hexagon *ABCDEF*. Then find the sum of the measures.
Sum of the angle measures = 720°

2. Name 1 pair of vertical angles and 1 pair of adjacent angles. Sample answers:
vertical angles: ∠APC and ∠DPB
adjacent angles: ∠APD and ∠DPB

3. A leather coat that regularly costs $325 is on sale for 20% off. What is the sale price?
Sale Price $260

4. Write in standard notation.
a. $(3 * 10^2) + (5 * 10^0) + (9 * 10^{-3})$ 305.009
b. 0.7 million 700,000
c. $(4 * 10^0) + (2 * 10^{-2}) + (7 * 10^{-4})$ 4.0207
d. 1.5 thousand 1,500

5. Add or subtract.
a. 15 + (−18) = −3
b. 14 − 16 = −2
c. 28 + (−30) = −2
d. 0 − 45 = −45

6. Compare using $<$, $>$, or $=$.
a. $8 + (3 + 10) = (8 + 3) + 10$
b. $12 \div 3 > 3 \div 12$
c. $15 * 25 = 25 * 15$
d. $20 - (15 - 3) > (20 - 15) - 3$

Math Journal 1, p. 168

▶ Math Boxes 5·2

INDEPENDENT ACTIVITY

(*Math Journal 1,* p. 168)

Mixed Practice Math Boxes in this lesson are paired with Math Boxes in Lesson 5-4. The skills in Problems 5 and 6 preview Unit 6 content.

Writing/Reasoning Have students write a response to the following: *Explain how you might find the sum of the interior angle measures in Problem 1 without using a protractor.* Sample answer: Use diagonals to divide the hexagon into 4 triangles. Multiply the number of triangles by the sum of the interior angle measures of each triangle ($4 * 180° = 720°$).

▶ Study Link 5·2

INDEPENDENT ACTIVITY

(*Math Masters,* p. 148)

Home Connection Students use angle relationships to find measures of angles without using a protractor.

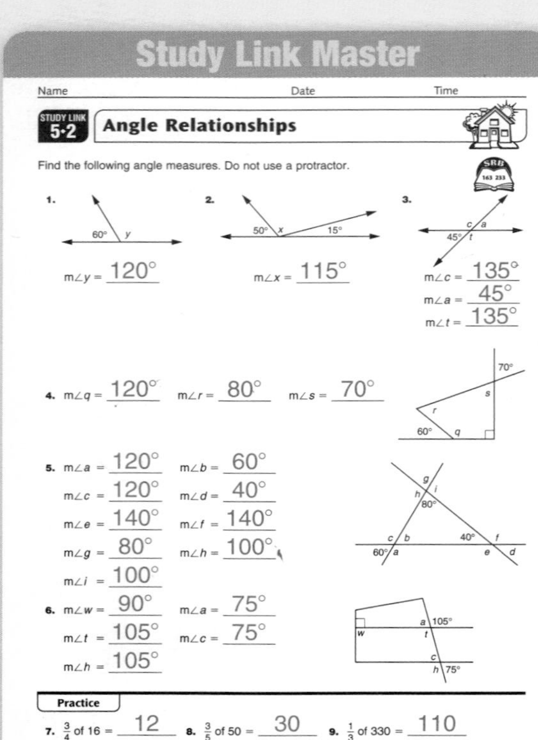
Study Link Master

Name Date Time

STUDY LINK 5·2 **Angle Relationships**

Find the following angle measures. Do not use a protractor.

1. m∠y = 120°
2. m∠x = 115°
3. m∠c = 135°, m∠a = 45°, m∠t = 135°
4. m∠q = 120° m∠r = 80° m∠s = 70°
5. m∠a = 120° m∠b = 60° m∠c = 120° m∠d = 40° m∠e = 140° m∠f = 140° m∠g = 80° m∠h = 100° m∠i = 100°
6. m∠w = 90° m∠a = 75° m∠t = 105° m∠c = 75° m∠h = 105°

Practice

7. $\frac{3}{4}$ of 16 = 12
8. $\frac{3}{5}$ of 50 = 30
9. $\frac{1}{3}$ of 330 = 110

Math Masters, p. 148

3 Differentiation Options

READINESS

SMALL-GROUP ACTIVITY

15–30 Min

▶ Finding Sums of Angle Measures in Triangles and Quadrangles

(*Math Masters,* pp. 149 and 150)

To provide experience finding sums of angle measures in triangles and quadrangles, have students carefully tear off each angle of one triangle and one quadrangle from *Math Masters,* page 149. Ask them to align the angles and explore the properties of the sums of angle measures in triangles and quadrangles.

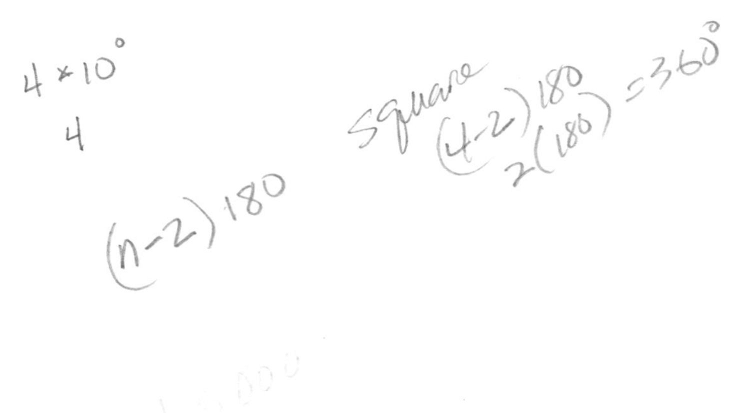

ENRICHMENT

INDEPENDENT ACTIVITY

5–15 Min

▶ Applying Angle Relationships

(*Math Masters,* p. 151)

To further explore angle relationships, students extend the sides of a regular pentagon to construct a five-pointed star. They apply their knowledge of angle relationships to find the measure of each angle in the construction.

EXTRA PRACTICE

INDEPENDENT ACTIVITY

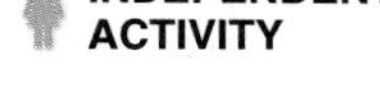

5–15 Min

▶ Writing Custom-Made Math Boxes

Use *Math Masters,* page 405 to generate Math Box questions that focus on a particular concept or skill for which students need extra practice.

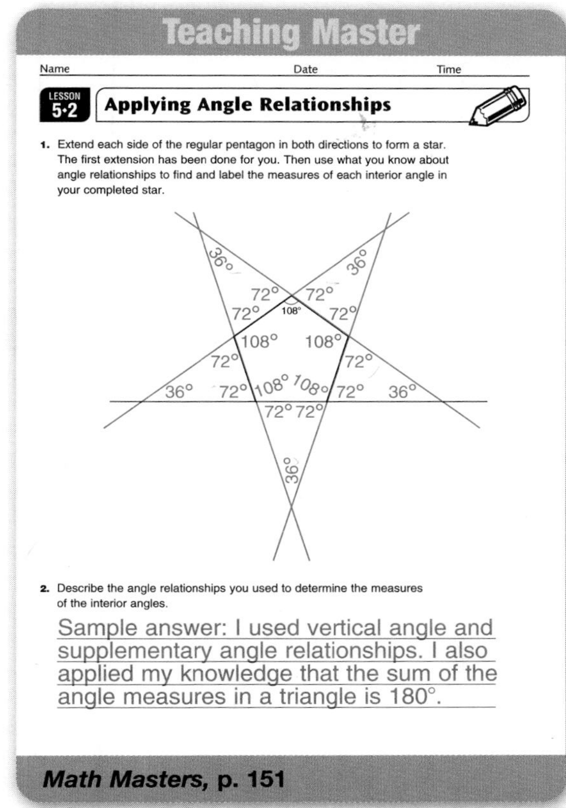

Teaching Master

Name Date Time

LESSON 5·2 **Applying Angle Relationships**

1. Extend each side of the regular pentagon in both directions to form a star. The first extension has been done for you. Then use what you know about angle relationships to find and label the measures of each interior angle in your completed star.

2. Describe the angle relationships you used to determine the measures of the interior angles.

Sample answer: I used vertical angle and supplementary angle relationships. I also applied my knowledge that the sum of the angle measures in a triangle is 180°.

Math Masters, p. 151

Teaching Master

Name Date Time

LESSON 5·2 **Finding Sums of Angle Measures**

1. Cut out one of the triangles on *Math Masters,* page 149. Carefully cut or tear off each angle. Use point *P* at the right to position the angles so they touch but do not overlap. The shaded regions should form a semicircle. Use tape or glue to hold the angles in place.

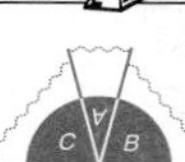

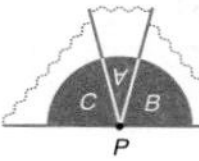

2. Notice that the combined shaded regions form an angle. How many degrees does this angle measure? 180°

3. Compare your results with those of other students. What do your triangles seem to have in common?

Sample answer: The sum of the 3 angle measures is 180°.

4. Complete the following statement.
The sum of the measures of the angles of any triangle is 180°.

5. Cut out one of the quadrangles on *Math Masters,* page 149. Carefully cut or tear off each angle. Use point *Q* at the right to position the angles so they touch but do not overlap. The shaded regions should form a circle. Use tape or glue to hold the angles in place.

6. Notice that the combined shaded regions form a figure. How many degrees are in this figure? 360°

7. Compare your results with those of other students. What do your quadrangles seem to have in common?

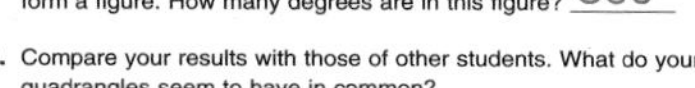

Sample answer: The sum of the 4 angle measures is 360°.

8. Complete the following statement.
The sum of the measures of the angles of any quadrangle is 360°.

Math Masters, p. 150

Using a Protractor to Make Circle Graphs

Objectives To introduce how to calculate degree measures of sectors; and to use a protractor to draw circle graphs.

1 Teaching the Lesson

Key Activities

Students use fractions, decimals, and percents to calculate the degree measures of sectors in a circle graph. They use a protractor to draw each sector.

Key Concepts and Skills

- Apply place-value concepts to round decimals to the nearest whole number. [Number and Numeration Goal 1]
- Recognize and use equivalent names for fractions, decimals, and percents. [Number and Numeration Goal 5]
- Use appropriate strategies to construct circle graphs. [Data and Chance Goal 1]
- Draw and measure angles to the nearest degree. [Measurement and Reference Frames Goal 1]

Key Vocabulary

sector

Ongoing Assessment: Recognizing Student Achievement Use journal page 169. [Geometry Goal 1]

materials

- ☐ *Math Journal 1,* pp. 169–171
- ☐ *Student Reference Book,* pp. 59, 60, and 147
- ☐ Study Link 5•2
- ☐ Transparencies (*Math Masters,* pp. 152 and 153; optional)
- ☐ compass
- ☐ Geometry Template/protractor
- ☐ calculator
- ☐ scissors
- ☐ tape
- ☐ board compass and protractor (for demonstration purposes)

2 Ongoing Learning & Practice

Students calculate percents of numbers to solve sale-price problems.

Students practice and maintain skills through Math Boxes and Study Link activities.

materials

- ☐ *Math Journal 1,* pp. 172 and 173
- ☐ Study Link Master (*Math Masters,* p. 154)
- ☐ Geometry Template/protractor
- ☐ calculator

3 Differentiation Options

READINESS

Students use a diagram of the full-circle protractor to find fractional parts of a circle and their degree equivalencies.

ENRICHMENT

Students use diagonals and apply properties of triangles to find the sums of angle measures in polygons.

materials

- ☐ *Student Reference Book,* p. 233
- ☐ Teaching Masters (*Math Masters,* pp. 155 and 156)
- ☐ color pencils or markers

Technology

Assessment Management System
Math Message
See the **iTLG.**

Getting Started

Mental Math and Reflexes

Students use a calculator to solve percent problems.
Suggestions:

- ●○○ 28% of 18 5.04
- ●●○ 3% of 42 1.26
- ●●● 12.5% of 62 7.75
- ●●● 7.25% of 52 3.77

Math Message ★

Complete the Math Message on journal page 169.

Study Link 5•2 Follow-Up

Ask students to explain how they determined the angle measures.

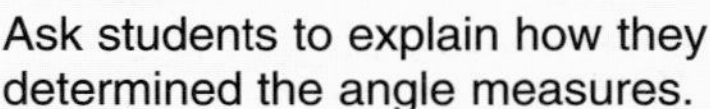

1 Teaching the Lesson

▶ Math Message Follow-Up

WHOLE-CLASS DISCUSSION

(*Math Journal 1,* p. 169)

Use Problems 1 and 2 of the Math Message to check students' understanding of the number of degrees in a circle. Students will need to know that there are 360 degrees in a circle when they calculate the degree measure of each **sector** in a circle graph.

Ongoing Assessment: Recognizing Student Achievement

Math Message ★

Use the **Math Message** to assess students' ability to apply the definitions of supplementary and vertical angles. Students are making adequate progress if they use the given angle measure (150°) to find the measures of vertical angles and their supplements.

[Geometry Goal 1]

▶ Calculating the Degree Measure of a Sector

WHOLE-CLASS ACTIVITY

(*Math Journal 1,* pp. 169 and 170; *Student Reference Book,* pp. 59, 60, and 147; *Math Masters,* pp. 152 and 153)

Use Problem 3 on journal page 169 to review strategies for renaming fractions as percents, an essential skill for this lesson. Circulate and assist as needed.

Student Page

Date ______ Time ______

LESSON 5•3 **Degree Measures of Sectors**

Math Message ★

SRB 163

1. Find the measures of the following angles in circle *O* without using a protractor.
   a. m∠*QOR* = 150°
   b. m∠*POS* = 150 °
   c. m∠*POQ* = 30 °
   d. m∠*SOR* = 30 °

P Q O 150° S R

2. Find the sum of the angle measures in Problem 1.
   150° + m∠*POS* + m∠*POQ* + m∠*SOR* = 360 °

SRB 59 60 147

3. Connie, Josh, and Manuel were running for student council representative. The table below shows the number of votes that each candidate received. Complete the table.

Candidate	Number of Votes Received	Fraction of Votes Received	Percent of Votes Received
Connie	7	$\frac{7}{25}$	28%
Josh	6	$\frac{6}{25}$	24%
Manuel	12	$\frac{12}{25}$	48%
Total	**25**	$\frac{25}{25}$	**100%**

4. Use the percents from the table above to calculate the degree measure of the sector representing each candidate.

Candidate	Percent of Votes Received	Degree Measure of Sector (to nearest degree)
Connie	28%	0.28 ∗ 360 = 100.8° ≈ 101°
Josh	24%	86°
Manuel	48%	173°
Total	**100%**	**360°**

Math Journal 1, p. 169

Student Page

Date ______ Time ______

LESSON 5·3 **Drawing Circle Graphs with a Protractor**

Mr. Li surveyed the students in his class to find out what kinds of pets they owned and how many of each kind they had. The results are shown in the first two columns of the table below.

Kind of Pet	Number of Pets	Fraction of Total Number of Pets	Decimal Equivalent (to nearest thousandth)	Percent of Total Number of Pets	Degree Measure of Sector
Dog	8	$\frac{8}{24}$	0.333	$33\frac{1}{3}\%$	$\frac{1}{3} * 360° =$ ___
Cat	6	$\frac{6}{24}$	0.25	25%	$\frac{1}{4} * 360° = 90°$
Guinea pig or hamster	3	$\frac{3}{24}$	0.125	12.5%	$0.125 * 360° = 45°$
Bird	3	$\frac{3}{24}$	0.125	12.5%	$0.125 * 360° = 45°$
Other	4	$\frac{4}{24}$	0.167	16.7%	$\frac{1}{6} * 360° = 60°$

1. Complete the table above. Study the first row.
2. At the right, or on a separate sheet of paper, use a compass and a protractor to make a circle graph of the data in the table. If you need to, tape your completed circle graph on this page. Write a title for the graph.

Pets Owned by Mr. Li's Students

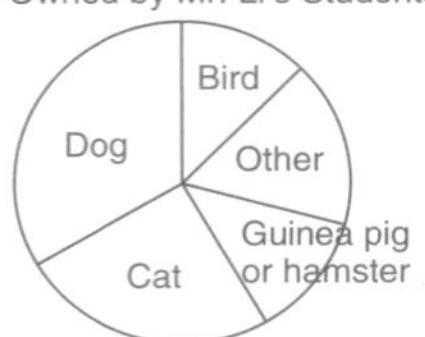

Math Journal 1, p. 170

NOTE The table on *Math Masters,* page 152 is identical to the table in Problem 4 on journal page 169.

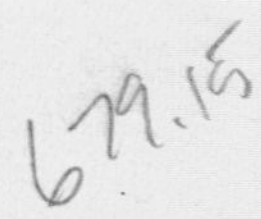

Student Page

Date ______ Time ______

LESSON 5·3 **Drawing Circle Graphs with a Protractor** *cont.*

3. Sixth-grade students at Hawthorn School took a survey about after-school activities. Students answering the survey named the activity on which they spent the most time after school. The results are shown in the table below. Complete the table.

Activity	Number of Students	Fraction of Students	Decimal Equivalent	Percent of Students (to nearest percent)	Size of Sector
Music	12	$\frac{12}{60}$	0.2	20%	72°
Math Club	28	$\frac{28}{60}$	$0.4\overline{6}$	47%	168°
Art	5	$\frac{5}{60}$	$0.08\overline{3}$	8%	30°
Sports	8	$\frac{8}{60}$	$0.1\overline{3}$	13%	48°
Computers	3	$\frac{3}{60}$	0.05	5%	18°
None	4	$\frac{4}{60}$	$0.0\overline{6}$	7%	24°

4. In the space below, or on a separate sheet of paper, use a compass and a protractor to make a circle graph of the data in the table. If you need to, tape your completed circle graph on this page. Write a title for the graph.

After-School Activities of Sixth Graders

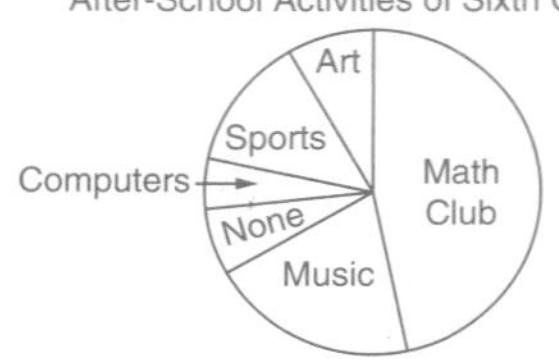

Math Journal 1, p. 171

Draw and shade in a sector of a circle on the board. Explain that in previous lessons, students used the Percent Circle on their Geometry Template to draw each wedge-shaped piece, or sector, of a circle graph. In this lesson, they will learn how to use a protractor to draw each sector.

Copy the table in Problem 4 on the board or use a transparency of *Math Masters,* page 152. (*See margin.*) Discuss solution strategies for finding the degree measure of each sector.

▷ One approach is to express the data as fractions and find those fractions of 360°. For example, Connie received 7 out of 25 votes, or $\frac{7}{25}$ of the votes.

$\frac{7}{25}$ of $360° = \frac{7}{25} * 360° = 100\frac{4}{5}°$

Similarly, Josh received $\frac{6}{25}$ of the votes.

$\frac{6}{25}$ of $360° = \frac{6}{25} * 360° = 86\frac{2}{5}°$

Manuel received twice as many votes as Josh ($\frac{12}{25}$), so the measure of the sector representing Manuel is $86\frac{2}{5}° * 2 = 172\frac{4}{5}°$. Since the protractors that students use are marked in whole-degree increments, round each degree measure to the nearest whole degree: $100\frac{4}{5}° \rightarrow 101°$; $86\frac{2}{5}° \rightarrow 86°$; $172\frac{4}{5}° \rightarrow 173°$.

▷ Another approach is to express the data as fractions, rename the fractions as decimals, and then multiply the decimal by 360°. *For example:*

$\frac{7}{25} = 7 \div 25 = 0.28$ and $0.28 * 360° = 100.8°$

$\frac{6}{25} = 6 \div 25 = 0.24$ and $0.24 * 360° = 86.4°$

$\frac{12}{25} = 12 \div 25 = 0.48$ and $0.48 * 360° = 172.8°$

Similarly, each degree measure should be rounded to the nearest whole degree.

When students have completed Problem 4 on journal page 169, demonstrate how to make the circle graph of the data. Draw a circle on the board or use the circle on the transparency (*Math Masters,* p. 152) and mark off sectors with a protractor. In order to make the graph as accurate as possible, graph the smallest category (Josh's votes) first; graph the largest category (Manuel's votes) last.

Allow students to make their circle graphs on a separate sheet of paper as you demonstrate the appropriate procedures. When the graphs have been completed and titled, have students check them with the Percent Circle.

Votes Received in the Student Council Election

Manuel

Connie

Josh

Next, work through the table on journal page 170 with the class. Have students complete the table as you do the same on the board or transparency (*Math Masters,* p. 153). The first row of the table has already been filled in. Because some data are easier to work with as fractions and other data as decimals, ask students to share and explain the approach that they find most efficient for finding the degree measures of each sector.

When students have completed the table, ask them to use a compass and a protractor to make a circle graph of the survey data. Students may construct the graph on the bottom of journal page 170 or on a separate sheet of paper.

▶ Drawing a Circle Graph

PARTNER ACTIVITY

(*Math Journal 1,* p. 171)

Students find fraction, decimal, and percent equivalencies, calculate degree measures of sectors, and use a compass and a protractor to create a circle graph of the after-school activities of sixth graders.

Remind students that to make the graph as accurate as possible, they should graph the smallest category (Computers) first; they should graph the largest category (Math Club) last.

2 Ongoing Learning & Practice

▶ Calculating Sale Price

INDEPENDENT ACTIVITY

(*Math Journal 1,* p. 172)

The problems on journal page 172 provide practice using a one- or two-step method for finding a sale price.

▶ Math Boxes 5•3

INDEPENDENT ACTIVITY

(*Math Journal 1,* p. 173)

Mixed Practice Math Boxes in this lesson are paired with Math Boxes in Lesson 5-1. The skills in Problems 5 and 6 preview Unit 6 content.

▶ Study Link 5•3

INDEPENDENT ACTIVITY

(*Math Masters,* p. 154)

Home Connection Students make a circle graph. They then interpret the graph and draw conclusions. Remind students to take home a protractor or their Geometry Template.

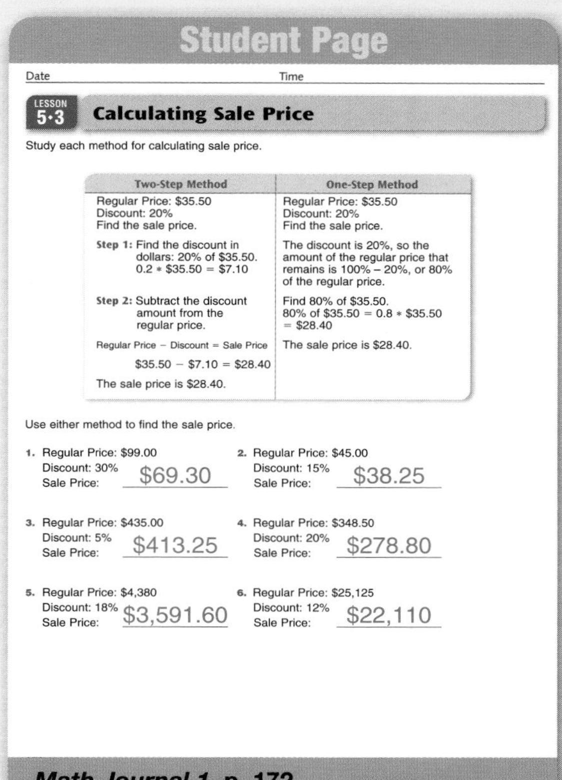

Student Page

Date Time

LESSON 5•3 **Calculating Sale Price**

Study each method for calculating sale price.

Two-Step Method	One-Step Method
Regular Price: \$35.50 Discount: 20% Find the sale price.	Regular Price: \$35.50 Discount: 20% Find the sale price.
Step 1: Find the discount in dollars: 20% of \$35.50. 0.2 * \$35.50 = \$7.10	The discount is 20%, so the amount of the regular price that remains is 100% – 20%, or 80% of the regular price.
Step 2: Subtract the discount amount from the regular price. Regular Price – Discount = Sale Price \$35.50 – \$7.10 = \$28.40 The sale price is \$28.40.	Find 80% of \$35.50. 80% of \$35.50 = 0.8 * \$35.50 = \$28.40 The sale price is \$28.40.

Use either method to find the sale price.

1. Regular Price: \$99.00
Discount: 30%
Sale Price: \$69.30
2. Regular Price: \$45.00
Discount: 15%
Sale Price: \$38.25
3. Regular Price: \$435.00
Discount: 5%
Sale Price: \$413.25
4. Regular Price: \$348.50
Discount: 20%
Sale Price: \$278.80
5. Regular Price: \$4,380
Discount: 18%
Sale Price: \$3,591.60
6. Regular Price: \$25,125
Discount: 12%
Sale Price: \$22,110

Math Journal 1, p. 172

NOTE A small error in a big percentage is relatively less important than a small error in a small percentage. For example, if a category is only 2% of the total and the sector is off by 1%, that is a fairly large error (50%). However, if a category is 34% of the total and the sector is off by 1%, the error is much less significant (only about 3%).

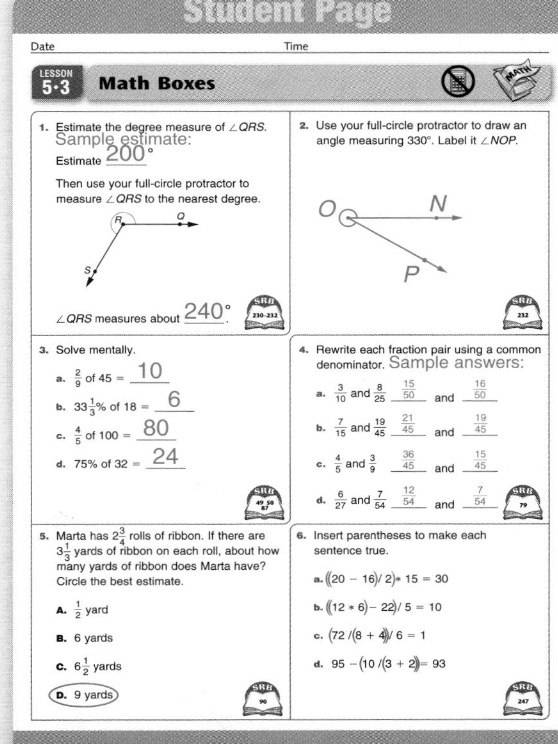

Student Page

Date Time

LESSON 5•3 **Math Boxes**

1. Estimate the degree measure of ∠*QRS*.
Sample estimate:
Estimate 200°
Then use your full-circle protractor to measure ∠*QRS* to the nearest degree.
∠*QRS* measures about 240°.
2. Use your full-circle protractor to draw an angle measuring 330°. Label it ∠*NOP*.
3. Solve mentally.
a. $\frac{2}{9}$ of 45 = 10
b. $33\frac{1}{3}$% of 18 = 6
c. $\frac{4}{5}$ of 100 = 80
d. 75% of 32 = 24
4. Rewrite each fraction pair using a common denominator. Sample answers:
a. $\frac{3}{10}$ and $\frac{8}{25}$ $\frac{15}{50}$ and $\frac{16}{50}$
b. $\frac{7}{15}$ and $\frac{19}{45}$ $\frac{21}{45}$ and $\frac{19}{45}$
c. $\frac{4}{5}$ and $\frac{3}{9}$ $\frac{36}{45}$ and $\frac{15}{45}$
d. $\frac{6}{27}$ and $\frac{7}{54}$ $\frac{12}{54}$ and $\frac{7}{54}$
5. Marta has $2\frac{3}{4}$ rolls of ribbon. If there are $3\frac{1}{3}$ yards of ribbon on each roll, about how many yards of ribbon does Marta have? Circle the best estimate.
A. $\frac{1}{2}$ yard
B. 6 yards
C. $6\frac{1}{2}$ yards
D. 9 yards
6. Insert parentheses to make each sentence true.
a. ((20 – 16) / 2) * 15 = 30
b. ((12 * 6) – 22) / 5 = 10
c. (72 / (8 + 4)) / 6 = 1
d. 95 – (10 / (3 + 2)) = 93

Math Journal 1, p. 173

Study Link Master

Name ________ Date ________ Time ________

STUDY LINK 5·3 **Circle Graphs**

1. The table below shows a breakdown, by age group, of adults who listen to classical music.
   a. Calculate the degree measure of each sector to the nearest degree.
   b. Use a protractor to make a circle graph. Do *not* use the Percent Circle. Write a title for the graph.

Age	Percent of Listeners	Degree Measure
18–24	11%	40°
25–34	18%	65°
35–44	24%	86°
45–54	20%	72°
55–64	11%	40°
65+	16%	58°

Source: *USA Today*, Snapshot

Age of Adult Classical Music Listeners

2. On average, about 8 million adults listen to classical music on the radio each day.
   a. Estimate how many adults between the ages of 35 and 44 listen to classical music on the radio each day. About 1,920,000 adults (unit)
   b. Estimate how many adults at least 45 years old listen to classical music on the radio each day. About 3,760,000 adults (unit)

Practice

Order each set of numbers from least to greatest.

3. 7, 0.07, −7, 0.7, 0 −7, 0, 0.07, 0.7, 7
4. 0.25, 0.75, 0.2, $\frac{4}{5}$, $\frac{4}{4}$, 0.06, 0.18, $\frac{1}{10}$ 0.06, $\frac{1}{10}$, 0.18, 0.2, 0.25, 0.75, $\frac{4}{5}$, $\frac{4}{4}$

Math Masters, p. 154

3 Differentiation Options

READINESS

INDEPENDENT ACTIVITY

5–15 Min

▶ Finding Fractions of 360°

(*Math Masters,* p. 155)

To provide experience finding fractions of 360°, have students use *Math Masters,* page 155 and coloring pencils or markers. Ask students to shade fractional parts of a full-circle protractor diagram. Then have them use the shaded regions to determine the number of degrees in each fractional part.

ENRICHMENT

INDEPENDENT ACTIVITY

5–15 Min

▶ Finding Sums of Angle Measures in Polygons

(*Math Masters,* p. 156; *Student Reference Book,* p. 233)

To further extend their knowledge of angle relationships, students find the sums of angle measures in various polygons. They use a pattern to calculate the sums of angle measures in a heptagon, nonagon, and dodecagon.

Teaching Master

Name ________ Date ________ Time ________

LESSON 5·3 **Fractions of 360°**

Shade each fractional part. Then record the number of degrees in each shaded region.

1. Shade $\frac{1}{2}$ of the circle. $\frac{1}{2}$ of 360° = 180°
2. Shade $\frac{1}{4}$ of the circle. $\frac{1}{4}$ of 360° = 90°
3. Shade $\frac{1}{6}$ of the circle. $\frac{1}{6}$ of 360° = 60°
4. Shade $\frac{1}{3}$ of the circle. $\frac{1}{3}$ of 360° = 120°
5. Shade $\frac{1}{12}$ of the circle. $\frac{1}{12}$ of 360° = 30°
6. Shade $\frac{3}{4}$ of the circle. $\frac{3}{4}$ of 360° = 270°

Math Masters, p. 155

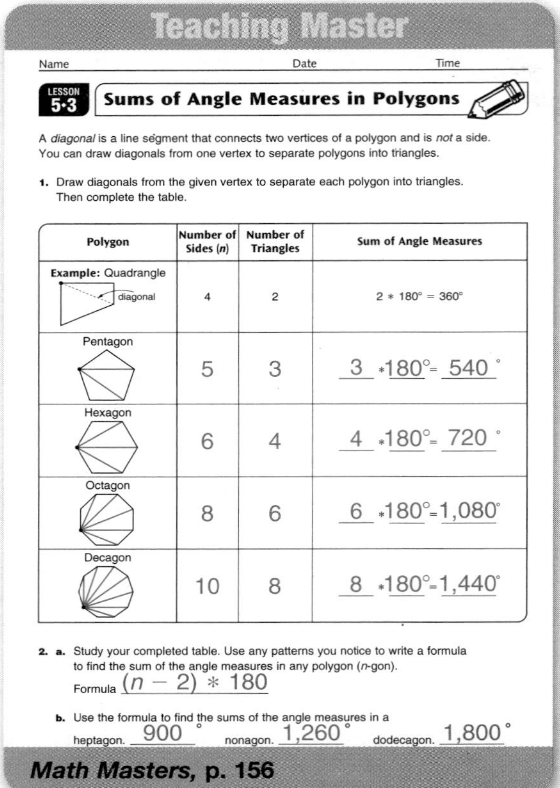

Teaching Master

Name ________ Date ________ Time ________

LESSON 5·3 **Sums of Angle Measures in Polygons**

A *diagonal* is a line segment that connects two vertices of a polygon and is *not* a side. You can draw diagonals from one vertex to separate polygons into triangles.

1. Draw diagonals from the given vertex to separate each polygon into triangles. Then complete the table.

Polygon	Number of Sides (*n*)	Number of Triangles	Sum of Angle Measures
Example: Quadrangle (diagonal)	4	2	2 ∗ 180° = 360°
Pentagon	5	3	3 ∗ 180° = 540°
Hexagon	6	4	4 ∗ 180° = 720°
Octagon	8	6	6 ∗ 180° = 1,080°
Decagon	10	8	8 ∗ 180° = 1,440°

2. a. Study your completed table. Use any patterns you notice to write a formula to find the sum of the angle measures in any polygon (*n*-gon). Formula $(n - 2) * 180$
   b. Use the formula to find the sums of the angle measures in a heptagon. 900° nonagon. 1,260° dodecagon. 1,800°

Math Masters, p. 156

5•4 Coordinate Geometry

Objectives To plot ordered number pairs; to apply properties of polygons; and to explore the relationship between endpoints and midpoints.

1 Teaching the Lesson

Key Activities

Students review how to plot ordered number pairs on a rectangular coordinate grid. They plot and name vertices of polygons. Students also explore the relationship between the coordinates of the endpoints and midpoints of line segments.

Key Concepts and Skills

- Add integers. [Operations and Computation Goal 1]
- Find the mean of two signed numbers. [Data and Chance Goal 2]
- Plot, name, and label points in any four quadrants of a coordinate grid. [Measurement and Reference Frames Goal 3]
- Extend a pattern to create a rule. [Patterns, Functions, and Algebra Goal 1]

Key Vocabulary

ordered number pair • rectangular coordinate grid • origin • axis • coordinate • midpoint

Ongoing Assessment: Informing Instruction See page 353.

materials

- ☐ *Math Journal 1,* pp. 174–176
- ☐ *Student Reference Book,* pp. 166, 169, and 234
- ☐ Study Link 5•3
- ☐ Transparency (*Math Masters,* p. 417; optional)

2 Ongoing Learning & Practice

Students practice identifying equivalent expressions involving fractions by playing *Spoon Scramble.*

Students practice and maintain skills through Math Boxes and Study Link activities.

Ongoing Assessment: Recognizing Student Achievement Use journal page 177. [Number and Numeration Goal 2]

materials

- ☐ *Math Journal 1,* p. 177 and Activity Sheets 1 and 2
- ☐ *Student Reference Book,* p. 333
- ☐ Study Link Master (*Math Masters,* p. 157)
- ☐ 3 spoons per group; 3" by 5" index cards (optional)

3 Differentiation Options

READINESS

Students practice plotting ordered number pairs by playing *X and O–Tic-Tac-Toe.*

ENRICHMENT

Students apply geometric properties to plot triangles and quadrangles in all four quadrants of a coordinate grid.

materials

- ☐ Teaching Masters (*Math Masters,* pp. 158 and 159)
- ☐ Teaching Aid Master (*Math Masters,* p. 417)
- ☐ Per partnership: 4 each of the number cards 0–10; straightedge

Technology

Assessment Management System
Math Boxes, Problem 3
See the **iTLG.**

Getting Started

Mental Math and Reflexes

Review adding signed numbers by posing the following problems.

●○○ $5 + (-12)$ -7

●●○ $-7\frac{1}{2} + 4\frac{1}{4}$ $-3\frac{1}{4}$

●●● $9\frac{3}{10} + (-11\frac{1}{5})$ $-1\frac{9}{10}$

Math Message

Read page 234 of the Student Reference Book. *Then complete the problems on journal page 174.*

Study Link 5·3 Follow-Up

Review answers. Students share the strategies they used to calculate the degree measure of each sector.

1 Teaching the Lesson

▶ Math Message Follow-Up

WHOLE-CLASS DISCUSSION

(*Math Journal 1,* p. 174; *Student Reference Book,* p. 234; *Math Masters,* p. 417)

Draw a 4-quadrant grid on the board. As you present and discuss each term, use it to label the grid.

Briefly review **ordered number pairs** and how to name points on a **rectangular coordinate grid.** Because students have worked with first-quadrant coordinate grids in *Third* and *Fourth Grade Everyday Mathematics* and with 4-quadrant grids in *Fifth Grade Everyday Mathematics,* you may not need to devote much time to guided instruction. However, a basic understanding of all 4 quadrants of the coordinate system is key to students' success with the activities in this and future lessons.

Go over the answers to the problems on journal page 174. Consider using a transparency of *Math Masters,* page 417 to demonstrate plotting and naming points. Emphasize the importance of the order of the numbers in an ordered pair.

You may want to discuss a method for plotting an ordered pair: start at the **origin**—the ordered number pair (0,0)—and move to the right or left of the vertical **axis,** depending on whether the first **coordinate** is a positive or a negative number. From that point, move up or down from the horizontal axis, depending on whether the second coordinate is positive or negative. *Suggestions:*

To Plot	Move
(4,6)	4 squares to the right and 6 squares up
(3,−1)	3 squares to the right and 1 square down
(−2,−8)	2 squares to the left and 8 squares down
(−4,4)	4 squares to the left and 4 squares up
(0,5)	5 squares up
(−3,0)	3 squares to the left

Student Page

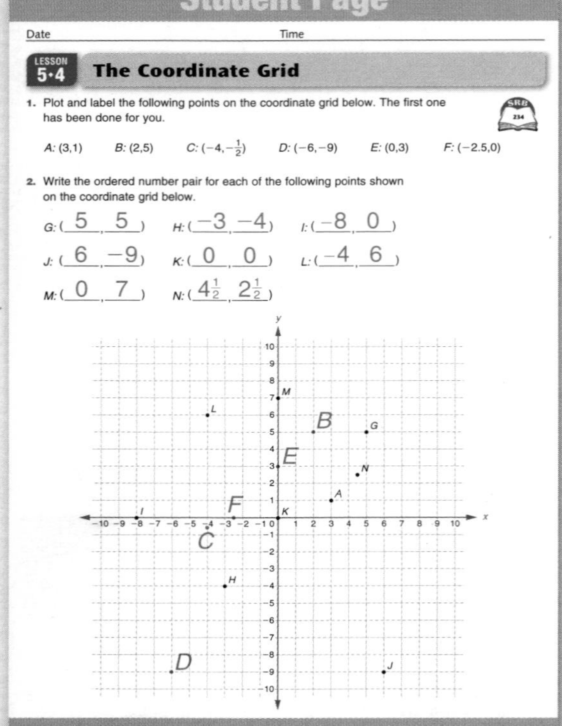

Date Time

LESSON 5·4 **The Coordinate Grid**

1. Plot and label the following points on the coordinate grid below. The first one has been done for you.

   A: (3,1) *B:* (2,5) *C:* $(-4,-\frac{1}{2})$ *D:* (−6,−9) *E:* (0,3) *F:* (−2.5,0)

2. Write the ordered number pair for each of the following points shown on the coordinate grid below.

   G: (5, 5) *H:* (−3, −4) *I:* (−8, 0)

   J: (6, −9) *K:* (0, 0) *L:* (−4, 6)

   M: (0, 7) *N:* $(4\frac{1}{2}, 2\frac{1}{2})$

Math Journal 1, p. 174

Ongoing Assessment: Informing Instruction

Watch for students who confuse the order of the coordinates of those points that lie on an axis, such as (−3,0) and (0,5). Remind students that the first coordinate indicates how far to move to the right or left of the *y*-axis; the second coordinate indicates how far to move above or below the *x*-axis. A coordinate value of 0 indicates no movement.

Adjusting the Activity

Use a ladder metaphor to help students plot ordered number pairs. The first number in the ordered number pair indicates where to put the ladder. The second number indicates how high to climb up or how low to climb down.

AUDITORY ◆ KINESTHETIC ◆ TACTILE ◆ VISUAL

▶ Applying Polygon Properties

PARTNER ACTIVITY

(*Math Journal 1,* p. 175)

Point out that the coordinate grid has been divided into 5 × 5 squares and that students should be able to complete each polygon within one 5 × 5 square. You might want to work on Problem 1 together to make sure students understand what they are to do. Students then work on the remaining problems while you circulate and assist. Some of the problems may prove challenging.

Bring the class together to share solutions. Some problems have only one correct solution; others have several. Encourage students to propose as many solutions as they can.

NOTE This activity assumes an understanding of various types of triangles and quadrangles. If students have forgotten some of them, suggest that they review pages 166 and 169 of the *Student Reference Book* or look in the Glossary.

▶ Finding Midpoints of Line Segments

PARTNER ACTIVITY

(*Math Journal 1,* p. 176)

This is a discovery activity. Students should have no trouble completing Problems 1 and 2. However, discovering the pattern in the accumulated information in Problem 2 and then applying that information to solve Problem 3 may require some ingenuity.

Student Page

Date Time

LESSON 5•4 **Polygons on a Coordinate Grid**

The names of polygons consist of letters that name the vertices, written in consecutive order. For example, the square at the right may be named square *ABCD, BCDA, CDAB,* or *DABC.*

The points shown on the grid below represent vertices of polygons. One or two vertices are missing for each polygon. Plot and name the missing vertices on the grid and then draw each polygon. List the number pairs for the missing vertices.

Sample answers:

1. Scalene triangle *ABC*
   C: (−2, 9)
2. Right triangle *DEF,* which is also an isosceles triangle
   F: (1, 6)
3. Square *GHIJ*
   I: (−3, 0)
   J: (−1, 2)
4. Rectangle *KLMN,* with $\overline{LM} = 2 * \overline{KL}$
   M: (3, 5)
   N: (1, 5)
5. Isosceles triangle *OPQ,* with $\overline{OP}$ the longest side
   Q: (−3, −2)
6. Parallelogram *RSTU*
   U: (4, −3)
7. Rhombus *VWXY*
   W: (−5, −7)
   Y: (−1, −7)
8. Kite *A'D'P'R'*
   P': (5, −7) *R'*: (3, −10)

Math Journal 1, p. 175

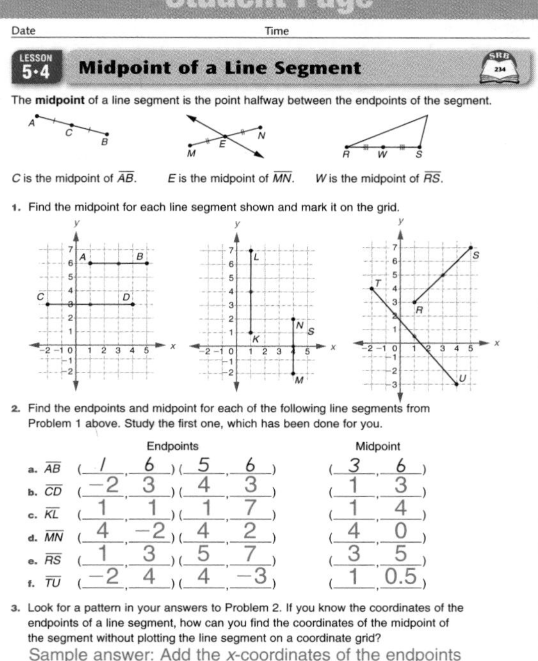

Student Page

Date Time

LESSON 5•4 **Midpoint of a Line Segment**

The **midpoint** of a line segment is the point halfway between the endpoints of the segment.

C is the midpoint of $\overline{AB}$. *E* is the midpoint of $\overline{MN}$. *W* is the midpoint of $\overline{RS}$.

1. Find the midpoint for each line segment shown and mark it on the grid.

2. Find the endpoints and midpoint for each of the following line segments from Problem 1 above. Study the first one, which has been done for you.

	Endpoints		Midpoint
a. $\overline{AB}$	(1, 6)	(5, 6)	(3, 6)
b. $\overline{CD}$	(−2, 3)	(4, 3)	(1, 3)
c. $\overline{KL}$	(1, 1)	(1, 7)	(1, 4)
d. $\overline{MN}$	(4, −2)	(4, 2)	(4, 0)
e. $\overline{RS}$	(1, 3)	(5, 7)	(3, 5)
f. $\overline{TU}$	(−2, 4)	(4, −3)	(1, 0.5)

3. Look for a pattern in your answers to Problem 2. If you know the coordinates of the endpoints of a line segment, how can you find the coordinates of the midpoint of the segment without plotting the line segment on a coordinate grid?
   Sample answer: Add the *x*-coordinates of the endpoints and divide by 2 to get the midpoint of the *x*-coordinate. Do the same for the *y*-coordinates.

Math Journal 1, p. 176

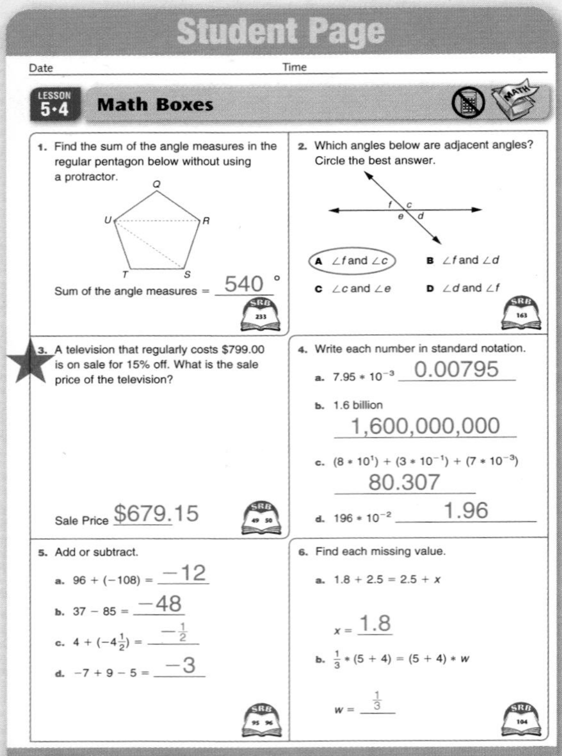
Student Page

Date Time

LESSON 5·4 Math Boxes

1. Find the sum of the angle measures in the regular pentagon below without using a protractor.

Sum of the angle measures = 540 °

2. Which angles below are adjacent angles? Circle the best answer.

A ∠f and ∠c (circled)
B ∠f and ∠d
C ∠c and ∠e
D ∠d and ∠f

3. A television that regularly costs $799.00 is on sale for 15% off. What is the sale price of the television?

Sale Price $679.15

4. Write each number in standard notation.

a. $7.95 * 10^{-3}$ 0.00795
b. 1.6 billion 1,600,000,000
c. $(8 * 10^{1}) + (3 * 10^{-1}) + (7 * 10^{-3})$ 80.307
d. $196 * 10^{-2}$ 1.96

5. Add or subtract.

a. 96 + (−108) = −12
b. 37 − 85 = −48
c. $4 + (-4\frac{1}{2}) =$ $-\frac{1}{2}$
d. −7 + 9 − 5 = −3

6. Find each missing value.

a. 1.8 + 2.5 = 2.5 + x

x = 1.8

b. $\frac{1}{3} * (5 + 4) = (5 + 4) * w$

w = $\frac{1}{3}$

Math Journal 1, p. 177

Study Link Master

Name Date Time

STUDY LINK 5·4 **More Polygons on a Coordinate Grid**

For each polygon described below, some vertices are plotted on the grid. Either one vertex or two vertices are missing.

- Plot and label the missing vertex or vertices on the grid. (There may be more than one place you can plot a point.)
- Write an ordered number pair for each vertex you plot.
- Draw the polygon. Sample answers for Problems 1–3:

1. Right triangle *ABC* Vertex *C*: (1, 2)
2. Parallelogram *DEFG* Vertex *F*: (5, 10) Vertex *G*: (3, 7)
3. Scalene triangle *HIJ* Vertex *J*: (2, 1)
4. Kite *KLMN* Vertex *M*: (−2, −3) 5. Square *PQRS* Vertex *Q*: (8, −3)

Math Masters, p. 157

Remind students of the definition of the **midpoint** of a line segment—the point halfway between the endpoints of the segment. Guide students to notice that in Problems 2a and 2b, the endpoints and midpoints have the same *y*-coordinate and that the *x*-coordinate of the midpoint is the number halfway between the *x*-coordinates of the endpoints. Problems 2c and 2d have a similar pattern. The *x*-coordinate is the same for endpoints and midpoint, and the *y*-coordinate of the midpoint is halfway between the *y*-coordinates of the endpoints.

The pattern in Problems 2e and 2f is a combination of the first two patterns. These patterns suggest the following conclusion:

To find the *x*- (or *y*-) coordinate of the midpoint, add the *x*- (or *y*-) coordinates of the endpoints and divide the sum by 2. In other words, find the mean of the coordinates.

2 Ongoing Learning & Practice

▶ Playing *Spoon Scramble*

(*Math Journal 1,* Activity Sheets 1 and 2; *Student Reference Book,* p. 333)

Read the directions with the class for *Spoon Scramble* on page 333 of the *Student Reference Book.* Demonstrate a round with a few volunteers. Use Activity Sheet 1 or 2, or have students use index cards to create their own sets of cards.

▶ Math Boxes 5·4

(*Math Journal 1,* p. 177)

Mixed Practice Math Boxes in this lesson are paired with Math Boxes in Lesson 5-2. The skills in Problems 5 and 6 preview Unit 6 content.

Ongoing Assessment: Recognizing Student Achievement

Math Boxes Problem 3

Use **Math Boxes, Problem 3** to assess students' ability to use a strategy for solving problems involving percents and discounts. Students are making adequate progress if they can calculate the sale price.

[Number and Numeration Goal 2]

▶ Study Link 5·4

(*Math Masters,* p. 157)

Home Connection Students plot and name missing vertices of polygons on a coordinate grid.

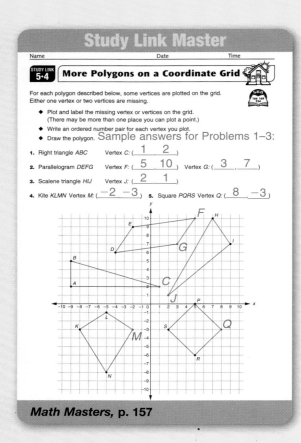

3 Differentiation Options

READINESS

PARTNER ACTIVITY

15–30 Min

▶ Playing *X and O—Tic-Tac-Toe*

(*Math Masters,* pp. 158 and 417)

To review ordered number pairs and how to find the location of ordered number pairs on a 4-quadrant coordinate grid, have students play *X and O—Tic-Tac-Toe.* In this game, students take turns drawing cards, forming ordered number pairs, and marking these ordered number pairs on a 4-quadrant coordinate grid.

Provide students with a copy of the game directions (*Math Masters,* p. 158) and a coordinate grid (*Math Masters,* p. 417).

ENRICHMENT

INDEPENDENT ACTIVITY

5–15 Min

▶ Plotting Triangles and Quadrangles in Four Quadrants

(*Math Masters,* pp. 417 and 159)

To extend their knowledge of geometric properties, students read descriptions of quadrangles and triangles and then plot the vertices on a 4-quadrant coordinate grid.

Teaching Master

Name Date Time

LESSON 5·4 **Plotting Triangles and Quadrangles**

Plot each of the described triangles and quadrangles on *Math Masters,* page 417. Record the coordinates of each vertex in the table below.

Sample answers:

	Description	Coordinates of Each Vertex
Example:	Square with side measuring 3 units	(6,−6); (6,−3); (9,−3); (9,−6)
1.	A rhombus that is *not* a square, which has at least one vertex with a negative *x*-coordinate and a positive *y*-coordinate	(−5,2); (−7,3); (−5,4); (−3,3)
2.	An isosceles triangle that has an area of 2 square units	(8,0); (9,2); (10,0)
3.	A rectangle that has a perimeter of 16 units	(2,4); (2,9); (5,9); (5,4)
4.	A right scalene triangle that has each vertex in a different quadrant	(−2,−2); (−2,1); (2,−2)
5.	A kite that has one vertex at the origin	(0,0); (−2,2); (0,5); (2,2)
6.	A parallelogram that has an area of 18 square units and one side on the *y*-axis	(0,−9); (0,−3); (3,−3); (3,−9)
7.	An obtuse scalene triangle that has at least two vertices with a negative *x*-coordinate and a negative *y*-coordinate	(−8,−6); (−9,−4); (−3,−6)
8.	Write your own description. Answers vary.	Answers vary.

***Math Masters,* p. 159**

Teaching Master

Name Date Time

LESSON 5·4 **X and O—Tic-Tac-Toe**

Materials □ 4 each of number cards 0–10 (from the Everything Math Deck, if available)

□ Coordinate Grid (*Math Masters,* p. 417)

Players 2

Object of the game To get 4 Xs or Os in a row, column, or diagonal on the coordinate grid.

Directions

1. Shuffle the cards and place the deck facedown on the playing surface.
2. In each round:
   - Player 1 draws 2 cards from the deck and uses the cards in any order to form an ordered pair. The player marks this ordered pair on the grid with an X and places the 2 cards in the discard pile.
   - Player 2 draws the next 2 cards from the deck and follows the same procedure, except that he or she uses an O to mark the ordered pair.
   - Players take turns drawing cards to form ordered pairs and marking the ordered pairs on the coordinate grid. If the 2 possible points that the player can make have already been marked, the player loses his or her turn.
3. The winner is the first player to get 4 Xs or 4 Os in a row, column, or diagonal.

***Math Masters,* p. 158**

5•5 Isometry Transformations

Objective To review transformations that produce another figure while maintaining the same size and shape of the original figure.

1 Teaching the Lesson

Key Activities

Students review and perform isometry transformations, including reflections, translations, and rotations.

Key Concepts and Skills

- Plot, name, and label points in any of the four quadrants of a coordinate grid. [Measurement and Reference Frames Goal 3]
- Identify congruent figures. [Geometry Goal 2]
- Practice and perform isometry transformations with geometric figures. [Geometry Goal 3]
- Classify a rotation by the number of degrees needed to produce a given image. [Geometry Goal 3]

Key Vocabulary

isometry transformation • transformation • translation (slide) • reflection (flip) • rotation (turn) • image • preimage • line of reflection

Ongoing Assessment: Recognizing Student Achievement Use an Exit Slip. [Measurement and Reference Frames Goal 3]

materials

- ☐ *Math Journal 1,* pp. 178–181
- ☐ *Student Reference Book,* pp. 180 and 181
- ☐ Teaching Aid Master (*Math Masters,* p. 404)
- ☐ Study Link 5•4
- ☐ transparent mirror
- ☐ tracing paper (optional)

2 Ongoing Learning & Practice

Students make a circle graph with a protractor.

Students practice and maintain skills through Math Boxes and Study Link activities.

materials

- ☐ *Math Journal 1,* pp. 182 and 183
- ☐ Study Link Master (*Math Masters,* p. 160)
- ☐ Geometry Template/protractor
- ☐ inch ruler; compass

3 Differentiation Options

READINESS

Students use an angle measurer to practice rotating a figure about a point.

ENRICHMENT

Students perform scaling transformations.

ELL SUPPORT

Students add terms associated with transformational geometry to their Math Word Banks.

materials

- ☐ Teaching Masters (*Math Masters,* pp. 161 and 162)
- ☐ *Differentiation Handbook*
- ☐ 1 trapezoid pattern block per student
- ☐ ruler

See Advance Preparation

Additional Information

Advance Preparation Set aside trapezoid pattern blocks for the optional Readiness activity.

Technology

Assessment Management System
Exit Slip
See the **iTLG.**

Getting Started

Mental Math and Reflexes

Students find the signed number that is halfway between each of the two given numbers. *Suggestions:*

●○○ between 5 and −5 0
between −7 and −3 −5
●●○ between −3 and 2 −0.5
●●● between 1.5 and −4.5 −1.5

Math Message

Study Problem 1 and complete Problem 2 on journal page 178.

Study Link 5·4 Follow-Up

Review answers.

1 Teaching the Lesson

▶ Math Message Follow-Up

WHOLE-CLASS DISCUSSION

(*Math Journal 1,* p. 178; *Student Reference Book,* pp. 180 and 181)

Students worked with **isometry transformations** in *Fifth Grade Everyday Mathematics,* but some of the vocabulary in this lesson may be new. Provide students with multiple opportunities to read, write, and say the vocabulary words. Whenever possible, relate vocabulary to students' experiences.

Briefly review each **transformation (translation, reflection,** and **rotation)** and go over the answers to Problems 2a–c. Draw students' attention to the fact that each new figure—the **image** (2)—is the same size and shape as the original figure—the **preimage** (1). Point out that the distance between points also remains unchanged.

Language Arts Link The word *isometry* comes from the Greek words *iso,* meaning *same,* and *metron,* meaning *measure.*

Adjusting the Activity

Have students identify the following locations on a coordinate grid:

- the origin (0,0)
- the *x*-axis (or horizontal axis)
- the *y*-axis (or vertical axis)

Write several ordered number pairs on the board. Ask students to identify the *x*- and *y*-coordinates for each ordered number pair.

AUDITORY ◆ KINESTHETIC ◆ TACTILE ◆ VISUAL

Student Page

Date Time

LESSON 5·5 **Isometry Transformations**

Math Message

SRB 180 181

Translations (slides), reflections (flips), and **rotations (turns)** are basic transformations that can be used to move a figure from one place to another without changing its size or shape.

1. Study each transformation shown below.

Translation (Slide)	Reflection (Flip)	Rotation (Turn)
A **translation** (slide) moves each point of a figure a certain distance in the same direction.	A **reflection** (flip) of a figure gives its mirror image over a line.	A **rotation** (turn) moves a figure around a point.

2. Identify whether the preimage (1) and image (2) are related by a translation, a reflection, or a rotation. Record your answer on the line below each coordinate grid.

a. reflection
b. translation
c. rotation

Math Journal 1, p. 178

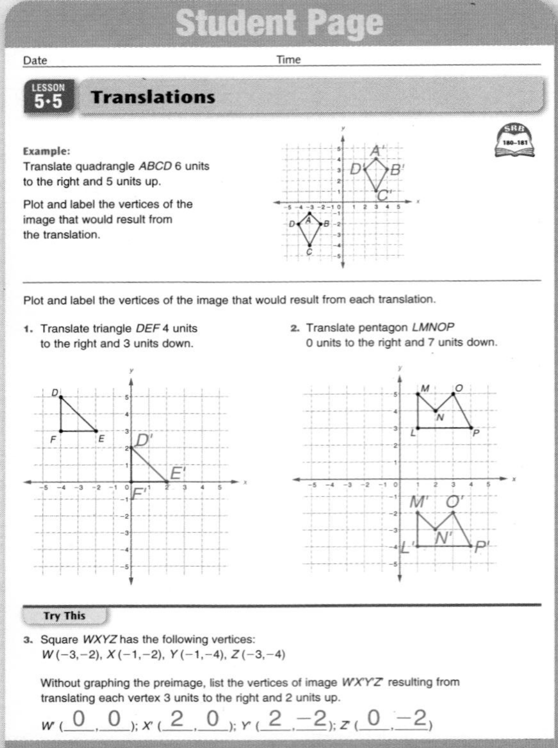

Student Page

Date Time

LESSON 5•5 **Translations**

Example:
Translate quadrangle *ABCD* 6 units to the right and 5 units up.

Plot and label the vertices of the image that would result from the translation.

Plot and label the vertices of the image that would result from each translation.

1. Translate triangle *DEF* 4 units to the right and 3 units down.
2. Translate pentagon *LMNOP* 0 units to the right and 7 units down.

Try This

3. Square *WXYZ* has the following vertices:
$W(-3,-2)$, $X(-1,-2)$, $Y(-1,-4)$, $Z(-3,-4)$

Without graphing the preimage, list the vertices of image *W'X'Y'Z'* resulting from translating each vertex 3 units to the right and 2 units up.

W' (0, 0); X' (2, 0); Y' (2, −2); Z' (0, −2)

***Math Journal 1*, p. 179**

▶ Translating Geometric Figures

WHOLE-CLASS ACTIVITY

(*Math Journal 1,* p. 179)

When a figure is translated, each point on the preimage slides the same distance in the same direction to create the image. If the translation is done on a coordinate plane, the image of a point can be found by adding translation numbers to the coordinates of the point being translated. In the example on journal page 179, each point of Figure *ABCD* is translated 6 units to the right (+6) and 5 units up (+5). Each point of the preimage has a corresponding point in the image. Point out that to distinguish between the image and the preimage, students should label an image point with the same letter as the preimage point and the additional symbol ($'$). For example, the image of A is A', read "A prime."

Ongoing Assessment: Recognizing Student Achievement

Exit Slip

Use the example on **journal page 179** to assess students' ability to name ordered number pairs in the third quadrant. Students are making adequate progress if they can correctly name the vertices of preimage *ABCD.* Ask students to record the number pairs on an **Exit Slip** (*Math Masters,* p. 404).

[Measurement and Reference Frames Goal 3]

List the coordinates of the vertices of $ABCD$ and $A'B'C'D'$. Show students how they can produce the image ($A'B'C'D'$) from the preimage ($ABCD$) by adding +6 units to each x-coordinate of a vertex and +5 units to each y-coordinate.

$$A = (-3,-1) \quad A' = (3,4)$$
$$B = (-2,-2) \quad B' = (4,3)$$
$$C = (-3,-4) \quad C' = (3,1)$$
$$D = (-4,-2) \quad D' = (2,3)$$

Ask students to pay attention to the coordinates of the vertices of preimages and images as they complete journal page 179.

Student Page

Date Time

LESSON 5•5 **Reflections**

Reflect each figure over the indicated axis or line of reflection. Then plot and label the vertices of the image that results from the reflection. Use a transparent mirror to check your placement of each image.

1. Reflect triangle *TAM* over the *x*-axis.
2. Reflect rectangle *STUV* over the *y*-axis.
3. Reflect triangle *PQR* over the *y*-axis.
4. Reflect square *DEFG* over line *m*.

***Math Journal 1*, p. 180**

▶ Reflecting Geometric Figures

WHOLE-CLASS ACTIVITY

(*Math Journal 1,* p. 180)

The reflection of a figure appears to be a reversal, or mirror image of the preimage. Each point on the preimage is the same distance from the **line of reflection** as the corresponding point on the image. When reflecting geometric figures over an axis on the coordinate grid, the axis is the line of reflection. The preimage and image are on opposite sides of the axis.

Have students complete journal page 180. Bring the class together to review answers by asking a volunteer to read the coordinates of each image or by having students check the reflections with a transparent mirror. Ask students to look closely at Problem 2 and decide whether the same image could be obtained by a horizontal translation of the preimage. Although the rectangles have the same orientation in relation to the x-axis, the order of the vertices changes from the preimage to the image. When a translation is performed, the order of the vertices remains unchanged.

Adjusting the Activity

Have students set a transparent mirror on the line of reflection to more clearly see the reversal of the points on a reflected image.

AUDITORY ◆ KINESTHETIC ◆ TACTILE ◆ VISUAL

▶ Rotating Geometric Figures

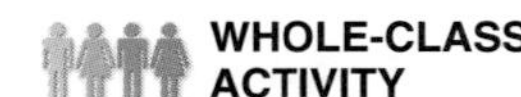

WHOLE-CLASS ACTIVITY

(*Math Journal 1,* pp. 178 and 181)

Draw attention again to Problem 2c of the Math Message on journal page 178. Point out that to rotate a figure, the following are needed:

▷ a specific point about which the figure is to rotate.

▷ a number of degrees the figure is to rotate about that specific point.

▷ a specific direction of rotation (clockwise or counterclockwise).

To support English language learners, discuss the meaning of *clockwise* and *counterclockwise.*

In Problem 2c, the preimage (1) is rotated 90° counterclockwise about the point (0,−3) to produce the image (2). A clockwise rotation of 270° of the preimage (1) will also produce the same image.

Have students work in partnerships on journal page 181.

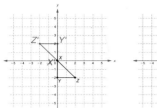

Adjusting the Activity

Make copies of journal page 181 from which students can cut out each preimage and perform each rotation manually. Students can also trace the preimage onto another sheet of paper and rotate the paper to help determine the orientation of the image.

AUDITORY ◆ KINESTHETIC ◆ TACTILE ◆ VISUAL

Student Page

Date Time

LESSON 5•5 **Rotations**

Rotate each figure around the point in the direction given. Then plot and label the vertices of the image that results from that rotation.

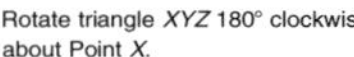

1. Rotate triangle *XYZ* 180° clockwise about Point *X*.

2. Rotate quadrangle *BCDE* 90° counterclockwise about the origin.

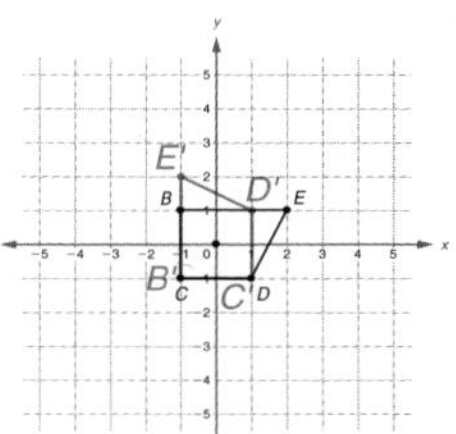

3. Rotate trapezoid *MNOP* 90° counterclockwise about point *M*.

4. Rotate triangle *SEV* 270° clockwise about (0,2).

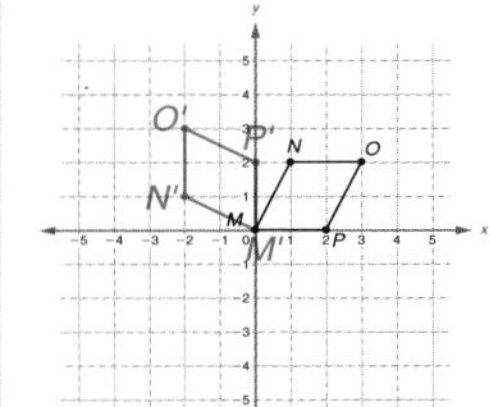

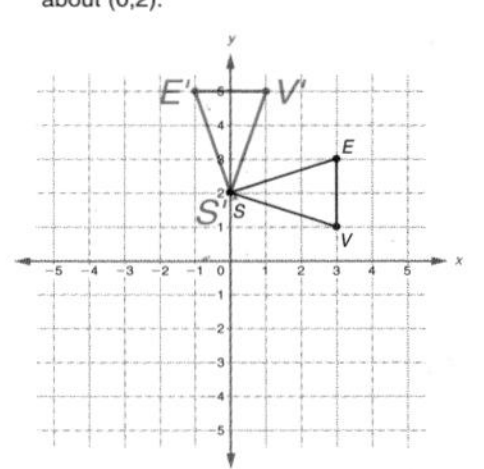

Math Journal 1, p. 181

Student Page

Date Time

LESSON 5•5 **Making a Circle Graph with a Protractor**

1. One way to convert a percent to the degree measure of a sector is to multiply 360° by the decimal equivalent of the percent.

Example: What is the degree measure of a sector that is 55% of a circle?
55% of 360° = 0.55 ∗ 360° = 198°

Complete the table below.

Percent of Circle	Decimal Equivalent	Degree Measure of Sector
40%	0.4	0.4 ∗ 360° = 144°
90%	0.9	0.9 ∗ 360° = 324°
65%	0.65	0.65 ∗ 360° = 234°
5%	0.05	0.05 ∗ 360° = 18°
1%	0.01	0.01 ∗ 360° = 3.6°

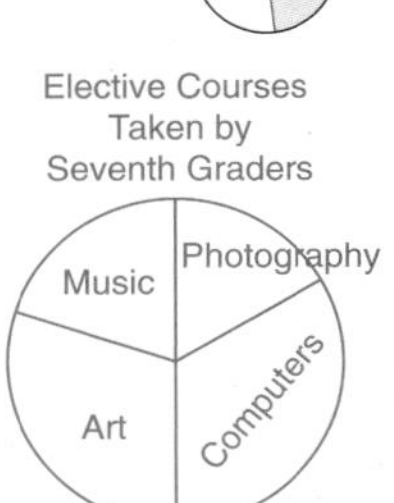

2. The table below shows the elective courses taken by a class of seventh graders. Complete the table. Then, in the space to the right, use a protractor to make a circle graph to display the information. Do not use the Percent Circle. (*Reminder:* Use a fraction or a decimal to find the degree measure of each sector.) Write a title for the graph.

Course	Number of Students	Fraction of Students	Decimal Equivalent	Percent of Students	Degree Measure of Sector
Music	6	$\frac{6}{30}$	0.2	20%	72°
Art	9	$\frac{9}{30}$	0.3	30%	108°
Computers	10	$\frac{10}{30}$	$0.3\overline{3}$	$33\frac{1}{3}$%	120°
Photography	5	$\frac{5}{30}$	$0.1\overline{6}$	$16\frac{2}{3}$%	60°

Math Journal 1, p. 182

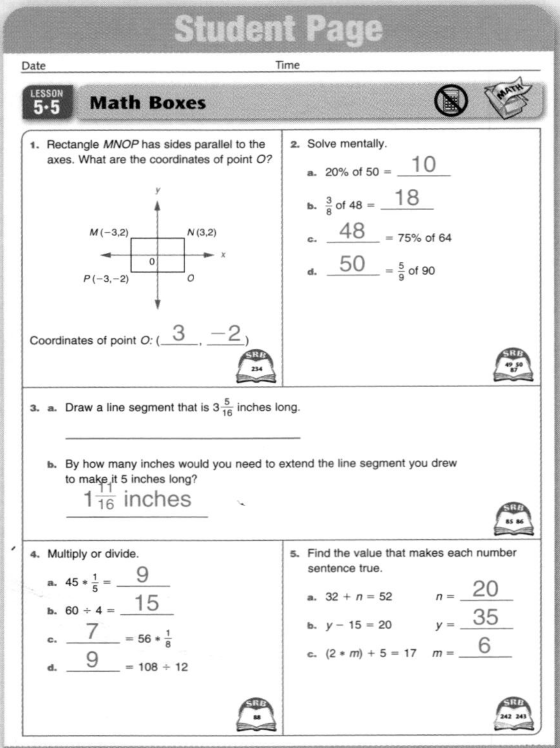

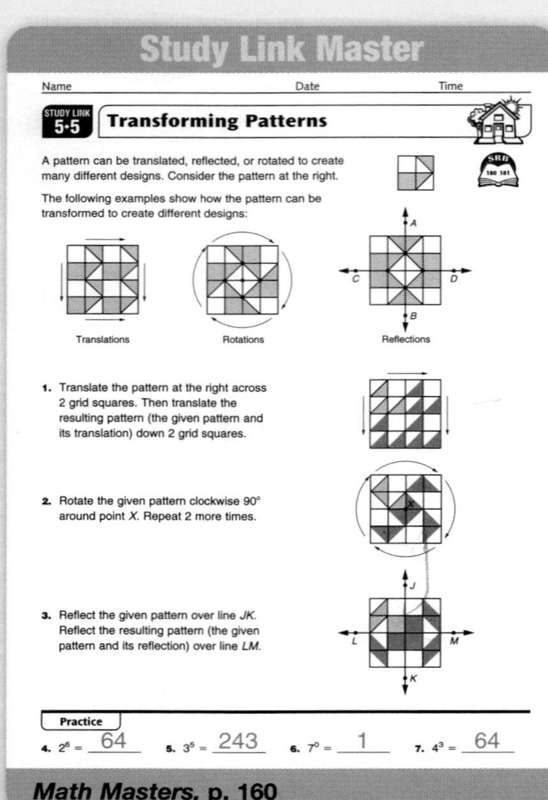

Links to the Future

Offer an example of a transformation that is not an isometry transformation. In Unit 8 of *Sixth Grade Everyday Mathematics,* students will study similar figures, which are produced by scaling transformations. A scaling transformation produces a figure that is the same shape as the original figure but not necessarily the same size. The following shows a scaling (but not an isometry) transformation:

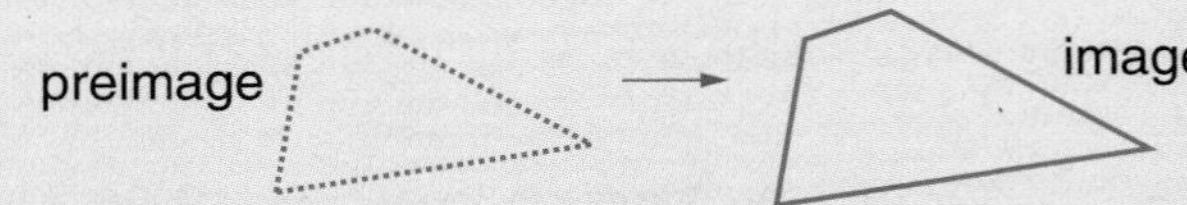

2 Ongoing Learning & Practice

▶ Making a Circle Graph with a Protractor

(*Math Journal 1,* p. 182)

Students find fraction, decimal, and percent equivalencies; calculate degree measures of sectors; and use a compass and a protractor to create a circle graph to display elective course information.

▶ Math Boxes 5•5

(*Math Journal 1,* p. 183)

Mixed Practice Math Boxes in this lesson are paired with Math Boxes in Lesson 5-7. The skills in Problems 4 and 5 preview Unit 6 content.

Writing and Reasoning Have students write a response to the following: *Explain how to rewrite Problems 4b and 4d as multiplication problems.* Sample answer: The division problem 60 ÷ 4 can be expressed as the fraction $\frac{60}{4}$. Because $\frac{60}{4} = 60 * \frac{1}{4}$, 60 ÷ 4 and $60 * \frac{1}{4}$ are equivalent expressions. Similarly, 108 ÷ 12 can be expressed as $\frac{108}{12}$ or $108 * \frac{1}{12}$.

▶ Study Link 5•5

INDEPENDENT ACTIVITY

(*Math Masters,* p. 160)

Home Connection Students practice performing transformations on a grid. If necessary, review the examples at the top of page 160 with the class.

3 Differentiation Options

READINESS

INDEPENDENT ACTIVITY

5–15 Min

▶ Reviewing Degrees and Directions of Rotation

(*Math Masters,* p. 161)

To provide experience using an angle measurer and rotating a figure, have students complete *Math Masters,* page 161. Students use an angle measurer with an embedded clock face to practice rotating a trapezoid pattern block a given number of degrees in a clockwise or counterclockwise direction. If necessary, provide additional opportunities to rotate the trapezoid.

ENRICHMENT

INDEPENDENT ACTIVITY

5–15 Min

▶ Performing a Scaling Transformation

(*Math Masters*, p. 162)

To deepen students' understanding of transformations and to introduce a size-change transformation, have students complete *Math Masters,* page 162. Students follow steps to perform scaling transformations to produce images that are twice and half the size of preimages. Have students describe the relationships between the original figure and the enlarged or reduced figure. Encourage them to use the vocabulary they have developed in this unit.

ELL SUPPORT

INDEPENDENT ACTIVITY

5–15 Min

▶ Building a Math Word Bank

(*Differentiation Handbook*)

To provide language support for transformational geometry terms, have students use the Word Bank template in the *Differentiation Handbook.* Ask students to write the terms *translation, reflection,* and *rotation,* draw pictures depicting each term, and write other related words. See the *Differentiation Handbook* for more information.

Teaching Master

Name Date Time

LESSON 5·5 **Degrees and Directions of Rotation**

When a figure is rotated, it is turned a certain number of degrees around a particular point. A figure can be rotated clockwise or counterclockwise.

Position a trapezoid pattern block on the center point of the angle measurer as shown at the right. Then rotate the pattern block as indicated and trace it in its new position.

Example: Rotate 90° clockwise.

For each problem below, rotate and then trace the pattern block in its new position.

1. Rotate 90° counterclockwise.
2. Rotate 270° clockwise.

Math Masters, **p. 161**

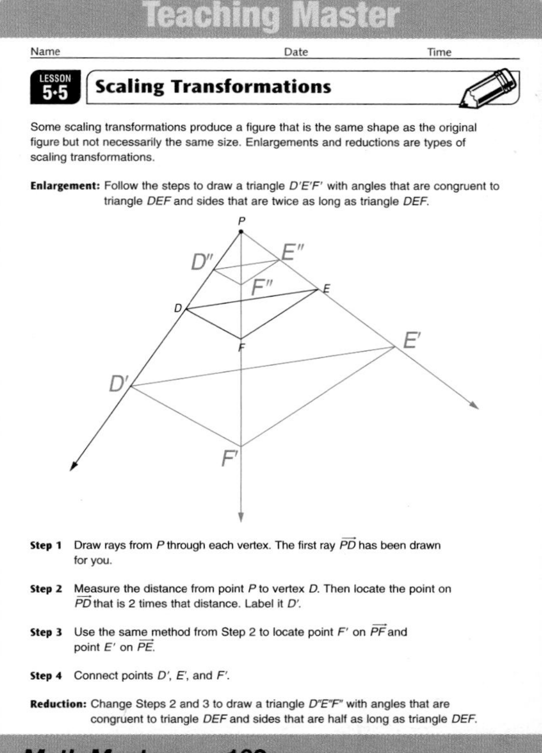

Teaching Master

Name Date Time

LESSON 5·5 **Scaling Transformations**

Some scaling transformations produce a figure that is the same shape as the original figure but not necessarily the same size. Enlargements and reductions are types of scaling transformations.

Enlargement: Follow the steps to draw a triangle *D'E'F'* with angles that are congruent to triangle *DEF* and sides that are twice as long as triangle *DEF.*

Step 1 Draw rays from *P* through each vertex. The first ray $\overrightarrow{PD}$ has been drawn for you.

Step 2 Measure the distance from point *P* to vertex *D.* Then locate the point on $\overrightarrow{PD}$ that is 2 times that distance. Label it *D'.*

Step 3 Use the same method from Step 2 to locate point *F'* on $\overrightarrow{PF}$ and point *E'* on $\overrightarrow{PE}$.

Step 4 Connect points *D', E',* and *F'.*

Reduction: Change Steps 2 and 3 to draw a triangle *D''E''F''* with angles that are congruent to triangle *DEF* and sides that are half as long as triangle *DEF.*

Math Masters, **p. 162**

Congruent Figures

Objectives To explore the meaning of congruence; and to use drawing tools to construct congruent figures.

1 Teaching the Lesson

Key Activities

Students explore the properties of congruent line segments, angles, and other figures. They also use drawing tools to construct congruent segments, angles, and 2-dimensional figures.

Key Concepts and Skills

- Identify congruent figures. [Geometry Goal 2]
- Use a straightedge and compass to construct a figure that is congruent to the original. [Geometry Goal 2]
- Apply the knowledge that a preimage and its image are congruent. [Geometry Goal 3]

Key Vocabulary

congruent • corresponding (sides, angles) • rough sketch • accurate drawing

materials

- ☐ *Math Journal 1,* pp. 184–186
- ☐ *Student Reference Book,* p. 178
- ☐ Study Link 5•5
- ☐ Transparency (Study Link 5•5; optional)
- ☐ compass; ruler
- ☐ Geometry Template/protractor
- ☐ board compass and protractor (for demonstration purposes)

See **Advance Preparation**

2 Ongoing Learning & Practice

Students practice and maintain skills through Math Boxes and Study Link activities.

Ongoing Assessment: Recognizing Student Achievement Use journal page 187. [Geometry Goal 3]

materials

- ☐ *Math Journal 1,* p. 187
- ☐ Study Link Master (*Math Masters,* p. 163)
- ☐ tracing paper (optional)

3 Differentiation Options

READINESS

Students sort quadrangles according to relationships between congruent angles and/or sides.

ENRICHMENT

Students explore isometry transformations using pentominoes.

EXTRA PRACTICE

Students practice using vocabulary terms to describe polygons and shapes.

materials

- ☐ Teaching Masters (*Math Masters,* pp. 164 and 165)
- ☐ Teaching Aid Master (*Math Masters,* p. 418)
- ☐ *5-Minute Math* pp. 57, 61, 64, 220, and 229
- ☐ metric ruler
- ☐ Geometry Template/protractor
- ☐ scissors; tape/glue
- ☐ 5 square tiles
- ☐ large sheets of paper

Additional Information

Advance Preparation For Part 1, draw and cut out two congruent polygons similar to those on page 178 of the *Student Reference Book.* Size them so both polygons fit on an overhead screen at the same time.

Technology

Assessment Management System
Math Boxes, Problem 1
See the **iTLG.**

Getting Started

Mental Math and Reflexes

Students mentally calculate 10%, 5%, 1%, and 6% of a number.
Suggestions:

●○○	●●○	●●●
10% of 100 10	10% of 360 36	10% of 90 9
5% of 100 5	5% of 360 18	5% of 90 4.5
1% of 100 1	1% of 360 3.6	1% of 90 0.9
6% of 100 6	6% of 360 21.6	6% of 90 5.4

Math Message

Complete the Math Message on journal page 184.

Study Link 5·5 Follow-Up

Students compare the designs resulting from the transformations. Consider making a transparency of Study Link 5-5 and have volunteers share their designs on the overhead.

1 Teaching the Lesson

▶ Math Message Follow-Up

WHOLE-CLASS DISCUSSION

(*Math Journal 1,* p. 184; *Student Reference Book,* p. 178)

Begin by discussing the need for definitions in mathematics. For example, definitions help avoid confusion when people make mathematical statements. You may also want to identify some characteristics of a good definition:

▷ It should name the term being defined.

▷ It should include only words that are easily understood or words that have been defined previously.

▷ It should be accurate and concise.

Ask students to share their definitions of *congruent polygons.* Then discuss the *Student Reference Book* definition. **Congruent** figures are figures that have the same size and the same shape. The word *shape* is difficult to define. Students should know intuitively that all squares have the same shape, all circles have the same shape, and so on. Discuss why all squares have the same shape but not all rectangles do. Some rectangles have sides that differ greatly in length; others have sides that are almost the same length.

Have students use the definition of *congruent* to explain why the pairs of polygons in Examples **d, e,** and **f** are not congruent. Explanations should include the following:

▷ The sides of the polygons in Example **d** are the same length, but the polygons are not the same shape—they don't have the same number of sides.

▷ The equilateral triangles in Example **e** are the same shape, but they are not the same size—their sides are not the same length.

▷ The polygons in Example **f** are not the same shape. Although their sides are the same length, their angles have different degree measures.

Student Page

Date Time

LESSON 5·6 **Congruent Figures**

Math Message

Carefully examine the figures in examples a–f.

The following pairs of figures are **congruent** to each other.

a.

b.

c.

The following pairs of figures are *not* congruent to each other.

d.

e.

f.

1. Write a definition of *congruent polygons.* Then compare your definition to the definition on page 178 in the *Student Reference Book.*
Answers vary.

Line segments are **congruent** if they have the same length.

Angles are **congruent** if they have the same degree measure.

2. Draw wavy lines to connect each pair of congruent line segments below. Use a ruler to measure line segments if needed.

3. Draw wavy lines to connect each pair of congruent angles below. Use a protractor to measure angles if needed.

Math Journal 1, p. 184

One way to determine whether two figures are congruent is to trace one of the figures, place the tracing on top of the other figure, and see whether the figures match exactly. One figure may have to be rotated or reflected to verify that it matches the other figure. Performing an isometry transformation is one way to decide if figures are congruent, especially when they appear to be the same shape and size.

To demonstrate the method described above, use the two congruent polygons you cut out. (*See Advance Preparation.*) Hold them up in different positions or place them on the overhead projector. Move one on top of the other so they match. Show how a combination of slides, flips, and turns can make one polygon fit exactly on top of the other. Mention that **corresponding sides** are the same length and **corresponding angles** have the same degree measure.

Adjusting the Activity

Use the demonstration polygons to show how to use slash marks and arcs to identify pairs of corresponding sides and angles. Also point out that when naming congruent polygons, the corresponding vertices of the polygons are listed in the same order for both polygons.

AUDITORY ◆ KINESTHETIC ◆ TACTILE ◆ VISUAL

Go over the answers to Problems 2 and 3. Note that in these problems, some line segments and angles may be difficult to match. If there are disagreements, have students check answers by measuring with a ruler or a protractor.

Links to the Future

In Unit 8, students will identify the corresponding sides and corresponding angles of figures that have the same shape but are not necessarily the same size. In their seventh- and eighth-grade mathematics courses, students will need to recognize congruent polygons when deriving and using formulas to calculate surface areas of polyhedrons.

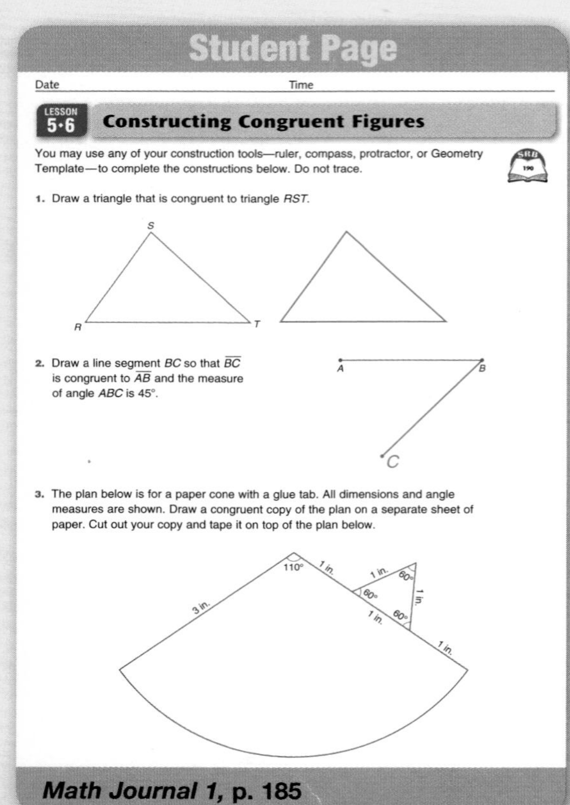

Math Journal 1, p. 185

▶ Constructing Congruent Figures

PARTNER ACTIVITY

(*Math Journal 1,* p. 185)

The problems on journal page 185 provide practice with drawing and measuring tools. Students may use any combination of tools they wish. Then bring the class together and ask students which tools they used for their constructions. Compare approaches. Ask students how they know that their drawings are congruent to the given figures.

▶ Making Accurate Drawings from Rough Sketches

(*Math Journal 1,* p. 186)

To support English language learners, discuss the differences between the verbs *draw, sketch,* and *construct.* Introduce the distinction between **rough sketches** and **accurate drawings.** Explain that lengths and angle measures may be written on a rough sketch, but that does not mean that they are drawn correctly. Draw a rough sketch on the board or overhead and then make a careful drawing from the sketch. (For drawing on the board, multiply the given lengths by 10.)

Example:

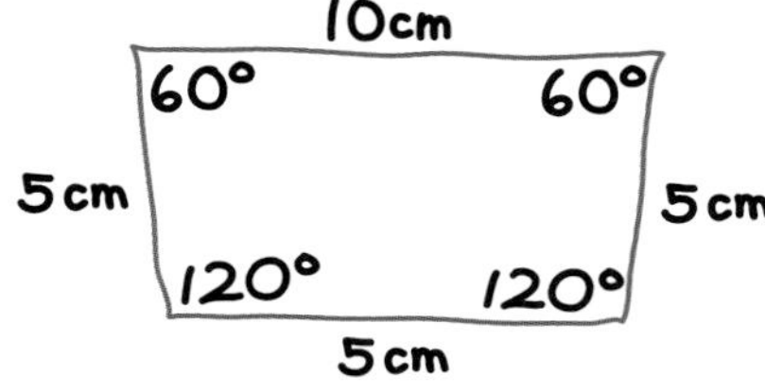

A rough sketch of a trapezoid

An accurate drawing of a trapezoid

Caution students that the diagram on journal page 186 is only a rough sketch, so they should not try to measure the angles or line segments. They need to work from the written measurements. Again, they may use any of their tools to make an accurate drawing of the rough sketch.

Bring the class together and have students describe how they made their drawings.

Although many of the angle measures and segment lengths are unknown, students have sufficient information to make a precise drawing.

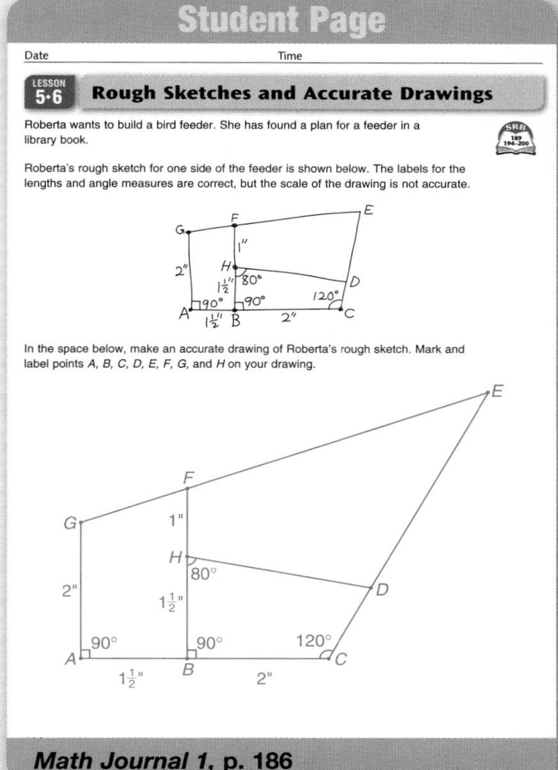

Student Page

Date Time

LESSON 5·6 **Rough Sketches and Accurate Drawings**

Roberta wants to build a bird feeder. She has found a plan for a feeder in a library book.

SRB 189 194–200

Roberta's rough sketch for one side of the feeder is shown below. The labels for the lengths and angle measures are correct, but the scale of the drawing is not accurate.

In the space below, make an accurate drawing of Roberta's rough sketch. Mark and label points *A, B, C, D, E, F, G,* and *H* on your drawing.

Math Journal 1, p. 186

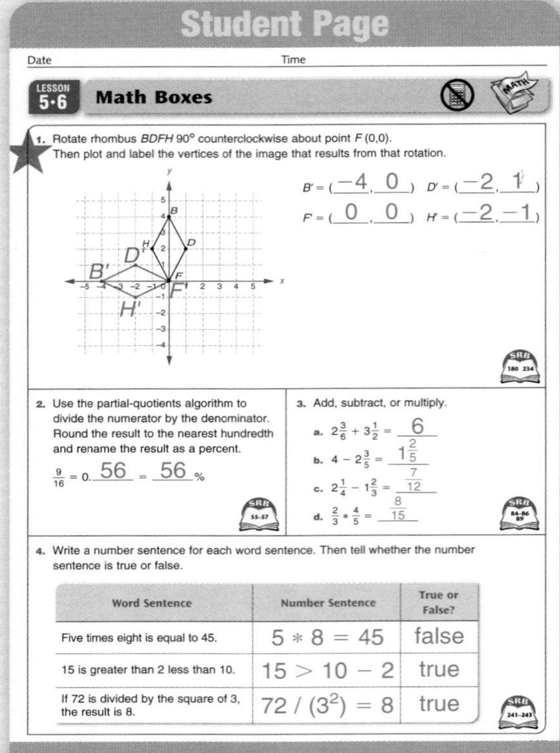
Student Page

Date Time

LESSON 5•6 **Math Boxes**

1. Rotate rhombus *BDFH* 90° counterclockwise about point *F* (0,0). Then plot and label the vertices of the image that results from that rotation.

B' = (−4, 0) D' = (−2, 1)

F = (0, 0) H' = (−2, −1)

2. Use the partial-quotients algorithm to divide the numerator by the denominator. Round the result to the nearest hundredth and rename the result as a percent.

$\frac{9}{16}$ = 0.56 = 56 %

3. Add, subtract, or multiply.

a. $2\frac{3}{6} + 3\frac{1}{2} = 6$

b. $4 - 2\frac{3}{5} = 1\frac{2}{5}$

c. $2\frac{1}{4} - 1\frac{2}{3} = \frac{7}{12}$

d. $\frac{2}{3} * \frac{4}{5} = \frac{8}{15}$

4. Write a number sentence for each word sentence. Then tell whether the number sentence is true or false.

Word Sentence	Number Sentence	True or False?
Five times eight is equal to 45.	5 ∗ 8 = 45	false
15 is greater than 2 less than 10.	15 > 10 − 2	true
If 72 is divided by the square of 3, the result is 8.	72 / (3²) = 8	true

Math Journal 1, p. 187

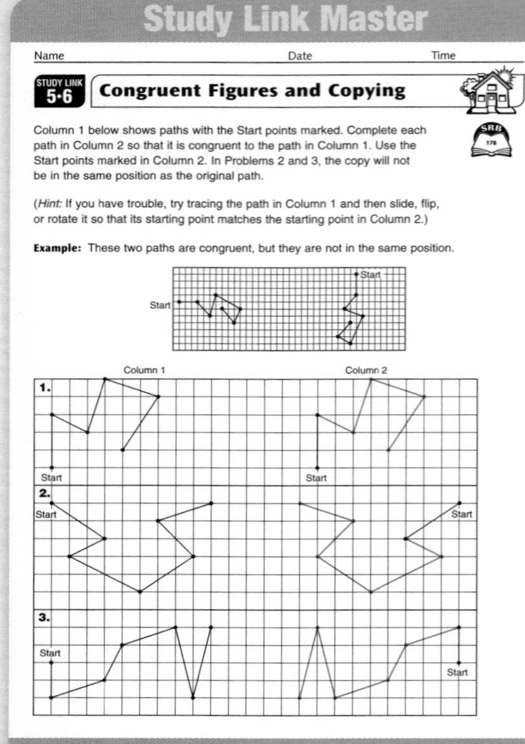
Study Link Master

Name Date Time

STUDY LINK 5•6 **Congruent Figures and Copying**

Column 1 below shows paths with the Start points marked. Complete each path in Column 2 so that it is congruent to the path in Column 1. Use the Start points marked in Column 2. In Problems 2 and 3, the copy will not be in the same position as the original path.

(*Hint:* If you have trouble, try tracing the path in Column 1 and then slide, flip, or rotate it so that its starting point matches the starting point in Column 2.)

Example: These two paths are congruent, but they are not in the same position.

Column 1 Column 2

Math Masters, p. 163

Here is one possible sequence of steps:

1. Draw a right angle with sides 2 inches and $3\frac{1}{2}$ inches. Label the angle *GAC*.
2. Mark point *B* on $\overline{AC}$, $1\frac{1}{2}$ inches from point *A*.
3. Draw a line segment perpendicular to $\overline{AC}$ at point *B*. Mark point *F* on this segment, $2\frac{1}{2}$ inches above point *B*. Mark point *H* on $\overline{BF}$, $1\frac{1}{2}$ inches above point *B*.
4. Draw a 120° angle at point *C*. (The sketch shows how to position this angle.)
5. Draw an 80° angle at point *H*. (The sketch shows how to position this angle.)
6. Draw a line segment from point *G* through point *F* and extend the side of the angle *C*. Label the intersection *E*.
7. Extend the side of angle *H* to $\overline{CE}$. Label the intersection *D*.

2 Ongoing Learning & Practice

▶ Math Boxes 5•6

INDEPENDENT ACTIVITY

(*Math Journal 1,* p. 187)

Mixed Practice Math Boxes in this lesson are paired with Math Boxes in Lesson 5-9. The skill in Problem 4 previews Unit 6 content.

Writing/Reasoning Have students write a response to the following: *Identify another rotation in Problem 1 that will produce an image with vertices at the same location as the image you got by performing a 90° counterclockwise rotation.* If *BDFH* is rotated 270° clockwise, the vertices of the image will be in the same location as when *BDFH* is rotated 90° counterclockwise.

Ongoing Assessment: Recognizing Student Achievement

Math Boxes Problem 1

Use **Math Boxes, Problem 1** to assess students' abilities to rotate a figure and name points on a coordinate grid. Students are making adequate progress if they can correctly plot the image and accurately name the coordinates of each vertex.

[Geometry Goal 3]

▶ Study Link 5•6

INDEPENDENT ACTIVITY

(*Math Masters,* p. 163)

Home Connection Students copy figures made of line segments, using a grid as a guide. In Problems 2 and 3, the copies have different orientations than the originals.

3 Differentiation Options

READINESS

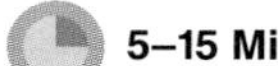

SMALL-GROUP ACTIVITY

5–15 Min

▶ Using Congruence to Sort Shapes

(*Math Masters,* p. 164 and 165)

To provide experience applying vocabulary and properties of congruence, have students cut out the 16 quadrangles and 6 set labels on *Math Masters,* page 164. They place the quadrangles in the rings of a Venn diagram on *Math Masters,* page 165 according to each pair of labels.

Pair A: All Right Angles; All Sides Congruent

Pair B: All Pairs Opposite Sides Congruent; At Least 2 Acute Angles

Pair C: Adjacent Sides Congruent; At Least 1 Right Angle

Students can use a ruler to compare side lengths and a protractor to compare angle measures.

NOTE Consider collecting and saving the quadrangles for the optional Readiness activity in Lesson 5-10.

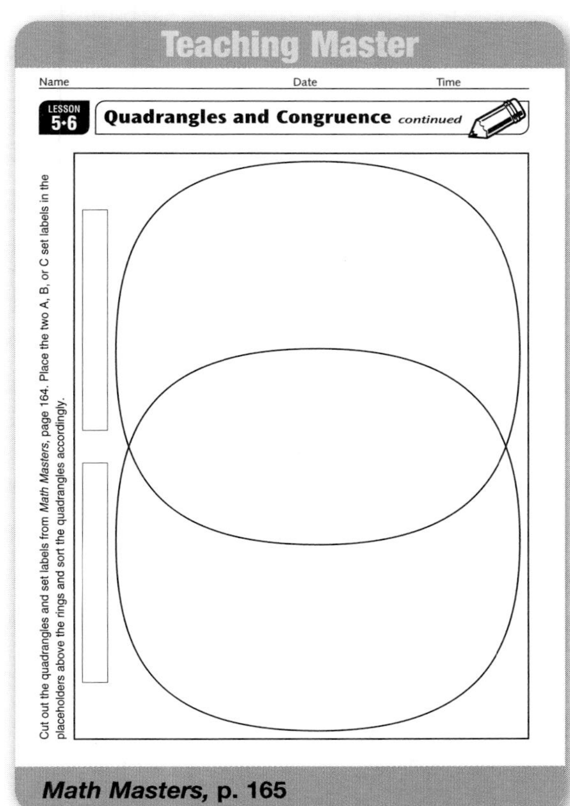
Teaching Master

Name Date Time

LESSON 5•6 **Quadrangles and Congruence** *continued*

Cut out the quadrangles and set labels from *Math Masters,* page 164. Place the two A, B, or C set labels in the placeholders above the rings and sort the quadrangles accordingly.

Math Masters, p. 165

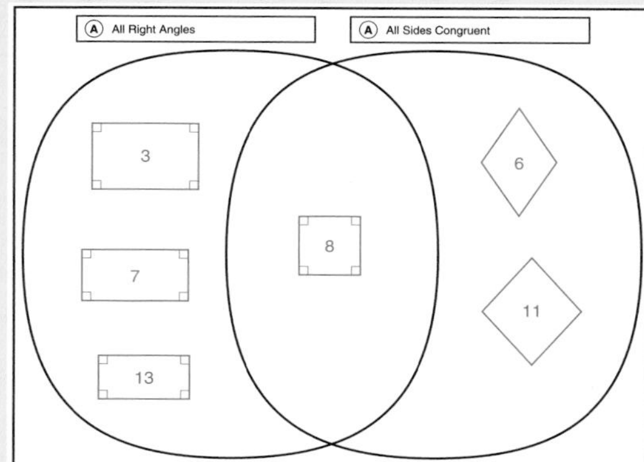

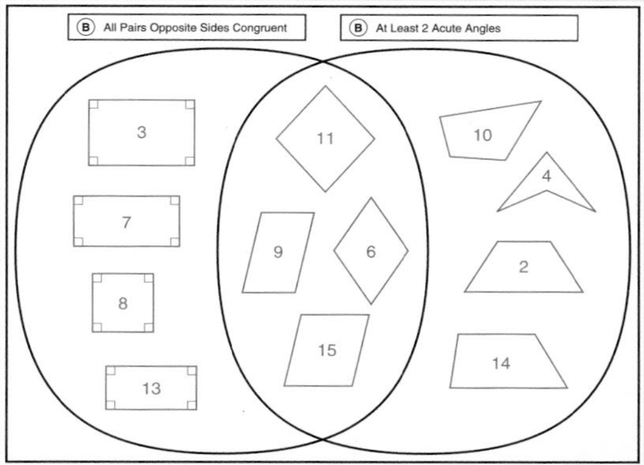

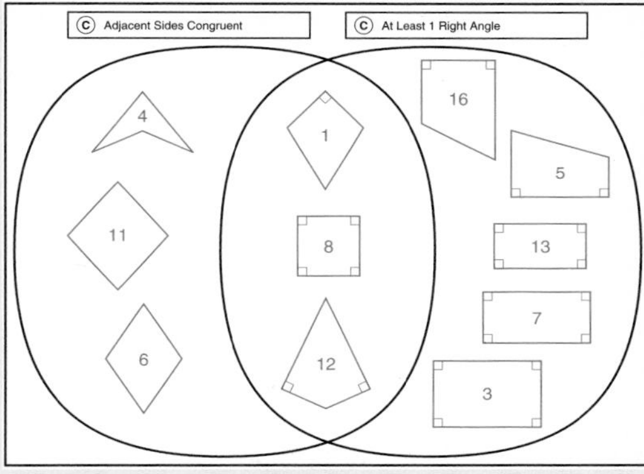

Teaching Aid Master

Name Date Time

Graph Paper (1 in.)

***Math Masters,* p. 418**

ENRICHMENT

SMALL-GROUP ACTIVITY

15–30 Min

Exploring Isometry Transformations and Congruence

(*Math Masters,* p. 418)

A *pentomino* is an arrangement of five unit squares that are joined along their edges.

This is a pentomino:

This is not a pentomino:

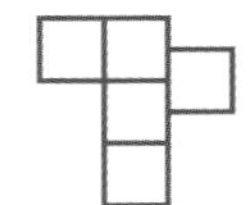

To further explore isometry transformations and congruence, students use five same-size square tiles to form as many different pentominoes as possible. They draw each pentomino on *Math Masters,* page 418, cut them out, and tape/glue them onto a large sheet of paper. Students apply their knowledge of isometry transformations (translations, reflections, rotations) to check that each pentomino is different.

The 12 possible pentominoes are shown below.

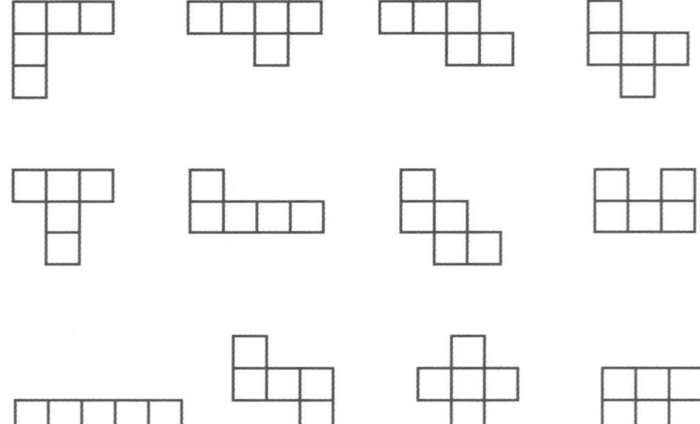

EXTRA PRACTICE

SMALL-GROUP ACTIVITY

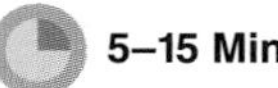

5–15 Min

5-Minute Math

To offer more practice using geometry vocabulary terms to describe polygons and other shapes, see *5-Minute Math,* pages 57, 61, 64, 220, and 229.

Compass-and-Straightedge Constructions Part 1

Objective To construct figures with a compass and a straightedge.

1 Teaching the Lesson

Key Activities

Students review two basic compass-and-straightedge constructions—copying a line segment and copying a triangle.

Key Concepts and Skills

- Use appropriate strategies to measure angles to the nearest degree. [Measurement and Reference Frames Goal 1]
- Label the points and vertices of a preimage and its image. [Measurement and Reference Frames Goal 3]
- Use a straightedge and compass to construct a figure that is congruent to the original. [Geometry Goal 2]

Key Vocabulary

compass-and-straightedge construction • anchor (of a compass) • concentric circles

Ongoing Assessment: Informing Instruction See page 371.

materials

- ☐ *Math Journal 1,* pp. 188 and 189
- ☐ *Student Reference Book,* pp. 188–190
- ☐ Study Link 5•6
- ☐ compass; straightedge
- ☐ ruler; Geometry Template/protractor
- ☐ tape
- ☐ board compass and meterstick (for demonstration purposes)

***See* Advance Preparation**

2 Ongoing Learning & Practice

Students practice renaming fractions as decimals by playing the decimal version of *2-4-8* or *3-6-9 Frac-Tac-Toe.*

Students practice and maintain skills through Math Boxes and Study Link activities.

Ongoing Assessment: Recognizing Student Achievement Use an Exit Slip. [Number and Numeration Goal 5]

materials

- ☐ *Math Journal 1,* p. 190
- ☐ *Student Reference Book,* pp. 314–316 and 372
- ☐ Study Link Master (*Math Masters,* p. 166)
- ☐ Teaching Aid Master (*Math Masters,* p. 404)
- ☐ Game Masters (*Math Masters,* pp. 439–441)
- ☐ Per partnership: 4 each of the number cards 0–10
- ☐ 2-color counters or pennies; ruler

3 Differentiation Options

READINESS

Students make circle constructions to practice anchoring and rotating a compass.

ENRICHMENT

Students construct an octagon using a compass and a straightedge.

EXTRA PRACTICE

Students make congruent shapes on geoboards or dot paper.

materials

- ☐ Teaching Masters (*Math Masters,* pp. 167 and 168)
- ☐ Teaching Aid Master (*Math Masters,* p. 419)
- ☐ compass; straightedge; scissors
- ☐ Per partnership: 2 geoboards with rubber bands, or dot paper

Additional Information

Advance Preparation Use a board compass and meterstick (or another long straightedge) to demonstrate Part 1 constructions on the board.

Technology

Assessment Management System
Exit Slip
See the **iTLG.**

Getting Started

Mental Math and Reflexes

Students write numbers in scientific notation. *Suggestions:*

●○○ 702,000,000 $7.02 * 10^8$
0.0000513 $5.13 * 10^{-5}$

●●○ 393.4 $3.934 * 10^2$

●●● $\frac{865}{10,000}$ $8.65 * 10^{-2}$

Math Message

Read the directions on page 188 of the Student Reference Book. *Use a compass to draw three concentric circles on a separate sheet of paper.*

Study Link 5·6 Follow-Up

Point out that the copy of the path in Problem 2 is the mirror image of the original path. The copy of the path in Problem 3 is obtained by rotating the original path 180° in either direction—clockwise or counterclockwise.

1 Teaching the Lesson

▶ Math Message Follow-Up

WHOLE-CLASS DISCUSSION

(*Student Reference Book,* p. 188)

Discuss page 188 in the *Student Reference Book*. Make sure students understand that in a **compass-and-straightedge construction,** they are allowed to use only a compass, a straightedge, and a pencil. They may not use rulers and protractors. Tracing is not allowed.

NOTE A straightedge is any tool used for drawing straight lines. A ruler is a straightedge and a measuring tool.

Remind students to work on top of a notebook or several sheets of paper when using a compass with a sharp point. Doing so will keep the **anchor** (the sharp point) of the compass from slipping as the pencil (or paper) is rotated.

Concentric circles are circles that have the same center but radiuses of different lengths. When drawing concentric circles, students should maintain the anchor's position at the center of the circle and change only the compass opening.

▶ Reviewing Compass-and-Straightedge Constructions

WHOLE-CLASS ACTIVITY

(*Student Reference Book,* pp. 189 and 190)

Pages 189 and 190 in the *Student Reference Book* give step-by-step directions for copying line segments and triangles. When copying figures, it is helpful to name points in the copied figure after points in the original. The symbol (′) can be added after the letter to distinguish between the original figure and its copy.

Student Page

Geometry and Constructions

Compass-and-Straightedge Constructions

Many geometric figures can be drawn using only a compass and straightedge. The compass is used to draw circles and mark off lengths. The straightedge is used to draw straight line segments.

Compass-and-straightedge constructions serve many purposes:

- Mathematicians use them to study properties of geometric figures.
- Architects use them to make blueprints and drawings.
- Engineers use them to develop their designs.
- Graphic artists use them to create illustrations on a computer.

Architect's drawing of a house plan

In addition to a compass and a straightedge, the only materials you need are a drawing tool (a pencil with a sharp point is the best) and some paper. For these constructions, you may not measure the lengths of line segments with a ruler or the sizes of angles with a protractor.

Draw on a surface that will hold the point of the compass (also called the **anchor**) so that it does not slip. You can draw on a stack of several sheets of paper.

Method 1

The directions below describe two ways to draw circles. For each method, begin in the same way:

- Draw a small point that will be the center of the circle.
- Press the compass anchor firmly on the center of the circle.

Method 1 Hold the compass at the top and rotate the pencil around the anchor. The pencil must go all the way around to make a circle. Some people find it easier to rotate the pencil as far as possible in one direction, and then rotate it in the other direction to complete the circle.

Method 2 This method works best with partners. One partner holds the compass in place while the other partner carefully turns the paper under the compass to form the circle.

Method 2

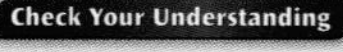

Concentric circles are circles that have the same center.

Use a compass to draw 3 concentric circles.

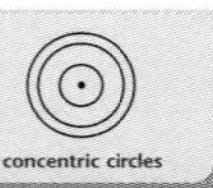
concentric circles

Student Reference Book, p. 188

Ongoing Assessment: Informing Instruction

Remind students that while doing a construction, they should not measure line segments with a ruler or measure angles with a protractor. They can, however, use a ruler and/or protractor to check their work when they have completed the construction.

▶ Constructing Line Segments and Triangles

INDEPENDENT ACTIVITY

(*Math Journal 1,* pp. 188 and 189)

After students have learned how to copy line segments and triangles, have them use these constructions to complete the problems on journal pages 188 and 189.

Adjusting the Activity

Have students complete the constructions on journal pages 188 and 189 in more than one way. Ask them to describe or demonstrate what they did.

AUDITORY ◆ KINESTHETIC ◆ TACTILE ◆ VISUAL

2 Ongoing Learning & Practice

▶ Playing *2-4-8* or *3-6-9 Frac-Tac-Toe* (Decimal versions)

PARTNER ACTIVITY

(*Student Reference Book,* pp. 314–316 and 372; *Math Masters,* pp. 439–441)

Students use *Math Masters,* page 439 to organize the cards when playing the game. Depending on students' needs and abilities, use *Math Masters,* page 441 to work with denominators of 3, 6, and 9 or *Math Masters,* page 440 to work with denominators of 2, 4, and 8. Players may use a calculator or the Table of Decimal Equivalents for Fractions (*Student Reference Book,* p. 372) to convert their fractions to decimals.

Student Page

Date Time

LESSON 5·7 **Constructing Line Segments**

Use only a compass, a straightedge, and a sharp pencil for the constructions below. Use rulers and protractors only to check your work. Do not trace.

SRB 189

1. Copy this line segment. Label the endpoints of your copy *A'* and *B'*. (These symbols are read A *prime* and B *prime*.)

A B A' B'

2. Construct a line segment twice as long as $\overline{CD}$. Label the endpoints of your segment *C'* and *D'*.

C D C' D'

3. Construct a line segment as long as $\overline{EF}$ and $\overline{GH}$ together. Label the endpoints of your segment *E'* and *H'*.

E F G H

E' H'

Try This

4. Construct a segment with a length equal to the length of $\overline{IJ}$ minus the length of $\overline{KL}$. Label the endpoints of your segment *I'* and *K'*.

I J I' K'

K L

Math Journal 1, p. 188

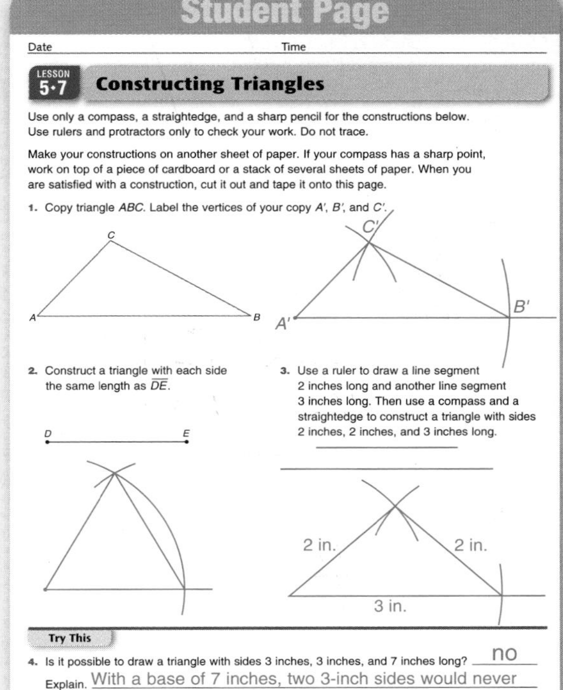

Student Page

Date Time

LESSON 5·7 **Constructing Triangles**

Use only a compass, a straightedge, and a sharp pencil for the constructions below. Use rulers and protractors only to check your work. Do not trace.

Make your constructions on another sheet of paper. If your compass has a sharp point, work on top of a piece of cardboard or a stack of several sheets of paper. When you are satisfied with a construction, cut it out and tape it onto this page.

1. Copy triangle *ABC*. Label the vertices of your copy *A'*, *B'*, and *C'*.

C A B C' A' B'

2. Construct a triangle with each side the same length as $\overline{DE}$.

D E

3. Use a ruler to draw a line segment 2 inches long and another line segment 3 inches long. Then use a compass and a straightedge to construct a triangle with sides 2 inches, 2 inches, and 3 inches long.

2 in. 2 in. 3 in.

Try This

4. Is it possible to draw a triangle with sides 3 inches, 3 inches, and 7 inches long? no

Explain. With a base of 7 inches, two 3-inch sides would never meet to form the third angle.

Math Journal 1, p. 189

Student Page

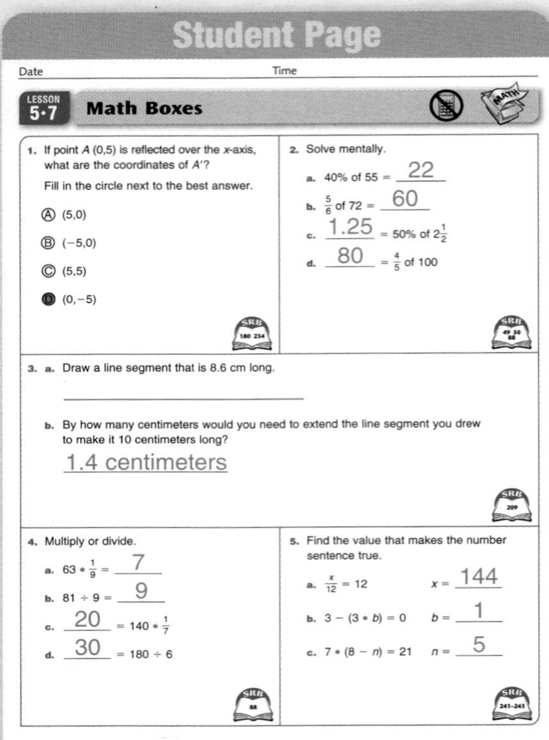

Date Time

LESSON 5·7 **Math Boxes**

1. If point A (0,5) is reflected over the x-axis, what are the coordinates of A'?
   Fill in the circle next to the best answer.
   - Ⓐ (5,0)
   - Ⓑ (−5,0)
   - Ⓒ (5,5)
   - ● (0,−5)

   SRB 180 234

2. Solve mentally.
   - a. 40% of 55 = 22
   - b. $\frac{5}{6}$ of 72 = 60
   - c. 1.25 = 50% of $2\frac{1}{2}$
   - d. 80 = $\frac{4}{5}$ of 100

   SRB 49 50 88

3. a. Draw a line segment that is 8.6 cm long.
   b. By how many centimeters would you need to extend the line segment you drew to make it 10 centimeters long?
   1.4 centimeters

   SRB 209

4. Multiply or divide.
   - a. $63 * \frac{1}{9}$ = 7
   - b. 81 ÷ 9 = 9
   - c. 20 = $140 * \frac{1}{7}$
   - d. 30 = 180 ÷ 6

   SRB 88

5. Find the value that makes the number sentence true.
   - a. $\frac{x}{12} = 12$ x = 144
   - b. $3 - (3 * b) = 0$ b = 1
   - c. $7 * (8 - n) = 21$ n = 5

   SRB 241–243

Math Journal 1, p. 190

Ongoing Assessment: Recognizing Student Achievement

Exit Slip 

Have students use an **Exit Slip** (*Math Masters,* p. 404) to record fraction and decimal equivalents they cover on the gameboard. Use students' recorded equivalencies to assess their ability to convert between fractions and decimals.
[Number and Numeration Goal 5]

▶ Math Boxes 5·7

INDEPENDENT ACTIVITY

(*Math Journal 1,* p. 190)

Mixed Practice Math Boxes in this lesson are paired with Math Boxes in Lesson 5-5. The skills in Problems 4 and 5 preview Unit 6 content.

▶ Study Link 5·7

INDEPENDENT ACTIVITY

(*Math Masters,* p. 166)

Home Connection Students solve problems involving angle relationships.

NOTE Study Links 5-7 and 5-8 do not reinforce the activities in these two lessons. Few students have the tools necessary to perform constructions at home. Instead, Study Links 5-7 and 5-8 provide practice with other skills and concepts presented in Unit 5.

Study Link Master

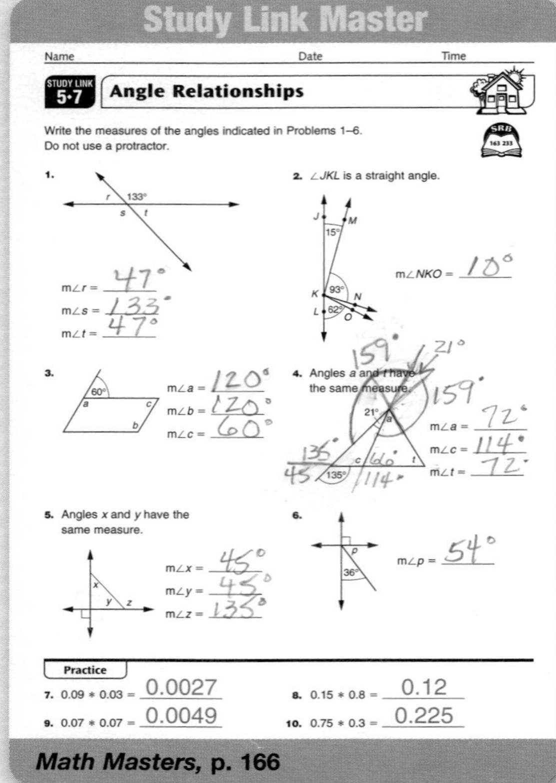

Name Date Time

STUDY LINK 5·7 **Angle Relationships**

Write the measures of the angles indicated in Problems 1–6.
Do not use a protractor.

SRB 163 233

1. m∠r = 47°, m∠s = 133°, m∠t = 47°
2. ∠JKL is a straight angle. m∠NKO = 10°
3. m∠a = 120°, m∠b = 120°, m∠c = 60°
4. Angles a and t have the same measure. m∠a = 72°, m∠c = 114°, m∠t = 72°
5. Angles x and y have the same measure. m∠x = 45°, m∠y = 45°, m∠z = 135°
6. m∠p = 54°

Practice

7. 0.09 ∗ 0.03 = 0.0027
8. 0.15 ∗ 0.8 = 0.12
9. 0.07 ∗ 0.07 = 0.0049
10. 0.75 ∗ 0.3 = 0.225

Math Masters, p. 166

3 Differentiation Options

READINESS

▶ Practicing Circle Constructions

INDEPENDENT ACTIVITY

15–30 Min

(*Math Masters,* p. 167)

To provide practice anchoring and rotating their compasses, have students complete *Math Masters,* page 167.

ENRICHMENT

▶ Constructing an Octagon

INDEPENDENT ACTIVITY

15–30 Min

(*Math Masters,* p. 168)

To extend students' knowledge of geometric constructions, they complete *Math Masters,* page 168. In this activity, students draw diameters and chords in circles, using a compass and a straightedge. Then they use these parts of the circle to construct an octagon.

EXTRA PRACTICE

▶ Making Congruent Shapes on Geoboards

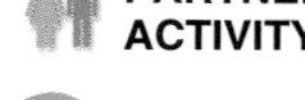

PARTNER ACTIVITY

5–15 Min

(*Math Masters,* p. 419)

To provide practice making and identifying congruent shapes, have students work in partnerships. One partner uses one or more rubber bands to make a shape on a geoboard. The other partner makes an exact copy of the shape on a different geoboard and explains why the two shapes are congruent. Then partners switch roles. If geoboards are not available, have students draw and copy shapes on dot paper (*Math Masters,* p. 419).

Teaching Aid Master

Name Date Time

Dot Paper (1 cm)

Math Masters, p. 419

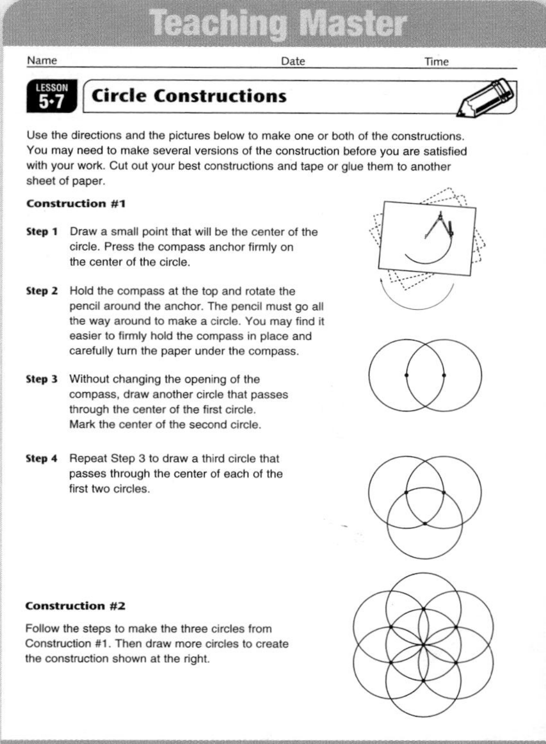

Teaching Master

Name Date Time

LESSON 5•7 **Circle Constructions**

Use the directions and the pictures below to make one or both of the constructions. You may need to make several versions of the construction before you are satisfied with your work. Cut out your best constructions and tape or glue them to another sheet of paper.

Construction #1

Step 1 Draw a small point that will be the center of the circle. Press the compass anchor firmly on the center of the circle.

Step 2 Hold the compass at the top and rotate the pencil around the anchor. The pencil must go all the way around to make a circle. You may find it easier to firmly hold the compass in place and carefully turn the paper under the compass.

Step 3 Without changing the opening of the compass, draw another circle that passes through the center of the first circle. Mark the center of the second circle.

Step 4 Repeat Step 3 to draw a third circle that passes through the center of each of the first two circles.

Construction #2

Follow the steps to make the three circles from Construction #1. Then draw more circles to create the construction shown at the right.

Math Masters, p. 167

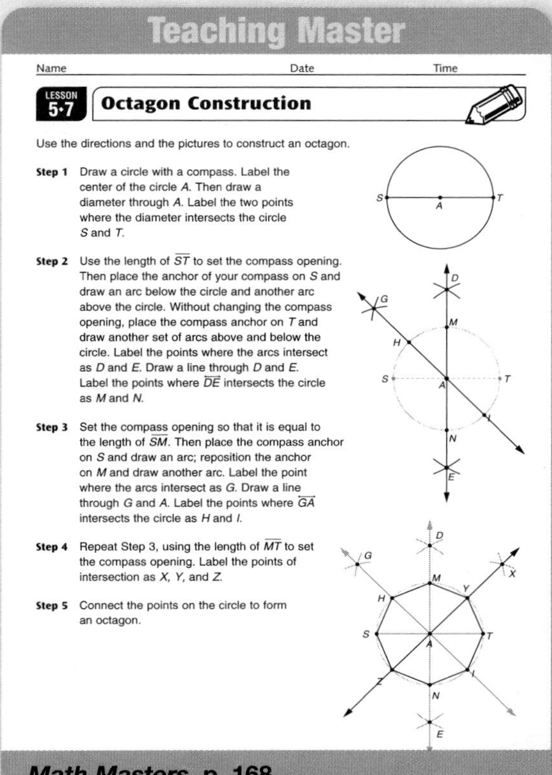

Teaching Master

Name Date Time

LESSON 5•7 **Octagon Construction**

Use the directions and the pictures to construct an octagon.

Step 1 Draw a circle with a compass. Label the center of the circle *A.* Then draw a diameter through *A.* Label the two points where the diameter intersects the circle *S* and *T.*

Step 2 Use the length of $\overline{ST}$ to set the compass opening. Then place the anchor of your compass on *S* and draw an arc below the circle and another arc above the circle. Without changing the compass opening, place the compass anchor on *T* and draw another set of arcs above and below the circle. Label the points where the arcs intersect as *D* and *E.* Draw a line through *D* and *E.* Label the points where $\overline{DE}$ intersects the circle as *M* and *N.*

Step 3 Set the compass opening so that it is equal to the length of $\overline{SM}$. Then place the compass anchor on *S* and draw an arc; reposition the anchor on *M* and draw another arc. Label the point where the arcs intersect as *G.* Draw a line through *G* and *A.* Label the points where $\overline{GA}$ intersects the circle as *H* and *I.*

Step 4 Repeat Step 3, using the length of $\overline{MT}$ to set the compass opening. Label the points of intersection as *X, Y,* and *Z.*

Step 5 Connect the points on the circle to form an octagon.

Math Masters, p. 168

5•8 Compass-and-Straightedge Constructions Part 2

Objectives To copy angles and construct perpendicular bisectors; and to solve construction problems.

1 Teaching the Lesson

Key Activities

Students learn methods for copying angles and constructing perpendicular bisectors. They apply these methods to solve construction problems.

Key Concepts and Skills

- Label the points and vertices of a preimage and its image. [Measurement and Reference Frames Goal 3]
- Apply the properties of perpendicular lines to draw, identify, and classify right angles. [Geometry Goal 1]
- Use appropriate tools to construct congruent figures. [Geometry Goal 2]
- Apply the knowledge that a preimage and its image are congruent. [Geometry Goal 3]

Key Vocabulary

perpendicular bisector • perpendicular • bisect • inscribed

Ongoing Assessment: Recognizing Student Achievement Use Mental Math and Reflexes. [Operations and Computation Goals 3 and 4]

materials

- ☐ *Math Journal 1,* pp. 192 and 193
- ☐ *Student Reference Book,* pp. 193–199
- ☐ Study Link 5•7
- ☐ compass; straightedge
- ☐ Geometry Template/protractor; ruler
- ☐ scissors; tape
- ☐ board compass; meterstick (for demonstration purposes)

2 Ongoing Learning & Practice

Students practice identifying the properties of polygons by playing *Polygon Capture*.

Students practice and maintain skills through Math Boxes and Study Link activities.

materials

- ☐ *Math Journal 1,* p. 191
- ☐ *Student Reference Book,* p. 330
- ☐ Study Link Master (*Math Masters,* p. 169)
- ☐ Game Masters (*Math Masters,* pp. 470 and 471)

***See* Advance Preparation**

3 Differentiation Options

READINESS

Students practice using a compass and a straightedge to bisect angles.

ENRICHMENT

Students apply knowledge of constructions to inscribe a circle in a triangle.

EXTRA PRACTICE

Students construct perpendicular bisectors.

materials

- ☐ *Student Reference Book,* pp. 195 and 197
- ☐ Teaching Masters (*Math Masters,* pp. 170 and 171)
- ☐ compass; straightedge

Additional Information

Advance Preparation Prior to playing *Polygon Capture* (Part 2), have students cut out the polygons and the Property Cards from *Math Masters,* pages 470 and 471.

Technology

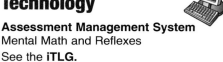

Assessment Management System
Mental Math and Reflexes
See the **iTLG.**

Getting Started

Mental Math and Reflexes 

Students solve addition, subtraction, and multiplication problems with fractions and mixed numbers.

Suggestions:

●○○ $\frac{3}{4} + \frac{3}{5}$ $\frac{27}{20}$, or $1\frac{7}{20}$

$\frac{4}{5} * \frac{1}{3}$ $\frac{4}{15}$

●●○ $2\frac{1}{6} - 1\frac{2}{3}$ $\frac{1}{2}$

$2 - \frac{1}{6}$ $\frac{11}{6}$, or $1\frac{5}{6}$

●●● $3\frac{13}{16} - 1\frac{1}{4}$ $\frac{41}{16}$, or $2\frac{9}{16}$

$2\frac{1}{4} * 1\frac{1}{3}$ 3

Math Message

Draw an angle. Copy your angle using only a compass and a straightedge.

Study Link 5•7 Follow-Up

Students explain how they determined the angle measures. Lessons 5-9 and 5-10 introduce additional angle relationships. To be successful in those lessons, students should understand the solutions to the problems on Study Link 5-7.

Ongoing Assessment: Recognizing Student Achievement

Mental Math and Reflexes 

Use **Mental Math and Reflexes** to assess students' abilities to add, subtract, and multiply fractions and mixed numbers.

[Operations and Computation Goals 3 and 4]

1 Teaching the Lesson

▶ Math Message Follow-Up

WHOLE-CLASS DISCUSSION

(*Student Reference Book,* p. 198)

Page 198 of the *Student Reference Book* explains the conventional method of copying an angle. Most students will not be familiar with this method. With some ingenuity, however, they might realize that they can copy an angle by making it part of a triangle and then copying the whole triangle.

1. Draw an angle to be copied.

2. Add a line segment to form a triangle.

3. Begin copying by drawing a ray.

Student Page

Geometry and Constructions

Copying an Angle

Follow each step carefully. Use a clean sheet of paper.

Step 1: Draw angle *B*.

Step 2: To start copying the angle, draw a ray. Label the endpoint of the ray as *B'*.

Step 3: Place the compass anchor on *B*. Draw an arc that crosses both sides of angle *B*. Label the point where the arc crosses one side as *A*. Label the point where the arc crosses the other side as *C*.

Step 4: Without changing the compass opening, place the compass anchor on *B'*. Draw an arc about the same size as the one you drew in Step 3. Label the point where the arc crosses the ray as *A'*.

Step 5: Place the compass anchor on *A* and the pencil point on *C*.

Step 6: Without changing the compass opening, place the compass anchor on *A'*. Draw a small arc where the pencil point crosses the larger arc and label the crossing point as *C'*.

Step 7: Draw a ray from point *B'* through point *C'*.

$\angle A'B'C'$ is **congruent** to $\angle ABC$. That is, the two angles have the same degree measure.

Check Your Understanding

Draw an angle. Use a compass and a straightedge to copy the angle. Then measure the two angles with a protractor to check that they are the same size.

Student Reference Book, p. 198

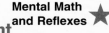

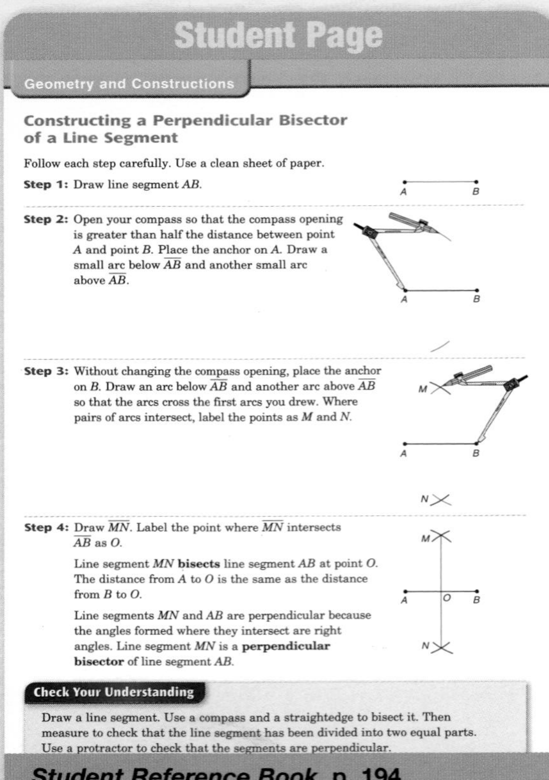
Student Page

Geometry and Constructions

Constructing a Perpendicular Bisector of a Line Segment

Follow each step carefully. Use a clean sheet of paper.

Step 1: Draw line segment *AB*.

Step 2: Open your compass so that the compass opening is greater than half the distance between point *A* and point *B*. Place the anchor on *A*. Draw a small arc below $\overline{AB}$ and another small arc above $\overline{AB}$.

Step 3: Without changing the compass opening, place the anchor on *B*. Draw an arc below $\overline{AB}$ and another arc above $\overline{AB}$ so that the arcs cross the first arcs you drew. Where pairs of arcs intersect, label the points as *M* and *N*.

Step 4: Draw $\overline{MN}$. Label the point where $\overline{MN}$ intersects $\overline{AB}$ as *O*.

Line segment *MN* **bisects** line segment *AB* at point *O*. The distance from *A* to *O* is the same as the distance from *B* to *O*.

Line segments *MN* and *AB* are perpendicular because the angles formed where they intersect are right angles. Line segment *MN* is a **perpendicular bisector** of line segment *AB*.

Check Your Understanding

Draw a line segment. Use a compass and a straightedge to bisect it. Then measure to check that the line segment has been divided into two equal parts. Use a protractor to check that the segments are perpendicular.

Student Reference Book, p. 194

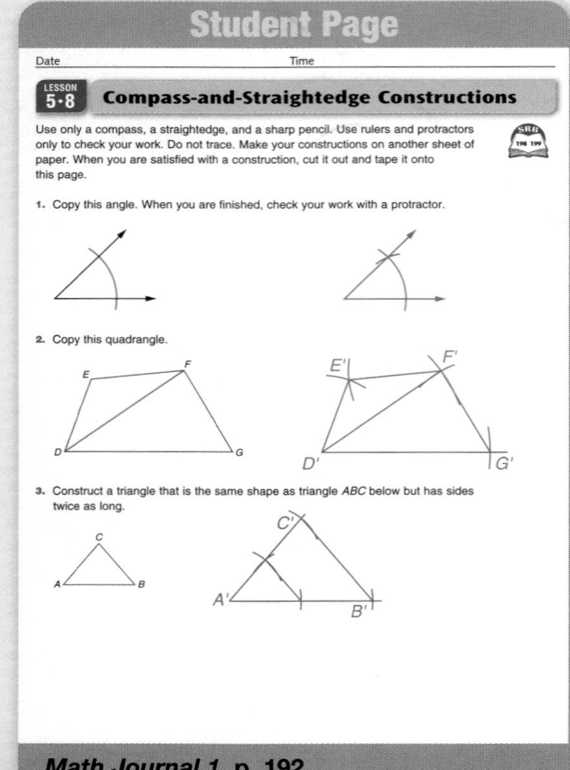
Student Page

Date Time

LESSON 5·8 **Compass-and-Straightedge Constructions**

Use only a compass, a straightedge, and a sharp pencil. Use rulers and protractors only to check your work. Do not trace. Make your constructions on another sheet of paper. When you are satisfied with a construction, cut it out and tape it onto this page.

1. Copy this angle. When you are finished, check your work with a protractor.

2. Copy this quadrangle.

3. Construct a triangle that is the same shape as triangle *ABC* below but has sides twice as long.

Math Journal 1, p. 192

4. Copy the first side.

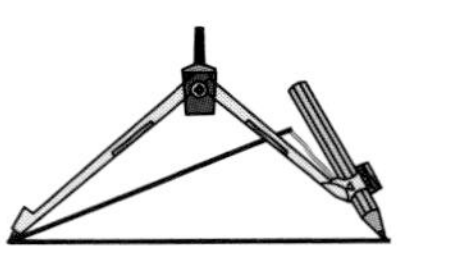
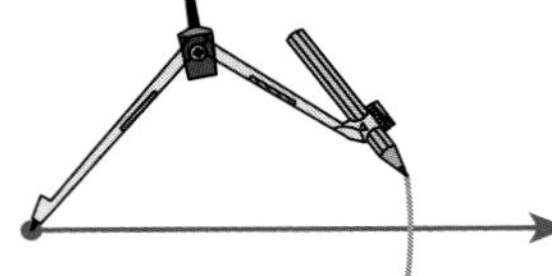

5. Draw arcs for the other two sides of the triangle.

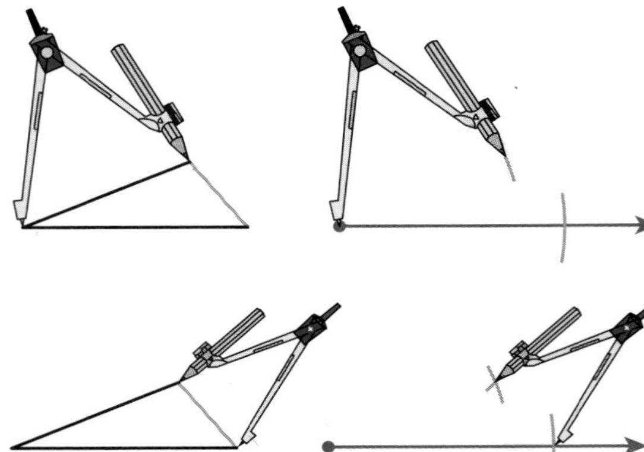

6. Draw the second side of the angle.

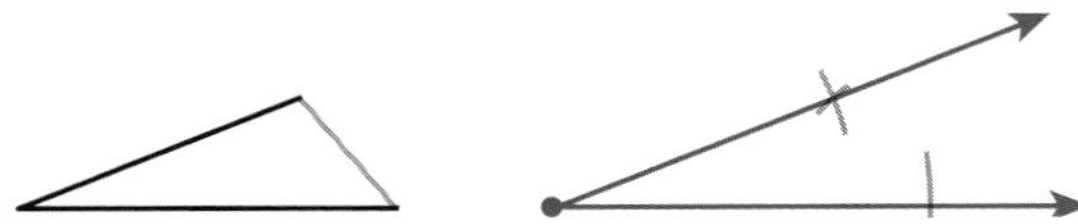

▶ Copying Angles and Constructing Perpendicular Bisectors

(*Student Reference Book,* pp. 194 and 198)

Ask volunteers to explain how they copied their angles. Demonstrate the standard methods for copying angles and constructing **perpendicular bisectors** (*Student Reference Book,* pages 194 and 198). Make sure students understand that **perpendicular** means *forming right angles,* and **bisect** means *to divide into two parts of equal measure.*

Ask students to read the directions for these constructions and practice on their own. Remind them that they should not use rulers and protractors to complete compass-and-straightedge constructions. They can, however, use these tools to check their constructions.

NOTE Many compass-and-straightedge constructions rely on the fact that if the sides of one triangle are equal in length to the sides of a second triangle, then the triangles are congruent. The most fundamental construction is to copy a triangle by copying all three sides. The classic angle-copying method shown in the *Student Reference Book* involves copying an isosceles triangle without actually drawing the third side.

▶ Solving Construction Problems

SMALL-GROUP ACTIVITY

(*Math Journal 1,* pp. 192 and 193; *Student Reference Book,* pp. 193–196 and 199)

These journal pages require students to solve construction problems. Point out the constructions described on pages 193–196 of the *Student Reference Book,* but explain that these problems can be solved in many ways. Encourage students to look for alternative solutions that use only a compass and a straightedge.

▷ Problem 2 requires students to copy a quadrangle. One method is shown on *Student Reference Book* page 199, but there are many other approaches. Two methods are shown below.

Method 1:
Divide the quadrangle into two triangles and copy both triangles.

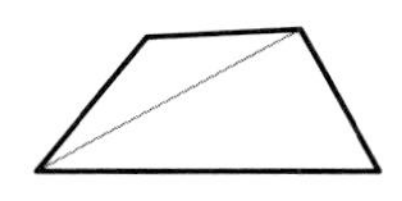

Original quadrangle

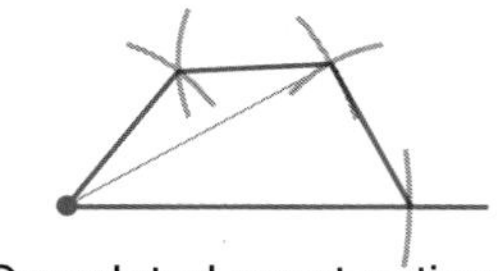

Completed construction

Method 2: Copy two angles and three sides.

1.

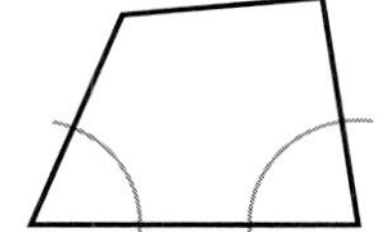

2.

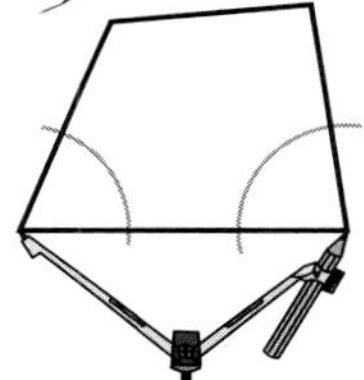

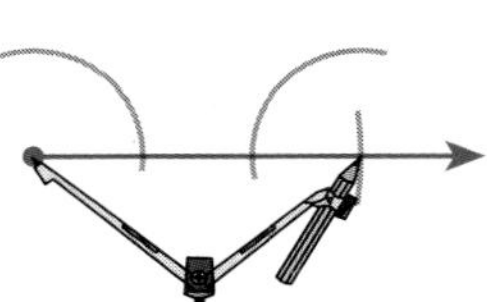

3.

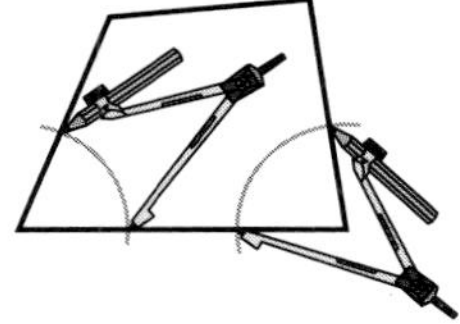

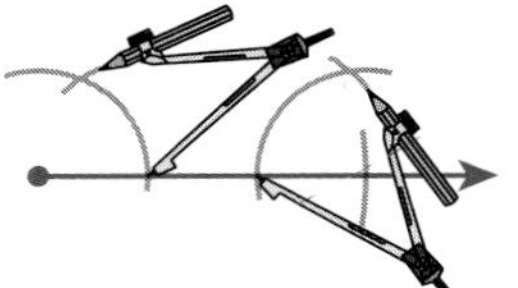

4.

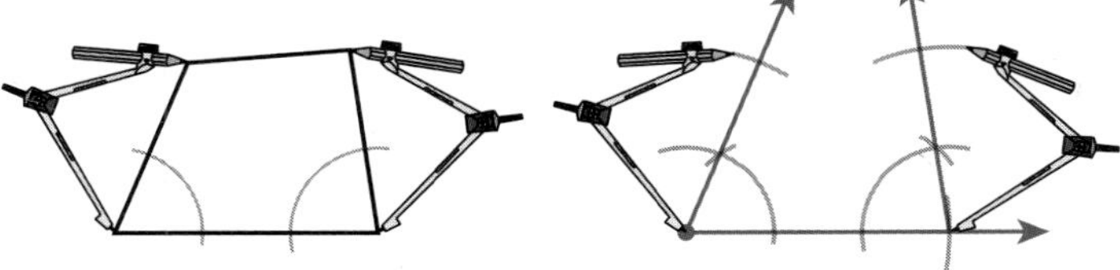

5.

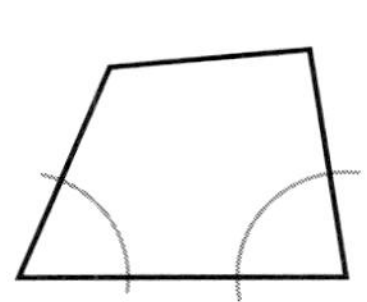

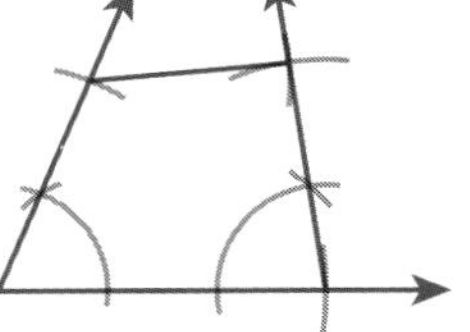

Student Page

Date Time

LESSON 5•8 **Compass-and-Straightedge Constructions** *cont.*

Use only a compass, a straightedge, and a sharp pencil. Use rulers and protractors only to check your work. Do not trace.

SRB 193–195

4. Construct a perpendicular bisector of this line segment.

5. Divide this line segment into four equal parts.

6. To **inscribe** a square in a circle means to construct a square inside a circle so that all four vertices (corners) of the square are on the circle. Draw a circle. Then inscribe a square in it.

7. Use your Geometry Template to draw a parallelogram. Then construct a line segment to show the height of the parallelogram. (That is, construct a perpendicular segment from one side to the opposite side.)

Math Journal 1, p. 193

Student Page

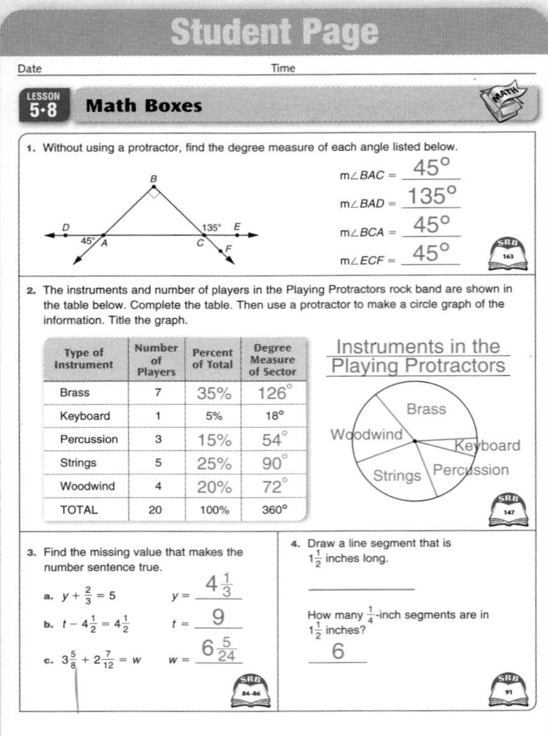

Date Time

LESSON 5•8 **Math Boxes**

1. Without using a protractor, find the degree measure of each angle listed below.

$m\angle BAC$ = 45°
$m\angle BAD$ = 135°
$m\angle BCA$ = 45°
$m\angle ECF$ = 45°

2. The instruments and number of players in the Playing Protractors rock band are shown in the table below. Complete the table. Then use a protractor to make a circle graph of the information. Title the graph.

Type of Instrument	Number of Players	Percent of Total	Degree Measure of Sector
Brass	7	35%	126°
Keyboard	1	5%	18°
Percussion	3	15%	54°
Strings	5	25%	90°
Woodwind	4	20%	72°
TOTAL	20	100%	360°

Instruments in the Playing Protractors

3. Find the missing value that makes the number sentence true.
a. $y + \frac{2}{3} = 5$ $y = 4\frac{1}{3}$
b. $t - 4\frac{1}{2} = 4\frac{1}{2}$ $t = 9$
c. $3\frac{5}{8} + 2\frac{7}{12} = w$ $w = 6\frac{5}{24}$

4. Draw a line segment that is $1\frac{1}{2}$ inches long.
How many $\frac{1}{4}$-inch segments are in $1\frac{1}{2}$ inches? 6

Math Journal 1, p. 191

Study Link Master

Name Date Time

STUDY LINK 5•8 **Isometry Transformations on a Grid**

1. Graph and label the following points on the coordinate grid. Connect the points to form quadrangle ABCD.
A: (−2,1) B: (−6,2)
C: (−8,4) D: (−5,7)

2. Translate each vertex of ABCD (in Problem 1) 0 units to the left or right and 8 units down. Plot and connect the new points. Label them A', B', C', and D'.
Record the coordinates of the image.
A': (−2,−7)
B': (−6,−6)
C': (−8,−4)
D': (−5,−1)

3. Reflect quadrangle ABCD across the y-axis. Plot and connect the new points. Label them A", B", C", and D". Record the coordinates of the image.
A": (2,1) B": (6,2) C": (8,4) D": (5,7)

Try This

4. Rotate quadrangle A"B"C"D" 90° clockwise around point (0,0). Plot and connect the new points. Label them A''', B''', C''', and D'''. Record the coordinates of the rotated image.
A''': (1,−2) B''': (2,−6) C''': (4,−8) D''': (7,−5)

Practice

5. $300 * 0.001 =$ 0.3 6. $143 * 10^{-3} =$ 0.143 7. $35.9 * \frac{1}{1{,}000} =$ 0.0359

Math Masters, p. 169

▷ Problem 3 requires students to construct a similar triangle—a triangle that is the same shape as the one on the page but with sides twice as long. One way is to copy an angle of the triangle, extending the sides; mark on the copy double the lengths of the sides of the original angle; and draw the third side.

▷ Problem 6 directs students to construct an **inscribed** square. An inscribed polygon is one whose vertices are points on a circle or other figure.

Bring the class together and have each group demonstrate at least one of its constructions.

2 Ongoing Learning & Practice

▶ Playing *Polygon Capture*

PARTNER ACTIVITY

(*Student Reference Book,* p. 330; *Math Masters,* pp. 470 and 471)

Have students cut out the polygons and the Property Cards from *Math Masters,* pages 470 and 471. They write *angles* or *sides* on the back of each Property Card to name the category.

Students capture polygons that match both the angle and side properties drawn. Properties include measures of angles, lengths of sides, and number of pairs of parallel sides.

▶ Math Boxes 5•8

INDEPENDENT ACTIVITY

(*Math Journal 1,* p. 191)

Mixed Practice Math Boxes in this lesson are paired with Math Boxes in Lesson 5-10. The skills in Problems 3 and 4 preview Unit 6 content.

Writing and Reasoning Have students write a response to the following: *Explain how you found the angle measures in Problem 1.* I applied vertical and supplementary angle relationships. For example, $\angle BAC$ and an angle marked 45° are vertical angles, so I know that the measure of $\angle BAC$ is 45°. The angle marked 45° and $\angle BAD$ are supplementary angles. Therefore, I know that $\angle BAD$ measures $180° - 45°$, or 135°. Similarly, $\angle BCE$ and $\angle BCA$ are supplementary angles, as well as $\angle BCE$ and $\angle ECF$. The measure of angle $\angle BCA$ and $\angle ECF$ can each be found by subtracting the measure of $\angle BCE$ (135°) from 180°.

▶ Study Link 5·8

INDEPENDENT ACTIVITY

(*Math Masters,* p. 169)

Home Connection Students graph points and perform translations, reflections, and rotations on a 4-quadrant coordinate grid.

3 Differentiation Options

READINESS

INDEPENDENT ACTIVITY

▶ Bisecting an Angle

5–15 Min

(*Student Reference Book,* p. 197)

Portfolio Ideas

To provide additional practice in how to set and maintain a compass opening and correctly anchor the compass point, have students read the steps on page 197 of the *Student Reference Book.* Then ask students to bisect an obtuse angle.

ENRICHMENT

INDEPENDENT ACTIVITY

▶ Inscribing a Circle in a Triangle

5–15 Min

(*Student Reference Book,* pp. 195 and 197; *Math Masters,* p. 170)

To further extend their knowledge of geometric constructions (bisecting an angle and constructing a perpendicular line segment), students complete *Math Masters,* page 170. Through this activity, students learn how to inscribe a circle in a triangle.

EXTRA PRACTICE

INDEPENDENT ACTIVITY

▶ Constructing Perpendicular Bisectors

15–30 Min

(*Math Masters,* p. 171)

To provide additional practice in geometric construction, have students complete *Math Masters,* page 171 by constructing perpendicular bisectors of the sides of a triangle and the diagonal of a square. Ask students to record their observations.

Teaching Master

Name ______ Date ______ Time ______

LESSON 5·8 **Inscribing a Circle in a Triangle**

Follow the steps to inscribe a circle in triangle *ABC.*

Step 1 Construct the bisectors of $\angle A$ and $\angle B$. Then label the intersection of the angle bisectors as *P.*

Step 2 Construct a line segment through point *P,* perpendicular to $\overline{AB}$. Label the point at which the line segment intersects $\overline{AB}$ as *Q.*

Step 3 Center the compass anchor on *P* and the pencil point on *Q.* Draw a circle through *Q.* The circle will be tangent to all three sides of the triangle.

Math Masters, p. 170

Teaching Master

Name ______ Date ______ Time ______

LESSON 5·8 **Constructing Perpendicular Bisectors**

1. Draw a large triangle. Construct perpendicular bisectors for each side of the triangle. What observations can you make? Sample answers: All three bisectors intersect at one point inside the triangle; they each bisect only one side; if all of the bisectors were extended, they would cut the triangle into six other figures.

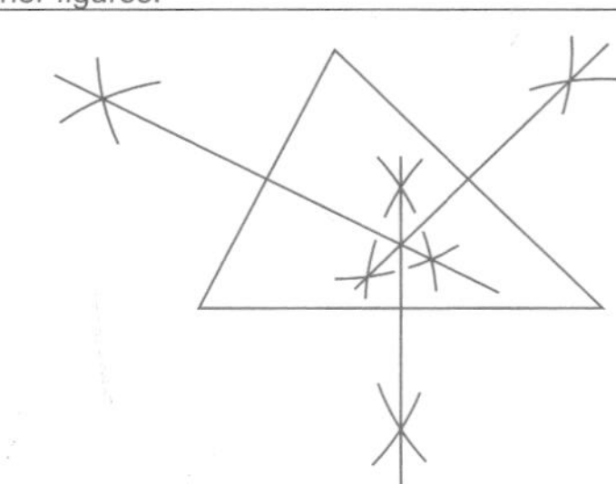

2. Use a protractor and a ruler to draw a large square. Draw a diagonal. Then construct the perpendicular bisector of the diagonal. What observations can you make? The bisector forms the second diagonal for the square.

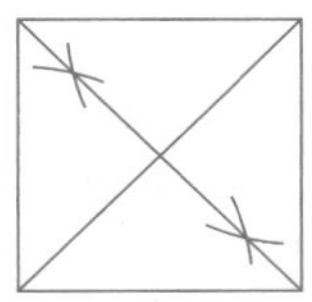

Math Masters, p. 171

Parallel Lines and Angle Relationships

Objective To explore and apply angle relationships.

1 Teaching the Lesson

Key Activities

Students explore and apply the special relationships between angles that are formed when parallel lines are cut by a transversal.

Key Concepts and Skills

- Add and subtract multidigit whole numbers. [Operations and Computation Goal 1]
- Determine angle measures by applying definitions and properties of angles, triangles, and quadrangles. [Geometry Goal 1]
- Identify congruent figures. [Geometry Goal 2]

Key Vocabulary

parallel lines • parallel line segments • skew • transversal • adjacent angles • supplementary angles • vertical angles

Ongoing Assessment: Recognizing Student Achievement Use journal page 194. [Geometry Goal 1]

Ongoing Assessment: Informing Instruction See page 383.

materials

- ☐ *Math Journal 1,* pp. 194–196
- ☐ *Student Reference Book,* pp. 163 and 233
- ☐ Study Link 5•8
- ☐ Transparency (Study Link 5•8; optional)
- ☐ compass
- ☐ straightedge
- ☐ ruler

2 Ongoing Learning & Practice

Students calculate percents of numbers to find total prices that include sales tax and tips.

Students practice and maintain skills through Math Boxes and Study Link activities.

materials

- ☐ *Math Journal 1,* pp. 197 and 198
- ☐ Study Link Master (*Math Masters,* p. 172)

3 Differentiation Options

ENRICHMENT

Students apply knowledge of angle relationships and algebraic expressions to find missing angle measures.

ENRICHMENT

Students find examples of parallel lines that are drawn in perspective.

ELL SUPPORT

Students use language-development techniques.

materials

- ☐ Teaching Master (*Math Masters,* p. 173)
- ☐ compass
- ☐ straightedge

***See* Advance Preparation**

Additional Information

Advance Preparation Ask the school's art instructor to discuss the second optional Enrichment activity with your students.

Technology

Assessment Management System
Math Message, Problems 1–6
See the **iTLG.**

Getting Started

Mental Math and Reflexes

Students mentally solve problems like the following. If time permits, have a volunteer share her or his strategy.

Suggestions and possible strategies:

●○○ 133 + 55 + 47 235; 140 + 40 + 55

●●○ 35 ∗ 12 420; (35 ∗10) + (35 ∗ 2)

360 – 155 205; 360 – 160 + 5

240 ÷ 5 48; Divide by 10, then multiply by 2

Math Message

Complete the problems on journal page 194.

Study Link 5·8 Follow-Up

You might want to make an overhead transparency of Study Link 5·8 and ask students to compare the coordinates of the preimages and images.

1 Teaching the Lesson

▶ Math Message Follow-Up

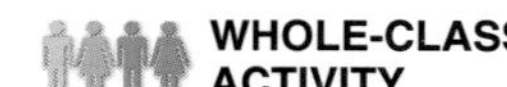

WHOLE-CLASS ACTIVITY

(*Math Journal 1,* p. 194)

Ongoing Assessment: Recognizing Student Achievement

Journal Page 194

Use **journal page 194, Problems 1–6** to assess students' ability to determine angle measures by applying the properties of adjacent angles, supplementary angles, and sums of angle measures in triangles and quadrangles. Students are making adequate progress if they are able to solve Problems 1–6.

[Geometry Goal 1]

When students have completed the page, discuss their answers and reasoning. To be successful with the content of this and the following lessons, it is important that students understand the solutions to the problems on journal page 194. Some students may benefit from reviewing pages 163 and 233 of the *Student Reference Book* and completing the Check Your Understanding problems at the bottom of each page.

▶ Exploring Angle Relationships

PARTNER ACTIVITY

(*Math Journal 1,* p. 195)

This is a discovery activity. No introduction is necessary. Students who complete journal page 195 before the rest of the class may go on to page 196.

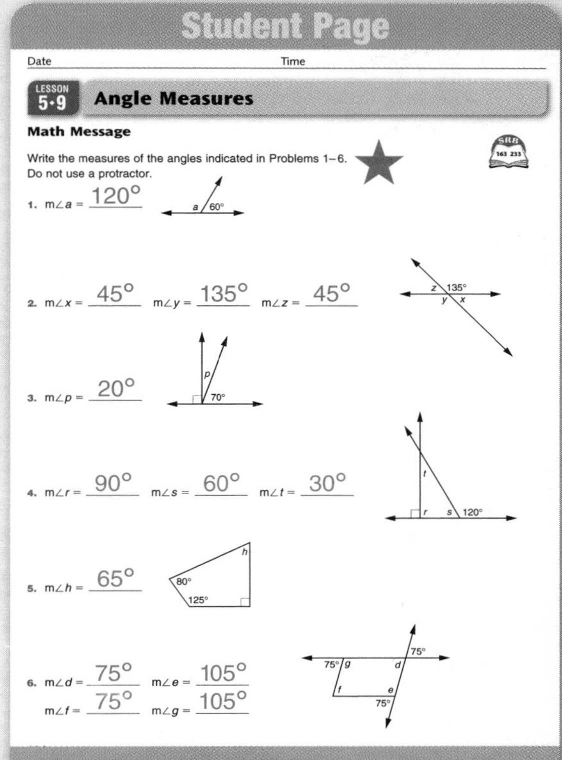

Student Page

Date Time

LESSON 5·9 **Angle Measures**

Math Message

Write the measures of the angles indicated in Problems 1–6. Do not use a protractor.

1. m∠*a* = 120°
2. m∠*x* = 45° m∠*y* = 135° m∠*z* = 45°
3. m∠*p* = 20°
4. m∠*r* = 90° m∠*s* = 60° m∠*t* = 30°
5. m∠*h* = 65°
6. m∠*d* = 75° m∠*e* = 105°
   m∠*f* = 75° m∠*g* = 105°

***Math Journal 1,* p. 194**

When most students have completed journal page 195, bring the class together to discuss what they have discovered. Ask them to define **parallel lines** and **parallel line segments.** Expect them to mention the following properties:

▷ Parallel lines never meet. They are always the same distance apart; that is, the shortest distance between two parallel lines is always the same, no matter where you measure the distance.

▷ The lines on notebook paper and the rails on a long stretch of straight railroad track are examples of parallel line segments. Lines, line segments, or rays in the same plane (a flat surface that extends forever) are parallel if they never cross or meet, no matter how far they are extended.

Adjusting the Activity

Help students remember the definition of *parallel* by pointing out that the three l's in *parallel* are, in fact, para**ll**e**l**. Some students may also be interested in the mathematical shorthand used for parallel lines or parallel line segments: *Line segment* AB *is parallel to line segment* CD is written as $\overline{AB} \parallel \overline{CD}$. Consider reviewing the mnemonic devices for *adjacent* and *supplementary* angles from Lesson 5-2 as well.

AUDITORY ◆ KINESTHETIC ◆ TACTILE ◆ VISUAL

Mention that if two lines (or line segments or rays) are in different planes, they may be neither intersecting nor parallel. For example, an east-west line on the floor and a north-south line on the ceiling never meet, but they are not parallel either. These lines are called **skew.**

Ask the class which pairs of lines on journal page 195 appear to be parallel. The lines in Problems 1, 3, and 6

Students should observe the following:

▷ When two parallel lines are cut by a **transversal** (a line that intersects both parallel lines), the pattern of the angle measures is the same at both intersections. There is no such pattern if the lines are not parallel.

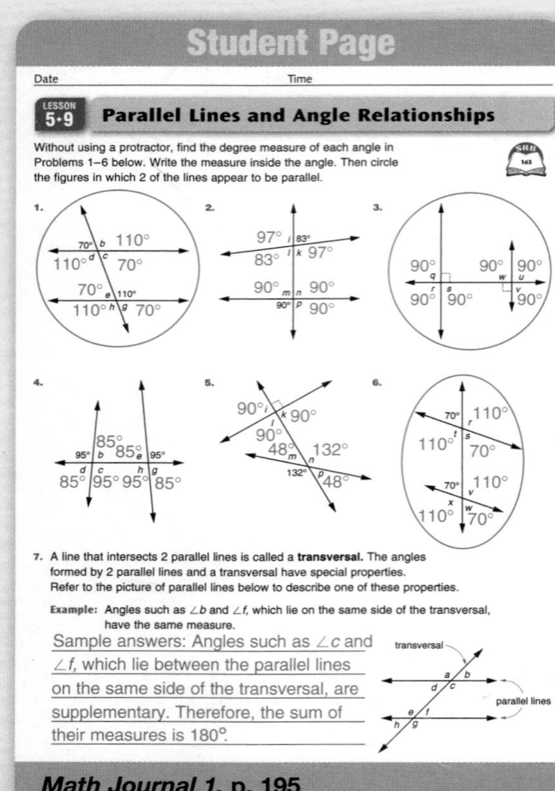

Math Journal 1, p. 195

Ask students to discuss their answers to Problem 7. Help them summarize the patterns they found. Some possible conclusions follow:

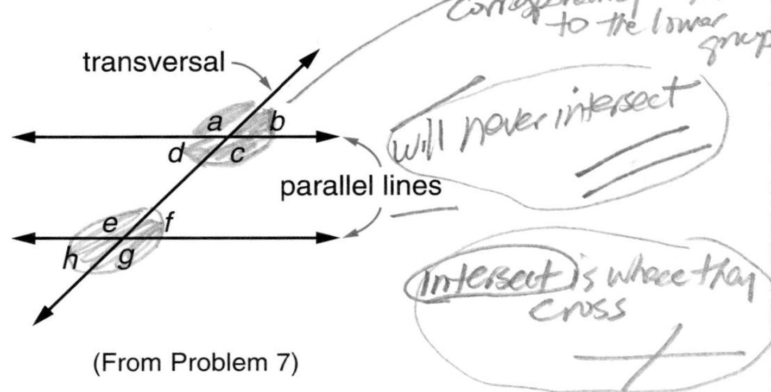

(From Problem 7)

- ▷ **Adjacent angles** above or below parallel lines (such as angles *a* and *b* in the diagram) are **supplementary angles.** The sum of their measures is 180°.
- ▷ There are two pairs of **vertical angles** at each intersection. Angles in each pair have the same measure.
- ▷ Angles between the parallel lines on the same side of the transversal (such as angles *c* and *f* in the diagram) are supplementary.
- ▷ Pairs of angles between the parallel lines and on opposite sides of the transversal (such as angles *d* and *f* in the diagram) have the same measure.
- ▷ Pairs of angles outside the parallel lines on opposite sides of the transversal (such as angles *b* and *h* in the diagram) have the same measure.
- ▷ Any two angles in the figure are either supplementary or congruent.

Ongoing Assessment: Informing Instruction

It may be easier for students to recognize lines as parallel if they extend the lines so they are about the same length (as students could do in Problems 3 and 6).

▶ Working with Parallel Lines

PARTNER ACTIVITY

(*Math Journal 1,* p. 196)

Students construct two parallel lines using only a compass and a straightedge. They draw two parallel lines and a parallelogram using only a ruler and a pencil. Students should only use the longer edges of the ruler to draw the parallel lines needed in Problems 2 and 3. If needed, refer students to the illustration at the top of journal page 199.

NOTE Discussion of this exercise will introduce the investigation of parallelograms in Lesson 5-10.

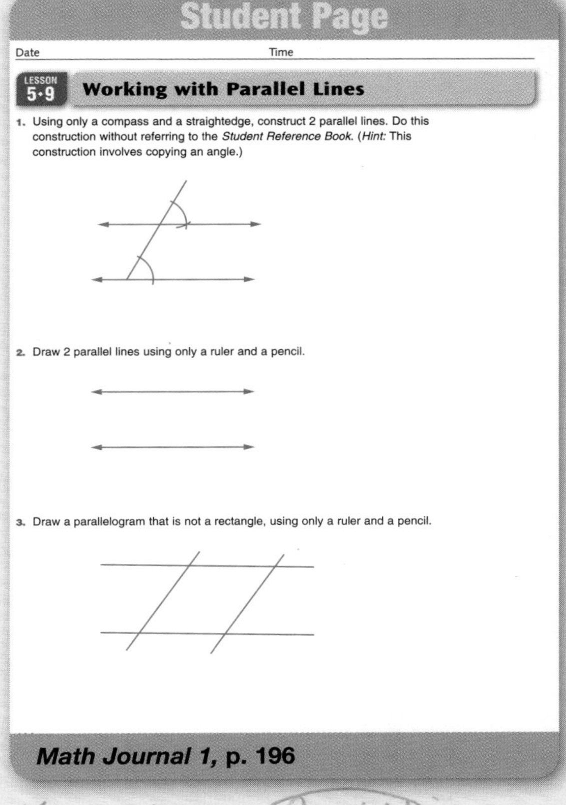

Student Page

Date Time

LESSON 5·9 **Working with Parallel Lines**

1. Using only a compass and a straightedge, construct 2 parallel lines. Do this construction without referring to the *Student Reference Book.* (*Hint:* This construction involves copying an angle.)

2. Draw 2 parallel lines using only a ruler and a pencil.

3. Draw a parallelogram that is not a rectangle, using only a ruler and a pencil.

Math Journal 1, p. 196

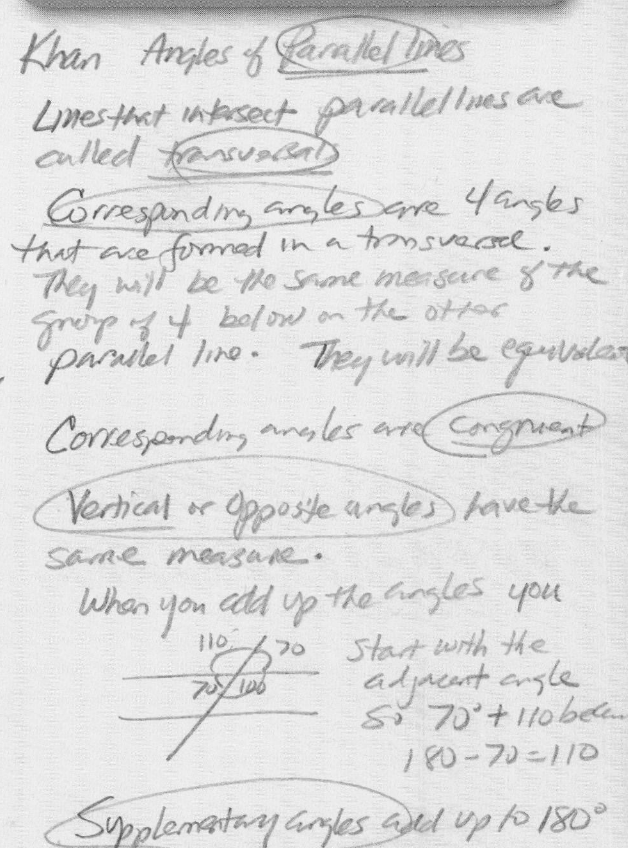

2 Ongoing Learning & Practice

▶ Calculating Total Price

INDEPENDENT ACTIVITY

(*Math Journal 1,* p. 197)

The problems on journal page 197 provide practice using a one- or two-step method for computing a total price that includes sales tax or tips.

▶ Math Boxes 5•9

INDEPENDENT ACTIVITY

(*Math Journal 1,* p. 198)

Mixed Practice Math Boxes in this lesson are paired with Math Boxes in Lesson 5-6. The skill in Problem 4 previews Unit 6 content.

▶ Study Link 5•9

INDEPENDENT ACTIVITY

(*Math Masters,* p. 172)

Home Connection Students explore relationships between angles formed by parallel lines cut by a transversal.

Student Page

Date Time

LESSON 5•9 **Calculating Total Price**

A total price is the sum of the price of an item (or subtotal) and the sales tax or tip that is a percentage of that item:

Total Price = Subtotal + Sales Tax (or Tip)

Two-Step Method	One-Step Method
Subtotal: $49.75 Sales Tax: 8% Find the total price.	Subtotal: $49.75 Sales Tax: 8% Find the total price.
Step 1: Find the sales tax in dollars: 8% of $49.75. 0.08 ∗ $49.75 = $3.98	The total price equals 100% of the subtotal plus 8% of the subtotal, so
Step 2: Add the sales tax amount to the subtotal.	Total = 100% ∗ subtotal + 8% ∗ subtotal = 1.08 ∗ subtotal
Subtotal + Sales Tax = Total Price $49.75 + $3.98 = $53.73	Find 108% of $49.75. 108% of $49.75 = 1.08 ∗ $49.75 = $53.73
The total price is $53.73.	The total price is $53.73.

Use either method to find the total price. Round your answer to the nearest cent, if necessary.

1. Subtotal: $89.00 Sales Tax: 6% Total Price: $94.34
2. Subtotal: $325.00 Sales Tax: 7% Total Price: $347.75
3. Subtotal: $25.20 Tip: 15% Total Price: $28.98
4. Subtotal: $103.50 Tip: 20% Total Price: $124.20
5. Subtotal: $448.40 Sales Tax: 4.5% Total Price: $468.58
6. Subtotal: $876.00 Sales Tax: 6.25% Total Price: $930.75

Math Journal 1, p. 197

Student Page

Date Time

LESSON 5•9 **Math Boxes**

1. Reflect figure *PQST* over the *x*-axis. Then plot and label the vertices of the image that results from that reflection.

P' = (−4, 1) Q' = (−2, 2)
S' = (−2, 4) T' = (−4, 3)

SRB 180 234

2. Use the partial-quotients algorithm to divide the numerator by the denominator. Round the result to the nearest hundredth and rename the result as a percent.

$\frac{11}{12}$ = 0.92 = 92 %

SRB 55-57

3. Choose the best estimate for the product $11\frac{2}{3} * \frac{1}{4}$.

- ○ 12
- ○ 11
- ○ 6
- ● 3

SRB 90

4. Write a number sentence for each word sentence. Then tell whether the number sentence is true or false.

Word Sentence	Number Sentence	True or False?
If 19 is subtracted from 55, the result is 36.	55 − 19 = 36	true
78 added to 62 is less than 160.	62 + 78 < 160	true
45 is 5 times as great as 9.	45 = 5 ∗ 9	true

SRB 241-243

Math Journal 1, p. 198

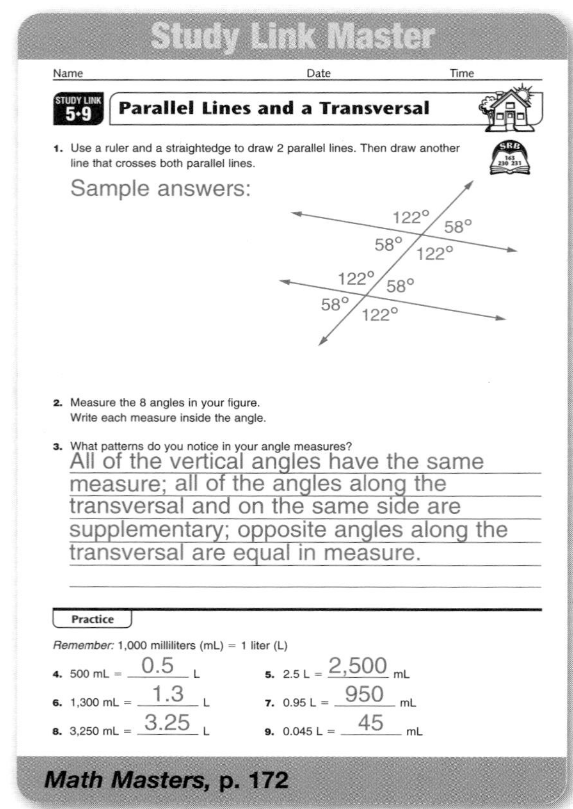
Study Link Master

Name Date Time

STUDY LINK 5•9 **Parallel Lines and a Transversal**

1. Use a ruler and a straightedge to draw 2 parallel lines. Then draw another line that crosses both parallel lines.

Sample answers:

2. Measure the 8 angles in your figure. Write each measure inside the angle.

3. What patterns do you notice in your angle measures?
All of the vertical angles have the same measure; all of the angles along the transversal and on the same side are supplementary; opposite angles along the transversal are equal in measure.

Practice

Remember: 1,000 milliliters (mL) = 1 liter (L)

4. 500 mL = 0.5 L
5. 2.5 L = 2,500 mL
6. 1,300 mL = 1.3 L
7. 0.95 L = 950 mL
8. 3,250 mL = 3.25 L
9. 0.045 L = 45 mL

Math Masters, p. 172

3 Differentiation Options

ENRICHMENT

INDEPENDENT ACTIVITY

▶ Applying Angle Relationships and Algebra

5–15 Min

(*Math Masters,* p. 173)

To apply their knowledge of adjacent, supplementary, and vertical angles, students find the missing values in algebraic expressions that represent angle measures. Encourage students to describe the strategies they used to find the missing measurements.

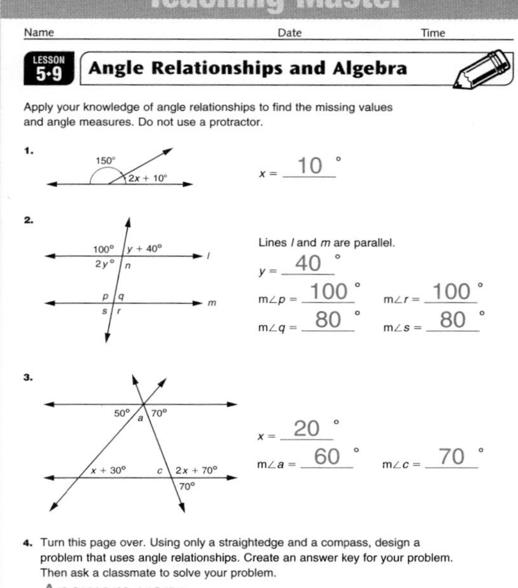

Teaching Master

Name Date Time

LESSON 5•9 **Angle Relationships and Algebra**

Apply your knowledge of angle relationships to find the missing values and angle measures. Do not use a protractor.

1. $x =$ 10°

2. Lines l and m are parallel.

$y =$ 40°

m∠p = 100° m∠r = 100°

m∠q = 80° m∠s = 80°

3. $x =$ 20°

m∠a = 60° m∠c = 70°

4. Turn this page over. Using only a straightedge and a compass, design a problem that uses angle relationships. Create an answer key for your problem. Then ask a classmate to solve your problem.

Answers vary.

Math Masters, p. 173

ENRICHMENT

INDEPENDENT ACTIVITY

▶ Finding Linear Perspective

30+ Min

Art Link Professional illustrators use linear perspective to represent special relationships as they appear to the human observer. All parallel lines that seem to go back into a picture (like rails of a railroad track) are angled so that the lines converge at a point in the distance, called a vanishing point. The vanishing point is always set on a real or imaginary horizontal line in a picture.

Have students look for examples of linear perspective in comic strips and sketches. Encourage them to talk to an artist, illustrator, or architect about the various techniques used to create the illusion of depth and distance.

ELL SUPPORT

SMALL-GROUP ACTIVITY

▶ Supporting Language with Drawings

5–15 Min

To provide language support for angle relationships, ask students to draw a pair of parallel lines cut by a transversal. Have them name the resulting angles and then use these names to identify pairs of vertical, supplementary, and adjacent angles.

Planning Ahead

For the optional Readiness activity in Lesson 5-10, use the cut-out quadrangles from Part 3 of Lesson 5-6, or make copies of *Math Masters,* page 164. Also set aside sheets of 11 in. by 17 in. paper.

Parallelograms

Objectives To introduce the relationships between angles of parallelograms; and to construct a parallelogram using a compass and a straightedge.

1 Teaching the Lesson

Key Activities

Students explore the relationships between angles of parallelograms. They also construct a parallelogram using a compass and a straightedge.

Key Concepts and Skills

- Add and subtract multidigit whole numbers. [Operations and Computation Goal 1]
- Determine angle measures by applying definitions and properties of angles, triangles, and quadrangles. [Geometry Goal 1]
- Use appropriate tools to construct congruent figures. [Geometry Goal 2]
- Apply the knowledge that a preimage and its image are congruent. [Geometry Goal 3]
- Write and evaluate algebraic expressions. [Patterns, Functions, and Algebra Goal 1]

Key Vocabulary

consecutive angles

materials

- ☐ *Math Journal 1,* pp. 196 and 199–201
- ☐ *Student Reference Book,* p. 200
- ☐ Study Link 5•9
- ☐ calculator; protractor
- ☐ compass; straightedge
- ☐ ruler
- ☐ board compass and meterstick (for demonstration purposes)

See **Advance Preparation**

2 Ongoing Learning & Practice

Students review properties of geometric solids by playing *3-D Shape Sort.*

Students practice and maintain skills through Math Boxes and Study Link activities.

Ongoing Assessment: Recognizing Student Achievement Use journal page 202. [Number and Numeration Goal 2; Measurement and Reference Frames Goal 1]

materials

- ☐ *Math Journal 1,* p. 202
- ☐ *Student Reference Book,* p. 335
- ☐ Study Link Master (*Math Masters,* p. 174)
- ☐ Game Masters (*Math Masters,* pp. 476 and 477)
- ☐ protractor

3 Differentiation Options

READINESS
Students use a tree diagram to review relationships among types of quadrangles.

ENRICHMENT
Students classify various quadrangles in terms of other quadrangles.

ELL SUPPORT
Students create a graphic organizer to support their understanding of parallelograms.

materials

- ☐ *Student Reference Book,* p. 169
- ☐ Teaching Masters (*Math Masters,* pp. 164 and 175)
- ☐ 11" by 17" paper; scissors

Additional Information

Advance Preparation Try the constructions on page 200 of the *Student Reference Book* before teaching the lesson.

Technology

Assessment Management System
Math Boxes, Problem 2
See the **iTLG.**

3 Differentiation Options

ENRICHMENT

INDEPENDENT ACTIVITY

▶ Applying Angle Relationships and Algebra

5–15 Min

(*Math Masters,* p. 173)

To apply their knowledge of adjacent, supplementary, and vertical angles, students find the missing values in algebraic expressions that represent angle measures. Encourage students to describe the strategies they used to find the missing measurements.

ENRICHMENT

INDEPENDENT ACTIVITY

▶ Finding Linear Perspective

30+ Min

Art Link Professional illustrators use linear perspective to represent special relationships as they appear to the human observer. All parallel lines that seem to go back into a picture (like rails of a railroad track) are angled so that the lines converge at a point in the distance, called a vanishing point. The vanishing point is always set on a real or imaginary horizontal line in a picture.

Have students look for examples of linear perspective in comic strips and sketches. Encourage them to talk to an artist, illustrator, or architect about the various techniques used to create the illusion of depth and distance.

ELL SUPPORT

SMALL-GROUP ACTIVITY

▶ Supporting Language with Drawings

5–15 Min

To provide language support for angle relationships, ask students to draw a pair of parallel lines cut by a transversal. Have them name the resulting angles and then use these names to identify pairs of vertical, supplementary, and adjacent angles.

Planning Ahead

For the optional Readiness activity in Lesson 5-10, use the cut-out quadrangles from Part 3 of Lesson 5-6, or make copies of *Math Masters,* page 164. Also set aside sheets of 11 in. by 17 in. paper.

Teaching Master

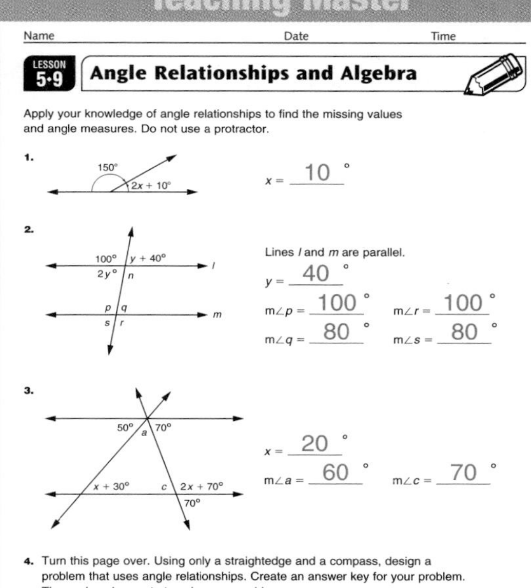

Name Date Time

LESSON 5•9 **Angle Relationships and Algebra**

Apply your knowledge of angle relationships to find the missing values and angle measures. Do not use a protractor.

1. $x =$ 10 °

2. Lines l and m are parallel.
$y =$ 40 °
$m\angle p =$ 100 ° $m\angle r =$ 100 °
$m\angle q =$ 80 ° $m\angle s =$ 80 °

3. $x =$ 20 °
$m\angle a =$ 60 ° $m\angle c =$ 70 °

4. Turn this page over. Using only a straightedge and a compass, design a problem that uses angle relationships. Create an answer key for your problem. Then ask a classmate to solve your problem.
Answers vary.

Math Masters, p. 173

Parallelograms

Objectives To introduce the relationships between angles of parallelograms; and to construct a parallelogram using a compass and a straightedge.

1 Teaching the Lesson

Key Activities

Students explore the relationships between angles of parallelograms. They also construct a parallelogram using a compass and a straightedge.

Key Concepts and Skills

- Add and subtract multidigit whole numbers. [Operations and Computation Goal 1]
- Determine angle measures by applying definitions and properties of angles, triangles, and quadrangles. [Geometry Goal 1]
- Use appropriate tools to construct congruent figures. [Geometry Goal 2]
- Apply the knowledge that a preimage and its image are congruent. [Geometry Goal 3]
- Write and evaluate algebraic expressions. [Patterns, Functions, and Algebra Goal 1]

Key Vocabulary

consecutive angles

materials

- ☐ *Math Journal 1,* pp. 196 and 199–201
- ☐ *Student Reference Book,* p. 200
- ☐ Study Link 5•9
- ☐ calculator; protractor
- ☐ compass; straightedge
- ☐ ruler
- ☐ board compass and meterstick (for demonstration purposes)

See **Advance Preparation**

2 Ongoing Learning & Practice

Students review properties of geometric solids by playing *3-D Shape Sort.*

Students practice and maintain skills through Math Boxes and Study Link activities.

Ongoing Assessment: Recognizing Student Achievement Use journal page 202. [Number and Numeration Goal 2; Measurement and Reference Frames Goal 1]

materials

- ☐ *Math Journal 1,* p. 202
- ☐ *Student Reference Book,* p. 335
- ☐ Study Link Master (*Math Masters,* p. 174)
- ☐ Game Masters (*Math Masters,* pp. 476 and 477)
- ☐ protractor

3 Differentiation Options

READINESS

Students use a tree diagram to review relationships among types of quadrangles.

ENRICHMENT

Students classify various quadrangles in terms of other quadrangles.

ELL SUPPORT

Students create a graphic organizer to support their understanding of parallelograms.

materials

- ☐ *Student Reference Book,* p. 169
- ☐ Teaching Masters (*Math Masters,* pp. 164 and 175)
- ☐ 11" by 17" paper; scissors

Additional Information

Advance Preparation Try the constructions on page 200 of the *Student Reference Book* before teaching the lesson.

Technology

Assessment Management System
Math Boxes, Problem 2
See the **iTLG.**

Getting Started

Mental Math and Reflexes

Students use calculators to find the degree measure of various sectors of a circle graph. They should round decimals to the nearest whole number.

Suggestions:

●○○ 70% 252°
$\frac{3}{5}$ 216°

●●○ 42% 151°
79% 284°

●●● $\frac{5}{16}$ 113°
35.25% 127°

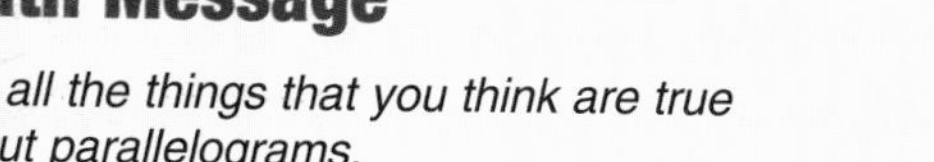

Math Message

List all the things that you think are true about parallelograms.

Study Link 5•9 Follow-Up

Review the patterns students found in their parallel lines cut by a transversal. Discuss why the measures they obtained using a protractor might not have been exactly what they theoretically should have been. The parallel lines that students drew may not be truly parallel, and the measures of the angles are approximations.

1 Teaching the Lesson

▶ Math Message Follow-Up

WHOLE-CLASS DISCUSSION

Ask students to share their lists of properties of parallelograms. Do not comment on the lists now. Just record properties on the board. The class will return to the list later in the lesson.

▶ Discussing Construction of Parallel Lines

WHOLE-CLASS ACTIVITY

(*Math Journal 1,* p. 196; *Student Reference Book,* p. 200)

Review journal page 196 from Lesson 5-9. Using a board compass, construct two parallel lines on the board. (Step-by-step directions are provided on page 200 of the *Student Reference Book.*)

Ask students to describe how they drew parallel lines using only a ruler and a pencil.

▷ One way is to draw two points, each the same distance from a line, and then to draw a line through the points.

▷ Another way is to lay the ruler on the paper and draw a line along each of the longer edges of the ruler. This is the method that will be used in Problem 1 on journal page 199.

NOTE The distance from a point to a line is defined to be along a line perpendicular to the given line. This means that drawing parallel lines by marking two points the same distance from a line depends on estimating or measuring 90° angles.

Student Page

Geometry and Constructions

Constructing Parallel Lines

Follow each step carefully. Use a clean sheet of paper.

Step 1: Draw line *AB* and ray *AC.*

Step 2: Place the compass anchor on *A.* Draw an arc that crosses both $\overline{AB}$ and $\overrightarrow{AC}$. Label the point where the arc crosses $\overline{AB}$ as *D.* Label the point where the arc crosses $\overrightarrow{AC}$ as *E.*

Step 3: Without changing the compass opening, place the compass anchor on *C.* Draw an arc the same size as the one you drew in Step 2. Label the point where the arc crosses $\overrightarrow{AC}$ as *F.*

Step 4: Place the compass anchor on *E* and the pencil point on *D.*

Step 5: Without changing the compass opening, place the compass anchor on *F.* Draw a small arc where the pencil point crosses the larger arc. Label the point where the small arc crosses the larger arc as *G.*

Step 6: Draw a line through points *C* and *G.*

Line *CG* is **parallel** to line *AB.* ∠*CAB* is **congruent** to ∠*FCG.*

Check Your Understanding

Draw a line. Use a compass and a straightedge to draw a line that is parallel to it.

Student Reference Book, p. 200

Adjusting the Activity

Have students extend the sides and the diagonal of the parallelogram in Problem 3 to see the parallel lines cut by the transversal. Also remind them that the sum of the measures of the angles of a triangle is 180°.

AUDITORY ◆ KINESTHETIC ◆ TACTILE ◆ VISUAL

When most students have completed journal pages 200 and 201, discuss their answers. Two possible methods for constructing a parallelogram are shown below. Other methods might combine copying some angles and some sides.

Method 1: This method is based on the relationship between pairs of opposite sides of a parallelogram and involves copying line segments.

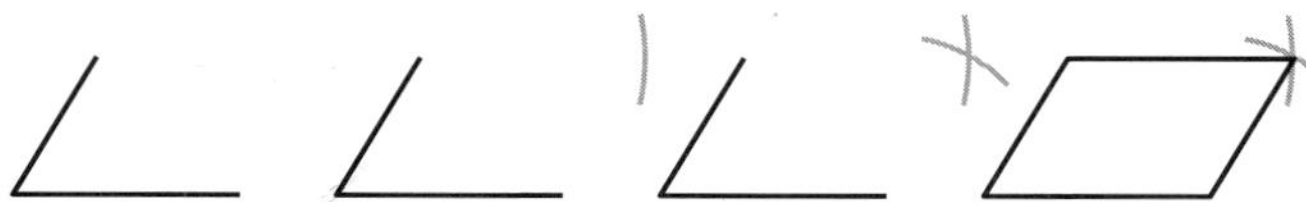

Method 2: This method is based on the relationship between angles formed by parallel lines cut by a transversal and involves copying angles.

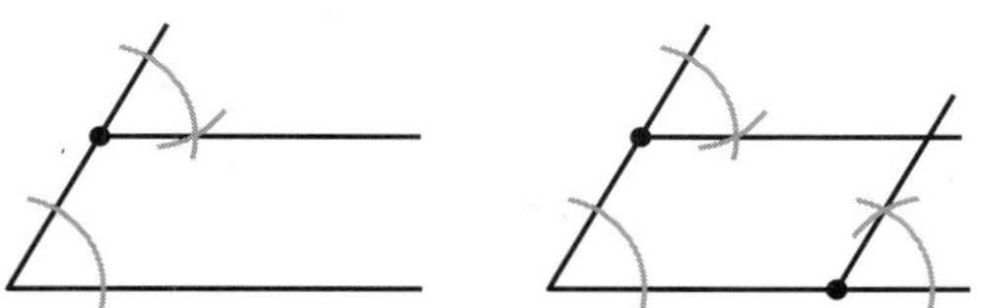

2 Ongoing Learning & Practice

▶ Playing *3-D Shape Sort*

PARTNER ACTIVITY

(*Student Reference Book*, p. 335; *Math Masters*, pp. 476 and 477)

Have students cut out the Shape Cards and the Property Cards from *Math Masters*, pages 476 and 477. They write either *vertex/edge* or *surfaces* on the back of each Property Card to name the category.

The rules are similar to those for *Polygon Capture*—students take shapes that match the vertex/edge property and the surface property.

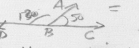

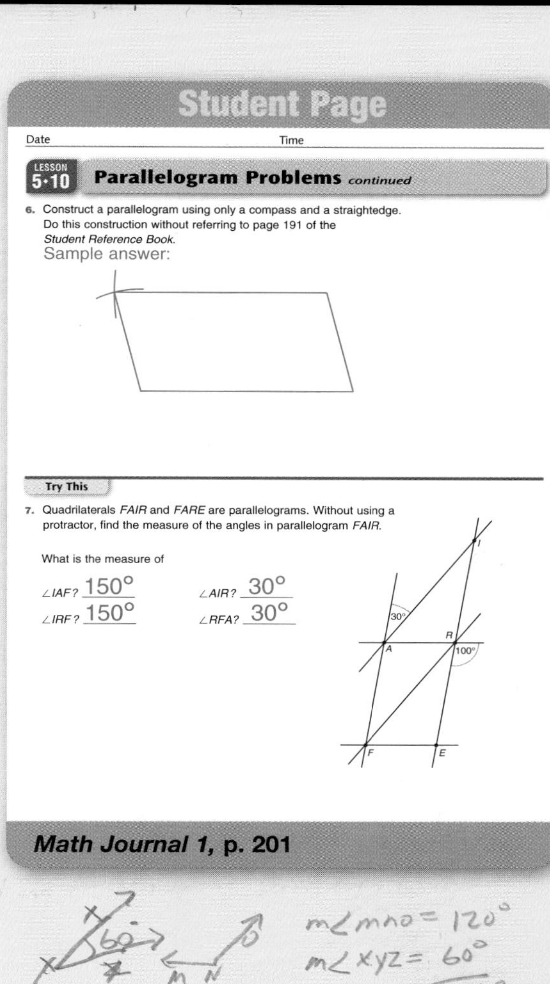

Student Page

Date Time

LESSON 5•10 **Parallelogram Problems** *continued*

6. Construct a parallelogram using only a compass and a straightedge. Do this construction without referring to page 191 of the *Student Reference Book*.

Sample answer:

Try This

7. Quadrilaterals *FAIR* and *FARE* are parallelograms. Without using a protractor, find the measure of the angles in parallelogram *FAIR*.

What is the measure of

∠IAF? 150° ∠AIR? 30°

∠IRF? 150° ∠RFA? 30°

Math Journal 1, p. 201

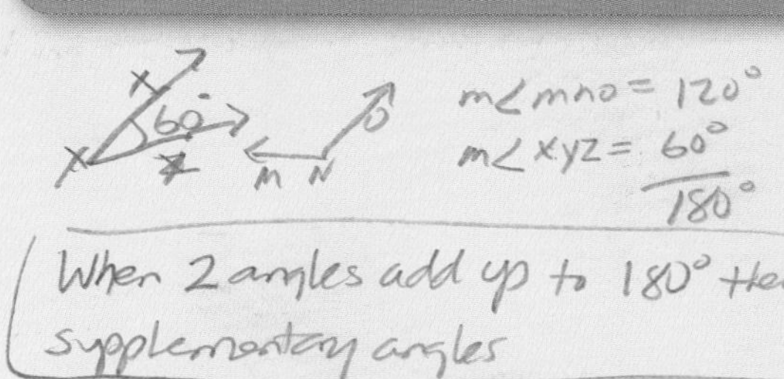

m∠MNO = 120°
m∠XYZ = 60°
180°
When 2 angles add up to 180° they are supplementary angles

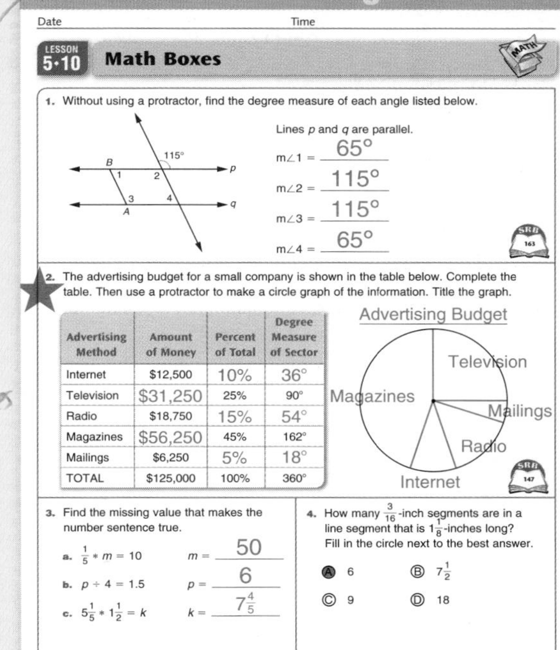

Student Page

Date Time

LESSON 5•10 **Math Boxes**

1. Without using a protractor, find the degree measure of each angle listed below.

Lines *p* and *q* are parallel.

m∠1 = 65°

m∠2 = 115°

m∠3 = 115°

m∠4 = 65°

2. The advertising budget for a small company is shown in the table below. Complete the table. Then use a protractor to make a circle graph of the information. Title the graph.

Advertising Method	Amount of Money	Percent of Total	Degree Measure of Sector
Internet	$12,500	10%	36°
Television	$31,250	25%	90°
Radio	$18,750	15%	54°
Magazines	$56,250	45%	162°
Mailings	$6,250	5%	18°
TOTAL	$125,000	100%	360°

Advertising Budget

3. Find the missing value that makes the number sentence true.

a. $\frac{1}{5} * m = 10$ m = 50

b. $p \div 4 = 1.5$ p = 6

c. $5\frac{1}{5} * 1\frac{1}{2} = k$ k = $7\frac{4}{5}$

4. How many $\frac{3}{16}$-inch segments are in a line segment that is $1\frac{1}{8}$-inches long? Fill in the circle next to the best answer.

(A) 6 (B) $7\frac{1}{2}$ (C) 9 (D) 18

Math Journal 1, p. 202

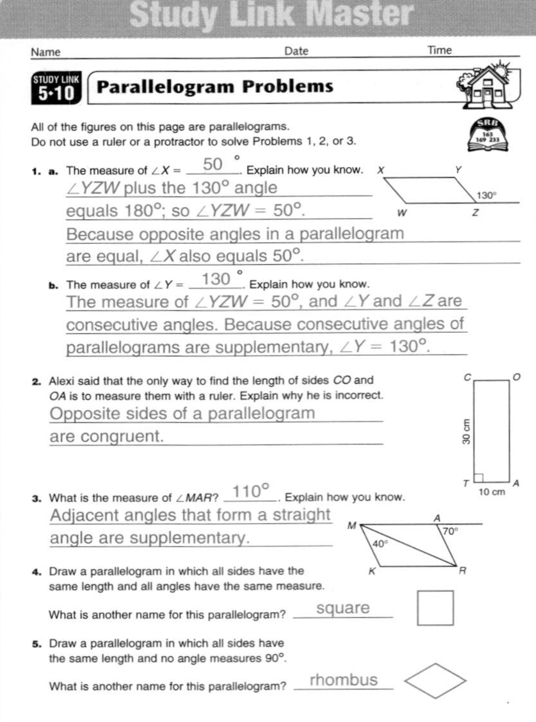
Study Link Master

Name Date Time

STUDY LINK 5·10 **Parallelogram Problems**

All of the figures on this page are parallelograms.
Do not use a ruler or a protractor to solve Problems 1, 2, or 3.

1. a. The measure of $\angle X$ = 50°. Explain how you know.
$\angle YZW$ plus the 130° angle equals 180°; so $\angle YZW$ = 50°. Because opposite angles in a parallelogram are equal, $\angle X$ also equals 50°.

   b. The measure of $\angle Y$ = 130°. Explain how you know.
The measure of $\angle YZW$ = 50°, and $\angle Y$ and $\angle Z$ are consecutive angles. Because consecutive angles of parallelograms are supplementary, $\angle Y$ = 130°.

2. Alexi said that the only way to find the length of sides *CO* and *OA* is to measure them with a ruler. Explain why he is incorrect.
Opposite sides of a parallelogram are congruent.

3. What is the measure of $\angle MAR$? 110°. Explain how you know.
Adjacent angles that form a straight angle are supplementary.

4. Draw a parallelogram in which all sides have the same length and all angles have the same measure.
What is another name for this parallelogram? square

5. Draw a parallelogram in which all sides have the same length and no angle measures 90°.
What is another name for this parallelogram? rhombus

Math Masters, p. 174

Quadrangle Tree Diagram

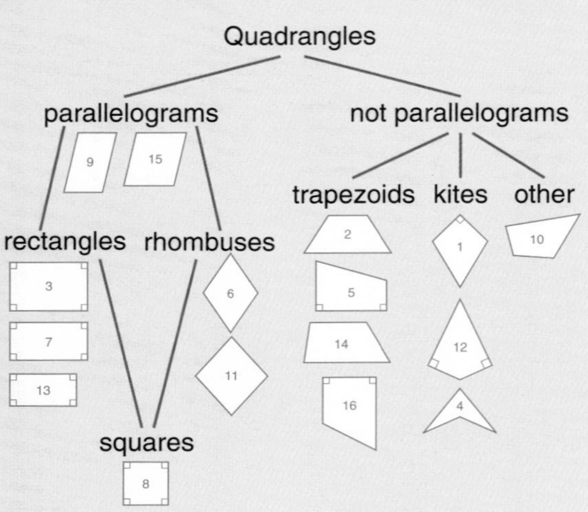

Math Boxes 5·10

INDEPENDENT ACTIVITY

(*Math Journal 1,* p. 202)

Mixed Practice Math Boxes in this lesson are paired with Math Boxes in Lesson 5-8. The skills in Problems 3 and 4 preview Unit 6 content.

Ongoing Assessment: Recognizing Student Achievement

Math Boxes Problem 2 ★

Use **Math Boxes, Problem 2** to assess students' ability to calculate the degree measures of the sectors of a circle graph. Students are making adequate progress if they can complete the table. Students' completed circle graphs indicate their ability to use a protractor to draw angles within ±2°.

[Number and Numeration Goal 2; Measurement and Reference Frames Goal 1]

Study Link 5·10

INDEPENDENT ACTIVITY

(*Math Masters,* p. 174)

Home Connection Students solve problems involving the sides and angles of parallelograms.

3 Differentiation Options

READINESS

PARTNER ACTIVITY

15–30 Min

Reviewing Quadrangle Relationships

(*Math Masters,* p. 164; *Student Reference Book,* p. 169)

To provide experience classifying quadrangles, have students copy the tree diagram from *Student Reference Book,* page 169 onto a sheet of 11 in. by 17 in. paper. Ask them to cut out the 16 quadrangles on *Math Masters,* page 164 and place each figure in the appropriate position on the tree diagram. Students will not need the set labels for this activity. (*See margin.*)

ENRICHMENT

▶ Using Quadrangles to Classify Quadrangles

PARTNER ACTIVITY

15–30 Min

(*Student Reference Book,* p. 169; *Math Masters,* p. 175)

To extend students' knowledge of quadrangle properties, have them read each statement on *Math Masters,* page 175 and classify various quadrangles in terms of other quadrangles. For example, a square is always a rectangle, but a rectangle is not always a square. Ask students to also identify cases for which statements are true.

ELL SUPPORT

▶ Understanding Parallelograms

SMALL-GROUP ACTIVITY

5–15 Min

To provide language support for parallelograms, have students create a graphic organizer. *Suggestion:*

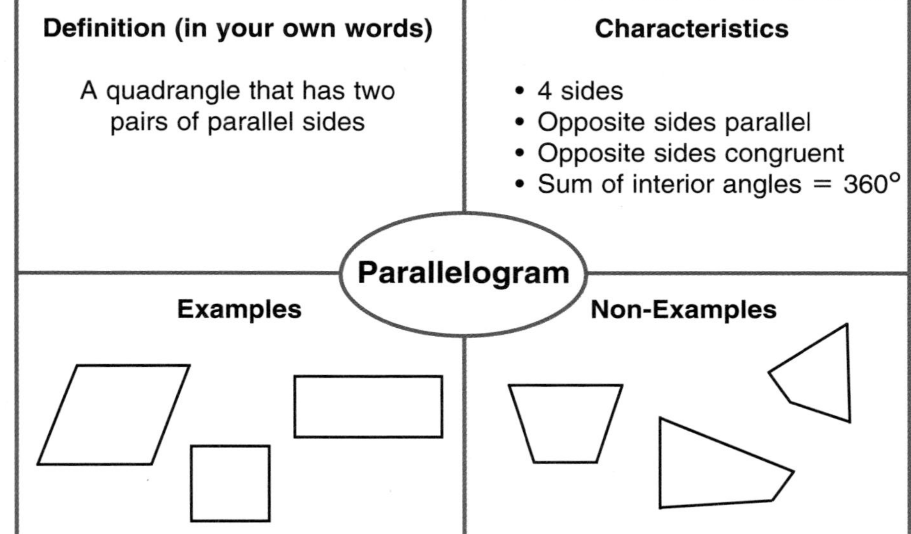

Planning Ahead

Have students remove *Algebra Election* Activity Sheets 3 and 4 from their journals (*Math Journal 1*). Collect and store these activity sheets for use in Unit 6.

Teaching Master

Name ____ Date ____ Time ____

LESSON 5•10 **Using Quadrangles to Classify Quadrangles**

Read each statement. Then decide if the statement is *always, sometimes,* or *never* true. If you write *sometimes,* identify a case for which the statement is true.

Example: A rectangle is a square. sometimes
A rectangle is a square when its 4 sides are the same length.

1. A square is a rectangle. always
2. A rhombus is a trapezoid. never
3. A square is a parallelogram. always
4. A rhombus is a parallelogram. always
5. A kite is a parallelogram. never
6. A rhombus is a rectangle. sometimes; A rhombus is a rectangle when it is a square.
7. A square is a rhombus. always
8. A trapezoid is a parallelogram. never

Fill in the blank using *always, sometimes,* or *never.* If you write *sometimes,* identify a case for which the statement is true.

9. A rectangle sometimes has consecutive sides that are congruent. A rectangle has consecutive sides that are congruent when it is a square.
10. The diagonals of a rhombus are sometimes congruent. The diagonals of a rhombus are congruent when the rhombus is a square.

Math Masters, p. 175

Student Page

Geometry and Constructions

Special types of quadrangles have been given names. Some of these are parallelograms; others are not.

The tree diagram below shows how the different types of quadrangles are related. For example, quadrangles are divided into two major groups—"parallelograms" and "not parallelograms." The special types of parallelograms include rectangles, rhombuses, and squares.

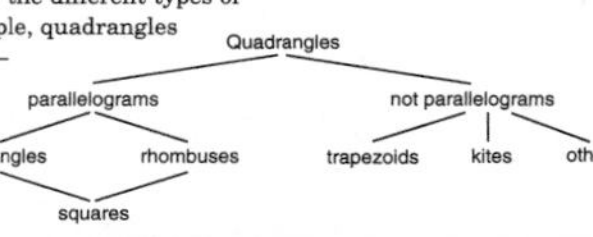

Quadrangles That Are Parallelograms		
rectangle		**Rectangles** are parallelograms. A rectangle has 4 right angles (square corners). The sides do not all have to be the same length.
rhombus		**Rhombuses** are parallelograms. A rhombus has 4 sides that are all the same length. The angles of a rhombus are usually not right angles, but they may be.
square		**Squares** are parallelograms. A square has 4 right angles (square corners). Its 4 sides are all the same length. *All* squares are rectangles. *All* squares are also rhombuses.

Quadrangles That Are NOT Parallelograms		
trapezoid		**Trapezoids** have exactly 1 pair of parallel sides. The 4 sides of a trapezoid can all have different lengths.
kite		**Kites** are quadrangles with 2 pairs of equal sides. The equal sides are next to each other. The 4 sides cannot all have the same length. (A rhombus is not a kite.)
other		Any polygon with 4 sides that is not a parallelogram, a trapezoid, or a kite.

Check Your Understanding

What is the difference between the quadrangles in each pair below?

1. a rhombus and a rectangle
2. a trapezoid and a square
3. a kite and a parallelogram

Check your answers on page 421.

Student Reference Book, p. 169

Progress Check 5

Objective To assess students' progress on mathematical content through the end of Unit 5.

1 Assessing Progress

Progress Check 5 is a cumulative assessment of concepts and skills taught in Unit 5 and in previous units.

See the Appendix for a complete list of Grade 6 Goals.

materials

- ☐ Study Link 5•10
- ☐ Assessment Masters (*Assessment Handbook,* pp. 161–165)
- ☐ slate; straightedge; protractor; compass

CONTENT ASSESSED	LESSON(S)	ASSESSMENT ITEMS			
		SELF	ORAL/SLATE	WRITTEN PART A	WRITTEN PART B
Rename fractions as decimals and percents. Calculate the percent of a number. [Number and Numeration Goal 2]	5•1, 5•3–5•10	1, 4	2, 4	8	14–15
Find sums of whole and signed numbers. [Operations and Computation Goal 1]	5•2–5•4, 5•9, 5•10		1	6	12–13
Estimate and find sums, differences, and products of fractions and mixed numbers. [Operations and Computation Goals 3–5]	5•1–5•3, 5•5–5•7, 5•9–5•11	2–3			9–11
Use a protractor to construct a circle graph. [Data and Chance Goal 1]	5•3	7		8	
Measure/draw angles to the nearest degree using a protractor. [Measurement, Reference Frames Goal 1]	5•1–5•3, 5•5			1–3	
Plot ordered number pairs in four quadrants. Use ordered pairs to name points. [Measurement and Reference Frames Goal 3]	5•4, 5•5			4	
Classify/describe angles. Apply properties of supplementary and vertical angles; of angles formed by two parallel lines and a transversal; of sums and angle measures of triangles and quadrangles [Geometry Goal 1]	5•1–5•10	5	1, 3	6–7	
Use a compass and straightedge to construct geometric and congruent figures. [Geometry Goal 2]	5•6–5•8, 5•10	6		5	
Perform isometry transformations on a coordinate grid. [Geometry Goal 3]	5•5–5•7 5–9	8		4	

2 Building Background for Unit 6

Math Boxes 5•11 previews and practices skills for Unit 6.

The **Unit 6 Family Letter** introduces families to Unit 6 topics and terms.

materials

- ☐ *Math Journal 1,* p. 203
- ☐ Study Link Masters (*Math Masters,* pp. 176–179)

Additional Information

See *Assessment Handbook,* pages 84–91 for additional assessment information. For assessment checklists, see pages 242–245.

Technology

Assessment Management System
Progress Check 5
See the **iTLG.**

Getting Started

Math Message • Self Assessment

Complete the Self Assessment (Assessment Handbook, *p. 161*).

Study Link 5•10 Follow-Up

Briefly review students' answers.

1 Assessing Progress

▶ Math Message Follow-Up

(Self Assessment, *Assessment Handbook,* p. 161)

The Self Assessment offers students the opportunity to reflect upon their progress.

▶ Oral and Slate Assessments

Problems 1 and 3 provide summative information and can be used for grading purposes. Problems 2 and 4 provide formative information that can be useful in planning future instruction.

Oral Assessment

1. Students mentally calculate the missing angle measure in triangles and quadrangles. *Suggestions:*
   - triangle: 68°, 54° 58°
   - quadrangle: 51°, 140°, 120° 49°

2. Students mentally solve percent problems. *Suggestions:*
   - 20% of 60 12
   - 25% of 32 8
   - 5% of 40 2
   - 110% of 50 55
   - 1% of 80 0.8
   - 6% of 90 5.4

Slate Assessment

3. Students draw and label specific angles on their slates. They describe the characteristics of each type of angle–acute, obtuse, right, reflex, straight, adjacent, supplementary, and vertical. Sample answer: The measure of an obtuse angle is between 90° and 180°; vertical angles are congruent.
4. Students write the decimal and percent equivalencies for each fraction. *Suggestions*:
   - $\frac{3}{5}$ 0.6; 60%
   - $2\frac{3}{4}$ 2.75; 275%
   - $\frac{1}{25}$ 0.04; 4%
   - $\frac{5}{4}$ 1.25; 125%
   - $\frac{11}{20}$ 0.55; 55%
   - $\frac{3}{8}$ 0.375; 37.5%

Assessment Master

Name Date Time

LESSON 5•11 **Self Assessment** Progress Check 5

Think about each skill listed below. Assess your own progress by checking the most appropriate box.

Skills	I can do this on my own and explain how to do this.	I can do this on my own.	I can do this if I get help or look at an example.
1. Rename fractions as mixed numbers, decimals, and percents.			
2. Estimate sums, differences, and products of fractions and mixed numbers.			
3. Add, subtract, and multiply fractions and mixed numbers.			
4. Find a percent of a number mentally.			
5. Identify, draw, and describe different types of angles (acute, obtuse, right, reflex, vertical, adjacent, supplementary).			
6. Copy a figure using a compass and a straightedge.			
7. Use a protractor to create a circle graph.			
8. Translate a figure on a coordinate grid.			

Assessment Handbook, **p. 161**

Assessment Master

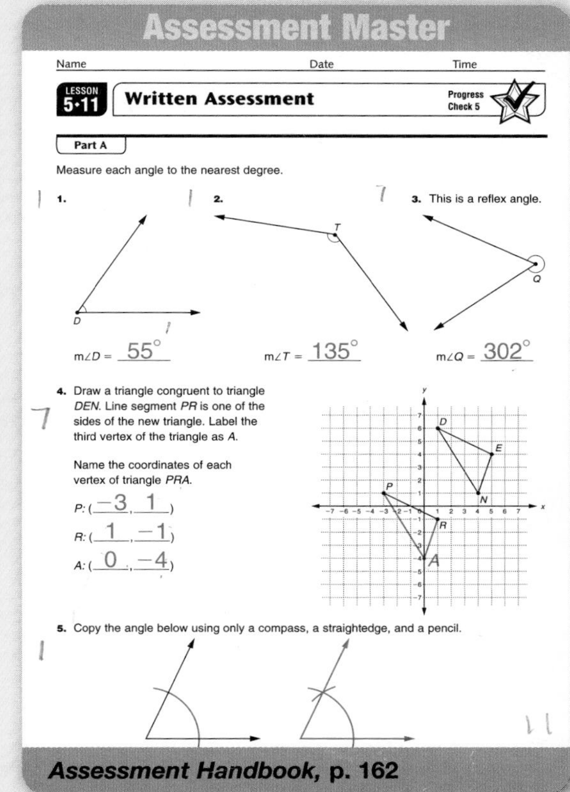

Name Date Time

LESSON 5•11 **Written Assessment** Progress Check 5

Part A

Measure each angle to the nearest degree.

1. m∠D = 55°
2. m∠T = 135°
3. This is a reflex angle. m∠Q = 302°

4. Draw a triangle congruent to triangle *DEN*. Line segment *PR* is one of the sides of the new triangle. Label the third vertex of the triangle as *A*.

Name the coordinates of each vertex of triangle *PRA*.

P: (−3, 1)
R: (1, −1)
A: (0, −4)

5. Copy the angle below using only a compass, a straightedge, and a pencil.

Assessment Handbook, **p. 162**

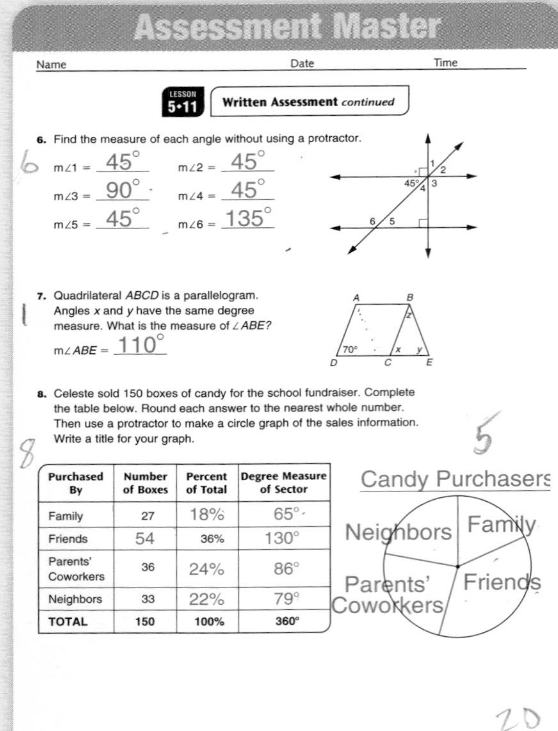
Assessment Master

Name Date Time

LESSON 5•11 Written Assessment *continued*

6. Find the measure of each angle without using a protractor.

m∠1 = 45° m∠2 = 45°
m∠3 = 90° m∠4 = 45°
m∠5 = 45° m∠6 = 135°

7. Quadrilateral *ABCD* is a parallelogram. Angles *x* and *y* have the same degree measure. What is the measure of ∠*ABE*?

m∠*ABE* = 110°

8. Celeste sold 150 boxes of candy for the school fundraiser. Complete the table below. Round each answer to the nearest whole number. Then use a protractor to make a circle graph of the sales information. Write a title for your graph.

Purchased By	Number of Boxes	Percent of Total	Degree Measure of Sector
Family	27	18%	65°
Friends	54	36%	130°
Parents' Coworkers	36	24%	86°
Neighbors	33	22%	79°
TOTAL	150	100%	360°

Assessment Handbook, p. 163

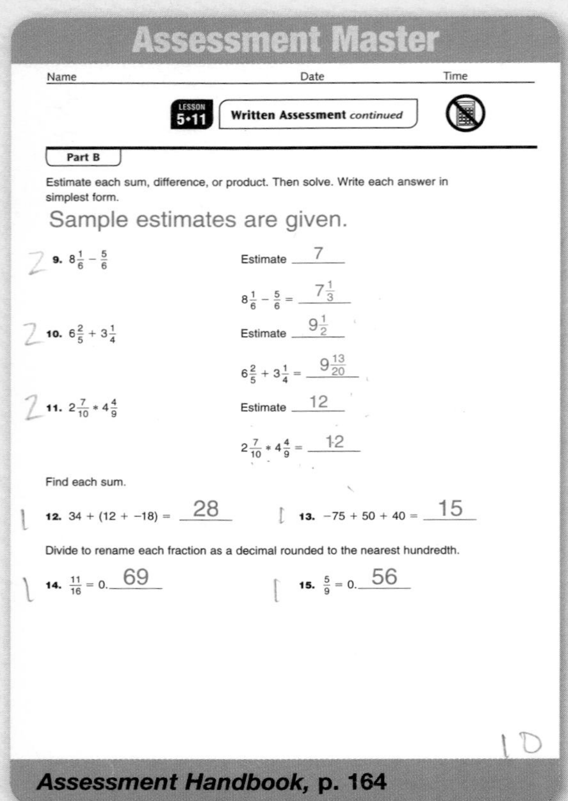
Assessment Master

Name Date Time

LESSON 5•11 Written Assessment *continued*

Part B

Estimate each sum, difference, or product. Then solve. Write each answer in simplest form.

Sample estimates are given.

9. $8\frac{1}{6} - \frac{5}{6}$ Estimate 7

$8\frac{1}{6} - \frac{5}{6} = 7\frac{1}{3}$

10. $6\frac{2}{5} + 3\frac{1}{4}$ Estimate $9\frac{1}{2}$

$6\frac{2}{5} + 3\frac{1}{4} = 9\frac{13}{20}$

11. $2\frac{7}{10} * 4\frac{4}{9}$ Estimate 12

$2\frac{7}{10} * 4\frac{4}{9} = 12$

Find each sum.

12. 34 + (12 + −18) = 28 **13.** −75 + 50 + 40 = 15

Divide to rename each fraction as a decimal rounded to the nearest hundredth.

14. $\frac{11}{16}$ = 0.69 **15.** $\frac{5}{9}$ = 0.56

Assessment Handbook, p. 164

▶ Written Assessment

INDEPENDENT ACTIVITY

(*Assessment Handbook,* pp. 162–164)

Part A Recognizing Student Achievement

Problems 1–8 provide summative information and may be used for grading purposes.

Problem(s)	Description
1–3	Measure angles to the nearest degree.
4	Translate a figure. Name points on a coordinate grid.
5	Copy a figure using a compass and a straightedge.
6, 7	Apply definitions and properties of angles and other figures.
8	Calculate the percent of a number. Create circle graphs.

Part B Informing Instruction

Problems 9–15 provide formative information that can be useful in planning future instruction.

Problem(s)	Description
9–11	Perform operations on fractions.
12–13	Add integers.
14–15	Divide to rename fractions as decimals.

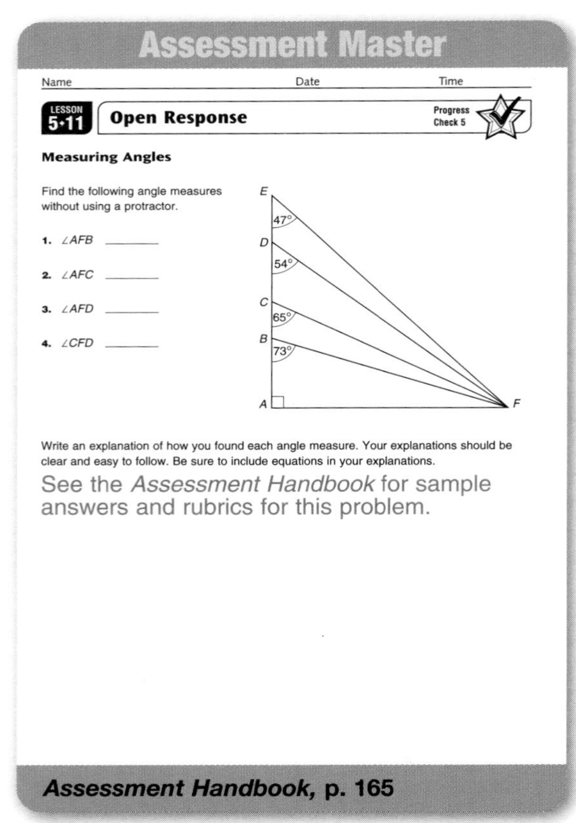
Assessment Master

Name Date Time

LESSON 5•11 Open Response Progress Check 5

Measuring Angles

Find the following angle measures without using a protractor.

1. ∠*AFB* ______
2. ∠*AFC* ______
3. ∠*AFD* ______
4. ∠*CFD* ______

Write an explanation of how you found each angle measure. Your explanations should be clear and easy to follow. Be sure to include equations in your explanations.

See the *Assessment Handbook* for sample answers and rubrics for this problem.

Assessment Handbook, p. 165

▶ Open Response

INDEPENDENT ACTIVITY

(*Assessment Handbook,* p. 165)

Measuring Angles

The open-response item requires students to apply skills and concepts from Unit 5 to solve a multistep problem. See *Assessment Handbook,* pages 87–91 for rubrics and students' work samples for this problem.

▶ Midyear Assessment

The Midyear Assessment (*Assessment Handbook,* pp. 203–210) provides an additional assessment opportunity that you may use as part of your balanced assessment plan. This assessment covers many of the important concepts and skills presented in *Sixth Grade Everyday Mathematics.* It should be used to complement the ongoing and periodic assessments that appear within lessons and at the end of the units. Please see pages 92 and 93 in the *Assessment Handbook* for further information.

2 Building Background for Unit 6

▶ Math Boxes 5•11

INDEPENDENT ACTIVITY

(*Math Journal 1,* p. 203)

Mixed Practice This Math Boxes page previews Unit 6 content.

▶ Study Link 5•11: Unit 6 Family Letter

INDEPENDENT ACTIVITY

(*Math Masters,* pp. 176–179)

Home Connection The Unit 6 Family Letter provides parents and guardians with information and activities related to Unit 6 topics.

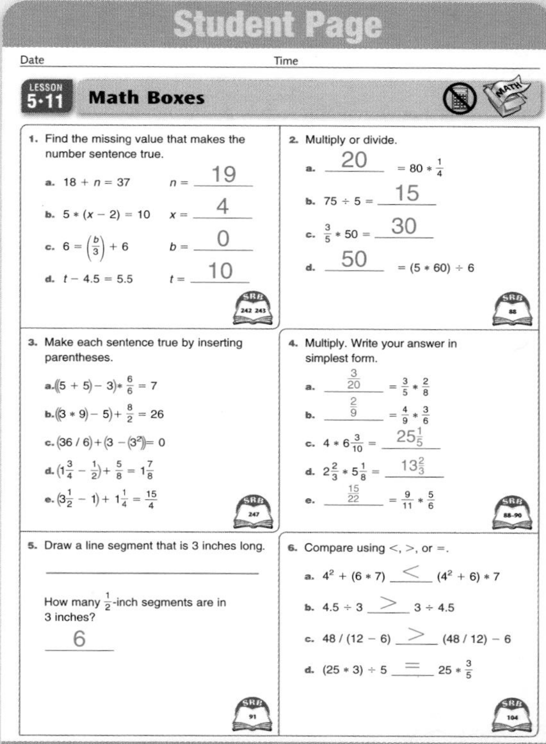

Student Page

Date Time

LESSON 5•11 **Math Boxes**

1. Find the missing value that makes the number sentence true.
   a. $18 + n = 37$ $n =$ 19
   b. $5 * (x - 2) = 10$ $x =$ 4
   c. $6 = \left(\frac{b}{3}\right) + 6$ $b =$ 0
   d. $t - 4.5 = 5.5$ $t =$ 10

   SRB 242 243

2. Multiply or divide.
   a. 20 $= 80 * \frac{1}{4}$
   b. $75 \div 5 =$ 15
   c. $\frac{3}{5} * 50 =$ 30
   d. 50 $= (5 * 60) \div 6$

   SRB 88

3. Make each sentence true by inserting parentheses.
   a. $((5 + 5) - 3) * \frac{6}{6} = 7$
   b. $((3 * 9) - 5) + \frac{8}{2} = 26$
   c. $(36 / 6) + (3 - (3^2)) = 0$
   d. $(1\frac{3}{4} - \frac{1}{2}) + \frac{5}{8} = 1\frac{7}{8}$
   e. $(3\frac{1}{2} - 1) + 1\frac{1}{4} = \frac{15}{4}$

   SRB 247

4. Multiply. Write your answer in simplest form.
   a. $\frac{3}{20}$ $= \frac{3}{5} * \frac{2}{8}$
   b. $\frac{2}{9}$ $= \frac{4}{9} * \frac{3}{6}$
   c. $4 * 6\frac{3}{10} =$ $25\frac{1}{5}$
   d. $2\frac{2}{3} * 5\frac{1}{8} =$ $13\frac{2}{3}$
   e. $\frac{15}{22}$ $= \frac{9}{11} * \frac{5}{6}$

   SRB 88-90

5. Draw a line segment that is 3 inches long.

   How many $\frac{1}{2}$-inch segments are in 3 inches?
   6

   SRB 91

6. Compare using <, >, or =.
   a. $4^2 + (6 * 7)$ $<$ $(4^2 + 6) * 7$
   b. $4.5 \div 3$ $>$ $3 \div 4.5$
   c. $48 / (12 - 6)$ $>$ $(48 / 12) - 6$
   d. $(25 * 3) \div 5$ $=$ $25 * \frac{3}{5}$

   SRB 104

Math Journal 1, p. 203

Study Link Master

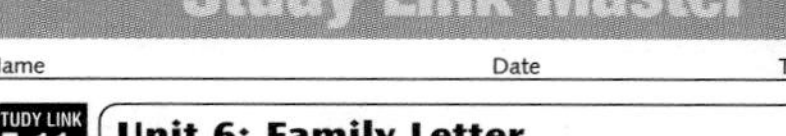

Name Date Time

STUDY LINK 5•11 **Unit 6: Family Letter**

Number Systems and Algebra Concepts

In *Fourth* and *Fifth Grade Everyday Mathematics,* your child worked with addition and subtraction of positive and negative numbers. In this unit, students use multiplication patterns to help them establish the rules for multiplying and dividing with positive and negative numbers. They also develop and use an algorithm for the division of fractions.

In the rest of the unit, your child will explore beginning algebra concepts. First, the class reviews how to determine whether a number sentence is true or false. This involves understanding what to do with numbers that are grouped within parentheses and knowing in what order to calculate if the groupings of numbers are not made explicit by parentheses.

Students then solve simple equations by trial and error to reinforce what it means to solve an equation—to replace a variable with a number that will make the number sentence true.

Next, they solve pan-balance problems, first introduced in *Fifth Grade Everyday Mathematics,* to develop a more systematic approach to solving equations. For example, to find out how many marbles weigh as much as 1 orange in the top balance at the right, you can first remove 1 orange from each pan and then remove half the remaining oranges from the left side and half the marbles from the right side. The pans will still balance.

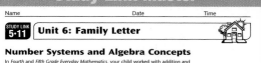

Students learn that each step in the solution of a pan-balance problem can be represented by an equation, thus leading to the solution of the original equation. You might ask your child to demonstrate how pan-balance problems work.

Finally, your child will learn how to solve inequalities—number sentences comparing two quantities that are not equal.

Please keep this Family Letter for reference as your child works through Unit 6.

Math Masters, pp. 176–179

Appendices

Contents

Exploring the Solar System

Objectives To learn about the solar system; and to read and compare large numbers.

1 Doing the Project

Recommended Use: During or after Unit 2

Key Activities

Students read about the solar system and examine a table showing the diameter, average distance from the Sun, and surface temperature of each planet. They use diameter and distance information to develop a second table comparing other planets to Earth.

Key Concepts and Skills

- Apply place-value concepts to read, write, interpret, and compare large numbers. [Number and Numeration Goal 1]
- Convert between scientific and standard notations. [Number and Numeration Goal 1]
- Apply extended multiplication and division facts to make ratio comparisons of large numbers. [Operations and Computation Goal 6]
- Use data to answer questions and draw conclusions. [Data and Chance Goal 2]
- Estimate metric equivalents for customary linear measurements. [Measurement and Reference Frames Goal 1]

Key Vocabulary

significant digits • diameter of a sphere • sphere • endpoints • ellipses • geocentric • heliocentric • astronomical unit

materials

- ☐ Project Masters (*Math Masters,* pp. 350–356)
- ☐ calculator (optional)

2 Extending the Project

Students discuss life on other planets.

materials

- ☐ Project Master (*Math Masters,* p. 354)

Additional Information

This project should take two days and is the first of five linked projects (Projects 1–5). *Math Masters,* page 354 is also referenced in Project 5, *Will It Be Possible to Travel to Other Planets in Your Lifetime?*

Background Information On July 29, 2005, Dr. Mike Brown and his colleagues announced the discovery of a tenth planet beyond Pluto. At that time, the planet's temporary name was 2003 UB313. The planet's permanent name, as well as information about its size and surface temperature, became available after this third edition of *Everyday Mathematics* had already gone to press. Consider having students extend planet data tables to include any available information about this tenth planet.

Advance Preparation Read "Projects" in the Management Guide section of the *Teacher's Reference Manual.*

Technology

See the **iTLG.**

1 Doing the Project

▶ Reading about the Solar System

WHOLE-CLASS DISCUSSION

(*Math Masters,* pp. 350 and 351)

Have students read the essays about the solar system and planetary movement on *Math Masters,* pages 350 and 351.

Discuss the essays and any additional information students may have read about specific planets, space probes, and so on.

▶ Considering Data about the Solar System

WHOLE-CLASS DISCUSSION

(*Math Masters,* pp. 352 and 353)

Read *Math Masters,* pages 352 and 353 as a class. Spend time discussing the meaning of **significant digits.** Digits that represent an actual measurement are significant digits. Nonzero digits (1–9) are always significant. If a zero indicates that a measurement was made and found to be zero, then the zero is significant.

Copy the following table on the board. Review each type of number and example. Have students identify the examples of 2-, 3-, and 4-significant digits from the table. 2-significant digits: 0.019, 4,200; 3-significant digits: 10.5; 4-significant digits: 0.003040, 607,800, 50.09

Numbers	Significant Zeros	Examples
Decimals between 0 and 1	Zeros to the left of all nonzero digits are not significant. All other zeros are significant.	Significant digits (red) 0.019 0.003040
Positive integer	Zeros to the right of all the nonzero digits are not significant. Zeros between nonzero digits are significant.	Significant digits (red) 4,200 607,800
Decimals greater than 1	All zeros are significant	Significant digits (red) 10.5 50.09

Project Master

Name Date Time

PROJECT 1 **The Solar System**

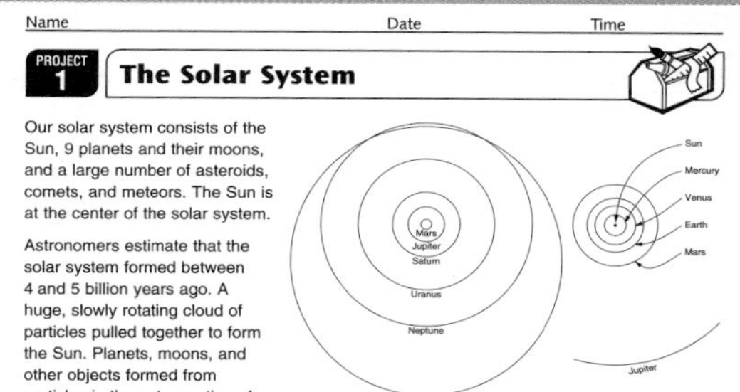

Our solar system consists of the Sun, 9 planets and their moons, and a large number of asteroids, comets, and meteors. The Sun is at the center of the solar system.

Astronomers estimate that the solar system formed between 4 and 5 billion years ago. A huge, slowly rotating cloud of particles pulled together to form the Sun. Planets, moons, and other objects formed from particles in the outer portion of the cloud.

From time to time, you can see Mercury, Venus, Mars, Jupiter, and Saturn in the night sky. For most of history, people thought these were the only planets other than Earth. Then, using increasingly powerful telescopes, astronomers spotted Uranus in 1781, Neptune in 1846, and Pluto in 1930. Astronomers might never have found Neptune and Pluto if they had not been guided by mathematical predictions that told them where to aim their telescopes.

The 4 planets closest to the Sun—Mercury, Venus, Earth, and Mars—are called the rocky dwarfs because they are small and made mostly of rock. Jupiter, Saturn, Uranus, and Neptune are huge balls of frozen gas and liquid with small solid cores. These planets are called the gas giants or Jovian planets. They have multiple moons and rings.

Knowledge of the solar system is growing rapidly. On July 29, 2005, Dr. Mike Brown and his colleagues announced the discovery of a tenth planet beyond Pluto. At that time, the planet's temporary name was 2003 UB313. The planet's permanent name, as well as information about its size and surface temperature, became available after this edition of *Everyday Mathematics* had already gone to press.

***Math Masters,* p. 350**

Project Master

Name Date Time

PROJECT 1 **Movement of the Planets**

Today most people know that Earth revolves around the Sun.

Long ago, almost everyone believed that the entire universe revolved around Earth. That idea certainly corresponds to what we can see with our own eyes: Every day the Sun rises in the east and sets in the west. At night, the Moon, planets, and stars move steadily through the sky.

In the second century A.D., an Egyptian mathematician and astronomer named Claudius Ptolemaeus (Ptolemy) published a book called the *Almagest.* In it, he gave a mathematical description of the universe as **geocentric,** or Earth-centered. Ptolemy's theory of how the Sun, planets, and stars move through space was widely accepted for the next 1,400 years.

In 1543, the Polish astronomer Nicolaus Copernicus (1473–1543) described a different view of the universe in his book *On the Revolutions of the Celestial Spheres.* After 30 years of research, he concluded that the planets—including Earth—have a **heliocentric** movement: They actually revolve around the Sun. The apparent motion of heavenly bodies through the sky is due primarily to Earth's rotation. This idea had been proposed by Greek scholars as early as the third century B.C. but had been ignored.

Copernicus's theory did not perfectly explain the movement of all the planets that were known at the time, but it led scientists in a new direction. Astronomer Tycho Brahe (1546–1601) gathered large quantities of data in a search for the true laws of planetary motion. Although Brahe died before he could complete his theory, his assistant, Johannes Kepler (1571–1630) developed mathematical models that correctly explained the observed motions of the planets. Kepler showed that planetary orbits are elliptical (oval) rather than circular. He also demonstrated that the Moon is a satellite of Earth.

In *Everyday Mathematics,* you have developed mathematical models to describe situations, represent relationships, and solve problems. These models include number sentences and graphs. You are solving problems that are simpler than Kepler's, but you are following the same approach that he used. You can read more about problem solving on pages 258 and 259 in the *Student Reference Book.*

***Math Masters,* p. 351**

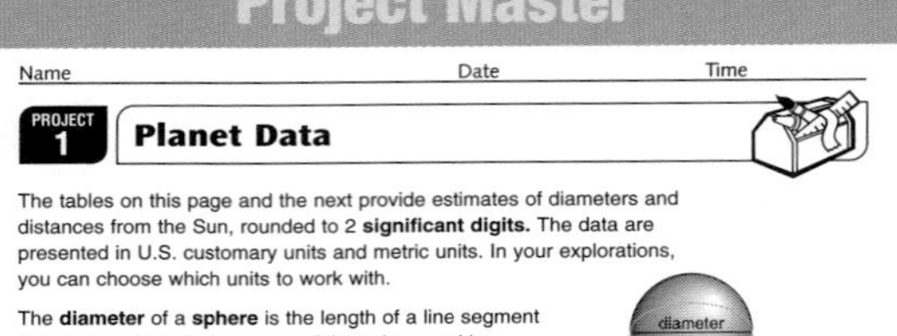

Project Master

Name Date Time

PROJECT 1 Planet Data

The tables on this page and the next provide estimates of diameters and distances from the Sun, rounded to 2 **significant digits.** The data are presented in U.S. customary units and metric units. In your explorations, you can choose which units to work with.

The **diameter** of a **sphere** is the length of a line segment that passes through the center of the sphere and has **endpoints** on the sphere. Planets are not quite spheres, so an average diameter is used in the data tables.

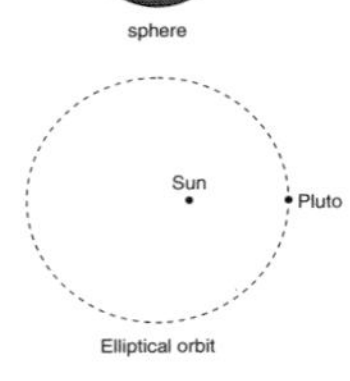

Planets move around the Sun in orbits that are **ellipses** (ovals), somewhat affected by the gravitational pulls of other planets. Estimates of average distances from the Sun are accurate enough for anything done in the *Sixth Grade Everyday Mathematics* solar system projects.

Sun
Pluto
Elliptical orbit

Solar System Data Table 1

Planet	Average Diameter (Miles)	Average Distance from the Sun (Miles)	Surface Temperature (Degrees Fahrenheit)
Mercury	3,000	36,000,000 or $3.6 * 10^7$	−290 to 800
Venus	7,500	67,000,000 or $6.7 * 10^7$	850 to 910
Earth	7,900	93,000,000 or $9.3 * 10^7$	−130 to 140
Mars	4,200	140,000,000 or $1.4 * 10^8$	−190 to 80
Jupiter	89,000	480,000,000 or $4.8 * 10^8$	−240 to −150
Saturn	75,000	890,000,000 or $8.9 * 10^8$	−290 to −150
Uranus	32,000	1,800,000,000 or $1.8 * 10^9$	−350
Neptune	31,000	2,800,000,000 or $2.8 * 10^9$	−350
Pluto	1,400	3,700,000,000 or $3.7 * 10^9$	−350
Sun	860,000		5,400 to 36,000,000

Math Masters, **p. 352**

If necessary, clarify terms such as *average diameter* and *average distance* in the table column headers. Solar system data are given in U.S. customary units (Table 1) and metric units (Table 2). This is done for comparison, because in later explorations the class will choose which units to use. Estimates of average distances from the Sun are accurate enough for the activities done in these solar system projects.

- ▷ The **diameter of a sphere** is the length of a line segment that passes through the center of the **sphere** and has **endpoints** on the sphere. Planets are not quite spheres, so average diameter is used in the data tables.
- ▷ Planets move around the Sun in orbits that are **ellipses** (ovals), somewhat altered by the gravitational pulls of other planets.

Large numbers in the table are expressed in standard and scientific notations. Ask students to convert average diameters from standard notation to number-and-word notation. Mercury: 3 thousand; Venus: 7.5 thousand; Earth: 7.9 thousand; Mars: 4.2 thousand; Jupiter: 89 thousand; Saturn: 75 thousand; Uranus: 32 thousand; Neptune: 31 thousand; Pluto: 1.4 thousand; Sun: 860 thousand, or 0.86 million

▶ Working with Solar System Data Tables

(*Math Masters,* pp. 352–355)

Students answer three questions on *Math Masters,* page 355 about the solar system data. When most students have finished, bring the class together to share answers and discuss ideas for each question.

The third question asks students to consider whether living things might exist on other planets based on temperature data. *Math Masters,* page 354 discusses this issue, including recent evidence that there may have been water on Mars long ago. Some students might want to research the current scientific consensus, if any, on the question of past life on Mars.

Project Master

Name Date Time

PROJECT 1 Planet Data *continued*

Solar System Data Table 2

Planet	Average Diameter (Kilometers)	Average Distance from the Sun (Kilometers)	Surface Temperature (Degrees Celsius)
Mercury	4,900	58,000,000 or $5.8 * 10^7$	−180 to 430
Venus	12,000	110,000,000 or $1.1 * 10^8$	450 to 490
Earth	13,000	150,000,000 or $1.5 * 10^8$	−90 to 60
Mars	6,800	230,000,000 or $2.3 * 10^8$	−90 to −10
Jupiter	140,000	780,000,000 or $7.8 * 10^8$	−150 to −100
Saturn	120,000	1,400,000,000 or $1.4 * 10^9$	−180 to −160
Uranus	51,000	2,900,000,000 or $2.9 * 10^9$	−200
Neptune	49,000	4,500,000,000 or $4.5 * 10^9$	−190
Pluto	2,300	5,900,000,000 or $5.9 * 10^9$	−230 to −220
Sun	1,400,000		3,000 to 20,000,000

Using Estimates and Comparing Big Numbers

Here is one strategy for comparing big numbers.

Problem Compare the distance of Earth from the Sun with the distances of Mars and Neptune from the Sun.

Think
Earth to Sun 150,000,000 km, or 150 million km
Mars to Sun 230,000,000 km, or 230 million km
Neptune to Sun 4,500,000,000 km, or 4,500 million km

Ask *About how many 150 millions are in 230 million? In 4,500 million?*

Another strategy is to compare distances in scientific notation. It is important to compare like powers of 10. Write equivalent names to make the division easier.

Think
Earth to Sun $1.5 * 10^8$ km, or $15 * 10^7$ km
Mars to Sun $2.3 * 10^8$ km, or $23 * 10^7$ km
Neptune to Sun $4.5 * 10^9$ km, or $45 * 10^8$ km, or $450 * 10^7$ km

Ask *About how many 15s are in 23? In 450?*

Math Masters, **p. 353**

▶ Comparing Other Planets to Earth

WHOLE-CLASS ACTIVITY

(*Math Masters,* pp. 352, 353, and 356)

Students make a data table on *Math Masters,* page 356 comparing the diameters of other planets to the diameter of Earth. They also compare the distances of other planets from the Sun to Earth's distance from the Sun.

Use questions such as the following to facilitate discussion:

- How does the diameter of Mars compare to the diameter of Earth? Is it more or less? less Express the diameter of Mars as a fraction of Earth's diameter. About $\frac{1}{2}$ Earth's diameter
- How does the distance from Mars to the Sun compare to the distance from Earth to the Sun? Is it larger or smaller? larger About how many times as large or as small? About $1\frac{1}{2}$ times as large

Calculators may be useful in this activity, but the main focus should be on mental estimates with large numbers. Many calculators can handle numbers in the billions and beyond only if the numbers are expressed in scientific notation. Regardless, entering large numbers is tedious, which is one reason why being able to perform mental estimates with large numbers is useful.

Math Masters, page 353 describes two strategies for comparing large numbers. One strategy is to think of 93,000,000 as 93 million. Ask: *About how many 93 millions are in 140 million? In 480 million?* Students can think of the distance to Neptune, 2,800,000,000 miles, as 2,800 million miles, so the question becomes: *How many 93 millions are in 2,800 million?*

Another strategy is to compare distances using scientific or exponential notation. It is important to compare like powers of 10. Encourage students to write equivalent names to make the division easier.

Earth to Sun: $9.3 * 10^7$ miles

Mars to Sun: $1.4 * 10^8$, or $14 * 10^7$ miles

Students can simplify ratio comparisons of numbers in standard notation by striking out the same number of zeros in each number (dividing both numbers by the appropriate power of 10).

Project Master

Name Date Time

PROJECT 1 **Life on Other Planets**

The unmanned Mariner 4 spacecraft flew past Mars on July 14, 1965, collecting the first close-up photographs of an inner solar-system planet. Since those first flyby images were taken, we have asked whether life ever arose on Mars. Life, as we understand it, requires water. Scientists believe that if life ever evolved on Mars, it did so in the presence of a long-standing supply of water.

Over 30 years ago, NASA launched two identical spacecraft (*Vikings 1 and 2*), each consisting of an orbiter and a lander. Each orbiter-lander pair flew together and entered Mars' orbit. After taking pictures, the orbiters separated and descended to the planet's surface for the purpose of data collection. The landers conducted three experiments designed to look for possible signs of life. While the experiments revealed unexpected chemical activity in the Martian soil, they provided no clear evidence for the presence of living microorganisms near the landing sites.

Exploration missions of the past decade have landed robotic rovers with far greater mobility than that of the *Viking* landers. The rovers carry a sophisticated set of instruments that collect and analyze surface samples. By studying rock and soil samples, scientists hope to determine whether water was involved in soil and rock formation and thereby identify areas on the planet that may have been favorable for life in the past.

In 1976, the *Viking I* orbiter took the first photographs of the Cydonia region of Mars, showing an unusual mountain that seemed to resemble a face. Some people suggested that the face was a monument built by an extraterrestrial civilization. But scientists believed this resemblance was accidental, partly due to the angle of light at the time the photo was taken and partly due to the complicated image enhancement used to process the data that was available at the time.

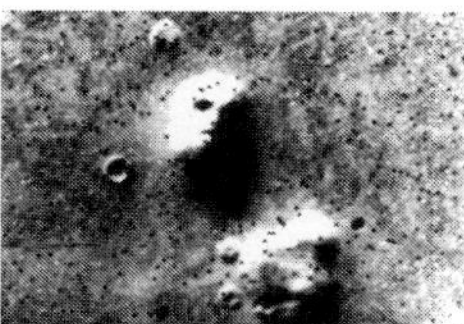

On May 28, 2001 the Mars Global Surveyor took a new photo of this feature. Although the landform has the same general shape as in earlier photographs, details provided by the higher-resolution photograph reveal the "face" to be a naturally formed hill.

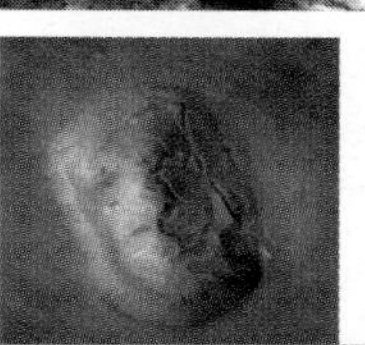

***Math Masters,* p. 354**

Project Master

Name Date Time

PROJECT 1 **What Can You Learn from the Data Tables?**

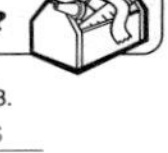

1. Look at the data on planet diameters on *Math Masters,* pages 352 and 353. Describe any patterns you see. Sample answer: The planets closest to the Sun have smaller diameters than planets farther from the Sun. The diameters of the planets beyond Jupiter decrease in size as their distances from the Sun increase.

   List some ideas or questions that the data suggest to you. Sample answer: Is there a relationship between diameter size of a planet and the planet's distance from the Sun? Is there a ratio or size-change factor that can be used to predict the diameter of a planet when the distance from the Sun is given or vice versa?

2. Look at the data on average distance from the Sun. Are the planets evenly spaced? No

   Describe any patterns you see in the average-distance data. Sample answer: The distance between planets increases as the distance from the Sun increases.

3. Look at the data on surface temperature. Is it likely that there is life on other planets today? Why or why not? Sample answer: Not life as we know it; temperatures are either too hot or too cold to support life.

For more information about life on other planets, read *Math Masters,* page 354.

***Math Masters,* p. 355**

Remind students that the problems ask only for estimates, not exact numbers, and that answers cannot be more accurate (have more significant figures) than the original data. Allow time to share strategies and solutions.

NOTE Encourage students to freely use estimates. The data in the tables are averages of many measurements, which are themselves estimates. Students should not be surprised if data from various sources do not agree, although they should question large discrepancies (±10% or more).

2 Extending the Project

▶ Discussing Life on Other Planets

Although *Math Masters,* page 354 is used in Project 5, you might want to allow time at the end of this project to discuss it briefly.

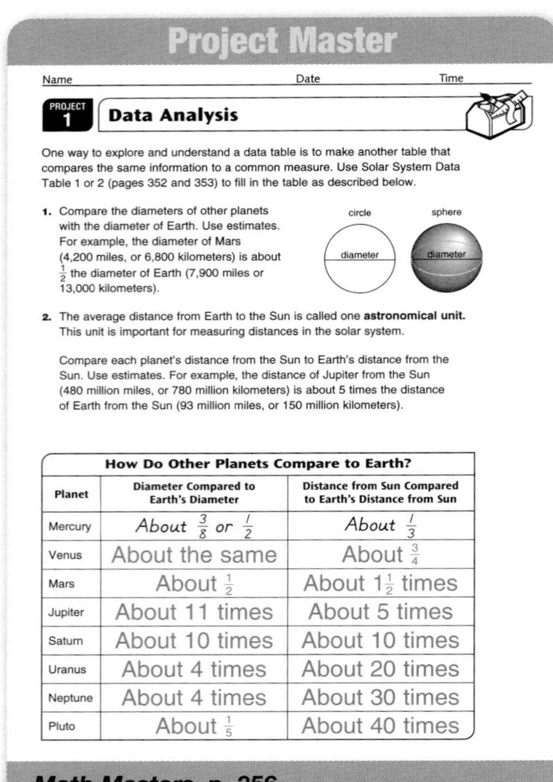

Project Master

Name ______ Date ______ Time ______

PROJECT 1 **Data Analysis**

One way to explore and understand a data table is to make another table that compares the same information to a common measure. Use Solar System Data Table 1 or 2 (pages 352 and 353) to fill in the table as described below.

1. Compare the diameters of other planets with the diameter of Earth. Use estimates. For example, the diameter of Mars (4,200 miles, or 6,800 kilometers) is about $\frac{1}{2}$ the diameter of Earth (7,900 miles or 13,000 kilometers).

2. The average distance from Earth to the Sun is called one **astronomical unit.** This unit is important for measuring distances in the solar system.

   Compare each planet's distance from the Sun to Earth's distance from the Sun. Use estimates. For example, the distance of Jupiter from the Sun (480 million miles, or 780 million kilometers) is about 5 times the distance of Earth from the Sun (93 million miles, or 150 million kilometers).

How Do Other Planets Compare to Earth?

Planet	Diameter Compared to Earth's Diameter	Distance from Sun Compared to Earth's Distance from Sun
Mercury	About $\frac{3}{8}$ or $\frac{1}{2}$	About $\frac{1}{3}$
Venus	About the same	About $\frac{3}{4}$
Mars	About $\frac{1}{2}$	About $1\frac{1}{2}$ times
Jupiter	About 11 times	About 5 times
Saturn	About 10 times	About 10 times
Uranus	About 4 times	About 20 times
Neptune	About 4 times	About 30 times
Pluto	About $\frac{1}{5}$	About 40 times

Math Masters, p. 356

Modeling the Solar System

Objective To apply a variety of skills to make a scale model of our solar system and its planets.

1 Doing the Project

Recommended Use: During or after Unit 2

Key Activities

In a two- to three-day exploration, the class makes a 2-dimensional scale model of our solar system. On the first day, students consider the sizes of the planets and the Sun and decide on a scale for their individual planet models. On the second day, teams assemble a model of the solar system and record information on a Planet Information Label.

Key Concepts and Skills

- Use extended facts to find products and quotients of very large numbers. [Operations and Computation Goal 2]
- Apply a scale to a drawing. [Operations and Computation Goal 6]
- Apply division rules to find *n*-to-1 ratios. [Operations and Computation Goal 6]
- Use data to answer questions and draw conclusions. [Data and Chance Goal 2]
- Convert units of measure within a measurement system. [Measurement and Reference Frames Goal 1]
- Measure side lengths to the nearest $\frac{1}{16}$ inch or 1 millimeter. [Measurement and Reference Frames Goal 1]

Key Vocabulary

metric units • U.S. customary units • scale model • scale • midpoint

materials

- ☐ Project Masters (*Math Masters,* pp. 352, 353, and 357–364)
- ☐ masking tape or transparent tape
- ☐ tape measure, yardstick, or meterstick
- ☐ construction paper (various colors)
- ☐ stick-on notes (optional)
- ☐ scissors
- ☐ compass
- ☐ ruler
- ☐ calculator

See Advance Preparation

2 Extending the Project

Students learn more about the solar system from outside sources.

materials

- ☐ reference books
- ☐ computer with Internet access

Additional Information

Because of the vast distances in the solar system, two scales are necessary: one for the sizes of planets and one for their distances from the Sun.

Advance Preparation Read "Projects" in the Management Guide section of the *Teacher's Reference Manual.*

Plan to spend two days on this project. The first time you do the project, it will require significant advance preparation. Decide how to divide the class into Planet Teams. Make nine copies of *Math Masters,* page 363—one per Planet Team and one for Earth.

Find suitable wall space to represent distances from the Sun. For the model of Pluto to be large enough, the model of the Sun must be at least 9 feet in diameter. An adequate representation, including a full model of the Sun, fits in about 55 feet of wall space. In this model, the scale for distance from the Sun is 1 inch to 10 million miles. You might find 55 feet available in a hallway, or possibly within the classroom, if you place the Sun in a corner or on adjoining walls.

The next two pages show several ways to set up the scale model of the solar system. If the walls you are using are less than 9 feet high, you can cut off the top and bottom of the Sun.

Technology

See the **iTLG.**

See Web site on page 410.

Background Information

Using U.S. Customary Units

Full model of the Sun, with planets on both sides

- Needs about 35.5 feet on one wall and 19.5 feet on an adjoining wall

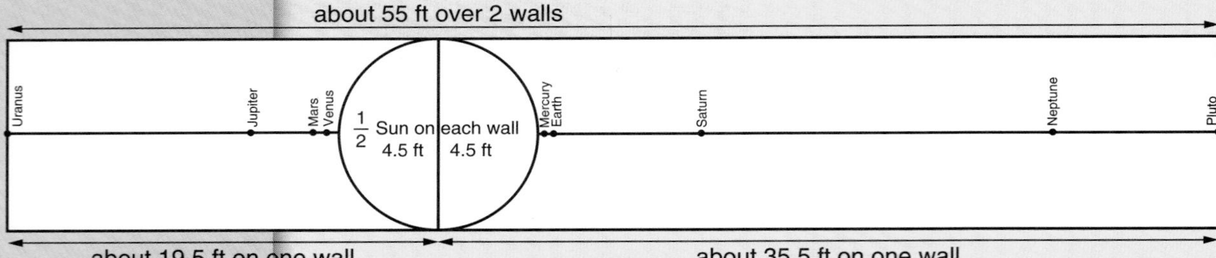

Half of the Sun, with planets all on one side

- Needs about 35.5 feet along one wall. Use the full model of the Sun if there is about 40 feet of wall space.

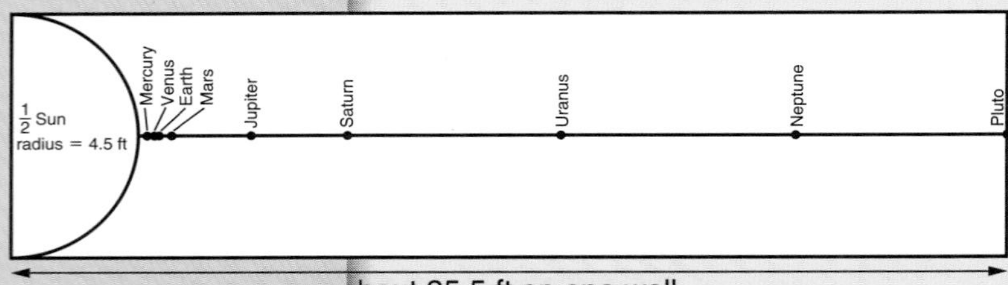

Using Metric Units

Full model of the Sun, with planets on both sides

- Needs about 24 feet (7.5 meters) along one wall and 14 feet (4.5 meters) along an adjoining wall

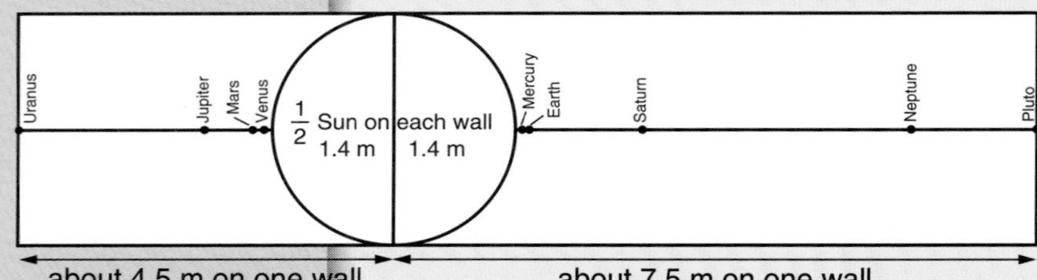

Half of the Sun, with all planets on one side

- Needs about 24 feet (7.5 meters) along one wall. Use the full model of the Sun if there is about 29 feet (9 meters) of wall space.

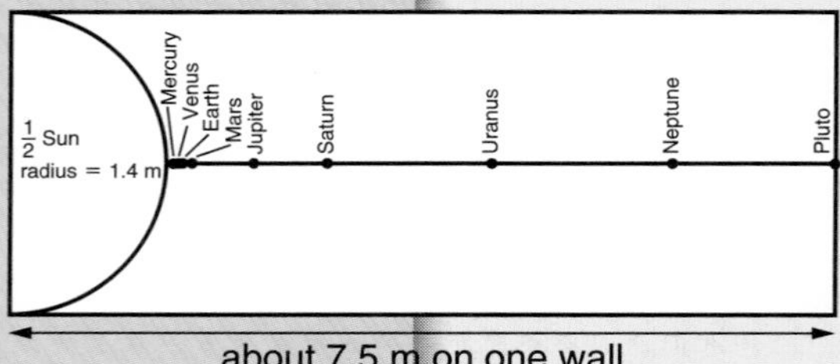

Estimate where to place the planets to make sure you avoid obstacles such as doors and bulletin boards. The planets' distances from the Sun for the two suggested scales on page 404 are given in the following table.

Planets' Distances from the Sun in a Model Solar System

Planet	1 inch represents 10 million miles	1 centimeter represents 10 million kilometers
Mercury	$3\frac{1}{2}$ in.	5.8 cm, or 6 cm
Venus	$6\frac{3}{4}$ in.	11 cm
Earth	9 in. or $9\frac{1}{4}$ in.	15 cm
Mars	14 in.	23 cm
Jupiter	48 in., or 4 ft	78 cm
Saturn	90 in., or 7 ft 6 in.	140 cm
Uranus	180 in., or 15 ft	290 cm
Neptune	280 in., or 23 ft	450 cm
Pluto	370 in., or 31 ft	590 cm

In addition to wall space, you will need supplies for making the Sun and planets. An art teacher may be able to help with such items as rolls of colored paper about three feet wide. Three pieces, each about nine feet long, can be taped together to make a square and then trimmed to form a circle representing the Sun. (*See Figure 1.*)

Another method is to outline the Sun with tape, construction paper, or stick-on notes. (*See Figure 2.*) Whatever method you choose, you should assemble the Sun and place it before Day 2 of the project.

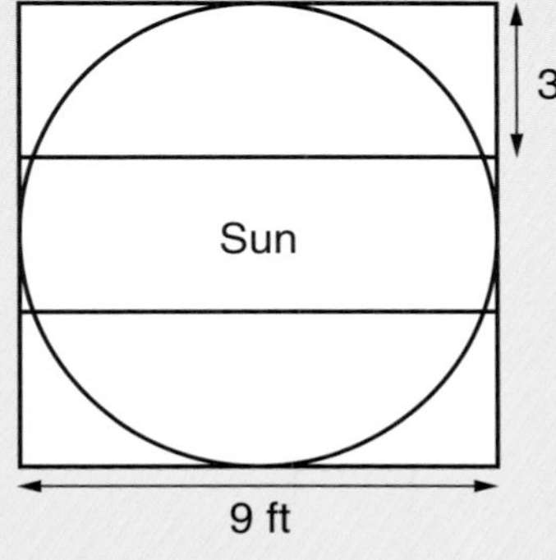

Figure 1

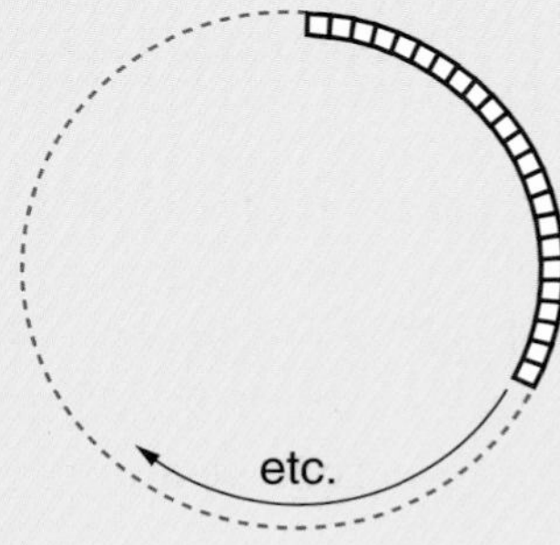

Figure 2

NOTE On July 29, 2005, Dr. Mike Brown and his colleagues announced the discovery of a tenth planet beyond Pluto. At that time, the planet's temporary name was 2003 UB313. The planet's permanent name, as well as information about its size and surface temperature, became available after this third edition of *Everyday Mathematics* had already gone to press. Consider having students extend planet data tables to include any available information about this tenth planet.

1 Doing the Project

▶ Day 1: Beginning Scale Models of the Sun and Planets

WHOLE-CLASS DISCUSSION

(*Math Masters,* p. 357)

Use your usual group reading procedure to read *Math Masters,* page 357. Students are asked to choose the units of measure they want to work with. **Metric units** are easy to work with and are used by astronomers and astronauts. On the other hand, **U.S. customary units** may provide vivid personal references.

Point out that students need to consider the space available to display the **scale model.** You may want to recommend one measurement system over the other, based on where you intend to display the model.

Students select the **scale** they will use to model the Sun and planets. If the suggested scale is not appropriate for your space, work with students to choose an alternative.

Divide the class into eight Planet Teams. There should not be a team for Earth, because Earth will be used for whole-class demonstrations. Assign planets or let the teams select. Students will work in these teams for Projects 2–5.

▶ Making the Planet Models

SMALL-GROUP ACTIVITY

(*Math Masters,* pp. 352, 353, and 357–359)

Students work with their Planet Teams to record the average diameter of their planets and the scale they will use. They consider how they can use this information to figure out the diameter of each planet model.

For example, if 1 inch represents 8,000 miles, students need to figure out about how many 8,000s are in their planet's diameter. In the case of Mercury, Venus, Mars, and Pluto, they need to figure out what fraction of 8,000 their planet's diameter is. Point out that students need only make estimates.

Project Master

Name Date Time

PROJECT 2 **Starting the Model**

1. Choose a Measurement System

In order to build a scale model of the solar system, the class needs to make some decisions.

- Will we measure in **U.S. customary units** (in. and mi) or in **metric units** (cm and km)?

Astronomers and astronauts use metric units. On the other hand, U.S. customary units may make the model easier to relate to personal references. For example, if the diameter of Earth is 1 inch (about the length of a toe), then the Sun's diameter is about 9 feet, almost twice the height of most sixth-grade students. Discuss the advantages and disadvantages of each measurement system. Then make a class decision.

We will use Answers vary. units.

2. Choose a Scale

Now the class needs to make another decision.

- Which scale will we use to model the relative sizes of the Sun and the planets?

The **scale** tells how many units in the real solar system are represented by 1 unit in the scale model of the solar system. *Suggestions:*

- **U.S. Customary Units** You might let 1 inch represent 8,000 miles (1 inch to 8,000 miles, or 1 in.:8,000 mi). 8,000 miles is approximately the diameter of Earth. If the diameter of Earth is represented by 1 inch, about how many inches would represent the diameter of Jupiter?
  11 in.
- **Metric Units** You might let 1 centimeter represent 5,000 kilometers (1 centimeter to 5,000 kilometers, or 1 cm:5,000 km). These are easy numbers to work with and to remember.

We will use this scale for size: Answers vary.

3. Divide into Planet Teams

The class should divide into 8 Planet Teams, a team for each planet except Earth.

My Planet Team will model this planet: Answers vary.

***Math Masters,* p. 357**

Some of the answers will be quite clear, but others will require more thought. One way to reason out some answers is by looking at a ruler. Mercury, for example, has a diameter of 3,000 miles. This is more than $\frac{1}{4}$ of 8,000 but less than $\frac{1}{2}$ of 8,000. Ask: *What marking on the ruler falls between $\frac{1}{4}$ and $\frac{1}{2}$?* Sample answer: $\frac{3}{8}$ Reasonable diameters for the two suggested scales are in the table below.

Diameters of Model Sun and Planets

Planet	1 inch represents 8,000 miles	1 centimeter represents 5,000 kilometers
Mercury	$\frac{3}{8}$ in.	1 cm
Venus	$\frac{15}{16}$ or $\frac{7}{8}$ in.	2.4 or 2.5 cm
Earth	1 in.	2.5 cm
Mars	$\frac{1}{2}$ in.	1.4 or 1.5 cm
Jupiter	11 in.	28 cm
Saturn	9 in.	24 cm
Uranus	4 in.	10 cm
Neptune	4 in.	10 cm
Pluto	$\frac{3}{16}$, or $\frac{1}{8}$ in.	0.5 cm, or 5 mm
Sun	108 in., or 9 ft	280 cm, or 2.8 m

Use Earth to demonstrate how to construct the planets. The chart on *Math Masters,* page 359 suggests the color of paper to use, if possible, to reflect each planet's actual appearance. Earth is blue, brown, and green. Construction procedures are suggested on *Math Masters,* page 359. Some students may need assistance drawing larger circles.

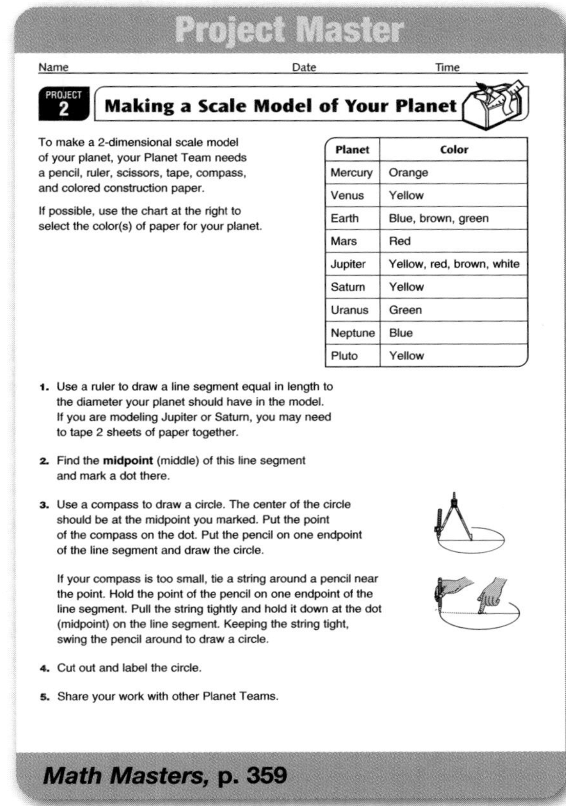

Project Master

Name Date Time

PROJECT 2 **Making a Scale Model of Your Planet**

To make a 2-dimensional scale model of your planet, your Planet Team needs a pencil, ruler, scissors, tape, compass, and colored construction paper.

If possible, use the chart at the right to select the color(s) of paper for your planet.

Planet	Color
Mercury	Orange
Venus	Yellow
Earth	Blue, brown, green
Mars	Red
Jupiter	Yellow, red, brown, white
Saturn	Yellow
Uranus	Green
Neptune	Blue
Pluto	Yellow

1. Use a ruler to draw a line segment equal in length to the diameter your planet should have in the model. If you are modeling Jupiter or Saturn, you may need to tape 2 sheets of paper together.
2. Find the **midpoint** (middle) of this line segment and mark a dot there.
3. Use a compass to draw a circle. The center of the circle should be at the midpoint you marked. Put the point of the compass on the dot. Put the pencil on one endpoint of the line segment and draw the circle.

   If your compass is too small, tie a string around a pencil near the point. Hold the point of the pencil on one endpoint of the line segment. Pull the string tightly and hold it down at the dot (midpoint) on the line segment. Keeping the string tight, swing the pencil around to draw a circle.
4. Cut out and label the circle.
5. Share your work with other Planet Teams.

Math Masters, p. 359

Project Master

Name Date Time

PROJECT 2 **Modeling the Sizes of Planets and the Sun**

1. My Planet Team's planet is Answers vary.
2. Its average diameter is ______

   (Remember to give the diameter in the same system of units—metric or U.S. customary—that you will use to build the model.)
3. In our scale model of planet size, ______ represents ______.
4. How can you use the scale to figure out how large your planet should be in the model? Discuss with your teammates and write your answer below.
5. What will be the diameter of your planet in the model? ______
6. a. What will be the diameter of the Sun in the model? ______

   b. How many feet or meters is this? ______

Math Masters, p. 358

Project Master

Name ______ Date ______ Time ______

PROJECT 2 **Modeling Distances in the Solar System**

1. My Planet Team's planet is Answers vary.
2. Its average distance from the Sun is ______
3. Now that you have modeled the size of your planet, you need to figure out how far to place it from the Sun. How could you do this?
   Answers vary.

To model the distances between planets and the Sun, your class needs to make several decisions.

Finding a Scale

4. Can you use the same **scale** for distance that you used for size? This would provide an excellent picture of planetary sizes and distances but may not be possible. Why not? Discuss with your classmates.
   Sample answer: There may not be room to accommodate the range of distances.
5. If 1 inch represents 8,000 miles, how many inches from the Sun should Earth be placed? 11,625 inches
6. How many feet is this? About 1,000 feet
7. Would a model of the entire solar system using this scale be possible anywhere in your school building? Answers vary.

Math Masters, **p. 360**

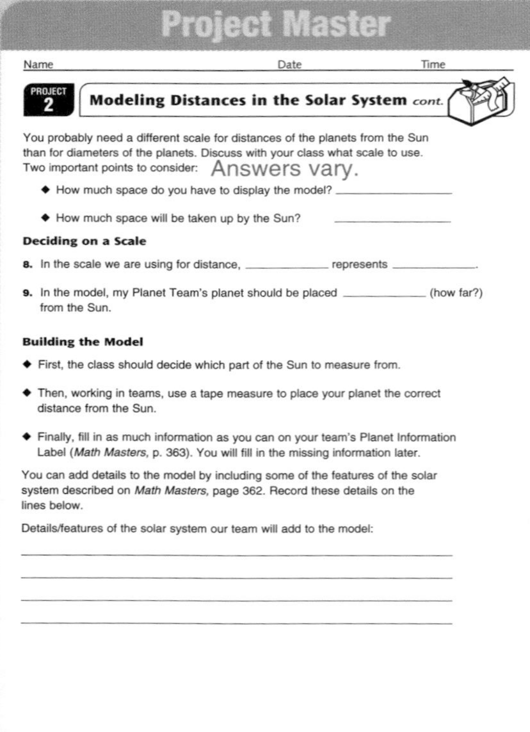

Project Master

Name ______ Date ______ Time ______

PROJECT 2 **Modeling Distances in the Solar System** *cont.*

You probably need a different scale for distances of the planets from the Sun than for diameters of the planets. Discuss with your class what scale to use. Two important points to consider: Answers vary.

- How much space do you have to display the model? ______
- How much space will be taken up by the Sun? ______

Deciding on a Scale

8. In the scale we are using for distance, ______ represents ______.
9. In the model, my Planet Team's planet should be placed ______ (how far?) from the Sun.

Building the Model

- First, the class should decide which part of the Sun to measure from.
- Then, working in teams, use a tape measure to place your planet the correct distance from the Sun.
- Finally, fill in as much information as you can on your team's Planet Information Label (*Math Masters,* p. 363). You will fill in the missing information later.

You can add details to the model by including some of the features of the solar system described on *Math Masters,* page 362. Record these details on the lines below.

Details/features of the solar system our team will add to the model:

Math Masters, **p. 361**

▶ Day 2: Modeling Distances in the Solar System

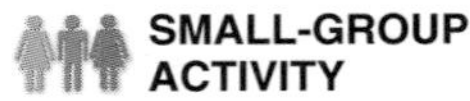

SMALL-GROUP ACTIVITY

(*Math Masters,* pp. 352, 353, 360, and 361)

Students continue to work with their Planet Teams. They should find their planet's average distance from the Sun for Problem 2 on *Math Masters,* page 360.

Next, they write their ideas for placing the planet models.

When most of the teams are at this point, a class discussion may be useful to consider several features of modeling distance. Read as a class the questions under Finding a Scale on page 360. Students answer the questions in their teams, and then the class shares solutions and strategies. Questions such as the following may facilitate discussion:

- Where should the planets be placed in the model? Find the positions by dividing the actual average distance of each planet from the Sun by the distance represented by one unit of the scale. *For example:* For Earth, 93,000,000 miles divided by 8,000 miles per inch equals almost 12,000 inches, or 1,000 feet.
- What are the pros and cons of using the same scale for size and distance? The same scale provides the most accurate picture of the solar system. However, such a model wouldn't fit in a classroom.
- If the scale used for planet size is also used for distance from the Sun, how far would Earth be from the Sun in the model solar system? How far would Pluto be? Answers depend on the scale used for planet size.

Discuss what scale students could use for distance, given the space available for the model. Suggest the scale that you have predetermined as being practical for the space available. Students record the scale in Problem 8 on *Math Masters,* page 361.

▶ Placing Planet Models

(*Math Masters,* pp. 361–363)

Each Planet Team calculates how far its planet will be from the Sun, using the agreed-upon scale. Then teams take turns placing their planets the proper distance from the Sun. They will need a tape measure, yardstick, or meterstick. Students can add details to the model by including some of the solar system features described on *Math Masters,* page 362.

Reasonable distances for inch and centimeter scales are provided in the table on page 405.

Teams fill in as much as they can on their Planet Information Label (*Math Masters,* p. 363). They can add the missing information as they work through Projects 3, 4, and 5. One student in each team should hang the Planet Information Label under the team's planet model.

▶ Answering the Conclusions Questions

(*Math Masters,* p. 364)

Students should work in their Planet Teams to answer the questions under Conclusions. When most students have finished, provide time for discussion.

Project Master

Name ____ Date ____ Time ____

PROJECT 2 **Some Solar System Features**

You can add more detail to the model by including some or all of the following celestial bodies.

Asteroids These are large pieces of rock that are too small to be considered planets. They range in size from big boulders to small mountains. Ceres, one of the largest asteroids, has a diameter of 580 miles, or 940 kilometers. Most asteroids are in what is known as the Asteroid Belt. The Asteroid Belt lies between Mars and Jupiter, about 180 to 270 million miles (290 to 430 million kilometers) from the Sun. To date, more than 18,000 asteroids have been identified in this region of the solar system. They can be represented in the model by small pen dots on pieces of paper or stick-on notes.

Moons Mars, Jupiter, Saturn, Uranus, and Neptune each have 2 or more moons. Mercury and Venus have no moons. The largest moons of Jupiter and Saturn are larger than Mercury and Pluto. Jupiter has at least 17 moons. Its 4 largest moons and their diameters are shown in the table.

Moon	Diameter
Ganymede	3,200 mi, or 5,300 km
Callisto	2,900 mi, or 4,800 km
Io	2,200 mi, or 3,600 km
Europa	1,900 mi, or 3,100 km

Saturn has at least 18 moons. The largest is Titan. Its diameter is 3,100 miles (5,200 kilometers). Earth's moon has a diameter of 2,200 miles (3,750 kilometers). It is slightly less than $\frac{1}{3}$ the size of Earth.

Rings Scientists have known for a long time that Saturn is surrounded by large, beautiful rings. When the *Voyager* spacecraft visited Jupiter, Neptune, and Uranus in the 1980s, scientists discovered that these planets also have rings, although they are considerably smaller than Saturn's. Saturn's rings are made up of frozen water particles ranging in size from tiny grains to blocks of ice that are 30 yards in diameter. The rings are only a few miles thick, but they extend from the planet for 50,000 miles (80,000 kilometers).

***Math Masters,* p. 362**

Project Master

Name ____ Date ____ Time ____

PROJECT 2 **Conclusions**

1. Suppose you had used the scale for planet diameters to also represent distances of planets from the Sun. Keep the same position for the Sun that you used in your model. Answers vary.
   a. How far away from your model Sun would Earth be? ____
   b. Where in your school or town might Earth be located? ____
   c. How far away from your model Sun would Neptune be? ____
   d. Where in your school or town might Neptune be located? ____
2. Suppose you had used the scale for distances of planets from the Sun to also represent the diameter of Earth. Answers vary.
   a. What would be the diameter of the model Earth? ____
   b. If the model Earth were made with exactly that diameter, could you see it without a magnifying glass? (*Hint:* Pencil leads in some mechanical pencils are 0.5 mm, or about $\frac{2}{1,000}$ of an inch, thick.) ____
3. Suppose you were explaining to someone how big the largest planet in the solar system is, compared to Earth.
   a. What would be an easy multiple to use? Sample answer: 11
   b. What other comparison might you use to make the difference easier to understand (for example, the costs or sizes of two common objects)? Answers vary.
4. Similarly, suppose you were explaining how big the Sun is, compared to even the largest planet in the solar system.
   a. What would be an easy multiple to use? Sample answer: 10
   b. What other comparison might you use to make the difference easier to understand? Answers vary.
5. Choose a fact you have learned about the solar system. Make up a question for a trivia game based on that fact. Answers vary.

***Math Masters,* p. 364**

Project Master

Name ____ Date ____ Time ____

PROJECT 2 **Planet Information Label**

Planet name: Answers vary. ____

Average diameter: ____

The planet's average diameter is about __?__ the diameter of Earth. ____

Average distance from the Sun: ____

How long would it take to fly from the planet to the Sun, assuming your rate of travel is 500 mph? ____

Time sunlight takes to reach the planet: ____

How long does it take the planet to orbit the Sun? ____

Since 1776, this planet has orbited the Sun about __?__ times. ____

What is the length of time it would take to reach the planet from Earth if you were to travel at a rate of 20,000 miles per hour? ____

In our lifetime, humans might be able to travel 50,000 miles per hour in space. At this rate, how long would it take to reach the planet? ____

***Math Masters,* p. 363**

2 Extending the Project

Finding Out about the Solar System

INDEPENDENT ACTIVITY

Invite students to learn more about the solar system by reading newspapers, magazines, and books, such as the following:

Janice VanCleave's The Solar System: Mind-Boggling Experiments You Can Turn into Science Fair Projects by Janice Pratt VanCleave (Wiley, 2000).

The New Solar System, J. Kelly Beatty, Carolyn Collins Petersen, and Andrew L. Chaikin, editors (Sky Publishing Corporation, 1999).

There are many NASA-sponsored Internet sites devoted to the solar system, astronomy, and space exploration.

Go to *www.nasa.gov/home/*

Distances in the Solar System

Objectives To compare large numbers; and to calculate travel times.

1 Doing the Project

Recommended Use: During or after Unit 2

Key Activities

Students compare distances in the solar system to more familiar distances. They work in their Planet Teams to calculate how long it would take to fly from each planet to the Sun at jet speed and how long sunlight takes to reach each planet. Then they share their findings with the class to compile the information.

Key Concepts and Skills

- Apply place-value concepts to read, compare, and round large whole numbers. [Number and Numeration Goal 1]
- Convert between scientific and standard notations with or without a calculator. [Number and Numeration Goal 1]
- Use a calculator to compute products and quotients of whole numbers. [Operations and Computation Goal 2]
- Apply extended multiplication and division facts to solve rate problems. [Operations and Computation Goal 6]
- Use data to answer questions and draw conclusions. [Data and Chance Goal 2]

Key Vocabulary

speed of light • light-year

materials

- ☐ Project Masters (*Math Masters,* pp. 363 and 365–367)
- ☐ Transparency (*Math Masters,* p. 366; optional)
- ☐ calculator

See **Advance Preparation**

2 Extending the Project

Students write a description of the distance of Pluto from the Sun to make the distance comprehensible to a friend. Students explore a light-year as a unit of distance.

materials

- ☐ Project Master (*Math Masters,* p. 367)

Additional Information

This project uses information obtained in Project 2.

Advance Preparation Read "Projects" in the Management Guide section of the *Teacher's Reference Manual.*

To help display data obtained by Planet Teams, make a transparency of *Math Masters,* page 366, or draw on the board a copy of the table on that page.

Technology

See the **iTLG.**

NOTE On July 29, 2005, Dr. Mike Brown and his colleagues announced the discovery of a tenth planet beyond Pluto. At that time, the planet's temporary name was 2003 UB313. The planet's permanent name, as well as information about its size and surface temperature, became available after this third edition of *Everyday Mathematics* had already gone to press. Consider having students extend planet data tables to include any available information about this tenth planet.

1 Doing the Project

▶ Estimating Travel Times between Earth and the Sun

PARTNER ACTIVITY

(*Math Masters,* p. 365)

Partners work the problems on *Math Masters,* page 365 to estimate how long it would take to fly from Earth to the Sun and how long it takes sunlight to reach Earth.

When most partnerships have finished, take a few minutes to share strategies and estimates.

If the calculators in your classroom do not accept entries in scientific notation, some numbers will be too large to work with. One way to overcome this is to drop the same number of zeros from each number in ratio comparisons (equivalent to dividing both numbers by the same multiple of 10). For example, 3,000 miles across the United States compared to 140,000,000 miles from Mars to the Sun is the same as 3 compared to 140,000.

▶ Estimating Distances and Travel Times in the Solar System

SMALL-GROUP ACTIVITY

(*Math Masters,* p. 366)

Discuss the best way to report flying time (hours, days, or years) and time for sunlight to reach a planet (seconds, minutes, or hours). Remind students that for the very large distances here, giving answers to two significant digits is fine. That means they will use rounding and write many zeros.

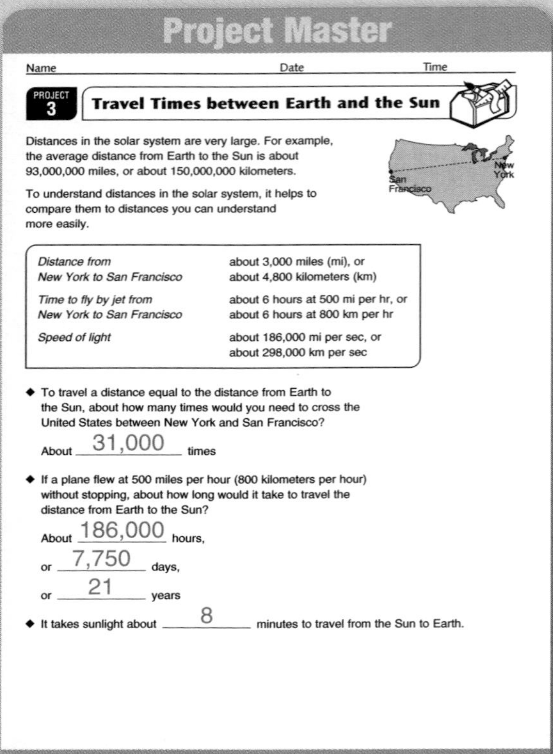
Project Master

Name Date Time

PROJECT 3 **Travel Times between Earth and the Sun**

Distances in the solar system are very large. For example, the average distance from Earth to the Sun is about 93,000,000 miles, or about 150,000,000 kilometers.

To understand distances in the solar system, it helps to compare them to distances you can understand more easily.

Distance from New York to San Francisco	about 3,000 miles (mi), or about 4,800 kilometers (km)
Time to fly by jet from New York to San Francisco	about 6 hours at 500 mi per hr, or about 6 hours at 800 km per hr
Speed of light	about 186,000 mi per sec, or about 298,000 km per sec

- To travel a distance equal to the distance from Earth to the Sun, about how many times would you need to cross the United States between New York and San Francisco?

  About 31,000 times

- If a plane flew at 500 miles per hour (800 kilometers per hour) without stopping, about how long would it take to travel the distance from Earth to the Sun?

  About 186,000 hours,
  or 7,750 days,
  or 21 years

- It takes sunlight about 8 minutes to travel from the Sun to Earth.

Math Masters, p. 365

▶ Completing Distance and Travel Time Data Tables

(*Math Masters,* pp. 363 and 366)

Students work in the same Planet Teams as they did in Project 2. Each team will make trip and time estimates for its own planet.

Teams complete *Math Masters,* page 366 for their planets.

As teams finish, have them enter the additional information on their Planet Information Labels (*Math Masters,* p. 363).

When all teams have finished, have them share their findings so everyone can complete the table on page 366. You may want to use a transparency of page 366 or copy the table onto the board. Use the last row to record any available information about the tenth planet.

The examples below show how the table might be completed. Remember that all values are estimates.

Examples:

Planet	Average Distance from Sun (Miles)	Number of Trips across US. to Equal Distance from Planet to Sun
Mercury	36,000,000	12,000
Venus	67,000,000	22,000
Earth	93,000,000	31,000
Mars	140,000,000	47,000
Jupiter	480,000,000	160,000
Saturn	890,000,000	300,000
Uranus	1,800,000,000	600,000
Neptune	2,800,000,000	930,000
Pluto	3,700,000,000	1,200,000

Planet	Time to Fly Distance from Planet to Sun (Years)	Time Sunlight Takes to Reach Planet (Minutes)
Mercury	8	3
Venus	15	6
Earth	21	8
Mars	32	13
Jupiter	110	43
Saturn	200	80
Uranus	410	160
Neptune	640	250
Pluto	840	330

Project Master

Name ____________ Date ____________ Time ____________

PROJECT 3 **Estimate Travel Times**

Use what you have learned about travel times between Earth and the Sun to make similar comparisons for your model planet. Answers vary.

- The planet I helped model is ____________.
- Its average distance from the Sun is ____________.
- This distance is equal to crossing the United States ____________ times.
- It would take about ____________ to fly this distance at 500 miles per hour.
- It takes sunlight about ____________ to reach this planet.

Add this information to your team's Planet Information Label.

Share your work with your classmates. Use their numbers to help you complete the following table. Answers are approximate.

Planet	Average Distance from Sun (Miles)	Number of Trips across U.S. to Equal Distance from Planet to Sun	Time to Fly the Distance from Planet to Sun (Years)	Time Sunlight Takes to Reach Planet (Minutes)
Mercury	36,000,000	12,000	8	3
Venus	67,000,000	22,000	15	6
Earth	93,000,000	31,000	21	8
Mars	140,000,000	47,000	32	13
Jupiter	480,000,000	160,000	110	43
Saturn	890,000,000	300,000	200	80
Uranus	1,800,000,000	600,000	410	160
Neptune	2,800,000,000	930,000	640	250
Pluto	3,700,000,000	1,200,000	840	330

***Math Masters,* p. 366**

2 Extending the Project

▶ Describing a Distance

WHOLE-CLASS DISCUSSION

(*Math Masters,* p. 367)

Students independently write a description of the distance from Pluto to the Sun using various distances on Earth as references; for example the coast-to-coast distance of the United States, the length of Africa from its top border to its southernmost tip, the circumference of Earth at the equator, and so on. Volunteers share their descriptions with the class.

Project Master

Name ______ Date ______ Time ______

PROJECT 3 **Describe a Distance**

1. The distance between Pluto and the Sun is very large. How could you describe this distance to help a friend understand it?
Sample answer: Pluto is about 40 times farther away from the Sun than Earth is. (Example: A plane flying at 500 mph and leaving Pluto in 2007 would not reach the Sun until 2852, more than 800 years later.)

2. The **speed of light** is about 300,000,000 meters per second. At that rate, light can travel around the world about 7 times in 1 second.
   a. Express the speed of light in scientific notation. $3.0 * 10^8$
   b. Express the speed of light in centimeters per second.
   The speed of light is about $3.0 * 10^{10}$ cm per second.
   c. A **light-year** is the distance that light travels in 1 year. Explain how you would estimate the number of centimeters in a light-year.
   Sample answer: First I would figure out the number of seconds in a year. There are 365 days in a year, 24 hours in a day, 60 minutes in an hour, and 60 seconds in a minute, so there are $365 * 24 * 60 * 60$, or 31,536,000, seconds in 1 year. Then I would use my calculator to multiply the number of seconds in a year by the speed of light in centimeters—$31{,}536{,}000 * 3.0 * 10^{10} = 9.461 * 10^{17}$.

Math Masters, p. 367

Movement of the Planets

Objectives To learn about Earth's rotation and revolution; and to calculate times of rotation and revolution.

1 Doing the Project

Recommended Use: During or after Unit 2

Key Activities

Students learn about the daily rotation of Earth on its axis and the yearly revolution of Earth around the Sun. They calculate how far they have revolved and rotated in the past hour and past minute. Students work in their Planet Teams to compare the movement of other planets with Earth and to estimate how many times each planet has traveled around the Sun since 1776. Students also estimate the minimum distance between each planet and Earth.

Key Concepts and Skills

- Apply place-value concepts to round numbers to two significant digits. [Number and Numeration Goal 1]
- Convert between scientific and standard notations with or without a calculator. [Number and Numeration Goal 1]
- Apply extended multiplication and division facts to make ratio comparisons of large numbers. [Operations and Computation Goal 6]
- Apply division rules to find *n*-to-1 ratios. [Operations and Computation Goal 6]
- Use data to answer questions and draw conclusions. [Data and Chance Goal 2]

Key Vocabulary

rotate • revolve • rotation • revolution

materials

- ☐ Project Masters (*Math Masters,* pp. 352, 353, and 368–372)
- ☐ calculator
- ☐ globe (optional)

See **Advance Preparation**

2 Extending the Project

Students calculate the maximum distance between each planet and Earth.

materials

- ☐ Project Masters (*Math Masters,* pp. 352, 353, and 372)
- ☐ calculator

Additional Information

Advance Preparation Read "Projects" in the Management Guide section of the *Teacher's Reference Manual.*

A globe will be useful.

Technology

See the **iTLG.**

Project Master

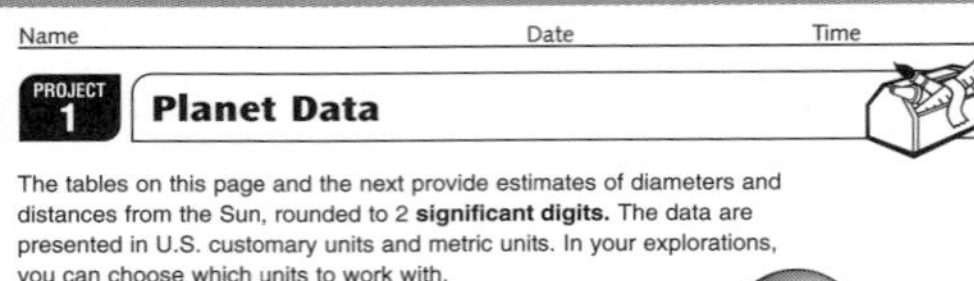

Name Date Time

PROJECT 1 **Planet Data**

The tables on this page and the next provide estimates of diameters and distances from the Sun, rounded to 2 **significant digits.** The data are presented in U.S. customary units and metric units. In your explorations, you can choose which units to work with.

The **diameter** of a **sphere** is the length of a line segment that passes through the center of the sphere and has **endpoints** on the sphere. Planets are not quite spheres, so an average diameter is used in the data tables.

Planets move around the Sun in orbits that are **ellipses** (ovals), somewhat affected by the gravitational pulls of other planets. Estimates of average distances from the Sun are accurate enough for anything done in the *Sixth Grade Everyday Mathematics* solar system projects.

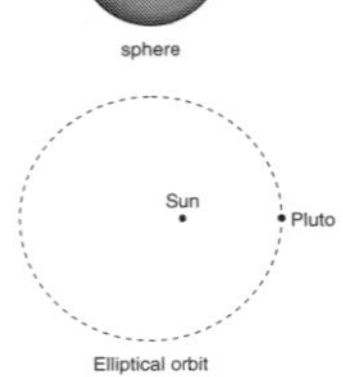

Solar System Data Table 1

Planet	Average Diameter (Miles)	Average Distance from the Sun (Miles)	Surface Temperature (Degrees Fahrenheit)
Mercury	3,000	36,000,000 or $3.6 * 10^7$	−290 to 800
Venus	7,500	67,000,000 or $6.7 * 10^7$	850 to 910
Earth	7,900	93,000,000 or $9.3 * 10^7$	−130 to 140
Mars	4,200	140,000,000 or $1.4 * 10^8$	−190 to 80
Jupiter	89,000	480,000,000 or $4.8 * 10^8$	−240 to −150
Saturn	75,000	890,000,000 or $8.9 * 10^8$	−290 to −150
Uranus	32,000	1,800,000,000 or $1.8 * 10^9$	−350
Neptune	31,000	2,800,000,000 or $2.8 * 10^9$	−350
Pluto	1,400	3,700,000,000 or $3.7 * 10^9$	−350
Sun	860,000		5,400 to 36,000,000

Math Masters, p. 352

NOTE On July 29, 2005, Dr. Mike Brown and his colleagues announced the discovery of a tenth planet beyond Pluto. At that time, the planet's temporary name was 2003 UB313. The planet's permanent name, as well as information about its size and surface temperature, became available after this third edition of *Everyday Mathematics* had already gone to press. Consider having students extend planet data tables to include any available information about this tenth planet.

Project Master

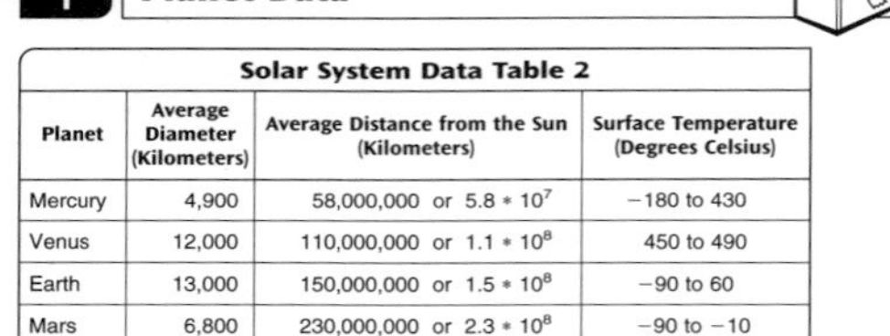

Name Date Time

PROJECT 1 **Planet Data** *continued*

Solar System Data Table 2

Planet	Average Diameter (Kilometers)	Average Distance from the Sun (Kilometers)	Surface Temperature (Degrees Celsius)
Mercury	4,900	58,000,000 or $5.8 * 10^7$	−180 to 430
Venus	12,000	110,000,000 or $1.1 * 10^8$	450 to 490
Earth	13,000	150,000,000 or $1.5 * 10^8$	−90 to 60
Mars	6,800	230,000,000 or $2.3 * 10^8$	−90 to −10
Jupiter	140,000	780,000,000 or $7.8 * 10^8$	−150 to −100
Saturn	120,000	1,400,000,000 or $1.4 * 10^9$	−180 to −160
Uranus	51,000	2,900,000,000 or $2.9 * 10^9$	−200
Neptune	49,000	4,500,000,000 or $4.5 * 10^9$	−190
Pluto	2,300	5,900,000,000 or $5.9 * 10^9$	−230 to −220
Sun	1,400,000		3,000 to 20,000,000

Using Estimates and Comparing Big Numbers

Here is one strategy for comparing big numbers.

Problem Compare the distance of Earth from the Sun with the distances of Mars and Neptune from the Sun.

Think Earth to Sun 150,000,000 km, or 150 million km
Mars to Sun 230,000,000 km, or 230 million km
Neptune to Sun 4,500,000,000 km, or 4,500 million km

Ask *About how many 150 millions are in 230 million? In 4,500 million?*

Another strategy is to compare distances in scientific notation. It is important to compare like powers of 10. Write equivalent names to make the division easier.

Think Earth to Sun $1.5 * 10^8$ km, or $15 * 10^7$ km
Mars to Sun $2.3 * 10^8$ km, or $23 * 10^7$ km
Neptune to Sun $4.5 * 10^9$ km, or $45 * 10^8$ km, or $450 * 10^7$ km

Ask *About how many 15s are in 23? In 450?*

Math Masters, p. 353

1 Doing the Project

▶ Estimating Distances of Rotation and Revolution

WHOLE-CLASS ACTIVITY

(*Math Masters,* pp. 368 and 369)

Use your usual group reading procedure to read the top of *Math Masters,* page 368. Ask students to suggest ways to find out how far they travel each day as Earth **rotates** on its axis and **revolves** around the Sun. If possible, use a globe to demonstrate Earth's **rotation** and **revolution.**

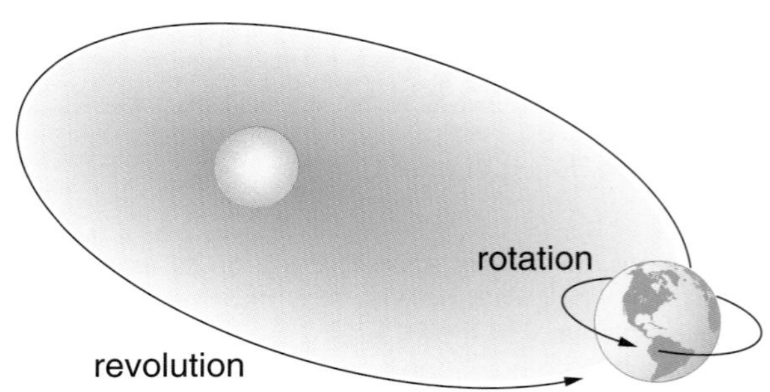

Discuss the text and the diagrams of Earth's movement. Ask whether your school is nearest the latitude lines at 25,000 miles (equator), at 21,000 miles, or at the North Pole. Ask students to suggest how to estimate the distance a person travels in a 24-hour rotation of Earth.

On *Math Masters,* page 369, students are asked to use the information from page 368 to estimate how far they have rotated and revolved in the past hour and minute. They should use a calculator and round their results.

When most students have finished, bring the class together to share strategies and solutions.

▶ Examining the Movements of Planets around the Sun

SMALL-GROUP ACTIVITY

(*Math Masters,* pp. 368 and 370)

Planet Teams examine Solar System Data Table 3 on *Math Masters,* page 368. Students look for patterns in the data and describe the patterns on page 370, sharing their thoughts with team members and with other Planet Teams.

Students use the information in the table to estimate how many times their team's planet has traveled around the Sun since 1776. Teams share results so all students can complete the table.

▶ Calculating Minimum Distances from Earth to Other Planets

SMALL-GROUP ACTIVITY

(*Math Masters,* pp. 352, 353, 371, and 372)

In their Planet Teams, students read *Math Masters,* page 371. The diagrams show that from time to time the distance between Earth and Mars reaches a minimum. This can be inferred to be true for the other planets, as well. Except for Pluto, the orbits are almost circular and in the same plane. Thus students can calculate the approximate minimum distance using Solar System Data Table 1 or 2 on *Math Masters,* pages 352 and 353, when Earth and another planet align on the same radius.

Because Pluto's eccentric orbit makes calculation difficult, you might have the Pluto Team disperse to other teams; or they might attempt to write an explanation of why estimating the minimum Earth-to-Pluto distance from the given data would be difficult.

When teams have finished, discuss their work and share results so students can complete the Estimated Minimum Distance from Earth column in the table on *Math Masters,* page 372.

Project Master

Name Date Time

PROJECT 4 **Spaceship Earth**

To be a successful space traveler, you must be able to find your way back to Earth. This may not be easy. You do not feel it, but at this moment you are traveling through space at incredible speeds.

Earth spins around like a top. In 24 hours, it makes 1 complete **rotation.** At the equator, the distance around Earth is about 25,000 miles. In the middle of the United States, the distance is about 21,000 miles. This means that if you live in the middle of the United States, you travel about 21,000 miles every day.

21,000 miles
25,000 miles

At the same time Earth is rotating, it is moving in its orbit around the Sun. In 1 year, Earth makes 1 complete **revolution,** or trip, around the Sun. This trip is approximately 600,000,000 (or $6 * 10^8$) miles long.

600,000,000 miles
Earth
Sun

Movement of the Planets around the Sun

All the planets are in motion, rotating like tops and revolving around the Sun. Compared to Earth, some planets move fast, but others are quite slow. Understanding planetary motion is key for space travel. You must know where to aim the spaceship.

Solar System Data Table 3

Planet	Average Speed in Orbit: Miles per Earth Day	Time to Revolve Once around the Sun: Earth Days or Years	Time to Rotate Once: Earth Days or Hours
Mercury	2,600,000	88 days	59 days
Venus	1,900,000	223 days	243 days
Earth	1,600,000	365 days	24 hours
Mars	1,300,000	686 days	25 hours
Jupiter	700,000	12 years	10 hours
Saturn	520,000	29 years	11 hours
Uranus	360,000	84 years	16 hours
Neptune	290,000	165 years	18 hours
Pluto	250,000	249 years	6 days

Source: Richard Lewis. *The Illustrated Encyclopedia of the Universe.* Harmony Books, 1983.

***Math Masters,* p. 368**

Project Master

Name Date Time

PROJECT 4 **Rotating and Revolving with Earth**

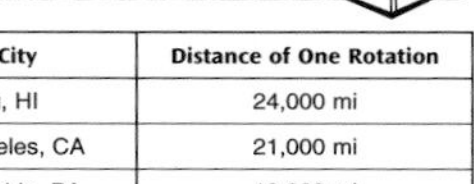

During 1 rotation of Earth, a person at the equator travels about 25,000 miles. The farther north of the equator a person is, the smaller the distance of rotation becomes.

City	Distance of One Rotation
Honolulu, HI	24,000 mi
Los Angeles, CA	21,000 mi
Philadelphia, PA	19,000 mi
Seattle, WA	17,000 mi
Anchorage, AK	13,000 mi

Sample answers:

1. Estimate how many miles a person travels during 1 hour of rotation.
   a. At the equator About 1,040 miles b. In Los Angeles About 880 miles
   c. In Seattle About 710 miles d. In Anchorage About 540 miles

2. a. Estimate the distance of 1 rotation for your location. For example, if you live in Chicago—which is farther from the equator than Philadelphia but closer than Seattle—you might say 18,000 miles. About ______ miles Answers vary.
   b. How far have you rotated in the past hour? About ______ miles
   c. How far have you rotated in the past minute? About ______ miles

3. Earth travels about 600,000,000 miles (in scientific notation: $6 * 10^8$) around the Sun in 1 year. Estimate how far Earth (with you on it) travels in its orbit around the Sun during various time periods. Complete the following statements.
   a. In 1 month, Earth travels about 50,000,000, or $(5 * 10^7)$ miles.
   b. In 1 day, Earth travels about 1,600,000 miles.
   c. In the past hour, Earth traveled about 68,000 miles.
   d. In the past minute, Earth traveled about 1,100 miles.

***Math Masters,* p. 369**

Project Master

Name Date Time

PROJECT 4 **Movement of Planets around the Sun**

Read the paragraph under Movement of the Planets around the Sun on *Math Masters,* page 368, and look at the information in Solar System Data Table 3. Then work with your Planet Team to complete the following.

1. Record some observations about the information in the table. For example, which planets rotate faster than Earth? About the same as Earth? Slower than Earth?
   Sample answer: Faster—Jupiter, Saturn, Uranus, and Neptune; slower—Mercury, Venus, and Pluto; about the same—Mars.

2. Since the Declaration of Independence was signed in 1776, about how many times has Earth revolved around the Sun? Sample answer: 230 times (as of 2006)

3. a. About how many times has your team's planet traveled around the Sun since 1776? Answers vary.
   b. Share results with your classmates to complete the list below.
   Sample answers: (as of 2006)

Approximate Number of Revolutions around the Sun Since 1776					
Mercury	953.98	Mars	122.38	Uranus	2.74
Venus	376.46	Jupiter	19.17	Neptune	1.39
Earth	230	Saturn	7.93	Pluto	0.92

4. Use what you have learned to add information to your team's Planet Information Label.

***Math Masters,* p. 370**

Project Master

Name Date Time

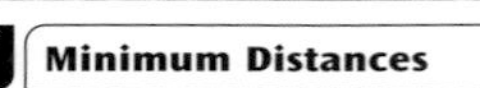

PROJECT 4 **Minimum Distances**

The constant movement of planets complicates space travel. Planets move at different speeds, so exact calculations are needed to figure out the directions spaceships should travel. Another challenge is that the distances between Earth and other planets are always changing.

Scientists use complex mathematical computer models to calculate the relationship of Earth to the other planets and to plot the data needed to send space probes to other planets. There are also some facts that we can use to make rough estimates of some things we might want to know for space travel.

All the planets except Pluto travel in nearly circular orbits, with the Sun at the center.

For all planets except Pluto, orbits are almost in the same plane. This means that when the planets pass each other on the same radius from the Sun, the minimum distance can be calculated from the information in the Solar System Data Tables on *Math Masters,* pages 352 and 353. This can be seen in the diagram below.

Earth revolves quickly around the Sun compared with all the planets except Mercury and Venus. This means that at least once every year, Earth and each of the outer planets line up on the same radius from the Sun, at the minimum distance. The times are predictable, too. It is harder to predict when Earth will line up with Mercury and Venus. (For Pluto the situation is even more difficult. You might want to take on the problem as a challenge, but it can't be done using only the information on these pages.)

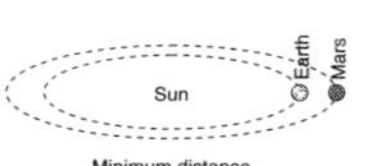

Minimum distance

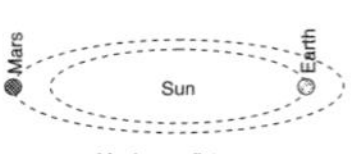

Maximum distance

***Math Masters,* p. 371**

▶ Using Data to Draw Conclusions

PARTNER ACTIVITY

(*Math Masters,* p. 372)

Students work in partnerships to complete Questions 1, 2, and 3 on *Math Masters,* page 372 and then share their answers with the class. Filling in the third column on the table is considered an extension. See Part 2 for a discussion of that activity.

2 Extending the Project

▶ Calculating Maximum Distances from Earth to Other Planets

SMALL-GROUP ACTIVITY

(*Math Masters,* pp. 352, 353, 371, and 372)

As Planet Teams finish finding minimum distances, you might have them calculate the estimated maximum distance from Earth to their planets. They use the information to fill in the third column of the table on *Math Masters,* page 372.

Project Master

Name Date Time

PROJECT 4 **Minimum/Maximum Distances of Planets**

Read Minimum Distances on *Math Masters,* page 371. Then work with your Planet Team, unless you are on the Pluto team. Your teacher will tell the Pluto team what to do.

Use the information on *Math Masters,* page 352 or 353 to estimate the distance between Earth and your planet when they are closest to each other. Round your estimate to 2 significant digits and write it in scientific notation. Share estimates with the other teams to fill in the estimated minimum distances in the table below. Then complete the Estimated Maximum Distance column. (*Hint:* Add Earth's distance from the Sun to each planet's distance from the Sun.)

Planet	Estimated Minimum Distance from Earth (mi or km)	Estimated Maximum Distance from Earth (mi or km)
Mercury	$5.7 * 10^7$ mi; $9.2 * 10^7$ km	$1.3 * 10^8$ mi; $2.1 * 10^8$ km
Venus	$2.6 * 10^7$ mi; $4.0 * 10^7$ km	$1.6 * 10^8$ mi; $2.6 * 10^8$ km
Mars	$4.7 * 10^7$ mi; $8.0 * 10^7$ km	$2.3 * 10^8$ mi; $3.8 * 10^8$ km
Jupiter	$3.9 * 10^8$ mi; $6.3 * 10^8$ km	$5.7 * 10^8$ mi; $9.3 * 10^8$ km
Saturn	$8.0 * 10^8$ mi; $1.3 * 10^9$ km	$9.8 * 10^8$ mi; $1.6 * 10^9$ km
Uranus	$1.7 * 10^9$ mi; $2.8 * 10^9$ km	$1.9 * 10^9$ mi; $3.1 * 10^9$ km
Neptune	$2.7 * 10^9$ mi; $4.4 * 10^9$ km	$2.9 * 10^9$ mi; $4.7 * 10^9$ km

Summary

1. How would you describe to a friend the motion of Earth on its axis and around the Sun? Answers vary.

2. When you return from a space trip, will Earth be in the same place as when you left? ____ Explain. Answers vary.

3. About how many times have you rotated and revolved since you were born?
   Rotated: 4,380 Revolved: 12 Answers based on the age of 12 years. If leap years are used, the "rotated" answer might be 4,383.

***Math Masters,* p. 372**

Will It Be Possible to Travel to Other Planets in Your Lifetime?

Objective **To use previously gathered data to decide whether it will be possible to travel to other planets in students' lifetimes.**

1 Doing the Project

Recommended Use: During or after Unit 2

Key Activities

Students use what they learned in the preceding projects as they explore the possibility of traveling to other planets in their lifetimes.

Key Concepts and Skills

- Apply place-value concepts to find values $\frac{1}{10}$ and 10 times as much. [Number and Numeration Goal 1]
- Use a calculator to compute products and quotients of whole numbers. [Operations and Computation Goal 2]
- Use estimation strategies to solve problems. [Operations and Computation Goal 5]
- Apply division rules to find n-to-1 ratios. [Operations and Computation Goal 6]
- Solve rate problems using unit rates. [Operations and Computation Goal 6]
- Use data to answer questions and draw conclusions. [Data and Chance Goal 2]
- Identify rules for patterns and use these patterns to complete a table. [Patterns, Functions, and Algebra Goal 1]

materials

- ☐ Project Masters (*Math Masters,* pp. 352–354, 368, and 372–375)

See **Advance Preparation**

2 Extending the Project

Students figure out how old they would be on another planet.

Students research space flight.

materials

- ☐ Project Masters (*Math Masters,* pp. 368 and 376)
- ☐ reference books and articles about space travel
- ☐ computer with Internet access

Additional Information

This project is designed to be a culminating activity.

In Projects 1–4, students worked with partners, Planet Teams, or as a class. In this project, have students work independently to consider the feasibility of space travel to a planet of their choice. They need not explore the planet they studied with their Planet Teams, but it is likely that many students will choose the same planet. Some planets may not be chosen by anyone. In an Extending the Project activity, students estimate how old they would be on three different planets: Venus, Mars, and Jupiter.

Advance Preparation Read "Projects" in the Management Guide section of the *Teacher's Reference Manual.*

Technology

See the **iTLG.**

See Web site on page 421.

Name ____________ Date ____________ Time ____________

PROJECT 1 **Life on Other Planets**

The unmanned Mariner 4 spacecraft flew past Mars on July 14, 1965, collecting the first close-up photographs of an inner solar-system planet. Since those first flyby images were taken, we have asked whether life ever arose on Mars. Life, as we understand it, requires water. Scientists believe that if life ever evolved on Mars, it did so in the presence of a long-standing supply of water.

Over 30 years ago, NASA launched two identical spacecraft (*Vikings 1 and 2*), each consisting of an orbiter and a lander. Each orbiter-lander pair flew together and entered Mars' orbit. After taking pictures, the orbiters separated and descended to the planet's surface for the purpose of data collection. The landers conducted three experiments designed to look for possible signs of life. While the experiments revealed unexpected chemical activity in the Martian soil, they provided no clear evidence for the presence of living microorganisms near the landing sites.

Exploration missions of the past decade have landed robotic rovers with far greater mobility than that of the *Viking* landers. The rovers carry a sophisticated set of instruments that collect and analyze surface samples. By studying rock and soil samples, scientists hope to determine whether water was involved in soil and rock formation and thereby identify areas on the planet that may have been favorable for life in the past.

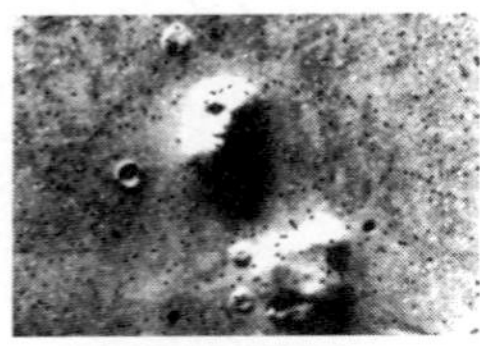

In 1976, the *Viking I* orbiter took the first photographs of the Cydonia region of Mars, showing an unusual mountain that seemed to resemble a face. Some people suggested that the face was a monument built by an extraterrestrial civilization. But scientists believed this resemblance was accidental, partly due to the angle of light at the time the photo was taken and partly due to the complicated image enhancement used to process the data that was available at the time.

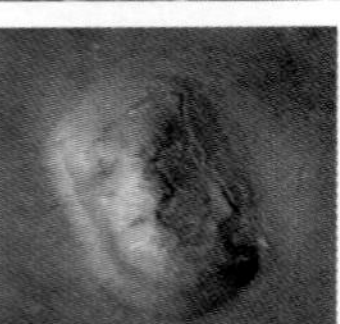

On May 28, 2001 the Mars Global Surveyor took a new photo of this feature. Although the landform has the same general shape as in earlier photographs, details provided by the higher-resolution photograph reveal the "face" to be a naturally formed hill.

***Math Masters,* p. 354**

NOTE On July 29, 2005, Dr. Mike Brown and his colleagues announced the discovery of a tenth planet beyond Pluto. At that time, the planet's temporary name was 2003 UB313. The planet's permanent name, as well as information about its size and surface temperature, became available after this third edition of *Everyday Mathematics* had already gone to press. Consider having students extend planet data tables to include any available information about this tenth planet.

Project Master

Name ____________ Date ____________ Time ____________

PROJECT 5 **Travel to Other Planets in Your Lifetime?**

You have explored the solar system. You have learned about the size, distance, and motion of each planet. You are ready to offer an informed opinion on travel to other planets.

Fill in the basic facts about the planet you plan to visit. Then estimate the answers to the questions on the rest of this page and the next page. Work on your own, but consult with your teacher or classmates if you are unsure about what to do.

My planet Answers vary.

Here are some facts I know about this planet.
(This information is on *Math Masters,* pp. 352, 353, and 368.)

- Surface temperature ____________
- Average diameter ____________
- Average distance from the Sun ____________
- Earth days or years to orbit the Sun ____________

How Far Will You Need to Travel?

Estimated minimum distance from Earth (See *Math Masters,* p. 372.) ____________

How Long Will It Take to Travel to Your Planet?

- Suppose a spaceship with people on it can travel at about 25,000 miles per hour. At this speed, how long will it take to reach your planet? See page 374
- If you could travel at 25,000 miles per hour, would it be possible to visit your planet and return to Earth in your lifetime? Answers vary.
- If not, how much faster would you need to travel? ____________ times faster
- At the faster speed, how long would it take to go to your planet and return? See page 374

***Math Masters,* p. 373**

1 Doing the Project

▶ Traveling to Other Planets

INDEPENDENT ACTIVITY

(*Math Masters,* pp. 352–354, 368, and 372–375)

Ask students to choose a planet to travel to and record their choice at the top of *Math Masters,* page 373. Encourage the class to choose a diversity of planets. Ask a few students to tell which planets they chose and why.

NOTE Students recorded their estimates of the minimum distance from Earth to each planet in our solar system (except Pluto) on *Math Masters,* page 372. Use these figures to estimate travel times.

Students work independently, perhaps using you or classmates as consultants. As much as possible, they should solve problems by themselves before checking with others.

After students have made calculations for their chosen planet, they pool their information to fill in the table on *Math Masters,* page 374. If some students finish early, ask them to make estimates for any planets that were not chosen, so all blanks in the table can be filled in.

As students finish their estimates, they add information to the Planet Information Labels posted next to each planet in the solar system model.

If time allows, or on another day, have students share responses to Conclusions on *Math Masters,* page 375.

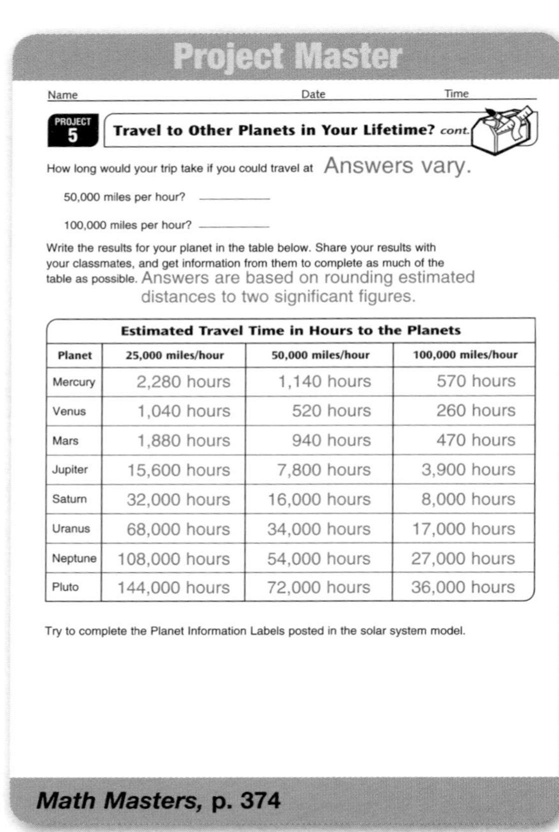

Project Master

Name ____________ Date ____________ Time ____________

PROJECT 5 **Travel to Other Planets in Your Lifetime?** *cont.*

How long would your trip take if you could travel at Answers vary.

50,000 miles per hour? ____________

100,000 miles per hour? ____________

Write the results for your planet in the table below. Share your results with your classmates, and get information from them to complete as much of the table as possible. Answers are based on rounding estimated distances to two significant figures.

Estimated Travel Time in Hours to the Planets

Planet	25,000 miles/hour	50,000 miles/hour	100,000 miles/hour
Mercury	2,280 hours	1,140 hours	570 hours
Venus	1,040 hours	520 hours	260 hours
Mars	1,880 hours	940 hours	470 hours
Jupiter	15,600 hours	7,800 hours	3,900 hours
Saturn	32,000 hours	16,000 hours	8,000 hours
Uranus	68,000 hours	34,000 hours	17,000 hours
Neptune	108,000 hours	54,000 hours	27,000 hours
Pluto	144,000 hours	72,000 hours	36,000 hours

Try to complete the Planet Information Labels posted in the solar system model.

***Math Masters,* p. 374**

2 Extending the Project

▶ Determining Age on Another Planet

INDEPENDENT ACTIVITY

(*Math Masters,* pp. 368 and 376)

Students estimate the number of Earth days they have been alive. Then they estimate how old they would be in Venus years, Mars years, and Jupiter years, using data from Solar System Data Table 3 on *Math Masters,* page 368. They can find the answers by dividing the number of days they have been alive by 223 for Venus, 686 for Mars, and 4,380 for Jupiter. Students should not be surprised to find discrepancies among various outside sources, because they are working with estimated figures.

▶ Finding Out More about Space Flight

INDEPENDENT ACTIVITY

Invite students to learn more about current space flight activity by reading newspapers, magazines, and books, and by visiting Internet sites such as *http://spaceflight.nasa.gov.*

Project Master

Name Date Time

PROJECT 4 Spaceship Earth

To be a successful space traveler, you must be able to find your way back to Earth. This may not be easy. You do not feel it, but at this moment you are traveling through space at incredible speeds.

Earth spins around like a top. In 24 hours, it makes 1 complete **rotation.** At the equator, the distance around Earth is about 25,000 miles. In the middle of the United States, the distance is about 21,000 miles. This means that if you live in the middle of the United States, you travel about 21,000 miles every day.

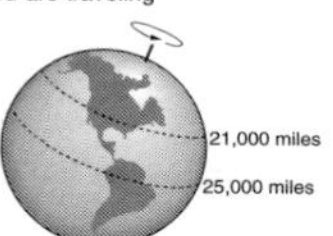

At the same time Earth is rotating, it is moving in its orbit around the Sun. In 1 year, Earth makes 1 complete **revolution,** or trip, around the Sun. This trip is approximately 600,000,000 (or $6 * 10^8$) miles long.

600,000,000 miles

Earth Sun

Movement of the Planets around the Sun

All the planets are in motion, rotating like tops and revolving around the Sun. Compared to Earth, some planets move fast, but others are quite slow. Understanding planetary motion is key for space travel. You must know where to aim the spaceship.

Solar System Data Table 3

Planet	Average Speed in Orbit: Miles per Earth Day	Time to Revolve Once around the Sun: Earth Days or Years	Time to Rotate Once: Earth Days or Hours
Mercury	2,600,000	88 days	59 days
Venus	1,900,000	223 days	243 days
Earth	1,600,000	365 days	24 hours
Mars	1,300,000	686 days	25 hours
Jupiter	700,000	12 years	10 hours
Saturn	520,000	29 years	11 hours
Uranus	360,000	84 years	16 hours
Neptune	290,000	165 years	18 hours
Pluto	250,000	249 years	6 days

Source: Richard Lewis. The Illustrated Encyclopedia of the Universe, Harmony Books, 1983.

***Math Masters,* p. 368**

Project Master

Name Date Time

PROJECT 5 Travel to Other Planets in Your Lifetime? *cont.*

Conclusions Answers vary.

1. Do you think it might be possible to travel to your planet and return in your lifetime? Why or why not?

2. Which planets are most likely to be explored by humans? Why do you think so?

3. Some scientists believe that it makes sense to send people to explore other planets. Some scientists believe that other planets should be explored only with computers, cameras, and scientific instruments aboard space probes. Choose one of these positions, or one in between, and defend your choice.

4. If you were one of the first people to go on a trip to another planet, what items would you take to represent your beliefs and interests?

***Math Masters,* p. 375**

Project Master

Name Date Time

PROJECT 5 Your Age on Another Planet

We use the time it takes Earth to make one trip around the Sun to keep track of our ages. When you tell someone how old you are, you are telling how many times Earth has traveled around the Sun since you were born.

Sample answer:

1. a. Today my age is 12 years, 0 months, and 0 days.
   b. I have been on Earth a total of about 4,383 days.

Planet	Time to Orbit the Sun (Earth Days)
Mercury	88
Venus	223
Earth	365
Mars	686
Jupiter	4,380
Saturn	10,585
Uranus	30,660
Neptune	60,225
Pluto	90,885

Source: Universal Almanac

Answers for Problem 3 based on the age of 12 years.

If you lived on a different planet, you would have a different age counted in the year of that planet. For example, on Venus, 1 year (the time it takes for Venus to travel around the Sun) equals 223 Earth days.

2. a. How many Earth days are there in a year on Mars? 686
   b. How many Earth days are there in a year on Jupiter? 4,380
3. Estimate how old you would be today on the following planets by finding the number of times they have revolved around the Sun since you were born.
   Venus 19.7 Mars 6.4 Jupiter 1

***Math Masters,* p. 376**

Anthropometry Project: Formulas for Body Height and Neck Circumference

Objectives **To measure body parts and to plot measurements as data pairs; and to investigate formulas that relate to body measurements.**

1 Doing the Project

Recommended Use: During or after Unit 3

Key Activities

Students investigate two rules for estimating body measurements. Each student measures two adults and himself or herself, and the class plots measurement data on two coordinate grids. Students use the class graphs to answer questions.

Key Concepts and Skills

- Convert between fractions and decimals. [Number and Numeration Goal 5]
- Multiply decimal numbers. [Operations and Computation Goal 2]
- Use the spread and shape of graphed data to draw conclusions. [Data and Chance Goal 2]
- Use a graph to represent and interpret a function. [Patterns, Functions, and Algebra Goal 1]
- Apply the order of operations to evaluate formulas. [Patterns, Functions, and Algebra Goal 3]

Key Vocabulary

anthropometry • anthropometrist • tibia (shinbone) • patella (kneecap) • prediction line

materials

- ☐ Project Masters (*Math Masters,* pp. 377–383)

For students:

- ☐ tape measure (inches)
- ☐ inch ruler and string (optional)
- ☐ yardstick
- ☐ calculator
- ☐ colored pencils (red, blue, black)

For the teacher:

- ☐ scissors
- ☐ transparent tape or thumbtacks

See **Advance Preparation**

2 Extending the Project

Students collect additional measurement data.

materials

- ☐ Project Masters (*Math Masters,* p. 383)

Additional Information

Background Information

Anthropometry is the study of human body sizes and proportions. An **anthropometrist** is a person who gathers data on the size of the human body and its components. Body-size data are useful to many professions. For example:

▷ Automotive engineers use body-size data in designing vehicles and child-safety seats.

▷ Architects take body-size data into account when designing stairs, planning safe kitchens and bathrooms, and providing access space for people who use wheelchairs.

▷ Clothing manufacturers use body-size data to create sewing patterns.

No two people, including identical twins, are exactly alike. There are always differences in body sizes and proportions due to age, sex, and ethnic or racial group.

There is no perfect formula that can be used to exactly predict one body measure by using another body measure. However, some imperfect formulas and rules of thumb can be very useful in describing how one body measure is related to another body measure. The project will focus on activities that investigate two such formulas.

Advance Preparation Read "Projects" in the Management Guide section of the *Teacher's Reference Manual.*

Make eight copies of *Math Masters,* page 383 to make two large coordinate grids. (See directions on page 423.) Fasten papers to the board or a bulletin board. This project will proceed smoothly if students complete several measurement and graphing activities before the class begins the project. The next page shows a suggested timetable.

Technology

See the **iTLG.**

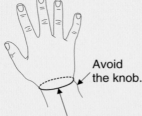

Avoid the knob.

Measure around skinny part of wrist.

7 school days before teaching the project: Have students read the background information about anthropometry on *Math Masters,* page 377. Distribute copies of *Math Masters,* pages 378 and 379, which explain how and with what precision students are to measure the following: their tibias and heights; the tibias and heights of two adults; their own necks and wrists; and the necks and wrists of two adults. Take time to demonstrate the measuring process so students know exactly where to measure. Remind students that all body measures should be in U.S. customary units—the tibia and neck to the nearest $\frac{1}{4}$ inch, the height to the nearest $\frac{1}{2}$ inch, and the wrist to the nearest $\frac{1}{8}$ inch. Allow students five to six days to complete this assignment.

6 days before teaching the project: Assemble two large coordinate grids.

- Cut four copies of *Math Masters,* page 383 and tape them to form a coordinate grid as shown on page 425. The assembled grid should measure eight 4 × 4 squares wide and twelve 4 × 4 squares high. Label the left axis *Height* and the bottom axis *Tibia Length.* Label the unit marks along the axes as follows:

  Left and right axes in inches from 51" to 75".

  Top and bottom axes in inches from 11" to 19".

- Cut four more copies of *Math Masters,* page 383 and assemble a second grid as shown on page 427. Label the left axis *Neck Circumference* and the bottom axis *Wrist Circumference.* Label the unit marks along the axes as follows:

  Left and right axes in half-inches from 7" to 19".

  Top and bottom axes in half-inches from $4\frac{1}{2}$" to $8\frac{1}{2}$".

- A prediction line is a line through the points that exactly follow a rule. On the second grid, draw the prediction line for the rule:

  Circumference of neck = 2 ∗ Circumference of wrist.

The prediction line for the first grid will be done as a class demonstration in Part 1. As students plot their neck-and-wrist data pairs during the next several days, they will be able to conclude immediately, by looking at the prediction line, whether any data pair they add to the grid satisfies the rule.

- Tape or tack the prepared coordinate grids to the board or a bulletin board.

5 days before teaching the project: Some students will have completed their body-size measurements. Demonstrate how they should plot their measures as data pairs on the two classroom coordinate grids. Include the following points:

▷ Each student will have measures for an adult male, an adult female, and for himself or herself. Therefore, each student will plot three points on each coordinate grid.

▷ Explain the color and symbol conventions for plotting:

   Use solid red circles for adult female data.

   Use open blue circles for adult male data.

   Use solid black squares for student data.

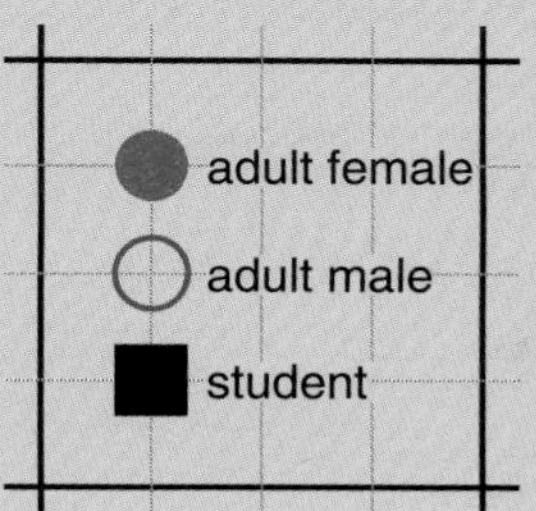

Each plotted point should be large—about 5 mm across—so students will be able to see the points from a distance. Students will probably make mistakes when plotting, so consider using erasable colored pencils rather than markers or pens.

Verify that students are correctly reading the scales when they locate number pairs. For example, the tibia axis has grid lines at each $\frac{1}{4}$ inch but is labeled only at whole inches. The height axis has grid lines at each $\frac{1}{2}$ inch but is labeled only at whole inches.

Have students discuss why a graph that visually differentiates adult male, adult female, and student data might be useful. There may be interesting patterns among plotted points. These patterns are more apparent when the points for men, women, and children are color-coded. These patterns may be overlooked if the points are not color-coded.

Remaining days before teaching the project: As students complete *Math Masters,* pages 378 and 379, have them plot their measures as data pairs onto the classroom grids. Encourage students who have not yet completed the measurements to do so.

It's likely that some number pairs will be identical. If the point for a student's number pair is already plotted, the student should plot the pair as near the correct point as possible, without overlapping any points already marked.

1 Doing the Project

▶ Applying a Rule

INDEPENDENT ACTIVITY

(*Math Masters,* p. 380)

Ask students to read and answer Problem 1 on *Math Masters,* page 380. Then have them share their responses. Students should have no difficulty understanding that anthropometric data cannot be described by perfect formulas that predict exactly. You may wish to share an example from the completed classroom plot of tibia/height measures to demonstrate this point.

Point out that the formula Height = (2.6 ∗ Length of Tibia) + 25.5 applies to adults. Anthropometrists typically use separate formulas for males and females to describe relationships between two different body measures. The rule used for the activities in this lesson, Height = (2.6 ∗ Length of Tibia) + 25.5, acceptably fits adult males and females.

▷ Find a **tibia** length that is common to several people. Notice that these people most likely do not all have the same height.

▷ Find a height that is common to several people. Notice that these people most likely do not all have the same tibia length.

Have students complete Problem 2 on *Math Masters,* page 380.

NOTE Measuring the tibia as directed on *Math Masters,* page 378 will likely yield results that overestimate the length of the tibia by $\frac{1}{2}$ inch. However, the average $\frac{1}{2}$-inch overestimate is not a problem because the formula takes it into account.

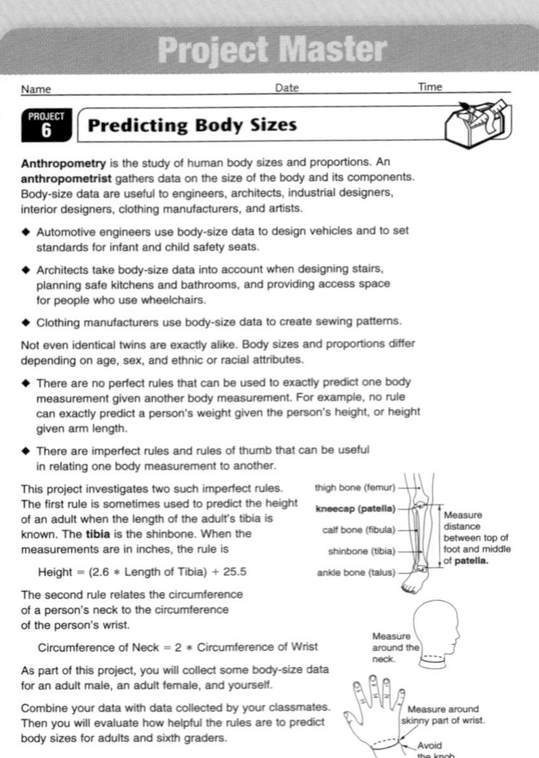

Project Master

Name Date Time

PROJECT 6 **Predicting Body Sizes**

Anthropometry is the study of human body sizes and proportions. An **anthropometrist** gathers data on the size of the body and its components. Body-size data are useful to engineers, architects, industrial designers, interior designers, clothing manufacturers, and artists.

- Automotive engineers use body-size data to design vehicles and to set standards for infant and child safety seats.
- Architects take body-size data into account when designing stairs, planning safe kitchens and bathrooms, and providing access space for people who use wheelchairs.
- Clothing manufacturers use body-size data to create sewing patterns.

Not even identical twins are exactly alike. Body sizes and proportions differ depending on age, sex, and ethnic or racial attributes.

- There are no perfect rules that can be used to exactly predict one body measurement given another body measurement. For example, no rule can exactly predict a person's weight given the person's height, or height given arm length.
- There are imperfect rules and rules of thumb that can be useful in relating one body measurement to another.

This project investigates two such imperfect rules. The first rule is sometimes used to predict the height of an adult when the length of the adult's tibia is known. The **tibia** is the shinbone. When the measurements are in inches, the rule is

Height = (2.6 ∗ Length of Tibia) + 25.5

The second rule relates the circumference of a person's neck to the circumference of the person's wrist.

Circumference of Neck = 2 ∗ Circumference of Wrist

As part of this project, you will collect some body-size data for an adult male, an adult female, and yourself.

Combine your data with data collected by your classmates. Then you will evaluate how helpful the rules are to predict body sizes for adults and sixth graders.

Math Masters, p. 377

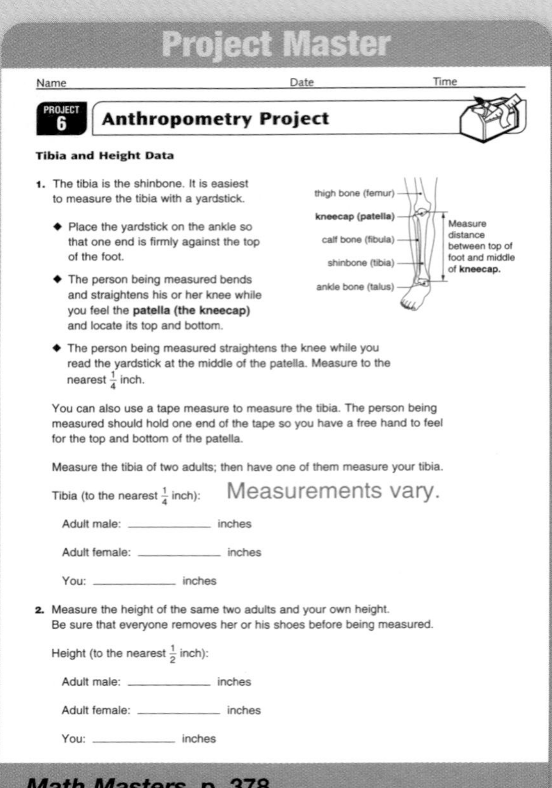

Project Master

Name Date Time

PROJECT 6 **Anthropometry Project**

Tibia and Height Data

1. The tibia is the shinbone. It is easiest to measure the tibia with a yardstick.
   - Place the yardstick on the ankle so that one end is firmly against the top of the foot.
   - The person being measured bends and straightens his or her knee while you feel the **patella (the kneecap)** and locate its top and bottom.
   - The person being measured straightens the knee while you read the yardstick at the middle of the patella. Measure to the nearest $\frac{1}{4}$ inch.

   You can also use a tape measure to measure the tibia. The person being measured should hold one end of the tape so you have a free hand to feel for the top and bottom of the patella.

   Measure the tibia of two adults; then have one of them measure your tibia.

   Tibia (to the nearest $\frac{1}{4}$ inch): Measurements vary.

   Adult male: ______ inches

   Adult female: ______ inches

   You: ______ inches

2. Measure the height of the same two adults and your own height. Be sure that everyone removes her or his shoes before being measured.

   Height (to the nearest $\frac{1}{2}$ inch):

   Adult male: ______ inches

   Adult female: ______ inches

   You: ______ inches

Math Masters, p. 378

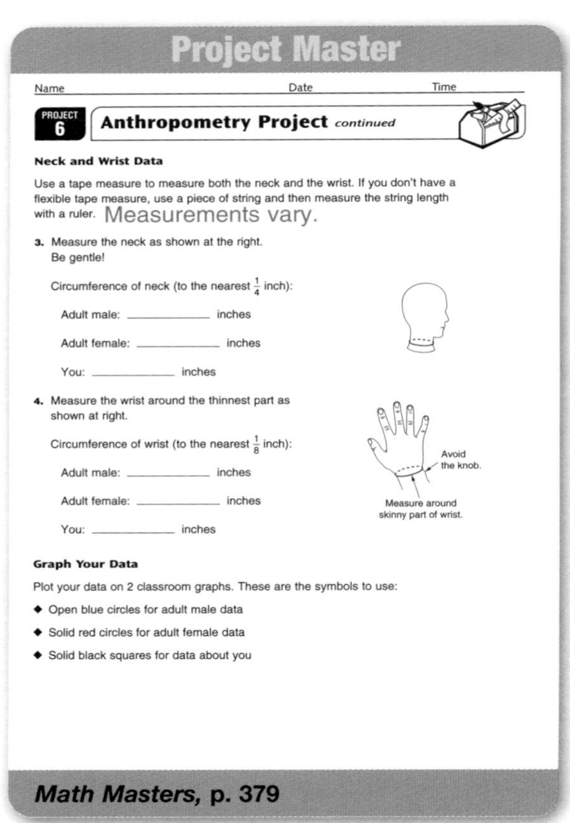

Project Master

Name Date Time

PROJECT 6 **Anthropometry Project** *continued*

Neck and Wrist Data

Use a tape measure to measure both the neck and the wrist. If you don't have a flexible tape measure, use a piece of string and then measure the string length with a ruler. Measurements vary.

3. Measure the neck as shown at the right. Be gentle!

   Circumference of neck (to the nearest $\frac{1}{4}$ inch):

   Adult male: ______ inches

   Adult female: ______ inches

   You: ______ inches

4. Measure the wrist around the thinnest part as shown at right.

   Circumference of wrist (to the nearest $\frac{1}{8}$ inch):

   Adult male: ______ inches

   Adult female: ______ inches

   You: ______ inches

Graph Your Data

Plot your data on 2 classroom graphs. These are the symbols to use:

- Open blue circles for adult male data
- Solid red circles for adult female data
- Solid black squares for data about you

Math Masters, p. 379

▶ Graphing the Prediction Line for Tibia and Height

WHOLE-CLASS ACTIVITY

(*Math Masters,* pp. 380 and 381)

Gather the class, with their project master copies and calculators, around the classroom grid on which they plotted their tibia and height data.

Have students read their answers to Problem 2 on *Math Masters,* page 380 as you mark the four points on the grid. Indicate that these points fall on a straight line, which is called the **prediction line** for the formula. Then draw the prediction line. (*See below.*) The prediction line is a graphic representation of the formula. It shows the values for which the formula is true.

Pose additional tibia lengths and have students use the formula and calculators to find the predicted heights for those lengths. In each case, verify that each of these new tibia-predicted height pairs also falls on the line drawn.

As a class, use the prediction line to complete Problems 3 and 4. The discussion need not be a sophisticated analysis of the grid. Rather, simply guide students to see and verbalize some simple features of the data that are quite clear from looking at the completed grid.

NOTE The grid below shows actual data collected from adults and students. It should give you a good idea of how your class's completed grid will look.

Tibia and Height Data

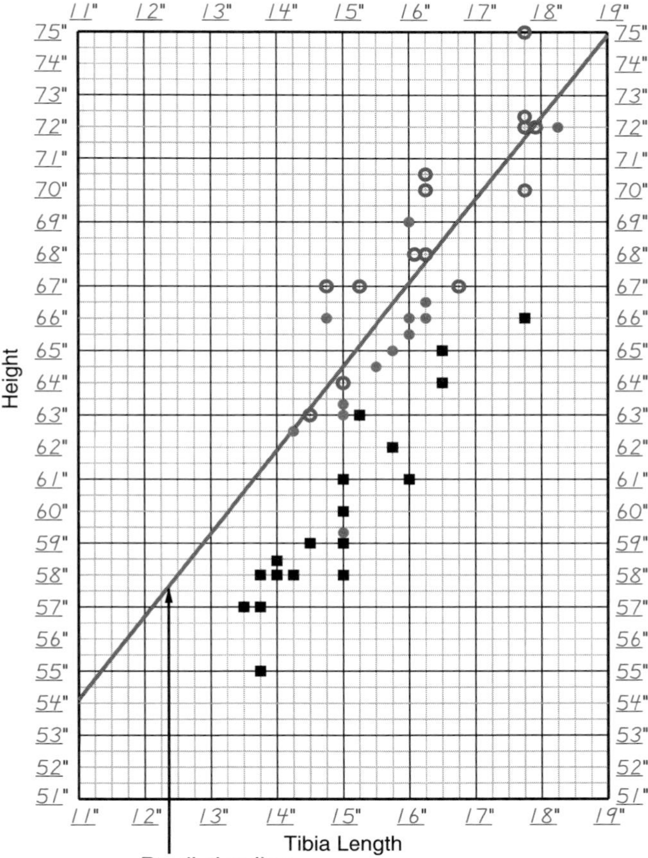

Project Master

Name Date Time

PROJECT 6 **Anthropometry Project: Tibia and Height**

1. The following rule is sometimes used to predict the height of an adult when the length of the adult's tibia is known. Measurements are in inches. (*Reminder:* Your tibia is your shinbone.)

   Height = (2.6 ∗ Length of Tibia) + 25.5

   Do you think that this rule can exactly predict a person's height when the length of the person's tibia is known? Sample answer: No

   Explain. People's proportions differ. The rule is intended to give only an approximate measurement.

2. Use the rule in Problem 1 to complete the table. Find the predicted height for each tibia length. You may use your calculator.

Tibia Length	Height Predicted
11 in.	54.1 in.
14 in.	61.9 in.
19 in.	74.9 in.
$17\frac{1}{2}$ in.	71 in.

3. Your teacher will draw a **prediction line** on the grid where you plotted your research data. It passes through points that exactly follow the rule for predicting height given the tibia length. Use the prediction line to answer the following questions.

   a. The predicted height for a person with a $15\frac{1}{4}$-inch tibia is about 65 inches.

   b. The predicted height for a person with a $13\frac{1}{4}$ -inch tibia is about 5 ft 0 in.

4. a. How closely does the prediction line approximate the actual data points for adult males? Sample answers: Somewhat closely

   Explain. Most of the data points fall near or slightly above the prediction line.

Math Masters, p. 380

Project Master

Name Date Time

PROJECT 6 **Anthropometry Project: Tibia and Height** *cont.*

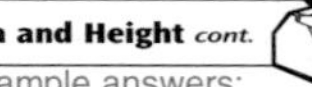

Sample answers:

b. How closely does the prediction line approximate the actual data points for adult females? Explain.
   The prediction line approximates the actual data somewhat closely. Most of the data points are close to or slightly below the prediction line.

c. How closely does the prediction line approximate the actual data points for students in your class? Explain.
   Predicted values are not as close as those for adults. Many of the student data points are far below the prediction line.

5. Scientists can use a single bone from a human skeleton to estimate the height of an adult who lived many centuries ago. If they have a tibia, they can use the rule:

   Height = (2.6 ∗ Length of Tibia) + 25.5

   a. The skeleton of a Neanderthal man who lived about 40,000 years ago contained a tibia about $14\frac{3}{4}$ inches long. Estimate the man's height. 64 in.

   b. The tibia of a partial skeleton of a 20,000-year-old adult was reconstructed and found to be about $12\frac{1}{2}$ inches long. Estimate the person's height. 58 in.

6. Paul measured his baby sister's tibia (4 inches long) and then used the rule to estimate her height. "That's crazy!" said Paul when he saw the result.

   a. What was Paul's estimate of his baby sister's height? 36 in.

   b. Why did he say that the estimate was "crazy"? Sample answer: Babies are not 3 feet long.

Math Masters, p. 381

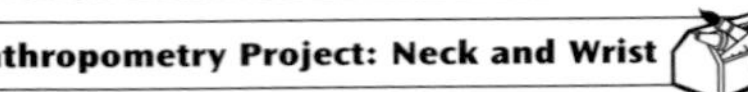

Name _______ Date _______ Time _______

PROJECT 6 **Anthropometry Project: Neck and Wrist**

Use the neck and wrist data that you and your classmates collected on the graph posted in the classroom to answer the following questions about the wrist-to-neck rule.

Circumference of Neck =
2 ∗ Circumference of Wrist

1. How closely does the prediction line approximate the actual data points
   for adult males? Not too closely
   for adult females? Not too closely
   for sixth graders? Fairly closely

The following passage is from *Gulliver's Travels* by Jonathan Swift. The setting is Lilliput, a country where the people are only 6 inches high.

"Two hundred seamstresses were employed to make me shirts … . The seamstresses took my measure as I lay on the ground, one standing at my neck, and another at my mid leg, with a strong cord extended, that each held by the end, while the third measured the length of the cord with a rule of an inch long. Then they measured my right thumb and desired no more; *for by a mathematical computation, that twice round the thumb is once round the wrist, and so on to the neck and the waist,* and by the help of my old shirt, which I displayed on the ground before them for a pattern, they fitted me exactly."

This passage provides three rules:

- Circumference of Wrist = 2 ∗ Circumference of Thumb
- Circumference of Neck = 2 ∗ Circumference of Wrist
- Circumference of Waist = 2 ∗ Circumference of Neck

2. Based on the data you and your classmates collected, how well do you think Gulliver's new clothes fit? Explain.
   Sample answer: They may be snug. Most of the data points for adult males fall above the prediction line.

***Math Masters,* p. 382**

Although the actual data pairs will vary from class to class, the following features are likely to be consistent:

▷ *Adult male data (open blue circles):* Some data points will fall on, or nearly on, the prediction line. For these people, the formula is predicting their height almost exactly. Of the remaining data points, more points will likely fall above the prediction line than below it. This means that, for men, the rule tends to predict heights that are a bit shorter than actual height. Very few of the data points will represent heights that differ from the predicted heights by more than three inches.

▷ *Adult female data (solid red circles):* These data points should be similar to those of the adult males. However, expect that more female points will fall below the prediction line than above it. This means that, for women, the rule tends to predict heights that are a bit taller than actual height.

▷ *Student data (solid black squares):* Most data points will fall below the prediction line. The rule predicts heights for students that are taller than actual height.

NOTE There has been no attempt to differentiate between sexes for students in this activity. There is very little difference in height, tibia length, and the tibia-to-height relationship between sexes until children reach their teen years.

Your class will probably conclude that the rule predicts fairly accurately for adults but poorly for students, usually predicting 2 to 6 inches taller than students' actual heights.

▶ Testing the Rule of Twice

(*Math Masters,* pp. 381 and 382)

Ask students to complete Problems 5 and 6 on *Math Masters,* page 381. Then have them work in partnerships to complete page 382. When most students have finished, discuss their conclusions.

Although actual data pairs will vary from class to class, the following features are likely to be consistent.

▷ *Adult male data (open blue circles):* More of the data points will likely fall above the prediction line than below it. This means that the rule tends to predict men's neck sizes that are a bit smaller than actual size. Few actual neck sizes will differ from the predicted sizes by more than three inches.

▷ *Adult female data (solid red circles):* These results should be similar to those of adult males. Expect that a few more female points than male points will fall below the prediction line. This means that the rule tends to predict women's neck sizes that are a bit smaller than actual size, but it is more accurate than for men's sizes.

▷ *Student data (solid black squares):* Some data points will fall on or near the prediction line. For these students, the rule predicts neck size almost exactly. Of the remaining data points, more will fall above the prediction line than below it.

Your class will probably conclude that the rule predicts fairly accurately for students but poorly for adults, usually predicting neck sizes smaller than actual size.

NOTE The completed grid below shows actual data collected from adults and students. It should give you a fairly good idea of how your class's completed grid will look.

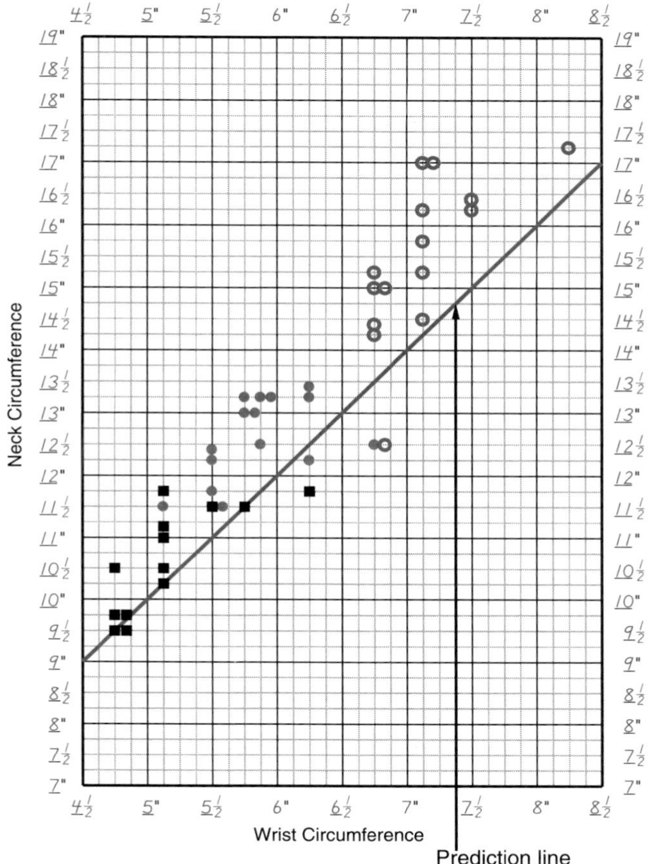

2 Extending the Project

▶ Collecting Data for Thumbs and Wrists

INDEPENDENT ACTIVITY

(*Math Masters,* p. 383)

Some students may be interested in collecting data for thumbs and wrists to test the other formulas from *Gulliver's Travels*. Have those students retitle *Math Masters,* page 383 as Thumb-and-Wrist Grid and then use the grid to graph their recorded data. Invite the students to share their findings with the class.

Project Master

Name Date Time

PROJECT 6 **Height-and-Tibia or Neck-and-Wrist Grid**

***Math Masters,* p. 383**

Paper-Throwing Experiments

Objectives To decide on a testing protocol and follow detailed instructions; to organize test data in tables and bar graphs; and to evaluate tested airplanes.

1 Doing the Project

Recommended Use: During or after Unit 1

Key Activities

Students design, assemble, and test a paper airplane. They make a second paper airplane using a prize-winning design. Students test their second airplanes, picking the three best. They compare data for the student-designed and prize-winning airplanes.

Key Concepts and Skills

- Construct a bar graph from collected data. [Data and Chance Goal 1]
- Use a graph key to distinguish represented data. [Data and Chance Goal 1]
- Calculate landmarks (maximum, minimum, median) of a data set. [Data and Chance Goal 2]
- Use data to answer questions and draw conclusions. [Data and Chance Goal 2]
- Use appropriate strategies to draw and measure angles to the nearest degree. [Measurement and Reference Frames Goal 1]

Key Vocabulary air resistance

materials

- ☐ Project Masters (*Math Masters,* pp. 384–395)

For students:

- ☐ sheets of $8\frac{1}{2}$"-by-11" paper, 20 lb or 24 lb
- ☐ transparent tape; inch ruler
- ☐ one tape measure or yardstick per group
- ☐ Geometry Template/protractor

For the teacher:

- ☐ 50-foot tape measure; masking tape

See **Advance Preparation**

2 Extending the Project

Students find out more about paper airplanes.

materials

- ☐ Project Masters (*Math Masters,* pp. 394 and 395)
- ☐ research books
- ☐ computer with Internet access

Additional Information

This is a four-day project.

To limit the project to one day, use the following version, which emphasizes geometry and minimizes data analysis.

1. Copy the design plan of the prize-winning airplane model.
2. Assemble the airplane.
3. Test each student's airplane for distance; compare the results.

Advance Preparation

Read "Projects" in the Management Guide section of the *Teacher's Reference Manual.*

Students will need a supply of $8\frac{1}{2}$ in. by 11 in. paper of a standard weight (not construction paper or card stock) and transparent tape. You will need a 50-foot tape measure and masking tape.

Technology

See the **iTLG.**

Day 1: Divide the class into groups of three or four students. An odd number of groups is helpful in determining median distances. Draw a table on the board similar to the following.

Class Distances						
Group	**Unfolded**	**1 Fold**	**2 Folds**	**3 Folds**	**4 Folds**	**5 Folds**
1						
2						
(etc.)						

Distance testing of the folded paper can also be done as a whole-class activity. In that case, you will not need the table of Class Distances, because there will be no group results to record.

Students will need a long space (at least 50 feet) in which to throw the folded paper. Consider using an empty school corridor, a gymnasium, a cafeteria, or an outside area that is sheltered from the wind. Place a strip of masking tape on the floor as a baseline from which to throw the paper airplanes

Day 2: Students will again require a long space in which to throw their paper airplanes. Stretch a 50-foot tape measure along the length of the area or put masking tape on the floor at 10-foot intervals, starting at the baseline. You will use this area again on Day 4.

Day 3: To help guide students, you might build a paper airplane yourself before Day 3, as directed on *Math Masters,* pages 390–392. You may want to make a master of your airplane for students who have difficulty copying the design.

Day 4: Use the same area as you did on Day 2.

Consider enlisting adult volunteers to help ensure that students follow safety procedures during the paper-throwing experiments.

1 Doing the Project

▶ Day 1: Throwing Paper

WHOLE-CLASS DISCUSSION

Ask: *How far do you think you can throw a sheet of paper?*

Expect that students will want to know whether the sheet of paper can be folded or crumpled or must remain flat. Some will want to know if there is a specific way in which they must fold or throw the paper. These are valid questions. Tell students that they will investigate how these factors affect the distance the paper will travel.

Project Master

Name Date Time

PROJECT 7 **How Far Can You Throw a Sheet of Paper?**

1. **Paper Folding**

   Work in a group of 3 or 4 students.
   You will need 6 sheets of paper, transparent tape, and a tape measure or yardstick.

   - Leave one paper unfolded.
   - Fold one paper in half.
   - Fold one paper in half 2 times.
   - Fold one paper in half 3 times.
   - Fold one paper in half 4 times.
   - Fold one paper in half 5 times.

For each of the folded papers, use tape to secure the edges and keep the paper from unfolding. *Use no more than 3 inches of tape* for each folded paper. Write the number of folds on each folded paper.

2. **Distance Testing**

   Agree on a baseline from which to throw each paper. Throw each paper (including the unfolded one) 3 times. Don't worry if the paper hits the floor, ceiling, or walls before it lands. You may throw the paper in any way you want. Try to throw each paper as far as possible.

   a. Measure all distances to the nearest foot. Record the best distance for each kind of paper in the table below. Answers vary.

Group Distances						
	Unfolded	**1 Fold**	**2 Folds**	**3 Folds**	**4 Folds**	**5 Folds**
Distance (to the nearest foot)						

   b. If your teacher has put a table of Class Distances on the board, record the distances collected by your group in the table.

Math Masters, p. 384

Project Master

Name ____ Date ____ Time ____

PROJECT 7 **How Far Can You Throw a Sheet of Paper?** *cont.*

3. Use the data in the completed table of Group Distances to complete the table below. Answers vary.

Landmarks for Class Distances						
Landmark	Unfolded	1 Fold	2 Folds	3 Folds	4 Folds	5 Folds
Maximum						
Median						
Minimum						

4. Which paper(s) consistently traveled the longest distance? ____

The shortest distance? ____

How do you think the surface area of the paper, its shape, the method of throwing, and other factors affected how far the paper traveled?
Answers vary. See the discussion on page 431 of the *Teacher's Lesson Guide.*

5. Generations of students, much to the dismay of generations of teachers, have perfected a way of using the air to throw a sheet of paper a great distance. Can you describe how they do it?
Answers vary.

***Math Masters,* p. 385**

▶ Testing How Far a Sheet of Paper Can Be Thrown

SMALL-GROUP ACTIVITY

(*Math Masters,* pp. 384–385)

Students work in groups of three or four to complete the paper-folding and distance-testing activities described on *Math Masters,* page 384. Alternatively, the whole class can do these activities. Review these procedures with the class before groups begin.

Tell students that they should use no more than three inches of tape on any sheet of paper. Students should consider this a rule of the testing procedure—more tape might give an unfair advantage over a sheet with less tape.

Have students throw each folded paper three times. Each group records the greatest distance for each kind of fold, using the table of Group Distances in Problem 2 on *Math Masters,* page 384. After completing this table, groups enter their results in the table of Class Distances on the board. (*See* Advance Preparation.)

If you prefer not to have individual groups conduct the distance-testing activities, consider the following procedure.

Allow about ten minutes for groups to complete the folding and taping. Remind students to write the number of folds on each sheet of paper. Place all the folded papers in separate piles—one pile for each number of folds. Students should take turns as measurers and throwers, testing one pile at a time. They should throw each paper only once. After they have thrown the last paper in a pile, they should identify the minimum, maximum, and median throws. The measurers then measure these distances from the baseline and report them to the class. Students should record each of the measurements in the table of Landmarks for Class Distances in Problem 3 on *Math Masters,* page 385. If you use this procedure, skip Problem 2 on *Math Masters,* page 384.

▶ Determining Landmarks for Class Distances

WHOLE-CLASS ACTIVITY

(*Math Masters,* p. 385)

Discuss the data recorded in the table of Class Distances on the board. Students then use this table to complete the table of Landmarks for Class Distances in Problem 3 on *Math Masters,* page 385.

▶ Discussing the Effects of Folds on Distance

(*Math Masters,* p. 385)

Problem 4 on *Math Masters,* page 385 asks students to consider why some of the folded papers might have traveled farther than others. Have students share ideas within their groups before opening the discussion to the entire class. Expect responses similar to the following:

▷ **Unfolded** The unfolded paper probably traveled the shortest distance. Many students may note that the paper flew back at them when they tried to throw it forward. Students may report a negative distance for a paper that lands behind the baseline. Because the surface area of the unfolded paper is so large, **air resistance** greatly affects the forward motion of the paper.

▷ **1 Fold** This paper probably traveled only slightly farther than the unfolded paper. Again, the paper may have flown back due to the amount of surface area.

▷ **2 and 3 Folds** Groups may have found that when these papers are thrown like flying discs, they travel a fair distance. The thickness of the folded paper makes a flying-disc throw possible—unlike the unfolded and 1-fold papers. Guide students to see that when they throw the paper like a flying disc, they are using air to their advantage.

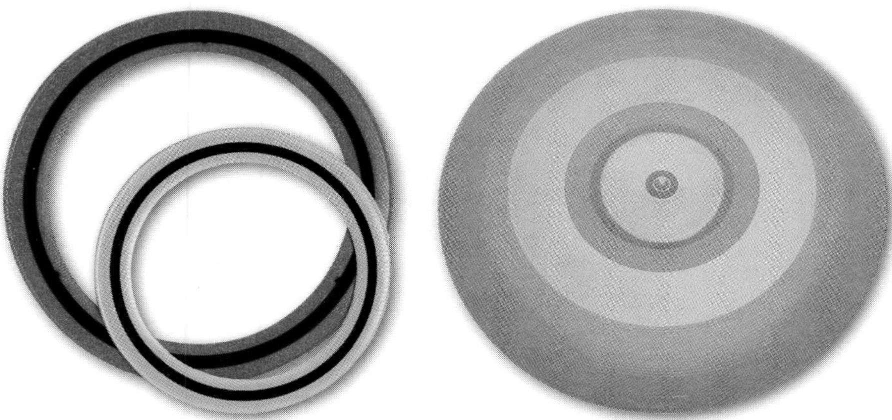

Flying Discs

▷ **4 and 5 Folds** These papers probably traveled the greatest distances. Some groups may have found that if they threw the paper with an edge slicing through the air, they could minimize the effect of air resistance. These papers have the smallest surface area, which also limits the effect of air resistance.

NOTE *Math Masters,* pages 394 and 395 describe simple experiments with the kite effect and vacuum effect on flight. You may want to conduct these experiments as whole-class demonstrations or suggest that students consult these pages as they design their paper airplanes in the assignment on *Math Masters,* page 387. (*See page 432.*)

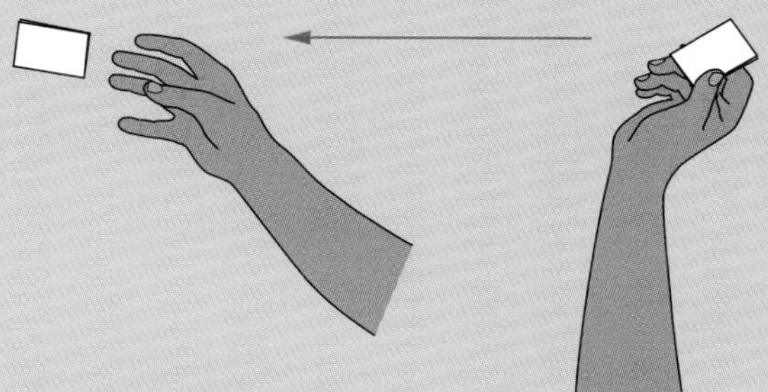

Overhand throw, viewed from the side

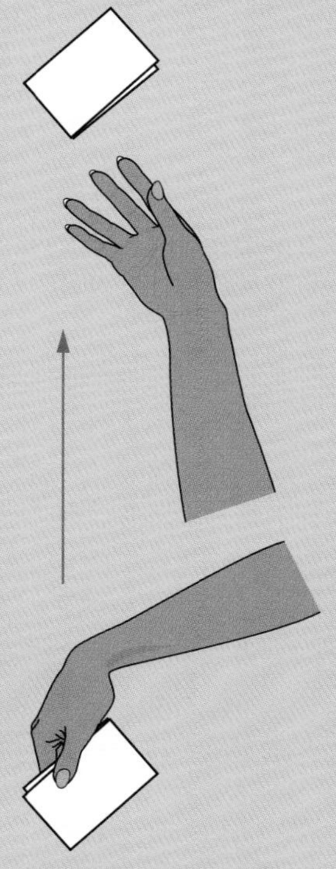

Flying-disc throw, viewed from above

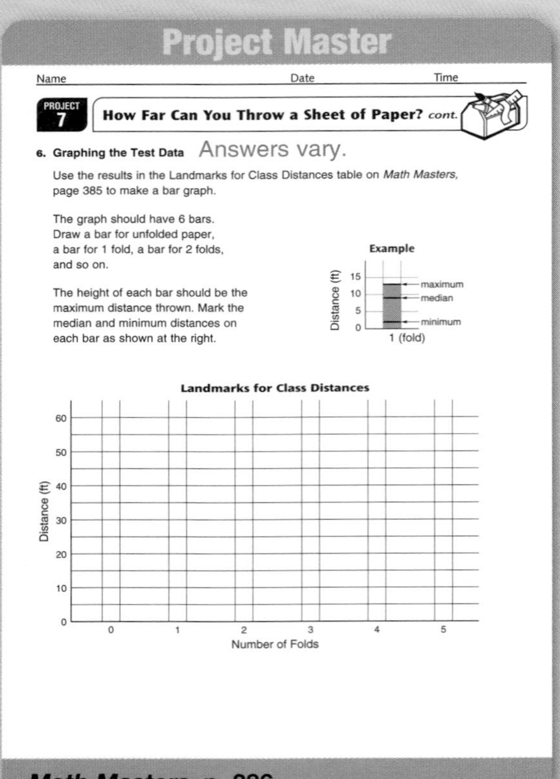

Project Master

Name Date Time

PROJECT 7 **How Far Can You Throw a Sheet of Paper?** *cont.*

6. Graphing the Test Data Answers vary.

Use the results in the Landmarks for Class Distances table on *Math Masters,* page 385 to make a bar graph.

The graph should have 6 bars. Draw a bar for unfolded paper, a bar for 1 fold, a bar for 2 folds, and so on.

The height of each bar should be the maximum distance thrown. Mark the median and minimum distances on each bar as shown at the right.

Math Masters, p. 386

NOTE The bar on *Math Masters,* page 386 is similar to a statistical display called a box-and-whiskers plot.

By the end of the discussion, students should conclude that the air resisted or assisted the forward motion of the paper, depending on the way the paper was folded and how it was thrown.

Problem 5 on *Math Masters,* page 385 refers to paper airplanes. Tell students that, during the next few days, they will experiment with paper airplane designs.

Graphing Class Distances

INDEPENDENT ACTIVITY

(*Math Masters,* pp. 385 and 386)

Students use the table of Landmarks for Class Distances on *Math Masters,* page 385 to complete the graph on page 386.

You may want to complete the first bar as a class to make sure students understand how to show the minimum and median with marks below the top of the bar. (See the example on *Math Masters,* p. 386.) Students should catch on quickly and easily complete the remaining bars on their own.

Designing a Paper Airplane

INDEPENDENT ACTIVITY

(*Math Masters,* p. 387)

Students design a paper airplane that they think will fly the greatest possible distance. Review the design rules with the class. Assign this after the Day 1 activities, to be completed in time for the Day 2 activities. You may want to assign it over a weekend or give students two nights to complete the assignment before beginning the Day 2 activities.

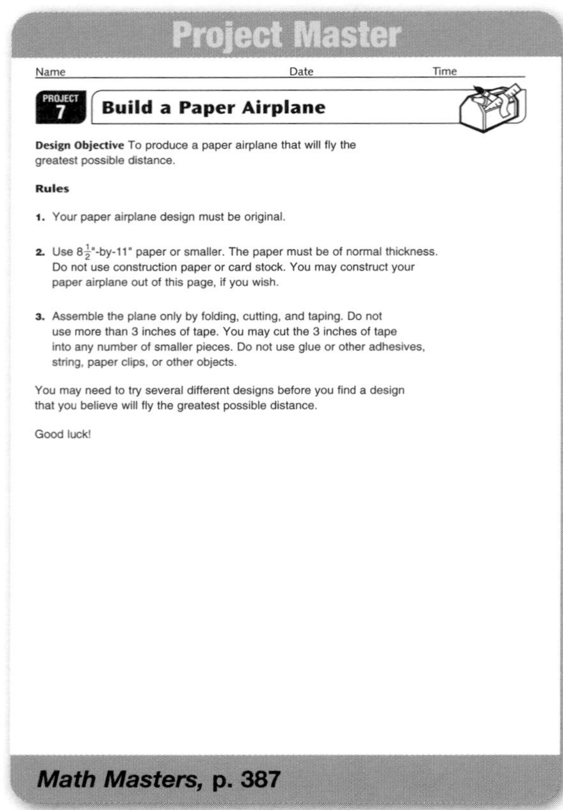

Project Master

Name Date Time

PROJECT 7 **Build a Paper Airplane**

Design Objective To produce a paper airplane that will fly the greatest possible distance.

Rules

1. Your paper airplane design must be original.
2. Use $8\frac{1}{2}$"-by-11" paper or smaller. The paper must be of normal thickness. Do not use construction paper or card stock. You may construct your paper airplane out of this page, if you wish.
3. Assemble the plane only by folding, cutting, and taping. Do not use more than 3 inches of tape. You may cut the 3 inches of tape into any number of smaller pieces. Do not use glue or other adhesives, string, paper clips, or other objects.

You may need to try several different designs before you find a design that you believe will fly the greatest possible distance.

Good luck!

Math Masters, p. 387

▶ Day 2: Testing Student-Designed Paper Airplanes

WHOLE-CLASS ACTIVITY

(*Math Masters,* p. 388)

Have students take their airplanes to the test area. Allow each student to throw an airplane one time. Leave the planes where they land.

After all the airplanes have been thrown, they will be lying at various distances from the baseline. Student helpers should then move each plane over to one of the walls, being careful not to change the plane's distance from the baseline. It is now possible to observe a line plot of flight-tested airplanes. Students can identify and measure the landmark flight distances as well as the three longest flights.

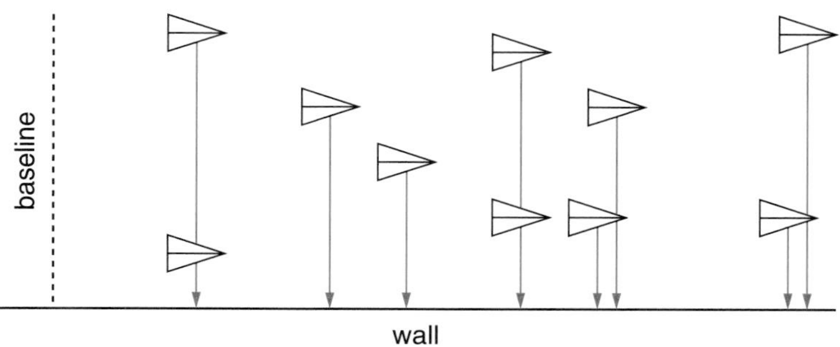

Have the class identify the airplanes that flew the minimum, maximum, and median distances. Measure these distances to the nearest foot. Students record these landmark distances in Problem 1 on *Math Masters,* page 388 to be used later with page 393.

Save the three airplanes that flew the farthest for more testing on Day 4.

Project Master

Name Date Time

PROJECT 7 **Testing Paper Airplane Designs, Part 1**

Student-Designed Airplanes

1. Complete the following after you conduct test flights of student-designed paper airplanes. Answers vary.
   a. Number of models tested ______
   b. Minimum distance ______ feet
   c. Median distance ______ feet
   d. Maximum distance ______ feet

Schultz-Designed Airplanes

2. Complete the following after you conduct test flights of Schultz-designed airplanes. Answers vary.
   a. Number of models tested ______
   b. Minimum distance ______ feet
   c. Median distance ______ feet
   d. Maximum distance ______ feet

3. Select the 3 student-designed and 3 Schultz-designed airplanes that flew the farthest. Test these 6 planes again. Record the results in the table below.

Name of Designer	Distance	Rank (1st to 6th)
Student	feet	
Student	feet	
Student	feet	
Louis Schultz	feet	
Louis Schultz	feet	
Louis Schultz	feet	

Math Masters, p. 388

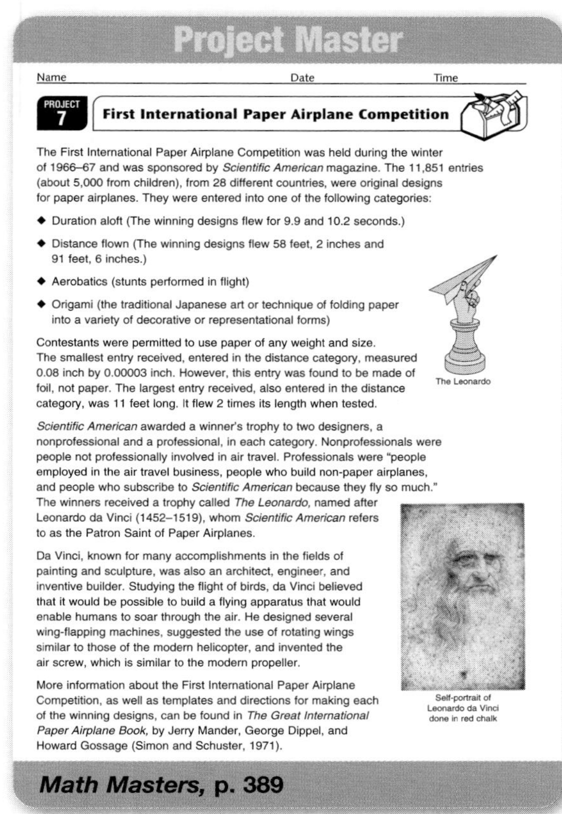

Project Master

Name Date Time

PROJECT 7 **First International Paper Airplane Competition**

The First International Paper Airplane Competition was held during the winter of 1966–67 and was sponsored by *Scientific American* magazine. The 11,851 entries (about 5,000 from children), from 28 different countries, were original designs for paper airplanes. They were entered into one of the following categories:

- Duration aloft (The winning designs flew for 9.9 and 10.2 seconds.)
- Distance flown (The winning designs flew 58 feet, 2 inches and 91 feet, 6 inches.)
- Aerobatics (stunts performed in flight)
- Origami (the traditional Japanese art or technique of folding paper into a variety of decorative or representational forms)

Contestants were permitted to use paper of any weight and size. The smallest entry received, entered in the distance category, measured 0.08 inch by 0.00003 inch. However, this entry was found to be made of foil, not paper. The largest entry received, also entered in the distance category, was 11 feet long. It flew 2 times its length when tested.

The Leonardo

Scientific American awarded a winner's trophy to two designers, a nonprofessional and a professional, in each category. Nonprofessionals were people not professionally involved in air travel. Professionals were "people employed in the air travel business, people who build non-paper airplanes, and people who subscribe to *Scientific American* because they fly so much." The winners received a trophy called *The Leonardo,* named after Leonardo da Vinci (1452–1519), whom *Scientific American* refers to as the Patron Saint of Paper Airplanes.

Da Vinci, known for many accomplishments in the fields of painting and sculpture, was also an architect, engineer, and inventive builder. Studying the flight of birds, da Vinci believed that it would be possible to build a flying apparatus that would enable humans to soar through the air. He designed several wing-flapping machines, suggested the use of rotating wings similar to those of the modern helicopter, and invented the air screw, which is similar to the modern propeller.

Self-portrait of Leonardo da Vinci done in red chalk

More information about the First International Paper Airplane Competition, as well as templates and directions for making each of the winning designs, can be found in *The Great International Paper Airplane Book,* by Jerry Mander, George Dippel, and Howard Gossage (Simon and Schuster, 1971).

Math Masters, p. 389

Project Master

Name Date Time

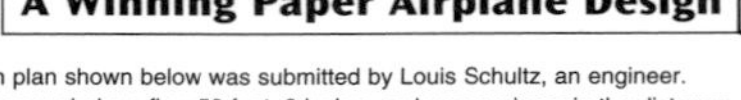

PROJECT 7 **A Winning Paper Airplane Design**

The design plan shown below was submitted by Louis Schultz, an engineer. Schultz's paper airplane flew 58 feet, 2 inches and was a winner in the distance category for nonprofessionals. The professional winner in the distance category was Robert Meuser. His paper airplane flew 91 feet, 6 inches.

1. Follow the directions below to make an accurate copy of the design plan on an $8\frac{1}{2}$"-by-11" sheet of paper.
   a. Use a ruler to find the midpoints at the top and bottom of the paper. Mark these points. Draw a center line connecting the midpoints to match the subsequent labels.
   b. Mark 2 points that are $\frac{1}{4}$ inch away from the midpoint at the top of the paper.
   c. Use a protractor to make two 45° angles as shown. Mark them with dashed lines.
   d. Use a protractor to make two 82° angles as shown. Mark them with dashed lines.

Louis Schultz's Paper Airplane Design Plan

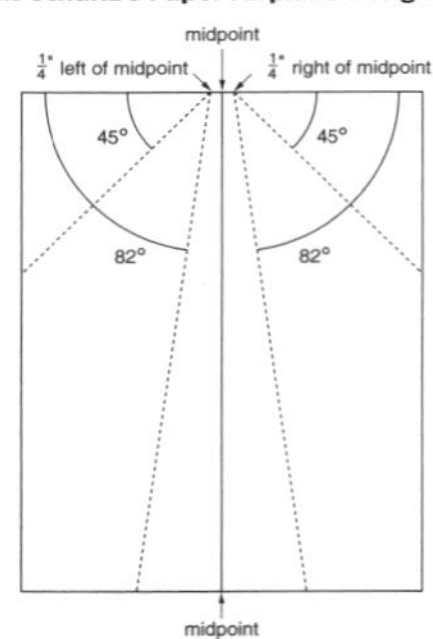

Math Masters, p. 390

▶ Day 3: Reading about the First International Paper Airplane Competition

WHOLE-CLASS ACTIVITY

(*Math Masters,* p. 389)

Use your usual group reading procedure to read *Math Masters,* page 389. Tell students that they will construct paper airplanes from the design made by Louis Schultz, the nonprofessional winner of The Leonardo trophy in the distance category. They will test the planes on Day 4, using the same procedure they used for their own planes on Day 2. Later students will test their best planes (Day 2 test-flight winners) against the best planes made according to Schultz's specifications (Day 4 test-flight winners).

▶ Copying a Design and Assembling an Airplane

PARTNER ACTIVITY

(*Math Masters,* pp. 390–392)

The design plan on *Math Masters,* page 390 is an accurate scale drawing of Schultz's design, but it is less than 50 percent the required size. Students are asked to copy this design, enlarging it to fit exactly on an $8\frac{1}{2}$ in. by 11 in. sheet of paper, while preserving all the ratios of lengths and angle measures. Enlarging the design plan of the winning airplane model provides practice with following an annotated plan, as well as measuring and drawing angles.

Expect that some students will have difficulty drawing the 45° and 82° angles, because the edge of the paper is one side of each angle. You might want to demonstrate how to draw these angles before students begin copying the design.

When students have copied the design plan, they should follow the directions on *Math Masters,* pages 391 and 392 for assembling the plane. Emphasize the need for precise folding.

Project Master

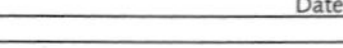

Name Date Time

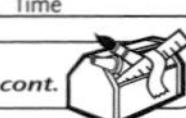

PROJECT 7 **A Winning Paper Airplane Design** *cont.*

2. Assemble the paper airplane as shown below. Be very careful to make precise folds. Make the folds on a table. When making a fold, first press down on the paper with your finger. Then go over this fold with a pen or a ruler on its side. It is important that you *do not* use your fingernails to make folds. (Using your fingernail causes more than one fold to be made in a small area. This fold will move as you attempt to make the rest of the plane.)
   a. Fold the paper back and forth along the center line to get a sharp crease. Then unfold.

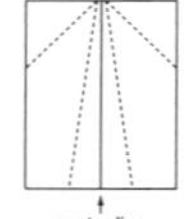

   b. Fold corners along the dashed lines as shown. Use a small piece of tape to secure each corner, as shown in the sketch.

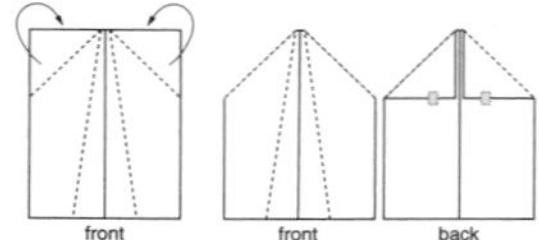

   c. With the back side of the paper facing you, fold the right side of the paper toward the center so that the edges highlighted in the sketch meet. Use a small piece of tape to secure the flap in the position shown in the sketch. Do the same to the other side.

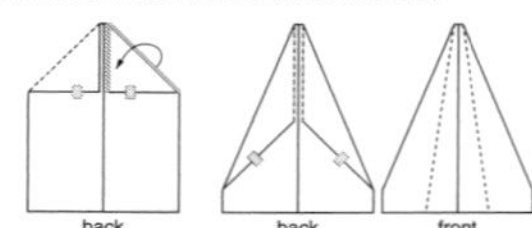

Math Masters, p. 391

▶ Day 4: Testing the Schultz-Designed Airplanes

(*Math Masters,* p. 388)

The Schultz-designed paper airplanes are tested in the same way the student-designed airplanes were tested on Day 2. Students record the minimum, maximum, and median distances in Problem 2 on *Math Masters,* page 388.

Save the three best Schultz-designed planes for additional testing.

▶ Testing Student Planes against Schultz Planes

(*Math Masters,* p. 388)

The final test pits the three best student-designed airplanes against the three best airplanes built using Louis Schultz's design. Throw each plane only once. After throwing the last plane, measure the distance each plane flew, to the nearest foot. Students record these distances in Problem 3 on *Math Masters,* page 388.

▶ Reporting Test Results

(*Math Masters,* pp. 388 and 393)

Students complete the bar graph on *Math Masters,* page 393. The report describing the test results (Problem 2) should make full use of all collected data.

- ▷ Problems 1 and 2 on *Math Masters,* page 388 show landmarks for the tests of all the paper airplanes that were made.
- ▷ Problem 3 on page 388 shows information for the three best paper airplanes of each type.

Project Master

Name ______ Date ______ Time ______

PROJECT 7 **A Winning Paper Airplane Design** *cont.*

d. Flip the paper to the front side. Fold in half along the center line so that the front side is now inside. Your paper airplane should look like this.

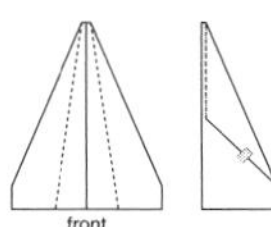

e. Take the top flap of the paper and fold it outward along the dashed lines. (Look for these dashed lines on the inside of the plane.) Do the same to the other flap. Your paper airplane should now look like this.

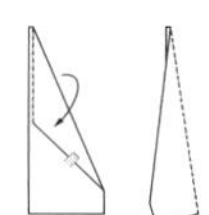

f. Tape the wings together on top of the airplane. Then tape the bottom as shown, making sure to secure all loose flaps.

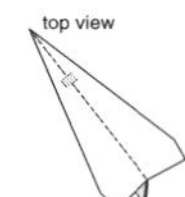

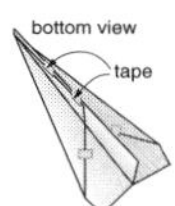

***Math Masters,* p. 392**

Project Master

Name ______ Date ______ Time ______

PROJECT 7 **Testing Paper Airplane Designs, Part 2**

Answers vary.

1. Draw a bar graph below to show the distance traveled by each of the 6 planes as recorded in the table on *Math Masters,* page 388.

Distance (ft): 0, 10, 20, 30, 40, 50

1st 2nd 3rd 4th 5th 6th

Name ______ ______ ______ ______ ______ ______

2. Describe the test-flight results. Did student-designed airplanes perform better or worse than airplanes built using Schultz's design?

______

3. Which do you think works best for distance:

a. a paper airplane that uses air to assist the motion of the paper?

b. a piece of paper, folded very tightly (like the 5-fold paper), which cuts through the air? Explain.

______

***Math Masters,* p. 393**

2 Extending the Project

▶ Finding Out More about Paper Airplanes

(*Math Masters,* pp. 394 and 395)

Invite students to learn more about paper airplanes. Some suggested books are listed on *Math Masters,* page 395. Students may also want to search the Internet for more information about paper airplanes.

Project Master

Name ______ Date ______ Time ______

Experiments with Air

Air is a real substance, just as water, earth, and maple syrup are real substances. Because air is a substance, it offers **resistance,** or opposition, to the movement of objects through it.

Imagine dropping a penny into a bottle of maple syrup. The penny will eventually fall to the bottom of the bottle, but the maple syrup will slow its progress. In other words, the maple syrup will offer resistance to the movement of the penny. Air works in much the same way—objects can move through it, but the air offers resistance to the movement of those objects.

Did you know that this resistance can serve a helpful purpose? Try the following experiments to see how resistance can help an object such as an airplane move through the air more efficiently.

The Kite Effect

1. Hold one end of an $8\frac{1}{2}$"-by-11" sheet of paper as shown—forefinger on top, supported by the thumb and second finger on the bottom. Notice that the paper in the illustration is tilted slightly, so the opposite end of the paper is a bit higher than the end being held.

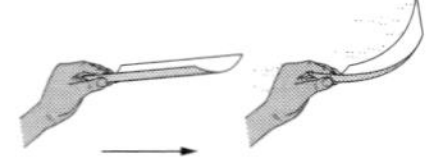

2. Push the paper directly forward as shown.

   You will notice that the end of the paper that is opposite the end you are holding tilts up. When the tilted surface of the paper pushes against the air, the air pushes back. This partially slows the paper down and partially lifts it up.

The sheet of paper has some of the characteristics of an airplane wing. The wings of an airplane are set at an angle so the front edge is higher than the back edge. In this way, the lower surface of the airplane wing uses the air resistance to achieve a small amount of lift.

Math Masters, p. 394

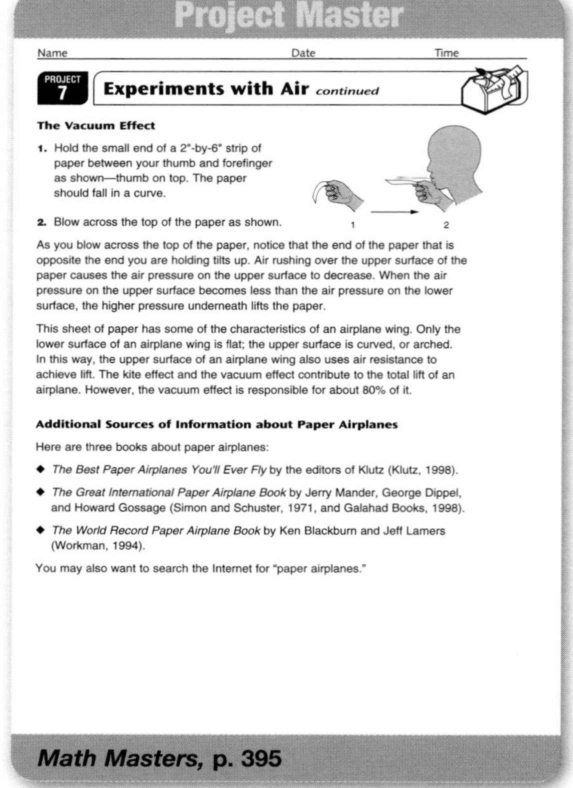

Project Master

Name ______ Date ______ Time ______

PROJECT 7 **Experiments with Air** *continued*

The Vacuum Effect

1. Hold the small end of a 2"-by-6" strip of paper between your thumb and forefinger as shown—thumb on top. The paper should fall in a curve.
2. Blow across the top of the paper as shown.

As you blow across the top of the paper, notice that the end of the paper that is opposite the end you are holding tilts up. Air rushing over the upper surface of the paper causes the air pressure on the upper surface to decrease. When the air pressure on the upper surface becomes less than the air pressure on the lower surface, the higher pressure underneath lifts the paper.

This sheet of paper has some of the characteristics of an airplane wing. Only the lower surface of an airplane wing is flat; the upper surface is curved, or arched. In this way, the upper surface of an airplane wing also uses air resistance to achieve lift. The kite effect and the vacuum effect contribute to the total lift of an airplane. However, the vacuum effect is responsible for about 80% of it.

Additional Sources of Information about Paper Airplanes

Here are three books about paper airplanes:

- *The Best Paper Airplanes You'll Ever Fly* by the editors of Klutz (Klutz, 1998).
- *The Great International Paper Airplane Book* by Jerry Mander, George Dippel, and Howard Gossage (Simon and Schuster, 1971, and Galahad Books, 1998).
- *The World Record Paper Airplane Book* by Ken Blackburn and Jeff Lamers (Workman, 1994).

You may also want to search the Internet for "paper airplanes."

Math Masters, p. 395

Cross Sections of Clay Solids

Objectives **To construct geometric solids out of clay; to visualize what happens when a plane slices a solid; and to describe the shapes of cross sections.**

1 Doing the Project

Recommended Use: During or after Unit 5

Key Activities

Students visualize what happens when a geometric solid is sliced at a particular location and angle. They test their visualizations by slicing clay models. Students name or describe the cross sections formed.

Key Concepts and Skills

- Compare and classify plane and solid figures using appropriate geometric terms. [Geometry Goal 2]
- Identify and describe similar and congruent figures. [Geometry Goal 2]

Key Vocabulary

cross section

materials

- ☐ Project Masters (*Math Masters,* pp. 396–398)

For demonstration purposes:

- ☐ 3 carrots, orange, sharp knife, cutting board

Per partnership:

- ☐ clay or modeling compound
- ☐ dental floss or cheese slicer
- ☐ conical paper cup (optional)
- ☐ cutting board
- ☐ slate
- ☐ *Incredible Cross Sections* and/or *Incredible Explosions* (optional)

See **Advance Preparation**

2 Extending the Project

Students solve cross-section problems.

materials

- ☐ Project Masters (*Math Masters,* pp. 399–401)

Additional Information

Advance Preparation

Read "Projects" in the Management Guide section of the *Teacher's Reference Manual.*

Oil-base clays work best for constructing clay solids to be used in the activities. Water-base clays dry out quickly if they are not stored correctly. A cheese slicer works well for slicing the cross sections. However, dental floss works almost as well and is easy to obtain. Knives and similar cutting tools tend to distort the clay as they move through it. Two books—*Incredible Cross Sections* and *Incredible Explosions*—show colorful cross sections of a variety of subjects, including a castle, a jumbo jet, and the Empire State Building. Both books are illustrated by Stephen Biesty with text by Richard Platt (Random House, 1992, 1996).

Technology

See the **iTLG.**

1 Doing the Project

▶ Defining a Cross Section

WHOLE-CLASS DISCUSSION

Have a volunteer read the definition of **cross section** in the *Student Reference Book.* Ask students to try to restate the definition in their own words. If this is difficult for many students, go on to the next activity and return to the definition.

If you were able to obtain either of the cross-section books described in **Advance Preparation,** now would be a good time to share them with the class.

▶ Cutting Fruits and Vegetables to Introduce Cross Sections

WHOLE-CLASS ACTIVITY

Display a carrot to students and ask them to predict answers to the following questions. Consider having students draw pictures of predictions on slates while volunteers share predictions on the board or overhead projector. After each prediction, make the cut so students can check their predictions.

- If I slice the carrot straight through, across its width, what will be the shape of the cross section I create? A circle, assuming the carrot is not lopsided

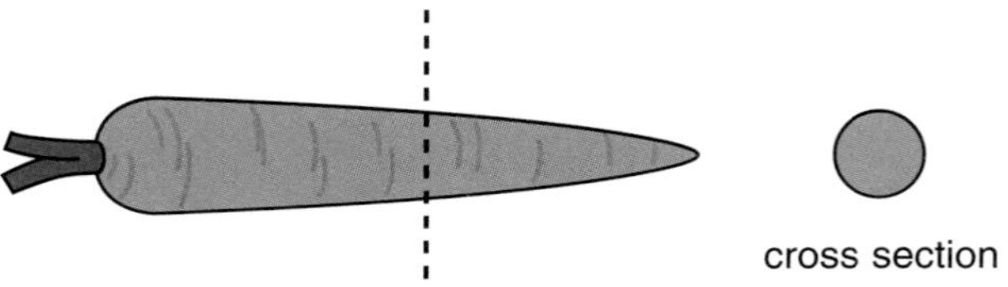

- If I make the cut on a slant instead of straight, what will be the shape of the cross section I create? An oval, or ellipse

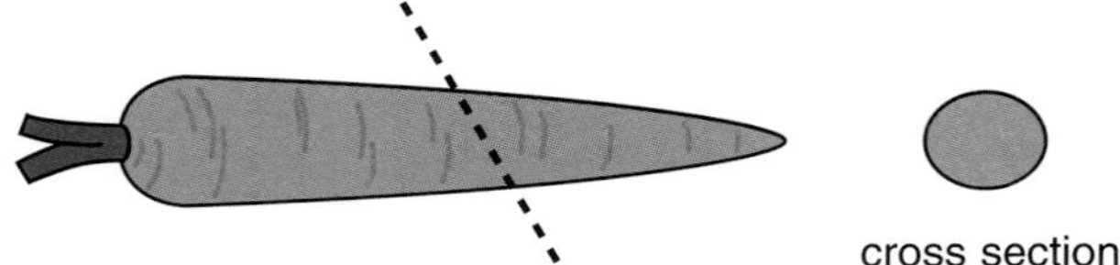

- **What shape will I get if the cut is slanted even more?** The more slanted the cut is, the flatter the ellipse will be.

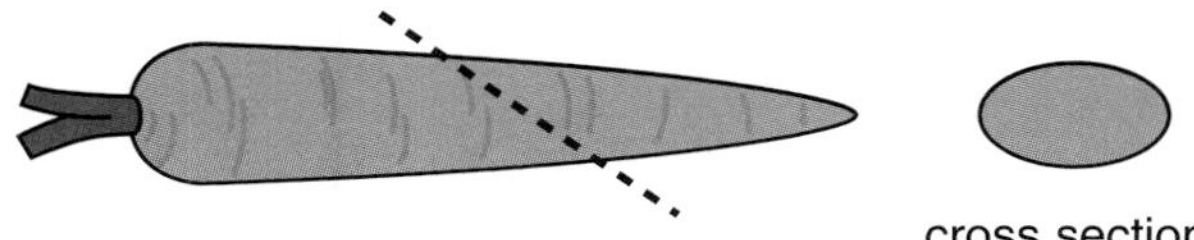

- **What will the cross section look like if I cut the carrot lengthwise from end to end?** It will resemble a thin isosceles triangle with a curved base.

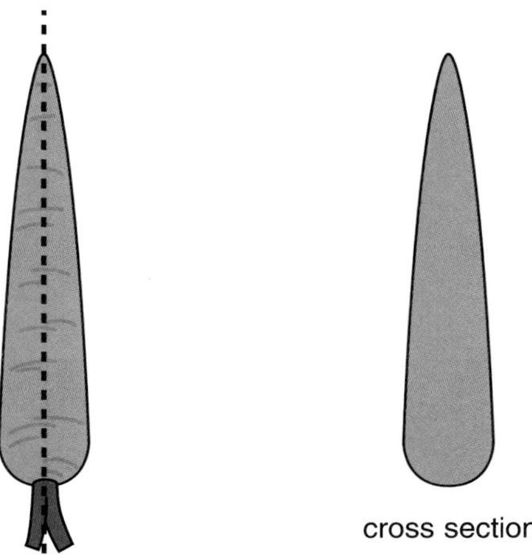

- **What will the cross section of an orange look like?** It will look like a circle, the size of which will vary, depending upon the location of the cut.

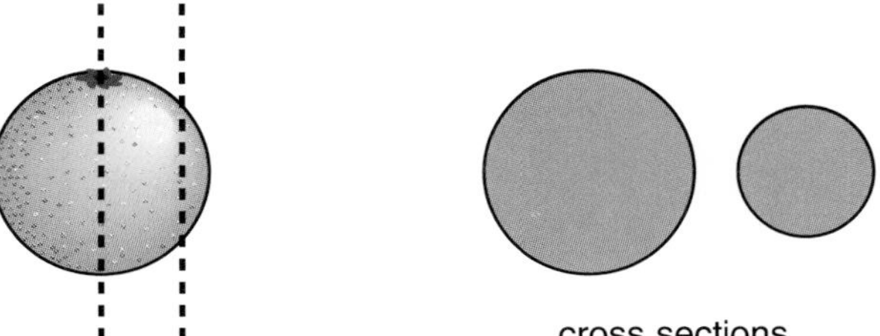

Project Master

Name ____ Date ____ Time ____

PROJECT 8 **Cross Sections of a Clay Cube**

Form a clay cube. Draw your prediction of the shape of the **cross section** that will be formed by the first cut shown below. After making the cut, draw the actual shape and describe (name) the shape. Re-form the cube and repeat these steps for the other cuts.

Clay Cube	Predicted Shape of Cross Section	Actual Shape of Cross Section	Description of Shape
	Answers vary.		rectangle
			square
			triangle
			rectangle

***Math Masters*, p. 396**

Project Master

Name Date Time

PROJECT 8 **Cross Sections of a Clay Cylinder**

Form a clay cylinder. Draw your prediction of the shape of the cross section that will be formed by the first cut shown below. After making the cut, draw the actual shape and describe (name) the shape. Re-form the cylinder and repeat these steps for the other cuts.

Clay Cylinder	Predicted Shape of Cross Section	Actual Shape of Cross Section	Description of Shape
	Answers vary.		rectangle
			closed parabola
			circle
			ellipse

Math Masters, p. 397

Project Master

Name Date Time

PROJECT 8 **Cross Sections of a Clay Cone**

Form a clay cone. Draw your prediction of the shape of the cross section that will be formed by the first cut shown below. After making the cut, draw the actual shape and describe (name) the shape. Re-form the cone and repeat these steps for the other cuts.

Clay Cone	Predicted Shape of Cross Section	Actual Shape of Cross Section	Description of Shape
	Answers vary.		circle
			ellipse
			Closed parabola
			ellipse

Math Masters, p. 398

▶ Finding Cross Sections of a Clay Cube

WHOLE-CLASS ACTIVITY

(*Math Masters,* p. 396)

For this activity, you will need to construct a clay cube that is large enough for students to see and for you to work with comfortably. Call students' attention to the cube shown at the top left corner of *Math Masters,* page 396. The dotted lines represent the hidden edges on the opposite sides of the cube.

The first column shows the cube again, with arrows indicating the direction and angle of the cut you will make. In the second column, students make a drawing representing their predictions of the shape of the cross section. Point out that they should draw only the 2-dimensional shape revealed by the cut, not the solid remaining. After you slice the cube, students draw the actual cross section in the third column. In the last column, students write the name or a description of the cross section's shape.

Ask students to predict the shape of the first cross section and to record it in the second column on *Math Masters,* page 396. Then make the cut. When slicing the clay, hold the slicer or dental floss taut and pull it slowly and smoothly through the clay. If the clay is on a cutting board or similar surface, it will be easier to make a clean cut. Ask a student to hold the cube while you cut.

In the third column, students record the actual shape of the cross section. Ask how the cross section compares to their predictions. In the fourth column, students should be able to describe the shapes of the first two cross sections as a rectangle and a square.

Let some students make slices for the third and fourth examples. They may need a little practice to make a reasonably straight slice through the clay. By the time students have completed the table on page 396, they will probably be ready to try some cross sections on their own.

Finding Cross Sections of Cylinders and Cones

PARTNER ACTIVITY

(*Math Masters,* pp. 397 and 398)

Students complete *Math Masters,* pages 397 and 398. One partner should hold the solid while the other slices it. Making an accurate cone can be difficult. If conical cups from a water dispenser are available, consider having students fill a cup with clay to form the shape.

Remember that this is an introductory experience with cross sections. Don't expect all students to come up with the correct answers, even after slicing the solids. Students will vary in their abilities to visualize the cross sections, to form and slice the clay solid, and to name the plane figures formed. For example, on *Math Masters,* pages 397 and 398, one of the cuts forms a parabola. Students are unlikely to be familiar with this term. When reviewing the answers on these two pages, suggest students find the word *parabola* in a dictionary.

2 Extending the Project

Solving Cross-Section Problems

PARTNER ACTIVITY

(*Math Masters,* pp. 399–401)

Math Masters, pages 399–401 provide interested students with more advanced cross-section problems.

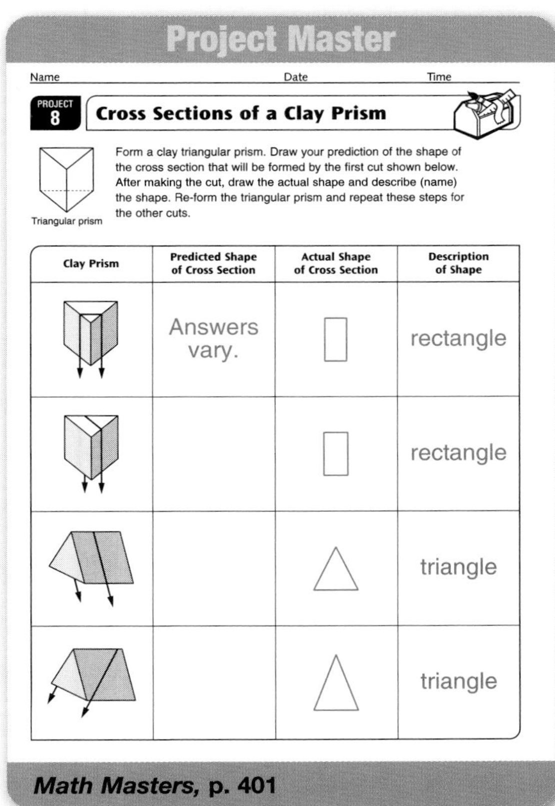

Project Master

Name Date Time

PROJECT 8 **Cross Sections of a Clay Prism**

Triangular prism

Form a clay triangular prism. Draw your prediction of the shape of the cross section that will be formed by the first cut shown below. After making the cut, draw the actual shape and describe (name) the shape. Re-form the triangular prism and repeat these steps for the other cuts.

Clay Prism	Predicted Shape of Cross Section	Actual Shape of Cross Section	Description of Shape
	Answers vary.		rectangle
			rectangle
			triangle
			triangle

Math Masters, p. 401

Project Master

Name Date Time

PROJECT 8 **Cross Sections of a Clay Pyramid**

Pyramid with square base

Form a clay pyramid with a square base. Draw your prediction of the shape of the cross section that will be formed by the first cut shown below. After making the cut, draw the actual shape and describe (name) the shape. Re-form the pyramid and repeat these steps for the other cuts.

Clay Pyramid	Predicted Shape of Cross Section	Actual Shape of Cross Section	Description of Shape
	Answers vary.		triangle
			square
			triangle
			trapezoid

Math Masters, p. 399

Project Master

Name Date Time

PROJECT 8 **Cross Sections of a Clay Torus**

Torus (doughnut)

Form a clay torus. Draw your prediction of the shape of the cross section that will be formed by the first cut shown below. After making the cut, draw the actual shape and describe (name) the shape. Re-form the torus and repeat these steps for the other cuts.

Clay Torus	Predicted Shape of Cross Section	Actual Shape of Cross Section	Description of Shape
	Answers vary.		Sample answers: Two circles
			A pinched oval
			Two "teardrops"
			A "smile"

Math Masters, p. 400

Sixth Grade Key Vocabulary

For a more comprehensive glossary that includes additional entries and illustrations, please refer to the *Teacher's Reference Manual.*

NOTE: In a definition, terms in italics are defined elsewhere in the glossary.

A

absolute value The distance between a number and 0 on a number line. The absolute value of a positive number is the number itself, and the absolute value of a negative number is the opposite of the number. The absolute value of 0 is 0. The notation for the absolute value of n is $|n|$.

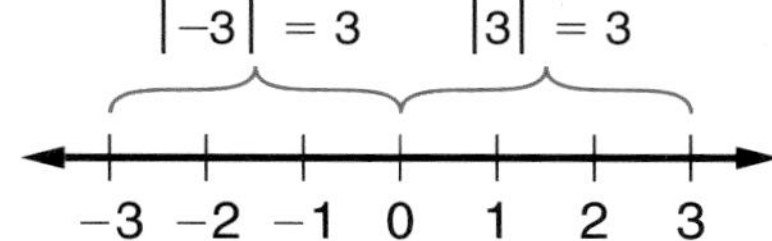

acute angle An angle with a measure less than 90°.

adjacent angles Two angles with a common side and *vertex* that do not otherwise overlap.

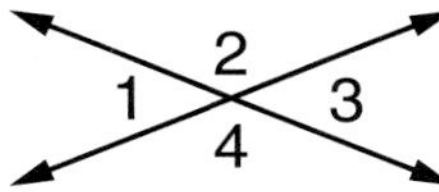

Angles 1 and 2, 2 and 3, 3 and 4, and 4 and 1 are pairs of adjacent angles.

adjacent sides Same as *consecutive sides.*

algebraic expression An *expression* that contains a *variable.* For example, if Maria is 2 inches taller than Joe and if the variable m represents Maria's height, then the algebraic expression $m-2$ represents Joe's height.

area The amount of surface inside a 2-dimensional figure. The figure might be a triangle or rectangle in a plane, the curved surface of a cylinder, or a state or country on Earth's surface. Commonly, area is measured in square units such as square miles, square inches, or square centimeters.

area model (1) A model for multiplication in which the length and width of a rectangle represent the *factors,* and the *area* of the rectangle represents the product.

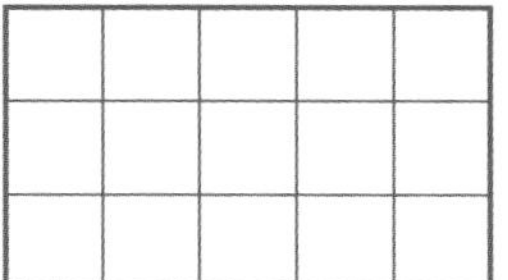

Area model for $3 * 5 = 15$

(2) A model showing *fractions* as parts of a whole. The whole is a region, such as a *circle* or a rectangle, representing the number ONE.

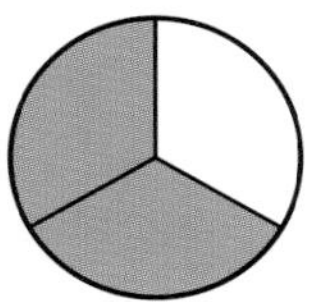

Area model for $\frac{2}{3}$

Associative Property of Addition A property of addition that three numbers can be added in any order without changing the sum. For example, $(4 + 3) + 7 = 4 + (3 + 7)$ because $7 + 7 = 4 + 10$. In symbols:

For any numbers a, b, and c,
$(a + b) + c = a + (b + c)$.

Subtraction is not associative. For example, $(4 - 3) + 7 \neq 4 - (3 + 7)$ because $8 \neq -6$.

Associative Property of Multiplication A property of multiplication that three numbers can be multiplied in any order without changing the product. For example, $(4 * 3) * 7 = 4 * (3 * 7)$ because $12 * 7 = 4 * 21$. In symbols:

For any numbers a, b, and c,
$(a * b) * c = a * (b * c)$.

Division is not associative. For example, $(8 / 2) / 4 \neq 8 / (2 / 4)$ because $1 \neq 16$.

average A typical value for a set of numbers. In everyday life, average usually refers to the *mean* of the set, found by adding all the numbers and dividing the sum by the number of numbers. In statistics, several different averages, or *landmarks,* are defined, including *mean, median,* and *mode.*

axis of a coordinate grid Either of the two number lines used to form a *coordinate grid.* Plural is axes.

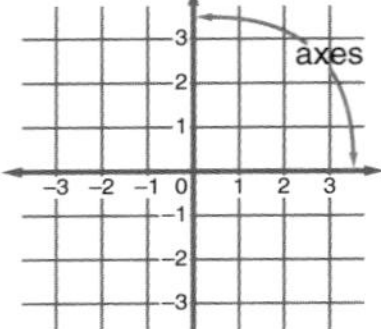

axis of rotation A line about which a solid figure rotates.

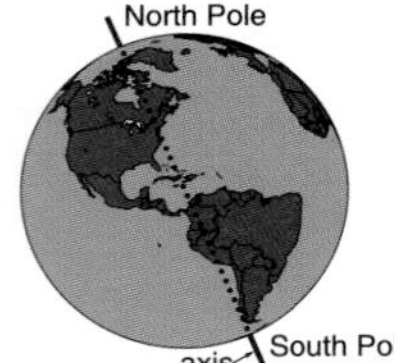

bar graph A graph with horizontal or vertical bars that represent data.

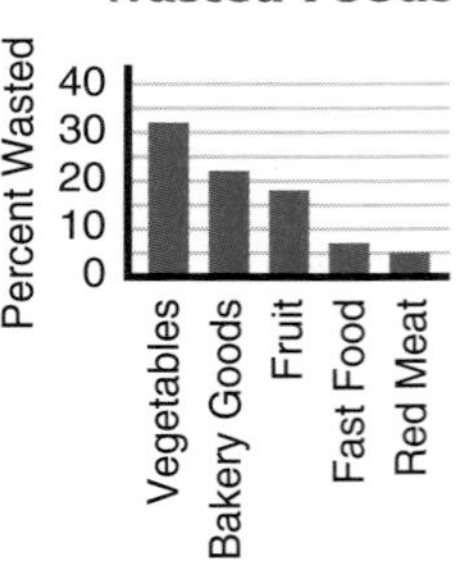

Source: The Garbage Product

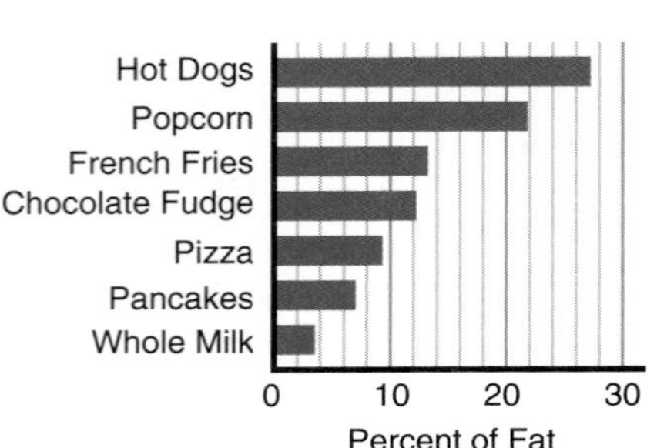

Source: The New York Public Library Desk Reference

base (in exponential notation) A number that is raised to a *power.* For example, the base in 5^3 is 5. See *exponential notation.*

base of a number system The foundation number for a numeration system. For example, our usual way of writing numbers uses a base-10 place-value system. In programming computers or other digital devices, bases of 2, 8, 16, or other *powers* of 2 are more common than base 10.

base of a parallelogram (1) The side of a parallelogram to which an altitude is drawn. (2) The length of this side. The *area* of a parallelogram is the length of the base times the altitude or height perpendicular to it. See *height of a parallelogram.*

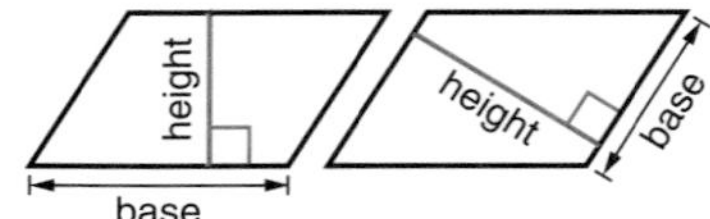

base of a prism or cylinder Either of the two parallel and congruent faces that define the shape of a prism or cylinder. In a cylinder, the base is a *circle.* See *height of a prism or cylinder.*

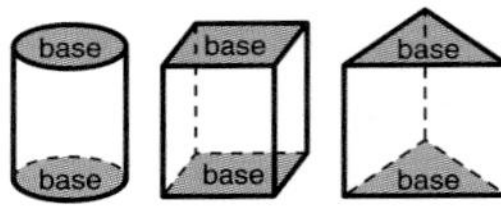

base of a triangle (1) Any side of a triangle to which an altitude is drawn. (2) The length of this side. The *area* of a triangle is half the length of the base times the altitude or height.

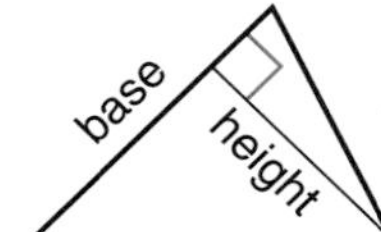

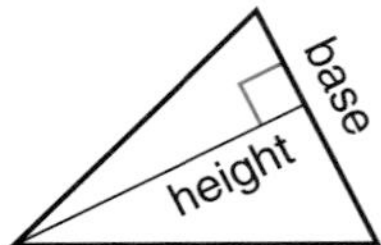

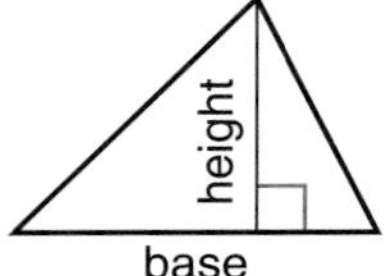

benchmark A count or measure that can be used to evaluate the reasonableness of other counts, measures, or estimates.

biased sample A sample that does not fairly represent the total population from which it was selected. A sample is biased if every member of the population does not have the same chance of being selected for the sample. See *random sample.*

bisect To divide a segment, angle, or figure into two parts of equal measure. See *bisector.*

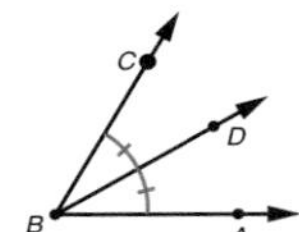

$\overrightarrow{BD}$ bisects angle $\angle ABC$

bisector A line, segment, or ray that divides a segment, an angle, or a figure into two parts of equal measure. See *bisect.*

broken-line graph Same as *line graph.*

cell (1) In a spreadsheet, the box where a vertical column and a horizontal row intersect. The address of a cell is the column letter followed by the row number. For example, cell B3 in column B, row 3, is highlighted below. (2) The box where a column and row in a table intersect.

	A	B	C	D
1				
2				
3				
4				

circle The set of all points in a plane that are equally distant from a fixed point in the plane called the center of the circle. The distance from the center to the circle is the *radius* of the circle. The diameter of a circle is twice its radius. Points inside a circle are not part of the circle. A circle together with its interior is called a disk or a circular region.

circle graph A graph in which a *circle* and its interior are divided into *sectors* corresponding to parts of a set of data. The whole circle represents the whole set of data. Same as pie graph and sometimes called a pie chart.

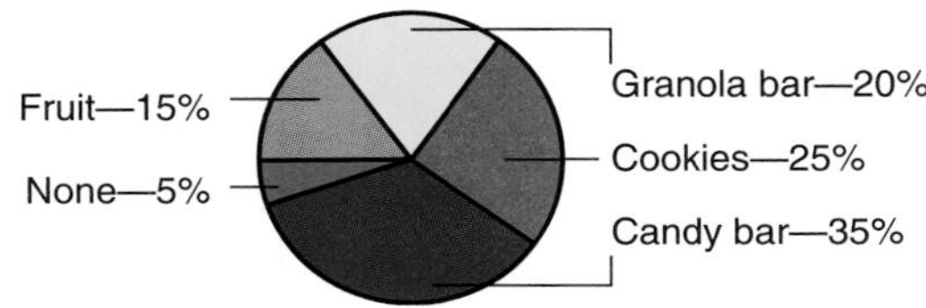

circumference The distance around a *circle;* its *perimeter.* The circumference of a *sphere* is the circumference of a circle on the sphere with the same center as the sphere.

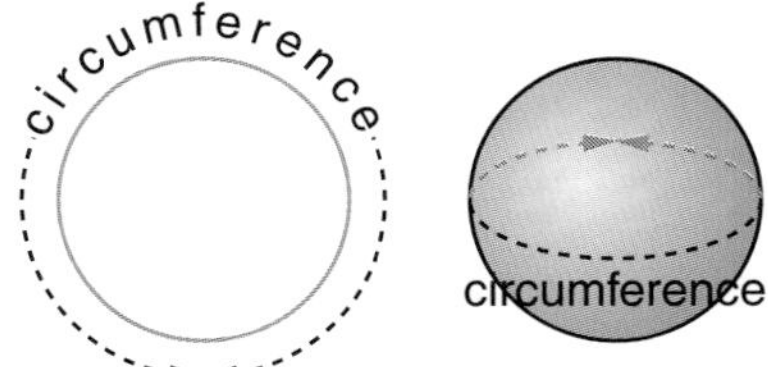

coefficient The number, or *constant,* factor in a *variable term* in an *expression.* For example, in $3c + 8d$, 3 and 8 are coefficients.

common denominator A nonzero number that is a multiple of the denominators of two or more *fractions.* For example, the fractions $\frac{1}{2}$ and $\frac{2}{3}$ have common denominators 6, 12, 18, and other multiples of 6. Fractions with the same denominator already have a common denominator.

common factor A *factor* of each of two or more counting numbers. For example, 4 is a common factor of 8 and 12.

Commutative Property of Addition A property of addition that two numbers can be added in either order without changing the sum. For example, $5 + 10 = 10 + 5$. In *Everyday Mathematics,* this is called a turn-around fact, and the two Commutative Properties are called turn-around rules. In symbols:

For any numbers a and b, $a + b = b + a$.

Subtraction is not commutative. For example, $8 - 5 \neq 5 - 8$ because $3 \neq -3$.

Commutative Property of Multiplication A property of multiplication that two numbers can be multiplied in either order without changing the product. For example, $5 * 10 = 10 * 5$. In *Everyday Mathematics,* this is called a turn-around fact, and the two Commutative Properties are called turn-around rules. In symbols:

For any numbers a and b, $a * b = b * a$.

Division is not commutative. For example, $10 / 5 \neq 5 / 10$ because $2 \neq \frac{1}{2}$.

compass-and-straightedge construction A drawing of a geometric figure made using only a compass and a *straightedge* with no measurement allowed.

complementary angles Two angles whose measures add to 90°. Complementary angles do not need to be *adjacent.* Compare to *supplementary angles.*

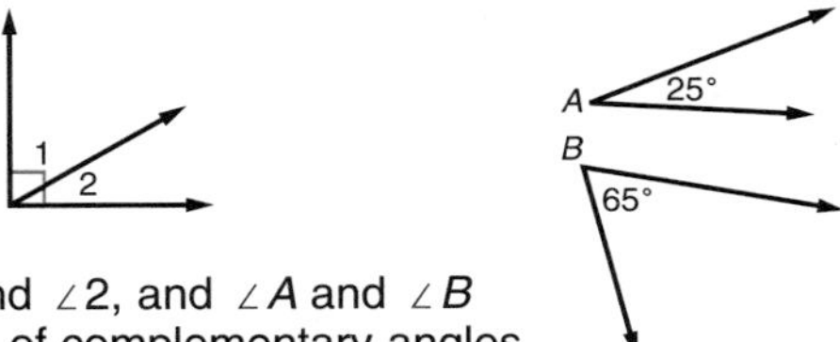

$\angle 1$ and $\angle 2$, and $\angle A$ and $\angle B$ are pairs of complementary angles.

composite number A *counting number* greater than 1 that has more than two *factors.* For example, 10 is a composite number because it has four factors: 1, 2, 5, and 10. A composite number is divisible by at least three whole numbers. Compare to *prime number.*

congruent figures (≅) Figures having the same size and shape. Two figures are congruent if they match exactly when one is placed on top of the other after a combination of *slides, flips,* and/or *turns.* In diagrams of congruent figures, the corresponding congruent sides may be marked with the same number of hash marks. The symbol ≅ means "is congruent to."

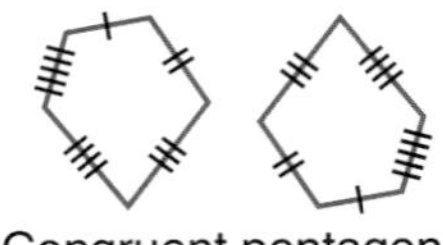

Congruent pentagons

consecutive angles Two angles in a polygon with a common side.

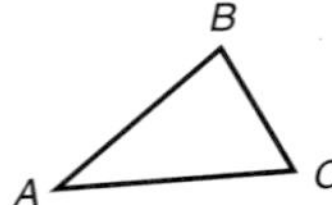

Angles *A* and *B, B* and *C,* and *C* and *A* are pairs of consecutive angles.

consecutive sides (1) Two sides of a polygon with a common *vertex.* (2) Two sides of a polyhedron with a common edge. Same as *adjacent sides.*

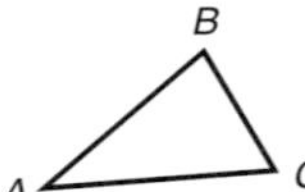

Sides *AB* and *BC, BC* and *CA,* and *CA* and *AB* are pairs of consecutive sides.

constant A quantity that does not change. For example, the ratio of the *circumference* of a *circle* to its diameter is the famous constant π. In $x + 3 = y$, 3 is the constant.

coordinate (1) A number used to locate a point on a number line; a point's distance from an *origin.* (2) One of the numbers in an *ordered pair* or triple that locates a point on a *coordinate grid* or in coordinate space, respectively.

coordinate grid (rectangular coordinate grid) A reference frame for locating points in a plane by means of *ordered pairs* of numbers. A rectangular coordinate grid is formed by two number lines that intersect at *right angles* at their zero points.

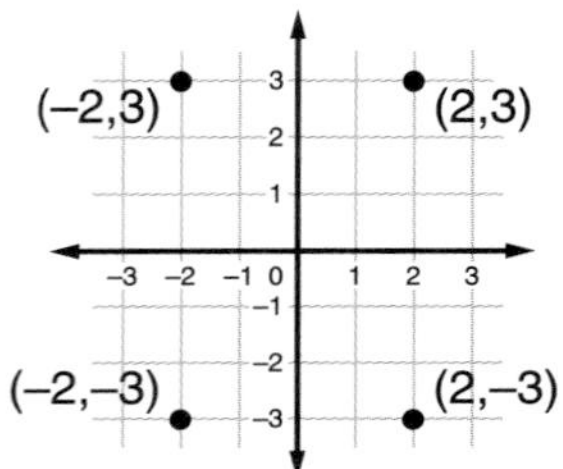

A coordinate grid

corresponding angles (1) Angles in the same relative position in *similar* or *congruent figures.* Pairs of corresponding angles are marked either by the same number of arcs or by the same number of hash marks per arc.

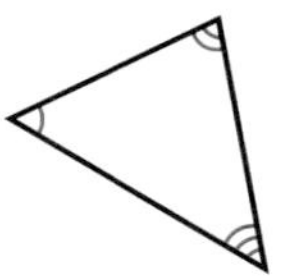
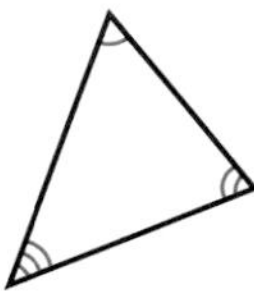
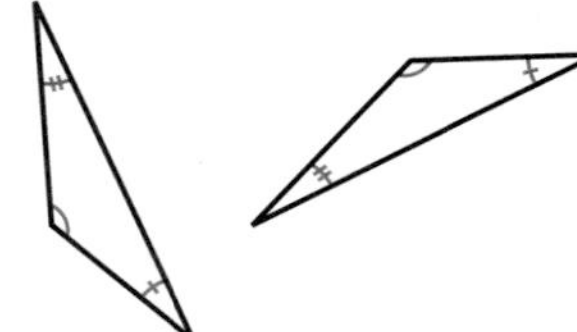

(2) Two angles in the same relative position when two lines are intersected by a *transversal.* In the diagram, $\angle a$ and $\angle e$, $\angle b$ and $\angle f$, $\angle d$ and $\angle h$, and $\angle c$ and $\angle g$ are pairs of corresponding angles. If any two corresponding angles in a pair are congruent, then the two lines are parallel.

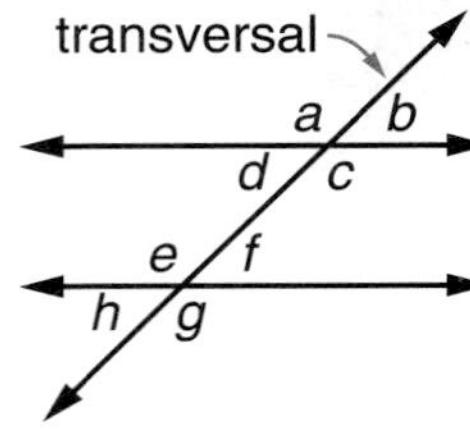

corresponding sides Sides in the same relative position in *similar* or *congruent figures.* Pairs of corresponding sides are marked with the same number of hash marks.

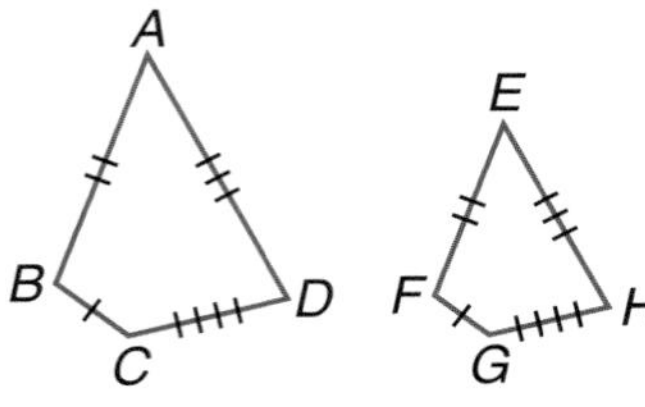

counting numbers The numbers used to count things. The set of counting numbers is {1, 2, 3, 4, . . .}. Sometimes 0 is included, but not in *Everyday Mathematics.* Counting numbers are in the sets of *whole numbers, integers, rational numbers,* and *real numbers,* but each of these sets include numbers that are not counting numbers.

cover-up method An informal method for finding a *solution of an open sentence* by covering up a part of the sentence containing a *variable.*

cross products The two products of the numerator of one *fraction* and the denominator of the other fraction in a *proportion.* The cross products of a proportion are equal. For example, in the proportion $\frac{2}{3} = \frac{6}{9}$, the cross products $9 * 2$ and $3 * 6$ are both 18.

$9 * 2 = 18$ $\quad \frac{2}{3} = \frac{6}{9} \quad$ $3 * 6 = 18$

cross section A shape formed by the intersection of a plane and a geometric solid.

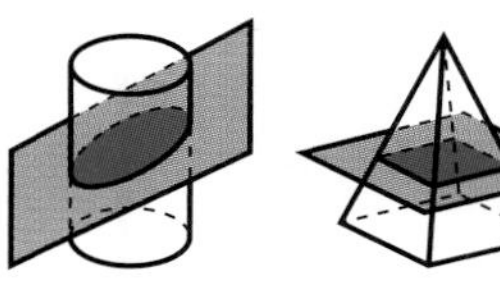

Cross sections of a cylinder and a pyramid

diagonal (1) A line segment joining two nonconsecutive *vertices* of a polygon.
(2) A segment joining two nonconsecutive vertices on different faces of a polyhedron.

diagonal

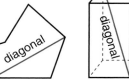

(3) A line of objects or numbers between opposite corners of an array or a table.

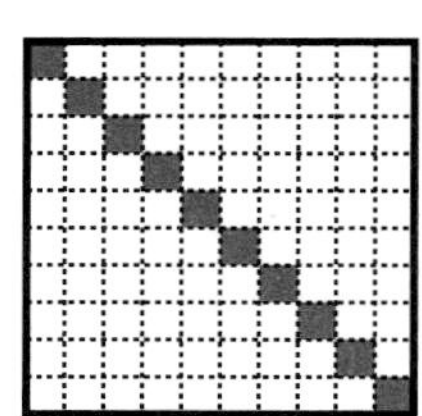

A diagonal of an array

Distributive Property of Multiplication over Addition A property relating multiplication to a sum of numbers by distributing a *factor* over the terms in the sum. For example, $2 * (5 + 3) = (2 * 5) + (2 * 3) = 10 + 6 = 16$. In symbols:

For any numbers a, b, and c:
$a * (b + c) = (a * b) + (a * c)$
or $a(b + c) = ab + ac$

Distributive Property of Multiplication over Subtraction A property relating multiplication to a difference of numbers by distributing a *factor* over the terms in the difference. For example, $2 * (5 - 3) = (2 * 5) - (2 * 3) = 10 - 6 = 4$. In symbols:

For any numbers a, b, and c:
$a * (b - c) = (a * b) - (a * c)$
or $a(b - c) = ab - ac$

dividend The number in division that is being divided. For example, in $35 / 7 = 5$, the dividend is 35.

Division of Fractions Property A property of dividing that says division by a *fraction* is the same as multiplication by the *reciprocal* of the fraction. Another name for this property is the "invert and multiply rule."

divisor In division, the number that divides another number, the *dividend.* For example, in $35 / 7 = 5$, the divisor is 7.

double-stem plot A *stem-and-leaf plot* in which each stem is split into two parts. Numbers on the original stem ending in 0 through 4 are plotted on one half of the split, and numbers ending in 5 through 9 are plotted on the other half. Double-stem plots are useful if the original stem-and-leaf plot has many leaves falling on few stems. The following plot shows eruption duration in minutes of the Old Faithful Geyser. For example, the first two stems show one observation each of durations lasting 42, 44, 45, 48, and 49 minutes.

Eruption Duration of Old Faithful (minutes)

Stems (tens)	**Leaves** (ones)
4	2 4
4	5 8 9
5	0 1 1 1 3 3 3 4
5	5 5 6 6 7 7 8
6	0 1 1
6	6 7 7 8 8 9

A double-stem plot

equally likely outcomes Outcomes of a chance experiment or situation that have the same *probability* of happening. If all the possible outcomes are equally likely, then the probability of an event is equal to:

$$\frac{\text{number of favorable outcomes}}{\text{number of possible outcomes}}$$

See *favorable outcome.*

equation A *number sentence* that contains an equal sign. For example, $5 + 10 = 15$ and $P = 2l + 2w$ are equations.

equivalent equations *Equations* with the same *solution.* For example, $2 + x = 4$ and $6 + x = 8$ are equivalent equations with common solution 2.

equivalent fractions *Fractions* with different denominators that name the same number.

equivalent rates *Rates* that make the same comparison. For example, the rates $\frac{60 \text{ miles}}{1 \text{ hour}}$ and $\frac{1 \text{ mile}}{1 \text{ minute}}$ are equivalent. *Equivalent fractions* represent equivalent rates if the units for the rates are the same. For example, $\frac{12 \text{ pages}}{4 \text{ minutes}}$ and $\frac{6 \text{ pages}}{2 \text{ minutes}}$ are equivalent rates because $\frac{12}{4}$ and $\frac{6}{2}$ are equivalent with the same rate of pages per minute.

equivalent ratios *Ratios* that make the same comparison. *Equivalent fractions* represent equivalent ratios. For example, $\frac{1}{2}$ and $\frac{4}{8}$ are equivalent ratios.

event A set of possible outcomes to an experiment. For example, in an experiment flipping two coins, getting 2 HEADS is an event, as is getting 1 HEAD and 1 TAIL. The *probability* of an event is the chance that the event will happen. For example, the probability that a fair coin will land HEADS up is $\frac{1}{2}$. If the probability of an event is 0, the event is impossible. If the probability is 1, the event is certain.

expanded notation A way of writing a number as the sum of the values of each digit. For example, 356 is $300 + 50 + 6$ or $(3 * 100) + (5 * 10) + (6 * 1)$ in expanded notation. Compare to *standard notation, scientific notation,* and *number-and-word notation.*

expected outcome The average outcome over a large number of repetitions of a random experiment. For example, the expected outcome of rolling one die is the average number of dots landing up over a large number of rolls. Because each face of a fair die has equal *probability* of landing up, the expected outcome is $(1 + 2 + 3 + 4 + 5 + 6)/6 = 21/6 = 3\frac{1}{2}$. This means that the average of many rolls of a fair die is expected to be about $3\frac{1}{2}$. More formally, the expected outcome is defined as a *mean* over infinitely many repetitions.

exponent A small raised number used in *exponential notation* to tell how many times the *base* is used as a *factor.* For example, in 5^3, the base is 5, the exponent is 3, and $5^3 = 5 * 5 * 5 = 125$. Same as *power.*

exponential notation A way of representing repeated multiplication by the same *factor.* For example, 2^3 is exponential notation for $2 * 2 * 2$. The *exponent* 3 tells how many times the *base* 2 is used as a factor.

expression (1) A mathematical phrase made up of numbers, *variables, operation symbols,* and/or grouping symbols. An expression does not contain *relation symbols* such as =, <, and ≤. (2) Either side of an *equation* or *inequality.*

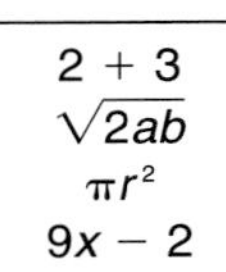

Expressions

factor (1) Each of the two or more numbers in a product. For example, in $6 * 0.5$, 6 and 0.5 are factors. (2) To represent a number as a product of factors. For example, factor 21 by rewriting as $7 * 3$.

fair game A game in which every player has the same chance of winning.

favorable outcome An outcome that satisfies the conditions of an *event* of interest. For example, suppose a 6-sided die is rolled and the event of interest is "roll an even number." There are six possible outcomes: 1, 2, 3, 4, 5, and 6. Of these, three are favorable: 2, 4, or 6. See also *equally likely outcomes.*

figurate numbers Numbers that can be illustrated by specific geometric patterns. *Square numbers* and *triangular numbers* are figurate numbers.

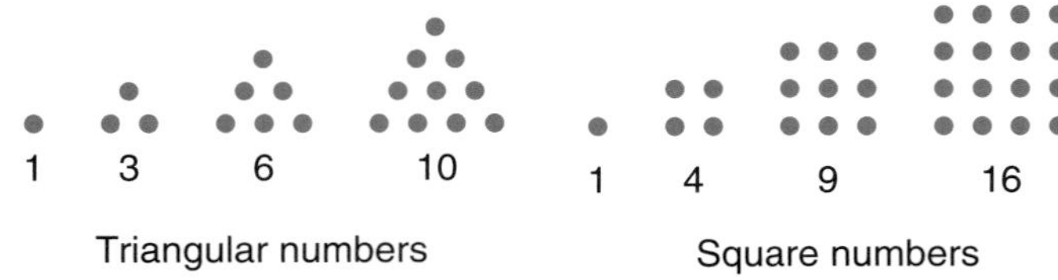

flip An informal name for a *reflection transformation.*

formula A general rule for finding the value of something. A formula is usually an *equation* with quantities represented by letter *variables.*

fraction A number in the form $\frac{a}{b}$ or a/b, where a and b are *whole numbers* and b is not 0. A fraction may be used to name part of an object or part of a collection of objects, to compare two quantities, or to represent division. For example, $\frac{12}{6}$ might mean 12 eggs divided into 6 groups of 2 eggs each, 12:6, or 12/6.

frequency (1) The number of times a value occurs in a set of data. (2) A number of repetitions per unit of time. For example, the vibrations per second in a sound wave.

function A set of *ordered pairs* (x,y) in which each value of x is paired with exactly one value of y. A function is typically represented in a table, by points on a coordinate graph, or by a rule such as an *equation.* For example, for a function with the rule "Double," 1 is paired with 2, 2 is paired with 4, 3 is paired with 6, and so on. In symbols, $y = 2 * x$ or $y = 2x$.

general pattern In *Everyday Mathematics,* a *number model* for a pattern or rule.

genus In *topology,* the number of holes in a geometric shape. Shapes with the same genus are topologically equivalent. For example, a donut and a teacup are equivalent because both are genus 1.

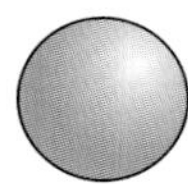

Genus 0

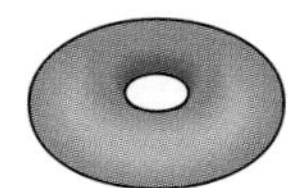

Genus 1

Golden Ratio The *ratio* of the length of the long side to the length of the short side of a *Golden Rectangle,* approximately equal to 1.618 to 1. The Greek letter ϕ (phi) sometimes stands for the Golden Ratio. The Golden Ratio is an *irrational number* equal to $\frac{1 + \sqrt{5}}{2}$.

Golden Rectangle A rectangle prized for its pleasing proportions in which the longer side is constructed with *compass and straightedge* from the shorter side. The *ratio* of these sides is the *Golden Ratio,* about 1.618 to 1. A 5-inch by 3-inch index card is roughly similar to a Golden Rectangle, as are the front faces of many ancient Greek buildings.

greatest common factor (GCF) The largest *factor* that two or more *counting numbers* have in common. For example, the common factors of 24 and 36 are 1, 2, 3, 4, 6, and 12, and their greatest common factor is 12.

height of a parallelogram (1) The length of the shortest line segment between a *base of a parallelogram* and the line containing the opposite side. The height is perpendicular to the base. (2) The line segment itself. See *base of a parallelogram.*

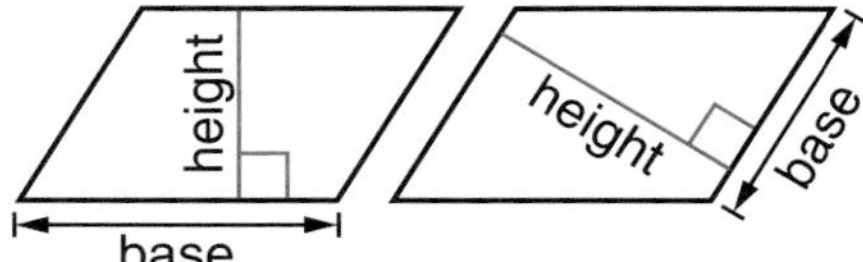

height of a prism or cylinder The length of the shortest line segment from a *base of a prism or cylinder* to the plane containing the opposite base. The height is perpendicular to the bases. (2) The line segment itself. See *base of a prism or cylinder.*

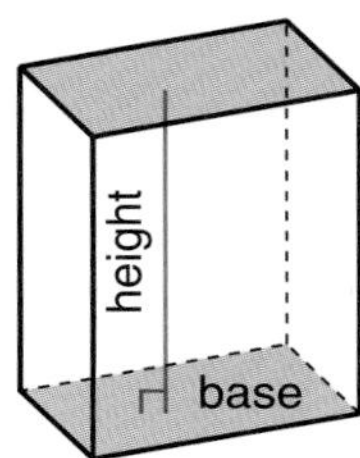

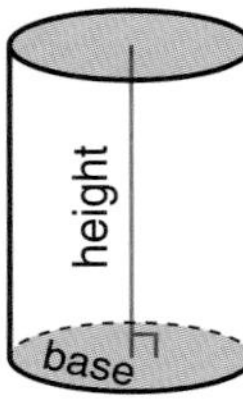

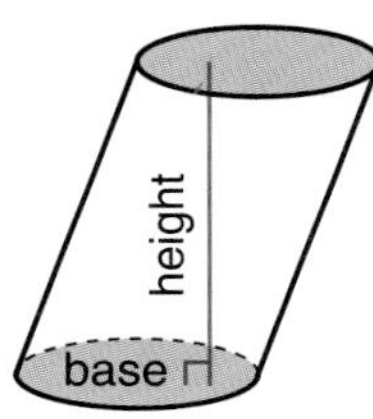

height of a triangle The length of the shortest segment from a *vertex* of a triangle to the line containing the opposite side. The height is perpendicular to the base. (2) The line segment itself. See *base of a triangle.*

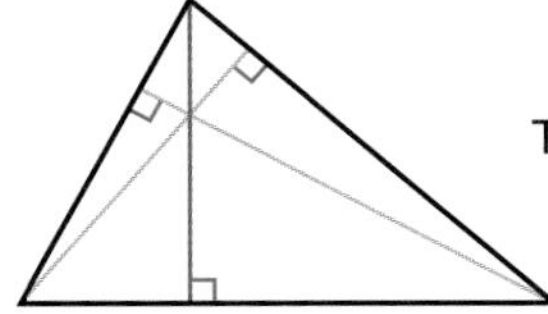

The heights of the triangle are shown in blue.

hypotenuse In a *right triangle,* the side opposite the *right angle.*

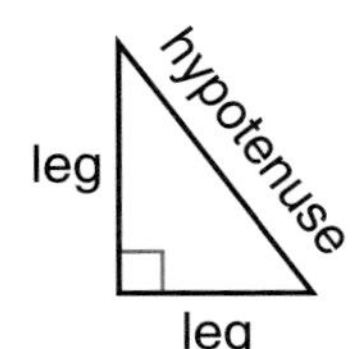

image A figure that is produced by a *transformation* of another figure called the *preimage.*

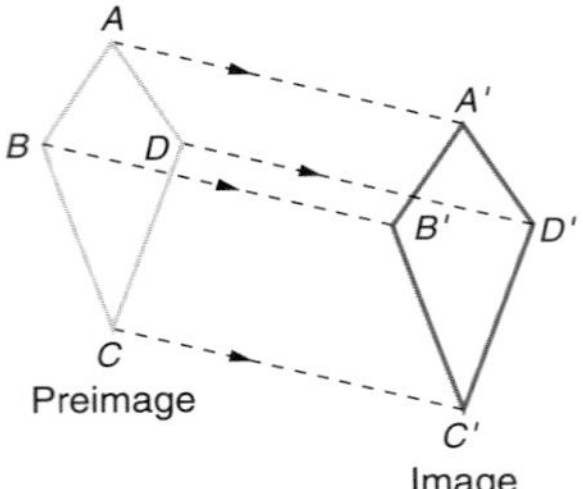

indirect measurement The determination of heights, distances, and other quantities that cannot be measured directly.

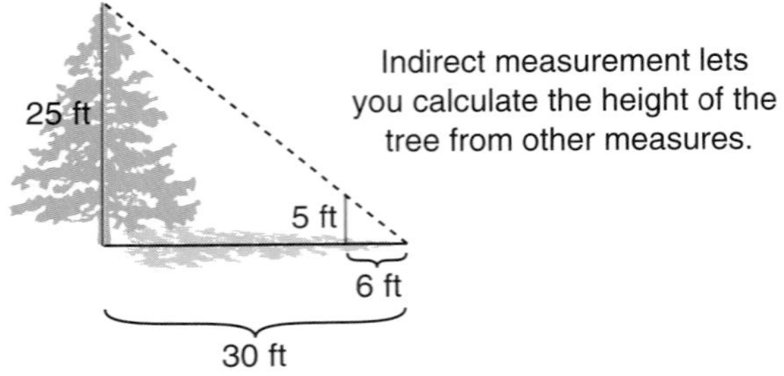

inequality A *number sentence* with a *relation symbol* other than =, such as >, <, ≥, ≤, ≠, or ≈.

integer A number in the set {. . ., −4, −3, −2, −1, 0, 1, 2, 3, 4, . . .}. A *whole number* or its opposite, where 0 is its own opposite. Compare to *rational number, irrational number,* and *real number.*

irrational numbers Numbers that cannot be written as *fractions* where both the numerator and denominator are *integers* and the denominator is not zero. For example, $\sqrt{2}$ and π are irrational numbers. An irrational number can be written as a nonterminating, nonrepeating decimal. For example, $\pi = 3.141592653\ldots$ continues forever without any known pattern. The number 1.10100100010000 . . . is irrational because its pattern does not repeat.

isometry transformation A *transformation* in which the *preimage* and *image* are *congruent. Reflections (flips), rotations (turns)* and *translations (slides)* are isometry transformations, while a *size-change* (stretch or shrink) is not. Although the size and shape of the figures in an isometry transformation are the same, their orientations may be different. From the Greek *isometros* meaning "of equal measure."

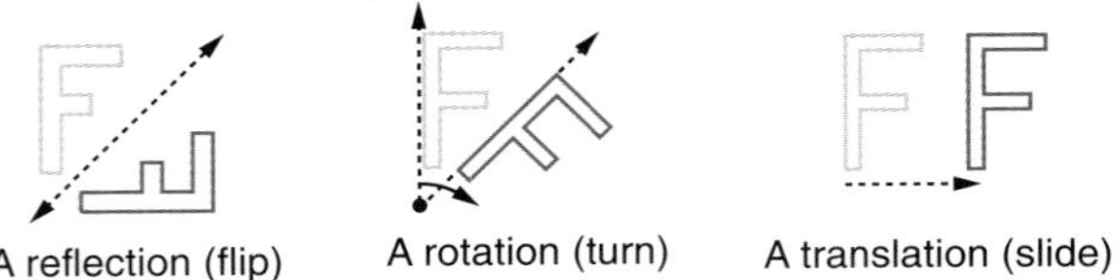

landmark In *Everyday Mathematics,* a notable feature of a data set. Landmarks include the *median, mode, mean, maximum, minimum,* and *range.*

lattice multiplication A very old algorithm for multiplying multidigit numbers that requires only basic multiplication facts and addition of 1-digit numbers in a lattice diagram.

least common denominator (LCD) The *least common multiple* of the denominators of every *fraction* in a given collection. For example, the least common denominator of $\frac{1}{2}$, $\frac{4}{5}$, and $\frac{3}{8}$ is 40.

least common multiple (LCM) The smallest number that is a multiple of two or more given numbers. For example, common multiples of 6 and 8 include 24, 48, and 72. The least common multiple of 6 and 8 is 24.

leg of a right triangle Either side of the *right angle* in a *right triangle;* a side that is not the *hypotenuse.*

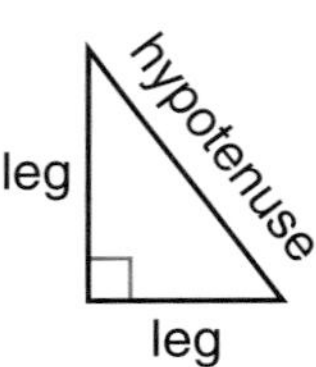

like terms In an *algebraic expression,* either the *constant terms* or any terms that contain the same *variable(s)* raised to the same *power(s).* For example, $4y$ and $7y$ are like terms in the expression $4y + 7y - z$.

line graph A graph in which data points are connected by line segments. Same as *broken-line graph.*

line of reflection (mirror line) (1) In *Everyday Mathematics,* a line halfway between a figure and its *reflection image* in a plane. (2) The *perpendicular bisector* of the line segments connecting points on a figure with their corresponding points on its reflection image. Compare to *line of symmetry.*

line of symmetry A line that divides a figure into two parts that are *reflection images* of each other. A figure may have zero, one, or more lines of symmetry. For example, the numeral 2 has no lines of symmetry, a square has four lines of symmetry, and a circle has infinitely many lines of symmetry. Also called a symmetry line.

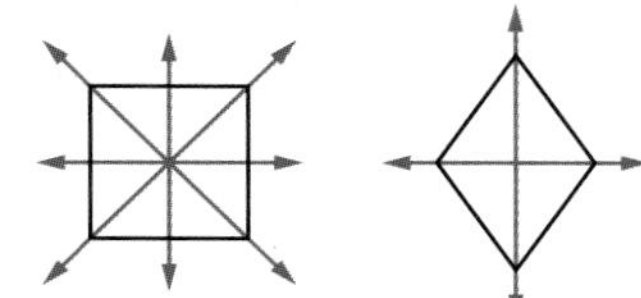

Lines of symmetry are shown in blue.

line plot A sketch of data in which check marks, Xs, or other symbols above a labeled line show the *frequency* of each value.

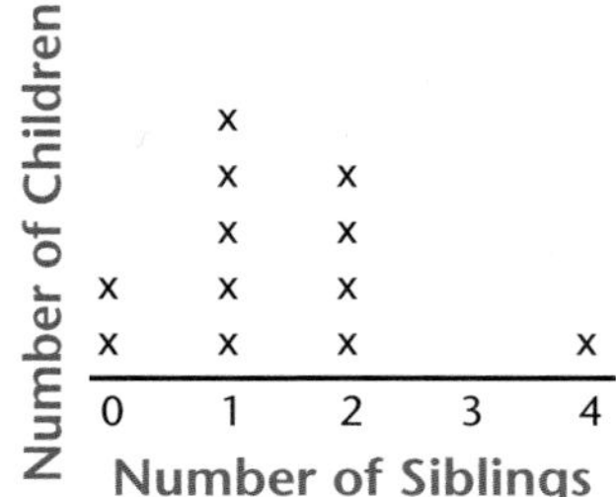

line symmetry A figure has line symmetry if a line can be drawn that divides it into two parts that are *reflection images* of each other. See *line of symmetry.*

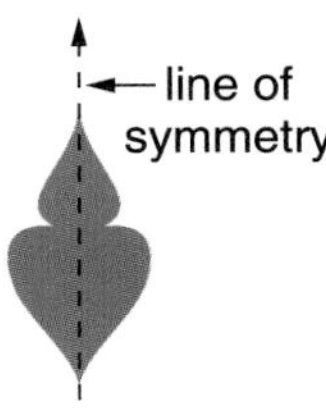

M

maximum The largest amount; the greatest number in a set of data. Compare to *minimum.*

mean For a set of numbers, their sum divided by the number of numbers. Often called the *average* value of the set. Compare to the other data *landmarks median* and *mode.*

median The middle value in a set of data when the data are listed in order from smallest to largest or vice versa. If there is an even number of data points, the median is the *mean* of the two middle values. Compare to other data *landmarks mean* and *mode.*

midpoint A point halfway between two other points. The midpoint of a line segment is the point halfway between the endpoints.

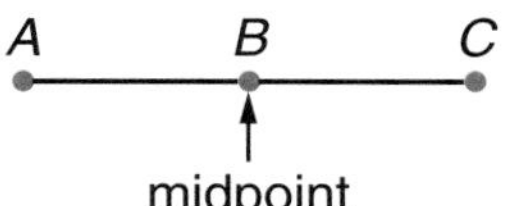

Length of $\overline{AB}$ = length of $\overline{BC}$

minimum The smallest amount; the smallest number in a set of data. Compare to *maximum.*

mixed number A number that is written using both a *whole number* and a *fraction.* For example, $2\frac{1}{4}$ is a mixed number equal to $2 + \frac{1}{4}$.

Möbius strip (Möbius band) A 3-dimensional figure with only one side and one edge, named for the German mathematician August Ferdinand Möbius (1790–1868).

Möbius strip

mode The value or values that occur most often in a set of data. Compare to other *landmarks median* and *mean.*

multiple of a number *n* (1) A product of *n* and a *counting number.* For example, the multiples of 7 are 7, 14, 21, 28, ... (2) A product of *n* and an *integer.* For example, the multiples of 7 are . . . , −21, −14, −7, 0, 7, 14, 21, ...

Multiplication Counting Principle A way of determining the total number of possible outcomes for two or more separate choices. For example, suppose you roll a typical die and then flip a coin. There are 6 choices for which a number on the die lands up (1, 2, 3, 4, 5, or 6) and 2 choices for which side of the coin lands up (HEADS *H* or TAILS *T*). So there are $6 * 2 = 12$ possible outcomes altogether: (1, *H*), (1, *T*), (2, *H*), (2, *T*), (3, *H*), (3, *T*), (4, *H*), (4, *T*), (5, *H*), (5, *T*), (6, *H*), (6, *T*).

Multiplication Property of -1 A property of multiplication that multiplying any number by -1 gives the opposite of the number. For example, $-1 * 5 = -5$ and $-1 * -3 = -(-3) = 3$. In symbols:

For any number a, $-1 * a = -a$.

Some calculators apply this property with a [+/−] key that toggles between a positive and negative value in the display.

multiplicative inverses Same as *reciprocals.*

N

name-collection box In *Everyday Mathematics,* a diagram that is used for collecting equivalent names for a number.

25
37 − 12
20 + 5
𝍸𝍸𝍸𝍸𝍸
twenty-five
veinticinco

natural numbers In *Everyday Mathematics,* same as *counting numbers.*

negative numbers Numbers less than 0; the opposites of the *positive numbers,* commonly written as a positive number preceded by a − or *OPP.* Negative numbers are plotted left of 0 on a horizontal number line or below 0 on a vertical number line.

nested parentheses Parentheses within parentheses in an *expression.* Expressions are evaluated from within the innermost parentheses outward.

number-and-word notation A notation consisting of the significant digits of a number and words for the place value. For example, 27 billion is number-and-word notation for 27,000,000,000.

number model A *number sentence, expression,* or other representation that models a number story or situation. For example, the story *Sally had $5, and then she earned $8* can be modeled as the number sentence $5 + 8 = 13$, or as the expression $5 + 8$.

number sentence Two *expressions* with a *relation symbol.* For example,

$$5 + 5 = 10 \qquad 2 - ? = 8$$
$$16 \leq a * b \qquad a^2 + b^2 = c^2$$

Number sentences

O

obtuse angle An angle with measure between 90° and 180°.

open proportion A *proportion* with one or more *variables.* An open proportion is an *open sentence* and is neither true nor false. For example, $\frac{2}{3} = \frac{a}{5}$ and $\frac{z}{15} = \frac{y}{3}$ are open proportions.

open sentence A *number sentence* with one or more *variables.* An open sentence is neither true nor false. For example, $9 + \_\_ = 15$, $? - 24 < 10$, and $7 = x + y$ are open sentences.

operation symbol A symbol used in *expressions* and *number sentences* to stand for a particular mathematical operation. Symbols for common arithmetic operations include +, −, *, / and ^.

OPP(*n*) In *Everyday Mathematics,* the symbol for the opposite of a number *n.*

order of operations Rules that tell the order in which operations in an *expression* should be carried out. The conventional order of operations is: grouping symbols, exponents, multiplication/division, addition/subtraction.

order of rotation symmetry The number of times a *rotation image* of a figure coincides with the figure before completing a 360° rotation.

A figure with order 5 rotation symmetry

ordered pair (1) Two numbers, or *coordinates,* used to locate a point on a *rectangular coordinate grid.* The first coordinate *x* gives the position along the horizontal *axis* of the grid, and the second coordinate *y* gives the position along the vertical axis. The pair is written (x,y).

origin The zero point in a coordinate system. On a number line, the origin is the point at 0. On a *coordinate grid,* the origin is the point (0,0) where the two *axes* intersect.

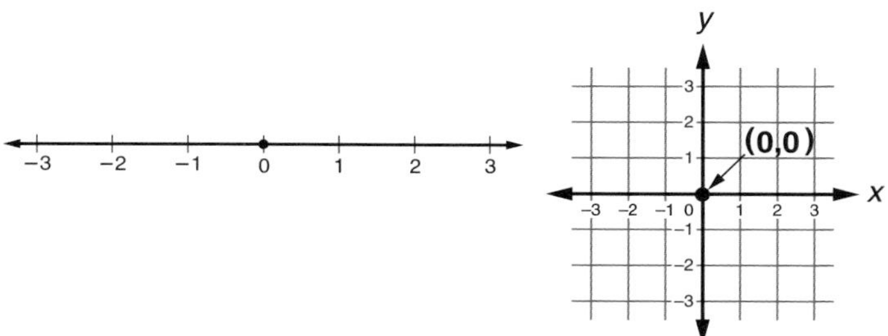

The points at 0 and (0,0) are origins.

outlier A value far from most of the others in a data set. Commonly, outliers are much larger or smaller than other values.

pan balance A device used to weigh objects or compare their weights.

part-to-part ratio A *ratio* that compares a part of a whole to another part of the same whole. For example, *There are 8 boys for every 12 girls* is a part-to-part ratio with a whole of 20 children. Compare to *part-to-whole ratio.*

part-to-whole ratio A *ratio* that compares a part of a whole to the whole. For example, *8 out of 20 students are boys and 12 out of 20 students are girls* are part-to-whole ratios. Compare to *part-to-part ratio.*

partial-products multiplication A multiplication algorithm in which partial products are computed by multiplying the value of each digit in one *factor* by the value of each digit in the other factor. The final product is the sum of the partial products.

partial-quotients division A division algorithm in which a partial quotient is computed in each of several steps. The final quotient is the sum of the partial quotients.

percent (%) Per hundred, for each hundred, or out of a hundred. $1\% = \frac{1}{100} = 0.01$. For example, *48% of the students in the school are boys* means that, on average, 48 of every 100 children in the school are boys.

Percent Circle A tool on the Geometry Template that is used to measure and draw figures that involve *percents,* such as *circle graphs.*

perimeter The distance around the boundary of a 2-dimensional figure. The perimeter of a *circle* is called its *circumference.* A formula for the perimeter P of a rectangle with length l and width w is $P = 2 * (l + w)$. Perimeter comes from the Greek words for "around measure."

perpendicular (⊥) Two lines or two planes that intersect at *right angles.* Line segments or rays that lie on perpendicular lines are perpendicular to each other. The symbol ⊥ means "is perpendicular to."

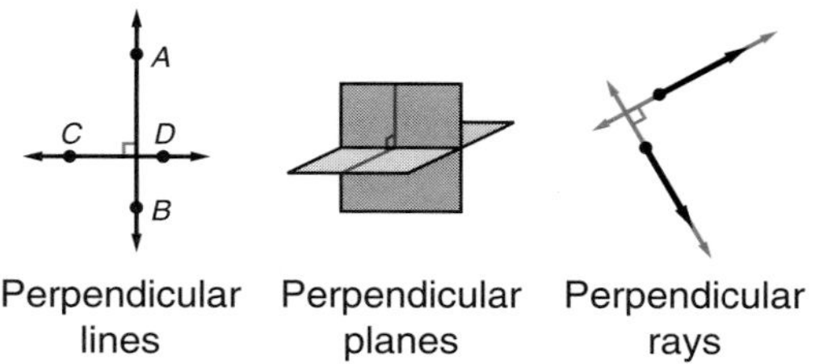

Perpendicular lines Perpendicular planes Perpendicular rays

perpendicular bisector A line, ray, or segment that *bisects* a line segment at a *right angle.*

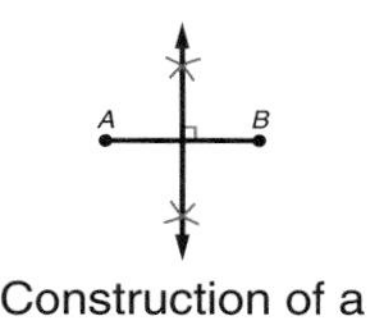

Construction of a perpendicular bisector of $\overline{AB}$

point symmetry (1) A figure has point symmetry if it is a *reflection image* of itself through a center of symmetry C. A line through C and a point M on the figure intersects the reflection image at point M' where the length of CM equals the length of CM'. (2) Point symmetry is the same as *rotation symmetry* around point C through a 180° turn.

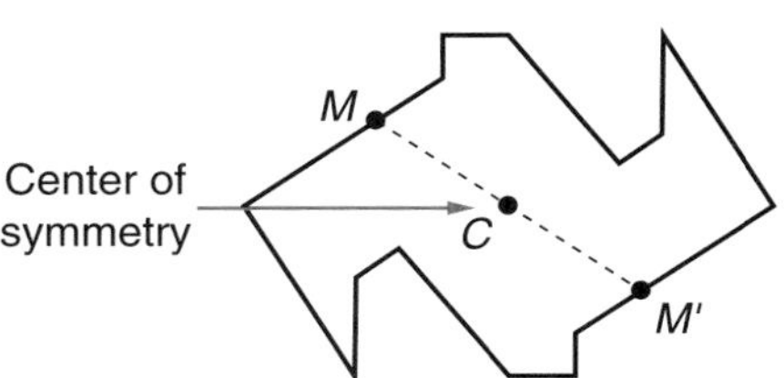

A polygon with point symmetry through C

positive numbers Numbers greater than 0; the opposites of the *negative numbers.* Positive numbers are plotted to the right of 0 on a horizontal number line or above 0 on a vertical number line.

power of a number A product of *factors* that are all the same; the result of a^b for any numbers a and b. For example, $5^3 = 5 * 5 * 5 = 125$ is read "5 to the third power" or "the third power of 5" because 5 is a factor 3 times. See *exponential notation.*

power of 10 (1) In *Everyday Mathematics,* a number that can be written in the form 10^a, where a is a *counting number.* That is, the numbers $10 = 10^1$, $100 = 10^2$, $1{,}000 = 10^3$, and so on, that can be written using only 10s as *factors.* Same as *positive power of 10.* (2) More generally, a number that can be written in the form 10^a, where a is an *integer,* that is, all the positive and negative powers of 10 together, along with $10^0 = 1$.

preimage The original figure in a *transformation.* Compare to *image.*

prime factorization A *counting number* written as a product of *prime number factors.* Every counting number greater than 1 has a unique prime factorization. For example, the prime factorization of 24 is $2 * 2 * 2 * 3$ or $2^3 * 3$.

prime number A *counting number* greater than 1 that has exactly two *whole number factors,* 1 and itself.

probability A number from 0 through 1 giving the likelihood of an *event* happening. The closer a probability is to 1, the more likely the event is to happen. The closer a probability is to 0, the less likely the event is to happen. For example, the probability that a fair coin will show HEADS is $\frac{1}{2}$.

probability tree diagram A drawing used to analyze a *probability* situation that consists of two or more choices or stages. For example, the branches of the probability tree diagram below represent the four *equally likely outcomes* when one coin is flipped two times.

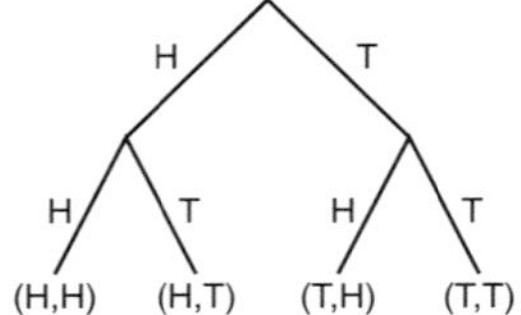

proportion A *number model* equating two *fractions.* Often the fractions in a proportion represent *rates* or *ratios.* For example, the problem *Alan's speed is 12 miles per hour. At the same speed, how far can he travel in 3 hours?* is modeled by the proportion:

$$\frac{12 \text{ miles}}{1 \text{ hour}} = \frac{n \text{ miles}}{3 \text{ hours}}$$

Pythagorean theorem If the *legs of a right triangle* have lengths a and b and the *hypotenuse* has length c, then $a^2 + b^2 = c^2$.

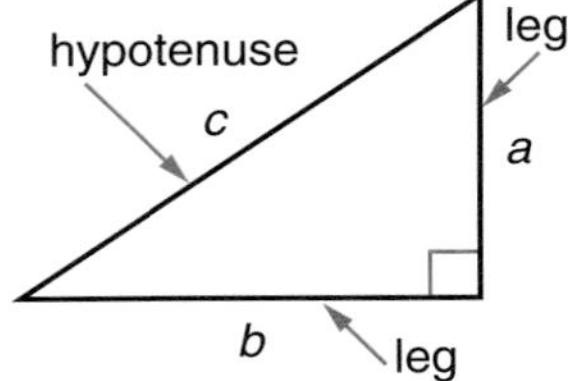

quadrant One of the four sections into which a rectangular *coordinate grid* is divided by the two *axes.* The quadrants are typically numbered I, II, III, and IV counterclockwise beginning at the upper right.

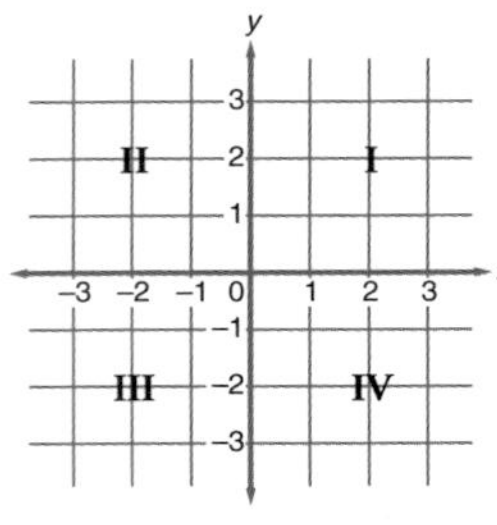

quick common denominator The product of the denominators of two or more *fractions.* For example, the quick common denominator of $\frac{3}{4}$ and $\frac{5}{6}$ is $4 * 6 = 24$. In general, the quick common denominator of $\frac{a}{b}$ and $\frac{c}{d}$ is $b * d$. As the name suggests, this is a quick way to get a *common denominator* for a collection of fractions, but it does not necessarily give the *least common denominator.*

quotient The result of dividing one number by another number. For example, in $10/5 = 2$, the quotient is 2.

radius (1) A line segment from the center of a *circle* (or *sphere*) to any point on the circle (or sphere). (2) The length of this line segment. The length of a radius is half the length of a diameter. Plural is radiuses or radii.

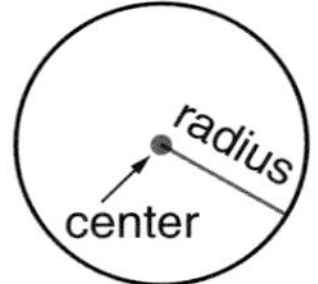

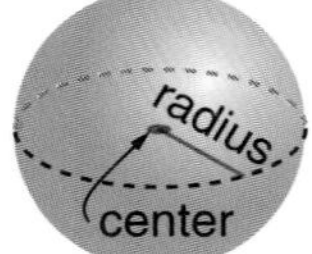

random number A number produced by a random experiment, such as rolling a die or spinning a spinner. For example, rolling a fair die produces random numbers because each of the six possible numbers 1, 2, 3, 4, 5, and 6 has the same chance of coming up.

random sample A sample that gives all members of the population the same chance of being selected.

range The difference between the *maximum* and the *minimum* in a set of data. Used as a measure of the spread of the data.

rate A comparison by division of two quantities with different units. For example, traveling 100 miles in 2 hours is an average rate of $\frac{100 \text{ mi}}{2 \text{ hr}}$, or 50 miles per hour. Rate information is often shown in a rate table. Compare to *ratio.*

rate unit A compound unit for a *rate.* For example, *miles per hour, dollars per pound,* and *words per minute* are rate units.

ratio A comparison by division of two quantities with the same units. Ratios can be *fractions,* decimals, *percents,* or stated in words. Ratios can also be written with a colon between the two numbers being compared. For example, if a team wins 3 games out of 5 games played, the ratio of wins to total games is $\frac{3}{5}$, 3/5, 0.6, 60%, 3 to 5, or 3:5 (read "three to five"). Compare to *rate.*

rational numbers Numbers that can be written in the form $\frac{a}{b}$, where a and nonzero b are *integers.* The decimal form of a rational number either terminates or repeats. For example, $\frac{2}{3}$, $-\frac{2}{3}$, 0.5, 20.5, and 0.333 . . . are rational numbers.

real numbers All *rational* and *irrational numbers;* all numbers that can be written as decimals. For every real number there is a corresponding point on a number line, and for every point on the number line there is a real number.

reciprocals Two numbers whose product is 1. For example, 5 and $\frac{1}{5}$, $\frac{3}{5}$ and $\frac{5}{3}$, and 0.2 and 5 are pairs of reciprocals. Same as *multiplicative inverses.*

reflection A point A' is a reflection *image* of point A over a *line of reflection* l if A' and A are the same distance from l on a line perpendicular to it. If all points on one figure are reflection images of all the points on another figure over the same line, the figures are reflection images. Informally called a *flip.*

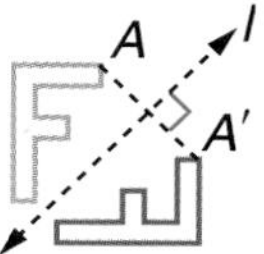

A reflection

reflex angle An angle with a measure between 180° and 360°.

regular polygon A polygon in which all sides are the same length and all angles have the same measure.

Regular polygons

regular polyhedron A polyhedron whose faces are all *congruent regular polygons* and in which the same number of faces meet at each *vertex.* The five regular polyhedrons, known as the Platonic solids, are shown below.

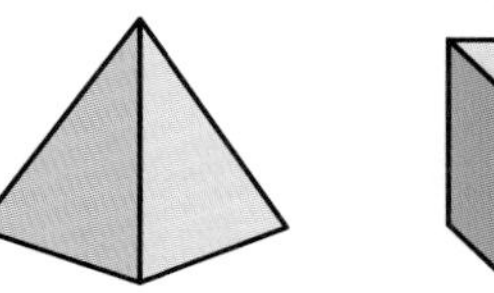
Tetrahedron
(4 equilateral triangles)

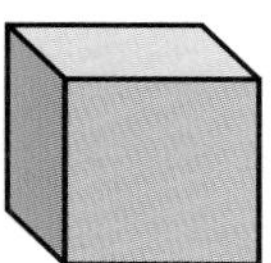
Cube
(6 squares)

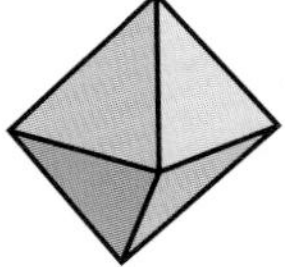
Octahedron
(8 equilateral triangles)

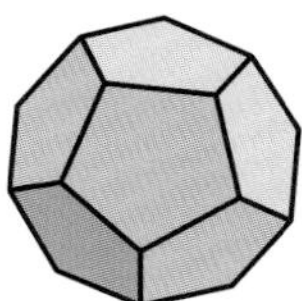
Dodecahedron
(12 regular pentagons)

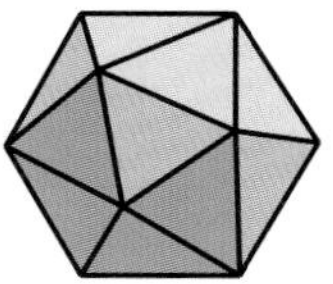
Icosahedron
(20 equilateral triangles)

regular tessellation A tessellation of one *regular polygon.* The only three regular tessellations are shown below.

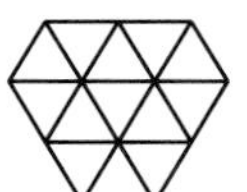
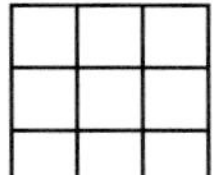

The three regular tessellations

relation symbol A symbol used to express a relationship between two quantities. Relation symbols include $=$, $\neq$, $<$, $>$, $\leq$, $\geq$, and $\approx$

repeating decimal A decimal in which one digit or a group of digits is repeated without end. For example, 0.3333. . . and $0.\overline{147}$ are repeating decimals. Compare to *terminating decimal.*

right angle A 90° angle.

right triangle A triangle with a *right angle.*

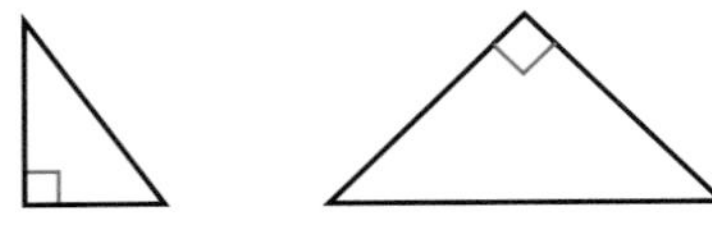

Right triangles

rotation (1) A point P' is a rotation *image* of a point P around a center of rotation C if P' is on the *circle* with center C and radius CP. If all the points in one figure are rotation images of all the points in another figure around the same center of rotation and with the same angle of rotation, the figures are rotation images. The center can be inside or outside of the original image. Informally called a *turn.*

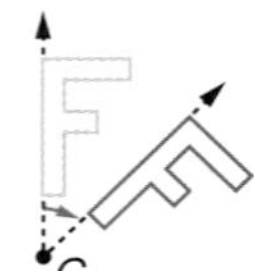

A rotation

rotation symmetry A figure has rotation symmetry if it is the *rotation image* of itself after less than a 360° turn around a center or *axis of rotation.*

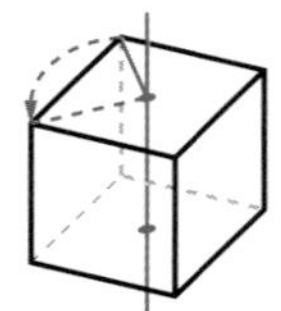

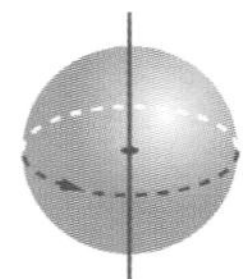

Shapes with rotation symmetry

scale factor (1) The *ratio* of lengths on an *image* and corresponding lengths on a *preimage* in a *size change.* Same as size-change factor. (2) The ratio of lengths in a scale drawing or scale model to the corresponding lengths in the object being drawn or modeled.

scientific notation A way of writing a number as the product of a *power of 10* and a number that is at least 1 and less than 10. Scientific notation allows you to write large and small numbers with only a few symbols. For example, in scientific notation, 4,300,000 is $4.3 * 10^6$, and 0.00001 is $1 * 10^{-5}$. Scientific calculators display numbers in scientific notation. Compare to *standard notation* and *expanded notation.*

sector A region bounded by, and including, an arc and two *radii* of a *circle.* A sector resembles a slice of pizza. *Circle graphs* are made with sectors corresponding to parts of a data set. Also called a wedge.

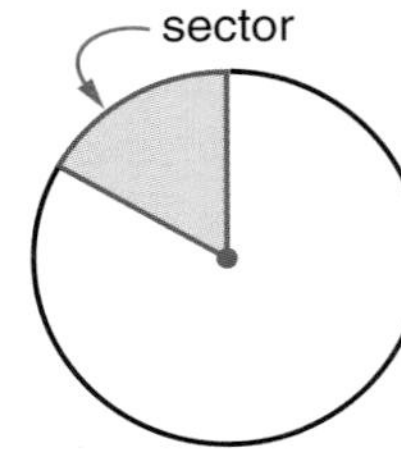

semi-regular tessellation A tessellation made with *congruent* copies of two or more different *regular polygons.* The same combination of polygons must meet in the same order at each *vertex point,* and the angles at each vertex point must add up to 360°. There are eight semiregular tessellations. Compare to *regular tessellation.*

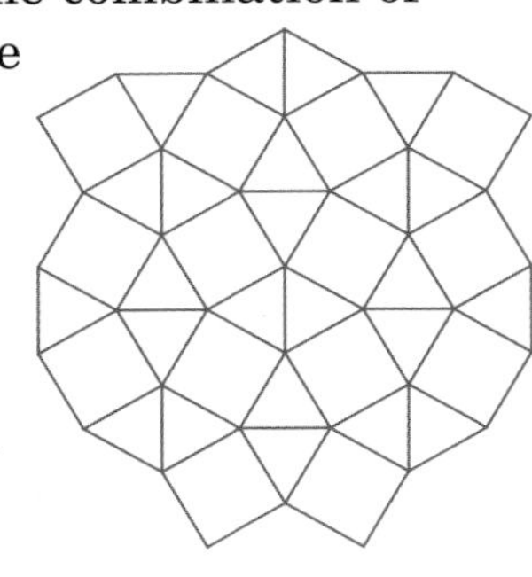

A 3.3.4.3.4 semiregular tessellation

side-by-side bar graph A *bar graph* that uses pairs of bars to compare two related data sets. The graph below compares road miles and air miles from Los Angeles to three different cities.

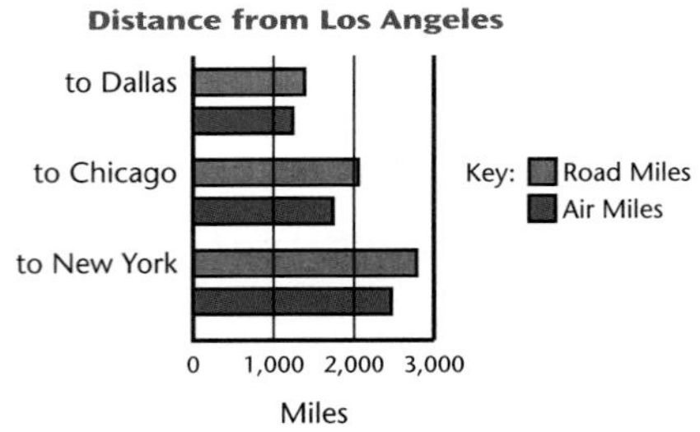

A side-by-side bar graph

similar figures Figures that have the same shape, but not necessarily the same size. Compare to *congruent figures.*

Similar polygons

simplify an expression To rewrite an *expression* by clearing grouping symbols and combining *like terms* and *constants.*

size change A *transformation* in which the *image* of a figure is an enlargement (stretch) or reduction (shrink) of the original figure by a given *scale factor.*

slide An informal name for a *translation.*

solution of an open sentence A value or values for the *variable(s)* in an *open sentence* that make the sentence true.

solution set The set of all *solutions of an open sentence.*

special case In *Everyday Mathematics,* a specific example of a *general pattern.*

sphere The set of all points in space that are an equal distance from a fixed point called the center of the sphere. The distance from the center to the sphere is the radius of the sphere. The diameter of a sphere is twice its radius. Points inside a sphere are not part of the sphere.

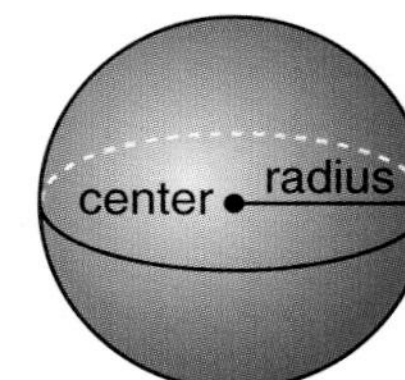

A sphere

square numbers *Figurate numbers* that are the product of a *counting number* and itself. For example, 25 is a square number because $25 = 5 * 5$. A square number can be represented by a square array and as a number squared, such as $25 = 5^2$.

square of a number *n* The product of n and itself, commonly written n^2. For example, $81 = 9 * 9 = 9^2$ and $3.5^2 = 3.5 * 3.5 = 12.25$.

square root of a number *n* A number that multiplied by itself is n, commonly written $\sqrt{n}$. For example, 4 is a square root of 16, because $4 * 4 = 16$. Normally, square root refers to the positive square root, but the opposite of a positive square root is also a square root. For example, -4 is also a square root of 16 because $-4 * -4 = 16$.

stacked bar graph A *bar graph* in which the bars are subdivided to show additional information. A stacked bar graph shows how a total is made up of several parts. In this example, of all the boys, 30% are on 0 teams, about 45% are on 1 team, and the rest are on 2 or more teams. Compare to *side-by-side bar graph.*

Number of Sports Teams

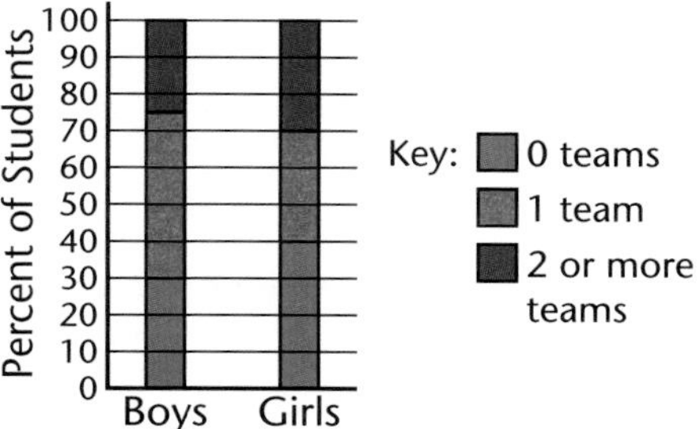

A stacked bar graph

standard notation Our most common way of representing *whole numbers, integers,* and decimals. Standard notation is base-10 place-value numeration. For example, standard notation for three hundred fifty-six is 356. Same as decimal notation.

stem-and-leaf plot A display of data values in which digits with larger place values are "stems" and digits with smaller place values are "leaves."

Data List: 24, 24, 25, 26, 27, 27, 31, 31, 32, 32, 36, 36, 41, 41, 43, 45, 48, 50, 52

Stems (tens)	**Leaves** (ones)
2	4 4 5 6 7 7
3	1 1 2 2 6 6
4	1 1 3 5 8
5	0 2

A stem-and-leaf plot

step graph A 2-dimensional coordinate graph that looks like steps because the vertical values of points are the same over an interval of horizontal values and then change, or step, for another interval. Horizontal values in a step graph often represent time.

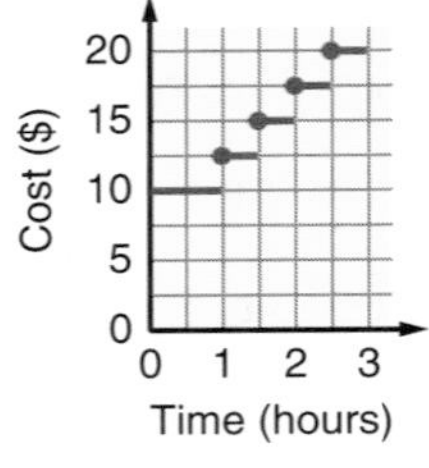

A step graph

straight angle A 180° angle.

straightedge A tool used to draw line segments. Strictly speaking, a straightedge does not have a measuring scale on it, so ignore the marks if you use a ruler as a straightedge. Together, a compass and straightedge are used to construct geometric figures.

supplementary angles Two angles whose measures add to 180°. Supplementary angles do not need to be adjacent. Compare to *complementary angles.*

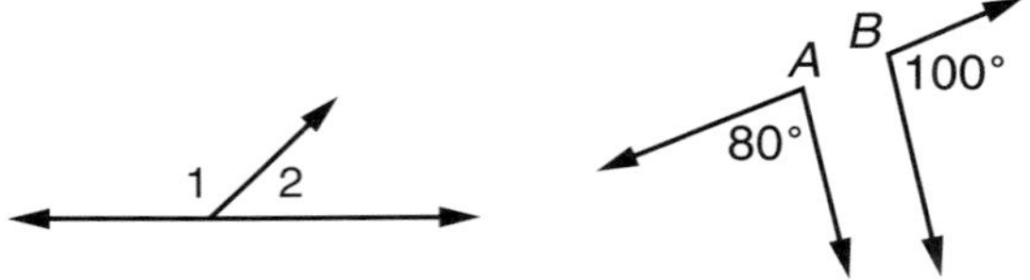

∠1 and ∠2 and ∠A and ∠B are two pairs of supplementary angles.

surface area The *area* of the surface of a 3-dimensional figure. The surface area of a polyhedron is the sum of the areas of its faces.

survey A study that collects data. Surveys are commonly used to study demographics such as people's characteristics, behaviors, interests, and opinions.

symmetry The balanced distribution of points over a line or around a point in a symmetric figure. See *line symmetry, point symmetry, rotation symmetry.*

A figure with line symmetry

A figure with rotation symmetry

term (1) In an *algebraic expression,* a number or a product of a number and one or more *variables.* For example, in the equation $5y + 3k = 8$, the terms are $5y$, $3k$, and 8. The 8 is a *constant term,* or simply a *constant,* because it has no variable part. (2) An element in a sequence. In the sequence of *square numbers,* the terms are 1, 4, 9, 16, and so on.

terminating decimal A decimal that ends. For example, 0.5 and 0.125 are terminating decimals.

test number A number used to replace a *variable* when solving an equation using the *trial-and-error method.* Test numbers are useful for closing in on an exact solution.

time graph A graph representing a story that takes place over time. The units on the horizontal axis are time units.

topological transformation A *transformation* that pairs a figure with its *image* after shrinking, stretching, twisting, bending, or turning inside out. Tearing, breaking, and sticking together are not allowed. Shapes that can be changed into one another by a topological transformation are called "topologically equivalent shapes." For example, a donut is topologically equivalent to a coffee cup. See *topology* and *genus.*

topology The study of the properties of shapes that are unchanged by shrinking, stretching, twisting, bending, and turning inside out. Tearing, breaking, and sticking together are not allowed. Same as rubber-sheet geometry. See *topological transformation.*

transformation An operation on a geometric figure (the *preimage*) that produces a new figure (the *image*). The study of transformations is called transformation geometry. Transformations are often based on rules for how points behave, as in the translation below. Although the preimage does not actually move under a transformation, it is convenient to think and talk about transformations as moving a figure from one place to another and sometimes changing its size or shape. So *Everyday Mathematics* encourages using informal terms such as *flip, turn,* and *slide.* See *isometry transformation, reflection, rotation, translation* and *size change.*

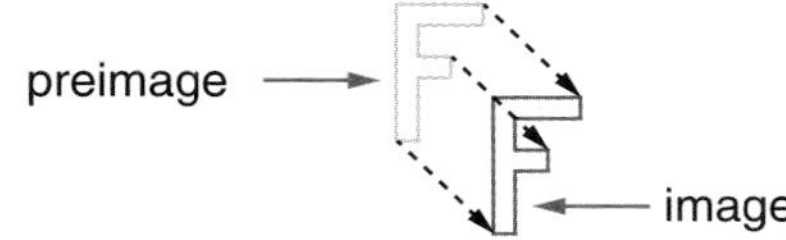

A translation

translation A *transformation* in which every point in the *image* of a figure is at the same distance in the same direction from its corresponding point in the figure. Informally called a *slide.* See *transformation* for an example.

translation tessellation A tessellation made of a tile in which one or more sides is a *translation image* of the opposite side(s). Dutch artist M.C. Escher (1898–1972) created many beautiful and elaborate translation tessellations.

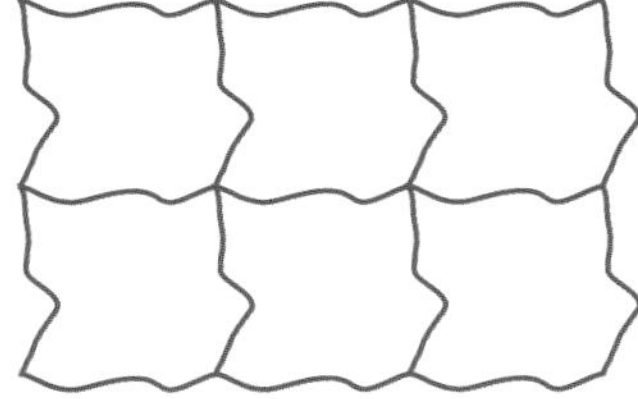

A translation tessellation

transversal A line that intersects two or more other lines.

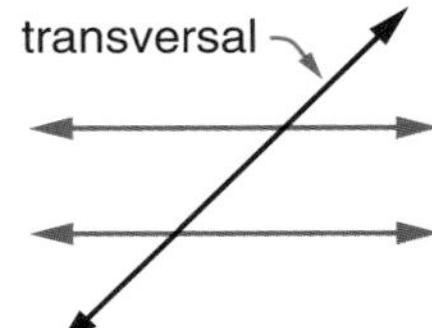

tree diagram A network of points connected by line segments and containing no closed loops. *Factor trees* and *probability trees* are tree diagrams used, respectively, to factor numbers and to represent probability situations in which there is a series of events. The first tree diagram below shows the prime factorization of 30. The second tree diagram models flipping one coin two times, to get a HEADS (H) or TAILS (T).

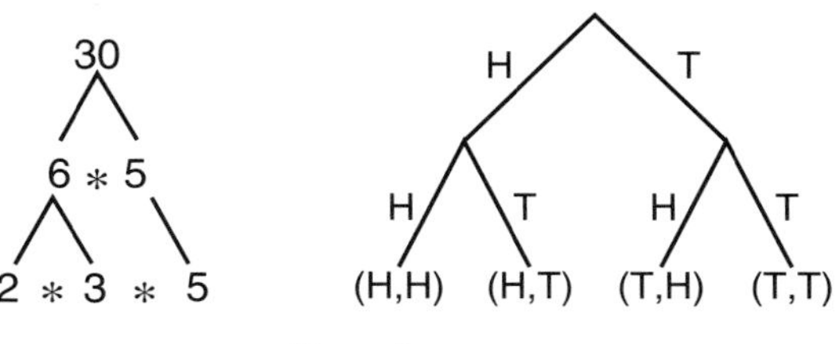

Tree diagrams

trial-and-error method A method for finding the solution of an equation by trying a sequence of *test numbers.*

triangular numbers *Figurate numbers* that can be shown by triangular arrangements of dots. The triangular numbers are {1, 3, 6, 10, 15, 21, 28, 36, 45, . . .}.

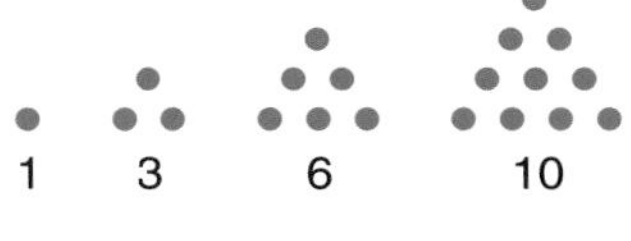

Triangular numbers

turn An informal name for a *rotation.*

unfair game A game in which every player does not have the same chance of winning.

unit fraction A *fraction* whose numerator is 1. For example, $\frac{1}{2}$, $\frac{1}{3}$, $\frac{1}{12}$, $\frac{1}{8}$, and $\frac{1}{20}$ are unit fractions.

unit percent One *percent* (1%).

unit ratio Same as *n*-to-1 ratio.

unit whole Same as whole or ONE.

variable A letter or other symbol that represents a number. A variable can represent a single number, as in $5 + n = 9$, because only $n = 4$ makes the sentence true. A variable may also stand for many different numbers, as in $x + 2 < 10$, because any number x less than 8 makes the sentence true. In *formulas* and properties, variables stand for all numbers. For example, $a + 3 = 3 + a$ for all numbers a.

variable term A *term* that contains at least one *variable.* For example, in $4b - 8 = b + 5$, $4b$ and b are variable terms.

Venn diagram A picture that uses circles or rings to show relationships between sets. In this diagram, $22 + 8 = 30$ girls are on the track team, and 8 are on both the track and the basketball teams. The rectangle in the diagram represents the universal set.

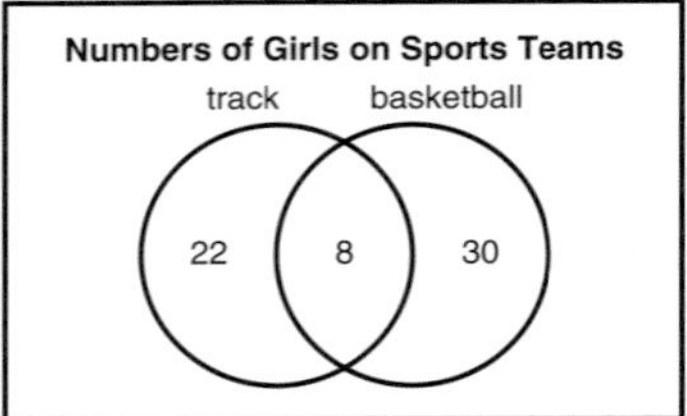

A Venn diagram

vertex The point at which the rays of an angle, the sides of a polygon, or the edges of a polyhedron meet. Plural is vertexes or vertices. In *Everyday Mathematics,* same as corner.

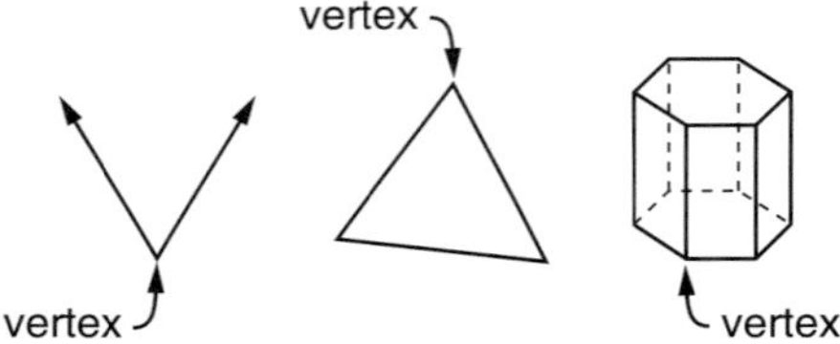

vertex point A point where the corners of tessellation tiles meet.

vertical angles The angles made by intersecting lines that do not share a common side. Same as opposite angles. Vertical angles have equal measures.

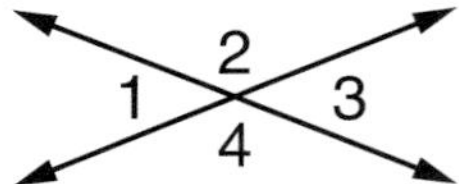

Angles 1 and 3 and angles 2 and 4 are pairs of vertical angles.

volume (1) The amount of space occupied by a 3-dimensional figure. Same as capacity. (2) The amount a container can hold. Volume is often measured in cubic units, such as cm^3, cubic inches, or cubic feet.

whole numbers The *counting numbers* and 0. The set of whole numbers is {0, 1, 2, 3, . . .}.

Grade-Level Goals

Everyday Mathematics organizes content through Program Goals and Grade-Level Goals. The Grade-Level Goals chart shows the units in which goal content is taught and then practiced. For more information, see the *Assessment Handbook*.

The Grade-Level Goals are divided according to the content strands below.

Content Strands — Pages

How to Read the Grade-Level Goals Chart

Each section of the chart includes Grade-Level Goals organized by content strand. The three grade-level columns divided into units indicate in which units the goal is addressed.

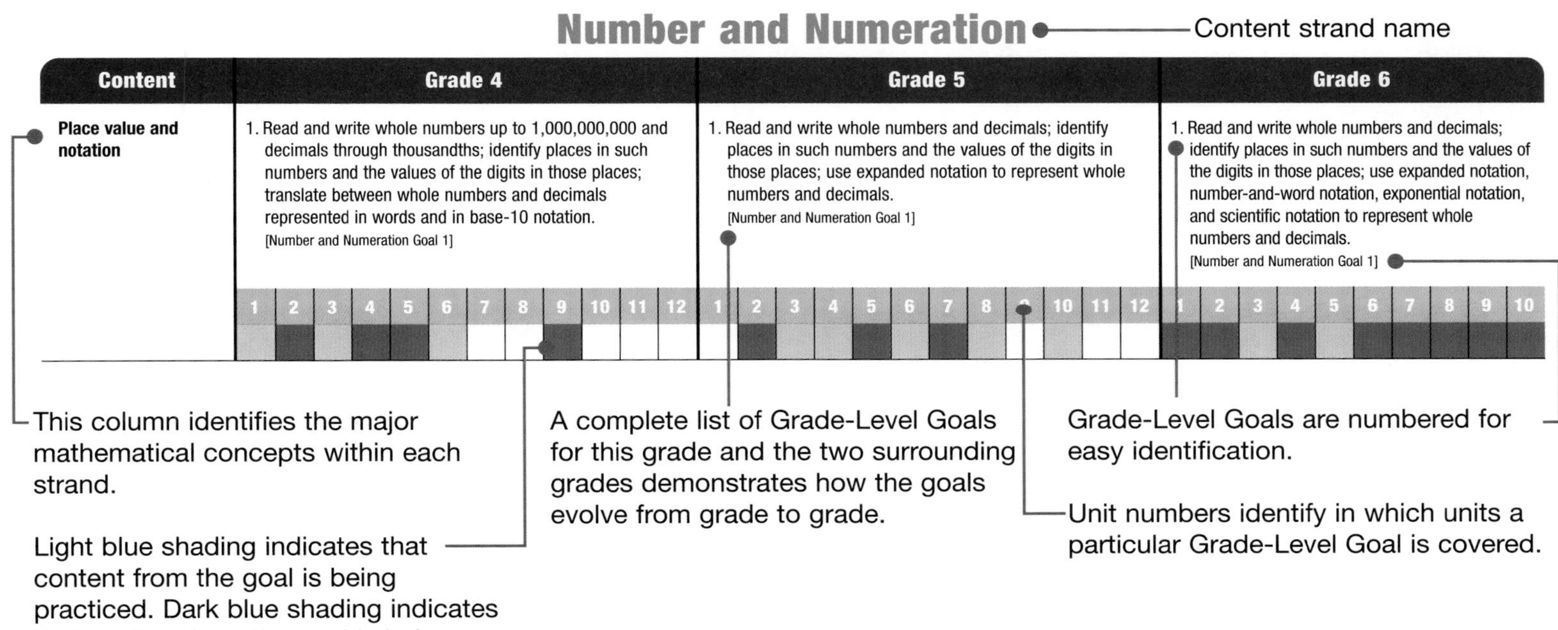

Number and Numeration
Content strand name
Content
Grade 4
Grade 5
Grade 6
Place value and notation
1. Read and write whole numbers up to 1,000,000,000 and decimals through thousandths; identify places in such numbers and the values of the digits in those places; translate between whole numbers and decimals represented in words and in base-10 notation. [Number and Numeration Goal 1]
1. Read and write whole numbers and decimals; identify places in such numbers and the values of the digits in those places; use expanded notation to represent whole numbers and decimals. [Number and Numeration Goal 1]
1. Read and write whole numbers and decimals; identify places in such numbers and the values of the digits in those places; use expanded notation, number-and-word notation, exponential notation, and scientific notation to represent whole numbers and decimals. [Number and Numeration Goal 1]
1 2 3 4 5 6 7 8 9 10 11 12
1 2 3 4 5 6 7 8 9 10 11 12
1 2 3 4 5 6 7 8 9 10
This column identifies the major mathematical concepts within each strand.
Light blue shading indicates that content from the goal is being practiced. Dark blue shading indicates that content from the goal is being taught.
A complete list of Grade-Level Goals for this grade and the two surrounding grades demonstrates how the goals evolve from grade to grade.
Grade-Level Goals are numbered for easy identification.
Unit numbers identify in which units a particular Grade-Level Goal is covered.

Number and Numeration

Content	Grade 4	Grade 5	Grade 6
Place value and notation	1. Read and write whole numbers up to 1,000,000,000 and decimals through thousandths; identify places in such numbers and the values of the digits in those places; translate between whole numbers and decimals represented in words and in base-10 notation. [Number and Numeration Goal 1] 1 2 3 4 5 6 7 8 9 10 11 12	1. Read and write whole numbers and decimals; identify places in such numbers and the values of the digits in those places; use expanded notation to represent whole numbers and decimals. [Number and Numeration Goal 1] 1 2 3 4 5 6 7 8 9 10 11 12	1. Read and write whole numbers and decimals; identify places in such numbers and the values of the digits in those places; use expanded notation, number-and-word notation, exponential notation, and scientific notation to represent whole numbers and decimals. [Number and Numeration Goal 1] 1 2 3 4 5 6 7 8 9 10
Meanings and uses of fractions	2. Read, write, and model fractions; solve problems involving fractional parts of a region or a collection; describe and explain strategies used; given a fractional part of a region or collection, identify the unit whole. [Number and Numeration Goal 2] 1 2 3 4 5 6 7 8 9 10 11 12	2. Solve problems involving percents and discounts; describe and explain strategies used; identify the unit whole in situations involving fractions. [Number and Numeration Goal 2] 1 2 3 4 5 6 7 8 9 10 11 12	2. Solve problems involving percents and discounts; explain strategies used; identify the unit whole in situations involving fractions, decimals, and percents. [Number and Numeration Goal 2] 1 2 3 4 5 6 7 8 9 10
Number theory	3. Find multiples of whole numbers less than 10; find whole-number factors of numbers. [Number and Numeration Goal 3] 1 2 3 4 5 6 7 8 9 10 11 12	3. Identify prime and composite numbers; factor numbers; find prime factorizations. [Number and Numeration Goal 3] 1 2 3 4 5 6 7 8 9 10 11 12	3. Use GCFs, LCMs, and divisibility rules to manipulate fractions. [Number and Numeration Goal 3] 1 2 3 4 5 6 7 8 9 10

Content	Grade 4	Grade 5	Grade 6
Equivalent names for whole numbers	4. Use numerical expressions involving one or more of the basic four arithmetic operations and grouping symbols to give equivalent names for whole numbers. [Number and Numeration Goal 4]	4. Use numerical expressions involving one or more of the basic four arithmetic operations, grouping symbols, and exponents to give equivalent names for whole numbers; convert between base-10, exponential, and repeated-factor notations. [Number and Numeration Goal 4]	4. Apply the order of operations to numerical expressions to give equivalent names for rational numbers. [Number and Numeration Goal 4]
	1 2 3 4 5 6 7 8 9 10 11 12	1 2 3 4 5 6 7 8 9 10 11 12	1 2 3 4 5 6 7 8 9 10
Equivalent names for fractions, decimals, and percents	5. Use numerical expressions to find and represent equivalent names for fractions and decimals; use and explain a multiplication rule to find equivalent fractions; rename fourths, fifths, tenths, and hundredths as decimals and percents. [Number and Numeration Goal 5]	5. Use numerical expressions to find and represent equivalent names for fractions, decimals, and percents; use and explain multiplication and division rules to find equivalent fractions and fractions in simplest form; convert between fractions and mixed numbers; convert between fractions, decimals, and percents. [Number and Numeration Goal 5]	5. Find equivalent fractions and fractions in simplest form by applying multiplication and division rules and concepts from number theory; convert between fractions, mixed numbers, decimals, and percents. [Number and Numeration Goal 5]
	1 2 3 4 5 6 7 8 9 10 11 12	1 2 3 4 5 6 7 8 9 10 11 12	1 2 3 4 5 6 7 8 9 10
Comparing and ordering numbers	6. Compare and order whole numbers up to 1,000,000,000 and decimals through thousandths; compare and order integers between -100 and 0; use area models, benchmark fractions, and analyses of numerators and denominators to compare and order fractions. [Number and Numeration Goal 6]	6. Compare and order rational numbers; use area models, benchmark fractions, and analyses of numerators and denominators to compare and order fractions and mixed numbers; describe strategies used to compare fractions and mixed numbers. [Number and Numeration Goal 6]	6. Choose and apply strategies for comparing and ordering rational numbers; explain those choices and strategies. [Number and Numeration Goal 6]
	1 2 3 4 5 6 7 8 9 10 11 12	1 2 3 4 5 6 7 8 9 10 11 12	1 2 3 4 5 6 7 8 9 10

Operations and Computation

Content	Grade 4	Grade 5	Grade 6
Addition and subtraction facts	1. Demonstrate automaticity with basic addition and subtraction facts and fact extensions. [Operations and Computation Goal 1]		
	1 2 3 4 5 6 7 8 9 10 11 12	1 2 3 4 5 6 7 8 9 10 11 12	1 2 3 4 5 6 7 8 9 10

Operations and Computation (cont.)

Content	Grade 4	Grade 5	Grade 6
Addition and subtraction procedures	2. Use manipulatives, mental arithmetic, paper-and-pencil algorithms, and calculators to solve problems involving the addition and subtraction of whole numbers and decimals through hundredths; describe the strategies used and explain how they work. [Operations and Computation Goal 2] 1 2 3 4 5 6 7 8 9 10 11 12	1. Use mental arithmetic, paper-and-pencil algorithms, and calculators to solve problems involving the addition and subtraction of whole numbers, decimals, and signed numbers; describe the strategies used and explain how they work. [Operations and Computation Goal 1] 1 2 3 4 5 6 7 8 9 10 11 12	1. Use mental arithmetic, paper-and-pencil algorithms, and calculators to solve problems involving the addition and subtraction of whole numbers, decimals, and signed numbers; describe the strategies used and explain how they work. [Operations and Computation Goal 1] 1 2 3 4 5 6 7 8 9 10
Multiplication and division facts	3. Demonstrate automaticity with multiplication facts through 10 * 10 and proficiency with related division facts; use basic facts to compute fact extensions such as 30 * 60. [Operations and Computation Goal 3] 1 2 3 4 5 6 7 8 9 10 11 12	2. Demonstrate automaticity with multiplication facts and proficiency with division facts and fact extensions. [Operations and Computation Goal 2] 1 2 3 4 5 6 7 8 9 10 11 12	1 2 3 4 5 6 7 8 9 10
Multiplication and division procedures	4. Use mental arithmetic, paper-and-pencil algorithms, and calculators to solve problems involving the multiplication of multidigit whole numbers by 2-digit whole numbers and the division of multidigit whole numbers by 1-digit whole numbers; describe the strategies used and explain how they work. [Operations and Computation Goal 4] 1 2 3 4 5 6 7 8 9 10 11 12	3. Use mental arithmetic, paper-and-pencil algorithms, and calculators to solve problems involving the multiplication of whole numbers and decimals and the division of multidigit whole numbers and decimals by whole numbers; express remainders as whole numbers or fractions as appropriate; describe the strategies used and explain how they work. [Operations and Computation Goal 3] 1 2 3 4 5 6 7 8 9 10 11 12	2. Use mental arithmetic, paper-and-pencil algorithms, and calculators to solve problems involving the multiplication and division of whole numbers, decimals, and signed numbers; describe the strategies used and explain how they work. [Operations and Computation Goal 2] 1 2 3 4 5 6 7 8 9 10
Procedures for addition and subtraction of fractions	5. Use manipulatives, mental arithmetic, and calculators to solve problems involving the addition and subtraction of fractions with like and unlike denominators; describe the strategies used. [Operations and Computation Goal 5] 1 2 3 4 5 6 7 8 9 10 11 12	4. Use mental arithmetic, paper-and-pencil algorithms, and calculators to solve problems involving the addition and subtraction of fractions and mixed numbers; describe the strategies used and explain how they work. [Operations and Computation Goal 4] 1 2 3 4 5 6 7 8 9 10 11 12	3. Use mental arithmetic, paper-and-pencil algorithms, and calculators to solve problems involving the addition and subtraction of fractions and mixed numbers; describe the strategies used and explain how they work. [Operations and Computation Goal 3] 1 2 3 4 5 6 7 8 9 10

Content	Grade 4	Grade 5	Grade 6
Procedures for multiplication and division of fractions		5. Use area models, mental arithmetic, paper-and-pencil algorithms, and calculators to solve problems involving the multiplication of fractions and mixed numbers; use diagrams, a common-denominator method, and calculators to solve problems involving the division of fractions; describe the strategies used. [Operations and Computation Goal 5]	4. Use mental arithmetic, paper-and-pencil algorithms, and calculators to solve problems involving the multiplication and division of fractions and mixed numbers; describe the strategies used and explain how they work. [Operations and Computation Goal 4]
	1 2 3 4 5 6 7 8 9 10 11 12	1 2 3 4 5 6 7 8 9 10 11 12	1 2 3 4 5 6 7 8 9 10
Computational estimation	6. Make reasonable estimates for whole number and decimal addition and subtraction problems and whole number multiplication and division problems; explain how the estimates were obtained. [Operations and Computation Goal 6]	6. Make reasonable estimates for whole number and decimal addition, subtraction, multiplication, and division problems and fraction and mixed number addition and subtraction problems; explain how the estimates were obtained. [Operations and Computation Goal 6]	5. Make reasonable estimates for whole number, decimal, fraction, and mixed number addition, subtraction, multiplication, and division problems; explain how the estimates were obtained. [Operations and Computation Goal 5]
	1 2 3 4 5 6 7 8 9 10 11 12	1 2 3 4 5 6 7 8 9 10 11 12	1 2 3 4 5 6 7 8 9 10
Models for the operations	7. Use repeated addition, skip counting, arrays, area, and scaling to model multiplication and division. [Operations and Computation Goal 7]	7. Use repeated addition, arrays, area, and scaling to model multiplication and division; use ratios expressed as words, fractions, percents, and with colons; solve problems involving ratios of parts of a set to the whole set. [Operations and Computation Goal 7]	6. Use ratios and scaling to model size changes and to solve size-change problems; represent ratios as fractions, percents, and decimals, and using a colon; model and solve problems involving part-to-whole and part-to-part ratios; model rate and ratio number stories with proportions; use and explain cross multiplication and other strategies to solve proportions. [Operations and Computation Goal 6]
	1 2 3 4 5 6 7 8 9 10 11 12	1 2 3 4 5 6 7 8 9 10 11 12	1 2 3 4 5 6 7 8 9 10

Data and Chance

Content	Grade 4	Grade 5	Grade 6
Data collection and representation	1. Collect and organize data or use given data to create charts, tables, bar graphs, line plots, and line graphs. [Data and Chance Goal 1]	1. Collect and organize data or use given data to create bar, line, and circle graphs with reasonable titles, labels, keys, and intervals. [Data and Chance Goal 1]	1. Collect and organize data or use given data to create bar, line, circle, and stem-and-leaf graphs with reasonable titles, labels, keys, and intervals. [Data and Chance Goal 1]
Data analysis	2. Use the maximum, minimum, range, median, mode, and graphs to ask and answer questions, draw conclusions, and make predictions. [Data and Chance Goal 2]	2. Use the maximum, minimum, range, median, mode, and mean and graphs to ask and answer questions, draw conclusions, and make predictions. [Data and Chance Goal 2]	2. Use the minimum, range, median, mode, and mean and graphs to ask and answer questions, draw conclusions, and make predictions; compare and contrast the median and mean of a data set. [Data and Chance Goal 2]
Qualitative probability	3. Describe events using *certain, very likely, likely, unlikely, very unlikely, impossible*, and other basic probability terms; use *more likely, equally likely, same chance, 50-50, less likely*, and other basic probability terms to compare events; explain the choice of language. [Data and Chance Goal 3]	3. Describe events using *certain, very likely, likely, unlikely, very unlikely, impossible*, and other basic probability terms; use *more likely, equally likely, same chance, 50-50, less likely*, and other basic probability terms to compare events; explain the choice of language. [Data and Chance Goal 3]	
Quantitative probability	4. Predict the outcomes of experiments and test the predictions using manipulatives; summarize the results and use them to predict future events; express the probability of an event as a fraction. [Data and Chance Goal 4]	4. Predict the outcomes of experiments, test the predictions using manipulatives, and summarize the results; compare predictions based on theoretical probability with experimental results; use summaries and comparisons to predict future events; express the probability of an event as a fraction, decimal, or percent. [Data and Chance Goal 4]	3. Use the Multiplication Counting Principle, tree diagrams, and other counting strategies to identify all possible outcomes for a situation; predict results of experiments, test the predictions using manipulatives, and summarize the findings; compare predictions based on theoretical probability with experimental results; calculate probabilities and express them as fractions, decimals, and percents; explain how sample size affects results; use the results to predict future events. [Data and Chance Goal 3]

Measurement and Reference Frames

Content	Grade 4	Grade 5	Grade 6
Length, weight, and angles	1. Estimate length with and without tools; measure length to the nearest $\frac{1}{4}$ inch and $\frac{1}{2}$ centimeter; estimate the size of angles without tools. [Measurement and Reference Frames Goal 1] 1 2 3 4 5 6 7 8 9 10 11 12	1. Estimate length with and without tools; measure length with tools to the nearest $\frac{1}{8}$ inch and millimeter; estimate the measure of angles with and without tools; use tools to draw angles with given measures. [Measurement and Reference Frames Goal 1] 1 2 3 4 5 6 7 8 9 10 11 12	1. Estimate length with and without tools; measure length with tools to the nearest $\frac{1}{16}$ inch and millimeter; estimate the measure of angles with and without tools; use tools to draw angles with given measures. [Measurement and Reference Frames Goal 1] 1 2 3 4 5 6 7 8 9 10
Area, perimeter, volume, and capacity	2. Describe and use strategies to measure the perimeter and area of polygons, to estimate the area of irregular shapes, and to find the volume of rectangular prisms. [Measurement and Reference Frames Goal 2] 1 2 3 4 5 6 7 8 9 10 11 12	2. Describe and use strategies to find the perimeter of polygons and the area of circles; choose and use appropriate formulas to calculate the areas of rectangles, parallelograms, and triangles, and the volume of a prism; define *pi* as the ratio of a circle's circumference to its diameter. [Measurement and Reference Frames Goal 2] 1 2 3 4 5 6 7 8 9 10 11 12	2. Choose and use appropriate formulas to calculate the circumference of circles and to solve area, perimeter, and volume problems. [Measurement and Reference Frames Goal 2] 1 2 3 4 5 6 7 8 9 10
Units and systems of measurement	3. Describe relationships among U.S. customary units of length and among metric units of length. [Measurement and Reference Frames Goal 3] 1 2 3 4 5 6 7 8 9 10 11 12	3. Describe relationships among U.S. customary units of length; among metric units of length; and among U.S. customary units of capacity. [Measurement and Reference Frames Goal 3] 1 2 3 4 5 6 7 8 9 10 11 12	1 2 3 4 5 6 7 8 9 10
Coordinate systems	4. Use ordered pairs of numbers to name, locate, and plot points in the first quadrant of a coordinate grid. [Measurement and Reference Frames Goal 4] 1 2 3 4 5 6 7 8 9 10 11 12	4. Use ordered pairs of numbers to name, locate, and plot points in all four quadrants of a coordinate grid. [Measurement and Reference Frames Goal 4] 1 2 3 4 5 6 7 8 9 10 11 12	3. Use ordered pairs of numbers to name, locate, and plot points in all four quadrants of a coordinate grid. [Measurement and Reference Frames Goal 3] 1 2 3 4 5 6 7 8 9 10

Geometry

Content	Grade 4	Grade 5	Grade 6
Lines and angles	1. Identify, draw, and describe points, intersecting and parallel line segments and lines, rays, and right, acute, and obtuse angles. [Geometry Goal 1] 1 2 3 4 5 6 7 8 9 10 11 12	1. Identify, describe, compare, name, and draw right, acute, obtuse, straight, and reflex angles; determine angle measures in vertical and supplementary angles and by applying properties of sums of angle measures in triangles and quadrangles. [Geometry Goal 1] 1 2 3 4 5 6 7 8 9 10 11 12	1. Identify, describe, classify, name, and draw angles; determine angle measures by applying properties of orientations of angles and of sums of angle measures in triangles and quadrangles. [Geometry Goal 1] 1 2 3 4 5 6 7 8 9 10
Plane and solid figures	2. Describe, compare, and classify plane and solid figures, including polygons, circles, spheres, cylinders, rectangular prisms, cones, cubes, and pyramids, using appropriate geometric terms including *vertex, base, face, edge,* and *congruent.* [Geometry Goal 2] 1 2 3 4 5 6 7 8 9 10 11 12	2. Describe, compare, and classify plane and solid figures using appropriate geometric terms; identify congruent figures and describe their properties. [Geometry Goal 2] 1 2 3 4 5 6 7 8 9 10 11 12	2. Identify and describe similar and congruent figures and describe their properties; construct a figure that is congruent to another figure using compass and straightedge. [Geometry Goal 2] 1 2 3 4 5 6 7 8 9 10
Transformations and symmetry	3. Identify, describe, and sketch examples of reflections; identify and describe examples of translations and rotations. [Geometry Goal 3] 1 2 3 4 5 6 7 8 9 10 11 12	3. Identify, describe, and sketch examples of reflections, translations, and rotations. [Geometry Goal 3] 1 2 3 4 5 6 7 8 9 10 11 12	3. Identify, describe, and sketch (including plotting on the coordinate plane) instances of reflections, translations, and rotations. [Geometry Goal 3] 1 2 3 4 5 6 7 8 9 10

Patterns, Functions, and Algebra

Content	Grade 4	Grade 5	Grade 6
Patterns and functions	1. Extend, describe, and create numeric patterns; describe rules for patterns and use them to solve problems; use words and symbols to describe and write rules for functions that involve the four basic arithmetic operations and use those rules to solve problems. [Patterns, Functions, and Algebra Goal 1]	1. Extend, describe, and create numeric patterns; describe rules for patterns and use them to solve problems; write rules for functions involving the four basic arithmetic operations; represent functions using words, symbols, tables, and graphs and use those representations to solve problems. [Patterns, Functions, and Algebra Goal 1]	1. Extend, describe, and create numeric patterns; describe rules for patterns and use them to solve problems; represent patterns and rules using algebraic notation; represent functions using words, algebraic notation, tables, and graphs; translate from one representation to another and use representations to solve problems involving functions. [Patterns, Functions, and Algebra Goal 1]
Algebraic notation and solving number sentences	2. Use conventional notation to write expressions and number sentences using the four basic arithmetic operations; determine whether number sentences are true or false; solve open sentences and explain the solutions; write expressions and number sentences to model number stories. [Patterns, Functions, and Algebra Goal 2]	2. Determine whether number sentences are true or false; solve open number sentences and explain the solutions; use a letter variable to write an open sentence to model a number story; use a pan-balance model to solve linear equations in one unknown. [Patterns, Functions, and Algebra Goal 2]	2. Determine whether equalities and inequalities are true or false; solve open number sentences and explain the solutions; use a pan-balance model to solve linear equations in one or two unknowns; use trial-and-error and equivalent equations strategies to solve linear equations in one unknown. [Patterns, Functions, and Algebra Goal 2]
Order of operations	3. Evaluate numeric expressions containing grouping symbols; insert grouping symbols to make number sentences true. [Patterns, Functions, and Algebra Goal 3]	3. Evaluate numeric expressions containing grouping symbols and nested grouping symbols; insert grouping symbols and nested grouping symbols to make number sentences true; describe and use the precedence of multiplication and division over addition and subtraction. [Patterns, Functions, and Algebra Goal 3]	3. Describe and apply the conventional order of operations. [Patterns, Functions, and Algebra Goal 3]
Properties of the arithmetic operations	4. Apply the Distributive Property of Multiplication over Addition to the partial-products multiplication algorithm. [Patterns, Functions, and Algebra Goal 4]	4. Describe and apply the properties of arithmetic. [Patterns, Functions, and Algebra Goal 4]	4. Describe and apply properties of arithmetic and multiplicative and additive inverses. [Patterns, Functions, and Algebra Goal 4]

Scope and Sequence Chart

Throughout *Everyday Mathematics*, students repeatedly encounter skills in each of the content strands. Each exposure builds on and extends students' understanding. They study important concepts over consecutive years through a variety of formats. The Scope and Sequence Chart shows the units in which these exposures occur. The symbol ● indicates that the skill is introduced or taught. The symbol ■ indicates that the skill is revisited, practiced, or extended. These levels refer to unit content within the *K–6 Everyday Mathematics* curriculum.

The skills are divided according to the content strands below.

Content Strands

Pages

How to Read the Scope and Sequence Chart

Each section of the chart includes a content strand title, three grade-level columns divided by units or sections, and a list of specific skills grouped by major concepts.

Number and Numeration — Content Strand

	Grade 4 Units												Grade 5 Units												Grade 6 Units									
Rote Counting	1	2	3	4	5	6	7	8	9	10	11	12	1	2	3	4	5	6	7	8	9	10	11	12	1	2	3	4	5	6	7	8	9	10
Count by tenths and hundredths				●																														
Place Value and Notation	1	2	3	4	5	6	7	8	9	10	11	12	1	2	3	4	5	6	7	8	9	10	11	12	1	2	3	4	5	6	7	8	9	10
Read and write numbers to hundred millions		●	■	■	■		■						■	■	●	■			■							●	■		■					
Read and write numbers to billions		●			●									■	■											●	■		■					

This row identifies the major mathematical concepts within each content strand. A list of related concepts and skills appear below this head.

Find specific skills in this list and then follow across the row to find where they appear at each grade level.

The colored circle indicates where the skill is introduced or taught.

The colored square indicates where the skill is primarily revisited, practiced, or extended.

Number and Numeration

	Grade 4 Units												Grade 5 Units												Grade 6 Units									
Rote Counting	1	2	3	4	5	6	7	8	9	10	11	12	1	2	3	4	5	6	7	8	9	10	11	12	1	2	3	4	5	6	7	8	9	10
Count by tenths and hundredths				●																														
Place Value and Notation	1	2	3	4	5	6	7	8	9	10	11	12	1	2	3	4	5	6	7	8	9	10	11	12	1	2	3	4	5	6	7	8	9	10
Read and write numbers to hundred millions		●	■	■	■		■						■	■	●	■			■							●	■		■					
Read and write numbers to billions		●			●									■	■											●	■		■					
Explore numbers to trillions					●									●					●						■	●	■				■			
Investigate or identify place value in numbers to hundred millions		●	■	■			■						■	■	■	■			■						■	●	■						■	
Identify place value in numbers to billions		●			●									■	■								■		■	●	■						■	
Name the values of digits in numbers to billions		●			●										■										■	●	■						■	
Make exchanges among place values		●		■										■			■	■	■							■					■			
Investigate and apply powers of 10					■														●							●	■	■						■
Investigate and apply expanded notation		■			■									●		■			●							■			■	■				
Read and write numbers to trillions in standard and expanded notation																									●	●	■				■			■
Investigate, use, or apply exponential notation					●	■		■					●	■			■	■	●							●	■	■	■	■		■		■
Investigate and apply scientific notation																			●							●	■	■		■				■
Use dollar-and-cents notation			■	●		■	●	■	●		■	●																						
Explore uses of decimals				■																														
Model decimals with base-10 materials				●																														
Read and write decimals to ten-thousandths in standard and expanded notation				●	■				●					●	■				■						■	●			■					
Identify place value in decimals through ten-thousandths; compare decimals				●	■	■							■	●	■				■						●	●	■	●				●	●	
Investigate and apply expanded notation of decimals				■											■					■						●								
Meanings and Uses of Fractions	1	2	3	4	5	6	7	8	9	10	11	12	1	2	3	4	5	6	7	8	9	10	11	12	1	2	3	4	5	6	7	8	9	10
Explore uses of fractions			■				●										●					■		■										
Identity fractional parts of regions					■	■	●	■	●	■							●	■		●					■			●						

Meanings and Uses of Fractions (cont.)	1	2	3	4	5	6	7	8	9	10	11	12	1	2	3	4	5	6	7	8	9	10	11	12	1	2	3	4	5	6	7	8	9	10
Identify fractional parts of a set				●		■	●	■									●			■									■	■	■			
Identify the whole for fractions							●		●						■		●	■	■	●								■				●		
Identify fractions on a number line						■	●	■				■					●	●									■							
Identify/find fractional parts of units of money							■													●												●		
Find a fraction of a number				●		■	●		●								●	■	■	●			■	●				●	■	■	■		■	
Use percents to describe real-life situations								■	●																							■		
Find a percent of a number								■	●			■					■	■	■	●			■	■			●	●	■	■	●	●	●	
Find the whole, given a percent of the whole									●											●				■								●	■	
Solve percent problems								■	■	■							●			●						■	●	●	■	■	●	●	●	
Estimate and calculate percent								■	●								●			●						■	●	●	■	■	●	●	●	
Find the unit fraction or unit percent to calculate unit prices												●								●		●									■	●		
Determine the better buy												●								■			●				●					●	■	

Number Theory	1	2	3	4	5	6	7	8	9	10	11	12	1	2	3	4	5	6	7	8	9	10	11	12	1	2	3	4	5	6	7	8	9	10
Identify even and odd numbers													●																	■				
Find the factors of numbers			●		■							■	●	■	■	■	■			■			■	●			■	■						
Investigate, identify, or apply the concepts of prime and composite numbers			■										●											●				●		■				
Find the prime factorization of numbers													●	■	■	■	■				■		■	●				■						
Find multiples of a number or the least common multiple of two numbers			●	■							■		●					■		■	■			●			■	●		●		■		
Find the greatest common factor of two numbers													●							■				●			■	●			●			
Investigate or identify square numbers, square roots, and absolute value			●										●										■				■			■			●	
Understand properties of rational numbers																										■				●	■			

Equivalent Names for Whole Numbers	1	2	3	4	5	6	7	8	9	10	11	12	1	2	3	4	5	6	7	8	9	10	11	12	1	2	3	4	5	6	7	8	9	10
Find equivalent names for numbers	■	●	■	■	■	■				■		■	●	■	■	●	■	■	●		■	■			●	●		■				■		■
Rename numbers written in exponential notation					●	■							●						●							●	■	■	■	■		■		■

Number and Numeration (cont.)

	Grade 4 Units												Grade 5 Units												Grade 6 Units									
Equivalent Names for Fractions, Decimals, and Percents	**1**	**2**	**3**	**4**	**5**	**6**	**7**	**8**	**9**	**10**	**11**	**12**	**1**	**2**	**3**	**4**	**5**	**6**	**7**	**8**	**9**	**10**	**11**	**12**	**1**	**2**	**3**	**4**	**5**	**6**	**7**	**8**	**9**	**10**
Find equivalent fractions						■	●	■	■							■	●	●	■	●			■	●				●			■	●		
Rename fractions as decimals				●			●		●	■							●	■									■	●	●	■	■	■		
Relate fractions and decimals				●			●		●								●								●	●		●	■	■	■	■	■	
Convert between fractions and decimals							●	■	●	■							●			■							■	●	■	■	■	■		
Estimate equivalent percents for fractions																	●											●	●	■	■	●	■	
Rename fractions and mixed numbers in simplest forms																	■	●	■	●			■	■			■	●		■	■	■	■	
Convert between fractions, mixed numbers, decimals, and/or percents			●	●			■		●	■			■	■	■		●	●		●	■			■	●	■	■	●	■	●	●	●	■	
Use a calculator to rename any fraction as a decimal or percent									●								●	●									■	●	●		●	●		
Comparing and Ordering Numbers	**1**	**2**	**3**	**4**	**5**	**6**	**7**	**8**	**9**	**10**	**11**	**12**	**1**	**2**	**3**	**4**	**5**	**6**	**7**	**8**	**9**	**10**	**11**	**12**	**1**	**2**	**3**	**4**	**5**	**6**	**7**	**8**	**9**	**10**
Compare numbers using <, >, and = symbols	■	■	■	■	■	■	●	■			■	■						●	●	●	■		■	■	●	■		●		●			■	
Compare larger numbers					●	■								■					●						■	■								
Compare and order decimals			■	●	■	■			■			■	■		■	■	■		■		■			■		●	■					■		
Compare and order integers										●	■	■							●						●	■			■	●	■	■		
Compare and order fractions with or without benchmarks							●		■	■		■		■		■	●	●	■	●	■			■			■	●				■		
Explore uses for positive and negative numbers										●	●								●		●								■	●	■			
Use properties of positive and negative numbers										●	■	■							●							■	●		■	●	■			
Explore reference points for zero										●	■												●	●										

Operations and Computation

	Grade 4 Units												Grade 5 Units												Grade 6 Units									
Addition and Subtraction Facts	1	2	3	4	5	6	7	8	9	10	11	12	1	2	3	4	5	6	7	8	9	10	11	12	1	2	3	4	5	6	7	8	9	10
Practice basic facts and extended facts	■	■											■	■		■			■			■	■			■			●		■	■		
Practice extensions of basic facts		■													■											■				■				
Add/subtract multiples of 10 or 100		●																																
Addition and Subtraction Procedures	1	2	3	4	5	6	7	8	9	10	11	12	1	2	3	4	5	6	7	8	9	10	11	12	1	2	3	4	5	6	7	8	9	10
Use addition/subtraction algorithms		●		●	■								■	●	■										■	●	■			■		■		
Add/subtract using a calculator		●		●																						■					■	■		
Add/subtract multidigit numbers	■	●	●		●								■	●	■										■	●		■	■		■			
Solve addition/subtraction number stories		■	●	■	●									●	■										■							■		
Add/subtract multidigit whole numbers and decimals		●	■	●	■		■							●	■	■					■	■			■	●	■			■		■		
Use estimation or algorithms to add/subtract money amounts/decimals; make change			■	●		■				●	●	●		●	■	■	■	■	■	■					■	●	■	■					■	
Solve decimal addition/subtraction number stories				●															■							●								
Add/subtract positive and negative numbers; model addition and subtraction on a number line										●	●	■							●			■	■				●	■	●	●		■		
Compute with positive and negative integers											■	■							●								■			●	■	■		
Multiplication and Division Facts	1	2	3	4	5	6	7	8	9	10	11	12	1	2	3	4	5	6	7	8	9	10	11	12	1	2	3	4	5	6	7	8	9	10
Use a Multiplication/Division Facts Table			●										■																					
Practice multiplication/division facts			●	■	■	■	■						●	■	■	●			■	■		■	■			●	●	●	■	●		●		
Practice extended multiplication/division facts			●		●	■							■	■	■	●										●	■					■		
Solve multiplication/division problems involving multiples of 10, 100, and 1,000					●	■							■	●	■	●									■	●	■	●	■		■	■		
Mulitplication and Division Procedures	1	2	3	4	5	6	7	8	9	10	11	12	1	2	3	4	5	6	7	8	9	10	11	12	1	2	3	4	5	6	7	8	9	10
Model multiplication with arrays			■		■								●																					
Use mental arithmetic to multiply/divide		■		■	●									■	■	●		■					■	■	●	●				■		■		
Use multiplication/division algorithms					●	●	■	■	●					●	■	●					■	■		■	●	●	■	■	■		■	●		
Relate fractions and division			■						●								●										■	●	■	■		■		

Operations and Computation (cont.)

	Grade 4 Units												Grade 5 Units												Grade 6 Units									
Mulitplication and Division Procedures (cont.)	**1**	**2**	**3**	**4**	**5**	**6**	**7**	**8**	**9**	**10**	**11**	**12**	**1**	**2**	**3**	**4**	**5**	**6**	**7**	**8**	**9**	**10**	**11**	**12**	**1**	**2**	**3**	**4**	**5**	**6**	**7**	**8**	**9**	**10**
Divide by 1-digit numbers						●			■				●			●		■						■	■	●				■		■		
Divide by 2-digit numbers						●			■							●	■									●				■		■		
Use a calculator to multiply/divide					■							●	●			●		■	■			■			●	●		●	■			■	■	
Identify or investigate square numbers			●										●														■						●	
Solve multiplication/division number stories		■	■		■	●			■		■	●				●	■	■								●		■	■			■	■	
Solve multidigit multiplication/division problems					●	■								●	■	●					■	■		■	●	●	■				■			
Multiply/divide decimals by powers of 10																										●	■	●		■		■		
Multiply decimals by whole numbers									●	■	■			●	■			■	■						●	●		●	■			●		
Divide decimals by whole numbers									●	■	■					●		■								●	■					■		
Multiply/divide money amounts						■			●	●		●		●		●				●	■	●				●	■					●	●	
Solve multiplication/division decimal number stories									●														■					●				■	●	
Interpret a remainder in division problems					■	●			■			●				●	■									■		●				■		
Express remainders as fractions or decimals						●						■				●										●	■	●		■		■	■	
Express quotients as mixed numbers or decimals						●											■	■								●	■	●		■		■		
Locate the decimal point in a product or quotient									●	■	■			●												●		●	■					
Round a decimal quotient to a specified place																		■			■					●		●				●		
Multiply decimals by decimals														●											■	●						●		
Multiply by positive and negative powers of 10																			●		■					●	■							
Multiply/divide positive and negative numbers																											■			●	■	■		
Use divisibility tests to determine if a number is divisible by another number													●		■	■	■	■			■	■				■	■	●						
Procedures for Addition and Subtraction of Fractions	**1**	**2**	**3**	**4**	**5**	**6**	**7**	**8**	**9**	**10**	**11**	**12**	**1**	**2**	**3**	**4**	**5**	**6**	**7**	**8**	**9**	**10**	**11**	**12**	**1**	**2**	**3**	**4**	**5**	**6**	**7**	**8**	**9**	**10**
Use models to add/subtract fractions and mixed numbers							●										●	●	■	●								■						
Add/subtract fractions with like denominators							●	■	■	■								●		●							■	●			●	■	●	
Add/subtract fractions with unlike denominators							●	■	■	■								●		●	■			■				●	■	■	●	■	●	

Procedures for Addition and Subtraction of Fractions (cont.)	1	2	3	4	5	6	7	8	9	10	11	12	1	2	3	4	5	6	7	8	9	10	11	12	1	2	3	4	5	6	7	8	9	10
Solve fraction addition/subtraction number stories; model addition and subtraction with pictures or words							■										●	■	■	■	■			■				●	■			■		
Use an algorithm to add/subtract mixed numbers with like denominators																				●				■			■	●						
Use an algorithm to add/subtract mixed numbers with unlike denominators																	■	■	■	●				■				●	■			■		
Procedures for Multiplication and Division of Fractions	**1**	**2**	**3**	**4**	**5**	**6**	**7**	**8**	**9**	**10**	**11**	**12**	**1**	**2**	**3**	**4**	**5**	**6**	**7**	**8**	**9**	**10**	**11**	**12**	**1**	**2**	**3**	**4**	**5**	**6**	**7**	**8**	**9**	**10**
Find common denominators																		●		●				■				●	■	●	●	■		
Use an algorithm to multiply fractions																				●	■			■				●	■	●	●	●	■	■
Use an algorithm to multiply mixed numbers																				●	■			■				●	■	●		●		■
Solve multiplication/division fraction number stories																				●	■							■	■			●		
Solve “fraction-of-a-fraction” problems																				●										■	●	■	■	
Use a common denominator to divide fractions																			■	●														
Use an algorithm to multiply/divide fractions and mixed numbers; use area models to demonstrate																				●	■							●	■	●		●	■	■
Computational Estimation	**1**	**2**	**3**	**4**	**5**	**6**	**7**	**8**	**9**	**10**	**11**	**12**	**1**	**2**	**3**	**4**	**5**	**6**	**7**	**8**	**9**	**10**	**11**	**12**	**1**	**2**	**3**	**4**	**5**	**6**	**7**	**8**	**9**	**10**
Round whole numbers to a given place				■	●	■							■	■		●		■							■	●	■						●	
Use estimation to add/subtract		●	■	●	●									●	■													■		●		●		
Use estimation to multiply/divide					●			■						●		●								■	■		■	■						■
Make magnitude estimates to solve *, ÷ problems					●									●		●						■			■	■		■						■
Estimate sums/differences of fractions																				■	■	■						■						
Round decimals to a given place									■		■	■		●	■	●										●	■	●	■			●	■	
Estimate costs				■		■			■								■								■									
Estimate products and multiply decimals									●	■	■			●										■	■	●								■
Estimate the quotient and divide a decimal by a whole number									●	■	■					●	■									●	■	●		■				

Operations and Computation (cont.)

	Grade 4 Units												Grade 5 Units												Grade 6 Units									
Models for the Operations	1	2	3	4	5	6	7	8	9	10	11	12	1	2	3	4	5	6	7	8	9	10	11	12	1	2	3	4	5	6	7	8	9	10
Find unit rates												●										●					■				■	●	■	
Collect and compare rate data; evaluate reasonableness of rate data												●										●		●			●					●		
Use rate tables to solve problems												●										●		●			●					●		
Represent rates with formulas, tables, and graphs												●										●		●			●			■	■	●	■	
Solve rate and ratio number stories; find equivalent ratios												●								■		●		●			●				■	●	●	
Explore uses of ratios and ways of expressing ratios; differentiate between rate and ratio												●										●		●							■	●	●	
Find opposites and reciprocals of numbers																				■										●		■		
Solve problems involving a size-change factor																																●	●	
Write open proportions to solve model problems																								●							■	●	●	
Use cross-multiplication to solve open proportions																															■	●	■	

Data and Chance

	Grade 4 Units												Grade 5 Units												Grade 6 Units									
Data Collection and Representation	1	2	3	4	5	6	7	8	9	10	11	12	1	2	3	4	5	6	7	8	9	10	11	12	1	2	3	4	5	6	7	8	9	10
Collect data by counting/interviewing		●							●			●					●	●							●		■	■						
Collect data from print sources		●	●	■	■	■	■	■	■	■	■	■						■	■						●	■								
Collect data from a map			●	■	●	●						■			■			●					■									●		
Find locations on a map or globe		●	●		●	●	■		■		■										●													
Collect and compare rate data												●										●		●			●					●		
Conduct a survey									●									●		●					●	■								
Organize and tabulate survey data									●									●							●									
Make a tally chart		●																●													■			
Record data in a table/chart		●	●						●	■		●						●		■		●	●	●	●		●			■	■	■	●	

Data Collection and Representation (cont.)	1	2	3	4	5	6	7	8	9	10	11	12	1	2	3	4	5	6	7	8	9	10	11	12	1	2	3	4	5	6	7	8	9	10
Record data on a map									●																									
Record/compare numerical data		●					●	■	●			●		●				●						●	●		●	●				■		
Create/interpret bar graphs		●		■	■	■			■	■	■	■		■			●	●							●			■			■			
Create/interpret broken-line graphs and line plots		■	●	■	■	■	■	■		■		■							●	■	■	●		●	●	■	●			■	■			
Create/interpret circle graphs with or without a Percent Circle			■	■	■	■										■	●	●		■		■	■		●	■		●	●	■		■		
Create/interpret step graphs																									●	■								
Create/interpret Venn diagrams	■		■		■						■						■		●				●	■					■		●	■		
Create/interpret number-line plots														●				●							●	■								
Create/interpret stem-and-leaf plots																		●	■			●			●	■		■					■	
Interpret mystery graphs																						●				■	■			■			■	
Use technology to create graphs																									■									
Use a spreadsheet																											●	■				■	●	
Explore misleading ways of presenting data																									●	■								

Data Analysis	1	2	3	4	5	6	7	8	9	10	11	12	1	2	3	4	5	6	7	8	9	10	11	12	1	2	3	4	5	6	7	8	9	10
Interpret tables, graphs, and maps	■		●	■	■	■			●					●	■	■	●	●	●	●	■	●	■	●	●	■	●	■				●	■	
Use a map scale			●	■	■	●	■	●	■					●		●																●	●	
Use a mileage map					●									●		●																●		
Make and interpret scale drawings								●													■											●	●	
Identify locations for given latitudes and longitudes						●															●													
Find latitude and longitude for given locations						●			■												●													
Summarize and interpret data		■		■				■				●		●				●	●	●		●		●	●	■	●	■				■	■	
Compare two sets of data; compare graphical representations of the same data		■						■	■			■		●	●		●	●	●	●		●		●	●	■								
Make predictions about data		■					●		●			■						●				●		●	●		●	●			●			
Find/use the minimum/maximum		●		■				●		■			■	●	●	■	■	●	■		■	■		●	●	■							■	
Find/use the range		●	■	■	■		■			■			■	●	■		■	●	■		■			●	●								■	
Find/use the median		●	●		■		■	●		■		●	■	●	●	■	■	●	■			●		●	●	■	■	■					■	

Data and Chance (cont.)

	Grade 4 Units												Grade 5 Units												Grade 6 Units									
Data Analysis (cont.)	1	2	3	4	5	6	7	8	9	10	11	12	1	2	3	4	5	6	7	8	9	10	11	12	1	2	3	4	5	6	7	8	9	10
Find/use the mode		●		■			■	●		■				●	■	■	■	●			■				●	■							■	
Find/use the mean		■	●	■			■					■		●	■	■	■	●			■				●	■	●	■	●				■	
Understand how sample size or outliers affect results		■					■											●							●	■		■						
Determine whether the mean, median, or mode provides the most useful information in a given situation		■	■									■						●							●	■	■	■						
Use data in problem solving		■	●					■				●						●				●			●		●				■	■		
Qualitative Probability	1	2	3	4	5	6	7	8	9	10	11	12	1	2	3	4	5	6	7	8	9	10	11	12	1	2	3	4	5	6	7	8	9	10
Explore likelihood of events						■	●		■		■	■		●										●						■	●			
Explore fair and unfair games							●										■	●													●			
Quantitative Probability	1	2	3	4	5	6	7	8	9	10	11	12	1	2	3	4	5	6	7	8	9	10	11	12	1	2	3	4	5	6	7	8	9	10
Predict outcomes; solve problems involving chance outcomes							●	■	■					●				■						●						■	●	■		
Conduct experiments							●							●				■						●							●			
Record outcomes							●							●				■						●							●	■		
Use fractions to record probabilities of events							●		■															●						■	■	■		
Compute the probability of equally-likely outcomes							●	■	■		■			■										●						■	●	■		
Calculate and express the probability of simple events						■	●	■	■	■	■	■					■		■		■			●						■	●			
Understand and apply the concept of random numbers to probability situations																															●			
Understand how increasing the number of trials affects experimental results																		●						■	●						●	■		
Investigate/apply the Multiplication Counting Principle, tree diagrams, lists, and other counting strategies to identify all possible outcomes for a situation			■																					●						■	●	■		
Explore random sampling									●									●							●						●			

Measurement and Reference Frames

	Grade 4 Units												Grade 5 Units												Grade 6 Units									
Length, Weight, and Angles	1	2	3	4	5	6	7	8	9	10	11	12	1	2	3	4	5	6	7	8	9	10	11	12	1	2	3	4	5	6	7	8	9	10
Estimate and compare lengths/heights of objects			■	●	■		■																●										●	●
Measure to the nearest foot								●																										
Measure to the nearest inch			■				■									●								●										
Measure to the nearest $\frac{1}{2}$ inch			●																■						■							●	●	●
Measure to the nearest $\frac{1}{4}$ inch					■	■		●						■		■	●			■					■				■			●	●	
Measure to the nearest $\frac{1}{8}$ inch														■				■							■			●	■	●		●	●	
Draw or measure line segments to the nearest centimeter		●	■	●				●								■		●							■				■				■	
Measure to the nearest $\frac{1}{2}$ centimeter		●		■																														
Draw or measure line segments to the nearest millimeter				●	■	■												●		■					■				■			●	●	
Investigate the meter				●																														
Express metric measures with decimals				●																						■								
Estimate and compare distances			●	●	●	●		●						●		●					■													●
Solve length/height/distance number stories			●																		■					■						●	■	
Estimate and compare weights										■	●																					■		
Estimate/weigh objects in ounces or grams											●																			■				
Use a pan balance/spring scale											●											●												
Solve weight number stories											●											●	●											
Estimate the measure of an angle			■			■	■			■					●	■												■	■					■
Use full-circle and half-circle protractors to measure and draw angles						●	■	■	■	■					●		■	●										■	●			■		
Measure angles with degree units to within 2°						●	■							■	●	■	■	●	■									■	●				■	■
Area, Perimeter, Volume, and Capacity	1	2	3	4	5	6	7	8	9	10	11	12	1	2	3	4	5	6	7	8	9	10	11	12	1	2	3	4	5	6	7	8	9	10
Investigate area and perimeter			■				■	●	■												●			■	●	■	●					■	●	

Measurement and Reference Frames (cont.)

	Grade 4 Units												Grade 5 Units												Grade 6 Units									
Area, Perimeter, Volume, and Capacity (cont.)	1	2	3	4	5	6	7	8	9	10	11	12	1	2	3	4	5	6	7	8	9	10	11	12	1	2	3	4	5	6	7	8	9	10
Find the areas of regular shapes								●	■	■							■			■	●	■	●		●	■	●	●		●		■	●	
Find the perimeters of regular shapes			■					●	■	■					■		■				■		■		■	■	●					■	●	
Find the areas of irregular shapes								●													●		■					■					■	
Find the perimeters of irregular shapes								■	■												■		■										■	■
Estimate area								●													●							■					●	
Compare perimeter and area								■	■			■									■		■	■	■								●	
Find the area of a figure by counting unit squares and fractions of unit squares inside the figure							■	●													●					■							■	
Use formulas to find areas of rectangles, parallelograms, and triangles; understand the relationship between these formulas								●	■												●		●		■	■	●			●		■	●	■
Find the surface areas of prisms, cylinders, and pyramids																					■		●					●					■	
Investigate/understand the concept of volume of a figure											●										●	■	■										●	■
Understand the relationships between the volumes of pyramids and prisms, and the volumes of cones and cylinders																							●										●	
Estimate volume or surface area								●			●										●												●	
Find and use an approximate value for π (pi)																						●											●	
Use a formula to find the circumference of a circle																						●		■									●	■
Use a formula to find the area of a circle																						●	●	■			●					■	●	■
Distinguish between circumference and area of a circle																						●		■									●	
Solve cube-stacking volume problems with unit cubes											■										●												■	
Use formulas to calculate volumes of 3-dimensional shapes											●	■									●	■	●			■							●	■
Investigate/understand the concept of capacity											●										●		●										●	
Estimate and calculate capacity											●										●		●										●	■
Solve capacity number stories											●												●										●	■

Units and Systems of Measurement	1	2	3	4	5	6	7	8	9	10	11	12	1	2	3	4	5	6	7	8	9	10	11	12	1	2	3	4	5	6	7	8	9	10
Identify equivalent customary units of length	■	■	■					●	■		■			●							■											●	●	■
Identify equivalent metric units of length				●		■												■			■				■						■		●	
Convert between metric/customary measures				●														■							●	●				■		■	●	■
Use personal references for metric/customary units of length				●	■										■			●			●													
Identify equivalent customary units of weight											●												■									■		
Identify equivalent metric units of weight											●												●									■		
Identify metric units of capacity																					●	■	●										●	
Identify equivalent metric units of capacity																					●		●										●	
Examine the relationships among the liter, milliliter, and cubic centimeter																					●		●										●	
Use personal references for common units of area																					●				■			■					■	
Money	1	2	3	4	5	6	7	8	9	10	11	12	1	2	3	4	5	6	7	8	9	10	11	12	1	2	3	4	5	6	7	8	9	10
Compare money amounts	■		■	■					■			●																						
Temperature	1	2	3	4	5	6	7	8	9	10	11	12	1	2	3	4	5	6	7	8	9	10	11	12	1	2	3	4	5	6	7	8	9	10
Read, record, and convert units of temperature									■													■					●					■	●	
Time	1	2	3	4	5	6	7	8	9	10	11	12	1	2	3	4	5	6	7	8	9	10	11	12	1	2	3	4	5	6	7	8	9	10
Investigate 1-minute intervals						●						●																						
Calculate elapsed time			●			●																●												
Convert units of time					●													●		■				■								■		
Solve time number stories			●		●								■																					
Coordinate Systems	1	2	3	4	5	6	7	8	9	10	11	12	1	2	3	4	5	6	7	8	9	10	11	12	1	2	3	4	5	6	7	8	9	10
Plot ordered number pairs on a one or four-quadrant coordinate grid						●	■	■	■	■		■								■	●	■		●	■	■	■		●		■		■	
Use ordered number pairs to name points in four quadrants																				■	●	■			■	■	■		■			■		■

Geometry

	Grade 4 Units												Grade 5 Units												Grade 6 Units									
Lines and Angles	1	2	3	4	5	6	7	8	9	10	11	12	1	2	3	4	5	6	7	8	9	10	11	12	1	2	3	4	5	6	7	8	9	10
Identify and name points	●														■										■			■	●					■
Identify and name line segments	●		■												■					■								■	●				■	
Draw line segments to a specified length	●	●													●						■				■				●					
Identify parallel and nonparallel line segments	●				■										■														●	■		■	■	
Identify and name lines	●														■														●	■		■	■	
Identify and name intersecting lines					■										■														●	■		■	■	
Identify and name rays	●			■																														
Name, draw, and label line segments, lines, and rays	●														■										■			■	●					■
Identify and name acute, obtuse, right, straight, and reflex angles	●					●			■					■	●	■				■				■				■	●				●	
Identify and describe right angles, parallel lines, skew lines, and line segments	●													■	■													■	●			■	■	
Use full-circle and half-circle protractors to measure and draw angles						●	■	■	■	■					●		■	●										■	●			■		■
Use a compass and a protractor to draw and measure angles formed by intersecting lines															●														●					■
Solve degree problems						●									■														●				■	
Determine angle measures based on relationships among common angles					■	●									●													■	●					■
Find angle sums for geometric shapes						■									●														●				■	■
Apply properties of adjacent, supplementary, complementary, and vertical angles; recognize properties in real-world settings															●														●	■		■	●	■
Apply properties of sums of angle measures of triangles and quadrilaterals															■	■								■				■	●			■	■	■
Apply properties of angles of parallelograms																													●				■	●
Apply properties of angles formed by two parallel lines and a transversal																													●	■		■	■	■
Explore the relationship between endpoints and midpoints																													●					

Lines and Angles (cont.)	1	2	3	4	5	6	7	8	9	10	11	12	1	2	3	4	5	6	7	8	9	10	11	12	1	2	3	4	5	6	7	8	9	10
Make turns and fractions of turns; relate turns to angles						●				■					●									■					●				■	●
Solve construction problems															●														●			■		
Plane and Solid Figures	**1**	**2**	**3**	**4**	**5**	**6**	**7**	**8**	**9**	**10**	**11**	**12**	**1**	**2**	**3**	**4**	**5**	**6**	**7**	**8**	**9**	**10**	**11**	**12**	**1**	**2**	**3**	**4**	**5**	**6**	**7**	**8**	**9**	**10**
Explore shape relationships	●						●	●		●					●						■								■			●	●	■
Identify characteristics of 2-dimensional shapes; use symbolic notation to denote these characteristics	●						●	●	■	●				■	●						●					■			●			●	●	
Identify 2-dimensional shapes	●	■	■				●	●							●					■	■					■			●			■	●	■
Construct/draw 2-dimensional shapes; create designs with 2-dimensional shapes	●	■					■	●		●					●										■				●			●	●	
Use a compass and a straightedge to construct geometric figures	●	■					■	■							●														●			■		
Identify the bases and heights of triangles and parallelograms								●													●											■	●	■
Use a compass to draw a circle with a given radius or diameter, and angles formed by intersecting lines															●														●				■	
Investigate the relationship between circumference and diameter																						●					■						■	
Form shapes by combining polygons							●	■																										
Identify properties and characteristics of polygons	●	■	■	■	■			●	■	●				■	●						■				■	■			●			●	●	●
Classify and name polygons	●						●	●	■						●						■				■				●				■	■
Classify triangles and quadrilaterals according to side and angle properties	●							●							●					■					■				●				●	●
Name, draw, and label angles, triangles, and quadrilaterals	●							●							●					■					●			■	●					■
Identify types of triangles								●							●	■				■					■									
Verify and apply the Pythagorean Theorem																																	●	
Solve problems involving 2-dimensional shapes	■	■					●	●							●						●				■				●			●	●	
Identify and classify 3-dimensional shapes											●									■	●		●						■				●	
Identify characteristics of 3-dimensional shapes; compare them with their 2-D faces											●										●	■	●						■				●	
Construct 3-dimensional shapes											●										●		●										●	
Describe properties of geometric solids											●										●		●						■				●	■

Geometry (cont.)

	Grade 4 Units												Grade 5 Units												Grade 6 Units									
Plane and Solid Figures (cont.)	1	2	3	4	5	6	7	8	9	10	11	12	1	2	3	4	5	6	7	8	9	10	11	12	1	2	3	4	5	6	7	8	9	10
Identify faces, edges, vertices, and bases of prisms and pyramids											●	■											●						■				●	
Perform and identify topological transformations																													■					●
Identify congruent figures															●					■			■					●	●	■		●		●
Draw or form a figure congruent to a given figure										●					●						■								●					■
Identify and draw similar figures								■							●														■			●	●	
Describe relationships among angles, side lengths, perimeter, and area of similar polygons								■																						■	■	●	●	
Transformations and Symmetry	1	2	3	4	5	6	7	8	9	10	11	12	1	2	3	4	5	6	7	8	9	10	11	12	1	2	3	4	5	6	7	8	9	10
Identify lines of reflection, reflected figures, and figures with line symmetry										●											●								●					■
Use a transparent mirror to draw the reflection of a figure										●																								■
Identify symmetrical figures										●											■													■
Identify lines of symmetry									■	●											■												■	■
Translate figures on a coordinate grid																					●								●					●
Rotate figures										■	■										●								●					●
Model clockwise/counterclockwise turns/rotations						●				■														■					●					
Explore transformations of geometric figures in a plane; identify preimage and image											■										●								●				■	●
Explore rotation and point symmetry										■					●																			●

Patterns, Functions, and Algebra

	Grade 4 Units												Grade 5 Units												Grade 6 Units									
Patterns and Functions	1	2	3	4	5	6	7	8	9	10	11	12	1	2	3	4	5	6	7	8	9	10	11	12	1	2	3	4	5	6	7	8	9	10
Explore and extend visual patterns	■						●			●			●							●	●	■							●					●
Create patterns with 2-dimensional shapes	■						●			●																								■
Define and create tessellations/frieze patterns										●					●																		■	●
Identify and use notation for semiregular tessellations																																	■	●
Identify regular tessellations															●																		■	●
Find and extend numerical patterns		■	■		■						●				■			■	■	■		●				●	●	■	●			●	●	
Make/complete a sequence with a number line		●		●	■		●	■				■	●			■		■				■												
Solve "What's My Rule?" (function machine); Find a rule for a set of problems		■	●	■	■	■	■		■	■							●	■	●	●	■					●	■			■			■	■
Solve pan-balance problems		■																				●	■	■						●	■		●	
Describe a pattern with a number sentence that has one to three variables																											●			●		■	●	■
Find patterns in addition, subtraction, multiplication, and division facts		■	■		■								●								■					●	■	●		●	■	●	●	
Find number patterns in data; complete a table of values								●				●										●		●		●	●	●				●	●	
Solve and graph solutions for inequalities																														●	■		■	
Combine like terms to simplify expressions and equations																																	●	■
Write and identify equivalent expressions and equivalent equations													●				■	■			●								●	●			●	
Write and solve equations that represent problem situations																●											■			●		■	●	■
Algebraic Notation and Solving Number Sentences	**1**	**2**	**3**	**4**	**5**	**6**	**7**	**8**	**9**	**10**	**11**	**12**	**1**	**2**	**3**	**4**	**5**	**6**	**7**	**8**	**9**	**10**	**11**	**12**	**1**	**2**	**3**	**4**	**5**	**6**	**7**	**8**	**9**	**10**
Compare numbers using <, >, and = symbols	■	■	■	■	■	■	●	■			■	■						●	●	●			■	■	●			●	■	●			■	
Evaluate expressions using <, >, =, and ≈ symbols																■						■			●		●	●	■	●	■	●	●	
Translate number stories into expressions														●		●			●			●		●			●	■	■	●			●	
Write/solve addition and subtraction number sentences	■	●											■	●	■						■				■	■	●	■	■	●			●	
Write/solve multiplication/division number sentences			●			■							■	●		●					■				■	■	●		■	●		●	●	■
Use variables to describe general patterns																											●	■		●		●	●	

Patterns, Functions, and Algebra (cont.)

	Grade 4 Units												Grade 5 Units												Grade 6 Units									
Algebraic Notation and Solving Number Sentences (cont.)	1	2	3	4	5	6	7	8	9	10	11	12	1	2	3	4	5	6	7	8	9	10	11	12	1	2	3	4	5	6	7	8	9	10
Determine the value of a variable		■		■		■		■		■	■	■		●	■	●		■	■	■	■	●	■	●			●	●	●	●	■	●	●	
Write and solve open sentences or number sentences with variables			●											●	■	●	■		●	●	■	●	■	●			●	●	●	●	■	●	●	
Determine if number sentences are true or false		■	●	■	■												■		●	■									■	●	■	■		
Write or evaluate algebraic expressions and formulas to describe situations			●																			●		■			●	■		●		■	●	■
Use variables and formulas in spreadsheets																											●	■				■	●	
Evaluate formulas																					●		●			■	●	■		●		■	●	■
Use formulas to solve problems																					●		●			■	●	●		●		■	●	■
Order of Operations	1	2	3	4	5	6	7	8	9	10	11	12	1	2	3	4	5	6	7	8	9	10	11	12	1	2	3	4	5	6	7	8	9	10
Apply the use of parentheses in number sentences			●	■	■	■	■		■		■							■	●	■	■			■	■		●		■	●		■	●	■
Understand and apply the order of operations to evaluate expressions and solve number sentences																			●	■	■	●	■		■	●		■	■	●	■	■	●	■
Simplify expressions and equations that have parentheses																			●										■	●		■	●	■
Properties of Arithmetic Operations	1	2	3	4	5	6	7	8	9	10	11	12	1	2	3	4	5	6	7	8	9	10	11	12	1	2	3	4	5	6	7	8	9	10
Investigate properties of multiplication/division			●			■							●	■		●										■				●	■	■	■	
Understand and apply the Commutative Property for addition and multiplication																				■										●	■		●	
Apply the Distributive Property					●	■	■	■	■																			●		●		■	●	■
Understand and apply the Identity Property for multiplication																												●		●		●		
Understand and apply the Associative Property for addition and multiplication																												●		●			●	

Index

Notes

Notes

Notes

Notes